DERIVATIVES AND INTEGRALS

D1308467

Basic Differentiation Rules

1. $\dfrac{d}{dx}[cu] = cu'$

2. $\dfrac{d}{dx}[u \pm v] = u' \pm v'$

3. $\dfrac{d}{dx}[uv] = uv' + vu'$

4. $\dfrac{d}{dx}\left[\dfrac{u}{v}\right] = \dfrac{vu' - uv'}{v^2}$

5. $\dfrac{d}{dx}[c] = 0$

6. $\dfrac{d}{dx}[u^n] = nu^{n-1}u'$

7. $\dfrac{d}{dx}[x] = 1$

8. $\dfrac{d}{dx}[|u|] = \dfrac{u}{|u|}(u'), \quad u \neq 0$

9. $\dfrac{d}{dx}[\ln u] = \dfrac{u'}{u}$

10. $\dfrac{d}{dx}[e^u] = e^u u'$

11. $\dfrac{d}{dx}[\log_a u] = \dfrac{u'}{(\ln a)u}$

12. $\dfrac{d}{dx}[a^u] = (\ln a)a^u u'$

13. $\dfrac{d}{dx}[\sin u] = (\cos u)u'$

14. $\dfrac{d}{dx}[\cos u] = -(\sin u)u'$

15. $\dfrac{d}{dx}[\tan u] = (\sec^2 u)u'$

16. $\dfrac{d}{dx}[\cot u] = -(\csc^2 u)u'$

17. $\dfrac{d}{dx}[\sec u] = (\sec u \tan u)u'$

18. $\dfrac{d}{dx}[\csc u] = -(\csc u \cot u)u'$

19. $\dfrac{d}{dx}[\arcsin u] = \dfrac{u'}{\sqrt{1 - u^2}}$

20. $\dfrac{d}{dx}[\arccos u] = \dfrac{-u'}{\sqrt{1 - u^2}}$

21. $\dfrac{d}{dx}[\arctan u] = \dfrac{u'}{1 + u^2}$

22. $\dfrac{d}{dx}[\text{arccot } u] = \dfrac{-u'}{1 + u^2}$

23. $\dfrac{d}{dx}[\text{arcsec } u] = \dfrac{u'}{|u|\sqrt{u^2 - 1}}$

24. $\dfrac{d}{dx}[\text{arccsc } u] = \dfrac{-u'}{|u|\sqrt{u^2 - 1}}$

25. $\dfrac{d}{dx}[\sinh u] = (\cosh u)u'$

26. $\dfrac{d}{dx}[\cosh u] = (\sinh u)u'$

27. $\dfrac{d}{dx}[\tanh u] = (\text{sech}^2 u)u'$

28. $\dfrac{d}{dx}[\coth u] = -(\text{csch}^2 u)u'$

29. $\dfrac{d}{dx}[\text{sech } u] = -(\text{sech } u \tanh u)u'$

30. $\dfrac{d}{dx}[\text{csch } u] = -(\text{csch } u \coth u)u'$

31. $\dfrac{d}{dx}[\sinh^{-1} u] = \dfrac{u'}{\sqrt{u^2 + 1}}$

32. $\dfrac{d}{dx}[\cosh^{-1} u] = \dfrac{u'}{\sqrt{u^2 - 1}}$

33. $\dfrac{d}{dx}[\tanh^{-1} u] = \dfrac{u'}{1 - u^2}$

34. $\dfrac{d}{dx}[\coth^{-1} u] = \dfrac{u'}{1 - u^2}$

35. $\dfrac{d}{dx}[\text{sech}^{-1} u] = \dfrac{-u'}{u\sqrt{1 - u^2}}$

36. $\dfrac{d}{dx}[\text{csch}^{-1} u] = \dfrac{-u'}{|u|\sqrt{1 + u^2}}$

Basic Integration Formulas

1. $\displaystyle\int kf(u)\,du = k\int f(u)\,du$

2. $\displaystyle\int [f(u) \pm g(u)]\,du = \int f(u)\,du \pm \int g(u)\,du$

3. $\displaystyle\int du = u + C$

4. $\displaystyle\int u^n\,du = \dfrac{u^{n+1}}{n+1} + C, \quad n \neq -1$

5. $\displaystyle\int \dfrac{du}{u} = \ln|u| + C$

6. $\displaystyle\int e^u\,du = e^u + C$

7. $\displaystyle\int a^u\,du = \left(\dfrac{1}{\ln a}\right)a^u + C$

8. $\displaystyle\int \sin u\,du = -\cos u + C$

9. $\displaystyle\int \cos u\,du = \sin u + C$

10. $\displaystyle\int \tan u\,du = -\ln|\cos u| + C$

11. $\displaystyle\int \cot u\,du = \ln|\sin u| + C$

12. $\displaystyle\int \sec u\,du = \ln|\sec u + \tan u| + C$

13. $\displaystyle\int \csc u\,du = -\ln|\csc u + \cot u| + C$

14. $\displaystyle\int \sec^2 u\,du = \tan u + C$

15. $\displaystyle\int \csc^2 u\,du = -\cot u + C$

16. $\displaystyle\int \sec u \tan u\,du = \sec u + C$

17. $\displaystyle\int \csc u \cot u\,du = -\csc u + C$

18. $\displaystyle\int \dfrac{du}{\sqrt{a^2 - u^2}} = \arcsin \dfrac{u}{a} + C$

19. $\displaystyle\int \dfrac{du}{a^2 + u^2} = \dfrac{1}{a}\arctan \dfrac{u}{a} + C$

20. $\displaystyle\int \dfrac{du}{u\sqrt{u^2 - a^2}} = \dfrac{1}{a}\text{arcsec} \dfrac{|u|}{a} + C$

TRIGONOMETRY

Definition of the Six Trigonometric Functions

Right triangle definitions, where $0 < \theta < \pi/2$.

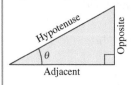

$$\sin \theta = \frac{\text{opp}}{\text{hyp}} \quad \csc \theta = \frac{\text{hyp}}{\text{opp}}$$

$$\cos \theta = \frac{\text{adj}}{\text{hyp}} \quad \sec \theta = \frac{\text{hyp}}{\text{adj}}$$

$$\tan \theta = \frac{\text{opp}}{\text{adj}} \quad \cot \theta = \frac{\text{adj}}{\text{opp}}$$

Circular function definitions, where θ is any angle.

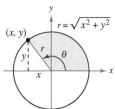

$$\sin \theta = \frac{y}{r} \quad \csc \theta = \frac{r}{y}$$

$$\cos \theta = \frac{x}{r} \quad \sec \theta = \frac{r}{x}$$

$$\tan \theta = \frac{y}{x} \quad \cot \theta = \frac{x}{y}$$

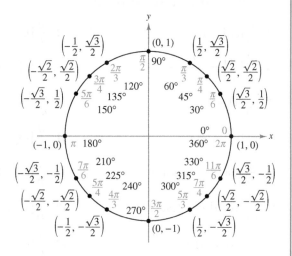

Reciprocal Identities

$$\sin x = \frac{1}{\csc x} \quad \sec x = \frac{1}{\cos x} \quad \tan x = \frac{1}{\cot x}$$

$$\csc x = \frac{1}{\sin x} \quad \cos x = \frac{1}{\sec x} \quad \cot x = \frac{1}{\tan x}$$

Quotient Identities

$$\tan x = \frac{\sin x}{\cos x} \quad \cot x = \frac{\cos x}{\sin x}$$

Pythagorean Identities

$$\sin^2 x + \cos^2 x = 1$$
$$1 + \tan^2 x = \sec^2 x \qquad 1 + \cot^2 x = \csc^2 x$$

Cofunction Identities

$$\sin\left(\frac{\pi}{2} - x\right) = \cos x \quad \cos\left(\frac{\pi}{2} - x\right) = \sin x$$

$$\csc\left(\frac{\pi}{2} - x\right) = \sec x \quad \tan\left(\frac{\pi}{2} - x\right) = \cot x$$

$$\sec\left(\frac{\pi}{2} - x\right) = \csc x \quad \cot\left(\frac{\pi}{2} - x\right) = \tan x$$

Even/Odd Identities

$$\sin(-x) = -\sin x \quad \cos(-x) = \cos x$$
$$\csc(-x) = -\csc x \quad \tan(-x) = -\tan x$$
$$\sec(-x) = \sec x \quad \cot(-x) = -\cot x$$

Sum and Difference Formulas

$$\sin(u \pm v) = \sin u \cos v \pm \cos u \sin v$$
$$\cos(u \pm v) = \cos u \cos v \mp \sin u \sin v$$
$$\tan(u \pm v) = \frac{\tan u \pm \tan v}{1 \mp \tan u \tan v}$$

Double-Angle Formulas

$$\sin 2u = 2 \sin u \cos u$$
$$\cos 2u = \cos^2 u - \sin^2 u = 2 \cos^2 u - 1 = 1 - 2 \sin^2 u$$
$$\tan 2u = \frac{2 \tan u}{1 - \tan^2 u}$$

Power-Reducing Formulas

$$\sin^2 u = \frac{1 - \cos 2u}{2}$$

$$\cos^2 u = \frac{1 + \cos 2u}{2}$$

$$\tan^2 u = \frac{1 - \cos 2u}{1 + \cos 2u}$$

Sum-to-Product Formulas

$$\sin u + \sin v = 2 \sin\left(\frac{u + v}{2}\right) \cos\left(\frac{u - v}{2}\right)$$

$$\sin u - \sin v = 2 \cos\left(\frac{u + v}{2}\right) \sin\left(\frac{u - v}{2}\right)$$

$$\cos u + \cos v = 2 \cos\left(\frac{u + v}{2}\right) \cos\left(\frac{u - v}{2}\right)$$

$$\cos u - \cos v = -2 \sin\left(\frac{u + v}{2}\right) \sin\left(\frac{u - v}{2}\right)$$

Product-to-Sum Formulas

$$\sin u \sin v = \frac{1}{2}[\cos(u - v) - \cos(u + v)]$$

$$\cos u \cos v = \frac{1}{2}[\cos(u - v) + \cos(u + v)]$$

$$\sin u \cos v = \frac{1}{2}[\sin(u + v) + \sin(u - v)]$$

$$\cos u \sin v = \frac{1}{2}[\sin(u + v) - \sin(u - v)]$$

Calculus 1 Early Transcendentals

6th Edition

Larson | Edwards

CENGAGE
Learning·

Australia • Brazil • Japan • Korea • Mexico • Singapore • Spain • United Kingdom • United States

**Calculus 1 Early Transcendentals
6th Edition**

Calculus: Early Transcendental Functions, 6th Edition
Ron Larson and Bruce Edwards

© 2015, 2011, 2010 Cengage Learning. All rights reserved.

For product information and technology assistance, contact us at
Cengage Learning Customer & Sales Support, 1-800-354-9706

For permission to use material from this text or product,
submit all requests online at **cengage.com/permissions**
Further permissions questions can be emailed to
permissionrequest@cengage.com

This book contains select works from existing Cengage Learning resources and was produced by Cengage Learning Custom Solutions for collegiate use. As such, those adopting and/or contributing to this work are responsible for editorial content accuracy, continuity and completeness.

Compilation © 2015 Cengage Learning

ISBN: 978-1-305-77219-9

WCN: 01-100-101

Cengage Learning
20 Channel Center Street
Boston, MA 02210
USA

Cengage Learning is a leading provider of customized learning solutions with office locations around the globe, including Singapore, the United Kingdom, Australia, Mexico, Brazil, and Japan. Locate your local office at:
www.international.cengage.com/region.

Cengage Learning products are represented in Canada by Nelson Education, Ltd.

For your lifelong learning solutions, visit **www.cengage.com/custom.**

Visit our corporate website at **www.cengage.com.**

Custom Contents

1 > Preparation for Calculus   1

1.1 Graphs and Models 2
1.2 Linear Models and Rates of Change 10
1.3 Functions and Their Graphs 19
1.4 Fitting Models to Data 31
1.5 Inverse Functions 37
1.6 Exponential and Logarithmic Functions 48
Review Exercises 56
P.S. Problem Solving 59

2 > Limits and Their Properties   61

2.1 A Preview of Calculus 62
2.2 Finding Limits Graphically and Numerically 68
2.3 Evaluating Limits Analytically 79
2.4 Continuity and One-Sided Limits 90
2.5 Infinite Limits 103
Section Project: Graphs and Limits of
Trigonometric Functions 110
Review Exercises 111
P.S. Problem Solving 113

3 > Differentiation   115

3.1 The Derivative and the Tangent Line Problem 116
3.2 Basic Differentiation Rules and Rates of Change 126
3.3 Product and Quotient Rules and
Higher-Order Derivatives 139
3.4 The Chain Rule 150
3.5 Implicit Differentiation 165
Section Project: Optical Illusions 173
3.6 Derivatives of Inverse Functions 174
3.7 Related Rates 181
3.8 Newton's Method 190
Review Exercises 196
P.S. Problem Solving 199

4 > Applications of Differentiation   201

4.1 Extrema on an Interval 202
4.2 Rolle's Theorem and the Mean Value Theorem 210
4.3 Increasing and Decreasing Functions and
the First Derivative Test 217
Section Project: Rainbows 226
4.4 Concavity and the Second Derivative Test 227
4.5 Limits at Infinity 235
4.6 A Summary of Curve Sketching 246
4.7 Optimization Problems 256
Section Project: Connecticut River 266

4.8 Differentials 267
Review Exercises 274
P.S. Problem Solving 277

5 > Integration 279

5.1 Antiderivatives and Indefinite Integration 280
5.2 Area 290
5.3 Riemann Sums and Definite Integrals 302
5.4 The Fundamental Theorem of Calculus 313
Section Project: Demonstrating the
Fundamental Theorem 327
5.5 Integration by Substitution 328
5.6 Numerical Integration 341
5.7 The Natural Logarithmic Function: Integration 348
5.8 Inverse Trigonometric Functions: Integration 357
5.9 Hyperbolic Functions 365
Section Project: St. Louis Arch 374
Review Exercises 375
P.S. Problem Solving 377

Appendices

Appendix A: Proofs of Selected Theorems A2
Appendix B: Integration Tables A3
Appendix C: Precalculus Review
C.1   Real Numbers and the Real Number Line A7
C.2   The Cartesian Plane A16
C.3   Review of Trigonometric Functions A23

Answers to Odd Numbered Exercises and Tests A35
Index A147

1 Preparation for Calculus

1.1 Graphs and Models
1.2 Linear Models and Rates of Change
1.3 Functions and Their Graphs
1.4 Fitting Models to Data
1.5 Inverse Functions
1.6 Exponential and Logarithmic Functions

Automobile Aerodynamics *(Exercise 96, p. 30)*

Hours of Daylight
(Example 3, p. 33)

Conveyor Design *(Exercise 23, p. 16)*

Cell Phone Subscribers
(Exercise 68, p. 9)

Modeling Carbon Dioxide Concentration *(Example 6, p. 7)*

Clockwise from top left, Gyi nesa/iStockphoto.com; hjschneider/iStockphoto.com;
Andy Dean Photography/Shutterstock.com; Gavriel Jecan/Terra/CORBIS; xtrekx/Shutterstock.com

1.1   Graphs and Models

- Sketch the graph of an equation.
- Find the intercepts of a graph.
- Test a graph for symmetry with respect to an axis and the origin.
- Find the points of intersection of two graphs.
- Interpret mathematical models for real-life data.

The Graph of an Equation

In 1637, the French mathematician René Descartes revolutionized the study of mathematics by combining its two major fields—algebra and geometry. With Descartes's coordinate plane, geometric concepts could be formulated analytically and algebraic concepts could be viewed graphically. The power of this approach was such that within a century of its introduction, much of calculus had been developed.

The same approach can be followed in your study of calculus. That is, by viewing calculus from multiple perspectives—*graphically*, *analytically*, and *numerically*—you will increase your understanding of core concepts.

Consider the equation $3x + y = 7$. The point $(2, 1)$ is a **solution point** of the equation because the equation is satisfied (is true) when 2 is substituted for x and 1 is substituted for y. This equation has many other solutions, such as $(1, 4)$ and $(0, 7)$. To find other solutions systematically, solve the original equation for y.

$$y = 7 - 3x \qquad \text{Analytic approach}$$

Then construct a **table of values** by substituting several values of x.

x	0	1	2	3	4
y	7	4	1	-2	-5

Numerical approach

From the table, you can see that $(0, 7)$, $(1, 4)$, $(2, 1)$, $(3, -2)$, and $(4, -5)$ are solutions of the original equation $3x + y = 7$. Like many equations, this equation has an infinite number of solutions. The set of all solution points is the **graph** of the equation, as shown in Figure 1.1. Note that the sketch shown in Figure 1.1 is referred to as the graph of $3x + y = 7$, even though it really represents only a *portion* of the graph. The entire graph would extend beyond the page.

In this course, you will study many sketching techniques. The simplest is point plotting—that is, you plot points until the basic shape of the graph seems apparent.

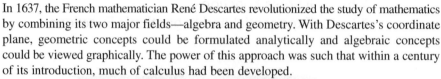

Graphical approach: $3x + y = 7$
Figure 1.1

RENÉ DESCARTES (1596–1650)

Descartes made many contributions to philosophy, science, and mathematics. The idea of representing points in the plane by pairs of real numbers and representing curves in the plane by equations was described by Descartes in his book *La Géométrie*, published in 1637. *See LarsonCalculus.com to read more of this biography.*

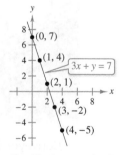

The parabola $y = x^2 - 2$
Figure 1.2

EXAMPLE 1   Sketching a Graph by Point Plotting

To sketch the graph of $y = x^2 - 2$, first construct a table of values. Next, plot the points shown in the table. Then connect the points with a smooth curve, as shown in Figure 1.2. This graph is a **parabola.** It is one of the conics you will study in Chapter 10.

x	-2	-1	0	1	2	3
y	2	-1	-2	-1	2	7

One disadvantage of point plotting is that to get a good idea about the shape of a graph, you may need to plot many points. With only a few points, you could badly misrepresent the graph. For instance, to sketch the graph of

$$y = \frac{1}{30}x(39 - 10x^2 + x^4)$$

you plot five points:

$$(-3, -3), \quad (-1, -1), \quad (0, 0), \quad (1, 1), \quad \text{and} \quad (3, 3)$$

as shown in Figure 1.3(a). From these five points, you might conclude that the graph is a line. This, however, is not correct. By plotting several more points, you can see that the graph is more complicated, as shown in Figure 1.3(b).

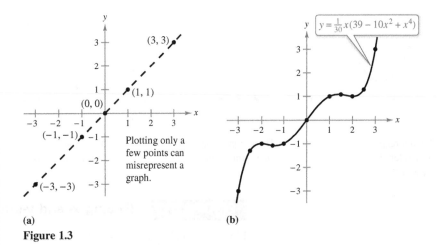

Plotting only a few points can misrepresent a graph.

(a)

(b)

Figure 1.3

▷ **TECHNOLOGY** Graphing an equation has been made easier by technology. Even with technology, however, it is possible to misrepresent a graph badly. For instance, each of the graphing utility* screens in Figure 1.4 shows a portion of the graph of

$$y = x^3 - x^2 - 25.$$

From the screen on the left, you might assume that the graph is a line. From the screen on the right, however, you can see that the graph is not a line. So, whether you are sketching a graph by hand or using a graphing utility, you must realize that different "viewing windows" can produce very different views of a graph. In choosing a viewing window, your goal is to show a view of the graph that fits well in the context of the problem.

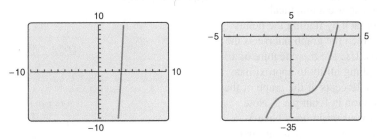

Graphing utility screens of $y = x^3 - x^2 - 25$
Figure 1.4

---

*In this text, the term *graphing utility* means either a graphing calculator, such as the *TI-Nspire*, or computer graphing software, such as *Maple* or *Mathematica*.

▷ ## Intercepts of a Graph

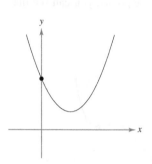

REMARK   Some texts denote the *x*-intercept as the *x*-coordinate of the point $(a, 0)$ rather than the point itself. Unless it is necessary to make a distinction, when the term *intercept* is used in this text, it will mean either the point or the coordinate.

Two types of solution points that are especially useful in graphing an equation are those having zero as their *x*- or *y*-coordinate. Such points are called **intercepts** because they are the points at which the graph intersects the *x*- or *y*-axis. The point $(a, 0)$ is an **x-intercept** of the graph of an equation when it is a solution point of the equation. To find the *x*-intercepts of a graph, let *y* be zero and solve the equation for *x*. The point $(0, b)$ is a **y-intercept** of the graph of an equation when it is a solution point of the equation. To find the *y*-intercepts of a graph, let *x* be zero and solve the equation for *y*.

It is possible for a graph to have no intercepts, or it might have several. For instance, consider the four graphs shown in Figure 1.5.

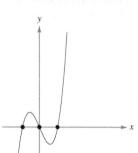
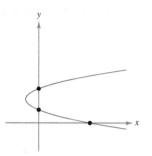
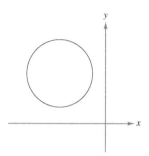

No *x*-intercepts
One *y*-intercept
Figure 1.5

Three *x*-intercepts
One *y*-intercept

One *x*-intercept
Two *y*-intercepts

No intercepts

| EXAMPLE 2 | **Finding *x*- and *y*-Intercepts** |

Find the *x*- and *y*-intercepts of the graph of $y = x^3 - 4x$.

Solution   To find the *x*-intercepts, let *y* be zero and solve for *x*.

$$x^3 - 4x = 0 \qquad \text{Let } y \text{ be zero.}$$
$$x(x - 2)(x + 2) = 0 \qquad \text{Factor.}$$
$$x = 0, 2, \text{ or } -2 \qquad \text{Solve for } x.$$

Because this equation has three solutions, you can conclude that the graph has three *x*-intercepts:

$$(0, 0), \quad (2, 0), \quad \text{and} \quad (-2, 0). \qquad \text{\textit{x}-intercepts}$$

To find the *y*-intercepts, let *x* be zero. Doing this produces $y = 0$. So, the *y*-intercept is

$$(0, 0). \qquad \text{\textit{y}-intercept}$$

(See Figure 1.6.)

▷ **TECHNOLOGY**   Example 2 uses an analytic approach to finding intercepts. When an analytic approach is not possible, you can use a graphical approach by finding the points at which the graph intersects the axes. Use the *trace* feature of a graphing utility to approximate the intercepts of the graph of the equation in Example 2. Note that your utility may have a built-in program that can find the *x*-intercepts of a graph. (Your utility may call this the *root* or *zero* feature.) If so, use the program to find the *x*-intercepts of the graph of the equation in Example 2.

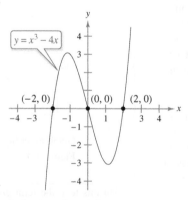

Intercepts of a graph
Figure 1.6

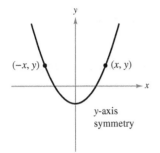

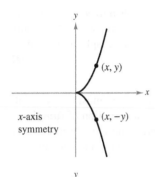

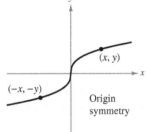

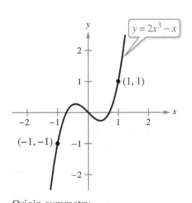

Figure 1.7

Symmetry of a Graph

Knowing the symmetry of a graph before attempting to sketch it is useful because you need only half as many points to sketch the graph. The three types of symmetry listed below can be used to help sketch the graphs of equations (see Figure 1.7).

1. A graph is **symmetric with respect to the y-axis** if, whenever (x, y) is a point on the graph, then $(-x, y)$ is also a point on the graph. This means that the portion of the graph to the left of the y-axis is a mirror image of the portion to the right of the y-axis.
2. A graph is **symmetric with respect to the x-axis** if, whenever (x, y) is a point on the graph, then $(x, -y)$ is also a point on the graph. This means that the portion of the graph below the x-axis is a mirror image of the portion above the x-axis.
3. A graph is **symmetric with respect to the origin** if, whenever (x, y) is a point on the graph, then $(-x, -y)$ is also a point on the graph. This means that the graph is unchanged by a rotation of $180°$ about the origin.

Tests for Symmetry

1. The graph of an equation in x and y is symmetric with respect to the y-axis when replacing x by $-x$ yields an equivalent equation.
2. The graph of an equation in x and y is symmetric with respect to the x-axis when replacing y by $-y$ yields an equivalent equation.
3. The graph of an equation in x and y is symmetric with respect to the origin when replacing x by $-x$ and y by $-y$ yields an equivalent equation.

The graph of a polynomial has symmetry with respect to the y-axis when each term has an even exponent (or is a constant). For instance, the graph of

$$y = 2x^4 - x^2 + 2$$

has symmetry with respect to the y-axis. Similarly, the graph of a polynomial has symmetry with respect to the origin when each term has an odd exponent, as illustrated in Example 3.

EXAMPLE 3   **Testing for Symmetry**

Test the graph of $y = 2x^3 - x$ for symmetry with respect to (a) the y-axis and (b) the origin.

Solution

a. $y = 2x^3 - x$ Write original equation.

    $y = 2(-x)^3 - (-x)$ Replace x by $-x$.

    $y = -2x^3 + x$ Simplify. It is not an equivalent equation.

Because replacing x by $-x$ does *not* yield an equivalent equation, you can conclude that the graph of $y = 2x^3 - x$ is *not* symmetric with respect to the y-axis.

b. $y = 2x^3 - x$ Write original equation.

    $-y = 2(-x)^3 - (-x)$ Replace x by $-x$ and y by $-y$.

    $-y = -2x^3 + x$ Simplify.

    $y = 2x^3 - x$ Equivalent equation

Because replacing x by $-x$ and y by $-y$ yields an equivalent equation, you can conclude that the graph of $y = 2x^3 - x$ is symmetric with respect to the origin, as shown in Figure 1.8.

Origin symmetry
Figure 1.8

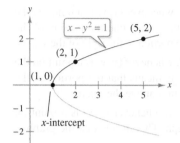

Figure 1.9

EXAMPLE 4 **Using Intercepts and Symmetry to Sketch a Graph**

•••▷ *See LarsonCalculus.com for an interactive version of this type of example.*

Sketch the graph of $x - y^2 = 1$.

Solution The graph is symmetric with respect to the x-axis because replacing y by $-y$ yields an equivalent equation.

$x - y^2 = 1$	Write original equation.
$x - (-y)^2 = 1$	Replace y by $-y$.
$x - y^2 = 1$	Equivalent equation

This means that the portion of the graph below the x-axis is a mirror image of the portion above the x-axis. To sketch the graph, first plot the x-intercept and the points above the x-axis. Then reflect in the x-axis to obtain the entire graph, as shown in Figure 1.9.

▷ **TECHNOLOGY** Graphing utilities are designed so that they most easily graph equations in which y is a function of x (see Section 1.3 for a definition of **function**). To graph other types of equations, you need to split the graph into two or more parts *or* you need to use a different graphing mode. For instance, to graph the equation in Example 4, you can split it into two parts.

$y_1 = \sqrt{x - 1}$	Top portion of graph
$y_2 = -\sqrt{x - 1}$	Bottom portion of graph

Points of Intersection

A **point of intersection** of the graphs of two equations is a point that satisfies both equations. You can find the point(s) of intersection of two graphs by solving their equations simultaneously.

EXAMPLE 5 **Finding Points of Intersection**

Find all points of intersection of the graphs of

$$x^2 - y = 3 \quad \text{and} \quad x - y = 1.$$

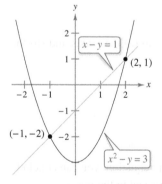

Two points of intersection
Figure 1.10

Solution Begin by sketching the graphs of both equations in the *same* rectangular coordinate system, as shown in Figure 1.10. From the figure, it appears that the graphs have two points of intersection. You can find these two points as follows.

$y = x^2 - 3$	Solve first equation for y.
$y = x - 1$	Solve second equation for y.
$x^2 - 3 = x - 1$	Equate y-values.
$x^2 - x - 2 = 0$	Write in general form.
$(x - 2)(x + 1) = 0$	Factor.
$x = 2 \text{ or } -1$	Solve for x.

The corresponding values of y are obtained by substituting $x = 2$ and $x = -1$ into either of the original equations. Doing this produces two points of intersection:

$$(2, 1) \quad \text{and} \quad (-1, -2). \qquad \text{Points of intersection}$$

You can check the points of intersection in Example 5 by substituting into *both* of the original equations or by using the *intersect* feature of a graphing utility.

Mathematical Models

Real-life applications of mathematics often use equations as **mathematical models.** In developing a mathematical model to represent actual data, you should strive for two (often conflicting) goals: accuracy and simplicity. That is, you want the model to be simple enough to be workable, yet accurate enough to produce meaningful results. Section 1.4 explores these goals more completely.

The Mauna Loa Observatory in Hawaii has been measuring the increasing concentration of carbon dioxide in Earth's atmosphere since 1958.

EXAMPLE 6   **Comparing Two Mathematical Models**

The Mauna Loa Observatory in Hawaii records the carbon dioxide concentration y (in parts per million) in Earth's atmosphere. The January readings for various years are shown in Figure 1.11. In the July 1990 issue of *Scientific American*, these data were used to predict the carbon dioxide level in Earth's atmosphere in the year 2035, using the quadratic model

$$y = 0.018t^2 + 0.70t + 316.2 \qquad \text{Quadratic model for 1960–1990 data}$$

where $t = 0$ represents 1960, as shown in Figure 1.11(a). The data shown in Figure 1.11(b) represent the years 1980 through 2010 and can be modeled by

$$y = 1.68t + 303.5 \qquad \text{Linear model for 1980–2010 data}$$

where $t = 0$ represents 1960. What was the prediction given in the *Scientific American* article in 1990? Given the new data for 1990 through 2010, does this prediction for the year 2035 seem accurate?

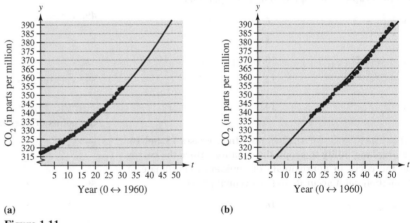

(a)   (b)

Figure 1.11

Solution   To answer the first question, substitute $t = 75$ (for 2035) into the quadratic model.

$$y = 0.018(75)^2 + 0.70(75) + 316.2 = 469.95 \qquad \text{Quadratic model}$$

So, the prediction in the *Scientific American* article was that the carbon dioxide concentration in Earth's atmosphere would reach about 470 parts per million in the year 2035. Using the linear model for the 1980–2010 data, the prediction for the year 2035 is

$$y = 1.68(75) + 303.5 = 429.5. \qquad \text{Linear model}$$

So, based on the linear model for 1980–2010, it appears that the 1990 prediction was too high.

The models in Example 6 were developed using a procedure called *least squares regression* (see Section 13.9). The quadratic and linear models have correlations given by $r^2 \approx 0.997$ and $r^2 \approx 0.994$, respectively. The closer r^2 is to 1, the "better" the model.

1.1 Exercises

See CalcChat.com for tutorial help and worked-out solutions to odd-numbered exercises.

Matching In Exercises 1–4, match the equation with its graph. [The graphs are labeled (a), (b), (c), and (d).]

(a)

(b)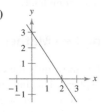

(c)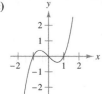

(d)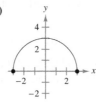

1. $y = -\frac{3}{2}x + 3$

2. $y = \sqrt{9 - x^2}$

3. $y = 3 - x^2$

4. $y = x^3 - x$

Sketching a Graph by Point Plotting In Exercises 5–14, sketch the graph of the equation by point plotting.

5. $y = \frac{1}{2}x + 2$

6. $y = 5 - 2x$

7. $y = 4 - x^2$

8. $y = (x - 3)^2$

9. $y = |x + 2|$

10. $y = |x| - 1$

11. $y = \sqrt{x} - 6$

12. $y = \sqrt{x + 2}$

13. $y = \frac{3}{x}$

14. $y = \frac{1}{x + 2}$

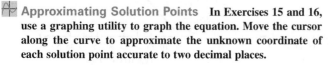 **Approximating Solution Points** In Exercises 15 and 16, use a graphing utility to graph the equation. Move the cursor along the curve to approximate the unknown coordinate of each solution point accurate to two decimal places.

15. $y = \sqrt{5 - x}$
  (a) $(2, y)$
  (b) $(x, 3)$

16. $y = x^5 - 5x$
  (a) $(-0.5, y)$
  (b) $(x, -4)$

Finding Intercepts In Exercises 17–26, find any intercepts.

17. $y = 2x - 5$

18. $y = 4x^2 + 3$

19. $y = x^2 + x - 2$

20. $y^2 = x^3 - 4x$

21. $y = x\sqrt{16 - x^2}$

22. $y = (x - 1)\sqrt{x^2 + 1}$

23. $y = \frac{2 - \sqrt{x}}{5x + 1}$

24. $y = \frac{x^2 + 3x}{(3x + 1)^2}$

25. $x^2y - x^2 + 4y = 0$

26. $y = 2x - \sqrt{x^2 + 1}$

Testing for Symmetry In Exercises 27–38, test for symmetry with respect to each axis and to the origin.

27. $y = x^2 - 6$

28. $y = x^2 - x$

29. $y^2 = x^3 - 8x$

30. $y = x^3 + x$

31. $xy = 4$

32. $xy^2 = -10$

33. $y = 4 - \sqrt{x + 3}$

34. $xy - \sqrt{4 - x^2} = 0$

35. $y = \frac{x}{x^2 + 1}$

36. $y = \frac{x^2}{x^2 + 1}$

37. $y = |x^3 + x|$

38. $|y| - x = 3$

Using Intercepts and Symmetry to Sketch a Graph In Exercises 39–56, find any intercepts and test for symmetry. Then sketch the graph of the equation.

39. $y = 2 - 3x$

40. $y = \frac{2}{3}x + 1$

41. $y = 9 - x^2$

42. $y = 2x^2 + x$

43. $y = x^3 + 2$

44. $y = x^3 - 4x$

45. $y = x\sqrt{x + 5}$

46. $y = \sqrt{25 - x^2}$

47. $x = y^3$

48. $x = y^2 - 4$

49. $y = \frac{8}{x}$

50. $y = \frac{10}{x^2 + 1}$

51. $y = 6 - |x|$

52. $y = |6 - x|$

53. $y^2 - x = 9$

54. $x^2 + 4y^2 = 4$

55. $x + 3y^2 = 6$

56. $3x - 4y^2 = 8$

Finding Points of Intersection In Exercises 57–62, find the points of intersection of the graphs of the equations.

57. $x + y = 8$
   $4x - y = 7$

58. $3x - 2y = -4$
   $4x + 2y = -10$

59. $x^2 + y = 6$
   $x + y = 4$

60. $x = 3 - y^2$
   $y = x - 1$

61. $x^2 + y^2 = 5$
   $x - y = 1$

62. $x^2 + y^2 = 25$
   $-3x + y = 15$

Finding Points of Intersection In Exercises 63–66, use a graphing utility to find the points of intersection of the graphs. Check your results analytically.

63. $y = x^3 - 2x^2 + x - 1$
   $y = -x^2 + 3x - 1$

64. $y = x^4 - 2x^2 + 1$
   $y = 1 - x^2$

65. $y = \sqrt{x + 6}$
   $y = \sqrt{-x^2 - 4x}$

66. $y = -|2x - 3| + 6$
   $y = 6 - x$

The symbol ⊕ indicates an exercise in which you are instructed to use graphing technology or a symbolic computer algebra system. The solutions of other exercises may also be facilitated by the use of appropriate technology.

67. Modeling Data The table shows the Gross Domestic Product, or GDP (in trillions of dollars), for selected years. *(Source: U.S. Bureau of Economic Analysis)*

Year	1980	1985	1990	1995
GDP	2.8	4.2	5.8	7.4

Year	2000	2005	2010
GDP	10.0	12.6	14.5

(a) Use the regression capabilities of a graphing utility to find a mathematical model of the form $y = at^2 + bt + c$ for the data. In the model, y represents the GDP (in trillions of dollars) and t represents the year, with $t = 0$ corresponding to 1980.

(b) Use a graphing utility to plot the data and graph the model. Compare the data with the model.

(c) Use the model to predict the GDP in the year 2020.

68. Modeling Data

The table shows the numbers of cellular phone subscribers (in millions) in the United States for selected years. *(Source: CTIA-The Wireless)*

Year	1995	1998	2001	2004	2007	2010
Number	34	69	128	182	255	303

(a) Use the regression capabilities of a graphing utility to find a mathematical model of the form $y = at^2 + bt + c$ for the data. In the model, y represents the number of subscribers (in millions) and t represents the year, with $t = 5$ corresponding to 1995.

(b) Use a graphing utility to plot the data and graph the model. Compare the data with the model.

(c) Use the model to predict the number of cellular phone subscribers in the United States in the year 2020.

69. Break-Even Point Find the sales necessary to break even $(R = C)$ when the cost C of producing x units is $C = 2.04x + 5600$ and the revenue R from selling x units is $R = 3.29x$.

70. Copper Wire The resistance y in ohms of 1000 feet of solid copper wire at 77°F can be approximated by the model

$$y = \frac{10{,}770}{x^2} - 0.37, \quad 5 \le x \le 100$$

where x is the diameter of the wire in mils (0.001 in.). Use a graphing utility to graph the model. By about what factor is the resistance changed when the diameter of the wire is doubled?

71. Using Solution Points For what values of k does the graph of $y = kx^3$ pass through the point?

(a) $(1, 4)$ (b) $(-2, 1)$ (c) $(0, 0)$ (d) $(-1, -1)$

72. Using Solution Points For what values of k does the graph of $y^2 = 4kx$ pass through the point?

(a) $(1, 1)$ (b) $(2, 4)$ (c) $(0, 0)$ (d) $(3, 3)$

WRITING ABOUT CONCEPTS

Writing Equations In Exercises 73 and 74, write an equation whose graph has the indicated property. (There may be more than one correct answer.)

73. The graph has intercepts at $x = -4$, $x = 3$, and $x = 8$.

74. The graph has intercepts at $x = -\frac{3}{2}$, $x = 4$, and $x = \frac{5}{2}$.

75. Proof

(a) Prove that if a graph is symmetric with respect to the x-axis and to the y-axis, then it is symmetric with respect to the origin. Give an example to show that the converse is not true.

(b) Prove that if a graph is symmetric with respect to one axis and to the origin, then it is symmetric with respect to the other axis.

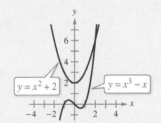

76. HOW DO YOU SEE IT? Use the graphs of the two equations to answer the questions below.

$y = x^2 + 2$ $y = x^3 - x$

(a) What are the intercepts for each equation?

(b) Determine the symmetry for each equation.

(c) Determine the point of intersection of the two equations.

True or False? In Exercises 77–80, determine whether the statement is true or false. If it is false, explain why or give an example that shows it is false.

77. If $(-4, -5)$ is a point on a graph that is symmetric with respect to the x-axis, then $(4, -5)$ is also a point on the graph.

78. If $(-4, -5)$ is a point on a graph that is symmetric with respect to the y-axis, then $(4, -5)$ is also a point on the graph.

79. If $b^2 - 4ac > 0$ and $a \ne 0$, then the graph of $y = ax^2 + bx + c$ has two x-intercepts.

80. If $b^2 - 4ac = 0$ and $a \ne 0$, then the graph of $y = ax^2 + bx + c$ has only one x-intercept.

1.2   Linear Models and Rates of Change

- ◾ Find the slope of a line passing through two points.
- ◾ Write the equation of a line with a given point and slope.
- ◾ Interpret slope as a ratio or as a rate in a real-life application.
- ◾ Sketch the graph of a linear equation in slope-intercept form.
- ◾ Write equations of lines that are parallel or perpendicular to a given line.

The Slope of a Line

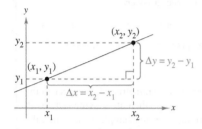

$\Delta y = y_2 - y_1 = $ change in y
$\Delta x = x_2 - x_1 = $ change in x
Figure 1.12

The **slope** of a nonvertical line is a measure of the number of units the line rises (or falls) vertically for each unit of horizontal change from left to right. Consider the two points (x_1, y_1) and (x_2, y_2) on the line in Figure 1.12. As you move from left to right along this line, a vertical change of

$$\Delta y = y_2 - y_1 \qquad \text{Change in } y$$

units corresponds to a horizontal change of

$$\Delta x = x_2 - x_1 \qquad \text{Change in } x$$

units. (Δ is the Greek uppercase letter *delta*, and the symbols Δy and Δx are read "delta y" and "delta x.")

Definition of the Slope of a Line

The **slope** m of the nonvertical line passing through (x_1, y_1) and (x_2, y_2) is

$$m = \frac{\Delta y}{\Delta x} = \frac{y_2 - y_1}{x_2 - x_1}, \quad x_1 \neq x_2.$$

Slope is not defined for vertical lines.

When using the formula for slope, note that

$$\frac{y_2 - y_1}{x_2 - x_1} = \frac{-(y_1 - y_2)}{-(x_1 - x_2)} = \frac{y_1 - y_2}{x_1 - x_2}.$$

So, it does not matter in which order you subtract *as long as* you are consistent and both "subtracted coordinates" come from the same point.

Figure 1.13 shows four lines: one has a positive slope, one has a slope of zero, one has a negative slope, and one has an "undefined" slope. In general, the greater the absolute value of the slope of a line, the steeper the line. For instance, in Figure 1.13, the line with a slope of -5 is steeper than the line with a slope of $\frac{1}{5}$.

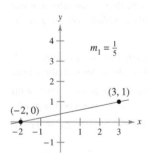

If m is positive, then the line rises from left to right.

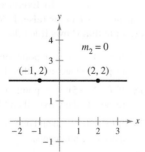

If m is zero, then the line is horizontal.

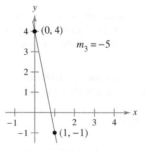

If m is negative, then the line falls from left to right.

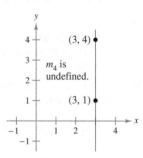

If m is undefined, then the line is vertical.

Figure 1.13

Exploration

Investigating Equations of Lines Use a graphing utility to graph each of the linear equations. Which point is common to all seven lines? Which value in the equation determines the slope of each line?

a. $y - 4 = -2(x + 1)$

b. $y - 4 = -1(x + 1)$

c. $y - 4 = -\frac{1}{2}(x + 1)$

d. $y - 4 = 0(x + 1)$

e. $y - 4 = \frac{1}{2}(x + 1)$

f. $y - 4 = 1(x + 1)$

g. $y - 4 = 2(x + 1)$

Use your results to write an equation of a line passing through $(-1, 4)$ with a slope of m.

Equations of Lines

Any two points on a nonvertical line can be used to calculate its slope. This can be verified from the similar triangles shown in Figure 1.14. (Recall that the ratios of corresponding sides of similar triangles are equal.)

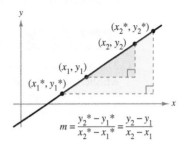

$$m = \frac{y_2^* - y_1^*}{x_2^* - x_1^*} = \frac{y_2 - y_1}{x_2 - x_1}$$

Any two points on a nonvertical line can be used to determine its slope.

Figure 1.14

If (x_1, y_1) is a point on a nonvertical line that has a slope of m and (x, y) is *any other* point on the line, then

$$\frac{y - y_1}{x - x_1} = m.$$

This equation in the variables x and y can be rewritten in the form

$$y - y_1 = m(x - x_1)$$

which is the **point-slope form** of the equation of a line.

Point-Slope Form of the Equation of a Line

The **point-slope form** of the equation of the line that passes through the point (x_1, y_1) and has a slope of m is

$$y - y_1 = m(x - x_1).$$

REMARK Remember that only nonvertical lines have a slope. Consequently, vertical lines cannot be written in point-slope form. For instance, the equation of the vertical line passing through the point $(1, -2)$ is $x = 1$.

EXAMPLE 1   **Finding an Equation of a Line**

Find an equation of the line that has a slope of 3 and passes through the point $(1, -2)$. Then sketch the line.

Solution

$$y - y_1 = m(x - x_1) \qquad \text{Point-slope form}$$
$$y - (-2) = 3(x - 1) \qquad \text{Substitute } -2 \text{ for } y_1, 1 \text{ for } x_1, \text{ and } 3 \text{ for } m.$$
$$y + 2 = 3x - 3 \qquad \text{Simplify.}$$
$$y = 3x - 5 \qquad \text{Solve for } y.$$

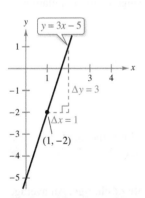

The line with a slope of 3 passing through the point $(1, -2)$

Figure 1.15

To sketch the line, first plot the point $(1, -2)$. Then, because the slope is $m = 3$, you can locate a second point on the line by moving one unit to the right and three units upward, as shown in Figure 1.15.

Ratios and Rates of Change

The slope of a line can be interpreted as either a *ratio* or a *rate*. If the *x*- and *y*-axes have the same unit of measure, then the slope has no units and is a **ratio.** If the *x*- and *y*-axes have different units of measure, then the slope is a rate or **rate of change.** In your study of calculus, you will encounter applications involving both interpretations of slope.

EXAMPLE 2 **Using Slope as a Ratio**

The maximum recommended slope of a wheelchair ramp is $\frac{1}{12}$. A business installs a wheelchair ramp that rises to a height of 22 inches over a length of 24 feet, as shown in Figure 1.16. Is the ramp steeper than recommended? *(Source: ADA Standards for Accessible Design)*

Figure 1.16

Solution The length of the ramp is 24 feet or 12(24) = 288 inches. The slope of the ramp is the ratio of its height (the rise) to its length (the run).

$$\text{Slope of ramp} = \frac{\text{rise}}{\text{run}}$$

$$= \frac{22 \text{ in.}}{288 \text{ in.}}$$

$$\approx 0.076$$

Because the slope of the ramp is less than $\frac{1}{12} \approx 0.083$, the ramp is not steeper than recommended. Note that the slope is a ratio and has no units.

EXAMPLE 3 **Using Slope as a Rate of Change**

The population of Colorado was about 4,302,000 in 2000 and about 5,029,000 in 2010. Find the average rate of change of the population over this 10-year period. What will the population of Colorado be in 2020? *(Source: U.S. Census Bureau)*

Solution Over this 10-year period, the average rate of change of the population of Colorado was

$$\text{Rate of change} = \frac{\text{change in population}}{\text{change in years}}$$

$$= \frac{5,029,000 - 4,302,000}{2010 - 2000}$$

$$= 72,700 \text{ people per year.}$$

Assuming that Colorado's population continues to increase at this same rate for the next 10 years, it will have a 2020 population of about 5,756,000 (see Figure 1.17). ∎

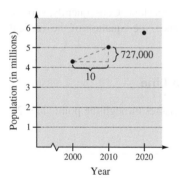

Population of Colorado
Figure 1.17

The rate of change found in Example 3 is an **average rate of change.** An average rate of change is always calculated over an interval. In this case, the interval is [2000, 2010]. In Chapter 3, you will study another type of rate of change called an *instantaneous rate of change.*

Graphing Linear Models

Many problems in coordinate geometry can be classified into two basic categories.

1. Given a graph (or parts of it), find its equation.
2. Given an equation, sketch its graph.

For lines, problems in the first category can be solved by using the point-slope form. The point-slope form, however, is not especially useful for solving problems in the second category. The form that is better suited to sketching the graph of a line is the **slope-intercept** form of the equation of a line.

The Slope-Intercept Form of the Equation of a Line

The graph of the linear equation

$$y = mx + b \qquad \text{Slope-intercept form}$$

is a line whose slope is m and whose y-intercept is $(0, b)$.

EXAMPLE 4   **Sketching Lines in the Plane**

Sketch the graph of each equation.

a. $y = 2x + 1$

b. $y = 2$

c. $3y + x - 6 = 0$

Solution

a. Because $b = 1$, the y-intercept is $(0, 1)$. Because the slope is $m = 2$, you know that the line rises two units for each unit it moves to the right, as shown in Figure 1.18(a).

b. By writing the equation $y = 2$ in slope-intercept form

$$y = (0)x + 2$$

you can see that the slope is $m = 0$ and the y-intercept is $(0, 2)$. Because the slope is zero, you know that the line is horizontal, as shown in Figure 1.18(b).

c. Begin by writing the equation in slope-intercept form.

$$
\begin{aligned}
3y + x - 6 &= 0 & &\text{Write original equation.} \\
3y &= -x + 6 & &\text{Isolate } y\text{-term on the left.} \\
y &= -\tfrac{1}{3}x + 2 & &\text{Slope-intercept form}
\end{aligned}
$$

In this form, you can see that the y-intercept is $(0, 2)$ and the slope is $m = -\tfrac{1}{3}$. This means that the line falls one unit for every three units it moves to the right, as shown in Figure 1.18(c).

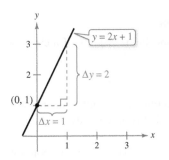

(a) $m = 2$; line rises

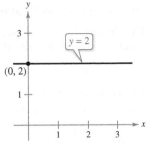

(b) $m = 0$; line is horizontal

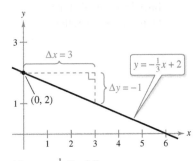

(c) $m = -\tfrac{1}{3}$; line falls

Figure 1.18

Because the slope of a vertical line is not defined, its equation cannot be written in slope-intercept form. However, the equation of any line can be written in the **general form**

$$Ax + By + C = 0 \qquad \text{General form of the equation of a line}$$

where A and B are not *both* zero. For instance, the vertical line

$$x = a \qquad \text{Vertical line}$$

can be represented by the general form

$$x - a = 0. \qquad \text{General form}$$

SUMMARY OF EQUATIONS OF LINES

1. General form: $Ax + By + C = 0$
2. Vertical line: $x = a$
3. Horizontal line: $y = b$
4. Slope-intercept form: $y = mx + b$
5. Point-slope form: $y - y_1 = m(x - x_1)$

Parallel and Perpendicular Lines

The slope of a line is a convenient tool for determining whether two lines are parallel or perpendicular, as shown in Figure 1.19. Specifically, nonvertical lines with the same slope are parallel, and nonvertical lines whose slopes are negative reciprocals are perpendicular.

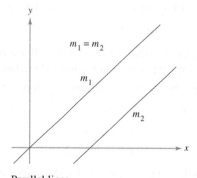

Parallel lines
Figure 1.19

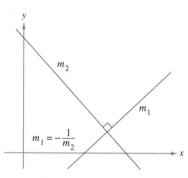

Perpendicular lines

•• REMARK   In mathematics, the phrase "if and only if" is a way of stating two implications in one statement. For instance, the first statement at the right could be rewritten as the following two implications.

a. If two distinct nonvertical lines are parallel, then their slopes are equal.

b. If two distinct nonvertical lines have equal slopes, then they are parallel.

Parallel and Perpendicular Lines

1. Two distinct nonvertical lines are **parallel** if and only if their slopes are equal—that is, if and only if

$$m_1 = m_2. \qquad \text{Parallel} \iff \text{Slopes are equal.}$$

2. Two nonvertical lines are **perpendicular** if and only if their slopes are negative reciprocals of each other—that is, if and only if

$$m_1 = -\frac{1}{m_2}. \qquad \text{Perpendicular} \iff \text{Slopes are negative reciprocals.}$$

EXAMPLE 5 **Finding Parallel and Perpendicular Lines**

∙ ∙ ∙ ∙ ▷ *See LarsonCalculus.com for an interactive version of this type of example.*

Find the general forms of the equations of the lines that pass through the point $(2, -1)$ and are (a) parallel to and (b) perpendicular to the line $2x - 3y = 5$.

Solution Begin by writing the linear equation $2x - 3y = 5$ in slope-intercept form.

$$2x - 3y = 5 \qquad \text{Write original equation.}$$
$$y = \tfrac{2}{3}x - \tfrac{5}{3} \qquad \text{Slope-intercept form}$$

So, the given line has a slope of $m = \tfrac{2}{3}$. (See Figure 1.20.)

a. The line through $(2, -1)$ that is parallel to the given line also has a slope of $\tfrac{2}{3}$.

$$y - y_1 = m(x - x_1) \qquad \text{Point-slope form}$$
$$y - (-1) = \tfrac{2}{3}(x - 2) \qquad \text{Substitute.}$$
$$3(y + 1) = 2(x - 2) \qquad \text{Simplify.}$$
$$3y + 3 = 2x - 4 \qquad \text{Distributive Property}$$
$$2x - 3y - 7 = 0 \qquad \text{General form}$$

Note the similarity to the equation of the given line, $2x - 3y = 5$.

b. Using the negative reciprocal of the slope of the given line, you can determine that the slope of a line perpendicular to the given line is $-\tfrac{3}{2}$.

$$y - y_1 = m(x - x_1) \qquad \text{Point-slope form}$$
$$y - (-1) = -\tfrac{3}{2}(x - 2) \qquad \text{Substitute.}$$
$$2(y + 1) = -3(x - 2) \qquad \text{Simplify.}$$
$$2y + 2 = -3x + 6 \qquad \text{Distributive Property}$$
$$3x + 2y - 4 = 0 \qquad \text{General form}$$

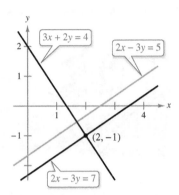

Lines parallel and perpendicular to
$2x - 3y = 5$
Figure 1.20

▷ **TECHNOLOGY PITFALL** The slope of a line will appear distorted if you use different tick-mark spacing on the x- and y-axes. For instance, the graphing utility screens in Figures 1.21(a) and 1.21(b) both show the lines

$$y = 2x \quad \text{and} \quad y = -\tfrac{1}{2}x + 3.$$

Because these lines have slopes that are negative reciprocals, they must be perpendicular. In Figure 1.21(a), however, the lines don't appear to be perpendicular because the tick-mark spacing on the x-axis is not the same as that on the y-axis. In Figure 1.21(b), the lines appear perpendicular because the tick-mark spacing on the x-axis is the same as on the y-axis. This type of viewing window is said to have a *square setting*.

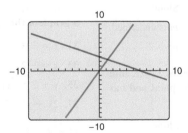

(a) Tick-mark spacing on the x-axis is not the same as tick-mark spacing on the y-axis.

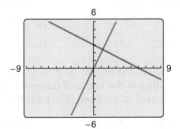

(b) Tick-mark spacing on the x-axis is the same as tick-mark spacing on the y-axis.

Figure 1.21

1.2 Exercises

See **CalcChat.com** for tutorial help and worked-out solutions to odd-numbered exercises.

Estimating Slope In Exercises 1–4, estimate the slope of the line from its graph. To print an enlarged copy of the graph, go to *MathGraphs.com*.

1.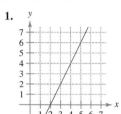

2.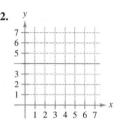

3.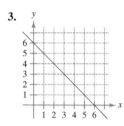

4.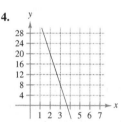

Finding the Slope of a Line In Exercises 5–10, plot the pair of points and find the slope of the line passing through them.

5. $(3, -4), (5, 2)$

6. $(1, 1), (-2, 7)$

7. $(4, 6), (4, 1)$

8. $(3, -5), (5, -5)$

9. $\left(-\frac{1}{2}, \frac{2}{3}\right), \left(-\frac{3}{4}, \frac{1}{6}\right)$

10. $\left(\frac{7}{8}, \frac{3}{4}\right), \left(\frac{5}{4}, -\frac{1}{4}\right)$

Sketching Lines In Exercises 11 and 12, sketch the lines through the point with the indicated slopes. Make the sketches on the same set of coordinate axes.

Point	Slopes

11. $(3, 4)$ (a) 1 (b) -2 (c) $-\frac{3}{2}$ (d) Undefined

12. $(-2, 5)$ (a) 3 (b) -3 (c) $\frac{1}{3}$ (d) 0

Finding Points on a Line In Exercises 13–16, use the point on the line and the slope of the line to find three additional points that the line passes through. (There is more than one correct answer.)

Point	Slope	Point	Slope

13. $(6, 2)$ $m = 0$ **14.** $(-4, 3)$ m is undefined.

15. $(1, 7)$ $m = -3$ **16.** $(-2, -2)$ $m = 2$

Finding an Equation of a Line In Exercises 17–22, find an equation of the line that passes through the point and has the indicated slope. Then sketch the line.

Point	Slope	Point	Slope

17. $(0, 3)$ $m = \frac{3}{4}$ **18.** $(-5, -2)$ m is undefined.

19. $(0, 0)$ $m = \frac{2}{3}$ **20.** $(0, 4)$ $m = 0$

21. $(3, -2)$ $m = 3$ **22.** $(-2, 4)$ $m = -\frac{3}{5}$

• • 23. Conveyor Design • • • • • • • • • • • • • •

A moving conveyor is built to rise 1 meter for each 3 meters of horizontal change.

(a) Find the slope of the conveyor.

(b) Suppose the conveyor runs between two floors in a factory. Find the length of the conveyor when the vertical distance between floors is 10 feet.

24. Modeling Data The table shows the populations y (in millions) of the United States for 2004 through 2009. The variable t represents the time in years, with $t = 4$ corresponding to 2004. *(Source: U.S. Census Bureau)*

t	4	5	6	7	8	9
y	293.0	295.8	298.6	301.6	304.4	307.0

(a) Plot the data by hand and connect adjacent points with a line segment.

(b) Use the slope of each line segment to determine the year when the population increased least rapidly.

(c) Find the average rate of change of the population of the United States from 2004 through 2009.

(d) Use the average rate of change of the population to predict the population of the United States in 2020.

Finding the Slope and y-Intercept In Exercises 25–30, find the slope and the y-intercept (if possible) of the line.

25. $y = 4x - 3$

26. $-x + y = 1$

27. $x + 5y = 20$

28. $6x - 5y = 15$

29. $x = 4$

30. $y = -1$

Sketching a Line in the Plane In Exercises 31–38, sketch a graph of the equation.

31. $y = -3$

32. $x = 4$

33. $y = -2x + 1$

34. $y = \frac{1}{3}x - 1$

35. $y - 2 = \frac{3}{2}(x - 1)$

36. $y - 1 = 3(x + 4)$

37. $2x - y - 3 = 0$

38. $x + 2y + 6 = 0$

Finding an Equation of a Line In Exercises 39–46, find an equation of the line that passes through the points. Then sketch the line.

39. $(0, 0), (4, 8)$

40. $(-2, -2), (1, 7)$

41. $(2, 8), (5, 0)$ **42.** $(-3, 6), (1, 2)$

43. $(6, 3), (6, 8)$ **44.** $(1, -2), (3, -2)$

45. $\left(\frac{1}{2}, \frac{7}{2}\right), \left(0, \frac{3}{4}\right)$ **46.** $\left(\frac{7}{8}, \frac{3}{4}\right), \left(\frac{5}{4}, -\frac{1}{4}\right)$

47. Finding an Equation of a Line Find an equation of the vertical line with x-intercept at 3.

48. Equation of a Line Show that the line with intercepts $(a, 0)$ and $(0, b)$ has the following equation.

$$\frac{x}{a} + \frac{y}{b} = 1, \quad a \neq 0, b \neq 0$$

Writing an Equation in General Form In Exercises 49–54, use the result of Exercise 48 to write an equation of the line in general form.

49. x-intercept: $(2, 0)$ **50.** x-intercept: $\left(-\frac{2}{3}, 0\right)$

  y-intercept: $(0, 3)$ y-intercept: $(0, -2)$

51. Point on line: $(1, 2)$ **52.** Point on line: $(-3, 4)$

  x-intercept: $(a, 0)$ x-intercept: $(a, 0)$

  y-intercept: $(0, a)$ y-intercept: $(0, a)$

  $(a \neq 0)$ $(a \neq 0)$

53. Point on line: $(9, -2)$ **54.** Point on line: $\left(-\frac{2}{3}, -2\right)$

  x-intercept: $(2a, 0)$ x-intercept: $(a, 0)$

  y-intercept: $(0, a)$ y-intercept: $(0, -a)$

  $(a \neq 0)$ $(a \neq 0)$

Finding Parallel and Perpendicular Lines In Exercises 55–62, write the general forms of the equations of the lines through the point (a) parallel to the given line and (b) perpendicular to the given line.

Point	Line		Point	Line
55. $(-7, -2)$	$x = 1$		**56.** $(-1, 0)$	$y = -3$
57. $(2, 5)$	$x - y = -2$		**58.** $(-3, 2)$	$x + y = 7$
59. $(2, 1)$	$4x - 2y = 3$		**60.** $\left(\frac{5}{6}, -\frac{1}{2}\right)$	$7x + 4y = 8$
61. $\left(\frac{3}{4}, \frac{7}{8}\right)$	$5x - 3y = 0$		**62.** $(4, -5)$	$3x + 4y = 7$

Rate of Change In Exercises 63–66, you are given the dollar value of a product in 2012 *and* the rate at which the value of the product is expected to change during the next 5 years. Write a linear equation that gives the dollar value V of the product in terms of the year t. (Let $t = 0$ represent 2010.)

2012 Value	Rate
63. $1850	$250 increase per year
64. $156	$4.50 increase per year
65. $17,200	$1600 decrease per year
66. $245,000	$5600 decrease per year

Collinear Points In Exercises 67 and 68, determine whether the points are collinear. (Three points are *collinear* if they lie on the same line.)

67. $(-2, 1), (-1, 0), (2, -2)$ **68.** $(0, 4), (7, -6), (-5, 11)$

 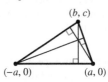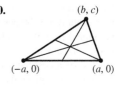
73. Analyzing a Line A line is represented by the equation $ax + by = 4$.

  (a) When is the line parallel to the x-axis?

  (b) When is the line parallel to the y-axis?

  (c) Give values for a and b such that the line has a slope of $\frac{5}{8}$.

  (d) Give values for a and b such that the line is perpendicular to $y = \frac{2}{5}x + 3$.

  (e) Give values for a and b such that the line coincides with the graph of $5x + 6y = 8$.

74. **HOW DO YOU SEE IT?** Several lines (labeled *a–f*) are shown in the figure below.

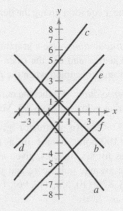

  (a) Which lines have a positive slope?

  (b) Which lines have a negative slope?

  (c) Which lines appear parallel?

  (d) Which lines appear perpendicular?

75. Temperature Conversion Find a linear equation that expresses the relationship between the temperature in degrees Celsius C and degrees Fahrenheit F. Use the fact that water freezes at $0°C$ ($32°F$) and boils at $100°C$ ($212°F$). Use the equation to convert $72°F$ to degrees Celsius.

76. Reimbursed Expenses A company reimburses its sales representatives $200 per day for lodging and meals plus $0.51 per mile driven. Write a linear equation giving the daily cost C to the company in terms of x, the number of miles driven. How much does it cost the company if a sales representative drives 137 miles on a given day?

77. Choosing a Job As a salesperson, you receive a monthly salary of $2000, plus a commission of 7% of sales. You are offered a new job at $2300 per month, plus a commission of 5% of sales.

(a) Write linear equations for your monthly wage W in terms of your monthly sales s for your current job and your job offer.

(b) Use a graphing utility to graph each equation and find the point of intersection. What does it signify?

(c) You think you can sell $20,000 worth of a product per month. Should you change jobs? Explain.

78. Straight-Line Depreciation A small business purchases a piece of equipment for $875. After 5 years, the equipment will be outdated, having no value.

(a) Write a linear equation giving the value y of the equipment in terms of the time x (in years), $0 \le x \le 5$.

(b) Find the value of the equipment when $x = 2$.

(c) Estimate (to two-decimal-place accuracy) the time when the value of the equipment is $200.

79. Apartment Rental A real estate office manages an apartment complex with 50 units. When the rent is $780 per month, all 50 units are occupied. However, when the rent is $825, the average number of occupied units drops to 47. Assume that the relationship between the monthly rent p and the demand x is linear. (*Note:* The term *demand* refers to the number of occupied units.)

(a) Write a linear equation giving the demand x in terms of the rent p.

(b) *Linear extrapolation* Use a graphing utility to graph the demand equation and use the *trace* feature to predict the number of units occupied when the rent is raised to $855.

(c) *Linear interpolation* Predict the number of units occupied when the rent is lowered to $795. Verify graphically.

80. Modeling Data An instructor gives regular 20-point quizzes and 100-point exams in a mathematics course. Average scores for six students, given as ordered pairs (x, y), where x is the average quiz score and y is the average exam score, are $(18, 87)$, $(10, 55)$, $(19, 96)$, $(16, 79)$, $(13, 76)$, and $(15, 82)$.

(a) Use the regression capabilities of a graphing utility to find the least squares regression line for the data.

(b) Use a graphing utility to plot the points and graph the regression line in the same viewing window.

(c) Use the regression line to predict the average exam score for a student with an average quiz score of 17.

(d) Interpret the meaning of the slope of the regression line.

(e) The instructor adds 4 points to the average exam score of everyone in the class. Describe the changes in the positions of the plotted points and the change in the equation of the line.

81. Tangent Line Find an equation of the line tangent to the circle $x^2 + y^2 = 169$ at the point $(5, 12)$.

82. Tangent Line Find an equation of the line tangent to the circle $(x - 1)^2 + (y - 1)^2 = 25$ at the point $(4, -3)$.

Distance In Exercises 83–86, find the distance between the point and line, or between the lines, using the formula for the distance between the point (x_1, y_1) and the line $Ax + By + C = 0$.

$$\text{Distance} = \frac{|Ax_1 + By_1 + C|}{\sqrt{A^2 + B^2}}$$

83. Point: $(-2, 1)$
Line: $x - y - 2 = 0$

84. Point: $(2, 3)$
Line: $4x + 3y = 10$

85. Line: $x + y = 1$
Line: $x + y = 5$

86. Line: $3x - 4y = 1$
Line: $3x - 4y = 10$

87. Distance Show that the distance between the point (x_1, y_1) and the line $Ax + By + C = 0$ is

$$\text{Distance} = \frac{|Ax_1 + By_1 + C|}{\sqrt{A^2 + B^2}}.$$

88. Distance Write the distance d between the point $(3, 1)$ and the line $y = mx + 4$ in terms of m. Use a graphing utility to graph the equation. When is the distance 0? Explain the result geometrically.

89. Proof Prove that the diagonals of a rhombus intersect at right angles. (A rhombus is a quadrilateral with sides of equal lengths.)

90. Proof Prove that the figure formed by connecting consecutive midpoints of the sides of any quadrilateral is a parallelogram.

91. Proof Prove that if the points (x_1, y_1) and (x_2, y_2) lie on the same line as (x_1^*, y_1^*) and (x_2^*, y_2^*), then

$$\frac{y_2^* - y_1^*}{x_2^* - x_1^*} = \frac{y_2 - y_1}{x_2 - x_1}.$$

Assume $x_1 \ne x_2$ and $x_1^* \ne x_2^*$.

92. Proof Prove that if the slopes of two nonvertical lines are negative reciprocals of each other, then the lines are perpendicular.

True or False? In Exercises 93–96, determine whether the statement is true or false. If it is false, explain why or give an example that shows it is false.

93. The lines represented by $ax + by = c_1$ and $bx - ay = c_2$ are perpendicular. Assume $a \ne 0$ and $b \ne 0$.

94. It is possible for two lines with positive slopes to be perpendicular to each other.

95. If a line contains points in both the first and third quadrants, then its slope must be positive.

96. The equation of any line can be written in general form.

1.3 Functions and Their Graphs

- Use function notation to represent and evaluate a function.
- Find the domain and range of a function.
- Sketch the graph of a function.
- Identify different types of transformations of functions.
- Classify functions and recognize combinations of functions.

Functions and Function Notation

A **relation** between two sets X and Y is a set of ordered pairs, each of the form (x, y), where x is a member of X and y is a member of Y. A **function** from X to Y is a relation between X and Y that has the property that any two ordered pairs with the same x-value also have the same y-value. The variable x is the **independent variable,** and the variable y is the **dependent variable.**

Many real-life situations can be modeled by functions. For instance, the area A of a circle is a function of the circle's radius r.

$$A = \pi r^2 \qquad \text{\small A is a function of r.}$$

In this case, r is the independent variable and A is the dependent variable.

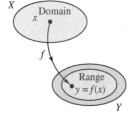

A real-valued function f of a real variable

Figure 1.22

Definition of a Real-Valued Function of a Real Variable

Let X and Y be sets of real numbers. A **real-valued function f of a real variable x** from X to Y is a correspondence that assigns to each number x in X exactly one number y in Y.

The **domain** of f is the set X. The number y is the **image** of x under f and is denoted by $f(x)$, which is called the **value of f at x.** The **range** of f is a subset of Y and consists of all images of numbers in X (see Figure 1.22).

Functions can be specified in a variety of ways. In this text, however, you will concentrate primarily on functions that are given by equations involving the dependent and independent variables. For instance, the equation

$$x^2 + 2y = 1 \qquad \text{\small Equation in implicit form}$$

defines y, the dependent variable, as a function of x, the independent variable. To **evaluate** this function (that is, to find the y-value that corresponds to a given x-value), it is convenient to isolate y on the left side of the equation.

$$y = \tfrac{1}{2}(1 - x^2) \qquad \text{\small Equation in explicit form}$$

Using f as the name of the function, you can write this equation as

$$f(x) = \tfrac{1}{2}(1 - x^2). \qquad \text{\small Function notation}$$

The original equation

$$x^2 + 2y = 1$$

implicitly defines y as a function of x. When you solve the equation for y, you are writing the equation in **explicit** form.

Function notation has the advantage of clearly identifying the dependent variable as $f(x)$ while at the same time telling you that x is the independent variable and that the function itself is "f." The symbol $f(x)$ is read "f of x." Function notation allows you to be less wordy. Instead of asking "What is the value of y that corresponds to $x = 3$?" you can ask "What is $f(3)$?"

FUNCTION NOTATION

The word *function* was first used by Gottfried Wilhelm Leibniz in 1694 as a term to denote any quantity connected with a curve, such as the coordinates of a point on a curve or the slope of a curve. Forty years later, Leonhard Euler used the word "function" to describe any expression made up of a variable and some constants. He introduced the notation $y = f(x)$.

In an equation that defines a function of x, the role of the variable x is simply that of a placeholder. For instance, the function

$$f(x) = 2x^2 - 4x + 1$$

can be described by the form

$$f(\quad) = 2(\quad)^2 - 4(\quad) + 1$$

where rectangles are used instead of x. To evaluate $f(-2)$, replace each rectangle with -2.

$$f(-2) = 2(-2)^2 - 4(-2) + 1 \qquad \text{Substitute } -2 \text{ for } x.$$
$$= 2(4) + 8 + 1 \qquad \text{Simplify.}$$
$$= 17 \qquad \text{Simplify.}$$

Although f is often used as a convenient function name and x as the independent variable, you can use other symbols. For instance, these three equations all define the same function.

$$f(x) = x^2 - 4x + 7 \qquad \text{Function name is } f, \text{ independent variable is } x.$$
$$f(t) = t^2 - 4t + 7 \qquad \text{Function name is } f, \text{ independent variable is } t.$$
$$g(s) = s^2 - 4s + 7 \qquad \text{Function name is } g, \text{ independent variable is } s.$$

EXAMPLE 1   **Evaluating a Function**

For the function f defined by $f(x) = x^2 + 7$, evaluate each expression.

a. $f(3a)$ **b.** $f(b - 1)$ **c.** $\dfrac{f(x + \Delta x) - f(x)}{\Delta x}$

Solution

a. $f(3a) = (3a)^2 + 7 \qquad \text{Substitute } 3a \text{ for } x.$
$$= 9a^2 + 7 \qquad \text{Simplify.}$$

b. $f(b - 1) = (b - 1)^2 + 7 \qquad \text{Substitute } b - 1 \text{ for } x.$
$$= b^2 - 2b + 1 + 7 \qquad \text{Expand binomial.}$$
$$= b^2 - 2b + 8 \qquad \text{Simplify.}$$

c. $\dfrac{f(x + \Delta x) - f(x)}{\Delta x} = \dfrac{[(x + \Delta x)^2 + 7] - (x^2 + 7)}{\Delta x}$

$$= \dfrac{x^2 + 2x\Delta x + (\Delta x)^2 + 7 - x^2 - 7}{\Delta x}$$

$$= \dfrac{2x\Delta x + (\Delta x)^2}{\Delta x}$$

$$= \dfrac{\Delta x(2x + \Delta x)}{\Delta x}$$

$$= 2x + \Delta x, \quad \Delta x \neq 0$$

> **· · REMARK** The expression in Example 1(c) is called a *difference quotient* and has a special significance in calculus. You will learn more about this in Chapter 3.

In calculus, it is important to specify the domain of a function or expression clearly. For instance, in Example 1(c), the two expressions

$$\dfrac{f(x + \Delta x) - f(x)}{\Delta x} \quad \text{and} \quad 2x + \Delta x, \quad \Delta x \neq 0$$

are equivalent because $\Delta x = 0$ is excluded from the domain of each expression. Without a stated domain restriction, the two expressions would not be equivalent.

The Domain and Range of a Function

The domain of a function can be described explicitly, or it may be described *implicitly* by an equation used to define the function. The implied domain is the set of all real numbers for which the equation is defined, whereas an explicitly defined domain is one that is given along with the function. For example, the function

$$f(x) = \frac{1}{x^2 - 4}, \quad 4 \le x \le 5$$

has an explicitly defined domain given by $\{x : 4 \le x \le 5\}$. On the other hand, the function

$$g(x) = \frac{1}{x^2 - 4}$$

has an implied domain that is the set $\{x : x \ne \pm 2\}$.

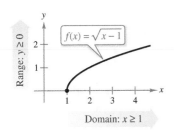

EXAMPLE 2 **Finding the Domain and Range of a Function**

a. The domain of the function

$$f(x) = \sqrt{x - 1}$$

is the set of all x-values for which $x - 1 \ge 0$, which is the interval $[1, \infty)$. To find the range, observe that $f(x) = \sqrt{x - 1}$ is never negative. So, the range is the interval $[0, \infty)$, as shown in Figure 1.23(a).

b. The domain of the tangent function

$$f(x) = \tan x$$

is the set of all x-values such that

$$x \ne \frac{\pi}{2} + n\pi, \quad n \text{ is an integer.} \qquad \text{Domain of tangent function}$$

The range of this function is the set of all real numbers, as shown in Figure 1.23(b). For a review of the characteristics of this and other trigonometric functions, see Appendix C.

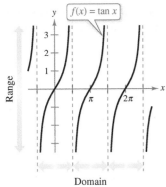

(a) The domain of f is $[1, \infty)$, and the range is $[0, \infty)$.

(b) The domain of f is all x-values such that $x \ne \frac{\pi}{2} + n\pi$, and the range is $(-\infty, \infty)$.

Figure 1.23

EXAMPLE 3 **A Function Defined by More than One Equation**

For the piecewise-defined function

$$f(x) = \begin{cases} 1 - x, & x < 1 \\ \sqrt{x - 1}, & x \ge 1 \end{cases}$$

f is defined for $x < 1$ and $x \ge 1$. So, the domain is the set of all real numbers. On the portion of the domain for which $x \ge 1$, the function behaves as in Example 2(a). For $x < 1$, the values of $1 - x$ are positive. So, the range of the function is the interval $[0, \infty)$. (See Figure 1.24.)

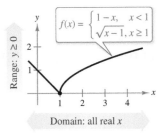

The domain of f is $(-\infty, \infty)$, and the range is $[0, \infty)$.

Figure 1.24

A function from X to Y is **one-to-one** when to each y-value in the range there corresponds exactly one x-value in the domain. For instance, the function in Example 2(a) is one-to-one, whereas the functions in Examples 2(b) and 3 are not one-to-one. A function from X to Y is **onto** when its range consists of all of Y.

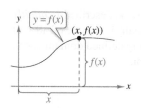

The graph of a function
Figure 1.25

The Graph of a Function

The graph of the function $y = f(x)$ consists of all points $(x, f(x))$, where x is in the domain of f. In Figure 1.25, note that

$$x = \text{the directed distance from the } y\text{-axis}$$

and

$$f(x) = \text{the directed distance from the } x\text{-axis}.$$

A vertical line can intersect the graph of a function of x at most *once*. This observation provides a convenient visual test, called the **Vertical Line Test,** for functions of x. That is, a graph in the coordinate plane is the graph of a function of x if and only if no vertical line intersects the graph at more than one point. For example, in Figure 1.26(a), you can see that the graph does not define y as a function of x because a vertical line intersects the graph twice, whereas in Figures 1.26(b) and (c), the graphs do define y as a function of x.

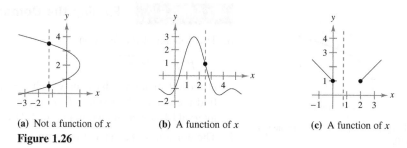

(a) Not a function of x (b) A function of x (c) A function of x
Figure 1.26

Figure 1.27 shows the graphs of eight basic functions. You should be able to recognize these graphs. (Graphs of the other four basic trigonometric functions are shown in Appendix C.)

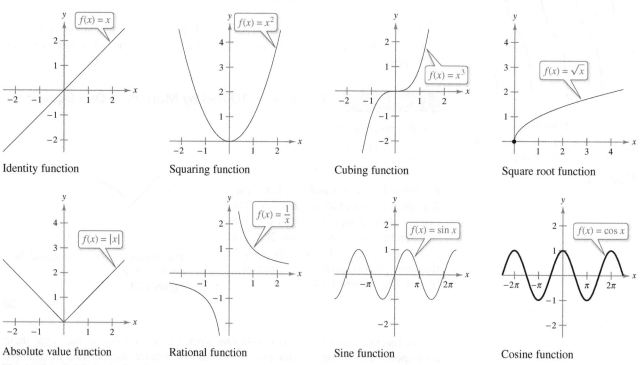

Identity function   Squaring function   Cubing function   Square root function

Absolute value function   Rational function   Sine function   Cosine function

The graphs of eight basic functions
Figure 1.27

Transformations of Functions

Some families of graphs have the same basic shape. For example, compare the graph of $y = x^2$ with the graphs of the four other quadratic functions shown in Figure 1.28.

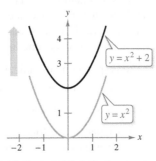

(a) Vertical shift upward

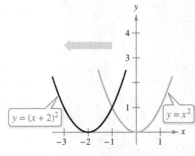

(b) Horizontal shift to the left

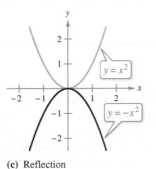

(c) Reflection

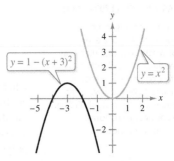

(d) Shift left, reflect, and shift upward

Figure 1.28

Each of the graphs in Figure 1.28 is a **transformation** of the graph of $y = x^2$. The three basic types of transformations illustrated by these graphs are vertical shifts, horizontal shifts, and reflections. Function notation lends itself well to describing transformations of graphs in the plane. For instance, using

$$f(x) = x^2 \qquad \text{Original function}$$

as the original function, the transformations shown in Figure 1.28 can be represented by these equations.

a. $y = f(x) + 2$ Vertical shift up two units

b. $y = f(x + 2)$ Horizontal shift to the left two units

c. $y = -f(x)$ Reflection about the x-axis

d. $y = -f(x + 3) + 1$ Shift left three units, reflect about the x-axis, and shift up one unit

---

Basic Types of Transformations $(c > 0)$

Original graph:	$y = f(x)$
Horizontal shift c units to the **right:**	$y = f(x - c)$
Horizontal shift c units to the **left:**	$y = f(x + c)$
Vertical shift c units **downward:**	$y = f(x) - c$
Vertical shift c units **upward:**	$y = f(x) + c$
Reflection (about the x-axis):	$y = -f(x)$
Reflection (about the y-axis):	$y = f(-x)$
Reflection (about the origin):	$y = -f(-x)$

LEONHARD EULER (1707–1783)

In addition to making major contributions to almost every branch of mathematics, Euler was one of the first to apply calculus to real-life problems in physics. His extensive published writings include such topics as shipbuilding, acoustics, optics, astronomy, mechanics, and magnetism. *See LarsonCalculus.com to read more of this biography.*

Classifications and Combinations of Functions

The modern notion of a function is derived from the efforts of many seventeenth- and eighteenth-century mathematicians. Of particular note was Leonhard Euler, who introduced the function notation $y = f(x)$. By the end of the eighteenth century, mathematicians and scientists had concluded that many real-world phenomena could be represented by mathematical models taken from a collection of functions called **elementary functions.** Elementary functions fall into three categories.

1. Algebraic functions (polynomial, radical, rational)

2. Trigonometric functions (sine, cosine, tangent, and so on)

3. Exponential and logarithmic functions

You can review the trigonometric functions in Appendix C. The other nonalgebraic functions, such as the inverse trigonometric functions and the exponential and logarithmic functions, are introduced in Sections 1.5 and 1.6.

The most common type of algebraic function is a **polynomial function**

$$f(x) = a_n x^n + a_{n-1} x^{n-1} + \cdots + a_2 x^2 + a_1 x + a_0$$

where n is a nonnegative integer. The numbers a_i are **coefficients,** with a_n the **leading coefficient** and a_0 the **constant term** of the polynomial function. If $a_n \neq 0$, then n is the **degree** of the polynomial function. The zero polynomial $f(x) = 0$ is not assigned a degree. It is common practice to use subscript notation for coefficients of general polynomial functions, but for polynomial functions of low degree, these simpler forms are often used. (Note that $a \neq 0$.)

Zeroth degree:	$f(x) = a$	Constant function
First degree:	$f(x) = ax + b$	Linear function
Second degree:	$f(x) = ax^2 + bx + c$	Quadratic function
Third degree:	$f(x) = ax^3 + bx^2 + cx + d$	Cubic function

Although the graph of a nonconstant polynomial function can have several turns, eventually the graph will rise or fall without bound as x moves to the right or left. Whether the graph of

$$f(x) = a_n x^n + a_{n-1} x^{n-1} + \cdots + a_2 x^2 + a_1 x + a_0$$

eventually rises or falls can be determined by the function's degree (odd or even) and by the leading coefficient a_n, as indicated in Figure 1.29. Note that the dashed portions of the graphs indicate that the **Leading Coefficient Test** determines *only* the right and left behavior of the graph.

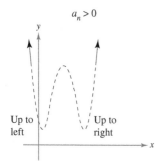

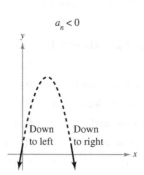

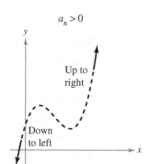

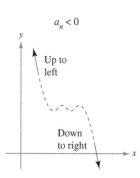

Graphs of polynomial functions of even degree

Graphs of polynomial functions of odd degree

The Leading Coefficient Test for polynomial functions

Figure 1.29

■ **FOR FURTHER INFORMATION**
For more on the history of the concept of a function, see the article "Evolution of the Function Concept: A Brief Survey" by Israel Kleiner in *The College Mathematics Journal*. To view this article, go to *MathArticles.com*.

Just as a rational number can be written as the quotient of two integers, a **rational function** can be written as the quotient of two polynomials. Specifically, a function f is rational when it has the form

$$f(x) = \frac{p(x)}{q(x)}, \quad q(x) \neq 0$$

where $p(x)$ and $q(x)$ are polynomials.

Polynomial functions and rational functions are examples of **algebraic functions.** An algebraic function of x is one that can be expressed as a finite number of sums, differences, multiples, quotients, and radicals involving x^n. For example,

$$f(x) = \sqrt{x + 1}$$

is algebraic. Functions that are not algebraic are **transcendental.** For instance, the trigonometric functions are transcendental.

Two functions can be combined in various ways to create new functions. For example, given $f(x) = 2x - 3$ and $g(x) = x^2 + 1$, you can form the functions shown.

$(f + g)(x) = f(x) + g(x) = (2x - 3) + (x^2 + 1)$	Sum
$(f - g)(x) = f(x) - g(x) = (2x - 3) - (x^2 + 1)$	Difference
$(fg)(x) = f(x)g(x) = (2x - 3)(x^2 + 1)$	Product
$(f/g)(x) = \dfrac{f(x)}{g(x)} = \dfrac{2x - 3}{x^2 + 1}$	Quotient

You can combine two functions in yet another way, called **composition.** The resulting function is called a **composite function.**

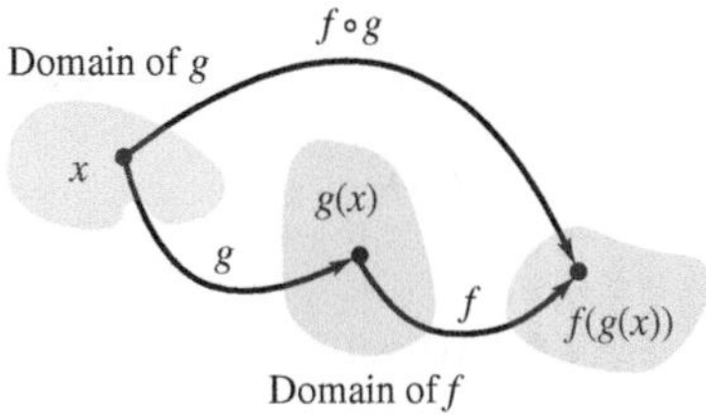

Domain of g $f \circ g$

x

$g(x)$

g

f

$f(g(x))$

Domain of f

The domain of the composite function $f \circ g$

Figure 1.30

Definition of Composite Function

Let f and g be functions. The function $(f \circ g)(x) = f(g(x))$ is the **composite** of f with g. The domain of $f \circ g$ is the set of all x in the domain of g such that $g(x)$ is in the domain of f (see Figure 1.30).

The composite of f with g is generally not the same as the composite of g with f. This is shown in the next example.

EXAMPLE 4   **Finding Composite Functions**

⋅ ⋅ ⋅ ⋅▷ *See LarsonCalculus.com for an interactive version of this type of example.*

For $f(x) = 2x - 3$ and $g(x) = \cos x$, find each composite function.

a. $f \circ g$ **b.** $g \circ f$

Solution

a.	$(f \circ g)(x) = f(g(x))$	Definition of $f \circ g$
	$= f(\cos x)$	Substitute $\cos x$ for $g(x)$.
	$= 2(\cos x) - 3$	Definition of $f(x)$
	$= 2 \cos x - 3$	Simplify.
b.	$(g \circ f)(x) = g(f(x))$	Definition of $g \circ f$
	$= g(2x - 3)$	Substitute $2x - 3$ for $f(x)$.
	$= \cos(2x - 3)$	Definition of $g(x)$

Note that $(f \circ g)(x) \neq (g \circ f)(x)$.

In Section 1.1, an *x*-intercept of a graph was defined to be a point $(a, 0)$ at which the graph crosses the *x*-axis. If the graph represents a function *f*, then the number *a* is a **zero** of *f*. In other words, *the zeros of a function f are the solutions of the equation* $f(x) = 0$. For example, the function

Exploration

Use a graphing utility to graph each function. Determine whether the function is *even, odd,* or *neither*.

$$f(x) = x^2 - x^4$$
$$g(x) = 2x^3 + 1$$
$$h(x) = x^5 - 2x^3 + x$$
$$j(x) = 2 - x^6 - x^8$$
$$k(x) = x^5 - 2x^4 + x - 2$$
$$p(x) = x^9 + 3x^5 - x^3 + x$$

Describe a way to identify a function as odd or even by inspecting the equation.

In Section 1.1, an *x*-intercept of a graph was defined to be a point $(a, 0)$ at which the graph crosses the *x*-axis. If the graph represents a function *f*, then the number *a* is a **zero** of *f*. In other words, *the zeros of a function f are the solutions of the equation* $f(x) = 0$. For example, the function

$$f(x) = x - 4$$

has a zero at $x = 4$ because $f(4) = 0$.

In Section 1.1, you also studied different types of symmetry. In the terminology of functions, a function is **even** when its graph is symmetric with respect to the *y*-axis, and is **odd** when its graph is symmetric with respect to the origin. The symmetry tests in Section 1.1 yield the following test for even and odd functions.

Test for Even and Odd Functions

The function $y = f(x)$ is **even** when

$$f(-x) = f(x).$$

The function $y = f(x)$ is **odd** when

$$f(-x) = -f(x).$$

EXAMPLE 5   **Even and Odd Functions and Zeros of Functions**

Determine whether each function is even, odd, or neither. Then find the zeros of the function.

a. $f(x) = x^3 - x$ **b.** $g(x) = 1 + \cos x$

Solution

a. This function is odd because

$$f(-x) = (-x)^3 - (-x) = -x^3 + x = -(x^3 - x) = -f(x).$$

The zeros of *f* are

$$x^3 - x = 0 \qquad \text{Let } f(x) = 0.$$
$$x(x^2 - 1) = 0 \qquad \text{Factor.}$$
$$x(x - 1)(x + 1) = 0 \qquad \text{Factor.}$$
$$x = 0, 1, -1. \qquad \text{Zeros of } f$$

See Figure 1.31(a).

b. This function is even because

$$g(-x) = 1 + \cos(-x) = 1 + \cos x = g(x). \qquad \cos(-x) = \cos(x)$$

The zeros of *g* are

$$1 + \cos x = 0 \qquad \text{Let } g(x) = 0.$$
$$\cos x = -1 \qquad \text{Subtract 1 from each side.}$$
$$x = (2n + 1)\pi, \; n \text{ is an integer.} \qquad \text{Zeros of } g$$

See Figure 1.31(b).

Each function in Example 5 is either even or odd. However, some functions, such as

$$f(x) = x^2 + x + 1$$

are neither even nor odd.

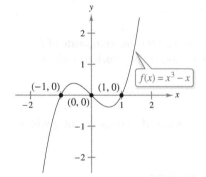

(a) Odd function

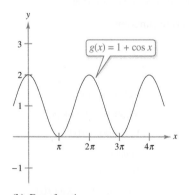

(b) Even function

Figure 1.31

1.3 Exercises

See CalcChat.com for tutorial help and worked-out solutions to odd-numbered exercises.

Evaluating a Function In Exercises 1–10, evaluate the function at the given value(s) of the independent variable. Simplify the results.

1. $f(x) = 7x - 4$
 (a) $f(0)$ (b) $f(-3)$
 (c) $f(b)$ (d) $f(x - 1)$

2. $f(x) = \sqrt{x + 5}$
 (a) $f(-4)$ (b) $f(11)$
 (c) $f(4)$ (d) $f(x + \Delta x)$

3. $g(x) = 5 - x^2$
 (a) $g(0)$ (b) $g(\sqrt{5})$
 (c) $g(-2)$ (d) $g(t - 1)$

4. $g(x) = x^2(x - 4)$
 (a) $g(4)$ (b) $g(\frac{3}{2})$
 (c) $g(c)$ (d) $g(t + 4)$

5. $f(x) = \cos 2x$
 (a) $f(0)$ (b) $f\left(-\dfrac{\pi}{4}\right)$
 (c) $f\left(\dfrac{\pi}{3}\right)$ (d) $f(\pi)$

6. $f(x) = \sin x$
 (a) $f(\pi)$ (b) $f\left(\dfrac{5\pi}{4}\right)$
 (c) $f\left(\dfrac{2\pi}{3}\right)$ (d) $f\left(-\dfrac{\pi}{6}\right)$

7. $f(x) = x^3$
$$\frac{f(x + \Delta x) - f(x)}{\Delta x}$$

8. $f(x) = 3x - 1$
$$\frac{f(x) - f(1)}{x - 1}$$

9. $f(x) = \dfrac{1}{\sqrt{x - 1}}$
$$\frac{f(x) - f(2)}{x - 2}$$

10. $f(x) = x^3 - x$
$$\frac{f(x) - f(1)}{x - 1}$$

Finding the Domain and Range of a Function In Exercises 11–22, find the domain and range of the function.

11. $f(x) = 4x^2$

12. $g(x) = x^2 - 5$

13. $f(x) = x^3$

14. $h(x) = 4 - x^2$

15. $g(x) = \sqrt{6x}$

16. $h(x) = -\sqrt{x + 3}$

17. $f(x) = \sqrt{16 - x^2}$

18. $f(x) = |x - 3|$

19. $f(t) = \sec \dfrac{\pi t}{4}$

20. $h(t) = \cot t$

21. $f(x) = \dfrac{3}{x}$

22. $f(x) = \dfrac{x - 2}{x + 4}$

Finding the Domain of a Function In Exercises 23–28, find the domain of the function.

23. $f(x) = \sqrt{x} + \sqrt{1 - x}$

24. $f(x) = \sqrt{x^2 - 3x + 2}$

25. $g(x) = \dfrac{2}{1 - \cos x}$

26. $h(x) = \dfrac{1}{\sin x - (1/2)}$

27. $f(x) = \dfrac{1}{|x + 3|}$

28. $g(x) = \dfrac{1}{|x^2 - 4|}$

Finding the Domain and Range of a Piecewise Function In Exercises 29–32, evaluate the function as indicated. Determine its domain and range.

29. $f(x) = \begin{cases} 2x + 1, & x < 0 \\ 2x + 2, & x \geq 0 \end{cases}$
 (a) $f(-1)$ (b) $f(0)$ (c) $f(2)$ (d) $f(t^2 + 1)$

30. $f(x) = \begin{cases} x^2 + 2, & x \leq 1 \\ 2x^2 + 2, & x > 1 \end{cases}$
 (a) $f(-2)$ (b) $f(0)$ (c) $f(1)$ (d) $f(s^2 + 2)$

31. $f(x) = \begin{cases} |x| + 1, & x < 1 \\ -x + 1, & x \geq 1 \end{cases}$
 (a) $f(-3)$ (b) $f(1)$ (c) $f(3)$ (d) $f(b^2 + 1)$

32. $f(x) = \begin{cases} \sqrt{x + 4}, & x \leq 5 \\ (x - 5)^2, & x > 5 \end{cases}$
 (a) $f(-3)$ (b) $f(0)$ (c) $f(5)$ (d) $f(10)$

Sketching a Graph of a Function In Exercises 33–40, sketch a graph of the function and find its domain and range. Use a graphing utility to verify your graph.

33. $f(x) = 4 - x$

34. $g(x) = \dfrac{4}{x}$

35. $h(x) = \sqrt{x - 6}$

36. $f(x) = \frac{1}{4}x^3 + 3$

37. $f(x) = \sqrt{9 - x^2}$

38. $f(x) = x + \sqrt{4 - x^2}$

39. $g(t) = 3 \sin \pi t$

40. $h(\theta) = -5 \cos \dfrac{\theta}{2}$

WRITING ABOUT CONCEPTS

41. Describing a Graph
 The graph of the distance that a student drives in a 10-minute trip to school is shown in the figure. Give a verbal description of the characteristics of the student's drive to school.

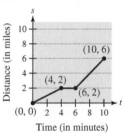

42. Sketching a Graph A student who commutes 27 miles to attend college remembers, after driving a few minutes, that a term paper that is due has been forgotten. Driving faster than usual, the student returns home, picks up the paper, and once again starts toward school. Sketch a possible graph of the student's distance from home as a function of time.

Using the Vertical Line Test In Exercises 43–46, use the Vertical Line Test to determine whether y is a function of x. To print an enlarged copy of the graph, go to *MathGraphs.com*.

43. $x - y^2 = 0$

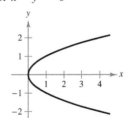

44. $\sqrt{x^2 - 4} - y = 0$

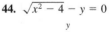
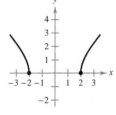

45. $y = \begin{cases} x + 1, & x \le 0 \\ -x + 2, & x > 0 \end{cases}$

46. $x^2 + y^2 = 4$

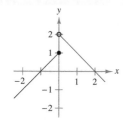 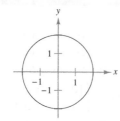

61. Sketching Transformations Use the graph of f shown in the figure to sketch the graph of each function. To print an enlarged copy of the graph, go to *MathGraphs.com*.

(a) $f(x + 3)$ (b) $f(x - 1)$

(c) $f(x) + 2$ (d) $f(x) - 4$

(e) $3f(x)$ (f) $\frac{1}{4}f(x)$

(g) $-f(x)$ (h) $-f(-x)$

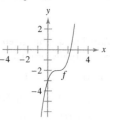

Deciding Whether an Equation Is a Function In Exercises 47–50, determine whether y is a function of x.

47. $x^2 + y^2 = 16$ **48.** $x^2 + y = 16$

49. $y^2 = x^2 - 1$ **50.** $x^2y - x^2 + 4y = 0$

Transformation of a Function In Exercises 51–54, the graph shows one of the eight basic functions on page 22 and a transformation of the function. Describe the transformation. Then use your description to write an equation for the transformation.

51.

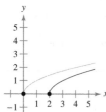

52.

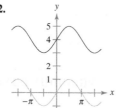

53.

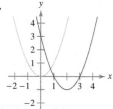

54.

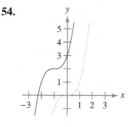

Matching In Exercises 55–60, use the graph of $y = f(x)$ to match the function with its graph.

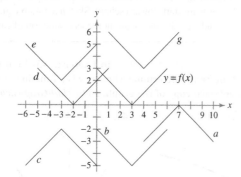

55. $y = f(x + 5)$ **56.** $y = f(x) - 5$

57. $y = -f(-x) - 2$ **58.** $y = -f(x - 4)$

59. $y = f(x + 6) + 2$ **60.** $y = f(x - 1) + 3$

62. Sketching Transformations Use the graph of f shown in the figure to sketch the graph of each function. To print an enlarged copy of the graph, go to *MathGraphs.com*.

(a) $f(x - 4)$ (b) $f(x + 2)$

(c) $f(x) + 4$ (d) $f(x) - 1$

(e) $2f(x)$ (f) $\frac{1}{2}f(x)$

(g) $f(-x)$ (h) $-f(x)$

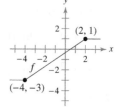

Combinations of Functions In Exercises 63 and 64, find (a) $f(x) + g(x)$, (b) $f(x) - g(x)$, (c) $f(x) \cdot g(x)$, and (d) $f(x)/g(x)$.

63. $f(x) = 3x - 4$
$g(x) = 4$

64. $f(x) = x^2 + 5x + 4$
$g(x) = x + 1$

65. Evaluating Composite Functions Given $f(x) = \sqrt{x}$ and $g(x) = x^2 - 1$, evaluate each expression.

(a) $f(g(1))$ (b) $g(f(1))$ (c) $g(f(0))$

(d) $f(g(-4))$ (e) $f(g(x))$ (f) $g(f(x))$

66. Evaluating Composite Functions Given $f(x) = \sin x$ and $g(x) = \pi x$, evaluate each expression.

(a) $f(g(2))$ (b) $f\left(g\left(\frac{1}{2}\right)\right)$ (c) $g(f(0))$

(d) $g\left(f\left(\frac{\pi}{4}\right)\right)$ (e) $f(g(x))$ (f) $g(f(x))$

Finding Composite Functions In Exercises 67–70, find the composite functions $f \circ g$ and $g \circ f$. Find the domain of each composite function. Are the two composite functions equal?

67. $f(x) = x^2$, $g(x) = \sqrt{x}$ **68.** $f(x) = x^2 - 1$, $g(x) = \cos x$

69. $f(x) = \dfrac{3}{x}$, $g(x) = x^2 - 1$ **70.** $f(x) = \dfrac{1}{x}$, $g(x) = \sqrt{x + 2}$

71. Evaluating Composite Functions Use the graphs of f and g to evaluate each expression. If the result is undefined, explain why.

(a) $(f \circ g)(3)$ (b) $g(f(2))$

(c) $g(f(5))$ (d) $(f \circ g)(-3)$

(e) $(g \circ f)(-1)$ (f) $f(g(-1))$

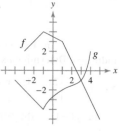

72. Ripples A pebble is dropped into a calm pond, causing ripples in the form of concentric circles. The radius (in feet) of the outer ripple is given by $r(t) = 0.6t$, where t is the time in seconds after the pebble strikes the water. The area of the circle is given by the function $A(r) = \pi r^2$. Find and interpret $(A \circ r)(t)$.

Think About It In Exercises 73 and 74, $F(x) = f \circ g \circ h$. Identify functions for f, g, and h. (There are many correct answers.)

73. $F(x) = \sqrt{2x - 2}$ **74.** $F(x) = -4 \sin(1 - x)$

Think About It In Exercises 75 and 76, find the coordinates of a second point on the graph of a function f when the given point is on the graph and the function is (a) even and (b) odd.

75. $\left(-\frac{3}{2}, 4\right)$ **76.** $(4, 9)$

77. Even and Odd Functions The graphs of f, g, and h are shown in the figure. Decide whether each function is even, odd, or neither.

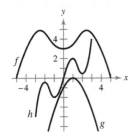

Figure for 77   Figure for 78

78. Even and Odd Functions The domain of the function f shown in the figure is $-6 \le x \le 6$.

(a) Complete the graph of f given that f is even.

(b) Complete the graph of f given that f is odd.

Even and Odd Functions and Zeros of Functions In Exercises 79–82, determine whether the function is even, odd, or neither. Then find the zeros of the function. Use a graphing utility to verify your result.

79. $f(x) = x^2(4 - x^2)$ **80.** $f(x) = \sqrt[3]{x}$

81. $f(x) = x \cos x$ **82.** $f(x) = \sin^2 x$

Writing Functions In Exercises 83–86, write an equation for a function that has the given graph.

83. Line segment connecting $(-2, 4)$ and $(0, -6)$

84. Line segment connecting $(3, 1)$ and $(5, 8)$

85. The bottom half of the parabola $x + y^2 = 0$

86. The bottom half of the circle $x^2 + y^2 = 36$

Sketching a Graph In Exercises 87–90, sketch a possible graph of the situation.

87. The speed of an airplane as a function of time during a 5-hour flight

88. The height of a baseball as a function of horizontal distance during a home run

89. The amount of a certain brand of sneaker sold by a sporting goods store as a function of the price of the sneaker

90. The value of a new car as a function of time over a period of 8 years

91. Domain Find the value of c such that the domain of $f(x) = \sqrt{c - x^2}$ is $[-5, 5]$.

92. Domain Find all values of c such that the domain of

$$f(x) = \frac{x + 3}{x^2 + 3cx + 6}$$

is the set of all real numbers.

93. Graphical Reasoning An electronically controlled thermostat is programmed to lower the temperature during the night automatically (see figure). The temperature T in degrees Celsius is given in terms of t, the time in hours on a 24-hour clock.

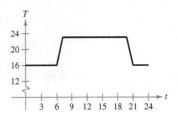

(a) Approximate $T(4)$ and $T(15)$.

(b) The thermostat is reprogrammed to produce a temperature $H(t) = T(t - 1)$. How does this change the temperature? Explain.

(c) The thermostat is reprogrammed to produce a temperature $H(t) = T(t) - 1$. How does this change the temperature? Explain.

 94. HOW DO YOU SEE IT? Water runs into a vase of height 30 centimeters at a constant rate. The vase is full after 5 seconds. Use this information and the shape of the vase shown to answer the questions when d is the depth of the water in centimeters and t is the time in seconds (see figure).

(a) Explain why d is a function of t.

(b) Determine the domain and range of the function.

(c) Sketch a possible graph of the function.

(d) Use the graph in part (c) to approximate $d(4)$. What does this represent?

95. Modeling Data The table shows the average numbers of acres per farm in the United States for selected years. *(Source: U.S. Department of Agriculture)*

Year	1960	1970	1980	1990	2000	2010
Acreage	297	374	429	460	436	418

(a) Plot the data, where A is the acreage and t is the time in years, with $t = 0$ corresponding to 1960. Sketch a freehand curve that approximates the data.

(b) Use the curve in part (a) to approximate $A(25)$.

96. Automobile Aerodynamics

The horsepower H required to overcome wind drag on a certain automobile is approximated by

$$H(x) = 0.002x^2 + 0.005x - 0.029, \quad 10 \le x \le 100$$

where x is the speed of the car in miles per hour.

(a) Use a graphing utility to graph H.

(b) Rewrite the power function so that x represents the speed in kilometers per hour. [Find $H(x/1.6)$.]

97. Think About It Write the function $f(x) = |x| + |x - 2|$ without using absolute value signs. (For a review of absolute value, see Appendix C.)

98. Writing Use a graphing utility to graph the polynomial functions $p_1(x) = x^3 - x + 1$ and $p_2(x) = x^3 - x$. How many zeros does each function have? Is there a cubic polynomial that has no zeros? Explain.

99. Proof Prove that the function is odd.

$$f(x) = a_{2n+1}x^{2n+1} + \cdots + a_3x^3 + a_1x$$

100. Proof Prove that the function is even.

$$f(x) = a_{2n}x^{2n} + a_{2n-2}x^{2n-2} + \cdots + a_2x^2 + a_0$$

101. Proof Prove that the product of two even (or two odd) functions is even.

102. Proof Prove that the product of an odd function and an even function is odd.

103. Length A right triangle is formed in the first quadrant by the x- and y-axes and a line through the point $(3, 2)$ (see figure). Write the length L of the hypotenuse as a function of x.

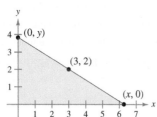

104. Volume An open box of maximum volume is to be made from a square piece of material 24 centimeters on a side by cutting equal squares from the corners and turning up the sides (see figure).

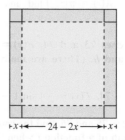
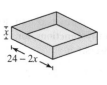

(a) Write the volume V as a function of x, the length of the corner squares. What is the domain of the function?

(b) Use a graphing utility to graph the volume function and approximate the dimensions of the box that yield a maximum volume.

(c) Use the *table* feature of a graphing utility to verify your answer in part (b). (The first two rows of the table are shown.)

Height, x	Length and Width	Volume, V
1	$24 - 2(1)$	$1[24 - 2(1)]^2 = 484$
2	$24 - 2(2)$	$2[24 - 2(2)]^2 = 800$

True or False? In Exercises 105–110, determine whether the statement is true or false. If it is false, explain why or give an example that shows it is false.

105. If $f(a) = f(b)$, then $a = b$.

106. A vertical line can intersect the graph of a function at most once.

107. If $f(x) = f(-x)$ for all x in the domain of f, then the graph of f is symmetric with respect to the y-axis.

108. If f is a function, then

$$f(ax) = af(x).$$

109. The graph of a function of x cannot have symmetry with respect to the x-axis.

110. If the domain of a function consists of a single number, then its range must also consist of only one number.

PUTNAM EXAM CHALLENGE

111. Let R be the region consisting of the points (x, y) of the Cartesian plane satisfying both $|x| - |y| \le 1$ and $|y| \le 1$. Sketch the region R and find its area.

112. Consider a polynomial $f(x)$ with real coefficients having the property $f(g(x)) = g(f(x))$ for every polynomial $g(x)$ with real coefficients. Determine and prove the nature of $f(x)$.

These problems were composed by the Committee on the Putnam Prize Competition.
© The Mathematical Association of America. All rights reserved.

1.4   Fitting Models to Data

■ Fit a linear model to a real-life data set.
■ Fit a quadratic model to a real-life data set.
■ Fit a trigonometric model to a real-life data set.

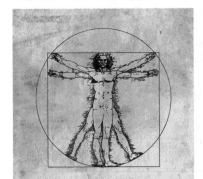

A computer graphics drawing based on the pen and ink drawing of Leonardo da Vinci's famous study of human proportions, called *Vitruvian Man*

Fitting a Linear Model to Data

A basic premise of science is that much of the physical world can be described mathematically and that many physical phenomena are predictable. This scientific outlook was part of the scientific revolution that took place in Europe during the late 1500s. Two early publications connected with this revolution were *On the Revolutions of the Heavenly Spheres* by the Polish astronomer Nicolaus Copernicus and *On the Fabric of the Human Body* by the Belgian anatomist Andreas Vesalius. Each of these books was published in 1543, and each broke with prior tradition by suggesting the use of a scientific method rather than unquestioned reliance on authority.

One basic technique of modern science is gathering data and then describing the data with a mathematical model. For instance, the data in Example 1 are inspired by Leonardo da Vinci's famous drawing that indicates that a person's height and arm span are equal.

EXAMPLE 1   **Fitting a Linear Model to Data**

• • • ▷ *See LarsonCalculus.com for an interactive version of this type of example.*

A class of 28 people collected the data shown below, which represent their heights x and arm spans y (rounded to the nearest inch).

(60, 61), (65, 65), (68, 67), (72, 73), (61, 62), (63, 63), (70, 71),

(75, 74), (71, 72), (62, 60), (65, 65), (66, 68), (62, 62), (72, 73),

(70, 70), (69, 68), (69, 70), (60, 61), (63, 63), (64, 64), (71, 71),

(68, 67), (69, 70), (70, 72), (65, 65), (64, 63), (71, 70), (67, 67)

Find a linear model to represent these data.

Solution   There are different ways to model these data with an equation. The simplest would be to observe that x and y are about the same and list the model as simply $y = x$. A more careful analysis would be to use a procedure from statistics called linear regression. (You will study this procedure in Section 13.9.) The least squares regression line for these data is

$$y = 1.006x - 0.23.$$ Least squares regression line

The graph of the model and the data are shown in Figure 1.32. From this model, you can see that a person's arm span tends to be about the same as his or her height.

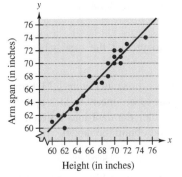

Linear model and data
Figure 1.32

▷ **TECHNOLOGY**   Many graphing utilities have built-in least squares regression programs. Typically, you enter the data into the calculator and then run the linear regression program. The program usually displays the slope and y-intercept of the best-fitting line and the *correlation coefficient r*. The correlation coefficient gives a measure of how well the data can be modeled by a line. The closer $|r|$ is to 1, the better the data can be modeled by a line. For instance, the correlation coefficient for the model in Example 1 is $r \approx 0.97$, which indicates that the linear model is a good fit for the data. If the r-value is positive, then the variables have a positive correlation, as in Example 1. If the r-value is negative, then the variables have a negative correlation.

Fitting a Quadratic Model to Data

A function that gives the height s of a falling object in terms of the time t is called a *position function*. If air resistance is not considered, then the position of a falling object can be modeled by

$$s(t) = \tfrac{1}{2}gt^2 + v_0 t + s_0$$

where g is the acceleration due to gravity, v_0 is the initial velocity, and s_0 is the initial height. The value of g depends on where the object is dropped. On Earth, g is approximately -32 feet per second per second, or -9.8 meters per second per second.

To discover the value of g experimentally, you could record the heights of a falling object at several increments, as shown in Example 2.

EXAMPLE 2 Fitting a Quadratic Model to Data

A basketball is dropped from a height of about $5\frac{1}{4}$ feet. The height of the basketball is recorded 23 times at intervals of about 0.02 second. The results are shown in the table.

Time	0.0	0.02	0.04	0.06	0.08	0.099996
Height	5.23594	5.20353	5.16031	5.0991	5.02707	4.95146

Time	0.119996	0.139992	0.159988	0.179988	0.199984	0.219984
Height	4.85062	4.74979	4.63096	4.50132	4.35728	4.19523

Time	0.23998	0.25993	0.27998	0.299976	0.319972	0.339961
Height	4.02958	3.84593	3.65507	3.44981	3.23375	3.01048

Time	0.359961	0.379951	0.399941	0.419941	0.439941
Height	2.76921	2.52074	2.25786	1.98058	1.63488

Find a model to fit these data. Then use the model to predict the time when the basketball will hit the ground.

Solution Begin by sketching a scatter plot of the data, as shown in Figure 1.33. From the scatter plot, you can see that the data do not appear to be linear. It does appear, however, that they might be quadratic. To check this, enter the data into a graphing utility that has a quadratic regression program. You should obtain the model

$$s = -15.45t^2 - 1.302t + 5.2340.$$ Least squares regression quadratic

Using this model, you can predict the time when the basketball hits the ground by substituting 0 for s and solving the resulting equation for t.

$$0 = -15.45t^2 - 1.302t + 5.2340 \qquad \text{Let } s = 0.$$

$$t = \frac{-b \pm \sqrt{b^2 - 4ac}}{2a} \qquad \text{Quadratic Formula}$$

$$t = \frac{-(-1.302) \pm \sqrt{(-1.302)^2 - 4(-15.45)(5.2340)}}{2(-15.45)} \qquad \begin{array}{l}\text{Substitute } a = -15.45, \\ b = -1.302, \text{ and } c = 5.2340.\end{array}$$

$$t \approx 0.54 \qquad \text{Choose positive solution.}$$

The solution is about 0.54 second. In other words, the basketball will continue to fall for about 0.1 second more before hitting the ground. (Note that the experimental value of g is $\tfrac{1}{2}g = -15.45$, or $g = -30.90$ feet per second per second.) ∎

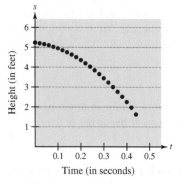

Scatter plot of data
Figure 1.33

Fitting a Trigonometric Model to Data

What is mathematical modeling? This is one of the questions that is asked in the book *Guide to Mathematical Modelling*. Here is part of the answer.*

1. Mathematical modeling consists of applying your mathematical skills to obtain useful answers to real problems.

2. Learning to apply mathematical skills is very different from learning mathematics itself.

3. Models are used in a very wide range of applications, some of which do not appear initially to be mathematical in nature.

4. Models often allow quick and cheap evaluation of alternatives, leading to optimal solutions that are not otherwise obvious.

5. There are no precise rules in mathematical modeling and no "correct" answers.

6. Modeling can be learned only by *doing*.

The amount of daylight received by locations on Earth varies with the time of year.

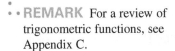

⋅⋅REMARK For a review of trigonometric functions, see Appendix C.

| **EXAMPLE 3** | **Fitting a Trigonometric Model to Data** |

The number of hours of daylight on a given day on Earth depends on the latitude and the time of year. Here are the numbers of minutes of daylight at a location of 20°N latitude on the longest and shortest days of the year: June 21, 801 minutes; December 22, 655 minutes. Use these data to write a model for the amount of daylight d (in minutes) on each day of the year at a location of 20°N latitude. How could you check the accuracy of your model?

Solution Here is one way to create a model. You can hypothesize that the model is a sine function whose period is 365 days. Using the given data, you can conclude that the amplitude of the graph is $(801 - 655)/2$, or 73. So, one possible model is

$$d = 728 - 73 \sin\left(\frac{2\pi t}{365} + \frac{\pi}{2}\right).$$

In this model, t represents the number of each day of the year, with December 22 represented by $t = 0$. A graph of this model is shown in Figure 1.34. To check the accuracy of this model, a weather almanac was used to find the numbers of minutes of daylight on different days of the year at the location of 20°N latitude.

Date	Value of t	Actual Daylight	Daylight Given by Model
Dec 22	0	655 min	655 min
Jan 1	10	657 min	656 min
Feb 1	41	676 min	672 min
Mar 1	69	705 min	701 min
Apr 1	100	740 min	739 min
May 1	130	772 min	773 min
Jun 1	161	796 min	796 min
Jun 21	181	801 min	801 min
Jul 1	191	799 min	800 min
Aug 1	222	782 min	785 min
Sep 1	253	752 min	754 min
Oct 1	283	718 min	716 min
Nov 1	314	685 min	681 min
Dec 1	344	661 min	660 min

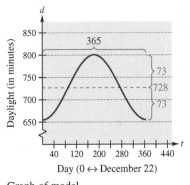

Graph of model
Figure 1.34

You can see that the model is fairly accurate.

---

* Text from Dilwyn Edwards and Mike Hamson, *Guide to Mathematical Modelling* (Boca Raton: CRC Press, 1990), p. 4. Used by permission of the authors.

1.4 Exercises

See CalcChat.com for tutorial help and worked-out solutions to odd-numbered exercises.

1. **Wages** Each ordered pair gives the average weekly wage x for federal government workers and the average weekly wage y for state government workers for 2001 through 2009. *(Source: U.S. Bureau of Labor Statistics)*

(941, 727), (1001, 754), (1043, 770), (1111, 791), (1151, 812), (1198, 844), (1248, 883), (1275, 923), (1303, 937)

(a) Plot the data. From the graph, do the data appear to be approximately linear?

(b) Visually find a linear model for the data. Graph the model.

(c) Use the model to approximate y when $x = 1075$.

2. **Quiz Scores** The ordered pairs represent the scores on two consecutive 15-point quizzes for a class of 15 students.

(7, 13), (9, 7), (14, 14), (15, 15), (10, 15), (9, 7), (11, 14), (7, 14), (14, 11), (14, 15), (8, 10), (15, 9), (10, 11), (9, 10), (11, 10)

(a) Plot the data. From the graph, does the relationship between consecutive scores appear to be approximately linear?

(b) If the data appear to be approximately linear, find a linear model for the data. If not, give some possible explanations.

3. **Hooke's Law** Hooke's Law states that the force F required to compress or stretch a spring (within its elastic limits) is proportional to the distance d that the spring is compressed or stretched from its original length. That is, $F = kd$, where k is a measure of the stiffness of the spring and is called the *spring constant*. The table shows the elongation d in centimeters of a spring when a force of F newtons is applied.

F	20	40	60	80	100
d	1.4	2.5	4.0	5.3	6.6

(a) Use the regression capabilities of a graphing utility to find a linear model for the data.

(b) Use a graphing utility to plot the data and graph the model. How well does the model fit the data? Explain.

(c) Use the model to estimate the elongation of the spring when a force of 55 newtons is applied.

4. **Falling Object** In an experiment, students measured the speed s (in meters per second) of a falling object t seconds after it was released. The results are shown in the table.

t	0	1	2	3	4
s	0	11.0	19.4	29.2	39.4

(a) Use the regression capabilities of a graphing utility to find a linear model for the data.

(b) Use a graphing utility to plot the data and graph the model. How well does the model fit the data? Explain.

(c) Use the model to estimate the speed of the object after 2.5 seconds.

5. **Energy Consumption and Gross National Product** The data show the per capita energy consumptions (in millions of Btu) and the per capita gross national incomes (in thousands of U.S. dollars) for several countries in 2008. *(Source: U.S. Energy Information Administration and The World Bank)*

Argentina	(81, 7.19)	India	(17, 1.04)
Australia	(274, 40.24)	Italy	(136, 35.46)
Bangladesh	(6, 0.52)	Japan	(172, 38.13)
Brazil	(54, 7.30)	Mexico	(66, 9.99)
Canada	(422, 43.64)	Poland	(101, 11.73)
Ecuador	(35, 3.69)	Turkey	(57, 9.02)
Hungary	(110, 12.81)	Venezuela	(121, 9.23)

(a) Use the regression capabilities of a graphing utility to find a linear model for the data. What is the correlation coefficient?

(b) Use a graphing utility to plot the data and graph the model.

(c) Interpret the graph in part (b). Use the graph to identify the three countries that differ most from the linear model.

(d) Delete the data for the three countries identified in part (c). Fit a linear model to the remaining data and give the correlation coefficient.

6. **HOW DO YOU SEE IT?** Determine whether the data can be modeled by a linear function, a quadratic function, or a trigonometric function, or that there appears to be no relationship between x and y.

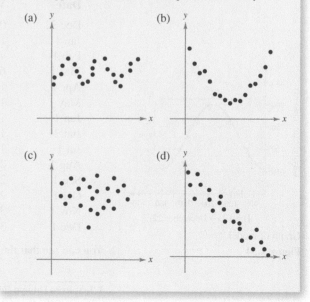

7. Beam Strength   Students in a lab measured the breaking strength S (in pounds) of wood 2 inches thick, x inches high, and 12 inches long. The results are shown in the table.

x	4	6	8	10	12
S	2370	5460	10,310	16,250	23,860

(a) Use the regression capabilities of a graphing utility to find a quadratic model for the data.

(b) Use a graphing utility to plot the data and graph the model.

(c) Use the model to approximate the breaking strength when $x = 2$.

(d) How many times greater is the breaking strength for a 4-inch-high board than for a 2-inch-high board?

(e) How many times greater is the breaking strength for a 12-inch-high board than for a 6-inch-high board? When the height of a board increases by a factor, does the breaking strength increase by the same factor? Explain.

8. Car Performance   The time t (in seconds) required to attain a speed of s miles per hour from a standing start for a Volkswagen Passat is shown in the table.   *(Source: Car & Driver)*

s	30	40	50	60	70	80	90
t	2.7	3.8	4.9	6.3	8.0	9.9	12.2

(a) Use the regression capabilities of a graphing utility to find a quadratic model for the data.

(b) Use a graphing utility to plot the data and graph the model.

(c) Use the graph in part (b) to state why the model is not appropriate for determining the times required to attain speeds of less than 20 miles per hour.

(d) Because the test began from a standing start, add the point $(0, 0)$ to the data. Fit a quadratic model to the revised data and graph the new model.

(e) Does the quadratic model in part (d) more accurately model the behavior of the car? Explain.

9. Engine Performance   A V8 car engine is coupled to a dynamometer, and the horsepower y is measured at different engine speeds x (in thousands of revolutions per minute). The results are shown in the table.

x	1	2	3	4	5	6
y	40	85	140	200	225	245

(a) Use the regression capabilities of a graphing utility to find a cubic model for the data.

(b) Use a graphing utility to plot the data and graph the model.

(c) Use the model to approximate the horsepower when the engine is running at 4500 revolutions per minute.

10. Boiling Temperature   The table shows the temperatures T (in degrees Fahrenheit) at which water boils at selected pressures p (in pounds per square inch).   *(Source: Standard Handbook for Mechanical Engineers)*

p	5	10	14.696 (1 atmosphere)	20
T	162.24°	193.21°	212.00°	227.96°

p	30	40	60	80	100
T	250.33°	267.25°	292.71°	312.03°	327.81°

(a) Use the regression capabilities of a graphing utility to find a cubic model for the data.

(b) Use a graphing utility to plot the data and graph the model.

(c) Use the graph to estimate the pressure required for the boiling point of water to exceed 300°F.

(d) Explain why the model would not be accurate for pressures exceeding 100 pounds per square inch.

11. Automobile Costs   The data in the table show the variable costs of operating an automobile in the United States for 2000 through 2010, where t is the year, with $t = 0$ corresponding to 2000. The functions y_1, y_2, and y_3 represent the costs in cents per mile for gas, maintenance, and tires, respectively.   *(Source: Bureau of Transportation Statistics)*

t	y_1	y_2	y_3
0	6.9	3.6	1.7
1	7.9	3.9	1.8
2	5.9	4.1	1.8
3	7.2	4.1	1.8
4	6.5	5.4	0.7
5	9.5	4.9	0.7
6	8.9	4.9	0.7
7	11.7	4.6	0.7
8	10.1	4.6	0.8
9	11.4	4.5	0.8
10	12.3	4.4	1.0

(a) Use the regression capabilities of a graphing utility to find cubic models for y_1 and y_3, and a quadratic model for y_2.

(b) Use a graphing utility to graph y_1, y_2, y_3, and $y_1 + y_2 + y_3$ in the same viewing window. Use the model to estimate the total variable cost per mile in 2014.

12. Health Maintenance Organizations The bar graph shows the numbers of people N (in millions) receiving care in HMOs for the years 1994 through 2008. *(Source: HealthLeaders-InterStudy)*

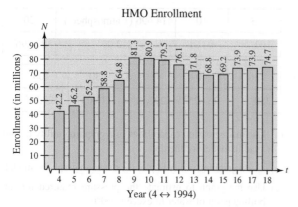

HMO Enrollment

(a) Let t be the time in years, with $t = 4$ corresponding to 1994. Use the regression capabilities of a graphing utility to find linear and cubic models for the data.

(b) Use a graphing utility to plot the data and graph the linear and cubic models.

(c) Use the graphs in part (b) to determine which is the better model.

(d) Use a graphing utility to find and graph a quadratic model for the data. How well does the model fit the data? Explain.

(e) Use the linear and cubic models to estimate the number of people receiving care in HMOs in the year 2014. What do you notice?

(f) Use a graphing utility to find other models for the data. Which models do you think best represent the data? Explain.

13. Harmonic Motion The motion of an oscillating weight suspended by a spring was measured by a motion detector. The data collected and the approximate maximum (positive and negative) displacements from equilibrium are shown in the figure. The displacement y is measured in centimeters, and the time t is measured in seconds.

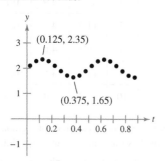

(a) Is y a function of t? Explain.

(b) Approximate the amplitude and period of the oscillations.

(c) Find a model for the data.

(d) Use a graphing utility to graph the model in part (c). Compare the result with the data in the figure.

14. Temperature The table shows the normal daily high temperatures for Miami M and Syracuse S (in degrees Fahrenheit) for month t, with $t = 1$ corresponding to January. *(Source: National Oceanic and Atmospheric Administration)*

t	1	2	3	4	5	6
M	76.5	77.7	80.7	83.8	87.2	89.5
S	31.4	33.5	43.1	55.7	68.5	77.0

t	7	8	9	10	11	12
M	90.9	90.6	89.0	85.4	81.2	77.5
S	81.7	79.6	71.4	59.8	47.4	36.3

(a) A model for Miami is

$$M(t) = 83.70 + 7.46 \sin(0.4912t - 1.95).$$

Find a model for Syracuse.

(b) Use a graphing utility to plot the data and graph the model for Miami. How well does the model fit?

(c) Use a graphing utility to plot the data and graph the model for Syracuse. How well does the model fit?

(d) Use the models to estimate the average annual temperature in each city. Which term of the model did you use? Explain.

(e) What is the period of each model? Is it what you expected? Explain.

(f) Which city has a greater variability in temperature throughout the year? Which factor of the models determines this variability? Explain.

WRITING ABOUT CONCEPTS

Modeling Data In Exercises 15 and 16, describe a possible real-life situation for each data set. Then describe how a model could be used in the real-life setting.

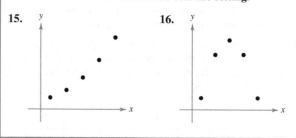

PUTNAM EXAM CHALLENGE

17. For $i = 1, 2$, let T_i be a triangle with side lengths a_i, b_i, c_i, and area A_i. Suppose that $a_1 \le a_2$, $b_1 \le b_2$, $c_1 \le c_2$, and that T_2 is an acute triangle. Does it follow that $A_1 \le A_2$?

1.5 Inverse Functions

■ Verify that one function is the inverse function of another function.
■ Determine whether a function has an inverse function.
■ Develop properties of the six inverse trigonometric functions.

Inverse Functions

Recall from Section 1.3 that a function can be represented by a set of ordered pairs. For instance, the function $f(x) = x + 3$ from $A = \{1, 2, 3, 4\}$ to $B = \{4, 5, 6, 7\}$ can be written as

$$f: \{(1, 4), (2, 5), (3, 6), (4, 7)\}.$$

By interchanging the first and second coordinates of each ordered pair, you can form the **inverse function** of f. This function is denoted by f^{-1}. It is a function from B to A, and can be written as

$$f^{-1}: \{(4, 1), (5, 2), (6, 3), (7, 4)\}.$$

Note that the domain of f is equal to the range of f^{-1}, and vice versa, as shown in Figure 1.35. The functions f and f^{-1} have the effect of "undoing" each other. That is, when you form the composition of f with f^{-1} or the composition of f^{-1} with f, you obtain the identity function.

$$f(f^{-1}(x)) = x \quad \text{and} \quad f^{-1}(f(x)) = x$$

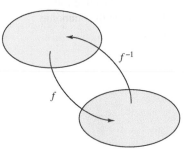

Domain of f = range of f^{-1}
Domain of f^{-1} = range of f
Figure 1.35

> • • **REMARK** Although the notation used to denote an inverse function resembles *exponential notation*, it is a different use of -1 as a superscript. That is, in general,
>
> $$f^{-1}(x) \neq \frac{1}{f(x)}.$$

Exploration

Finding Inverse Functions
Explain how to "undo" each of the functions below. Then use your explanation to write the inverse function of f.

a. $f(x) = x - 5$

b. $f(x) = 6x$

c. $f(x) = \dfrac{x}{2}$

d. $f(x) = 3x + 2$

e. $f(x) = x^3$

f. $f(x) = 4(x - 2)$

Use a graphing utility to graph each function and its inverse function in the same "square" viewing window. What observation can you make about each pair of graphs?

Definition of Inverse Function

A function g is the **inverse function** of the function f when

$$f(g(x)) = x \text{ for each } x \text{ in the domain of } g$$

and

$$g(f(x)) = x \text{ for each } x \text{ in the domain of } f.$$

The function g is denoted by f^{-1} (read "f inverse").

Here are some important observations about inverse functions.

1. If g is the inverse function of f, then f is the inverse function of g.
2. The domain of f^{-1} is equal to the range of f, and the range of f^{-1} is equal to the domain of f.
3. A function need not have an inverse function, but when it does, the inverse function is unique (see Exercise 140).

You can think of f^{-1} as undoing what has been done by f. For example, subtraction can be used to undo addition, and division can be used to undo multiplication. So,

$$f(x) = x + c \quad \text{and} \quad f^{-1}(x) = x - c \qquad \text{Subtraction can be used to undo addition.}$$

are inverse functions of each other and

$$f(x) = cx \quad \text{and} \quad f^{-1}(x) = \frac{x}{c}, \ c \neq 0 \qquad \text{Division can be used to undo multiplication.}$$

are inverse functions of each other.

EXAMPLE 1 **Verifying Inverse Functions**

Show that the functions are inverse functions of each other.

$$f(x) = 2x^3 - 1 \qquad \text{and} \qquad g(x) = \sqrt[3]{\frac{x+1}{2}}$$

•••••••••••••••▷
> **REMARK** In Example 1, try comparing the functions f and g verbally.
>   For f: First cube x, then multiply by 2, then subtract 1.
>   For g: First add 1, then divide by 2, then take the cube root.
> Do you see the "undoing pattern"?

Solution Because the domains and ranges of both f and g consist of all real numbers, you can conclude that both composite functions exist for all x. The composition of f with g is

$$f(g(x)) = 2\left(\sqrt[3]{\frac{x+1}{2}}\right)^3 - 1$$

$$= 2\left(\frac{x+1}{2}\right) - 1$$

$$= x + 1 - 1$$

$$= x.$$

The composition of g with f is

$$g(f(x)) = \sqrt[3]{\frac{(2x^3 - 1) + 1}{2}} = \sqrt[3]{\frac{2x^3}{2}} = \sqrt[3]{x^3} = x.$$

Because $f(g(x)) = x$ and $g(f(x)) = x$, you can conclude that f and g are inverse functions of each other (see Figure 1.36).

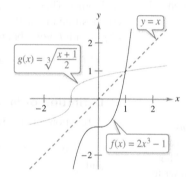

f and g are inverse functions of each other.
Figure 1.36

In Figure 1.36, the graphs of f and $g = f^{-1}$ appear to be mirror images of each other with respect to the line $y = x$. The graph of f^{-1} is a **reflection** of the graph of f in the line $y = x$. This idea is generalized in the next definition.

Reflective Property of Inverse Functions

The graph of f contains the point (a, b) if and only if the graph of f^{-1} contains the point (b, a).

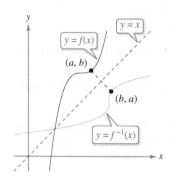

The graph of f^{-1} is a reflection of the graph of f in the line $y = x$.
Figure 1.37

To see the validity of the Reflective Property of Inverse Functions, consider the point (a, b) on the graph of f. This implies $f(a) = b$ and you can write

$$f^{-1}(b) = f^{-1}(f(a)) = a.$$

So, (b, a) is on the graph of f^{-1}, as shown in Figure 1.37. A similar argument will verify this result in the other direction.

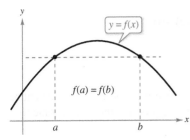

If a horizontal line intersects the graph of f twice, then f is not one-to-one.
Figure 1.38

Existence of an Inverse Function

Not every function has an inverse, and the Reflective Property of Inverse Functions suggests a graphical test for those that do—the **Horizontal Line Test** for an inverse function. This test states that a function f has an inverse function if and only if every horizontal line intersects the graph of f at most once (see Figure 1.38). The next definition formally states why the Horizontal Line Test is valid.

> ### The Existence of an Inverse Function
>
> A function has an inverse function if and only if it is one-to-one.

EXAMPLE 2   **The Existence of an Inverse Function**

Which of the functions has an inverse function?

a. $f(x) = x^3 - 1$

b. $f(x) = x^3 - x + 1$

Solution

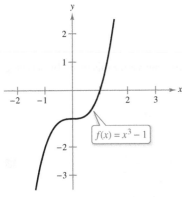

(a) Because f is one-to-one over its entire domain, it has an inverse function.

a. From the graph of f shown in Figure 1.39(a), it appears that f is one-to-one over its entire domain. To verify this, suppose that there exist x_1 and x_2 such that $f(x_1) = f(x_2)$. By showing that $x_1 = x_2$, it follows that f is one-to-one.

$$f(x_1) = f(x_2)$$
$$x_1^3 - 1 = x_2^3 - 1$$
$$x_1^3 = x_2^3$$
$$\sqrt[3]{x_1^3} = \sqrt[3]{x_2^3}$$
$$x_1 = x_2$$

Because f is one-to-one, you can conclude that f must have an inverse function.

b. From the graph of f shown in Figure 1.39(b), you can see that the function does not pass the Horizontal Line Test. In other words, it is not one-to-one. For instance, f has the same value when $x = -1, 0,$ and 1.

$$f(-1) = f(1) = f(0) = 1 \qquad \text{Not one-to-one}$$

Therefore, f does not have an inverse function.

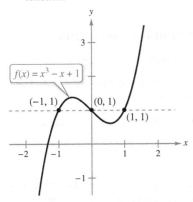

(b) Because f is not one-to-one, it does not have an inverse function.
Figure 1.39

Often it is easier to prove that a function has an inverse function than to find the inverse function. For instance, by sketching the graph of

$$f(x) = x^3 + x - 1$$

you can see that it is one-to-one. Yet it would be difficult to determine the inverse of this function algebraically.

> ### Guidelines for Finding an Inverse of a Function
>
> **1.** Determine whether the function given by $y = f(x)$ has an inverse function.
> **2.** Solve for x as a function of y: $x = g(y) = f^{-1}(y)$.
> **3.** Interchange x and y. The resulting equation is $y = f^{-1}(x)$.
> **4.** Define the domain of f^{-1} as the range of f.
> **5.** Verify that $f(f^{-1}(x)) = x$ and $f^{-1}(f(x)) = x$.

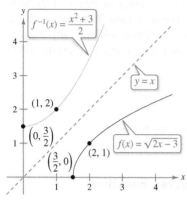

The domain of f^{-1}, $[0, \infty)$, is the range of f.
Figure 1.40

EXAMPLE 3 **Finding an Inverse Function**

Find the inverse function of

$$f(x) = \sqrt{2x - 3}.$$

Solution The function has an inverse function because it is one-to-one on its entire domain, $\left[\frac{3}{2}, \infty\right)$, as shown in Figure 1.40. To find an equation for the inverse function, let $y = f(x)$ and solve for x in terms of y.

$$\sqrt{2x - 3} = y \qquad \text{Let } y = f(x).$$
$$2x - 3 = y^2 \qquad \text{Square each side.}$$
$$x = \frac{y^2 + 3}{2} \qquad \text{Solve for } x.$$
$$y = \frac{x^2 + 3}{2} \qquad \text{Interchange } x \text{ and } y.$$
$$f^{-1}(x) = \frac{x^2 + 3}{2} \qquad \text{Replace } y \text{ by } f^{-1}(x).$$

The domain of f^{-1} is the range of f, which is $[0, \infty)$. You can verify this result by showing that $f(f^{-1}(x)) = x$ and $f^{-1}(f(x)) = x$.

$$f(f^{-1}(x)) = \sqrt{2\left(\frac{x^2 + 3}{2}\right) - 3} = \sqrt{x^2} = x, \quad x \geq 0$$

$$f^{-1}(f(x)) = \frac{\left(\sqrt{2x - 3}\right)^2 + 3}{2} = \frac{2x - 3 + 3}{2} = x, \quad x \geq \frac{3}{2}$$

Consider a function that is *not* one-to-one on its entire domain. By restricting the domain to an interval on which the function is one-to-one, you can conclude that the new function has an inverse function on the restricted domain.

EXAMPLE 4 **Testing Whether a Function Is One-to-One**

•••▷ *See LarsonCalculus.com for an interactive version of this type of example.*

Show that the sine function $f(x) = \sin x$ is not one-to-one on the entire real line. Then show that f is one-to-one on the closed interval $[-\pi/2, \pi/2]$.

Solution It is clear that f is not one-to-one, because many different x-values yield the same y-value. For instance,

$$\sin(0) = 0 = \sin(\pi).$$

Moreover, from the graph of $f(x) = \sin x$ in Figure 1.41, you can see that when f is restricted to the interval $[-\pi/2, \pi/2]$, then the restricted function is one-to-one.

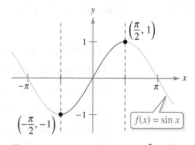

f is one-to-one on the interval $[-\pi/2, \pi/2]$.
Figure 1.41

Inverse Trigonometric Functions

From the graphs of the six basic trigonometric functions, you can see that they do not have inverse functions. (Graphs of the six basic trigonometric functions are shown in Appendix C.) The functions that are called "inverse trigonometric functions" are actually inverses of trigonometric functions whose domains have been restricted.

For instance, in Example 4, you saw that the sine function is one-to-one on the interval $[-\pi/2, \pi/2]$ (see Figure 1.42). On this interval, you can define the inverse of the *restricted* sine function as

$$y = \arcsin x \qquad \text{if and only if} \qquad \sin y = x$$

where

$$-1 \le x \le 1 \qquad \text{and} \qquad -\frac{\pi}{2} \le \arcsin x \le \frac{\pi}{2}.$$

From Figures 1.42 (a) and (b), you can see that you can obtain the graph of $y = \arcsin x$ by reflecting the graph of $y = \sin x$ in the line $y = x$ on the interval $[-\pi/2, \pi/2]$.

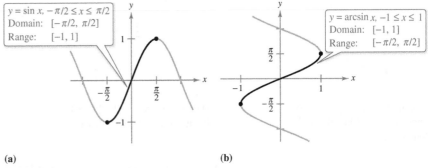

$y = \sin x, -\pi/2 \le x \le \pi/2$
Domain: $[-\pi/2, \pi/2]$
Range: $[-1, 1]$

$y = \arcsin x, -1 \le x \le 1$
Domain: $[-1, 1]$
Range: $[-\pi/2, \pi/2]$

(a)   **(b)**

Figure 1.42

Under suitable restrictions, each of the six trigonometric functions is one-to-one and so has an inverse function, as indicated in the next definition. (The term "iff" is used to represent the phrase "if and only if.")

Definition of Inverse Trigonometric Function

Function	Domain	Range
$y = \arcsin x$ iff $\sin y = x$	$-1 \le x \le 1$	$-\dfrac{\pi}{2} \le y \le \dfrac{\pi}{2}$
$y = \arccos x$ iff $\cos y = x$	$-1 \le x \le 1$	$0 \le y \le \pi$
$y = \arctan x$ iff $\tan y = x$	$-\infty < x < \infty$	$-\dfrac{\pi}{2} < y < \dfrac{\pi}{2}$
$y = \operatorname{arccot} x$ iff $\cot y = x$	$-\infty < x < \infty$	$0 < y < \pi$
$y = \operatorname{arcsec} x$ iff $\sec y = x$	$\lvert x \rvert \ge 1$	$0 \le y \le \pi, \;\; y \ne \dfrac{\pi}{2}$
$y = \operatorname{arccsc} x$ iff $\csc y = x$	$\lvert x \rvert \ge 1$	$-\dfrac{\pi}{2} \le y \le \dfrac{\pi}{2}, \;\; y \ne 0$

The term arcsin x is read as "the arcsine of x" or sometimes "the angle whose sine is x." An alternative notation for the inverse sine function is $\sin^{-1} x$.

The graphs of the six inverse trigonometric functions are shown in Figure 1.43.

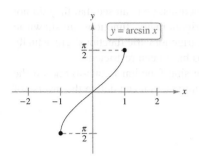

Domain: $[-1, 1]$
Range: $[-\pi/2, \pi/2]$

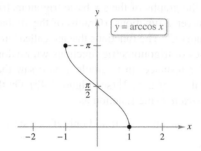

Domain: $[-1, 1]$
Range: $[0, \pi]$

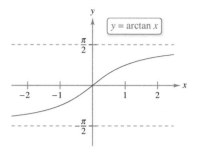

Domain: $(-\infty, \infty)$
Range: $(-\pi/2, \pi/2)$

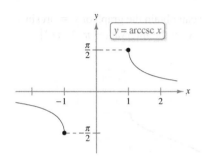

Domain: $(-\infty, -1] \cup [1, \infty)$
Range: $[-\pi/2, 0) \cup (0, \pi/2]$

Figure 1.43

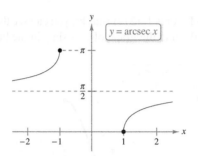

Domain: $(-\infty, -1] \cup [1, \infty)$
Range: $[0, \pi/2) \cup (\pi/2, \pi]$

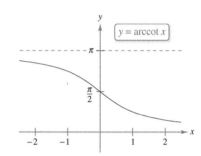

Domain: $(-\infty, \infty)$
Range: $(0, \pi)$

When evaluating inverse trigonometric functions, remember that they denote angles in *radian measure*.

EXAMPLE 5   **Evaluating Inverse Trigonometric Functions**

Evaluate each expression.

a. $\arcsin\left(-\dfrac{1}{2}\right)$ **b.** $\arccos 0$ **c.** $\arctan \sqrt{3}$ **d.** $\arcsin(0.3)$

Solution

a. By definition, $y = \arcsin\left(-\frac{1}{2}\right)$ implies that $\sin y = -\frac{1}{2}$. In the interval $[-\pi/2, \pi/2]$, the correct value of y is $-\pi/6$.

$$\arcsin\left(-\frac{1}{2}\right) = -\frac{\pi}{6}$$

b. By definition, $y = \arccos 0$ implies that $\cos y = 0$. In the interval $[0, \pi]$, you have $y = \pi/2$.

$$\arccos 0 = \frac{\pi}{2}$$

c. By definition, $y = \arctan \sqrt{3}$ implies that $\tan y = \sqrt{3}$. In the interval $(-\pi/2, \pi/2)$, you have $y = \pi/3$.

$$\arctan \sqrt{3} = \frac{\pi}{3}$$

d. Using a calculator set in *radian* mode produces

$$\arcsin(0.3) \approx 0.3047.$$

Inverse functions have the properties

$$f(f^{-1}(x)) = x \quad \text{and} \quad f^{-1}(f(x)) = x.$$

When applying these properties to inverse trigonometric functions, remember that the trigonometric functions have inverse functions only in restricted domains. For x-values outside these domains, these two properties do not hold. For example, $\arcsin(\sin \pi)$ is equal to 0, not π.

Properties of Inverse Trigonometric Functions

1. If $-1 \le x \le 1$ and $-\pi/2 \le y \le \pi/2$, then

$$\sin(\arcsin x) = x \quad \text{and} \quad \arcsin(\sin y) = y.$$

2. If $-\pi/2 < y < \pi/2$, then

$$\tan(\arctan x) = x \quad \text{and} \quad \arctan(\tan y) = y.$$

3. If $|x| \ge 1$ and $0 \le y < \pi/2$ or $\pi/2 < y \le \pi$, then

$$\sec(\arcsec x) = x \quad \text{and} \quad \arcsec(\sec y) = y.$$

Similar properties hold for the other inverse trigonometric functions.

EXAMPLE 6   **Solving an Equation**

Solve $\arctan(2x - 3) = \dfrac{\pi}{4}$ for x.

Solution

$\arctan(2x - 3) = \dfrac{\pi}{4}$	Write original equation.
$\tan[\arctan(2x - 3)] = \tan \dfrac{\pi}{4}$	Take tangent of each side.
$2x - 3 = 1$	$\tan(\arctan x) = x$
$x = 2$	Solve for x.

Some problems in calculus require that you evaluate expressions such as $\cos(\arcsin x)$, as shown in Example 7.

EXAMPLE 7   **Using Right Triangles**

a. Given $y = \arcsin x$, where $0 < y < \pi/2$, find $\cos y$.

b. Given $y = \arcsec\left(\sqrt{5}/2\right)$, find $\tan y$.

Solution

a. Because $y = \arcsin x$, you know that $\sin y = x$. This relationship between x and y can be represented by a right triangle, as shown in Figure 1.44.

$$\cos y = \cos(\arcsin x) = \frac{\text{adj.}}{\text{hyp.}} = \sqrt{1 - x^2}$$

(This result is also valid for $-\pi/2 < y < 0$.)

b. Use the right triangle shown in Figure 1.45.

$$\tan y = \tan\left[\arcsec\left(\frac{\sqrt{5}}{2}\right)\right] = \frac{\text{opp.}}{\text{adj.}} = \frac{1}{2}$$

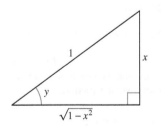

$y = \arcsin x$
Figure 1.44

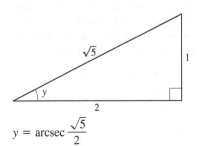

$y = \arcsec \dfrac{\sqrt{5}}{2}$
Figure 1.45

1.5 Exercises   See CalcChat.com for tutorial help and worked-out solutions to odd-numbered exercises.

Verifying Inverse Functions   In Exercises 1–8, show that f and g are inverse functions (a) analytically and (b) graphically.

1. $f(x) = 5x + 1$, $g(x) = \dfrac{x - 1}{5}$

2. $f(x) = 3 - 4x$, $g(x) = \dfrac{3 - x}{4}$

3. $f(x) = x^3$, $g(x) = \sqrt[3]{x}$

4. $f(x) = 1 - x^3$, $g(x) = \sqrt[3]{1 - x}$

5. $f(x) = \sqrt{x - 4}$, $g(x) = x^2 + 4$, $x \geq 0$

6. $f(x) = 16 - x^2$, $x \geq 0$, $g(x) = \sqrt{16 - x}$

7. $f(x) = \dfrac{1}{x}$, $g(x) = \dfrac{1}{x}$

8. $f(x) = \dfrac{1}{1 + x}$, $x \geq 0$, $g(x) = \dfrac{1 - x}{x}$, $0 < x \leq 1$

Matching   In Exercises 9–12, match the graph of the function with the graph of its inverse function. [The graphs of the inverse functions are labeled (a), (b), (c), and (d).]

(a)
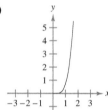

(b)
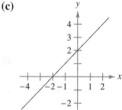

(c)
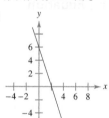

(d)
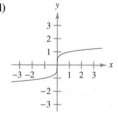

9.
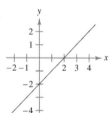

10.
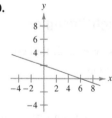

11.
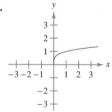

12.
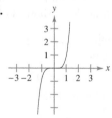

Using the Horizontal Line Test   In Exercises 13–16, use the Horizontal Line Test to determine whether the function is one-to-one on its entire domain and therefore has an inverse function. To print an enlarged copy of the graph, go to *MathGraphs.com*.

13. $f(x) = \frac{3}{4}x + 6$

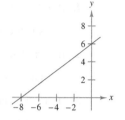

14. $f(x) = 5x - 3$

15. $f(\theta) = \sin \theta$

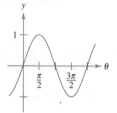

16. $f(x) = \dfrac{x^2}{x^2 + 4}$

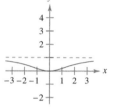

The Existence of an Inverse Function   In Exercises 17–22, use a graphing utility to graph the function. Determine whether the function is one-to-one on its entire domain and therefore has an inverse function.

17. $h(s) = \dfrac{1}{s - 2} - 3$

18. $f(x) = \dfrac{6x}{x^2 + 4}$

19. $g(t) = \dfrac{1}{\sqrt{t^2 + 1}}$

20. $f(x) = 5x\sqrt{x - 1}$

21. $g(x) = (x + 5)^3$

22. $h(x) = |x + 4| - |x - 4|$

The Existence of an Inverse Function   In Exercises 23–26, determine whether the function is one-to-one on its entire domain and therefore has an inverse function.

23. $f(x) = \dfrac{x^4}{4} - 2x^2$

24. $f(x) = \sin \dfrac{3x}{2}$

25. $f(x) = 2 - x - x^3$

26. $f(x) = \sqrt[3]{x + 1}$

Finding an Inverse Function   In Exercises 27–34, (a) find the inverse function of f, (b) graph f and f^{-1} on the same set of coordinate axes, (c) describe the relationship between the graphs, and (d) state the domains and ranges of f and f^{-1}.

27. $f(x) = 2x - 3$

28. $f(x) = 7 - 4x$

29. $f(x) = x^5$

30. $f(x) = x^3 - 1$

31. $f(x) = \sqrt{x}$

32. $f(x) = x^2$, $x \geq 0$

33. $f(x) = \sqrt{4 - x^2}$, $0 \leq x \leq 2$

34. $f(x) = \sqrt{x^2 - 4}$, $x \geq 2$

Finding an Inverse Function In Exercises 35–40, (a) find the inverse function of f, (b) use a graphing utility to graph f and f^{-1} in the same viewing window, (c) describe the relationship between the graphs, and (d) state the domains and ranges of f and f^{-1}.

35. $f(x) = \sqrt[3]{x - 1}$

36. $f(x) = 3\sqrt[5]{2x - 1}$

37. $f(x) = x^{2/3}, \quad x \geq 0$

38. $f(x) = x^{3/5}$

39. $f(x) = \dfrac{x}{\sqrt{x^2 + 7}}$

40. $f(x) = \dfrac{x + 2}{x}$

Finding an Inverse Function In Exercises 41 and 42, use the graph of the function f to make a table of values for the given points. Then make a second table that can be used to find f^{-1}, and sketch the graph of f^{-1}. To print an enlarged copy of the graph, go to *MathGraphs.com*.

41.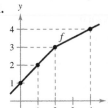

42.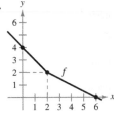

43. Cost You need 50 pounds of two commodities costing $1.25 and $1.60 per pound.

(a) Verify that the total cost is $y = 1.25x + 1.60(50 - x)$, where x is the number of pounds of the less expensive commodity.

(b) Find the inverse function of the cost function. What does each variable represent in the inverse function?

(c) What is the domain of the inverse function? Validate or explain your answer using the context of the problem.

(d) Determine the number of pounds of the less expensive commodity purchased when the total cost is $73.

44. Temperature The formula $C = \frac{5}{9}(F - 32)$, where $F \geq -459.6$, represents the Celsius temperature C as a function of the Fahrenheit temperature F.

(a) Find the inverse function of C.

(b) What does the inverse function represent?

(c) What is the domain of the inverse function? Validate or explain your answer using the context of the problem.

(d) The temperature is 22°C. What is the corresponding temperature in degrees Fahrenheit?

Testing Whether a Function Is One-to-One In Exercises 45–50, determine whether the function is one-to-one. If it is, find its inverse function.

45. $f(x) = \sqrt{x - 2}$

46. $f(x) = \sqrt{9 - x^2}$

47. $f(x) = -3$

48. $f(x) = |x - 2|, \quad x \leq 2$

49. $f(x) = ax + b, \quad a \neq 0$

50. $f(x) = (x + a)^3 + b$

Showing a Function Is One-to-One In Exercises 51–56, show that f is one-to-one on the given interval and therefore has an inverse function on that interval.

Function	Interval
51. $f(x) = (x - 4)^2$	$[4, \infty)$
52. $f(x) = |x + 2|$	$[-2, \infty)$
53. $f(x) = \dfrac{4}{x^2}$	$(0, \infty)$
54. $f(x) = \cot x$	$(0, \pi)$
55. $f(x) = \cos x$	$[0, \pi]$
56. $f(x) = \sec x$	$\left[0, \dfrac{\pi}{2}\right)$

Making a Function One-to-One In Exercises 57 and 58, delete part of the domain so that the function that remains is one-to-one. Find the inverse function of the remaining function and give the domain of the inverse function. (*Note:* There is more than one correct answer.)

57. $f(x) = (x - 3)^2$

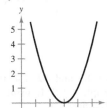

58. $f(x) = |x - 3|$

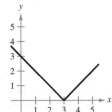

Finding an Inverse Function In Exercises 59–64, (a) sketch a graph of the function f, (b) determine an interval on which f is one-to-one, (c) find the inverse function of f on the interval found in part (b), and (d) give the domain of the inverse function. (*Note:* There is more than one correct answer.)

59. $f(x) = (x + 5)^2$

60. $f(x) = (7 - x)^2$

61. $f(x) = \sqrt{x^2 - 4x}$

62. $f(x) = -\sqrt{25 - x^2}$

63. $f(x) = 3 \cos x$

64. $f(x) = 2 \sin x$

Finding Values In Exercises 65–70, find $f^{-1}(a)$ for the function f and real number a.

Function	Real Number
65. $f(x) = x^3 + 2x - 1$	$a = 2$
66. $f(x) = 2x^5 + x^3 + 1$	$a = -2$
67. $f(x) = \sin x, \quad -\dfrac{\pi}{2} \leq x \leq \dfrac{\pi}{2}$	$a = \dfrac{1}{2}$
68. $f(x) = \cos 2x, \quad 0 \leq x \leq \dfrac{\pi}{2}$	$a = 1$
69. $f(x) = x^3 - \dfrac{4}{x}, \quad x > 0$	$a = 6$
70. $f(x) = \sqrt{x - 4}$	$a = 2$

Using Composite and Inverse Functions In Exercises 71–74, use the functions $f(x) = \frac{1}{8}x - 3$ and $g(x) = x^3$ to find the indicated value.

71. $(f^{-1} \circ g^{-1})(1)$ 72. $(g^{-1} \circ f^{-1})(-3)$

73. $(f^{-1} \circ f^{-1})(6)$ 74. $(g^{-1} \circ g^{-1})(-4)$

Using Composite and Inverse Functions In Exercises 75–78, use the functions $f(x) = x + 4$ and $g(x) = 2x - 5$ to find the indicated function.

75. $g^{-1} \circ f^{-1}$ 76. $f^{-1} \circ g^{-1}$

77. $(f \circ g)^{-1}$ 78. $(g \circ f)^{-1}$

Graphical Reasoning In Exercises 79 and 80, (a) use the graph of the function f to determine whether f is one-to-one, (b) state the domain of f^{-1}, and (c) estimate the value of $f^{-1}(2)$.

79. 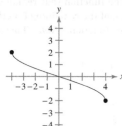   80.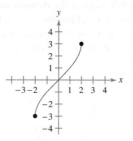

Graphical Reasoning In Exercises 81 and 82, use the graph of the function f to sketch the graph of f^{-1}. To print an enlarged copy of the graph, go to *MathGraphs.com*.

81. 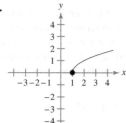   82.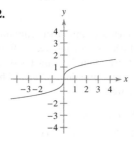

Numerical and Graphical Analysis In Exercises 83 and 84, (a) use a graphing utility to complete the table, (b) plot the points in the table and graph the function by hand, (c) use a graphing utility to graph the function and compare the result with your hand-drawn graph in part (b), and (d) determine any intercepts and symmetry of the graph.

x	-1	-0.8	-0.6	-0.4	-0.2	0	0.2	0.4	0.6	0.8	1
y											

83. $y = \arcsin x$ 84. $y = \arccos x$

85. **Missing Coordinates**
Determine the missing coordinates of the points on the graph of the function.

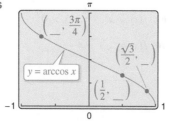

86. **HOW DO YOU SEE IT?** You use a graphing utility to graph $f(x) = \sin x$ and then use the *draw inverse* feature to graph g (see figure). Is g the inverse function of f? Why or why not?

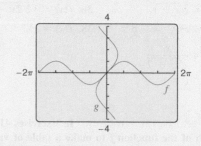

Evaluating Inverse Trigonometric Functions In Exercises 87–94, evaluate the expression without using a calculator.

87. $\arcsin \frac{1}{2}$ 88. $\arcsin 0$

89. $\arccos \frac{1}{2}$ 90. $\arccos 1$

91. $\arctan \dfrac{\sqrt{3}}{3}$ 92. $\text{arccot}(-\sqrt{3})$

93. $\text{arccsc}(-\sqrt{2})$ 94. $\text{arcsec}(-\sqrt{2})$

Approximating Inverse Trigonometric Functions In Exercises 95–98, use a calculator to approximate the value. Round your answer to two decimal places.

95. $\arccos(-0.8)$ 96. $\arcsin(-0.39)$

97. $\text{arcsec }1.269$ 98. $\arctan(-5)$

Using Properties In Exercises 99 and 100, use the properties of inverse trigonometric functions to evaluate the expression.

99. $\cos[\arccos(-0.1)]$ 100. $\arcsin(\sin 3\pi)$

Using a Right Triangle In Exercises 101–106, use the figure to write the expression in algebraic form given $y = \arccos x$, where $0 < y < \pi/2$.

101. $\cos y$

102. $\sin y$

103. $\tan y$

104. $\cot y$

105. $\sec y$

106. $\csc y$

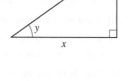

Evaluating an Expression In Exercises 107–110, evaluate the expression without using a calculator. [*Hint:* Sketch a right triangle, as demonstrated in Example 7(b).]

107. (a) $\sin\left(\arctan \dfrac{3}{4}\right)$ 108. (a) $\tan\left(\arccos \dfrac{\sqrt{2}}{2}\right)$

   (b) $\sec\left(\arcsin \dfrac{4}{5}\right)$ (b) $\cos\left(\arcsin \dfrac{5}{13}\right)$

109. (a) $\cot\left[\arcsin\left(-\tfrac{1}{2}\right)\right]$ 110. (a) $\sec\left[\arctan\left(-\tfrac{3}{5}\right)\right]$

   (b) $\csc\left[\arctan\left(-\tfrac{5}{12}\right)\right]$ (b) $\tan\left[\arcsin\left(-\tfrac{5}{6}\right)\right]$

Simplifying an Expression   In Exercises 111–116, write the expression in algebraic form. [*Hint:* Sketch a right triangle, as demonstrated in Example 7(a).]

111. $\cos(\arcsin 2x)$

112. $\sec(\arctan 4x)$

113. $\sin(\text{arcsec } x)$

114. $\sec[\arcsin(x - 1)]$

115. $\tan\left(\text{arcsec } \dfrac{x}{3}\right)$

116. $\csc\left(\arctan \dfrac{x}{\sqrt{2}}\right)$

Solving an Equation   In Exercises 117–120, solve the equation for *x*.

117. $\arcsin(3x - \pi) = \frac{1}{2}$

118. $\arctan(2x - 5) = -1$

119. $\arcsin \sqrt{2x} = \arccos \sqrt{x}$

120. $\arccos x = \text{arcsec } x$

Point of Intersection   In Exercises 121 and 122, find the point of intersection of the graphs of the functions.

121. $y = \arccos x$
   $y = \arctan x$

122. $y = \arcsin x$
   $y = \arccos x$

WRITING ABOUT CONCEPTS

123. Inverse Functions   Describe how to find the inverse function of a one-to-one function given by an equation in *x* and *y*. Give an example.

124. Describing Relationships   Describe the relationship between the graph of a function and the graph of its inverse function.

125. Inverse Trigonometric Functions   Explain why $\tan \pi = 0$ does not imply that $\arctan 0 = \pi$.

126. Inverse Trigonometric Functions and Technology   Explain how to graph $y = \text{arccot } x$ on a graphing utility that does not have the arccotangent function.

Fill in the Blank   In Exercises 127 and 128, fill in the blank.

127. $\arctan \dfrac{9}{x} = \arcsin(\quad)$, $x > 0$

128. $\arcsin \dfrac{\sqrt{36 - x^2}}{6} = \arccos(\quad)$

Verifying an Identity   In Exercises 129 and 130, verify each identity.

129. (a) $\text{arccsc } x = \arcsin \dfrac{1}{x}$, $|x| \geq 1$

   (b) $\arctan x + \arctan \dfrac{1}{x} = \dfrac{\pi}{2}$, $x > 0$

130. (a) $\arcsin(-x) = -\arcsin x$, $|x| \leq 1$

   (b) $\arccos(-x) = \pi - \arccos x$, $|x| \leq 1$

Sketching a Graph   In Exercises 131–134, sketch the graph of the function. Use a graphing utility to verify your graph.

131. $f(x) = \arcsin(x - 1)$

132. $f(x) = \text{arcsec } 2x$

133. $f(x) = \arctan x + \dfrac{\pi}{2}$

134. $f(x) = \arccos \dfrac{x}{4}$

135. Think About It   Given that *f* is a one-to-one function and $f(-3) = 8$, find $f^{-1}(8)$.

136. Think About It   Given $f(x) = 5 + \arccos x$, find $f^{-1}\left(5 + \dfrac{\pi}{2}\right)$.

137. Proof   Prove that if *f* and *g* are one-to-one functions, then $(f \circ g)^{-1}(x) = (g^{-1} \circ f^{-1})(x)$.

138. Proof   Prove that if *f* has an inverse function, then $(f^{-1})^{-1} = f$.

139. Proof   Prove that $\cos(\sin^{-1} x) = \sqrt{1 - x^2}$.

140. Proof   Prove that if a function has an inverse function, then the inverse function is unique.

True or False?   In Exercises 141–146, determine whether the statement is true or false. If it is false, explain why or give an example that shows it is false.

141. If *f* is an even function, then f^{-1} exists.

142. If the inverse function of *f* exists, then the *y*-intercept of *f* is an *x*-intercept of f^{-1}.

143. $\arcsin^2 x + \arccos^2 x = 1$

144. The range of $y = \arcsin x$ is $[0, \pi]$.

145. If $f(x) = x^n$ where *n* is odd, then f^{-1} exists.

146. There exists no function *f* such that $f = f^{-1}$.

147. Verifying an Identity   Verify each identity.

   (a) $\text{arccot } x = \begin{cases} \pi + \arctan(1/x), & x < 0 \\ \pi/2, & x = 0 \\ \arctan(1/x), & x > 0 \end{cases}$

   (b) $\text{arcsec } x = \arccos(1/x)$, $|x| \geq 1$

   (c) $\text{arccsc } x = \arcsin(1/x)$, $|x| \geq 1$

148. Using an Identity   Use the results of Exercise 147 and a graphing utility to evaluate each expression.

   (a) $\text{arccot } 0.5$

   (b) $\text{arcsec } 2.7$

   (c) $\text{arccsc}(-3.9)$

   (d) $\text{arccot}(-1.4)$

149. Proof   Prove that
$$\arctan x + \arctan y = \arctan \frac{x + y}{1 - xy}, \quad xy \neq 1.$$
Use this formula to show that
$$\arctan \frac{1}{2} + \arctan \frac{1}{3} = \frac{\pi}{4}.$$

150. Think About It   Use a graphing utility to graph $f(x) = \sin x$ and $g(x) = \arcsin(\sin x)$. Why isn't the graph of *g* the line $y = x$?

151. Determining Conditions   Let $f(x) = ax^2 + bx + c$, where $a > 0$ and the domain is all real numbers such that $x \leq -\dfrac{b}{2a}$. Find f^{-1}.

152. Determining Conditions   Determine conditions on the constants *a*, *b*, and *c* such that the graph of $f(x) = \dfrac{ax + b}{cx - a}$ is symmetric about the line $y = x$.

153. Determining Conditions   Determine conditions on the constants *a*, *b*, *c*, and *d* such that $f(x) = \dfrac{ax + b}{cx + d}$ has an inverse function. Then find f^{-1}.

1.6 Exponential and Logarithmic Functions

■ Develop and use properties of exponential functions.
■ Understand the definition of the number *e*.
■ Understand the definition of the natural logarithmic function, and develop and use properties of the natural logarithmic function.

Exponential Functions

An **exponential function** involves a constant raised to a power, such as $f(x) = 2^x$. You already know how to evaluate 2^x for *rational* values of x. For instance,

$$2^0 = 1, \quad 2^2 = 4, \quad 2^{-1} = \frac{1}{2}, \quad \text{and} \quad 2^{1/2} = \sqrt{2} \approx 1.4142136.$$

For *irrational* values of x, you can define 2^x by considering a sequence of rational numbers that approach x. A full discussion of this process would not be appropriate now, but here is the general idea. To define the number $2^{\sqrt{2}}$, note that

$$\sqrt{2} = 1.414213 \ldots$$

and consider the numbers below (which are of the form 2^r, where r is rational).

$$2^1 = 2 < 2^{\sqrt{2}} < 4 = 2^2$$
$$2^{1.4} = 2.639015 \ldots < 2^{\sqrt{2}} < 2.828427 \ldots = 2^{1.5}$$
$$2^{1.41} = 2.657371 \ldots < 2^{\sqrt{2}} < 2.675855 \ldots = 2^{1.42}$$
$$2^{1.414} = 2.664749 \ldots < 2^{\sqrt{2}} < 2.666597 \ldots = 2^{1.415}$$
$$2^{1.4142} = 2.665119 \ldots < 2^{\sqrt{2}} < 2.665303 \ldots = 2^{1.4143}$$
$$2^{1.41421} = 2.665137 \ldots < 2^{\sqrt{2}} < 2.665156 \ldots = 2^{1.41422}$$
$$2^{1.414213} = 2.665143 \ldots < 2^{\sqrt{2}} < 2.665144 \ldots = 2^{1.414214}$$

From these calculations, it seems reasonable to conclude that

$$2^{\sqrt{2}} \approx 2.66514.$$

In practice, you can use a calculator to approximate numbers such as $2^{\sqrt{2}}$.

In general, you can use any positive base a, $a \neq 1$, to define an exponential function. So, the exponential function with base a is written as $f(x) = a^x$. Exponential functions, even those with irrational values of x, obey the familiar properties of exponents.

Properties of Exponents

Let a and b be positive real numbers, and let x and y be any real numbers.

1. $a^0 = 1$ **2.** $a^x a^y = a^{x+y}$ **3.** $(a^x)^y = a^{xy}$ **4.** $(ab)^x = a^x b^x$

5. $\dfrac{a^x}{a^y} = a^{x-y}$ **6.** $\left(\dfrac{a}{b}\right)^x = \dfrac{a^x}{b^x}$ **7.** $a^{-x} = \dfrac{1}{a^x}$

EXAMPLE 1   Using Properties of Exponents

a. $(2^2)(2^3) = 2^{2+3} = 2^5$ **b.** $\dfrac{2^2}{2^3} = 2^{2-3} = 2^{-1} = \dfrac{1}{2}$

c. $(3^x)^3 = 3^{3x}$ **d.** $\left(\dfrac{1}{3}\right)^{-x} = (3^{-1})^{-x} = 3^x$

EXAMPLE 2 **Sketching Graphs of Exponential Functions**

⋯⋯▷ *See LarsonCalculus.com for an interactive version of this type of example.*

Sketch the graphs of the functions

$$f(x) = 2^x, \quad g(x) = \left(\tfrac{1}{2}\right)^x = 2^{-x}, \quad \text{and} \quad h(x) = 3^x.$$

Solution To sketch the graphs of these functions by hand, you can complete a table of values, plot the corresponding points, and connect the points with smooth curves.

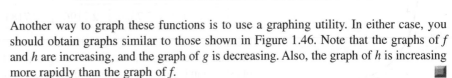

x	-3	-2	-1	0	1	2	3	4
2^x	$\frac{1}{8}$	$\frac{1}{4}$	$\frac{1}{2}$	1	2	4	8	16
2^{-x}	8	4	2	1	$\frac{1}{2}$	$\frac{1}{4}$	$\frac{1}{8}$	$\frac{1}{16}$
3^x	$\frac{1}{27}$	$\frac{1}{9}$	$\frac{1}{3}$	1	3	9	27	81

Another way to graph these functions is to use a graphing utility. In either case, you should obtain graphs similar to those shown in Figure 1.46. Note that the graphs of f and h are increasing, and the graph of g is decreasing. Also, the graph of h is increasing more rapidly than the graph of f. ∎

The shapes of the graphs in Figure 1.46 are typical of the exponential functions $f(x) = a^x$ and $g(x) = a^{-x}$ where $a > 1$, as shown in Figure 1.47.

Figure 1.46

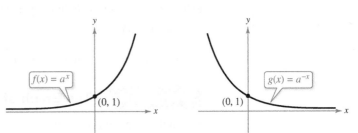

Figure 1.47

Properties of Exponential Functions

Let a be a real number that is greater than 1.

1. The domain of $f(x) = a^x$ and $g(x) = a^{-x}$ is $(-\infty, \infty)$.

2. The range of $f(x) = a^x$ and $g(x) = a^{-x}$ is $(0, \infty)$.

3. The y-intercept of $f(x) = a^x$ and $g(x) = a^{-x}$ is $(0, 1)$.

4. The functions $f(x) = a^x$ and $g(x) = a^{-x}$ are one-to-one.

▷ **TECHNOLOGY** Functions of the form $h(x) = b^{cx}$ have the same types of properties and graphs as functions of the form $f(x) = a^x$ and $g(x) = a^{-x}$. To see why this is true, notice that

$$b^{cx} = (b^c)^x.$$

For instance, $f(x) = 2^{3x}$ can be written as

$$f(x) = (2^3)^x \quad \text{or} \quad f(x) = 8^x.$$

Try confirming this by graphing $f(x) = 2^{3x}$ and $g(x) = 8^x$ in the same viewing window.

The Number *e*

In calculus, the natural (or convenient) choice for a base of an exponential number is the irrational number *e*, whose decimal approximation is

$$e \approx 2.71828182846.$$

This choice may seem anything but natural. The convenience of this particular base, however, will become apparent as you continue in this course.

EXAMPLE 3   **Investigating the Number *e***

Describe the behavior of the function $f(x) = (1 + x)^{1/x}$ at values of x that are close to 0.

Solution   One way to examine the values of $f(x)$ near 0 is to construct a table.

x	-0.01	-0.001	-0.0001	0.0001	0.001	0.01
$(1 + x)^{1/x}$	2.7320	2.7196	2.7184	2.7181	2.7169	2.7048

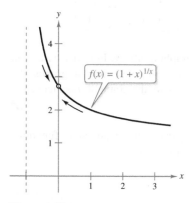

Figure 1.48

From the table, it appears that the closer x gets to 0, the closer $(1 + x)^{1/x}$ gets to e. The graph of f shown in Figure 1.48 supports this conclusion. Try using a graphing calculator to obtain this graph. Then zoom in closer and closer to $x = 0$. Although f is not defined when $x = 0$, it is defined for x-values that are arbitrarily close to zero. By zooming in, you can see that the value of $f(x)$ gets closer and closer to $e \approx 2.71828182846$ as x gets closer and closer to 0. Later, when you study limits, you will learn that this result can be written as

$$\lim_{x \to 0} (1 + x)^{1/x} = e$$

which is read as "the limit of $(1 + x)^{1/x}$ as x approaches 0 is e."

EXAMPLE 4   **The Graph of the Natural Exponential Function**

Sketch the graph of $f(x) = e^x$.

Solution   To sketch the graph of f by hand, you can complete a table of values, plot the corresponding points, and connect the points with a smooth curve (see Figure 1.49).

x	-2	-1	0	1	2
e^x	$\frac{1}{e^2} \approx 0.135$	$\frac{1}{e} \approx 0.368$	1	$e \approx 2.718$	$e^2 \approx 7.389$

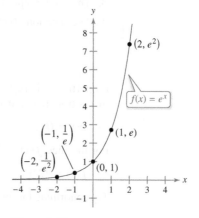

Figure 1.49

The Natural Logarithmic Function

Because the natural exponential function

$$f(x) = e^x$$

is one-to-one, it must have an inverse function. Its inverse is called the **natural logarithmic function.** The domain of the natural logarithmic function is the set of positive real numbers.

•• REMARK   The notation $\ln x$ is read as "el en of x" or "the natural log of x."

Definition of the Natural Logarithmic Function

Let x be a positive real number. The **natural logarithmic function,** denoted by $\ln x$, is defined as

$$\ln x = b \quad \text{if and only if} \quad e^b = x.$$

This definition tells you that a logarithmic equation can be written in an equivalent exponential form, and vice versa. Here are some examples.

Logarithmic Form	*Exponential Form*
$\ln 1 = 0$	$e^0 = 1$
$\ln e = 1$	$e^1 = e$
$\ln e^{-1} = -1$	$e^{-1} = \dfrac{1}{e}$

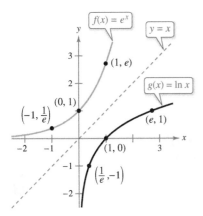

Figure 1.50

Because the function $g(x) = \ln x$ is defined to be the inverse of $f(x) = e^x$, it follows that the graph of the natural logarithmic function is a reflection of the graph of the natural exponential function in the line $y = x$, as shown in Figure 1.50. Several other properties of the natural logarithmic function also follow directly from its definition as the inverse of the natural exponential function.

Properties of the Natural Logarithmic Function

1. The domain of $g(x) = \ln x$ is $(0, \infty)$.

2. The range of $g(x) = \ln x$ is $(-\infty, \infty)$.

3. The x-intercept of $g(x) = \ln x$ is $(1, 0)$.

4. The function $g(x) = \ln x$ is one-to-one.

Because $f(x) = e^x$ and $g(x) = \ln x$ are inverses of each other, you can conclude that

$$\ln e^x = x \quad \text{and} \quad e^{\ln x} = x.$$

One of the properties of exponents states that when you multiply two exponential functions (having the same base), you add their exponents. For instance,

$$e^x e^y = e^{x+y}.$$

The logarithmic version of this property states that the natural logarithm of the product of two numbers is equal to the sum of the natural logs of the numbers. That is,

$$\ln xy = \ln x + \ln y.$$

This property and the properties dealing with the natural log of a quotient and the natural log of a power are listed on the next page.

Exploration

A graphing utility is used to graph $f(x) = \ln x^2$ and $g(x) = 2 \ln x$. Which of the graphs below is the graph of f? Which is the graph of g?

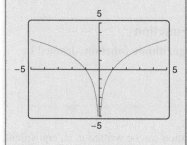

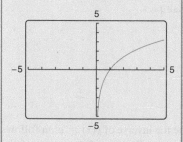

Properties of Logarithms

Let x, y, and z be real numbers such that $x > 0$ and $y > 0$.

1. $\ln xy = \ln x + \ln y$

2. $\ln \dfrac{x}{y} = \ln x - \ln y$

3. $\ln x^z = z \ln x$

EXAMPLE 5   **Expanding Logarithmic Expressions**

a. $\ln \dfrac{10}{9} = \ln 10 - \ln 9$ Property 2

b. $\ln \sqrt{3x + 2} = \ln(3x + 2)^{1/2}$ Rewrite with rational exponent.

$\qquad\qquad = \dfrac{1}{2} \ln(3x + 2)$ Property 3

c. $\ln \dfrac{6x}{5} = \ln(6x) - \ln 5$ Property 2

$\qquad\quad = \ln 6 + \ln x - \ln 5$ Property 1

d. $\ln \dfrac{(x^2 + 3)^2}{x\sqrt[3]{x^2 + 1}} = \ln(x^2 + 3)^2 - \ln\left(x\sqrt[3]{x^2 + 1}\right)$

$\qquad\qquad = 2 \ln(x^2 + 3) - \left[\ln x + \ln(x^2 + 1)^{1/3}\right]$

$\qquad\qquad = 2 \ln(x^2 + 3) - \ln x - \ln(x^2 + 1)^{1/3}$

$\qquad\qquad = 2 \ln(x^2 + 3) - \ln x - \dfrac{1}{3} \ln(x^2 + 1)$

When using the properties of logarithms to rewrite logarithmic functions, you must check to see whether the domain of the rewritten function is the same as the domain of the original function. For instance, the domain of $f(x) = \ln x^2$ is all real numbers except $x = 0$, and the domain of $g(x) = 2 \ln x$ is all positive real numbers.

EXAMPLE 6   **Solving Exponential and Logarithmic Equations**

Solve for x.

a. $7 = e^{x+1}$ **b.** $\ln(2x - 3) = 5$

Solution

a. $7 = e^{x+1}$ Write original equation.

$\qquad \ln 7 = \ln(e^{x+1})$ Take natural log of each side.

$\qquad \ln 7 = x + 1$ Apply inverse property.

$\quad -1 + \ln 7 = x$ Solve for x.

$\qquad 0.946 \approx x$ Use a calculator.

b. $\ln(2x - 3) = 5$ Write original equation.

$\qquad e^{\ln(2x-3)} = e^5$ Exponentiate each side.

$\qquad 2x - 3 = e^5$ Apply inverse property.

$\qquad x = \dfrac{1}{2}(e^5 + 3)$ Solve for x.

$\qquad x \approx 75.707$ Use a calculator.

1.6 Exercises

See CalcChat.com for tutorial help and worked-out solutions to odd-numbered exercises.

Evaluating an Expression In Exercises 1 and 2, evaluate the expressions.

1. (a) $25^{3/2}$ (b) $81^{1/2}$ (c) 3^{-2} (d) $27^{-1/3}$

2. (a) $64^{1/3}$ (b) 5^{-4} (c) $\left(\frac{1}{8}\right)^{1/3}$ (d) $\left(\frac{1}{4}\right)^{3}$

Using Properties of Exponents In Exercises 3–6, use the properties of exponents to simplify the expressions.

3. (a) $(5^2)(5^3)$
  (b) $(5^2)(5^{-3})$
  (c) $\dfrac{5^3}{25^2}$
  (d) $\left(\dfrac{1}{4}\right)^2 2^6$

4. (a) $(2^2)^3$
  (b) $(5^4)^{1/2}$
  (c) $[(27^{-1})(27^{2/3})]^3$
  (d) $(25^{3/2})(3^2)$

5. (a) $e^2(e^4)$
  (b) $(e^3)^4$
  (c) $(e^3)^{-2}$
  (d) $\dfrac{e^5}{e^3}$

6. (a) $\left(\dfrac{1}{e}\right)^{-2}$
  (b) $\left(\dfrac{e^5}{e^2}\right)^{-1}$
  (c) e^0
  (d) $\dfrac{1}{e^{-3}}$

Solving an Equation In Exercises 7–22, solve for x.

7. $3^x = 81$
8. $4^x = 64$
9. $6^{x-2} = 36$
10. $5^{x+1} = 125$
11. $\left(\frac{1}{2}\right)^x = 32$
12. $\left(\frac{1}{4}\right)^x = 16$
13. $\left(\frac{1}{3}\right)^{x-1} = 27$
14. $\left(\frac{1}{5}\right)^{2x} = 625$
15. $4^3 = (x+2)^3$
16. $18^2 = (5x-7)^2$
17. $x^{3/4} = 8$
18. $(x+3)^{4/3} = 16$
19. $e^x = 5$
20. $e^x = 1$
21. $e^{-2x} = e^5$
22. $e^{3x} = e^{-4}$

Comparing Numbers In Exercises 23 and 24, compare the given number with the number e. Is the number less than or greater than e?

23. $\left(1 + \dfrac{1}{1,000,000}\right)^{1,000,000}$

24. $1 + 1 + \frac{1}{2} + \frac{1}{6} + \frac{1}{24} + \frac{1}{120} + \frac{1}{720} + \frac{1}{5040}$

Sketching the Graph of a Function In Exercises 25–38, sketch the graph of the function.

25. $y = 3^x$
26. $y = 3^{x-1}$
27. $y = \left(\frac{1}{3}\right)^x$
28. $y = 2^{-x^2}$
29. $f(x) = 3^{-x^2}$
30. $f(x) = 3^{|x|}$
31. $y = e^{-x}$
32. $y = \frac{1}{2}e^x$
33. $y = e^x + 2$
34. $y = e^{x-1}$
35. $h(x) = e^{x-2}$
36. $g(x) = -e^{x/2}$
37. $y = e^{-x^2}$
38. $y = e^{-x/4}$

Finding the Domain In Exercises 39–44, find the domain of the function.

39. $f(x) = \dfrac{1}{3 + e^x}$
40. $f(x) = \dfrac{1}{2 - e^x}$
41. $f(x) = \sqrt{1 - 4^x}$
42. $f(x) = \sqrt{1 + 3^{-x}}$
43. $f(x) = \sin e^{-x}$
44. $f(x) = \cos e^{-x}$

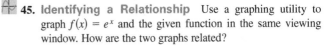

45. Identifying a Relationship Use a graphing utility to graph $f(x) = e^x$ and the given function in the same viewing window. How are the two graphs related?

  (a) $g(x) = e^{x-2}$ (b) $h(x) = -\frac{1}{2}e^x$ (c) $q(x) = e^{-x} + 3$

46. Describing the Shape of a Graph Use a graphing utility to graph the function. Describe the shape of the graph for very large and very small values of x.

  (a) $f(x) = \dfrac{8}{1 + e^{-0.5x}}$ (b) $g(x) = \dfrac{8}{1 + e^{-0.5/x}}$

Matching In Exercises 47–50, match the equation with the correct graph. Assume that a and C are positive real numbers. [The graphs are labeled (a), (b), (c), and (d).]

(a)
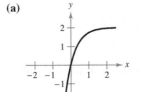

(b)
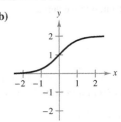

(c)
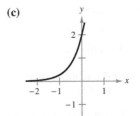

(d)
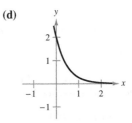

47. $y = Ce^{ax}$
48. $y = Ce^{-ax}$
49. $y = C(1 - e^{-ax})$
50. $y = \dfrac{C}{1 + e^{-ax}}$

Finding an Exponential Function In Exercises 51 and 52, find the exponential function $y = Ca^x$ that fits the graph.

51.
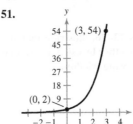

52.
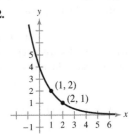

Matching In Exercises 53–56, match the function with its graph. [The graphs are labeled (a), (b), (c), and (d).]

(a)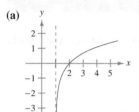

(b)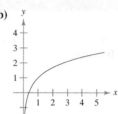

(c)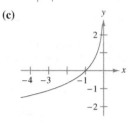

(d)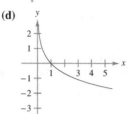

53. $f(x) = \ln x + 1$

54. $f(x) = -\ln x$

55. $f(x) = \ln(x - 1)$

56. $f(x) = -\ln(-x)$

Writing Exponential or Logarithmic Equations In Exercises 57–60, write the exponential equation as a logarithmic equation, or vice versa.

57. $e^0 = 1$

58. $e^{-2} = 0.1353\ldots$

59. $\ln 2 = 0.6931\ldots$

60. $\ln 0.5 = -0.6931\ldots$

Sketching a Graph In Exercises 61–68, sketch the graph of the function and state its domain.

61. $f(x) = 3 \ln x$

62. $f(x) = -2 \ln x$

63. $f(x) = \ln 2x$

64. $f(x) = \ln|x|$

65. $f(x) = \ln(x - 3)$

66. $f(x) = \ln x - 4$

67. $f(x) = \ln(x + 2)$

68. $f(x) = \ln(x - 2) + 1$

Writing an Equation In Exercises 69–72, write an equation for the function having the given characteristics.

69. The shape of $f(x) = e^x$, but shifted eight units upward and reflected in the x-axis

70. The shape of $f(x) = e^x$, but shifted two units to the left and six units downward

71. The shape of $f(x) = \ln x$, but shifted five units to the right and one unit downward

72. The shape of $f(x) = \ln x$, but shifted three units upward and reflected in the y-axis

Inverse Functions In Exercises 73–76, illustrate that the functions f and g are inverses of each other by using a graphing utility to graph them in the same viewing window.

73. $f(x) = e^{2x}$, $g(x) = \ln \sqrt{x}$

74. $f(x) = e^{x/3}$, $g(x) = \ln x^3$

75. $f(x) = e^x - 1$, $g(x) = \ln(x + 1)$

76. $f(x) = e^{x-1}$, $g(x) = 1 + \ln x$

Finding Inverse Functions In Exercises 77–80, (a) find the inverse of the function, (b) use a graphing utility to graph f and f^{-1} in the same viewing window, and (c) verify that $f^{-1}(f(x)) = x$ and $f(f^{-1}(x)) = x$.

77. $f(x) = e^{4x-1}$

78. $f(x) = 3e^{-x}$

79. $f(x) = 2\ln(x - 1)$

80. $f(x) = 3 + \ln(2x)$

Applying Inverse Properties In Exercises 81–86, apply the inverse properties of $\ln x$ and e^x to simplify the given expression.

81. $\ln e^{x^2}$

82. $\ln e^{2x-1}$

83. $e^{\ln(5x+2)}$

84. $e^{\ln \sqrt{x}}$

85. $-1 + \ln e^{2x}$

86. $-8 + e^{\ln x^3}$

Using Properties of Logarithms In Exercises 87 and 88, use the properties of logarithms to approximate the indicated logarithms, given that $\ln 2 \approx 0.6931$ and $\ln 3 \approx 1.0986$.

87. (a) $\ln 6$ (b) $\ln \frac{2}{3}$ (c) $\ln 81$ (d) $\ln \sqrt{3}$

88. (a) $\ln 0.25$ (b) $\ln 24$ (c) $\ln \sqrt[3]{12}$ (d) $\ln \frac{1}{72}$

Expanding a Logarithmic Expression In Exercises 89–98, use the properties of logarithms to expand the logarithmic expression.

89. $\ln \dfrac{x}{4}$

90. $\ln \sqrt{x^5}$

91. $\ln \dfrac{xy}{z}$

92. $\ln(xyz)$

93. $\ln\left(x\sqrt{x^2 + 5}\right)$

94. $\ln \sqrt[3]{z + 1}$

95. $\ln \sqrt{\dfrac{x - 1}{x}}$

96. $\ln z(z - 1)^2$

97. $\ln(3e^2)$

98. $\ln \dfrac{1}{e}$

Condensing a Logarithmic Expression In Exercises 99–106, write the expression as the logarithm of a single quantity.

99. $\ln x + \ln 7$

100. $\ln y + \ln x^2$

101. $\ln(x - 2) - \ln(x + 2)$

102. $3 \ln x + 2 \ln y - 4 \ln z$

103. $\frac{1}{3}[2 \ln(x + 3) + \ln x - \ln(x^2 - 1)]$

104. $2[\ln x - \ln(x + 1) - \ln(x - 1)]$

105. $2 \ln 3 - \frac{1}{2} \ln(x^2 + 1)$

106. $\frac{3}{2}[\ln(x^2 + 1) - \ln(x + 1) - \ln(x - 1)]$

Solving an Exponential or Logarithmic Equation In Exercises 107–110, solve for x accurate to three decimal places.

107. (a) $e^{\ln x} = 4$
(b) $\ln e^{2x} = 3$

108. (a) $e^{\ln 2x} = 12$
(b) $\ln e^{-x} = 0$

109. (a) $\ln x = 2$
(b) $e^x = 4$

110. (a) $\ln x^2 = 8$
(b) $e^{-2x} = 5$

Solving an Inequality In Exercises 111–114, solve the inequality for x.

111. $e^x > 5$

112. $e^{1-x} < 6$

113. $-2 < \ln x < 0$

114. $1 < \ln x < 100$

Solving an Inequality In Exercises 115 and 116, show that $f = g$ by using a graphing utility to graph f and g in the same viewing window. (Assume $x > 0$.)

115. $f(x) = \ln \dfrac{x^2}{4}$

$g(x) = 2 \ln x - \ln 4$

116. $f(x) = \ln \sqrt{x(x^2 + 1)}$

$g(x) = \frac{1}{2}[\ln x + \ln(x^2 + 1)]$

WRITING ABOUT CONCEPTS

117. Stating Properties In your own words, state the properties of the natural logarithmic function.

118. Think About It Explain why $\ln e^x = x$.

119. Stating Properties In your own words, state the properties of the natural exponential function.

120. Describe the Relationship Describe the relationship between the graphs of $f(x) = \ln x$ and $g(x) = e^x$.

121. Analyze a Statement The table of values below was obtained by evaluating a function. Determine which of the statements may be true and which must be false, and explain why.

(a) y is an exponential function of x.

(b) y is a logarithmic function of x.

(c) x is an exponential function of y.

(d) y is a linear function of x.

x	1	2	8
y	0	1	3

---

122. HOW DO YOU SEE IT? The figure below shows the graph of $y_1 = \ln e^x$ or $y_2 = e^{\ln x}$. Which graph is it? What are the domains of y_1 and y_2? Does $\ln e^x = e^{\ln x}$ for all real values of x? Explain.

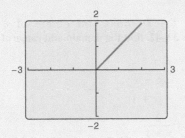

Sound Intensity In Exercises 123 and 124, use the following information. The relationship between the number of decibels β and the intensity of a sound in watts per centimeter squared is

$$\beta = \frac{10}{\ln 10} \ln\left(\frac{I}{10^{-16}}\right).$$

123. Use the properties of logarithms to write the formula in simpler form.

124. Determine the number of decibels of a sound with an intensity of 10^{-5} watt per square centimeter.

True or False? In Exercises 125 and 126, determine whether the statement is true or false. If it is false, explain why or give an example that shows it is false.

125. $\ln(x + 25) = \ln x + \ln 25$ **126.** $\ln xy = \ln x \ln y$

127. Comparing Functions Use a graphing utility to graph the functions

$$f(x) = 6^x \quad \text{and} \quad g(x) = x^6$$

in the same viewing window. Where do these graphs intersect? As x increases, which function grows more rapidly?

128. Comparing Functions Use a graphing utility to graph the functions

$$f(x) = \ln x \quad \text{and} \quad g(x) = x^{1/4}$$

in the same viewing window. Where do these graphs intersect? As x increases, which function grows more rapidly?

129. Analyzing a Function Let $f(x) = \ln\left(x + \sqrt{x^2 + 1}\right)$.

(a) Use a graphing utility to graph f and determine its domain.

(b) Show that f is an odd function.

(c) Find the inverse function of f.

130. Prime Number Theorem There are 25 prime numbers less than 100. The **Prime Number Theorem** states that the number of primes less than x approaches

$$p(x) \approx \frac{x}{\ln x}.$$

Use this approximation to estimate the rate (in primes per 100 integers) at which the prime numbers occur when

(a) $x = 1000$.

(b) $x = 1,000,000$.

(c) $x = 1,000,000,000$.

Stirling's Formula For large values of n,

$$n! = 1 \cdot 2 \cdot 3 \cdot 4 \cdots (n - 1) \cdot n$$

can be approximated by Stirling's Formula,

$$n! \approx \left(\frac{n}{e}\right)^n \sqrt{2\pi n}.$$

In Exercises 131 and 132, find the exact value of $n!$, and then approximate $n!$ using Stirling's Formula.

131. $n = 12$ **132.** $n = 15$

133. Proof Prove that $\ln(x/y) = \ln x - \ln y$, $x > 0, y > 0$.

134. Proof Prove that $\ln x^y = y \ln x$.

Review Exercises See CalcChat.com for tutorial help and worked-out solutions to odd-numbered exercises.

Finding Intercepts In Exercises 1–4, find any intercepts.

1. $y = 5x - 8$

2. $y = x^2 - 8x + 12$

3. $y = \dfrac{x - 3}{x - 4}$

4. $y = (x - 3)\sqrt{x + 4}$

Testing for Symmetry In Exercises 5–8, test for symmetry with respect to each axis and to the origin.

5. $y = x^2 + 4x$

6. $y = x^4 - x^2 + 3$

7. $y^2 = x^2 - 5$

8. $xy = -2$

Using Intercepts and Symmetry to Sketch a Graph In Exercises 9–14, sketch the graph of the equation. Identify any intercepts and test for symmetry.

9. $y = -\frac{1}{2}x + 3$

10. $y = -x^2 + 4$

11. $y = x^3 - 4x$

12. $y^2 = 9 - x$

13. $y = 2\sqrt{4 - x}$

14. $y = |x - 4| - 4$

Finding Points of Intersection In Exercises 15–18, find the points of intersection of the graphs of the equations.

15. $5x + 3y = -1$
   $x - y = -5$

16. $2x + 4y = 9$
   $6x - 4y = 7$

17. $x - y = -5$
   $x^2 - y = 1$

18. $x^2 + y^2 = 1$
   $-x + y = 1$

Finding the Slope of a Line In Exercises 19 and 20, plot the points and find the slope of the line passing through them.

19. $\left(\frac{3}{2}, 1\right), \left(5, \frac{5}{2}\right)$

20. $(-7, 8), (-1, 8)$

Finding an Equation of a Line In Exercises 21–24, find an equation of the line that passes through the point and has the indicated slope. Then sketch the line.

	Point	Slope
21.	$(3, -5)$	$m = \frac{7}{4}$
22.	$(-8, 1)$	m is undefined.
23.	$(-3, 0)$	$m = -\frac{2}{3}$
24.	$(5, 4)$	$m = 0$

Sketching Lines in the Plane In Exercises 25–28, use the slope and y-intercept to sketch a graph of the equation.

25. $y = 6$

26. $x = -3$

27. $y = 4x - 2$

28. $3x + 2y = 12$

Finding an Equation of a Line In Exercises 29 and 30, find an equation of the line that passes through the points. Then sketch the line.

29. $(0, 0), (8, 2)$

30. $(-5, 5), (10, -1)$

31. Finding Equations of Lines Find equations of the lines passing through $(-3, 5)$ and having the following characteristics.

(a) Slope of $\frac{7}{16}$

(b) Parallel to the line $5x - 3y = 3$

(c) Perpendicular to the line $3x + 4y = 8$

(d) Parallel to the y-axis

32. Finding Equations of Lines Find equations of the lines passing through $(2, 4)$ and having the following characteristics.

(a) Slope of $-\frac{2}{3}$

(b) Perpendicular to the line $x + y = 0$

(c) Passing through the point $(6, 1)$

(d) Parallel to the x-axis

33. Rate of Change The purchase price of a new machine is $12,500, and its value will decrease by $850 per year. Use this information to write a linear equation that gives the value V of the machine t years after it is purchased. Find its value at the end of 3 years.

34. Break-Even Analysis A contractor purchases a piece of equipment for $36,500 that costs an average of $9.25 per hour for fuel and maintenance. The equipment operator is paid $13.50 per hour, and customers are charged $30 per hour.

(a) Write an equation for the cost C of operating this equipment for t hours.

(b) Write an equation for the revenue R derived from t hours of use.

(c) Find the break-even point for this equipment by finding the time at which $R = C$.

Evaluating a Function In Exercises 35–38, evaluate the function at the given value(s) of the independent variable. Simplify the result.

35. $f(x) = 5x + 4$

(a) $f(0)$

(b) $f(5)$

(c) $f(-3)$

(d) $f(t + 1)$

36. $f(x) = x^3 - 2x$

(a) $f(-3)$

(b) $f(2)$

(c) $f(-1)$

(d) $f(c - 1)$

37. $f(x) = 4x^2$
   $\dfrac{f(x + \Delta x) - f(x)}{\Delta x}$

38. $f(x) = 2x - 6$
   $\dfrac{f(x) - f(-1)}{x - 1}$

Finding the Domain and Range of a Function In Exercises 39–42, find the domain and range of the function.

39. $f(x) = x^2 + 3$

40. $g(x) = \sqrt{6 - x}$

41. $f(x) = -|x + 1|$

42. $h(x) = \dfrac{2}{x + 1}$

Using the Vertical Line Test In Exercises 43–46, sketch the graph of the equation and use the Vertical Line Test to determine whether *y* is a function of *x*.

43. $x - y^2 = 6$

44. $x^2 - y = 0$

45. $y = \dfrac{|x - 2|}{x - 2}$

46. $x = 9 - y^2$

47. Transformations of Functions Use a graphing utility to graph $f(x) = x^3 - 3x^2$. Use the graph to write a formula for the function *g* shown in the figure. To print an enlarged copy of the graph, go to *MathGraphs.com.*

(a)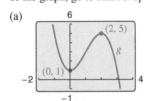

(b)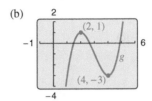

48. Conjecture

(a) Use a graphing utility to graph the functions *f*, *g*, and *h* in the same viewing window. Write a description of any similarities and differences you observe among the graphs.

Odd powers: $f(x) = x$, $g(x) = x^3$, $h(x) = x^5$

Even powers: $f(x) = x^2$, $g(x) = x^4$, $h(x) = x^6$

(b) Use the result in part (a) to make a conjecture about the graphs of the functions $y = x^7$ and $y = x^8$. Use a graphing utility to verify your conjecture.

49. Think About It Use the results of Exercise 48 to guess the shapes of the graphs of the functions *f*, *g*, and *h*. Then use a graphing utility to graph each function and compare the result with your guess.

(a) $f(x) = x^2(x - 6)^2$

(b) $g(x) = x^3(x - 6)^2$

(c) $h(x) = x^3(x - 6)^3$

50. Think About It What is the minimum degree of the polynomial function whose graph approximates the given graph? What sign must the leading coefficient have?

(a)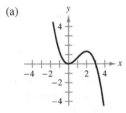

(b)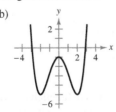

(c)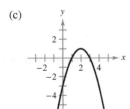

(d)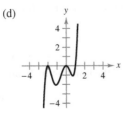

51. Writing The following graphs give the profits *P* for two small companies over a period *p* of 2 years. Create a story to describe the behavior of each profit function for some hypothetical product the company produces.

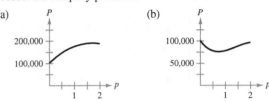

52. Area A wire 24 inches long is to be cut into four pieces to form a rectangle whose shortest side has a length of *x*.

(a) Write the area *A* of the rectangle as a function of *x*.

(b) Determine the domain of the function and use a graphing utility to graph the function over that domain.

(c) Use the graph of the function to approximate the maximum area of the rectangle. Make a conjecture about the dimensions that yield a maximum area.

53. Stress Test A machine part was tested by bending it *x* centimeters 10 times per minute until the time *y* (in hours) of failure. The results are recorded in the table.

x	3	6	9	12	15
y	61	56	53	55	48

x	18	21	24	27	30
y	35	36	33	44	23

(a) Use the regression capabilities of a graphing utility to find a linear model for the data.

(b) Use a graphing utility to plot the data and graph the model.

(c) Use the graph to determine whether there may have been an error made in conducting one of the tests or in recording the results. If so, eliminate the erroneous point and find the model for the remaining data.

54. Median Income The data in the table show the median income *y* (in thousands of dollars) for males of various ages *x* in the United States in 2009. *(Source: U.S. Census Bureau)*

x	20	30	40	50	60	70
y	10.0	31.9	42.2	44.7	41.3	25.9

(a) Use the regression capabilities of a graphing utility to find a quadratic model for the data.

(b) Use a graphing utility to plot the data and graph the model.

(c) Use the model to approximate the median income for a male who is 26 years old.

(d) Use the model to approximate the median income for a male who is 34 years old.

55. Summer Olympics The table lists the U.S. media rights fees y (in millions of dollars) for the Summer Olympics in year t, where $t = 4$ corresponds to 1984. *(Source: 2012 Olympics Media Guide, NBC Sports Group)*

t	4	8	12	16
y	225	300	401	456

t	20	24	28	32
y	705	793	894	1180

(a) Use the regression capabilities of a graphing utility to find a quadratic model for the data.

(b) Use a graphing utility to plot the data and graph the model. How well does the model fit the data? Explain your reasoning.

56. Harmonic Motion The motion of an oscillating weight suspended by a spring was measured by a motion detector. The data collected and the approximate maximum (positive and negative) displacements from equilibrium are shown in the figure. The displacement y is measured in feet, and the time t is measured in seconds.

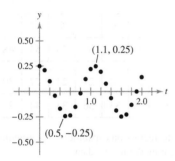

(a) Is y a function of t? Explain.

(b) Approximate the amplitude and period of the oscillations.

(c) Find a model for the data.

(d) Use a graphing utility to graph the model in part (c). Compare the result with the data in the figure.

Finding an Inverse Function In Exercises 57–62, (a) find the inverse of the function, (b) use a graphing utility to graph f and f^{-1} in the same viewing window, and (c) verify that $f^{-1}(f(x)) = x$ and $f(f^{-1}(x)) = x$.

57. $f(x) = \frac{1}{2}x - 3$

58. $f(x) = 5x - 7$

59. $f(x) = \sqrt{x + 1}$

60. $f(x) = x^3 + 2$

61. $f(x) = \sqrt[3]{x + 1}$

62. $f(x) = x^2 - 5, \quad x \geq 0$

Sketching a Graph In Exercises 63 and 64, sketch the graph of the function by hand.

63. $f(x) = 2 \arctan(x + 3)$ **64.** $h(x) = -3 \arcsin 2x$

Evaluating an Expression In Exercises 65 and 66, evaluate the expression without using a calculator. (*Hint:* Make a sketch of a right triangle.)

65. $\sin\left(\arcsin \frac{1}{2}\right)$ **66.** $\tan(\text{arccot } 2)$

Matching In Exercises 67–70, match the function with its graph. [The graphs are labeled (a), (b), (c), and (d).]

(a) 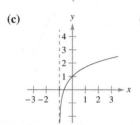   (b)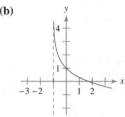

(c)   (d)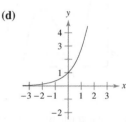

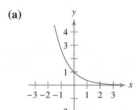

67. $f(x) = e^x$ **68.** $f(x) = e^{-x}$

69. $f(x) = \ln(x + 1) + 1$ **70.** $f(x) = -\ln(x + 1) + 1$

Sketching a Graph In Exercises 71 and 72, sketch the graph of the function by hand.

71. $f(x) = \ln x + 3$ **72.** $f(x) = \ln(x - 1)$

Expanding a Logarithmic Expression In Exercises 73 and 74, use the properties of logarithms to expand the logarithmic function.

73. $\ln \sqrt[5]{\dfrac{4x^2 - 1}{4x^2 + 1}}$ **74.** $\ln[(x^2 + 1)(x - 1)]$

Condensing a Logarithmic Expression In Exercises 75 and 76, write the expression as the logarithm of a single quantity.

75. $\ln 3 + \frac{1}{3}\ln(4 - x^2) - \ln x$

76. $3[\ln x - 2\ln(x^2 + 1)] + 2\ln 5$

Solving an Equation In Exercises 77 and 78, solve the equation for x.

77. $\ln \sqrt{x + 1} = 2$ **78.** $\ln x + \ln(x - 3) = 0$

Finding Inverse Functions In Exercises 79 and 80, (a) find the inverse function of f, (b) use a graphing utility to graph f and f^{-1} in the same viewing window, and (c) verify that $f^{-1}(f(x)) = x$ and $f(f^{-1}(x)) = x$.

79. $f(x) = \ln \sqrt{x}$ **80.** $f(x) = e^{1-x}$

Sketching a Graph In Exercises 81 and 82, sketch the graph of the function by hand.

81. $y = e^{-x/2}$ **82.** $y = 4e^{-x^2}$

P.S. Problem Solving

See **CalcChat.com** for tutorial help and worked-out solutions to odd-numbered exercises.

1. Finding Tangent Lines   Consider the circle

$$x^2 + y^2 - 6x - 8y = 0,$$

as shown in the figure.

(a) Find the center and radius of the circle.

(b) Find an equation of the tangent line to the circle at the point $(0, 0)$.

(c) Find an equation of the tangent line to the circle at the point $(6, 0)$.

(d) Where do the two tangent lines intersect?

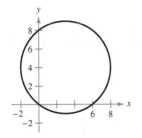

Figure for 1   Figure for 2

2. Finding Tangent Lines   There are two tangent lines from the point $(0, 1)$ to the circle $x^2 + (y + 1)^2 = 1$ (see figure). Find equations of these two lines by using the fact that each tangent line intersects the circle at *exactly* one point.

3. Heaviside Function   The Heaviside function $H(x)$ is widely used in engineering applications.

$$H(x) = \begin{cases} 1, & x \geq 0 \\ 0, & x < 0 \end{cases}$$

Sketch the graph of the Heaviside function and the graphs of the following functions by hand.

(a) $H(x) - 2$ (b) $H(x - 2)$ (c) $-H(x)$

(d) $H(-x)$ (e) $\frac{1}{2}H(x)$ (f) $-H(x - 2) + 2$

OLIVER HEAVISIDE (1850–1925)

Heaviside was a British mathematician and physicist who contributed to the field of applied mathematics, especially applications of mathematics to electrical engineering. The *Heaviside function* is a classic type of "on-off" function that has applications to electricity and computer science.

4. Sketching Transformations   Consider the graph of the function f shown below. Use this graph to sketch the graphs of the following functions. To print an enlarged copy of the graph, go to *MathGraphs.com*.

(a) $f(x + 1)$ (b) $f(x) + 1$

(c) $2f(x)$ (d) $f(-x)$

(e) $-f(x)$ (f) $|f(x)|$

(g) $f(|x|)$

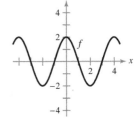

5. Maximum Area   A rancher plans to fence a rectangular pasture adjacent to a river. The rancher has 100 meters of fencing, and no fencing is needed along the river (see figure).

(a) Write the area A of the pasture as a function of x, the length of the side parallel to the river. What is the domain of A?

(b) Graph the area function and estimate the dimensions that yield the maximum amount of area for the pasture.

(c) Find the dimensions that yield the maximum amount of area for the pasture by completing the square.

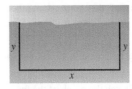   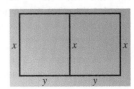

Figure for 5   Figure for 6

6. Maximum Area   A rancher has 300 feet of fencing to enclose two adjacent pastures (see figure).

(a) Write the total area A of the two pastures as a function of x. What is the domain of A?

(b) Graph the area function and estimate the dimensions that yield the maximum amount of area for the pastures.

(c) Find the dimensions that yield the maximum amount of area for the pastures by completing the square.

7. Writing a Function   You are in a boat 2 miles from the nearest point on the coast. You are to go to a point Q located 3 miles down the coast and 1 mile inland (see figure). You can row at 2 miles per hour and walk at 4 miles per hour. Write the total time T of the trip as a function of x.

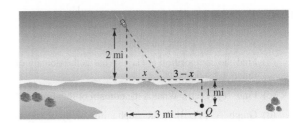

8. Analyzing a Function Graph the function $f(x) = e^x - e^{-x}$. From the graph, the function appears to be one-to-one. Assuming that the function has an inverse, find $f^{-1}(x)$.

9. Slope of a Tangent Line One of the fundamental themes of calculus is to find the slope of the tangent line to a curve at a point. To see how this can be done, consider the point $(2, 4)$ on the graph of $f(x) = x^2$ (see figure).

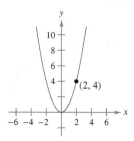

(a) Find the slope of the line joining $(2, 4)$ and $(3, 9)$. Is the slope of the tangent line at $(2, 4)$ greater than or less than this number?

(b) Find the slope of the line joining $(2, 4)$ and $(1, 1)$. Is the slope of the tangent line at $(2, 4)$ greater than or less than this number?

(c) Find the slope of the line joining $(2, 4)$ and $(2.1, 4.41)$. Is the slope of the tangent line at $(2, 4)$ greater than or less than this number?

(d) Find the slope of the line joining $(2, 4)$ and $(2 + h, f(2 + h))$ in terms of the nonzero number h. Verify that $h = 1, -1$, and 0.1 yield the solutions to parts (a)–(c) above.

(e) What is the slope of the tangent line at $(2, 4)$? Explain how you arrived at your answer.

10. Slope of a Tangent Line Sketch the graph of the function $f(x) = \sqrt{x}$ and label the point $(4, 2)$ on the graph.

(a) Find the slope of the line joining $(4, 2)$ and $(9, 3)$. Is the slope of the tangent line at $(4, 2)$ greater than or less than this number?

(b) Find the slope of the line joining $(4, 2)$ and $(1, 1)$. Is the slope of the tangent line at $(4, 2)$ greater than or less than this number?

(c) Find the slope of the line joining $(4, 2)$ and $(4.41, 2.1)$. Is the slope of the tangent line at $(4, 2)$ greater than or less than this number?

(d) Find the slope of the line joining $(4, 2)$ and $(4 + h, f(4 + h))$ in terms of the nonzero number h.

(e) What is the slope of the tangent line at $(4, 2)$? Explain how you arrived at your answer.

11. Composite Functions Let $f(x) = \dfrac{1}{1 - x}$.

(a) What are the domain and range of f?

(b) Find the composition $f(f(x))$. What is the domain of this function?

(c) Find $f(f(f(x)))$. What is the domain of this function?

(d) Graph $f(f(f(x)))$. Is the graph a line? Why or why not?

12. Graphing an Equation Explain how you would graph the equation

$$y + |y| = x + |x|.$$

Then sketch the graph.

13. Sound Intensity A large room contains two speakers that are 3 meters apart. The sound intensity I of one speaker is twice that of the other, as shown in the figure. (To print an enlarged copy of the graph, go to *MathGraphs.com*.) Suppose the listener is free to move about the room to find those positions that receive equal amounts of sound from both speakers. Such a location satisfies two conditions: (1) the sound intensity at the listener's position is directly proportional to the sound level of a source, and (2) the sound intensity is inversely proportional to the square of the distance from the source.

(a) Find the points on the x-axis that receive equal amounts of sound from both speakers.

(b) Find and graph the equation of all locations (x, y) where one could stand and receive equal amounts of sound from both speakers.

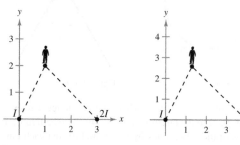

Figure for 13   Figure for 14

14. Sound Intensity Suppose the speakers in Exercise 13 are 4 meters apart and the sound intensity of one speaker is k times that of the other, as shown in the figure. To print an enlarged copy of the graph, go to *MathGraphs.com*.

(a) Find the equation of all locations (x, y) where one could stand and receive equal amounts of sound from both speakers.

(b) Graph the equation for the case $k = 3$.

(c) Describe the set of locations of equal sound as k becomes very large.

15. Lemniscate Let d_1 and d_2 be the distances from the point (x, y) to the points $(-1, 0)$ and $(1, 0)$, respectively, as shown in the figure. Show that the equation of the graph of all points (x, y) satisfying $d_1 d_2 = 1$ is

$$(x^2 + y^2)^2 = 2(x^2 - y^2).$$

This curve is called a **lemniscate**. Graph the lemniscate and identify three points on the graph.

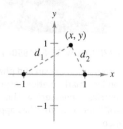

2 Limits and Their Properties

- **2.1** A Preview of Calculus
- **2.2** Finding Limits Graphically and Numerically
- **2.3** Evaluating Limits Analytically
- **2.4** Continuity and One-Sided Limits
- **2.5** Infinite Limits

Inventory Management *(Exercise 114, p. 101)*

Average Speed *(Exercise 68, p. 109)*

Free-Falling Object *(Exercises 107 and 108, p. 89)*

Sports *(Exercise 64, p. 77)*

Bicyclist *(Exercise 3, p. 67)*

2.1 A Preview of Calculus

- ■ Understand what calculus is and how it compares with precalculus.
- ■ Understand that the tangent line problem is basic to calculus.
- ■ Understand that the area problem is also basic to calculus.

What Is Calculus?

Calculus is the mathematics of change. For instance, calculus is the mathematics of velocities, accelerations, tangent lines, slopes, areas, volumes, arc lengths, centroids, curvatures, and a variety of other concepts that have enabled scientists, engineers, and economists to model real-life situations.

Although precalculus mathematics also deals with velocities, accelerations, tangent lines, slopes, and so on, there is a fundamental difference between precalculus mathematics and calculus. Precalculus mathematics is more static, whereas calculus is more dynamic. Here are some examples.

- An object traveling at a constant velocity can be analyzed with precalculus mathematics. To analyze the velocity of an accelerating object, you need calculus.
- The slope of a line can be analyzed with precalculus mathematics. To analyze the slope of a curve, you need calculus.
- The curvature of a circle is constant and can be analyzed with precalculus mathematics. To analyze the variable curvature of a general curve, you need calculus.
- The area of a rectangle can be analyzed with precalculus mathematics. To analyze the area under a general curve, you need calculus.

Each of these situations involves the same general strategy—the reformulation of precalculus mathematics through the use of a limit process. So, one way to answer the question "What is calculus?" is to say that calculus is a "limit machine" that involves three stages. The first stage is precalculus mathematics, such as the slope of a line or the area of a rectangle. The second stage is the limit process, and the third stage is a new calculus formulation, such as a derivative or integral.

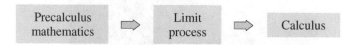

Some students try to learn calculus as if it were simply a collection of new formulas. This is unfortunate. If you reduce calculus to the memorization of differentiation and integration formulas, you will miss a great deal of understanding, self-confidence, and satisfaction.

On the next two pages are listed some familiar precalculus concepts coupled with their calculus counterparts. Throughout the text, your goal should be to learn how precalculus formulas and techniques are used as building blocks to produce the more general calculus formulas and techniques. Don't worry if you are unfamiliar with some of the "old formulas" listed on the next two pages—you will be reviewing all of them.

As you proceed through this text, come back to this discussion repeatedly. Try to keep track of where you are relative to the three stages involved in the study of calculus. For instance, note how these chapters relate to the three stages.

Chapter 1: Preparation for Calculus	Precalculus
Chapter 2: Limits and Their Properties	Limit process
Chapter 3: Differentiation	Calculus

This cycle is repeated many times on a smaller scale throughout the text.

Without Calculus	**With Differential Calculus**
Value of $f(x)$ when $x = c$	Limit of $f(x)$ as x approaches c
Slope of a line	Slope of a curve
Secant line to a curve	Tangent line to a curve
Average rate of change between $t = a$ and $t = b$	Instantaneous rate of change at $t = c$
Curvature of a circle	Curvature of a curve
Height of a curve when $x = c$	Maximum height of a curve on an interval
Tangent plane to a sphere	Tangent plane to a surface
Direction of motion along a line	Direction of motion along a curve

Without Calculus		With Integral Calculus	
Area of a rectangle		Area under a curve	
Work done by a constant force		Work done by a variable force	
Center of a rectangle		Centroid of a region	
Length of a line segment		Length of an arc	
Surface area of a cylinder		Surface area of a solid of revolution	
Mass of a solid of constant density		Mass of a solid of variable density	
Volume of a rectangular solid		Volume of a region under a surface	
Sum of a finite number of terms	$a_1 + a_2 + \cdots + a_n = S$	Sum of an infinite number of terms	$a_1 + a_2 + a_3 + \cdots = S$

The tangent line to the graph of f at P
Figure 2.1

The Tangent Line Problem

The notion of a limit is fundamental to the study of calculus. The following brief descriptions of two classic problems in calculus—*the tangent line problem* and *the area problem*—should give you some idea of the way limits are used in calculus.

In the tangent line problem, you are given a function f and a point P on its graph and are asked to find an equation of the tangent line to the graph at point P, as shown in Figure 2.1.

Except for cases involving a vertical tangent line, the problem of finding the **tangent line** at a point P is equivalent to finding the *slope* of the tangent line at P. You can approximate this slope by using a line through the point of tangency and a second point on the curve, as shown in Figure 2.2(a). Such a line is called a **secant line.** If $P(c, f(c))$ is the point of tangency and

$$Q(c + \Delta x, f(c + \Delta x))$$

is a second point on the graph of f, then the slope of the secant line through these two points can be found using precalculus and is

$$m_{\text{sec}} = \frac{f(c + \Delta x) - f(c)}{c + \Delta x - c} = \frac{f(c + \Delta x) - f(c)}{\Delta x}.$$

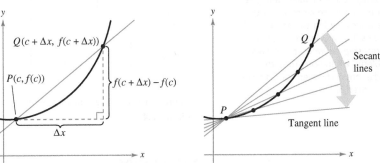

(a) The secant line through $(c, f(c))$ and $(c + \Delta x, f(c + \Delta x))$

(b) As Q approaches P, the secant lines approach the tangent line.

Figure 2.2

As point Q approaches point P, the slopes of the secant lines approach the slope of the tangent line, as shown in Figure 2.2(b). When such a "limiting position" exists, the slope of the tangent line is said to be the **limit** of the slopes of the secant lines. (Much more will be said about this important calculus concept in Chapter 3.)

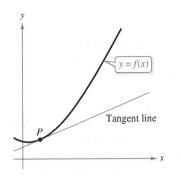

**GRACE CHISHOLM YOUNG
(1868–1944)**

Grace Chisholm Young received her degree in mathematics from Girton College in Cambridge, England. Her early work was published under the name of William Young, her husband. Between 1914 and 1916, Grace Young published work on the foundations of calculus that won her the Gamble Prize from Girton College.

Exploration

The following points lie on the graph of $f(x) = x^2$.

$Q_1(1.5, f(1.5))$, $Q_2(1.1, f(1.1))$, $Q_3(1.01, f(1.01))$,
$Q_4(1.001, f(1.001))$, $Q_5(1.0001, f(1.0001))$

Each successive point gets closer to the point $P(1, 1)$. Find the slopes of the secant lines through Q_1 and P, Q_2 and P, and so on. Graph these secant lines on a graphing utility. Then use your results to estimate the slope of the tangent line to the graph of f at the point P.

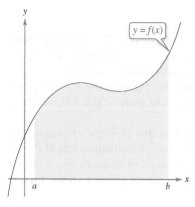

Area under a curve
Figure 2.3

The Area Problem

In the tangent line problem, you saw how the limit process can be applied to the slope of a line to find the slope of a general curve. A second classic problem in calculus is finding the area of a plane region that is bounded by the graphs of functions. This problem can also be solved with a limit process. In this case, the limit process is applied to the area of a rectangle to find the area of a general region.

As a simple example, consider the region bounded by the graph of the function $y = f(x)$, the x-axis, and the vertical lines $x = a$ and $x = b$, as shown in Figure 2.3. You can approximate the area of the region with several rectangular regions, as shown in Figure 2.4. As you increase the number of rectangles, the approximation tends to become better and better because the amount of area missed by the rectangles decreases. Your goal is to determine the limit of the sum of the areas of the rectangles as the number of rectangles increases without bound.

HISTORICAL NOTE

In one of the most astounding events ever to occur in mathematics, it was discovered that the tangent line problem and the area problem are closely related. This discovery led to the birth of calculus. You will learn about the relationship between these two problems when you study the Fundamental Theorem of Calculus in Chapter 5.

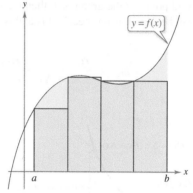

Approximation using four rectangles
Figure 2.4

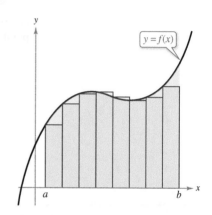

Approximation using eight rectangles

Exploration

Consider the region bounded by the graphs of

$$f(x) = x^2, \quad y = 0, \quad \text{and} \quad x = 1$$

as shown in part (a) of the figure. The area of the region can be approximated by two sets of rectangles—one set inscribed within the region and the other set circumscribed over the region, as shown in parts (b) and (c). Find the sum of the areas of each set of rectangles. Then use your results to approximate the area of the region.

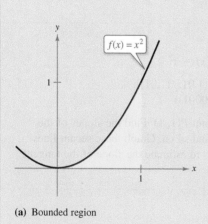

(a) Bounded region

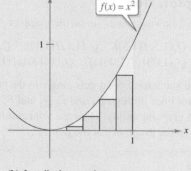

(b) Inscribed rectangles

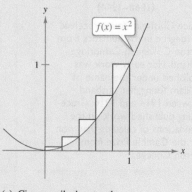

(c) Circumscribed rectangles

2.1 Exercises

See **CalcChat.com** for tutorial help and worked-out solutions to odd-numbered exercises.

Precalculus or Calculus   In Exercises 1–5, decide whether the problem can be solved using precalculus or whether calculus is required. If the problem can be solved using precalculus, solve it. If the problem seems to require calculus, explain your reasoning and use a graphical or numerical approach to estimate the solution.

1. Find the distance traveled in 15 seconds by an object traveling at a constant velocity of 20 feet per second.

2. Find the distance traveled in 15 seconds by an object moving with a velocity of $v(t) = 20 + 7 \cos t$ feet per second.

3. Rate of Change

A bicyclist is riding on a path modeled by the function $f(x) = 0.04(8x - x^2)$, where x and $f(x)$ are measured in miles (see figure). Find the rate of change of elevation at $x = 2$.

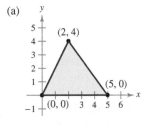

4. A bicyclist is riding on a path modeled by the function $f(x) = 0.08x$, where x and $f(x)$ are measured in miles (see figure). Find the rate of change of elevation at $x = 2$.

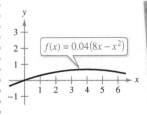

5. Find the area of the shaded region.

(a)

(b)

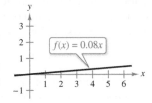
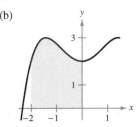

6. **Secant Lines**   Consider the function

$$f(x) = \sqrt{x}$$

and the point $P(4, 2)$ on the graph of f.

(a) Graph f and the secant lines passing through $P(4, 2)$ and $Q(x, f(x))$ for x-values of 1, 3, and 5.

(b) Find the slope of each secant line.

(c) Use the results of part (b) to estimate the slope of the tangent line to the graph of f at $P(4, 2)$. Describe how to improve your approximation of the slope.

7. **Secant Lines**   Consider the function $f(x) = 6x - x^2$ and the point $P(2, 8)$ on the graph of f.

(a) Graph f and the secant lines passing through $P(2, 8)$ and $Q(x, f(x))$ for x-values of 3, 2.5, and 1.5.

(b) Find the slope of each secant line.

(c) Use the results of part (b) to estimate the slope of the tangent line to the graph of f at $P(2, 8)$. Describe how to improve your approximation of the slope.

8. **HOW DO YOU SEE IT?**   How would you describe the instantaneous rate of change of an automobile's position on a highway?

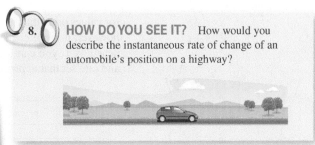

9. **Approximating Area**   Use the rectangles in each graph to approximate the area of the region bounded by $y = 5/x$, $y = 0$, $x = 1$, and $x = 5$. Describe how you could continue this process to obtain a more accurate approximation of the area.

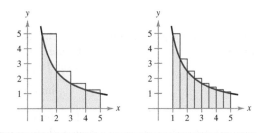

WRITING ABOUT CONCEPTS

10. **Approximating the Length of a Curve**   Consider the length of the graph of $f(x) = 5/x$ from $(1, 5)$ to $(5, 1)$.

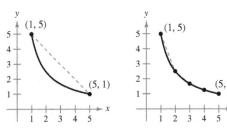

(a) Approximate the length of the curve by finding the distance between its two endpoints, as shown in the first figure.

(b) Approximate the length of the curve by finding the sum of the lengths of four line segments, as shown in the second figure.

(c) Describe how you could continue this process to obtain a more accurate approximation of the length of the curve.

2.2 Finding Limits Graphically and Numerically

- ■ Estimate a limit using a numerical or graphical approach.
- ■ Learn different ways that a limit can fail to exist.
- ■ Study and use a formal definition of limit.

An Introduction to Limits

To sketch the graph of the function

$$f(x) = \frac{x^3 - 1}{x - 1}$$

for values other than $x = 1$, you can use standard curve-sketching techniques. At $x = 1$, however, it is not clear what to expect. To get an idea of the behavior of the graph of f near $x = 1$, you can use two sets of x-values—one set that approaches 1 from the left and one set that approaches 1 from the right, as shown in the table.

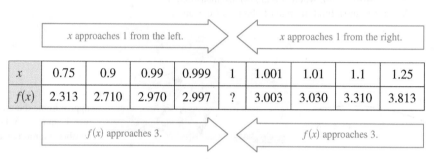

	x approaches 1 from the left.					x approaches 1 from the right.			
x	0.75	0.9	0.99	0.999	1	1.001	1.01	1.1	1.25
$f(x)$	2.313	2.710	2.970	2.997	?	3.003	3.030	3.310	3.813
	f(x) approaches 3.					f(x) approaches 3.			

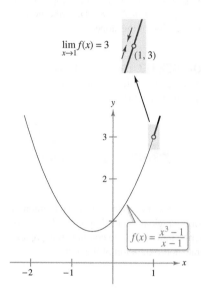

$\lim\limits_{x\to1} f(x) = 3$

$(1, 3)$

$f(x) = \dfrac{x^3 - 1}{x - 1}$

The limit of $f(x)$ as x approaches 1 is 3.
Figure 2.5

The graph of f is a parabola that has a gap at the point $(1, 3)$, as shown in Figure 2.5. Although x cannot equal 1, you can move arbitrarily close to 1, and as a result $f(x)$ moves arbitrarily close to 3. Using limit notation, you can write

$$\lim_{x\to1} f(x) = 3. \qquad \text{This is read as "the limit of } f(x) \text{ as } x \text{ approaches 1 is 3."}$$

This discussion leads to an informal definition of limit. If $f(x)$ becomes arbitrarily close to a single number L as x approaches c from either side, then the **limit** of $f(x)$, as x approaches c, is L. This limit is written as

$$\lim_{x\to c} f(x) = L.$$

Exploration

The discussion above gives an example of how you can estimate a limit *numerically* by constructing a table and *graphically* by drawing a graph. Estimate the following limit numerically by completing the table.

$$\lim_{x\to2} \frac{x^2 - 3x + 2}{x - 2}$$

x	1.75	1.9	1.99	1.999	2	2.001	2.01	2.1	2.25
$f(x)$	?	?	?	?	?	?	?	?	?

Then use a graphing utility to estimate the limit graphically.

EXAMPLE 1   **Estimating a Limit Numerically**

Evaluate the function $f(x) = x/(\sqrt{x + 1} - 1)$ at several x-values near 0 and use the results to estimate the limit

$$\lim_{x \to 0} \frac{x}{\sqrt{x + 1} - 1}.$$

Solution   The table lists the values of $f(x)$ for several x-values near 0.

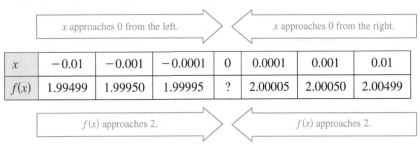

x	-0.01	-0.001	-0.0001	0	0.0001	0.001	0.01
$f(x)$	1.99499	1.99950	1.99995	?	2.00005	2.00050	2.00499

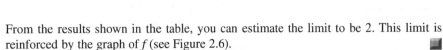

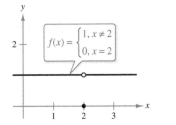

f is undefined at $x = 0$.

$f(x) = \dfrac{x}{\sqrt{x + 1} - 1}$

The limit of $f(x)$ as x approaches 0 is 2.
Figure 2.6

From the results shown in the table, you can estimate the limit to be 2. This limit is reinforced by the graph of f (see Figure 2.6).

In Example 1, note that the function is undefined at $x = 0$, and yet $f(x)$ appears to be approaching a limit as x approaches 0. This often happens, and it is important to realize that *the existence or nonexistence of $f(x)$ at $x = c$ has no bearing on the existence of the limit of $f(x)$ as x approaches c.*

EXAMPLE 2   **Finding a Limit**

Find the limit of $f(x)$ as x approaches 2, where

$$f(x) = \begin{cases} 1, & x \neq 2 \\ 0, & x = 2 \end{cases}.$$

$f(x) = \begin{cases} 1, x \neq 2 \\ 0, x = 2 \end{cases}$

The limit of $f(x)$ as x approaches 2 is 1.
Figure 2.7

Solution   Because $f(x) = 1$ for all x other than $x = 2$, you can estimate that the limit is 1, as shown in Figure 2.7. So, you can write

$$\lim_{x \to 2} f(x) = 1.$$

The fact that $f(2) = 0$ has no bearing on the existence or value of the limit as x approaches 2. For instance, as x approaches 2, the function

$$g(x) = \begin{cases} 1, & x \neq 2 \\ 2, & x = 2 \end{cases}$$

has the same limit as f.

So far in this section, you have been estimating limits numerically and graphically. Each of these approaches produces an estimate of the limit. In Section 2.3, you will study analytic techniques for evaluating limits. Throughout the course, try to develop a habit of using this three-pronged approach to problem solving.

1. Numerical approach   Construct a table of values.

2. Graphical approach   Draw a graph by hand or using technology.

3. Analytic approach   Use algebra or calculus.

Limits That Fail to Exist

In the next three examples, you will examine some limits that fail to exist.

EXAMPLE 3 **Different Right and Left Behavior**

Show that the limit $\lim\limits_{x \to 0} \dfrac{|x|}{x}$ does not exist.

Solution Consider the graph of the function

$$f(x) = \frac{|x|}{x}.$$

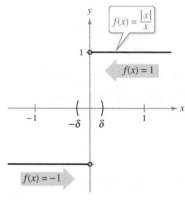

$\lim\limits_{x \to 0} f(x)$ does not exist.

Figure 2.8

In Figure 2.8 and from the definition of absolute value,

$$|x| = \begin{cases} x, & x \geq 0 \\ -x, & x < 0 \end{cases} \qquad \text{Definition of absolute value}$$

you can see that

$$\frac{|x|}{x} = \begin{cases} 1, & x > 0 \\ -1, & x < 0 \end{cases}.$$

So, no matter how close x gets to 0, there will be both positive and negative x-values that yield $f(x) = 1$ or $f(x) = -1$. Specifically, if δ (the lowercase Greek letter *delta*) is a positive number, then for x-values satisfying the inequality $0 < |x| < \delta$, you can classify the values of $|x|/x$ as

$$(-\delta, 0) \qquad \text{or} \qquad (0, \delta).$$

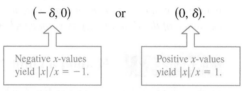

Negative x-values yield $|x|/x = -1$.

Positive x-values yield $|x|/x = 1$.

Because $|x|/x$ approaches a different number from the right side of 0 than it approaches from the left side, the limit $\lim\limits_{x \to 0} (|x|/x)$ does not exist.

EXAMPLE 4 **Unbounded Behavior**

Discuss the existence of the limit $\lim\limits_{x \to 0} \dfrac{1}{x^2}$.

Solution Consider the graph of the function

$$f(x) = \frac{1}{x^2}.$$

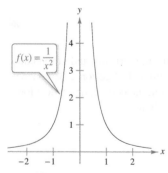

$\lim\limits_{x \to 0} f(x)$ does not exist.

Figure 2.9

In Figure 2.9, you can see that as x approaches 0 from either the right or the left, $f(x)$ increases without bound. This means that by choosing x close enough to 0, you can force $f(x)$ to be as large as you want. For instance, $f(x)$ will be greater than 100 when you choose x within $\frac{1}{10}$ of 0. That is,

$$0 < |x| < \frac{1}{10} \quad \Longrightarrow \quad f(x) = \frac{1}{x^2} > 100.$$

Similarly, you can force $f(x)$ to be greater than 1,000,000, as shown.

$$0 < |x| < \frac{1}{1000} \quad \Longrightarrow \quad f(x) = \frac{1}{x^2} > 1,000,000$$

Because $f(x)$ does not become arbitrarily close to a single number L as x approaches 0, you can conclude that the limit does not exist.

Oscillating Behavior

•••▷ *See LarsonCalculus.com for an interactive version of this type of example.*

Discuss the existence of the limit $\lim\limits_{x \to 0} \sin \dfrac{1}{x}$.

Solution Let $f(x) = \sin(1/x)$. In Figure 2.10, you can see that as x approaches 0, $f(x)$ oscillates between -1 and 1. So, the limit does not exist because no matter how small you choose δ, it is possible to choose x_1 and x_2 within δ units of 0 such that $\sin(1/x_1) = 1$ and $\sin(1/x_2) = -1$, as shown in the table.

x	$\dfrac{2}{\pi}$	$\dfrac{2}{3\pi}$	$\dfrac{2}{5\pi}$	$\dfrac{2}{7\pi}$	$\dfrac{2}{9\pi}$	$\dfrac{2}{11\pi}$	$x \to 0$
$\sin \dfrac{1}{x}$	1	-1	1	-1	1	-1	Limit does not exist.

$\lim\limits_{x \to 0} f(x)$ does not exist.
Figure 2.10

Common Types of Behavior Associated with Nonexistence of a Limit

1. $f(x)$ approaches a different number from the right side of c than it approaches from the left side.

2. $f(x)$ increases or decreases without bound as x approaches c.

3. $f(x)$ oscillates between two fixed values as x approaches c.

There are many other interesting functions that have unusual limit behavior. An often cited one is the *Dirichlet function*

$$f(x) = \begin{cases} 0, & \text{if } x \text{ is rational} \\ 1, & \text{if } x \text{ is irrational} \end{cases}.$$

Because this function has *no limit* at any real number c, it is *not continuous* at any real number c. You will study continuity more closely in Section 2.4.

▷ **TECHNOLOGY PITFALL** When you use a graphing utility to investigate the behavior of a function near the x-value at which you are trying to evaluate a limit, remember that you can't always trust the pictures that graphing utilities draw. When you use a graphing utility to graph the function in Example 5 over an interval containing 0, you will most likely obtain an incorrect graph such as that shown in Figure 2.11. The reason that a graphing utility can't show the correct graph is that the graph has infinitely many oscillations over any interval that contains 0.

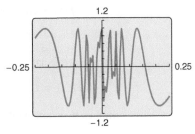

Incorrect graph of $f(x) = \sin(1/x)$
Figure 2.11

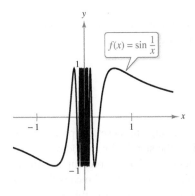

PETER GUSTAV DIRICHLET (1805–1859)

In the early development of calculus, the definition of a function was much more restricted than it is today, and "functions" such as the Dirichlet function would not have been considered. The modern definition of function is attributed to the German mathematician Peter Gustav Dirichlet.

See LarsonCalculus.com to read more of this biography.

■ **FOR FURTHER INFORMATION**
For more on the introduction of rigor to calculus, see "Who Gave You the Epsilon? Cauchy and the Origins of Rigorous Calculus" by Judith V. Grabiner in *The American Mathematical Monthly*. To view this article, go to *MathArticles.com*.

A Formal Definition of Limit

Consider again the informal definition of limit. If $f(x)$ becomes arbitrarily close to a single number L as x approaches c from either side, then the limit of $f(x)$ as x approaches c is L, written as

$$\lim_{x \to c} f(x) = L.$$

At first glance, this definition looks fairly technical. Even so, it is informal because exact meanings have not yet been given to the two phrases

"$f(x)$ becomes arbitrarily close to L"

and

"x approaches c."

The first person to assign mathematically rigorous meanings to these two phrases was Augustin-Louis Cauchy. His **ε-δ definition of limit** is the standard used today.

In Figure 2.12, let ε (the lowercase Greek letter *epsilon*) represent a (small) positive number. Then the phrase "$f(x)$ becomes arbitrarily close to L" means that $f(x)$ lies in the interval $(L - \varepsilon, L + \varepsilon)$. Using absolute value, you can write this as

$$|f(x) - L| < \varepsilon.$$

Similarly, the phrase "x approaches c" means that there exists a positive number δ such that x lies in either the interval $(c - \delta, c)$ or the interval $(c, c + \delta)$. This fact can be concisely expressed by the double inequality

$$0 < |x - c| < \delta.$$

The first inequality

$$0 < |x - c| \qquad \text{The distance between } x \text{ and } c \text{ is more than 0.}$$

expresses the fact that $x \neq c$. The second inequality

$$|x - c| < \delta \qquad x \text{ is within } \delta \text{ units of } c.$$

says that x is within a distance δ of c.

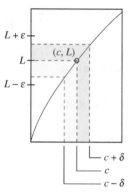

The ε-δ definition of the limit of $f(x)$ as x approaches c

Figure 2.12

Definition of Limit

Let f be a function defined on an open interval containing c (except possibly at c), and let L be a real number. The statement

$$\lim_{x \to c} f(x) = L$$

means that for each ε > 0 there exists a δ > 0 such that if

$$0 < |x - c| < \delta$$

then

$$|f(x) - L| < \varepsilon.$$

REMARK Throughout this text, the expression

$$\lim_{x \to c} f(x) = L$$

implies two statements—the limit exists *and* the limit is L.

Some functions do not have limits as x approaches c, but those that do cannot have two different limits as x approaches c. That is, *if the limit of a function exists, then the limit is unique* (see Exercise 77).

The next three examples should help you develop a better understanding of the ε-δ definition of limit.

EXAMPLE 6   **Finding a δ for a Given ε**

Given the limit

$$\lim_{x \to 3} (2x - 5) = 1$$

find δ such that

$$|(2x - 5) - 1| < 0.01$$

whenever

$$0 < |x - 3| < \delta.$$

•• REMARK In Example 6, note that 0.005 is the *largest* value of δ that will guarantee

$$|(2x - 5) - 1| < 0.01$$

whenever

$$0 < |x - 3| < \delta.$$

Any *smaller* positive value of δ would also work.

Solution In this problem, you are working with a given value of ε—namely, $\varepsilon = 0.01$. To find an appropriate δ, try to establish a connection between the absolute values

$$|(2x - 5) - 1| \quad \text{and} \quad |x - 3|.$$

Notice that

$$|(2x - 5) - 1| = |2x - 6| = 2|x - 3|.$$

Because the inequality $|(2x - 5) - 1| < 0.01$ is equivalent to $2|x - 3| < 0.01$, you can choose

$$\delta = \tfrac{1}{2}(0.01) = 0.005.$$

This choice works because

$$0 < |x - 3| < 0.005$$

implies that

$$|(2x - 5) - 1| = 2|x - 3| < 2(0.005) = 0.01.$$

As you can see in Figure 2.13, for x-values within 0.005 of 3 ($x \neq 3$), the values of $f(x)$ are within 0.01 of 1.

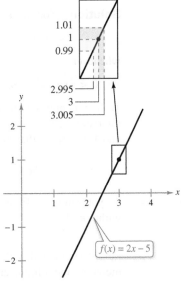

The limit of $f(x)$ as x approaches 3 is 1.
Figure 2.13

In Example 6, you found a δ-value for a *given* ε. This does not prove the existence of the limit. To do that, you must prove that you can find a δ for *any* ε, as shown in the next example.

EXAMPLE 7 Using the ε-δ Definition of Limit

Use the ε-δ definition of limit to prove that

$$\lim_{x \to 2} (3x - 2) = 4.$$

Solution You must show that for each $\varepsilon > 0$, there exists a $\delta > 0$ such that

$$|(3x - 2) - 4| < \varepsilon$$

whenever

$$0 < |x - 2| < \delta.$$

Because your choice of δ depends on ε, you need to establish a connection between the absolute values $|(3x - 2) - 4|$ and $|x - 2|$.

$$|(3x - 2) - 4| = |3x - 6| = 3|x - 2|$$

So, for a given $\varepsilon > 0$, you can choose $\delta = \varepsilon/3$. This choice works because

$$0 < |x - 2| < \delta = \frac{\varepsilon}{3}$$

implies that

$$|(3x - 2) - 4| = 3|x - 2| < 3\left(\frac{\varepsilon}{3}\right) = \varepsilon.$$

As you can see in Figure 2.14, for x-values within δ of 2 ($x \neq 2$), the values of $f(x)$ are within ε of 4.

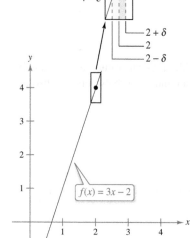

The limit of $f(x)$ as x approaches 2 is 4.
Figure 2.14

EXAMPLE 8 Using the ε-δ Definition of Limit

Use the ε-δ definition of limit to prove that

$$\lim_{x \to 2} x^2 = 4.$$

Solution You must show that for each $\varepsilon > 0$, there exists a $\delta > 0$ such that

$$|x^2 - 4| < \varepsilon$$

whenever

$$0 < |x - 2| < \delta.$$

To find an appropriate δ, begin by writing $|x^2 - 4| = |x - 2||x + 2|$. For all x in the interval $(1, 3)$, $x + 2 < 5$ and thus $|x + 2| < 5$. So, letting δ be the minimum of $\varepsilon/5$ and 1, it follows that, whenever $0 < |x - 2| < \delta$, you have

$$|x^2 - 4| = |x - 2||x + 2| < \left(\frac{\varepsilon}{5}\right)(5) = \varepsilon.$$

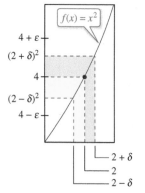

The limit of $f(x)$ as x approaches 2 is 4.
Figure 2.15

As you can see in Figure 2.15, for x-values within δ of 2 ($x \neq 2$), the values of $f(x)$ are within ε of 4.

Throughout this chapter, you will use the ε-δ definition of limit primarily to prove theorems about limits and to establish the existence or nonexistence of particular types of limits. For *finding* limits, you will learn techniques that are easier to use than the ε-δ definition of limit.

2.2 Exercises

See **CalcChat.com** for tutorial help and worked-out solutions to odd-numbered exercises.

Estimating a Limit Numerically In Exercises 1–6, complete the table and use the result to estimate the limit. Use a graphing utility to graph the function to confirm your result.

1. $\lim\limits_{x \to 4} \dfrac{x - 4}{x^2 - 3x - 4}$

x	3.9	3.99	3.999	4	4.001	4.01	4.1
$f(x)$				?			

2. $\lim\limits_{x \to 0} \dfrac{\sqrt{x + 1} - 1}{x}$

x	−0.1	−0.01	−0.001	0	0.001	0.01	0.1
$f(x)$				?			

3. $\lim\limits_{x \to 0} \dfrac{\sin x}{x}$

x	−0.1	−0.01	−0.001	0	0.001	0.01	0.1
$f(x)$				?			

4. $\lim\limits_{x \to 0} \dfrac{\cos x - 1}{x}$

x	−0.1	−0.01	−0.001	0	0.001	0.01	0.1
$f(x)$				?			

5. $\lim\limits_{x \to 0} \dfrac{e^x - 1}{x}$

x	−0.1	−0.01	−0.001	0	0.001	0.01	0.1
$f(x)$				?			

6. $\lim\limits_{x \to 0} \dfrac{\ln(x + 1)}{x}$

x	−0.1	−0.01	−0.001	0	0.001	0.01	0.1
$f(x)$				?			

Estimating a Limit Numerically In Exercises 7–16, create a table of values for the function and use the result to estimate the limit. Use a graphing utility to graph the function to confirm your result.

7. $\lim\limits_{x \to 1} \dfrac{x - 2}{x^2 + x - 6}$

8. $\lim\limits_{x \to -4} \dfrac{x + 4}{x^2 + 9x + 20}$

9. $\lim\limits_{x \to 1} \dfrac{x^4 - 1}{x^6 - 1}$

10. $\lim\limits_{x \to -3} \dfrac{x^3 + 27}{x + 3}$

11. $\lim\limits_{x \to -6} \dfrac{\sqrt{10 - x} - 4}{x + 6}$

12. $\lim\limits_{x \to 2} \dfrac{[x/(x + 1)] - (2/3)}{x - 2}$

13. $\lim\limits_{x \to 0} \dfrac{\sin 2x}{x}$

14. $\lim\limits_{x \to 0} \dfrac{\tan x}{\tan 2x}$

15. $\lim\limits_{x \to 2} \dfrac{\ln x - \ln 2}{x - 2}$

16. $\lim\limits_{x \to 0} \dfrac{4}{1 + e^{1/x}}$

Finding a Limit Graphically In Exercises 17–24, use the graph to find the limit (if it exists). If the limit does not exist, explain why.

17. $\lim\limits_{x \to 3} (4 - x)$

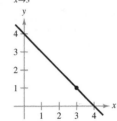

18. $\lim\limits_{x \to 0} \sec x$

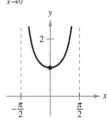

19. $\lim\limits_{x \to 2} f(x)$

$f(x) = \begin{cases} 4 - x, & x \neq 2 \\ 0, & x = 2 \end{cases}$

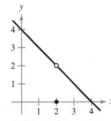

20. $\lim\limits_{x \to 1} f(x)$

$f(x) = \begin{cases} x^2 + 3, & x \neq 1 \\ 2, & x = 1 \end{cases}$

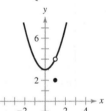

21. $\lim\limits_{x \to 2} \dfrac{|x - 2|}{x - 2}$

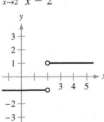

22. $\lim\limits_{x \to 0} \dfrac{4}{2 + e^{1/x}}$

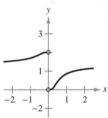

23. $\lim\limits_{x \to 0} \cos \dfrac{1}{x}$

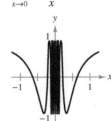

24. $\lim\limits_{x \to \pi/2} \tan x$

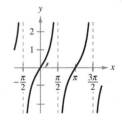

Graphical Reasoning In Exercises 25 and 26, use the graph of the function f to decide whether the value of the given quantity exists. If it does, find it. If not, explain why.

25. (a) $f(1)$

(b) $\lim\limits_{x \to 1} f(x)$

(c) $f(4)$

(d) $\lim\limits_{x \to 4} f(x)$

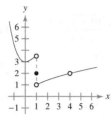

26. (a) $f(-2)$

(b) $\lim\limits_{x \to -2} f(x)$

(c) $f(0)$

(d) $\lim\limits_{x \to 0} f(x)$

(e) $f(2)$

(f) $\lim\limits_{x \to 2} f(x)$

(g) $f(4)$

(h) $\lim\limits_{x \to 4} f(x)$

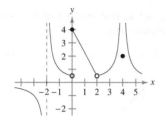

Limits of a Piecewise Function In Exercises 27 and 28, sketch the graph of f. Then identify the values of c for which $\lim\limits_{x \to c} f(x)$ exists.

27. $f(x) = \begin{cases} x^2, & x \le 2 \\ 8 - 2x, & 2 < x < 4 \\ 4, & x \ge 4 \end{cases}$

28. $f(x) = \begin{cases} \sin x, & x < 0 \\ 1 - \cos x, & 0 \le x \le \pi \\ \cos x, & x > \pi \end{cases}$

Sketching a Graph In Exercises 29 and 30, sketch a graph of a function f that satisfies the given values. (There are many correct answers.)

29. $f(0)$ is undefined.

$\lim\limits_{x \to 0} f(x) = 4$

$f(2) = 6$

$\lim\limits_{x \to 2} f(x) = 3$

30. $f(-2) = 0$

$f(2) = 0$

$\lim\limits_{x \to -2} f(x) = 0$

$\lim\limits_{x \to 2} f(x)$ does not exist.

31. Finding a δ for a Given ε The graph of $f(x) = x + 1$ is shown in the figure. Find δ such that if $0 < |x - 2| < \delta$, then $|f(x) - 3| < 0.4$.

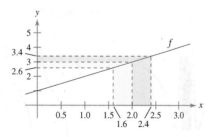

32. Finding a δ for a Given ε The graph of

$$f(x) = \frac{1}{x - 1}$$

is shown in the figure. Find δ such that if $0 < |x - 2| < \delta$, then $|f(x) - 1| < 0.01$.

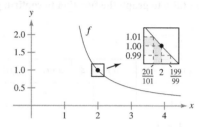

33. Finding a δ for a Given ε The graph of

$$f(x) = 2 - \frac{1}{x}$$

is shown in the figure. Find δ such that if $0 < |x - 1| < \delta$, then $|f(x) - 1| < 0.1$.

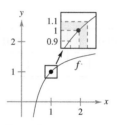
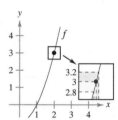

Figure for 33   Figure for 34

34. Finding a δ for a Given ε The graph of

$$f(x) = x^2 - 1$$

is shown in the figure. Find δ such that if $0 < |x - 2| < \delta$, then $|f(x) - 3| < 0.2$.

Finding a δ for a Given ε In Exercises 35–38, find the limit L. Then find $\delta > 0$ such that $|f(x) - L| < 0.01$ whenever $0 < |x - c| < \delta$.

35. $\lim\limits_{x \to 2} (3x + 2)$

36. $\lim\limits_{x \to 6} \left(6 - \dfrac{x}{3}\right)$

37. $\lim\limits_{x \to 2} (x^2 - 3)$

38. $\lim\limits_{x \to 4} (x^2 + 6)$

Using the ε-δ Definition of Limit In Exercises 39–50, find the limit L. Then use the ε-δ definition to prove that the limit is L.

39. $\lim\limits_{x \to 4} (x + 2)$

40. $\lim\limits_{x \to -2} (4x + 5)$

41. $\lim\limits_{x \to -4} \left(\tfrac{1}{2}x - 1\right)$

42. $\lim\limits_{x \to 3} \left(\tfrac{3}{4}x + 1\right)$

43. $\lim\limits_{x \to 6} 3$

44. $\lim\limits_{x \to 2} (-1)$

45. $\lim\limits_{x \to 0} \sqrt[3]{x}$

46. $\lim\limits_{x \to 4} \sqrt{x}$

47. $\lim\limits_{x \to -5} |x - 5|$

48. $\lim\limits_{x \to 3} |x - 3|$

49. $\lim\limits_{x \to 1} (x^2 + 1)$

50. $\lim\limits_{x \to -4} (x^2 + 4x)$

51. Finding a Limit What is the limit of $f(x) = 4$ as x approaches π?

52. Finding a Limit What is the limit of $g(x) = x$ as x approaches π?

Writing In Exercises 53–56, use a graphing utility to graph the function and estimate the limit (if it exists). What is the domain of the function? Can you detect a possible error in determining the domain of a function solely by analyzing the graph generated by a graphing utility? Write a short paragraph about the importance of examining a function analytically as well as graphically.

53. $f(x) = \dfrac{\sqrt{x+5}-3}{x-4}$

$$\lim_{x \to 4} f(x)$$

54. $f(x) = \dfrac{x-3}{x^2-4x+3}$

$$\lim_{x \to 3} f(x)$$

55. $f(x) = \dfrac{x-9}{\sqrt{x}-3}$

$$\lim_{x \to 9} f(x)$$

56. $f(x) = \dfrac{e^{x/2}-1}{x}$

$$\lim_{x \to 0} f(x)$$

57. Modeling Data For a long distance phone call, a hotel charges $9.99 for the first minute and $0.79 for each additional minute or fraction thereof. A formula for the cost is given by

$$C(t) = 9.99 - 0.79 [\![-(t-1)]\!]$$

where t is the time in minutes.

(*Note:* $[\![x]\!]$ = greatest integer n such that $n \le x$. For example, $[\![3.2]\!] = 3$ and $[\![-1.6]\!] = -2$.)

(a) Use a graphing utility to graph the cost function for $0 < t \le 6$.

(b) Use the graph to complete the table and observe the behavior of the function as t approaches 3.5. Use the graph and the table to find $\displaystyle \lim_{t \to 3.5} C(t)$.

t	3	3.3	3.4	3.5	3.6	3.7	4
C				?			

(c) Use the graph to complete the table and observe the behavior of the function as t approaches 3.

t	2	2.5	2.9	3	3.1	3.5	4
C				?			

Does the limit of $C(t)$ as t approaches 3 exist? Explain.

58. Modeling Data Repeat Exercise 57 for

$$C(t) = 5.79 - 0.99 [\![-(t-1)]\!].$$

63. Jewelry A jeweler resizes a ring so that its inner circumference is 6 centimeters.

(a) What is the radius of the ring?

(b) The inner circumference of the ring varies between 5.5 centimeters and 6.5 centimeters. How does the radius vary?

(c) Use the ε-δ definition of limit to describe this situation. Identify ε and δ.

64. Sports

A sporting goods manufacturer designs a golf ball having a volume of 2.48 cubic inches.

(a) What is the radius of the golf ball?

(b) The volume of the golf ball varies between 2.45 cubic inches and 2.51 cubic inches. How does the radius vary?

(c) Use the ε-δ definition of limit to describe this situation. Identify ε and δ.

65. Estimating a Limit Consider the function

$$f(x) = (1+x)^{1/x}.$$

Estimate

$$\lim_{x \to 0} (1+x)^{1/x}$$

by evaluating f at x-values near 0. Sketch the graph of f.

The symbol ⌘ indicates an exercise in which you are instructed to use graphing technology or a symbolic computer algebra system. The solutions of other exercises may also be facilitated by the use of appropriate technology.

Tony Bowler/Shutterstock.com

66. Estimating a Limit Consider the function

$$f(x) = \frac{|x + 1| - |x - 1|}{x}.$$

Estimate

$$\lim_{x \to 0} \frac{|x + 1| - |x - 1|}{x}$$

by evaluating f at x-values near 0. Sketch the graph of f.

67. Graphical Analysis The statement

$$\lim_{x \to 2} \frac{x^2 - 4}{x - 2} = 4$$

means that for each $\varepsilon > 0$ there corresponds a $\delta > 0$ such that if $0 < |x - 2| < \delta$, then

$$\left| \frac{x^2 - 4}{x - 2} - 4 \right| < \varepsilon.$$

If $\varepsilon = 0.001$, then

$$\left| \frac{x^2 - 4}{x - 2} - 4 \right| < 0.001.$$

Use a graphing utility to graph each side of this inequality. Use the *zoom* feature to find an interval $(2 - \delta, 2 + \delta)$ such that the graph of the left side is below the graph of the right side of the inequality.

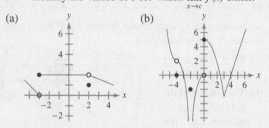

68. HOW DO YOU SEE IT? Use the graph of f to identify the values of c for which $\lim_{x \to c} f(x)$ exists.

(a)

(b)

True or False? In Exercises 69–72, determine whether the statement is true or false. If it is false, explain why or give an example that shows it is false.

69. If f is undefined at $x = c$, then the limit of $f(x)$ as x approaches c does not exist.

70. If the limit of $f(x)$ as x approaches c is 0, then there must exist a number k such that $f(k) < 0.001$.

71. If $f(c) = L$, then $\lim_{x \to c} f(x) = L$.

72. If $\lim_{x \to c} f(x) = L$, then $f(c) = L$.

Determining a Limit In Exercises 73 and 74, consider the function $f(x) = \sqrt{x}$.

73. Is $\lim_{x \to 0.25} \sqrt{x} = 0.5$ a true statement? Explain.

74. Is $\lim_{x \to 0} \sqrt{x} = 0$ a true statement? Explain.

75. Evaluating Limits Use a graphing utility to evaluate

$$\lim_{x \to 0} \frac{\sin nx}{x}$$

for several values of n. What do you notice?

76. Evaluating Limits Use a graphing utility to evaluate

$$\lim_{x \to 0} \frac{\tan nx}{x}$$

for several values of n. What do you notice?

77. Proof Prove that if the limit of $f(x)$ as x approaches c exists, then the limit must be unique. [*Hint:* Let $\lim_{x \to c} f(x) = L_1$ and $\lim_{x \to c} f(x) = L_2$ and prove that $L_1 = L_2$.]

78. Proof Consider the line $f(x) = mx + b$, where $m \neq 0$. Use the ε-δ definition of limit to prove that $\lim_{x \to c} f(x) = mc + b$.

79. Proof Prove that

$$\lim_{x \to c} f(x) = L$$

is equivalent to

$$\lim_{x \to c} [f(x) - L] = 0.$$

80. Proof

(a) Given that

$$\lim_{x \to 0} (3x + 1)(3x - 1)x^2 + 0.01 = 0.01$$

prove that there exists an open interval (a, b) containing 0 such that $(3x + 1)(3x - 1)x^2 + 0.01 > 0$ for all $x \neq 0$ in (a, b).

(b) Given that $\lim_{x \to c} g(x) = L$, where $L > 0$, prove that there exists an open interval (a, b) containing c such that $g(x) > 0$ for all $x \neq c$ in (a, b).

PUTNAM EXAM CHALLENGE

81. Inscribe a rectangle of base b and height h in a circle of radius one, and inscribe an isosceles triangle in a region of the circle cut off by one base of the rectangle (with that side as the base of the triangle). For what value of h do the rectangle and triangle have the same area?

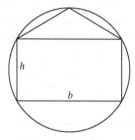

82. A right circular cone has base of radius 1 and height 3. A cube is inscribed in the cone so that one face of the cube is contained in the base of the cone. What is the side-length of the cube?

2.3 Evaluating Limits Analytically

- Evaluate a limit using properties of limits.
- Develop and use a strategy for finding limits.
- Evaluate a limit using the dividing out technique.
- Evaluate a limit using the rationalizing technique.
- Evaluate a limit using the Squeeze Theorem.

Properties of Limits

In Section 2.2, you learned that the limit of $f(x)$ as x approaches c does not depend on the value of f at $x = c$. It may happen, however, that the limit is precisely $f(c)$. In such cases, the limit can be evaluated by **direct substitution.** That is,

$$\lim_{x \to c} f(x) = f(c). \qquad \text{Substitute } c \text{ for } x.$$

Such *well-behaved* functions are **continuous at c.** You will examine this concept more closely in Section 2.4.

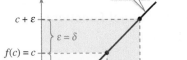

Figure 2.16

> **THEOREM 2.1   Some Basic Limits**
>
> Let b and c be real numbers, and let n be a positive integer.
>
> **1.** $\lim\limits_{x \to c} b = b$ **2.** $\lim\limits_{x \to c} x = c$ **3.** $\lim\limits_{x \to c} x^n = c^n$

Proof The proofs of Properties 1 and 3 of Theorem 2.1 are left as exercises (see Exercises 113 and 114). To prove Property 2, you need to show that for each $\varepsilon > 0$ there exists a $\delta > 0$ such that $|x - c| < \varepsilon$ whenever $0 < |x - c| < \delta$. To do this, choose $\delta = \varepsilon$. The second inequality then implies the first, as shown in Figure 2.16.
See LarsonCalculus.com for Bruce Edwards's video of this proof.

- **REMARK** When encountering new notations or symbols in mathematics, be sure you know how the notations are read. For instance, the limit in Example 1(c) is read as "the limit of x^2 as x approaches 2 is 4."

EXAMPLE 1   Evaluating Basic Limits

a. $\lim\limits_{x \to 2} 3 = 3$ **b.** $\lim\limits_{x \to -4} x = -4$ **c.** $\lim\limits_{x \to 2} x^2 = 2^2 = 4$

- **REMARK** The proof of Property 1 is left as an exercise (see Exercise 115).

> **THEOREM 2.2   Properties of Limits**
>
> Let b and c be real numbers, let n be a positive integer, and let f and g be functions with the limits
>
> $$\lim_{x \to c} f(x) = L \quad \text{and} \quad \lim_{x \to c} g(x) = K.$$
>
> **1.** Scalar multiple: $\lim\limits_{x \to c} [b f(x)] = bL$
>
> **2.** Sum or difference: $\lim\limits_{x \to c} [f(x) \pm g(x)] = L \pm K$
>
> **3.** Product: $\lim\limits_{x \to c} [f(x)g(x)] = LK$
>
> **4.** Quotient: $\lim\limits_{x \to c} \dfrac{f(x)}{g(x)} = \dfrac{L}{K}, \quad K \neq 0$
>
> **5.** Power: $\lim\limits_{x \to c} [f(x)]^n = L^n$
>
> A proof of this theorem is given in Appendix A.
> *See LarsonCalculus.com for Bruce Edwards's video of this proof.*

EXAMPLE 2   **The Limit of a Polynomial**

Find the limit: $\displaystyle\lim_{x \to 2} (4x^2 + 3)$.

Solution

$$\lim_{x \to 2} (4x^2 + 3) = \lim_{x \to 2} 4x^2 + \lim_{x \to 2} 3 \qquad \text{Property 2, Theorem 2.2}$$

$$= 4\left(\lim_{x \to 2} x^2\right) + \lim_{x \to 2} 3 \qquad \text{Property 1, Theorem 2.2}$$

$$= 4(2^2) + 3 \qquad \text{Properties 1 and 3, Theorem 2.1}$$

$$= 19 \qquad \text{Simplify.}$$

In Example 2, note that the limit (as x approaches 2) of the *polynomial function* $p(x) = 4x^2 + 3$ is simply the value of p at $x = 2$.

$$\lim_{x \to 2} p(x) = p(2) = 4(2^2) + 3 = 19$$

This *direct substitution* property is valid for all polynomial and rational functions with nonzero denominators.

THEOREM 2.3   Limits of Polynomial and Rational Functions

If p is a polynomial function and c is a real number, then

$$\lim_{x \to c} p(x) = p(c).$$

If r is a rational function given by $r(x) = p(x)/q(x)$ and c is a real number such that $q(c) \neq 0$, then

$$\lim_{x \to c} r(x) = r(c) = \frac{p(c)}{q(c)}.$$

EXAMPLE 3   **The Limit of a Rational Function**

Find the limit: $\displaystyle\lim_{x \to 1} \frac{x^2 + x + 2}{x + 1}$.

Solution   Because the denominator is not 0 when $x = 1$, you can apply Theorem 2.3 to obtain

$$\lim_{x \to 1} \frac{x^2 + x + 2}{x + 1} = \frac{1^2 + 1 + 2}{1 + 1} = \frac{4}{2} = 2.$$

Polynomial functions and rational functions are two of the three basic types of algebraic functions. The next theorem deals with the limit of the third type of algebraic function—one that involves a radical.

THE SQUARE ROOT SYMBOL

The first use of a symbol to denote the square root can be traced to the sixteenth century. Mathematicians first used the symbol $\sqrt{}$, which had only two strokes. This symbol was chosen because it resembled a lowercase r, to stand for the Latin word *radix*, meaning root.

THEOREM 2.4   The Limit of a Function Involving a Radical

Let n be a positive integer. The limit below is valid for all c when n is odd, and is valid for $c > 0$ when n is even.

$$\lim_{x \to c} \sqrt[n]{x} = \sqrt[n]{c}$$

A proof of this theorem is given in Appendix A.
See LarsonCalculus.com for Bruce Edwards's video of this proof.

The next theorem greatly expands your ability to evaluate limits because it shows how to analyze the limit of a composite function.

> **THEOREM 2.5   The Limit of a Composite Function**
>
> If f and g are functions such that $\lim_{x \to c} g(x) = L$ and $\lim_{x \to L} f(x) = f(L)$, then
>
> $$\lim_{x \to c} f(g(x)) = f\left(\lim_{x \to c} g(x)\right) = f(L).$$
>
> A proof of this theorem is given in Appendix A.
> *See LarsonCalculus.com for Bruce Edwards's video of this proof.*

Exploration

Your goal in this section is to become familiar with limits that can be evaluated by direct substitution. In the following library of elementary functions, what are the values of c for which

$$\lim_{x \to c} f(x) = f(c)?$$

Polynomial function:

$$f(x) = a_n x^n + \cdots + a_1 x + a_0$$

Rational function: (p and q are polynomials):

$$f(x) = \frac{p(x)}{q(x)}$$

Trigonometric functions:

$f(x) = \sin x, \quad f(x) = \cos x$

$f(x) = \tan x, \quad f(x) = \cot x$

$f(x) = \sec x, \quad f(x) = \csc x$

Exponential functions:

$f(x) = a^x, \quad f(x) = e^x$

Natural logarithmic function:

$f(x) = \ln x$

EXAMPLE 4   The Limit of a Composite Function

$\triangleright$ *See LarsonCalculus.com for an interactive version of this type of example.*

a. Because

$$\lim_{x \to 0} (x^2 + 4) = 0^2 + 4 = 4 \quad \text{and} \quad \lim_{x \to 4} \sqrt{x} = \sqrt{4} = 2$$

you can conclude that

$$\lim_{x \to 0} \sqrt{x^2 + 4} = \sqrt{4} = 2.$$

b. Because

$$\lim_{x \to 3} (2x^2 - 10) = 2(3^2) - 10 = 8 \quad \text{and} \quad \lim_{x \to 8} \sqrt[3]{x} = \sqrt[3]{8} = 2$$

you can conclude that

$$\lim_{x \to 3} \sqrt[3]{2x^2 - 10} = \sqrt[3]{8} = 2.$$

You have seen that the limits of many algebraic functions can be evaluated by direct substitution. The basic transcendental functions (trigonometric, exponential, and logarithmic) also possess this desirable quality, as shown in the next theorem (presented without proof).

> **THEOREM 2.6   Limits of Transcendental Functions**
>
> Let c be a real number in the domain of the given trigonometric function.
>
> **1.** $\lim_{x \to c} \sin x = \sin c$ **2.** $\lim_{x \to c} \cos x = \cos c$ **3.** $\lim_{x \to c} \tan x = \tan c$
>
> **4.** $\lim_{x \to c} \cot x = \cot c$ **5.** $\lim_{x \to c} \sec x = \sec c$ **6.** $\lim_{x \to c} \csc x = \csc c$
>
> **7.** $\lim_{x \to c} a^x = a^c, \ a > 0$ **8.** $\lim_{x \to c} \ln x = \ln c$

EXAMPLE 5   Limits of Trigonometric Functions

a. $\lim_{x \to 0} \tan x = \tan(0) = 0$

b. $\lim_{x \to 0} \sin^2 x = \lim_{x \to 0} (\sin x)^2 = 0^2 = 0$

c. $\lim_{x \to -1} x e^x = \left(\lim_{x \to -1} x\right)\left(\lim_{x \to -1} e^x\right) = (-1)(e^{-1}) = -e^{-1}$

d. $\lim_{x \to e} \ln x^3 = \lim_{x \to e} 3 \ln x = 3 \ln(e) = 3(1) = 3$

A Strategy for Finding Limits

On the previous three pages, you studied several types of functions whose limits can be evaluated by direct substitution. This knowledge, together with the next theorem, can be used to develop a strategy for finding limits.

> **THEOREM 2.7** **Functions That Agree at All but One Point**
>
> Let c be a real number, and let $f(x) = g(x)$ for all $x \neq c$ in an open interval containing c. If the limit of $g(x)$ as x approaches c exists, then the limit of $f(x)$ also exists and
>
> $$\lim_{x \to c} f(x) = \lim_{x \to c} g(x).$$
>
> A proof of this theorem is given in Appendix A.
> See LarsonCalculus.com for Bruce Edwards's video of this proof.

EXAMPLE 6 **Finding the Limit of a Function**

Find the limit.

$$\lim_{x \to 1} \frac{x^3 - 1}{x - 1}$$

Solution Let $f(x) = (x^3 - 1)/(x - 1)$. By factoring and dividing out like factors, you can rewrite f as

$$f(x) = \frac{(x - 1)(x^2 + x + 1)}{(x - 1)} = x^2 + x + 1 = g(x), \quad x \neq 1.$$

So, for all x-values other than $x = 1$, the functions f and g agree, as shown in Figure 2.17. Because $\lim_{x \to 1} g(x)$ exists, you can apply Theorem 2.7 to conclude that f and g have the same limit at $x = 1$.

$$\lim_{x \to 1} \frac{x^3 - 1}{x - 1} = \lim_{x \to 1} \frac{(x - 1)(x^2 + x + 1)}{x - 1} \qquad \text{Factor.}$$

$$= \lim_{x \to 1} \frac{(x - 1)(x^2 + x + 1)}{x - 1} \qquad \text{Divide out like factors.}$$

$$= \lim_{x \to 1}(x^2 + x + 1) \qquad \text{Apply Theorem 2.7.}$$

$$= 1^2 + 1 + 1 \qquad \text{Use direct substitution.}$$

$$= 3 \qquad \text{Simplify.}$$

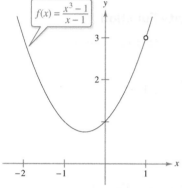

$f(x) = \dfrac{x^3 - 1}{x - 1}$

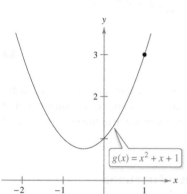

$g(x) = x^2 + x + 1$

f and g agree at all but one point.
Figure 2.17

• • • • • • • • • • • • • • • ▷
• **REMARK** When applying this strategy for finding a limit, remember that some functions do not have a limit (as x approaches c). For instance, the limit below does not exist.

$$\lim_{x \to 1} \frac{x^3 + 1}{x - 1}$$

A Strategy for Finding Limits

1. Learn to recognize which limits can be evaluated by direct substitution. (These limits are listed in Theorems 2.1 through 2.6.)

2. When the limit of $f(x)$ as x approaches c *cannot* be evaluated by direct substitution, try to find a function g that agrees with f for all x other than $x = c$. [Choose g such that the limit of $g(x)$ *can* be evaluated by direct substitution.] Then apply Theorem 2.7 to conclude *analytically* that

$$\lim_{x \to c} f(x) = \lim_{x \to c} g(x) = g(c).$$

3. Use a *graph* or *table* to reinforce your conclusion.

Dividing Out Technique

One procedure for finding a limit analytically is the **dividing out technique.** This technique involves dividing out common factors, as shown in Example 7.

EXAMPLE 7 Dividing Out Technique

 ⋅ ⋅ ⋅ ▷ *See LarsonCalculus.com for an interactive version of this type of example.*

Find the limit: $\displaystyle\lim_{x \to -3} \frac{x^2 + x - 6}{x + 3}$.

REMARK In the solution to Example 7, be sure you see the usefulness of the Factor Theorem of Algebra. This theorem states that if c is a zero of a polynomial function, then $(x - c)$ is a factor of the polynomial. So, when you apply direct substitution to a rational function and obtain

$$r(c) = \frac{p(c)}{q(c)} = \frac{0}{0}$$

you can conclude that $(x - c)$ must be a common factor of both $p(x)$ and $q(x)$.

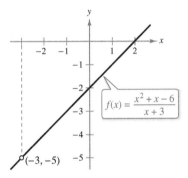

f is undefined when $x = -3$.
Figure 2.18

Solution Although you are taking the limit of a rational function, you *cannot* apply Theorem 2.3 because the limit of the denominator is 0.

$$\lim_{x \to -3} \frac{x^2 + x - 6}{x + 3}$$

$$\lim_{x \to -3} (x^2 + x - 6) = 0$$

$$\lim_{x \to -3} (x + 3) = 0$$

Direct substitution fails.

Because the limit of the numerator is also 0, the numerator and denominator have a *common factor* of $(x + 3)$. So, for all $x \neq -3$, you can divide out this factor to obtain

$$f(x) = \frac{x^2 + x - 6}{x + 3} = \frac{(x + 3)(x - 2)}{x + 3} = x - 2 = g(x), \quad x \neq -3.$$

Using Theorem 2.7, it follows that

$$\lim_{x \to -3} \frac{x^2 + x - 6}{x + 3} = \lim_{x \to -3} (x - 2) \qquad \text{Apply Theorem 2.7.}$$

$$= -5. \qquad \text{Use direct substitution.}$$

This result is shown graphically in Figure 2.18. Note that the graph of the function f coincides with the graph of the function $g(x) = x - 2$, except that the graph of f has a gap at the point $(-3, -5)$.

In Example 7, direct substitution produced the meaningless fractional form $0/0$. An expression such as $0/0$ is called an **indeterminate form** because you cannot (from the form alone) determine the limit. When you try to evaluate a limit and encounter this form, remember that you must rewrite the fraction so that the new denominator does not have 0 as its limit. One way to do this is to *divide out like factors*. Another way is to use the *rationalizing technique* shown on the next page.

▷ **TECHNOLOGY PITFALL** A graphing utility can give misleading information about the graph of a function. For instance, try graphing the function from Example 7

$$f(x) = \frac{x^2 + x - 6}{x + 3}$$

on a standard viewing window (see Figure 2.19). On most graphing utilities, the graph appears to be defined at every real number. However, because f is undefined when $x = -3$, you know that the graph of f has a hole at $x = -3$. You can verify this on a graphing utility using the *trace* or *table* feature.

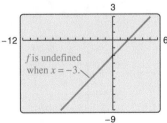

Misleading graph of f
Figure 2.19

Rationalizing Technique

Another way to find a limit analytically is the **rationalizing technique,** which involves rationalizing the numerator of a fractional expression. Recall that rationalizing the numerator means multiplying the numerator and denominator by the conjugate of the numerator. For instance, to rationalize the numerator of

$$\frac{\sqrt{x}+4}{x}$$

multiply the numerator and denominator by the conjugate of $\sqrt{x}+4$, which is

$$\sqrt{x}-4.$$

EXAMPLE 8 Rationalizing Technique

Find the limit: $\displaystyle\lim_{x\to 0}\frac{\sqrt{x+1}-1}{x}$.

Solution By direct substitution, you obtain the indeterminate form $0/0$.

$$\lim_{x\to 0}\frac{\sqrt{x+1}-1}{x}\qquad\nearrow\quad\lim_{x\to 0}\left(\sqrt{x+1}-1\right)=0$$

$$\searrow\quad\lim_{x\to 0}x=0$$

Direct substitution fails.

In this case, you can rewrite the fraction by rationalizing the numerator.

$$\frac{\sqrt{x+1}-1}{x}=\left(\frac{\sqrt{x+1}-1}{x}\right)\left(\frac{\sqrt{x+1}+1}{\sqrt{x+1}+1}\right)$$

$$=\frac{(x+1)-1}{x\left(\sqrt{x+1}+1\right)}$$

$$=\frac{\cancel{x}}{\cancel{x}\left(\sqrt{x+1}+1\right)}$$

$$=\frac{1}{\sqrt{x+1}+1},\quad x\neq 0$$

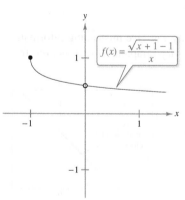

$\bullet\bullet$ **REMARK** The rationalizing technique for evaluating limits is based on multiplication by a convenient form of 1. In Example 8, the convenient form is

$$1=\frac{\sqrt{x+1}+1}{\sqrt{x+1}+1}.$$

Now, using Theorem 2.7, you can evaluate the limit as shown.

$$\lim_{x\to 0}\frac{\sqrt{x+1}-1}{x}=\lim_{x\to 0}\frac{1}{\sqrt{x+1}+1}$$

$$=\frac{1}{1+1}$$

$$=\frac{1}{2}$$

A table or a graph can reinforce your conclusion that the limit is $\frac{1}{2}$. (See Figure 2.20.)

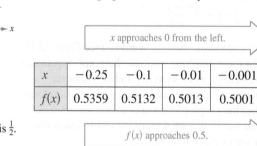

$f(x)=\dfrac{\sqrt{x+1}-1}{x}$

The limit of $f(x)$ as x approaches 0 is $\frac{1}{2}$.
Figure 2.20

	x approaches 0 from the left.					x approaches 0 from the right.			
x	-0.25	-0.1	-0.01	-0.001	0	0.001	0.01	0.1	0.25
$f(x)$	0.5359	0.5132	0.5013	0.5001	?	0.4999	0.4988	0.4881	0.4721
	$f(x)$ approaches 0.5.					$f(x)$ approaches 0.5.			

$h(x) \leq f(x) \leq g(x)$

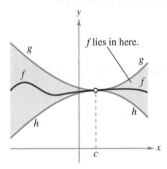

The Squeeze Theorem
Figure 2.21

The Squeeze Theorem

The next theorem concerns the limit of a function that is squeezed between two other functions, each of which has the same limit at a given x-value, as shown in Figure 2.21.

THEOREM 2.8   The Squeeze Theorem

If $h(x) \leq f(x) \leq g(x)$ for all x in an open interval containing c, except possibly at c itself, and if

$$\lim_{x \to c} h(x) = L = \lim_{x \to c} g(x)$$

then $\lim_{x \to c} f(x)$ exists and is equal to L.

A proof of this theorem is given in Appendix A.

See LarsonCalculus.com for Bruce Edwards's video of this proof.

•• **REMARK**   The third limit of Theorem 2.9 will be used in Chapter 3 in the development of the formula for the derivative of the exponential function $f(x) = e^x$.

$\triangleright$

You can see the usefulness of the Squeeze Theorem (also called the Sandwich Theorem or the Pinching Theorem) in the proof of Theorem 2.9.

THEOREM 2.9   Three Special Limits

1. $\displaystyle\lim_{x \to 0} \frac{\sin x}{x} = 1$ **2.** $\displaystyle\lim_{x \to 0} \frac{1 - \cos x}{x} = 0$ **3.** $\displaystyle\lim_{x \to 0} (1 + x)^{1/x} = e$

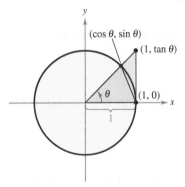

A circular sector is used to prove Theorem 2.9.
Figure 2.22

Proof   The proof of the second limit is left as an exercise (see Exercise 127). Recall from Section 1.6 that the third limit is actually the definition of the number e. To avoid the confusion of two different uses of x, the proof of the first limit is presented using the variable θ, where θ is an acute positive angle *measured in radians*. Figure 2.22 shows a circular sector that is squeezed between two triangles.

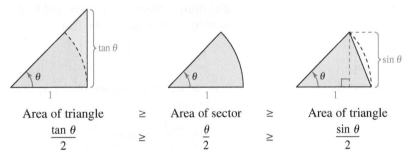

Area of triangle	$\geq$	Area of sector	$\geq$	Area of triangle
$\dfrac{\tan \theta}{2}$	$\geq$	$\dfrac{\theta}{2}$	$\geq$	$\dfrac{\sin \theta}{2}$

Multiplying each expression by $2/\sin \theta$ produces

$$\frac{1}{\cos \theta} \geq \frac{\theta}{\sin \theta} \geq 1$$

and taking reciprocals and reversing the inequalities yields

$$\cos \theta \leq \frac{\sin \theta}{\theta} \leq 1.$$

Because $\cos \theta = \cos(-\theta)$ and $(\sin \theta)/\theta = [\sin(-\theta)]/(-\theta)$, you can conclude that this inequality is valid for *all* nonzero θ in the open interval $(-\pi/2, \pi/2)$. Finally, because $\lim_{\theta \to 0} \cos \theta = 1$ and $\lim_{\theta \to 0} 1 = 1$, you can apply the Squeeze Theorem to conclude that $\lim_{\theta \to 0} (\sin \theta)/\theta = 1$.

See LarsonCalculus.com for Bruce Edwards's video of this proof.

EXAMPLE 9 **A Limit Involving a Trigonometric Function**

Find the limit: $\lim\limits_{x \to 0} \dfrac{\tan x}{x}$.

Solution Direct substitution yields the indeterminate form $0/0$. To solve this problem, you can write $\tan x$ as $(\sin x)/(\cos x)$ and obtain

$$\lim_{x \to 0} \frac{\tan x}{x} = \lim_{x \to 0} \left(\frac{\sin x}{x} \right) \left(\frac{1}{\cos x} \right).$$

Now, because

$$\lim_{x \to 0} \frac{\sin x}{x} = 1$$

and

$$\lim_{x \to 0} \frac{1}{\cos x} = 1$$

you can obtain

$$\lim_{x \to 0} \frac{\tan x}{x} = \left(\lim_{x \to 0} \frac{\sin x}{x} \right) \left(\lim_{x \to 0} \frac{1}{\cos x} \right)$$
$$= (1)(1)$$
$$= 1.$$

(See Figure 2.23.)

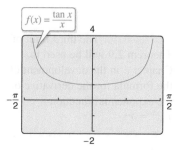

The limit of $f(x)$ as x approaches 0 is 1.
Figure 2.23

•• **REMARK** Be sure you understand the mathematical conventions regarding parentheses and trigonometric functions. For instance, in Example 10, $\sin 4x$ means $\sin(4x)$.

EXAMPLE 10 **A Limit Involving a Trigonometric Function**

Find the limit: $\lim\limits_{x \to 0} \dfrac{\sin 4x}{x}$.

Solution Direct substitution yields the indeterminate form $0/0$. To solve this problem, you can rewrite the limit as

$$\lim_{x \to 0} \frac{\sin 4x}{x} = 4 \left(\lim_{x \to 0} \frac{\sin 4x}{4x} \right). \qquad \text{Multiply and divide by 4.}$$

Now, by letting $y = 4x$ and observing that x approaches 0 if and only if y approaches 0, you can write

$$\lim_{x \to 0} \frac{\sin 4x}{x} = 4 \left(\lim_{x \to 0} \frac{\sin 4x}{4x} \right)$$
$$= 4 \left(\lim_{y \to 0} \frac{\sin y}{y} \right) \qquad \text{Let } y = 4x.$$
$$= 4(1) \qquad \text{Apply Theorem 2.9(1).}$$
$$= 4.$$

(See Figure 2.24.)

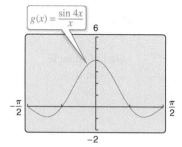

The limit of $g(x)$ as x approaches 0 is 4.
Figure 2.24

▷ TECHNOLOGY Use a graphing utility to confirm the limits in the examples and in the exercise set. For instance, Figures 2.23 and 2.24 show the graphs of

$$f(x) = \frac{\tan x}{x} \quad \text{and} \quad g(x) = \frac{\sin 4x}{x}.$$

Note that the first graph appears to contain the point $(0, 1)$ and the second graph appears to contain the point $(0, 4)$, which lends support to the conclusions obtained in Examples 9 and 10.

Estimating Limits In Exercises 1–4, use a graphing utility to graph the function and visually estimate the limits.

1. $h(x) = -x^2 + 4x$

(a) $\lim_{x \to 4} h(x)$

(b) $\lim_{x \to -1} h(x)$

2. $g(x) = \dfrac{12(\sqrt{x} - 3)}{x - 9}$

(a) $\lim_{x \to 4} g(x)$

(b) $\lim_{x \to 9} g(x)$

3. $f(x) = x \cos x$

(a) $\lim_{x \to 0} f(x)$

(b) $\lim_{x \to \pi/3} f(x)$

4. $f(t) = t|t - 4|$

(a) $\lim_{t \to 4} f(t)$

(b) $\lim_{t \to -1} f(t)$

Finding a Limit In Exercises 5–36, find the limit.

5. $\lim_{x \to 2} x^3$

6. $\lim_{x \to -3} x^4$

7. $\lim_{x \to 0} (2x - 1)$

8. $\lim_{x \to -4} (2x + 3)$

9. $\lim_{x \to -3} (x^2 + 3x)$

10. $\lim_{x \to 2} (-x^3 + 1)$

11. $\lim_{x \to -3} (2x^2 + 4x + 1)$

12. $\lim_{x \to 1} (2x^3 - 6x + 5)$

13. $\lim_{x \to 3} \sqrt{x + 1}$

14. $\lim_{x \to 2} \sqrt[3]{12x + 3}$

15. $\lim_{x \to -4} (x + 3)^2$

16. $\lim_{x \to 0} (3x - 2)^4$

17. $\lim_{x \to 2} \dfrac{1}{x}$

18. $\lim_{x \to -5} \dfrac{5}{x + 3}$

19. $\lim_{x \to 1} \dfrac{x}{x^2 + 4}$

20. $\lim_{x \to 1} \dfrac{3x + 5}{x + 1}$

21. $\lim_{x \to 7} \dfrac{3x}{\sqrt{x + 2}}$

22. $\lim_{x \to 3} \dfrac{\sqrt{x + 6}}{x + 2}$

23. $\lim_{x \to \pi/2} \sin x$

24. $\lim_{x \to \pi} \tan x$

25. $\lim_{x \to 1} \cos \dfrac{\pi x}{3}$

26. $\lim_{x \to 2} \sin \dfrac{\pi x}{2}$

27. $\lim_{x \to 0} \sec 2x$

28. $\lim_{x \to \pi} \cos 3x$

29. $\lim_{x \to 5\pi/6} \sin x$

30. $\lim_{x \to 5\pi/3} \cos x$

31. $\lim_{x \to 3} \tan\left(\dfrac{\pi x}{4}\right)$

32. $\lim_{x \to 7} \sec\left(\dfrac{\pi x}{6}\right)$

33. $\lim_{x \to 0} e^x \cos 2x$

34. $\lim_{x \to 0} e^{-x} \sin \pi x$

35. $\lim_{x \to 1} (\ln 3x + e^x)$

36. $\lim_{x \to 1} \ln\left(\dfrac{x}{e^x}\right)$

Finding Limits In Exercises 37–40, find the limits.

37. $f(x) = 5 - x, \ g(x) = x^3$

(a) $\lim_{x \to 1} f(x)$ (b) $\lim_{x \to 4} g(x)$ (c) $\lim_{x \to 1} g(f(x))$

38. $f(x) = x + 7, \ g(x) = x^2$

(a) $\lim_{x \to -3} f(x)$ (b) $\lim_{x \to 4} g(x)$ (c) $\lim_{x \to -3} g(f(x))$

39. $f(x) = 4 - x^2, \ g(x) = \sqrt{x + 1}$

(a) $\lim_{x \to 1} f(x)$ (b) $\lim_{x \to 3} g(x)$ (c) $\lim_{x \to 1} g(f(x))$

40. $f(x) = 2x^2 - 3x + 1, \ g(x) = \sqrt[3]{x + 6}$

(a) $\lim_{x \to 4} f(x)$ (b) $\lim_{x \to 21} g(x)$ (c) $\lim_{x \to 4} g(f(x))$

Evaluating Limits In Exercises 41–44, use the information to evaluate the limits.

41. $\lim_{x \to c} f(x) = 3$

$\lim_{x \to c} g(x) = 2$

(a) $\lim_{x \to c} [5g(x)]$

(b) $\lim_{x \to c} [f(x) + g(x)]$

(c) $\lim_{x \to c} [f(x)g(x)]$

(d) $\lim_{x \to c} \dfrac{f(x)}{g(x)}$

42. $\lim_{x \to c} f(x) = 2$

$\lim_{x \to c} g(x) = \frac{3}{4}$

(a) $\lim_{x \to c} [4f(x)]$

(b) $\lim_{x \to c} [f(x) + g(x)]$

(c) $\lim_{x \to c} [f(x)g(x)]$

(d) $\lim_{x \to c} \dfrac{f(x)}{g(x)}$

43. $\lim_{x \to c} f(x) = 4$

(a) $\lim_{x \to c} [f(x)]^3$

(b) $\lim_{x \to c} \sqrt{f(x)}$

(c) $\lim_{x \to c} [3f(x)]$

(d) $\lim_{x \to c} [f(x)]^{3/2}$

44. $\lim_{x \to c} f(x) = 27$

(a) $\lim_{x \to c} \sqrt[3]{f(x)}$

(b) $\lim_{x \to c} \dfrac{f(x)}{18}$

(c) $\lim_{x \to c} [f(x)]^2$

(d) $\lim_{x \to c} [f(x)]^{2/3}$

Finding a Limit In Exercises 45–50, write a simpler function that agrees with the given function at all but one point. Then find the limit of the function. Use a graphing utility to confirm your result.

45. $\lim_{x \to -1} \dfrac{x^2 - 1}{x + 1}$

46. $\lim_{x \to -2} \dfrac{3x^2 + 5x - 2}{x + 2}$

47. $\lim_{x \to 2} \dfrac{x^3 - 8}{x - 2}$

48. $\lim_{x \to -1} \dfrac{x^3 + 1}{x + 1}$

49. $\lim_{x \to -4} \dfrac{(x + 4) \ln(x + 6)}{x^2 - 16}$

50. $\lim_{x \to 0} \dfrac{e^{2x} - 1}{e^x - 1}$

Finding a Limit In Exercises 51–66, find the limit.

51. $\lim_{x \to 0} \dfrac{x}{x^2 - x}$

52. $\lim_{x \to 0} \dfrac{2x}{x^2 + 4x}$

53. $\lim_{x \to 4} \dfrac{x - 4}{x^2 - 16}$

54. $\lim_{x \to 5} \dfrac{5 - x}{x^2 - 25}$

55. $\lim_{x \to -3} \dfrac{x^2 + x - 6}{x^2 - 9}$

56. $\lim_{x \to 2} \dfrac{x^2 + 2x - 8}{x^2 - x - 2}$

57. $\lim_{x \to 4} \dfrac{\sqrt{x + 5} - 3}{x - 4}$

58. $\lim_{x \to 3} \dfrac{\sqrt{x + 1} - 2}{x - 3}$

59. $\lim_{x \to 0} \dfrac{\sqrt{x + 5} - \sqrt{5}}{x}$

60. $\lim_{x \to 0} \dfrac{\sqrt{2 + x} - \sqrt{2}}{x}$

61. $\lim_{x \to 0} \dfrac{[1/(3 + x)] - (1/3)}{x}$

62. $\lim_{x \to 0} \dfrac{[1/(x + 4)] - (1/4)}{x}$

63. $\lim\limits_{\Delta x \to 0} \dfrac{2(x + \Delta x) - 2x}{\Delta x}$ **64.** $\lim\limits_{\Delta x \to 0} \dfrac{(x + \Delta x)^2 - x^2}{\Delta x}$

65. $\lim\limits_{\Delta x \to 0} \dfrac{(x + \Delta x)^2 - 2(x + \Delta x) + 1 - (x^2 - 2x + 1)}{\Delta x}$

66. $\lim\limits_{\Delta x \to 0} \dfrac{(x + \Delta x)^3 - x^3}{\Delta x}$

Finding a Limit of a Transcendental Function In Exercises 67–80, find the limit of the transcendental function.

67. $\lim\limits_{x \to 0} \dfrac{\sin x}{5x}$ **68.** $\lim\limits_{x \to 0} \dfrac{3(1 - \cos x)}{x}$

69. $\lim\limits_{x \to 0} \dfrac{\sin x (1 - \cos x)}{x^2}$ **70.** $\lim\limits_{\theta \to 0} \dfrac{\cos \theta \tan \theta}{\theta}$

71. $\lim\limits_{x \to 0} \dfrac{\sin^2 x}{x}$ **72.** $\lim\limits_{x \to 0} \dfrac{\tan^2 x}{x}$

73. $\lim\limits_{h \to 0} \dfrac{(1 - \cos h)^2}{h}$ **74.** $\lim\limits_{\phi \to \pi} \phi \sec \phi$

75. $\lim\limits_{x \to \pi/2} \dfrac{\cos x}{\cot x}$ **76.** $\lim\limits_{x \to \pi/4} \dfrac{1 - \tan x}{\sin x - \cos x}$

77. $\lim\limits_{x \to 0} \dfrac{1 - e^{-x}}{e^x - 1}$ **78.** $\lim\limits_{x \to 0} \dfrac{4(e^{2x} - 1)}{e^x - 1}$

79. $\lim\limits_{t \to 0} \dfrac{\sin 3t}{2t}$

80. $\lim\limits_{x \to 0} \dfrac{\sin 2x}{\sin 3x}$ $\left[\textit{Hint: Find } \lim\limits_{x \to 0} \left(\dfrac{2 \sin 2x}{2x}\right)\left(\dfrac{3x}{3 \sin 3x}\right).\right]$

Graphical, Numerical, and Analytic Analysis In Exercises 81–90, use a graphing utility to graph the function and estimate the limit. Use a table to reinforce your conclusion. Then find the limit by analytic methods.

81. $\lim\limits_{x \to 0} \dfrac{\sqrt{x + 2} - \sqrt{2}}{x}$ **82.** $\lim\limits_{x \to 16} \dfrac{4 - \sqrt{x}}{x - 16}$

83. $\lim\limits_{x \to 0} \dfrac{[1/(2 + x)] - (1/2)}{x}$ **84.** $\lim\limits_{x \to 2} \dfrac{x^5 - 32}{x - 2}$

85. $\lim\limits_{t \to 0} \dfrac{\sin 3t}{t}$ **86.** $\lim\limits_{x \to 0} \dfrac{\cos x - 1}{2x^2}$

87. $\lim\limits_{x \to 0} \dfrac{\sin x^2}{x}$ **88.** $\lim\limits_{x \to 0} \dfrac{\sin x}{\sqrt[3]{x}}$

89. $\lim\limits_{x \to 1} \dfrac{\ln x}{x - 1}$ **90.** $\lim\limits_{x \to \ln 2} \dfrac{e^{3x} - 8}{e^{2x} - 4}$

Finding a Limit In Exercises 91–94, find

$$\lim\limits_{\Delta x \to 0} \dfrac{f(x + \Delta x) - f(x)}{\Delta x}.$$

91. $f(x) = 3x - 2$ **92.** $f(x) = x^2 - 4x$

93. $f(x) = \dfrac{1}{x + 3}$ **94.** $f(x) = \sqrt{x}$

Using the Squeeze Theorem In Exercises 95 and 96, use the Squeeze Theorem to find $\lim\limits_{x \to c} f(x)$.

95. $c = 0; \ 4 - x^2 \le f(x) \le 4 + x^2$

96. $c = a; \ b - |x - a| \le f(x) \le b + |x - a|$

Using the Squeeze Theorem In Exercises 97–100, use a graphing utility to graph the given function and the equations $y = |x|$ and $y = -|x|$ in the same viewing window. Using the graphs to observe the Squeeze Theorem visually, find $\lim\limits_{x \to 0} f(x)$.

97. $f(x) = |x| \sin x$ **98.** $f(x) = |x| \cos x$

99. $f(x) = x \sin \dfrac{1}{x}$ **100.** $h(x) = x \cos \dfrac{1}{x}$

WRITING ABOUT CONCEPTS

101. Functions That Agree at All but One Point

(a) In the context of finding limits, discuss what is meant by two functions that agree at all but one point.

(b) Give an example of two functions that agree at all but one point.

102. Indeterminate Form What is meant by an indeterminate form?

103. Squeeze Theorem In your own words, explain the Squeeze Theorem.

104. **HOW DO YOU SEE IT?** Would you use the dividing out technique or the rationalizing technique to find the limit of the function? Explain your reasoning.

(a) $\lim\limits_{x \to -2} \dfrac{x^2 + x - 2}{x + 2}$ (b) $\lim\limits_{x \to 0} \dfrac{\sqrt{x + 4} - 2}{x}$

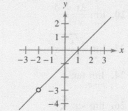
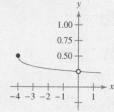

105. Writing Use a graphing utility to graph

$$f(x) = x, \quad g(x) = \sin x, \quad \text{and} \quad h(x) = \dfrac{\sin x}{x}$$

in the same viewing window. Compare the magnitudes of $f(x)$ and $g(x)$ when x is close to 0. Use the comparison to write a short paragraph explaining why

$$\lim\limits_{x \to 0} h(x) = 1.$$

106. Writing Use a graphing utility to graph

$$f(x) = x, \quad g(x) = \sin^2 x, \quad \text{and} \quad h(x) = \dfrac{\sin^2 x}{x}$$

in the same viewing window. Compare the magnitudes of $f(x)$ and $g(x)$ when x is close to 0. Use the comparison to write a short paragraph explaining why

$$\lim\limits_{x \to 0} h(x) = 0.$$

• • **Free-Falling Object** • • • • • • • • • • • • • • • •

In Exercises 107 and 108, use the position function $s(t) = -16t^2 + 500$, which gives the height (in feet) of an object that has fallen for t seconds from a height of 500 feet. The velocity at time $t = a$ seconds is given by

$$\lim_{t \to a} \frac{s(a) - s(t)}{a - t}.$$

107. A construction worker drops a full paint can from a height of 500 feet. How fast will the paint can be falling after 2 seconds?

108. A construction worker drops a full paint can from a height of 500 feet. When will the paint can hit the ground? At what velocity will the paint can impact the ground?

Free-Falling Object In Exercises 109 and 110, use the position function $s(t) = -4.9t^2 + 200$, which gives the height (in meters) of an object that has fallen for t seconds from a height of 200 meters. The velocity at time $t = a$ seconds is given by

$$\lim_{t \to a} \frac{s(a) - s(t)}{a - t}.$$

109. Find the velocity of the object when $t = 3$.

110. At what velocity will the object impact the ground?

111. Finding Functions Find two functions f and g such that $\lim_{x \to 0} f(x)$ and $\lim_{x \to 0} g(x)$ do not exist, but

$$\lim_{x \to 0} [f(x) + g(x)]$$

does exist.

112. Proof Prove that if $\lim_{x \to c} f(x)$ exists and $\lim_{x \to c} [f(x) + g(x)]$ does not exist, then $\lim_{x \to c} g(x)$ does not exist.

113. Proof Prove Property 1 of Theorem 2.1.

114. Proof Prove Property 3 of Theorem 2.1. (You may use Property 3 of Theorem 2.2.)

115. Proof Prove Property 1 of Theorem 2.2.

116. Proof Prove that if $\lim_{x \to c} f(x) = 0$, then $\lim_{x \to c} |f(x)| = 0$.

117. Proof Prove that if $\lim_{x \to c} f(x) = 0$ and $|g(x)| \le M$ for a fixed number M and all $x \ne c$, then $\lim_{x \to c} f(x)g(x) = 0$.

118. Proof

(a) Prove that if $\lim_{x \to c} |f(x)| = 0$, then $\lim_{x \to c} f(x) = 0$.

   (*Note:* This is the converse of Exercise 116.)

(b) Prove that if $\lim_{x \to c} f(x) = L$, then $\lim_{x \to c} |f(x)| = |L|$.

   [*Hint:* Use the inequality $\big||f(x)| - |L|\big| \le |f(x) - L|$.]

119. Think About It Find a function f to show that the converse of Exercise 118(b) is not true. [*Hint:* Find a function f such that $\lim_{x \to c} |f(x)| = |L|$ but $\lim_{x \to c} f(x)$ does not exist.]

120. Think About It When using a graphing utility to generate a table to approximate

$$\lim_{x \to 0} \frac{\sin x}{x}$$

a student concluded that the limit was 0.01745 rather than 1. Determine the probable cause of the error.

True or False? In Exercises 121–126, determine whether the statement is true or false. If it is false, explain why or give an example that shows it is false.

121. $\lim_{x \to 0} \dfrac{|x|}{x} = 1$

122. $\lim_{x \to \pi} \dfrac{\sin x}{x} = 1$

123. If $f(x) = g(x)$ for all real numbers other than $x = 0$, and $\lim_{x \to 0} f(x) = L$, then $\lim_{x \to 0} g(x) = L$.

124. If $\lim_{x \to c} f(x) = L$, then $f(c) = L$.

125. $\lim_{x \to 2} f(x) = 3$, where $f(x) = \begin{cases} 3, & x \le 2 \\ 0, & x > 2 \end{cases}$

126. If $f(x) < g(x)$ for all $x \ne a$, then $\lim_{x \to a} f(x) < \lim_{x \to a} g(x)$.

127. Proof Prove the second part of Theorem 2.9.

$$\lim_{x \to 0} \frac{1 - \cos x}{x} = 0$$

128. Piecewise Functions Let

$$f(x) = \begin{cases} 0, & \text{if } x \text{ is rational} \\ 1, & \text{if } x \text{ is irrational} \end{cases}$$

and

$$g(x) = \begin{cases} 0, & \text{if } x \text{ is rational} \\ x, & \text{if } x \text{ is irrational} \end{cases}.$$

Find (if possible) $\lim_{x \to 0} f(x)$ and $\lim_{x \to 0} g(x)$.

129. Graphical Reasoning Consider $f(x) = \dfrac{\sec x - 1}{x^2}$.

(a) Find the domain of f.

(b) Use a graphing utility to graph f. Is the domain of f obvious from the graph? If not, explain.

(c) Use the graph of f to approximate $\lim_{x \to 0} f(x)$.

(d) Confirm your answer to part (c) analytically.

130. Approximation

(a) Find $\lim_{x \to 0} \dfrac{1 - \cos x}{x^2}$.

(b) Use your answer to part (a) to derive the approximation $\cos x \approx 1 - \frac{1}{2}x^2$ for x near 0.

(c) Use your answer to part (b) to approximate $\cos(0.1)$.

(d) Use a calculator to approximate $\cos(0.1)$ to four decimal places. Compare the result with part (c).

2.4 Continuity and One-Sided Limits

- Determine continuity at a point and continuity on an open interval.
- Determine one-sided limits and continuity on a closed interval.
- Use properties of continuity.
- Understand and use the Intermediate Value Theorem.

Continuity at a Point and on an Open Interval

In mathematics, the term *continuous* has much the same meaning as it has in everyday usage. Informally, to say that a function f is continuous at $x = c$ means that there is no interruption in the graph of f at c. That is, its graph is unbroken at c, and there are no holes, jumps, or gaps. Figure 2.25 identifies three values of x at which the graph of f is *not* continuous. At all other points in the interval (a, b), the graph of f is uninterrupted and **continuous.**

Exploration

Informally, you might say that a function is *continuous* on an open interval when its graph can be drawn with a pencil without lifting the pencil from the paper. Use a graphing utility to graph each function on the given interval. From the graphs, which functions would you say are continuous on the interval? Do you think you can trust the results you obtained graphically? Explain your reasoning.

Function	Interval
a. $y = x^2 + 1$	$(-3, 3)$
b. $y = \dfrac{1}{x - 2}$	$(-3, 3)$
c. $y = \dfrac{\sin x}{x}$	$(-\pi, \pi)$
d. $y = \dfrac{x^2 - 4}{x + 2}$	$(-3, 3)$

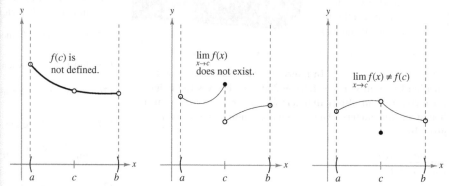

Three conditions exist for which the graph of f is not continuous at $x = c$.
Figure 2.25

In Figure 2.25, it appears that continuity at $x = c$ can be destroyed by any one of three conditions.

1. The function is not defined at $x = c$.
2. The limit of $f(x)$ does not exist at $x = c$.
3. The limit of $f(x)$ exists at $x = c$, but it is not equal to $f(c)$.

If *none* of the three conditions is true, then the function f is called **continuous at c,** as indicated in the important definition below.

■ **FOR FURTHER INFORMATION**
For more information on the concept of continuity, see the article "Leibniz and the Spell of the Continuous" by Hardy Grant in *The College Mathematics Journal.* To view this article, go to *MathArticles.com.*

Definition of Continuity

Continuity at a Point
A function f is **continuous at c** when these three conditions are met.

1. $f(c)$ is defined.
2. $\lim\limits_{x \to c} f(x)$ exists.
3. $\lim\limits_{x \to c} f(x) = f(c)$

Continuity on an Open Interval
A function is **continuous on an open interval (a, b)** when the function is continuous at each point in the interval. A function that is continuous on the entire real number line $(-\infty, \infty)$ is **everywhere continuous.**

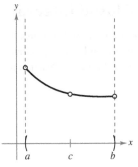

(a) Removable discontinuity

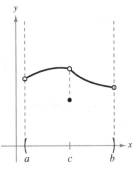

(b) Nonremovable discontinuity

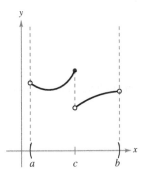

(c) Removable discontinuity
Figure 2.26

Consider an open interval I that contains a real number c. If a function f is defined on I (except possibly at c), and f is not continuous at c, then f is said to have a **discontinuity** at c. Discontinuities fall into two categories: **removable** and **nonremovable.** A discontinuity at c is called removable when f can be made continuous by appropriately defining (or redefining) $f(c)$. For instance, the functions shown in Figures 2.26(a) and (c) have removable discontinuities at c and the function shown in Figure 2.26(b) has a nonremovable discontinuity at c.

> **EXAMPLE 1** **Continuity of a Function**

Discuss the continuity of each function.

a. $f(x) = \dfrac{1}{x}$ **b.** $g(x) = \dfrac{x^2 - 1}{x - 1}$ **c.** $h(x) = \begin{cases} x + 1, & x \le 0 \\ e^x, & x > 0 \end{cases}$ **d.** $y = \sin x$

Solution

a. The domain of f is all nonzero real numbers. From Theorem 2.3, you can conclude that f is continuous at every x-value in its domain. At $x = 0$, f has a nonremovable discontinuity, as shown in Figure 2.27(a). In other words, there is no way to define $f(0)$ so as to make the function continuous at $x = 0$.

b. The domain of g is all real numbers except $x = 1$. From Theorem 2.3, you can conclude that g is continuous at every x-value in its domain. At $x = 1$, the function has a removable discontinuity, as shown in Figure 2.27(b). By defining $g(1)$ as 2, the "redefined" function is continuous for all real numbers.

c. The domain of h is all real numbers. The function h is continuous on $(-\infty, 0)$ and $(0, \infty)$, and, because

$$\lim_{x \to 0} h(x) = 1$$

h is continuous on the entire real number line, as shown in Figure 2.27(c).

d. The domain of y is all real numbers. From Theorem 2.6, you can conclude that the function is continuous on its entire domain, $(-\infty, \infty)$, as shown in Figure 2.27(d).

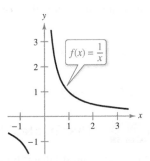

(a) Nonremovable discontinuity at $x = 0$

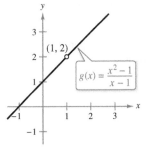

(b) Removable discontinuity at $x = 1$

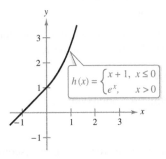

(c) Continuous on entire real number line

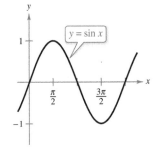

(d) Continuous on entire real number line
Figure 2.27

•••••••••••••••••••▷

••REMARK Some people may refer to the function in Example 1(a) as "discontinuous." We have found that this terminology can be confusing. Rather than saying that the function is discontinuous, we prefer to say that it has a discontinuity at $x = 0$.

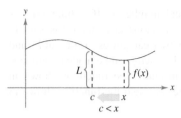

(a) Limit as x approaches c from the right.

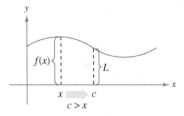

(b) Limit as x approaches c from the left.
Figure 2.28

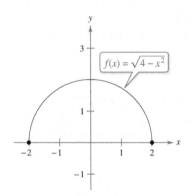

The limit of $f(x)$ as x approaches -2 from the right is 0.
Figure 2.29

One-Sided Limits and Continuity on a Closed Interval

To understand continuity on a closed interval, you first need to look at a different type of limit called a **one-sided limit.** For instance, the **limit from the right** (or right-hand limit) means that x approaches c from values greater than c [see Figure 2.28(a)]. This limit is denoted as

$$\lim_{x \to c^+} f(x) = L. \qquad \text{Limit from the right}$$

Similarly, the **limit from the left** (or left-hand limit) means that x approaches c from values less than c [see Figure 2.28(b)]. This limit is denoted as

$$\lim_{x \to c^-} f(x) = L. \qquad \text{Limit from the left}$$

One-sided limits are useful in taking limits of functions involving radicals. For instance, if n is an even integer, then

$$\lim_{x \to 0^+} \sqrt[n]{x} = 0.$$

EXAMPLE 2   **A One-Sided Limit**

Find the limit of $f(x) = \sqrt{4 - x^2}$ as x approaches -2 from the right.

Solution   As shown in Figure 2.29, the limit as x approaches -2 from the right is

$$\lim_{x \to -2^+} \sqrt{4 - x^2} = 0.$$

One-sided limits can be used to investigate the behavior of **step functions.** One common type of step function is the **greatest integer function** $[\![x]\!]$, defined as

$$[\![x]\!] = \text{greatest integer } n \text{ such that } n \le x. \qquad \text{Greatest integer function}$$

For instance, $[\![2.5]\!] = 2$ and $[\![-2.5]\!] = -3$.

EXAMPLE 3   **The Greatest Integer Function**

Find the limit of the greatest integer function $f(x) = [\![x]\!]$ as x approaches 0 from the left and from the right.

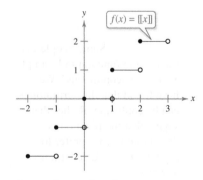

Solution   As shown in Figure 2.30, the limit as x approaches 0 *from the left* is

$$\lim_{x \to 0^-} [\![x]\!] = -1$$

and the limit as x approaches 0 *from the right* is

$$\lim_{x \to 0^+} [\![x]\!] = 0.$$

The greatest integer function has a discontinuity at zero because the left- and right-hand limits at zero are different. By similar reasoning, you can see that the greatest integer function has a discontinuity at any integer n.

Greatest integer function
Figure 2.30

When the limit from the left is not equal to the limit from the right, the (two-sided) limit *does not exist*. The next theorem makes this more explicit. The proof of this theorem follows directly from the definition of a one-sided limit.

THEOREM 2.10 The Existence of a Limit

Let f be a function, and let c and L be real numbers. The limit of $f(x)$ as x approaches c is L if and only if

$$\lim_{x \to c^-} f(x) = L \quad \text{and} \quad \lim_{x \to c^+} f(x) = L.$$

The concept of a one-sided limit allows you to extend the definition of continuity to closed intervals. Basically, a function is continuous on a closed interval when it is continuous in the interior of the interval and exhibits one-sided continuity at the endpoints. This is stated formally in the next definition.

Definition of Continuity on a Closed Interval

A function f is **continuous on the closed interval $[a, b]$** when f is continuous on the open interval (a, b) and

$$\lim_{x \to a^+} f(x) = f(a)$$

and

$$\lim_{x \to b^-} f(x) = f(b).$$

The function f is **continuous from the right** at a and **continuous from the left** at b (see Figure 2.31).

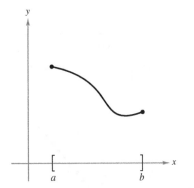

Continuous function on a closed interval
Figure 2.31

Similar definitions can be made to cover continuity on intervals of the form $(a, b]$ and $[a, b)$ that are neither open nor closed, or on infinite intervals. For example,

$$f(x) = \sqrt{x}$$

is continuous on the infinite interval $[0, \infty)$, and the function

$$g(x) = \sqrt{2 - x}$$

is continuous on the infinite interval $(-\infty, 2]$.

EXAMPLE 4   **Continuity on a Closed Interval**

Discuss the continuity of

$$f(x) = \sqrt{1 - x^2}.$$

Solution   The domain of f is the closed interval $[-1, 1]$. At all points in the open interval $(-1, 1)$, the continuity of f follows from Theorems 2.4 and 2.5. Moreover, because

$$\lim_{x \to -1^+} \sqrt{1 - x^2} = 0 = f(-1) \qquad \text{Continuous from the right}$$

and

$$\lim_{x \to 1^-} \sqrt{1 - x^2} = 0 = f(1) \qquad \text{Continuous from the left}$$

you can conclude that f is continuous on the closed interval $[-1, 1]$, as shown in Figure 2.32.

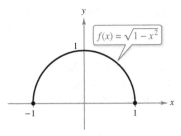

f is continuous on $[-1, 1]$.
Figure 2.32

The next example shows how a one-sided limit can be used to determine the value of absolute zero on the Kelvin scale.

EXAMPLE 5   **Charles's Law and Absolute Zero**

On the Kelvin scale, *absolute zero* is the temperature 0 K. Although temperatures very close to 0 K have been produced in laboratories, absolute zero has never been attained. In fact, evidence suggests that absolute zero *cannot* be attained. How did scientists determine that 0 K is the "lower limit" of the temperature of matter? What is absolute zero on the Celsius scale?

Solution   The determination of absolute zero stems from the work of the French physicist Jacques Charles (1746–1823). Charles discovered that the volume of gas at a constant pressure increases linearly with the temperature of the gas. The table illustrates this relationship between volume and temperature. To generate the values in the table, one mole of hydrogen is held at a constant pressure of one atmosphere. The volume V is approximated and is measured in liters, and the temperature T is measured in degrees Celsius.

T	-40	-20	0	20	40	60	80
V	19.1482	20.7908	22.4334	24.0760	25.7186	27.3612	29.0038

The points represented by the table are shown in Figure 2.33. Moreover, by using the points in the table, you can determine that T and V are related by the linear equation

$$V = 0.08213T + 22.4334.$$

Solving for T, you get an equation for the temperature of the gas.

$$T = \frac{V - 22.4334}{0.08213}$$

By reasoning that the volume of the gas can approach 0 (but can never equal or go below 0), you can determine that the "least possible temperature" is

$$\lim_{V \to 0^+} T = \lim_{V \to 0^+} \frac{V - 22.4334}{0.08213}$$

$$= \frac{0 - 22.4334}{0.08213} \qquad \text{Use direct substitution.}$$

$$\approx -273.15.$$

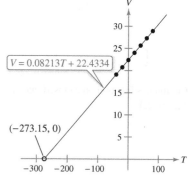

The volume of hydrogen gas depends on its temperature.
Figure 2.33

So, absolute zero on the Kelvin scale (0 K) is approximately $-273.15°$ on the Celsius scale.

In 2003, researchers at the Massachusetts Institute of Technology used lasers and evaporation to produce a super-cold gas in which atoms overlap. This gas is called a Bose-Einstein condensate. They measured a temperature of about 450 pK (picokelvin), or approximately $-273.14999999955°C$. *(Source: Science magazine, September 12, 2003)*

The table below shows the temperatures in Example 5 converted to the Fahrenheit scale. Try repeating the solution shown in Example 5 using these temperatures and volumes. Use the result to find the value of absolute zero on the Fahrenheit scale.

T	-40	-4	32	68	104	140	176
V	19.1482	20.7908	22.4334	24.0760	25.7186	27.3612	29.0038

Properties of Continuity

In Section 2.3, you studied several properties of limits. Each of those properties yields a corresponding property pertaining to the continuity of a function. For instance, Theorem 2.11 follows directly from Theorem 2.2.

AUGUSTIN-LOUIS CAUCHY
(1789–1857)

The concept of a continuous function was first introduced by Augustin-Louis Cauchy in 1821. The definition given in his text *Cours d'Analyse* stated that indefinite small changes in *y* were the result of indefinite small changes in *x*. "... $f(x)$ will be called a *continuous* function if ... the numerical values of the difference $f(x + \alpha) - f(x)$ decrease indefinitely with those of α...."
See LarsonCalculus.com to read more of this biography.

THEOREM 2.11   Properties of Continuity

If *b* is a real number and *f* and *g* are continuous at $x = c$, then the functions listed below are also continuous at *c*.

1. Scalar multiple: bf **2.** Sum or difference: $f \pm g$

3. Product: fg **4.** Quotient: $\dfrac{f}{g}$, $g(c) \neq 0$

A proof of this theorem is given in Appendix A.
See LarsonCalculus.com for Bruce Edwards's video of this proof.

The list below summarizes the functions you have studied so far that are continuous at every point in their domains.

1. Polynomial: $p(x) = a_n x^n + a_{n-1} x^{n-1} + \cdots + a_1 x + a_0$

2. Rational: $r(x) = \dfrac{p(x)}{q(x)}$, $q(x) \neq 0$

3. Radical: $f(x) = \sqrt[n]{x}$

4. Trigonometric: $\sin x$, $\cos x$, $\tan x$, $\cot x$, $\sec x$, $\csc x$

5. Exponential and logarithmic: $f(x) = a^x$, $f(x) = e^x$, $f(x) = \ln x$

By combining Theorem 2.11 with this list, you can conclude that a wide variety of elementary functions are continuous at every point in their domains.

EXAMPLE 6   **Applying Properties of Continuity**

⋯⋯▷ *See LarsonCalculus.com for an interactive version of this type of example.*

By Theorem 2.11, it follows that each of the functions below is continuous at every point in its domain.

$$f(x) = x + e^x, \quad f(x) = 3 \tan x, \quad f(x) = \frac{x^2 + 1}{\cos x}$$

The next theorem, which is a consequence of Theorem 2.5, allows you to determine the continuity of *composite* functions such as

$$f(x) = \ln 3x, \quad f(x) = \sqrt{x^2 + 1}, \quad \text{and} \quad f(x) = \tan \frac{1}{x}.$$

THEOREM 2.12   Continuity of a Composite Function

If *g* is continuous at *c* and *f* is continuous at $g(c)$, then the composite function given by $(f \circ g)(x) = f(g(x))$ is continuous at *c*.

⋯⋯⋯⋯⋯⋯⋯▷

REMARK   One consequence of Theorem 2.12 is that when *f* and *g* satisfy the given conditions, you can determine the limit of $f(g(x))$ as *x* approaches *c* to be

$$\lim_{x \to c} f(g(x)) = f(g(c)).$$

Proof   By the definition of continuity, $\lim\limits_{x \to c} g(x) = g(c)$ and $\lim\limits_{x \to g(c)} f(x) = f(g(c))$.

Apply Theorem 2.5 with $L = g(c)$ to obtain $\lim\limits_{x \to c} f(g(x)) = f\left(\lim\limits_{x \to c} g(x)\right) = f(g(c))$. So,

$(f \circ g)(x) = f(g(x))$ is continuous at *c*.

See LarsonCalculus.com for Bruce Edwards's video of this proof.

EXAMPLE 7 **Testing for Continuity**

Describe the interval(s) on which each function is continuous.

a. $f(x) = \tan x$ **b.** $g(x) = \begin{cases} \sin \dfrac{1}{x}, & x \neq 0 \\ 0, & x = 0 \end{cases}$ **c.** $h(x) = \begin{cases} x \sin \dfrac{1}{x}, & x \neq 0 \\ 0, & x = 0 \end{cases}$

Solution

a. The tangent function $f(x) = \tan x$ is undefined at

$$x = \frac{\pi}{2} + n\pi, \quad n \text{ is an integer.}$$

At all other points, f is continuous. So, $f(x) = \tan x$ is continuous on the open intervals

$$\ldots, \left(-\frac{3\pi}{2}, -\frac{\pi}{2}\right), \left(-\frac{\pi}{2}, \frac{\pi}{2}\right), \left(\frac{\pi}{2}, \frac{3\pi}{2}\right), \ldots$$

as shown in Figure 2.34(a).

b. Because $y = 1/x$ is continuous except at $x = 0$ and the sine function is continuous for all real values of x, it follows from Theorem 2.12 that

$$y = \sin \frac{1}{x}$$

is continuous at all real values except $x = 0$. At $x = 0$, the limit of $g(x)$ does not exist (see Example 5, Section 2.2). So, g is continuous on the intervals $(-\infty, 0)$ and $(0, \infty)$, as shown in Figure 2.34(b).

c. This function is similar to the function in part (b) except that the oscillations are damped by the factor x. Using the Squeeze Theorem, you obtain

$$-|x| \leq x \sin \frac{1}{x} \leq |x|, \quad x \neq 0$$

and you can conclude that

$$\lim_{x \to 0} h(x) = 0.$$

So, h is continuous on the entire real number line, as shown in Figure 2.34(c).

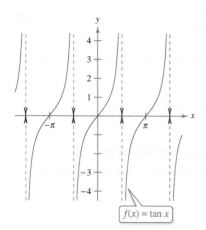

(a) f is continuous on each open interval in its domain.

Figure 2.34

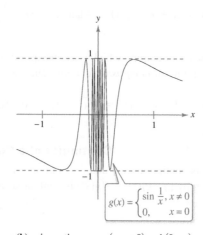

(b) g is continuous on $(-\infty, 0)$ and $(0, \infty)$.

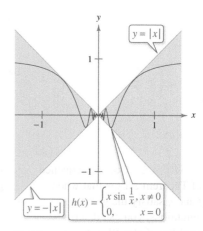

(c) h is continuous on the entire real number line.

The Intermediate Value Theorem

Theorem 2.13 is an important theorem concerning the behavior of functions that are continuous on a closed interval.

> **THEOREM 2.13   Intermediate Value Theorem**
>
> If f is continuous on the closed interval $[a, b]$, $f(a) \neq f(b)$, and k is any number between $f(a)$ and $f(b)$, then there is at least one number c in $[a, b]$ such that
>
> $$f(c) = k.$$

REMARK   The Intermediate Value Theorem tells you that at least one number c exists, but it does not provide a method for finding c. Such theorems are called **existence theorems.** By referring to a text on advanced calculus, you will find that a proof of this theorem is based on a property of real numbers called *completeness*. The Intermediate Value Theorem states that for a continuous function f, if x takes on all values between a and b, then $f(x)$ must take on all values between $f(a)$ and $f(b)$.

As an example of the application of the Intermediate Value Theorem, consider a person's height. A girl is 5 feet tall on her thirteenth birthday and 5 feet 7 inches tall on her fourteenth birthday. Then, for any height h between 5 feet and 5 feet 7 inches, there must have been a time t when her height was exactly h. This seems reasonable because human growth is continuous and a person's height does not abruptly change from one value to another.

The Intermediate Value Theorem guarantees the existence of *at least one* number c in the closed interval $[a, b]$. There may, of course, be more than one number c such that

$$f(c) = k$$

as shown in Figure 2.35. A function that is not continuous does not necessarily exhibit the intermediate value property. For example, the graph of the function shown in Figure 2.36 jumps over the horizontal line

$$y = k$$

and for this function there is no value of c in $[a, b]$ such that $f(c) = k$.

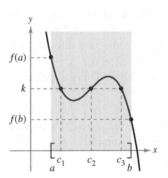

f is continuous on $[a, b]$.
[There exist three c's such that $f(c) = k$.]
Figure 2.35

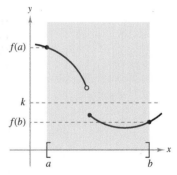

f is not continuous on $[a, b]$.
[There are no c's such that $f(c) = k$.]
Figure 2.36

The Intermediate Value Theorem often can be used to locate the zeros of a function that is continuous on a closed interval. Specifically, if f is continuous on $[a, b]$ and $f(a)$ and $f(b)$ differ in sign, then the Intermediate Value Theorem guarantees the existence of at least one zero of f in the closed interval $[a, b]$.

| EXAMPLE 8 | **An Application of the Intermediate Value Theorem** |

Use the Intermediate Value Theorem to show that the polynomial function

$$f(x) = x^3 + 2x - 1$$

has a zero in the interval $[0, 1]$.

Solution   Note that f is continuous on the closed interval $[0, 1]$. Because

$$f(0) = 0^3 + 2(0) - 1 = -1 \quad \text{and} \quad f(1) = 1^3 + 2(1) - 1 = 2$$

it follows that $f(0) < 0$ and $f(1) > 0$. You can therefore apply the Intermediate Value Theorem to conclude that there must be some c in $[0, 1]$ such that

$$f(c) = 0 \qquad \text{\small f has a zero in the closed interval $[0, 1]$.}$$

as shown in Figure 2.37.

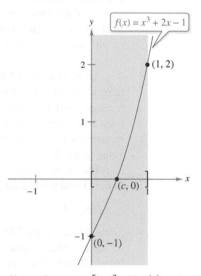

f is continuous on $[0, 1]$ with $f(0) < 0$ and $f(1) > 0$.
Figure 2.37

The **bisection method** for approximating the real zeros of a continuous function is similar to the method used in Example 8. If you know that a zero exists in the closed interval $[a, b]$, then the zero must lie in the interval $[a, (a + b)/2]$ or $[(a + b)/2, b]$. From the sign of $f([a + b]/2)$, you can determine which interval contains the zero. By repeatedly bisecting the interval, you can "close in" on the zero of the function.

▷ **TECHNOLOGY**   You can use the *root* or *zero* feature of a graphing utility to approximate the real zeros of a continuous function. Using this feature, the zero of the function in Example 8, $f(x) = x^3 + 2x - 1$, is approximately 0.453, as shown in Figure 2.38.

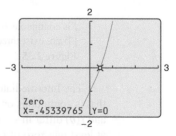

Zero of $f(x) = x^3 + 2x - 1$
Figure 2.38

2.4 Exercises

See CalcChat.com for tutorial help and worked-out solutions to odd-numbered exercises.

Limits and Continuity In Exercises 1–6, use the graph to determine the limit, and discuss the continuity of the function.

(a) $\lim_{x \to c^+} f(x)$ (b) $\lim_{x \to c^-} f(x)$ (c) $\lim_{x \to c} f(x)$

1.
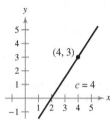

2.
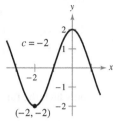

3.
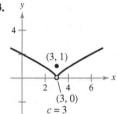

4.
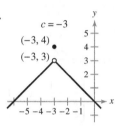

5.
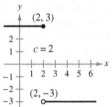

6.
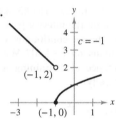

Finding a Limit In Exercises 7–28, find the limit (if it exists). If it does not exist, explain why.

7. $\lim_{x \to 8^+} \dfrac{1}{x + 8}$

8. $\lim_{x \to 2^-} \dfrac{2}{x + 2}$

9. $\lim_{x \to 5^+} \dfrac{x - 5}{x^2 - 25}$

10. $\lim_{x \to 4^+} \dfrac{4 - x}{x^2 - 16}$

11. $\lim_{x \to -3^-} \dfrac{x}{\sqrt{x^2 - 9}}$

12. $\lim_{x \to 4^-} \dfrac{\sqrt{x} - 2}{x - 4}$

13. $\lim_{x \to 0^-} \dfrac{|x|}{x}$

14. $\lim_{x \to 10^+} \dfrac{|x - 10|}{x - 10}$

15. $\lim_{\Delta x \to 0^-} \dfrac{\dfrac{1}{x + \Delta x} - \dfrac{1}{x}}{\Delta x}$

16. $\lim_{\Delta x \to 0^+} \dfrac{(x + \Delta x)^2 + x + \Delta x - (x^2 + x)}{\Delta x}$

17. $\lim_{x \to 3^-} f(x)$, where $f(x) = \begin{cases} \dfrac{x + 2}{2}, & x \le 3 \\ \dfrac{12 - 2x}{3}, & x > 3 \end{cases}$

18. $\lim_{x \to 3} f(x)$, where $f(x) = \begin{cases} x^2 - 4x + 6, & x < 3 \\ -x^2 + 4x - 2, & x \ge 3 \end{cases}$

19. $\lim_{x \to \pi} \cot x$

20. $\lim_{x \to \pi/2} \sec x$

21. $\lim_{x \to 4^-} (5[\![x]\!] - 7)$

22. $\lim_{x \to 2^+} (2x - [\![x]\!])$

23. $\lim_{x \to 3} (2 - [\![-x]\!])$

24. $\lim_{x \to 1} \left(1 - \left[\!\!\left[-\dfrac{x}{2} \right]\!\!\right]\right)$

25. $\lim_{x \to 3^+} \ln(x - 3)$

26. $\lim_{x \to 6^-} \ln(6 - x)$

27. $\lim_{x \to 2^-} \ln[x^2(3 - x)]$

28. $\lim_{x \to 5^+} \ln \dfrac{x}{\sqrt{x - 4}}$

Continuity of a Function In Exercises 29–32, discuss the continuity of each function.

29. $f(x) = \dfrac{1}{x^2 - 4}$

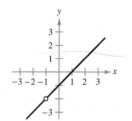

30. $f(x) = \dfrac{x^2 - 1}{x + 1}$

31. $f(x) = \frac{1}{2}[\![x]\!] + x$

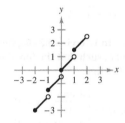

32. $f(x) = \begin{cases} x, & x < 1 \\ 2, & x = 1 \\ 2x - 1, & x > 1 \end{cases}$

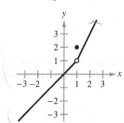

Continuity on a Closed Interval In Exercises 33–36, discuss the continuity of the function on the closed interval.

Function	Interval
33. $g(x) = \sqrt{49 - x^2}$	$[-7, 7]$
34. $f(t) = 3 - \sqrt{9 - t^2}$	$[-3, 3]$
35. $f(x) = \begin{cases} 3 - x, & x \le 0 \\ 3 + \frac{1}{2}x, & x > 0 \end{cases}$	$[-1, 4]$
36. $g(x) = \dfrac{1}{x^2 - 4}$	$[-1, 2]$

Removable and Nonremovable Discontinuities In Exercises 37–62, find the x-values (if any) at which f is not continuous. Which of the discontinuities are removable?

37. $f(x) = \dfrac{6}{x}$

38. $f(x) = \dfrac{4}{x - 6}$

39. $f(x) = 3x - \cos x$

40. $f(x) = x^2 - 4x + 4$

41. $f(x) = \dfrac{1}{4 - x^2}$ **42.** $f(x) = \cos\dfrac{\pi x}{2}$

43. $f(x) = \dfrac{x}{x^2 - x}$ **44.** $f(x) = \dfrac{x}{x^2 - 4}$

45. $f(x) = \dfrac{x}{x^2 + 1}$ **46.** $f(x) = \dfrac{x - 5}{x^2 - 25}$

47. $f(x) = \dfrac{x + 2}{x^2 - 3x - 10}$ **48.** $f(x) = \dfrac{x + 2}{x^2 - x - 6}$

49. $f(x) = \dfrac{|x + 7|}{x + 7}$ **50.** $f(x) = \dfrac{|x - 5|}{x - 5}$

51. $f(x) = \begin{cases} x, & x \le 1 \\ x^2, & x > 1 \end{cases}$ **52.** $f(x) = \begin{cases} -2x + 3, & x < 1 \\ x^2, & x \ge 1 \end{cases}$

53. $f(x) = \begin{cases} \frac{1}{2}x + 1, & x \le 2 \\ 3 - x, & x > 2 \end{cases}$

54. $f(x) = \begin{cases} -2x, & x \le 2 \\ x^2 - 4x + 1, & x > 2 \end{cases}$

55. $f(x) = \begin{cases} \tan\frac{\pi x}{4}, & |x| < 1 \\ x, & |x| \ge 1 \end{cases}$

56. $f(x) = \begin{cases} \csc\frac{\pi x}{6}, & |x - 3| \le 2 \\ 2, & |x - 3| > 2 \end{cases}$

57. $f(x) = \begin{cases} \ln(x + 1), & x \ge 0 \\ 1 - x^2, & x < 0 \end{cases}$

58. $f(x) = \begin{cases} 10 - 3e^{5-x}, & x > 5 \\ 10 - \frac{3}{5}x, & x \le 5 \end{cases}$

59. $f(x) = \csc 2x$ **60.** $f(x) = \tan\dfrac{\pi x}{2}$

61. $f(x) = [\![x - 8]\!]$ **62.** $f(x) = 5 - [\![x]\!]$

Making a Function Continuous In Exercises 63–68, find the constant a, or the constants a and b, such that the function is continuous on the entire real number line.

63. $f(x) = \begin{cases} 3x^2, & x \ge 1 \\ ax - 4, & x < 1 \end{cases}$ **64.** $g(x) = \begin{cases} \dfrac{4\sin x}{x}, & x < 0 \\ a - 2x, & x \ge 0 \end{cases}$

65. $f(x) = \begin{cases} 2, & x \le -1 \\ ax + b, & -1 < x < 3 \\ -2, & x \ge 3 \end{cases}$

66. $g(x) = \begin{cases} \dfrac{x^2 - a^2}{x - a}, & x \ne a \\ 8, & x = a \end{cases}$

67. $f(x) = \begin{cases} ae^{x-1} + 3, & x < 1 \\ \arctan(x - 1) + 2, & x \ge 1 \end{cases}$

68. $f(x) = \begin{cases} 2e^{ax} - 2, & x \le 4 \\ \ln(x - 3) + x^2, & x > 4 \end{cases}$

Continuity of a Composite Function In Exercises 69–72, discuss the continuity of the composite function $h(x) = f(g(x))$.

69. $f(x) = x^2$ **70.** $f(x) = \dfrac{1}{\sqrt{x}}$

$g(x) = x - 1$ $g(x) = x - 1$

71. $f(x) = \dfrac{1}{x - 6}$ **72.** $f(x) = \sin x$

$g(x) = x^2 + 5$ $g(x) = x^2$

Finding Discontinuities In Exercises 73–76, use a graphing utility to graph the function. Use the graph to determine any x-values at which the function is not continuous.

73. $f(x) = [\![x]\!] - x$ **74.** $h(x) = \dfrac{1}{x^2 + 2x - 15}$

75. $g(x) = \begin{cases} x^2 - 3x, & x > 4 \\ 2x - 5, & x \le 4 \end{cases}$ **76.** $f(x) = \begin{cases} \dfrac{\cos x - 1}{x}, & x < 0 \\ 5x, & x \ge 0 \end{cases}$

Testing for Continuity In Exercises 77–84, describe the interval(s) on which the function is continuous.

77. $f(x) = \dfrac{x}{x^2 + x + 2}$ **78.** $f(x) = \dfrac{x + 1}{\sqrt{x}}$

79. $f(x) = 3 - \sqrt{x}$ **80.** $f(x) = x\sqrt{x + 3}$

81. $f(x) = \sec\dfrac{\pi x}{4}$ **82.** $f(x) = \cos\dfrac{1}{x}$

83. $f(x) = \begin{cases} \dfrac{x^2 - 1}{x - 1}, & x \ne 1 \\ 2, & x = 1 \end{cases}$ **84.** $f(x) = \begin{cases} 2x - 4, & x \ne 3 \\ 1, & x = 3 \end{cases}$

Writing In Exercises 85–88, use a graphing utility to graph the function on the interval $[-4, 4]$. Does the graph of the function appear to be continuous on this interval? Is the function continuous on $[-4, 4]$? Write a short paragraph about the importance of examining a function analytically as well as graphically.

85. $f(x) = \dfrac{\sin x}{x}$ **86.** $f(x) = \dfrac{x^3 - 8}{x - 2}$

87. $f(x) = \dfrac{\ln(x^2 + 1)}{x}$ **88.** $f(x) = \dfrac{e^{-x} + 1}{e^x - 1}$

Writing In Exercises 89–92, explain why the function has a zero in the given interval.

Function	Interval
89. $f(x) = \frac{1}{12}x^4 - x^3 + 4$	$[1, 2]$
90. $f(x) = -\dfrac{5}{x} + \tan\left(\dfrac{\pi x}{10}\right)$	$[1, 4]$
91. $h(x) = -2e^{-x/2}\cos 2x$	$\left[0, \dfrac{\pi}{2}\right]$
92. $g(t) = (t^3 + 2t - 2)\ln(t^2 + 4)$	$[0, 1]$

Using the Intermediate Value Theorem In Exercises 93–98, use the Intermediate Value Theorem and a graphing utility to approximate the zero of the function in the interval $[0, 1]$. Repeatedly "zoom in" on the graph of the function to approximate the zero accurate to two decimal places. Use the *zero* or *root* feature of the graphing utility to approximate the zero accurate to four decimal places.

93. $f(x) = x^3 + x - 1$

94. $f(x) = x^4 - x^2 + 3x - 1$

95. $g(t) = 2 \cos t - 3t$ **96.** $h(\theta) = \tan \theta + 3\theta - 4$

97. $f(x) = x + e^x - 3$ **98.** $g(x) = 5 \ln(x + 1) - 2$

Using the Intermediate Value Theorem In Exercises 99–102, verify that the Intermediate Value Theorem applies to the indicated interval and find the value of c guaranteed by the theorem.

99. $f(x) = x^2 + x - 1$, $[0, 5]$, $f(c) = 11$

100. $f(x) = x^2 - 6x + 8$, $[0, 3]$, $f(c) = 0$

101. $f(x) = x^3 - x^2 + x - 2$, $[0, 3]$, $f(c) = 4$

102. $f(x) = \dfrac{x^2 + x}{x - 1}$, $\left[\dfrac{5}{2}, 4\right]$, $f(c) = 6$

WRITING ABOUT CONCEPTS

103. Using the Definition of Continuity State how continuity is destroyed at $x = c$ for each of the following graphs.

(a)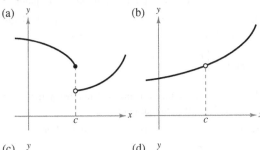

(b)

(c)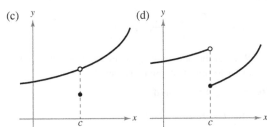

(d)

104. Sketching a Graph Sketch the graph of any function f such that

$$\lim_{x \to 3^+} f(x) = 1 \quad \text{and} \quad \lim_{x \to 3^-} f(x) = 0.$$

Is the function continuous at $x = 3$? Explain.

105. Continuity of Combinations of Functions If the functions f and g are continuous for all real x, is $f + g$ always continuous for all real x? Is f/g always continuous for all real x? If either is not continuous, give an example to verify your conclusion.

106. Removable and Nonremovable Discontinuities Describe the difference between a discontinuity that is removable and one that is nonremovable. In your explanation, give examples of the following descriptions.

(a) A function with a nonremovable discontinuity at $x = 4$

(b) A function with a removable discontinuity at $x = -4$

(c) A function that has both of the characteristics described in parts (a) and (b)

True or False? In Exercises 107–110, determine whether the statement is true or false. If it is false, explain why or give an example that shows it is false.

107. If $\lim\limits_{x \to c} f(x) = L$ and $f(c) = L$, then f is continuous at c.

108. If $f(x) = g(x)$ for $x \neq c$ and $f(c) \neq g(c)$, then either f or g is not continuous at c.

109. A rational function can have infinitely many x-values at which it is not continuous.

110. The function

$$f(x) = \frac{|x - 1|}{x - 1}$$

is continuous on $(-\infty, \infty)$.

111. Think About It Describe how the functions

$$f(x) = 3 + [\![x]\!] \quad \text{and} \quad g(x) = 3 - [\![-x]\!]$$

differ.

112. HOW DO YOU SEE IT? Every day you dissolve 28 ounces of chlorine in a swimming pool. The graph shows the amount of chlorine $f(t)$ in the pool after t days. Estimate and interpret $\lim\limits_{t \to 4^-} f(t)$ and $\lim\limits_{t \to 4^+} f(t)$.

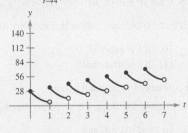

113. Telephone Charges A long distance phone service charges $0.40 for the first 10 minutes and $0.05 for each additional minute or fraction thereof. Use the greatest integer function to write the cost C of a call in terms of time t (in minutes). Sketch the graph of this function and discuss its continuity.

114. Inventory Management The number of units in inventory in a small company is given by

$$N(t) = 25\left(2\left[\!\!\left[\frac{t + 2}{2}\right]\!\!\right] - t\right)$$

where t is the time in months. Sketch the graph of this function and discuss its continuity. How often must this company replenish its inventory?

115. Déjà Vu At 8:00 A.M. on Saturday, a man begins running up the side of a mountain to his weekend campsite (see figure). On Sunday morning at 8:00 A.M., he runs back down the mountain. It takes him 20 minutes to run up, but only 10 minutes to run down. At some point on the way down, he realizes that he passed the same place at exactly the same time on Saturday. Prove that he is correct. [*Hint:* Let $s(t)$ and $r(t)$ be the position functions for the runs up and down, and apply the Intermediate Value Theorem to the function $f(t) = s(t) - r(t)$.]

Saturday 8:00 A.M.   Sunday 8:00 A.M.

Not drawn to scale

116. Volume Use the Intermediate Value Theorem to show that for all spheres with radii in the interval $[5, 8]$, there is one with a volume of 1500 cubic centimeters.

117. Proof Prove that if f is continuous and has no zeros on $[a, b]$, then either

$$f(x) > 0 \text{ for all } x \text{ in } [a, b] \quad \text{or} \quad f(x) < 0 \text{ for all } x \text{ in } [a, b].$$

118. Dirichlet Function Show that the Dirichlet function

$$f(x) = \begin{cases} 0, & \text{if } x \text{ is rational} \\ 1, & \text{if } x \text{ is irrational} \end{cases}$$

is not continuous at any real number.

119. Continuity of a Function Show that the function

$$f(x) = \begin{cases} 0, & \text{if } x \text{ is rational} \\ kx, & \text{if } x \text{ is irrational} \end{cases}$$

is continuous only at $x = 0$. (Assume that k is any nonzero real number.)

120. Signum Function The **signum function** is defined by

$$\text{sgn}(x) = \begin{cases} -1, & x < 0 \\ 0, & x = 0. \\ 1, & x > 0 \end{cases}$$

Sketch a graph of $\text{sgn}(x)$ and find the following (if possible).

(a) $\lim\limits_{x \to 0^-} \text{sgn}(x)$ (b) $\lim\limits_{x \to 0^+} \text{sgn}(x)$ (c) $\lim\limits_{x \to 0} \text{sgn}(x)$

121. Modeling Data The table lists the speeds S (in feet per second) of a falling object at various times t (in seconds).

t	0	5	10	15	20	25	30
S	0	48.2	53.5	55.2	55.9	56.2	56.3

(a) Create a line graph of the data.

(b) Does there appear to be a limiting speed of the object? If there is a limiting speed, identify a possible cause.

122. Creating Models A swimmer crosses a pool of width b by swimming in a straight line from $(0, 0)$ to $(2b, b)$. (See figure.)

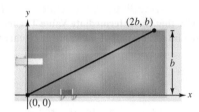

(a) Let f be a function defined as the y-coordinate of the point on the long side of the pool that is nearest the swimmer at any given time during the swimmer's crossing of the pool. Determine the function f and sketch its graph. Is f continuous? Explain.

(b) Let g be the minimum distance between the swimmer and the long sides of the pool. Determine the function g and sketch its graph. Is g continuous? Explain.

123. Making a Function Continuous Find all values of c such that f is continuous on $(-\infty, \infty)$.

$$f(x) = \begin{cases} 1 - x^2, & x \le c \\ x, & x > c \end{cases}$$

124. Proof Prove that for any real number y there exists x in $(-\pi/2, \pi/2)$ such that $\tan x = y$.

125. Making a Function Continuous Let

$$f(x) = \frac{\sqrt{x + c^2} - c}{x}, \quad c > 0.$$

What is the domain of f? How can you define f at $x = 0$ in order for f to be continuous there?

126. Proof Prove that if

$$\lim_{\Delta x \to 0} f(c + \Delta x) = f(c)$$

then f is continuous at c.

127. Continuity of a Function Discuss the continuity of the function $h(x) = x[\![x]\!]$.

128. Proof

(a) Let $f_1(x)$ and $f_2(x)$ be continuous on the closed interval $[a, b]$. If $f_1(a) < f_2(a)$ and $f_1(b) > f_2(b)$, prove that there exists c between a and b such that $f_1(c) = f_2(c)$.

(b) Show that there exists c in $[0, \pi/2]$ such that $\cos x = x$. Use a graphing utility to approximate c to three decimal places.

PUTNAM EXAM CHALLENGE

129. Prove or disprove: If x and y are real numbers with $y \ge 0$ and $y(y + 1) \le (x + 1)^2$, then $y(y - 1) \le x^2$.

130. Determine all polynomials $P(x)$ such that

$$P(x^2 + 1) = (P(x))^2 + 1 \quad \text{and} \quad P(0) = 0.$$

2.5   Infinite Limits

■ **Determine infinite limits from the left and from the right.**
■ **Find and sketch the vertical asymptotes of the graph of a function.**

Infinite Limits

Consider the function $f(x) = 3/(x - 2)$. From Figure 2.39 and the table, you can see that $f(x)$ *decreases without bound* as x approaches 2 from the left, and $f(x)$ *increases without bound* as x approaches 2 from the right.

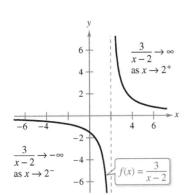

$f(x)$ increases and decreases without bound as x approaches 2.

Figure 2.39

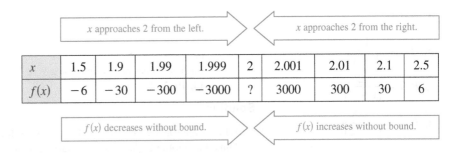

	x approaches 2 from the left.					x approaches 2 from the right.			
x	1.5	1.9	1.99	1.999	2	2.001	2.01	2.1	2.5
$f(x)$	-6	-30	-300	-3000	?	3000	300	30	6

| | $f(x)$ decreases without bound. | | | | $f(x)$ increases without bound. | | | |

This behavior is denoted as

$$\lim_{x \to 2^-} \frac{3}{x - 2} = -\infty \qquad f(x) \text{ decreases without bound as } x \text{ approaches 2 from the left.}$$

and

$$\lim_{x \to 2^+} \frac{3}{x - 2} = \infty. \qquad f(x) \text{ increases without bound as } x \text{ approaches 2 from the right.}$$

The symbols ∞ and $-\infty$ refer to positive infinity and negative infinity, respectively. These symbols do not represent real numbers. They are convenient symbols used to describe unbounded conditions more concisely. A limit in which $f(x)$ increases or decreases without bound as x approaches c is called an **infinite limit.**

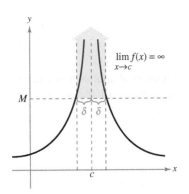

Infinite limits

Figure 2.40

Definition of Infinite Limits

Let f be a function that is defined at every real number in some open interval containing c (except possibly at c itself). The statement

$$\lim_{x \to c} f(x) = \infty$$

means that for each $M > 0$ there exists a $\delta > 0$ such that $f(x) > M$ whenever $0 < |x - c| < \delta$ (see Figure 2.40). Similarly, the statement

$$\lim_{x \to c} f(x) = -\infty$$

means that for each $N < 0$ there exists a $\delta > 0$ such that $f(x) < N$ whenever

$$0 < |x - c| < \delta.$$

To define the **infinite limit from the left,** replace $0 < |x - c| < \delta$ by $c - \delta < x < c$. To define the **infinite limit from the right,** replace $0 < |x - c| < \delta$ by $c < x < c + \delta$.

Be sure you see that the equal sign in the statement $\lim f(x) = \infty$ does not mean that the limit exists! On the contrary, it tells you how the limit **fails to exist** by denoting the unbounded behavior of $f(x)$ as x approaches c.

EXAMPLE 1   **Determining Infinite Limits from a Graph**

Determine the limit of each function shown in Figure 2.41 as x approaches 1 from the left and from the right.

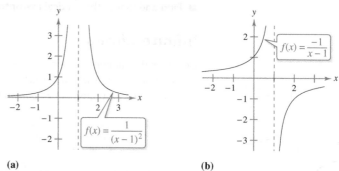

(a)   **(b)**

Each graph has an asymptote at $x = 1$.

Figure 2.41

Solution

a. When x approaches 1 from the left or the right, $(x - 1)^2$ is a small positive number. Thus, the quotient $1/(x - 1)^2$ is a large positive number, and $f(x)$ approaches infinity from each side of $x = 1$. So, you can conclude that

$$\lim_{x \to 1} \frac{1}{(x - 1)^2} = \infty. \qquad \text{Limit from each side is infinity.}$$

Figure 2.41(a) confirms this analysis.

b. When x approaches 1 from the left, $x - 1$ is a small negative number. Thus, the quotient $-1/(x - 1)$ is a large positive number, and $f(x)$ approaches infinity from the left of $x = 1$. So, you can conclude that

$$\lim_{x \to 1^-} \frac{-1}{x - 1} = \infty. \qquad \text{Limit from the left side is infinity.}$$

When x approaches 1 from the right, $x - 1$ is a small positive number. Thus, the quotient $-1/(x - 1)$ is a large negative number, and $f(x)$ approaches negative infinity from the right of $x = 1$. So, you can conclude that

$$\lim_{x \to 1^+} \frac{-1}{x - 1} = -\infty. \qquad \text{Limit from the right side is negative infinity.}$$

Figure 2.41(b) confirms this analysis.

▷ **TECHNOLOGY**   Remember that you can use a numerical approach to analyze a limit. For instance, you can use a graphing utility to create a table of values to analyze the limit in Example 1(a), as shown in Figure 2.42.

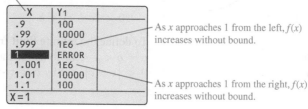

Figure 2.42

Use a graphing utility to make a table of values to analyze the limit in Example 1(b).

Vertical Asymptotes

If it were possible to extend the graphs in Figure 2.41 toward positive and negative infinity, you would see that each graph becomes arbitrarily close to the vertical line $x = 1$. This line is a **vertical asymptote** of the graph of f. (You will study other types of asymptotes in Sections 4.5 and 4.6.)

Definition of Vertical Asymptote

If $f(x)$ approaches infinity (or negative infinity) as x approaches c from the right or the left, then the line $x = c$ is a **vertical asymptote** of the graph of f.

In Example 1, note that each of the functions is a *quotient* and that the vertical asymptote occurs at a number at which the denominator is 0 (and the numerator is not 0). The next theorem generalizes this observation.

THEOREM 2.14 Vertical Asymptotes

Let f and g be continuous on an open interval containing c. If $f(c) \neq 0$, $g(c) = 0$, and there exists an open interval containing c such that $g(x) \neq 0$ for all $x \neq c$ in the interval, then the graph of the function

$$h(x) = \frac{f(x)}{g(x)}$$

has a vertical asymptote at $x = c$.

A proof of this theorem is given in Appendix A.
See LarsonCalculus.com for Bruce Edwards's video of this proof.

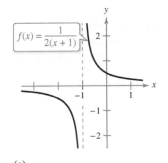

$f(x) = \dfrac{1}{2(x+1)}$

(a)

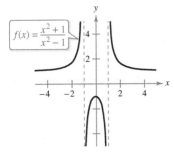

$f(x) = \dfrac{x^2+1}{x^2-1}$

(b)

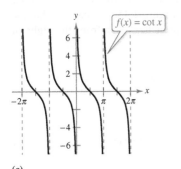

$f(x) = \cot x$

(c)

Functions with vertical asymptotes
Figure 2.43

EXAMPLE 2   Finding Vertical Asymptotes

• • • • ▷ *See LarsonCalculus.com for an interactive version of this type of example.*

a. When $x = -1$, the denominator of

$$f(x) = \frac{1}{2(x+1)}$$

is 0 and the numerator is not 0. So, by Theorem 2.14, you can conclude that $x = -1$ is a vertical asymptote, as shown in Figure 2.43(a).

b. By factoring the denominator as

$$f(x) = \frac{x^2+1}{x^2-1} = \frac{x^2+1}{(x-1)(x+1)}$$

you can see that the denominator is 0 at $x = -1$ and $x = 1$. Also, because the numerator is not 0 at these two points, you can apply Theorem 2.14 to conclude that the graph of f has two vertical asymptotes, as shown in Figure 2.43(b).

c. By writing the cotangent function in the form

$$f(x) = \cot x = \frac{\cos x}{\sin x}$$

you can apply Theorem 2.14 to conclude that vertical asymptotes occur at all values of x such that $\sin x = 0$ and $\cos x \neq 0$, as shown in Figure 2.43(c). So, the graph of this function has infinitely many vertical asymptotes. These asymptotes occur at $x = n\pi$, where n is an integer.

Theorem 2.14 requires that the value of the numerator at $x = c$ be nonzero. When both the numerator and the denominator are 0 at $x = c$, you obtain the *indeterminate form* 0/0, and you cannot determine the limit behavior at $x = c$ without further investigation, as illustrated in Example 3.

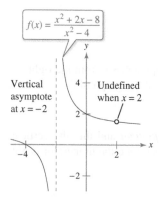

$f(x)$ increases and decreases without bound as x approaches -2.
Figure 2.44

EXAMPLE 3   **A Rational Function with Common Factors**

Determine all vertical asymptotes of the graph of

$$f(x) = \frac{x^2 + 2x - 8}{x^2 - 4}.$$

Solution   Begin by simplifying the expression, as shown.

$$f(x) = \frac{x^2 + 2x - 8}{x^2 - 4}$$

$$= \frac{(x + 4)(x - 2)}{(x + 2)(x - 2)}$$

$$= \frac{x + 4}{x + 2}, \quad x \neq 2$$

At all x-values other than $x = 2$, the graph of f coincides with the graph of $g(x) = (x + 4)/(x + 2)$. So, you can apply Theorem 2.14 to g to conclude that there is a vertical asymptote at $x = -2$, as shown in Figure 2.44. From the graph, you can see that

$$\lim_{x \to -2^-} \frac{x^2 + 2x - 8}{x^2 - 4} = -\infty \quad \text{and} \quad \lim_{x \to -2^+} \frac{x^2 + 2x - 8}{x^2 - 4} = \infty.$$

Note that $x = 2$ is *not* a vertical asymptote.

EXAMPLE 4   **Determining Infinite Limits**

Find each limit.

$$\lim_{x \to 1^-} \frac{x^2 - 3x}{x - 1} \quad \text{and} \quad \lim_{x \to 1^+} \frac{x^2 - 3x}{x - 1}$$

Solution   Because the denominator is 0 when $x = 1$ (and the numerator is not zero), you know that the graph of

$$f(x) = \frac{x^2 - 3x}{x - 1}$$

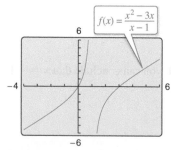

f has a vertical asymptote at $x = 1$.
Figure 2.45

has a vertical asymptote at $x = 1$. This means that each of the given limits is either ∞ or $-\infty$. You can determine the result by analyzing f at values of x close to 1, or by using a graphing utility. From the graph of f shown in Figure 2.45, you can see that the graph approaches ∞ from the left of $x = 1$ and approaches $-\infty$ from the right of $x = 1$. So, you can conclude that

$$\lim_{x \to 1^-} \frac{x^2 - 3x}{x - 1} = \infty \qquad \text{The limit from the left is infinity.}$$

and

$$\lim_{x \to 1^+} \frac{x^2 - 3x}{x - 1} = -\infty. \qquad \text{The limit from the right is negative infinity.}$$

▷ **TECHNOLOGY PITFALL**   When using a graphing utility, be careful to interpret correctly the graph of a function with a vertical asymptote—some graphing utilities have difficulty drawing this type of graph.

> **THEOREM 2.15 Properties of Infinite Limits**
>
> Let c and L be real numbers, and let f and g be functions such that
>
> $$\lim_{x \to c} f(x) = \infty \quad \text{and} \quad \lim_{x \to c} g(x) = L.$$
>
> 1. Sum or difference: $\displaystyle\lim_{x \to c} \left[f(x) \pm g(x) \right] = \infty$
>
> 2. Product:
> $$\lim_{x \to c} \left[f(x)g(x) \right] = \infty, \quad L > 0$$
> $$\lim_{x \to c} \left[f(x)g(x) \right] = -\infty, \quad L < 0$$
>
> 3. Quotient: $\displaystyle\lim_{x \to c} \frac{g(x)}{f(x)} = 0$
>
> Similar properties hold for one-sided limits and for functions for which the limit of $f(x)$ as x approaches c is $-\infty$ [see Example 5(d)].

Proof Here is a proof of the sum property. (The proofs of the remaining properties are left as an exercise [see Exercise 76].) To show that the limit of $f(x) + g(x)$ is infinite, choose $M > 0$. You then need to find $\delta > 0$ such that $[f(x) + g(x)] > M$ whenever $0 < |x - c| < \delta$. For simplicity's sake, you can assume L is positive. Let $M_1 = M + 1$. Because the limit of $f(x)$ is infinite, there exists δ_1 such that $f(x) > M_1$ whenever $0 < |x - c| < \delta_1$. Also, because the limit of $g(x)$ is L, there exists δ_2 such that $|g(x) - L| < 1$ whenever $0 < |x - c| < \delta_2$. By letting δ be the smaller of δ_1 and δ_2, you can conclude that $0 < |x - c| < \delta$ implies $f(x) > M + 1$ and $|g(x) - L| < 1$. The second of these two inequalities implies that $g(x) > L - 1$, and, adding this to the first inequality, you can write

$$f(x) + g(x) > (M + 1) + (L - 1) = M + L > M.$$

So, you can conclude that

$$\lim_{x \to c} \left[f(x) + g(x) \right] = \infty.$$

See LarsonCalculus.com for Bruce Edwards's video of this proof.

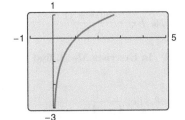

With a graphing utility, you can confirm that the natural logarithmic function has a vertical asymptote at $x = 0$. This implies that $\displaystyle\lim_{x \to 0^+} \ln x = -\infty$.

Figure 2.46

•• REMARK Note that the solution to Example 5(d) uses Property 1 from Theorem 2.15 for which the limit of $f(x)$ as x approaches c is $-\infty$.

EXAMPLE 5 **Determining Limits**

a. Because $\displaystyle\lim_{x \to 0} 1 = 1$ and $\displaystyle\lim_{x \to 0} \frac{1}{x^2} = \infty$, you can write

$$\lim_{x \to 0} \left(1 + \frac{1}{x^2} \right) = \infty. \qquad \text{Property 1, Theorem 2.15}$$

b. Because $\displaystyle\lim_{x \to 1^-} (x^2 + 1) = 2$ and $\displaystyle\lim_{x \to 1^-} (\cot \pi x) = -\infty$, you can write

$$\lim_{x \to 1^-} \frac{x^2 + 1}{\cot \pi x} = 0. \qquad \text{Property 3, Theorem 2.15}$$

c. Because $\displaystyle\lim_{x \to 0^+} 3 = 3$ and $\displaystyle\lim_{x \to 0^+} \ln x = -\infty$, you can write

$$\lim_{x \to 0^+} 3 \ln x = -\infty. \qquad \text{Property 2, Theorem 2.15 (See Figure 2.46.)}$$

d. Because $\displaystyle\lim_{x \to 0^-} x^2 = 0$ and $\displaystyle\lim_{x \to 0^-} \frac{1}{x} = -\infty$, you can write

$$\lim_{x \to 0^-} \left(x^2 + \frac{1}{x} \right) = -\infty. \qquad \text{Property 1, Theorem 2.15}$$

2.5 Exercises

See CalcChat.com for tutorial help and worked-out solutions to odd-numbered exercises.

Determining Infinite Limits from a Graph In Exercises 1–4, determine whether $f(x)$ approaches ∞ or $-\infty$ as x approaches -2 from the left and from the right.

1. $f(x) = 2\left|\dfrac{x}{x^2 - 4}\right|$

2. $f(x) = \dfrac{1}{x + 2}$

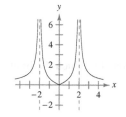

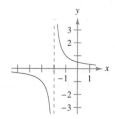

3. $f(x) = \tan\dfrac{\pi x}{4}$

4. $f(x) = \sec\dfrac{\pi x}{4}$

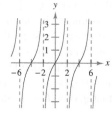

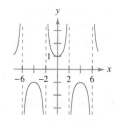

Determining Infinite Limits In Exercises 5–8, determine whether $f(x)$ approaches ∞ or $-\infty$ as x approaches 4 from the left and from the right.

5. $f(x) = \dfrac{1}{x - 4}$

6. $f(x) = \dfrac{-1}{x - 4}$

7. $f(x) = \dfrac{1}{(x - 4)^2}$

8. $f(x) = \dfrac{-1}{(x - 4)^2}$

Numerical and Graphical Analysis In Exercises 9–12, determine whether $f(x)$ approaches ∞ or $-\infty$ as x approaches -3 from the left and from the right by completing the table. Use a graphing utility to graph the function to confirm your answer.

x	-3.5	-3.1	-3.01	-3.001	-3
$f(x)$					?

x	-2.999	-2.99	-2.9	-2.5
$f(x)$				

9. $f(x) = \dfrac{1}{x^2 - 9}$

10. $f(x) = \dfrac{x}{x^2 - 9}$

11. $f(x) = \dfrac{x^2}{x^2 - 9}$

12. $f(x) = \cot\dfrac{\pi x}{3}$

Finding Vertical Asymptotes In Exercises 13–32, find the vertical asymptotes (if any) of the graph of the function.

13. $f(x) = \dfrac{1}{x^2}$

14. $f(x) = \dfrac{2}{(x - 3)^3}$

15. $f(x) = \dfrac{x^2}{x^2 - 4}$

16. $f(x) = \dfrac{3x}{x^2 + 9}$

17. $g(t) = \dfrac{t - 1}{t^2 + 1}$

18. $h(s) = \dfrac{3s + 4}{s^2 - 16}$

19. $f(x) = \dfrac{3}{x^2 + x - 2}$

20. $g(x) = \dfrac{x^3 - 8}{x - 2}$

21. $f(x) = \dfrac{x^2 - 2x - 15}{x^3 - 5x^2 + x - 5}$

22. $h(x) = \dfrac{x^2 - 9}{x^3 + 3x^2 - x - 3}$

23. $f(x) = \dfrac{e^{-2x}}{x - 1}$

24. $g(x) = xe^{-2x}$

25. $h(t) = \dfrac{\ln(t^2 + 1)}{t + 2}$

26. $f(z) = \ln(z^2 - 4)$

27. $f(x) = \dfrac{1}{e^x - 1}$

28. $f(x) = \ln(x + 3)$

29. $f(x) = \csc \pi x$

30. $f(x) = \tan \pi x$

31. $s(t) = \dfrac{t}{\sin t}$

32. $g(\theta) = \dfrac{\tan \theta}{\theta}$

Vertical Asymptote or Removable Discontinuity In Exercises 33–36, determine whether the graph of the function has a vertical asymptote or a removable discontinuity at $x = -1$. Graph the function using a graphing utility to confirm your answer.

33. $f(x) = \dfrac{x^2 - 1}{x + 1}$

34. $f(x) = \dfrac{x^2 - 2x - 8}{x + 1}$

35. $f(x) = \dfrac{x^2 + 1}{x + 1}$

36. $f(x) = \dfrac{\ln(x^2 + 1)}{x + 1}$

Finding a One-Sided Limit In Exercises 37–54, find the one-sided limit (if it exists).

37. $\displaystyle\lim_{x \to -1^+} \dfrac{1}{x + 1}$

38. $\displaystyle\lim_{x \to 1^-} \dfrac{-1}{(x - 1)^2}$

39. $\displaystyle\lim_{x \to 2^+} \dfrac{x}{x - 2}$

40. $\displaystyle\lim_{x \to 2^-} \dfrac{x^2}{x^2 + 4}$

41. $\displaystyle\lim_{x \to -3^-} \dfrac{x + 3}{x^2 + x - 6}$

42. $\displaystyle\lim_{x \to (-1/2)^+} \dfrac{6x^2 + x - 1}{4x^2 - 4x - 3}$

43. $\displaystyle\lim_{x \to 0^-} \left(1 + \dfrac{1}{x}\right)$

44. $\displaystyle\lim_{x \to 0^+} \left(6 - \dfrac{1}{x^3}\right)$

45. $\displaystyle\lim_{x \to -4^-} \left(x^2 + \dfrac{2}{x + 4}\right)$

46. $\displaystyle\lim_{x \to 3^+} \left(\dfrac{x}{3} + \cot\dfrac{\pi x}{2}\right)$

47. $\displaystyle\lim_{x \to 0^+} \dfrac{2}{\sin x}$

48. $\displaystyle\lim_{x \to (\pi/2)^+} \dfrac{-2}{\cos x}$

49. $\displaystyle\lim_{x \to 8^-} \dfrac{e^x}{(x - 8)^3}$

50. $\displaystyle\lim_{x \to 4^+} \ln(x^2 - 16)$

51. $\displaystyle\lim_{x \to (\pi/2)^-} \ln|\cos x|$

52. $\displaystyle\lim_{x \to 0^+} e^{-0.5x} \sin x$

53. $\lim\limits_{x\to(1/2)^-} x \sec \pi x$ **54.** $\lim\limits_{x\to(1/2)^+} x^2 \tan \pi x$

One-Sided Limit In Exercises 55–58, use a graphing utility to graph the function and determine the one-sided limit.

55. $f(x) = \dfrac{x^2 + x + 1}{x^3 - 1}$ **56.** $f(x) = \dfrac{x^3 - 1}{x^2 + x + 1}$

$\lim\limits_{x\to1^+} f(x)$ $\lim\limits_{x\to1^-} f(x)$

57. $f(x) = \dfrac{1}{x^2 - 25}$ **58.** $f(x) = \sec \dfrac{\pi x}{8}$

$\lim\limits_{x\to5^-} f(x)$ $\lim\limits_{x\to4^+} f(x)$

WRITING ABOUT CONCEPTS

59. Infinite Limit In your own words, describe the meaning of an infinite limit. Is ∞ a real number?

60. Asymptote In your own words, describe what is meant by an asymptote of a graph.

61. Writing a Rational Function Write a rational function with vertical asymptotes at $x = 6$ and $x = -2$, and with a zero at $x = 3$.

62. Rational Function Does the graph of every rational function have a vertical asymptote? Explain.

63. Sketching a Graph Use the graph of the function f (see figure) to sketch the graph of $g(x) = 1/f(x)$ on the interval $[-2, 3]$. To print an enlarged copy of the graph, go to *MathGraphs.com*.

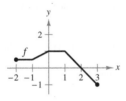

64. Relativity According to the theory of relativity, the mass m of a particle depends on its velocity v. That is,

$$m = \frac{m_0}{\sqrt{1 - (v^2/c^2)}}$$

where m_0 is the mass when the particle is at rest and c is the speed of light. Find the limit of the mass as v approaches c from the left.

65. Numerical and Graphical Analysis Use a graphing utility to complete the table for each function and graph each function to estimate the limit. What is the value of the limit when the power of x in the denominator is greater than 3?

x	1	0.5	0.2	0.1	0.01	0.001	0.0001
$f(x)$							

(a) $\lim\limits_{x\to0^+} \dfrac{x - \sin x}{x}$ (b) $\lim\limits_{x\to0^+} \dfrac{x - \sin x}{x^2}$

(c) $\lim\limits_{x\to0^+} \dfrac{x - \sin x}{x^3}$ (d) $\lim\limits_{x\to0^+} \dfrac{x - \sin x}{x^4}$

WendellandCarolyn/iStockphoto.com

 66. HOW DO YOU SEE IT? For a quantity of gas at a constant temperature, the pressure P is inversely proportional to the volume V. What is the limit of P as V approaches 0 from the right? Explain what this means in the context of the problem.

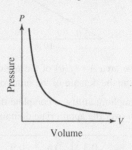

67. Rate of Change A 25-foot ladder is leaning against a house (see figure). If the base of the ladder is pulled away from the house at a rate of 2 feet per second, then the top will move down the wall at a rate of

$$r = \frac{2x}{\sqrt{625 - x^2}} \text{ ft/sec}$$

where x is the distance between the base of the ladder and the house, and r is the rate in feet per second.

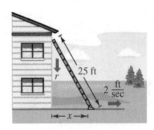

(a) Find the rate r when x is 7 feet.

(b) Find the rate r when x is 15 feet.

(c) Find the limit of r as x approaches 25 from the left.

68. Average Speed

On a trip of d miles to another city, a truck driver's average speed was x miles per hour. On the return trip, the average speed was y miles per hour. The average speed for the round trip was 50 miles per hour.

(a) Verify that

$$y = \frac{25x}{x - 25}.$$

What is the domain?

(b) Complete the table.

x	30	40	50	60
y				

Are the values of y different than you expected? Explain.

(c) Find the limit of y as x approaches 25 from the right and interpret its meaning.

69. Numerical and Graphical Analysis Consider the shaded region outside the sector of a circle of radius 10 meters and inside a right triangle (see figure).

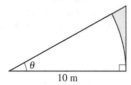

10 m

(a) Write the area $A = f(\theta)$ of the region as a function of θ. Determine the domain of the function.

(b) Use a graphing utility to complete the table and graph the function over the appropriate domain.

θ	0.3	0.6	0.9	1.2	1.5
$f(\theta)$					

(c) Find the limit of A as θ approaches $\pi/2$ from the left.

70. Numerical and Graphical Reasoning A crossed belt connects a 20-centimeter pulley (10-cm radius) on an electric motor with a 40-centimeter pulley (20-cm radius) on a saw arbor (see figure). The electric motor runs at 1700 revolutions per minute.

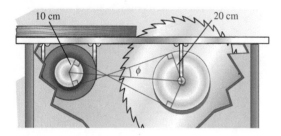

(a) Determine the number of revolutions per minute of the saw.

(b) How does crossing the belt affect the saw in relation to the motor?

(c) Let L be the total length of the belt. Write L as a function of ϕ, where ϕ is measured in radians. What is the domain of the function? (*Hint:* Add the lengths of the straight sections of the belt and the length of the belt around each pulley.)

(d) Use a graphing utility to complete the table.

ϕ	0.3	0.6	0.9	1.2	1.5
L					

(e) Use a graphing utility to graph the function over the appropriate domain.

(f) Find $\displaystyle\lim_{\phi \to (\pi/2)^-} L$. Use a geometric argument as the basis of a second method of finding this limit.

(g) Find $\displaystyle\lim_{\phi \to 0^+} L$.

True or False? In Exercises 71–74, determine whether the statement is true or false. If it is false, explain why or give an example that shows it is false.

71. The graph of a rational function has at least one vertical asymptote.

72. The graphs of polynomial functions have no vertical asymptotes.

73. The graphs of trigonometric functions have no vertical asymptotes.

74. If f has a vertical asymptote at $x = 0$, then f is undefined at $x = 0$.

75. Finding Functions Find functions f and g such that $\displaystyle\lim_{x \to c} f(x) = \infty$ and $\displaystyle\lim_{x \to c} g(x) = \infty$, but $\displaystyle\lim_{x \to c} [f(x) - g(x)] \neq 0$.

76. Proof Prove the difference, product, and quotient properties in Theorem 2.15.

77. Proof Prove that if $\displaystyle\lim_{x \to c} f(x) = \infty$, then $\displaystyle\lim_{x \to c} \frac{1}{f(x)} = 0$.

78. Proof Prove that if

$$\lim_{x \to c} \frac{1}{f(x)} = 0$$

then $\displaystyle\lim_{x \to c} f(x)$ does not exist.

Infinite Limits In Exercises 79 and 80, use the ε–δ definition of infinite limits to prove the statement.

79. $\displaystyle\lim_{x \to 3^+} \frac{1}{x - 3} = \infty$

80. $\displaystyle\lim_{x \to 5^-} \frac{1}{x - 5} = -\infty$

SECTION PROJECT

Graphs and Limits of Trigonometric Functions

Recall from Theorem 2.9 that the limit of $f(x) = (\sin x)/x$ as x approaches 0 is 1.

(a) Use a graphing utility to graph the function f on the interval $-\pi \le x \le \pi$. Explain how the graph helps confirm this theorem.

(b) Explain how you could use a table of values to confirm the value of this limit numerically.

(c) Graph $g(x) = \sin x$ by hand. Sketch a tangent line at the point $(0, 0)$ and visually estimate the slope of this tangent line.

(d) Let $(x, \sin x)$ be a point on the graph of g near $(0, 0)$, and write a formula for the slope of the secant line joining $(x, \sin x)$ and $(0, 0)$. Evaluate this formula at $x = 0.1$ and $x = 0.01$. Then find the exact slope of the tangent line to g at the point $(0, 0)$.

(e) Sketch the graph of the cosine function $h(x) = \cos x$. What is the slope of the tangent line at the point $(0, 1)$? Use limits to find this slope analytically.

(f) Find the slope of the tangent line to $k(x) = \tan x$ at $(0, 0)$.

Review Exercises

See CalcChat.com for tutorial help and worked-out solutions to odd-numbered exercises.

Precalculus or Calculus In Exercises 1 and 2, determine whether the problem can be solved using precalculus or whether calculus is required. If the problem can be solved using precalculus, solve it. If the problem seems to require calculus, explain your reasoning and use a graphical or numerical approach to estimate the solution.

1. Find the distance between the points $(1, 1)$ and $(3, 9)$ along the curve $y = x^2$.

2. Find the distance between the points $(1, 1)$ and $(3, 9)$ along the line $y = 4x - 3$.

Estimating a Limit Numerically In Exercises 3 and 4, complete the table and use the result to estimate the limit. Use a graphing utility to graph the function to confirm your result.

3. $\lim\limits_{x \to 3} \dfrac{x - 3}{x^2 - 7x + 12}$

x	2.9	2.99	2.999	3	3.001	3.01	3.1
$f(x)$				?			

4. $\lim\limits_{x \to 0} \dfrac{\sqrt{x + 4} - 2}{x}$

x	-0.1	-0.01	-0.001	0	0.001	0.01	0.1
$f(x)$				?			

Finding a Limit Graphically In Exercises 5 and 6, use the graph to find the limit (if it exists). If the limit does not exist, explain why.

5. $h(x) = \dfrac{4x - x^2}{x}$

6. $f(t) = \dfrac{\ln(t + 2)}{t}$

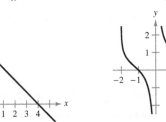

(a) $\lim\limits_{x \to 0} h(x)$ (b) $\lim\limits_{x \to -1} h(x)$ (a) $\lim\limits_{t \to 0} f(t)$ (b) $\lim\limits_{t \to -1} f(t)$

Using the ε–δ Definition of a Limit In Exercises 7–10, find the limit L. Then use the ε–δ definition to prove that the limit is L.

7. $\lim\limits_{x \to 1} (x + 4)$

8. $\lim\limits_{x \to 9} \sqrt{x}$

9. $\lim\limits_{x \to 2} (1 - x^2)$

10. $\lim\limits_{x \to 5} 9$

Finding a Limit In Exercises 11–28, find the limit.

11. $\lim\limits_{x \to -6} x^2$

12. $\lim\limits_{x \to 0} (5x - 3)$

13. $\lim\limits_{x \to 6} (x - 2)^2$

14. $\lim\limits_{x \to -5} \sqrt[3]{x - 3}$

15. $\lim\limits_{x \to 4} \dfrac{4}{x - 1}$

16. $\lim\limits_{x \to 2} \dfrac{x}{x^2 + 1}$

17. $\lim\limits_{x \to -2} \dfrac{t + 2}{t^2 - 4}$

18. $\lim\limits_{x \to 4} \dfrac{t^2 - 16}{t - 4}$

19. $\lim\limits_{x \to 4} \dfrac{\sqrt{x - 3} - 1}{x - 4}$

20. $\lim\limits_{x \to 0} \dfrac{\sqrt{4 + x} - 2}{x}$

21. $\lim\limits_{x \to 0} \dfrac{[1/(x + 1)] - 1}{x}$

22. $\lim\limits_{s \to 0} \dfrac{(1/\sqrt{1 + s}) - 1}{s}$

23. $\lim\limits_{x \to 0} \dfrac{1 - \cos x}{\sin x}$

24. $\lim\limits_{x \to \pi/4} \dfrac{4x}{\tan x}$

25. $\lim\limits_{x \to 1} e^{x - 1} \sin \dfrac{\pi x}{2}$

26. $\lim\limits_{x \to 2} \dfrac{\ln(x - 1)^2}{\ln(x - 1)}$

27. $\lim\limits_{\Delta x \to 0} \dfrac{\sin[(\pi/6) + \Delta x] - (1/2)}{\Delta x}$

[*Hint:* $\sin(\theta + \phi) = \sin \theta \cos \phi + \cos \theta \sin \phi$]

28. $\lim\limits_{\Delta x \to 0} \dfrac{\cos(\pi + \Delta x) + 1}{\Delta x}$

[*Hint:* $\cos(\theta + \phi) = \cos \theta \cos \phi - \sin \theta \sin \phi$]

Evaluating a Limit In Exercises 29–32, evaluate the limit given $\lim\limits_{x \to c} f(x) = -6$ and $\lim\limits_{x \to c} g(x) = \frac{1}{2}$.

29. $\lim\limits_{x \to c} [f(x)g(x)]$

30. $\lim\limits_{x \to c} \dfrac{f(x)}{g(x)}$

31. $\lim\limits_{x \to c} [f(x) + 2g(x)]$

32. $\lim\limits_{x \to c} [f(x)]^2$

Graphical, Numerical, and Analytic Analysis In Exercises 33–36, use a graphing utility to graph the function and estimate the limit. Use a table to reinforce your conclusion. Then find the limit by analytic methods.

33. $\lim\limits_{x \to 0} \dfrac{\sqrt{2x + 9} - 3}{x}$

34. $\lim\limits_{x \to 0} \dfrac{[1/(x + 4)] - (1/4)}{x}$

35. $\lim\limits_{x \to 0} \dfrac{20(e^{x/2} - 1)}{x - 1}$

36. $\lim\limits_{x \to 0} \dfrac{\ln(x + 1)}{x + 1}$

Free-Falling Object In Exercises 37 and 38, use the position function $s(t) = -4.9t^2 + 250$, which gives the height (in meters) of an object that has fallen for t seconds from a height of 250 meters. The velocity at time $t = a$ seconds is given by

$$\lim\limits_{t \to a} \dfrac{s(a) - s(t)}{a - t}.$$

37. Find the velocity of the object when $t = 4$.

38. At what velocity will the object impact the ground?

Finding a Limit In Exercises 39–48, find the limit (if it exists). If it does not exist, explain why.

39. $\lim\limits_{x \to 3^+} \dfrac{1}{x + 3}$

40. $\lim\limits_{x \to 6^-} \dfrac{x - 6}{x^2 - 36}$

41. $\lim\limits_{x \to 4^-} \dfrac{\sqrt{x} - 2}{x - 4}$

42. $\lim\limits_{x \to 3^-} \dfrac{|x - 3|}{x - 3}$

43. $\lim\limits_{x \to 2^-} (2[[x]] + 1)$ **44.** $\lim\limits_{x \to 4} [[x - 1]]$

45. $\lim\limits_{x \to 2} f(x)$, where $f(x) = \begin{cases} (x-2)^2, & x \le 2 \\ 2 - x, & x > 2 \end{cases}$

46. $\lim\limits_{x \to 1^+} g(x)$, where $g(x) = \begin{cases} \sqrt{1-x}, & x \le 1 \\ x + 1, & x > 1 \end{cases}$

47. $\lim\limits_{t \to 1} h(t)$, where $h(t) = \begin{cases} t^3 + 1, & t < 1 \\ \frac{1}{2}(t + 1), & t \ge 1 \end{cases}$

48. $\lim\limits_{s \to -2} f(s)$, where $f(s) = \begin{cases} -s^2 - 4s - 2, & s \le -2 \\ s^2 + 4s + 6, & s > -2 \end{cases}$

Removable and Nonremovable Discontinuities In Exercises 49–54, find the x-values (if any) at which f is not continuous. Which of the discontinuities are removable?

49. $f(x) = x^2 - 4$ **50.** $f(x) = x^2 - x + 20$

51. $f(x) = \dfrac{4}{x - 5}$ **52.** $f(x) = \dfrac{1}{x^2 - 9}$

53. $f(x) = \dfrac{x}{x^3 - x}$ **54.** $f(x) = \dfrac{x + 3}{x^2 - 3x - 18}$

55. Making a Function Continuous Determine the value of c such that the function is continuous on the entire real number line.

$$f(x) = \begin{cases} x + 3, & x \le 2 \\ cx + 6, & x > 2 \end{cases}$$

56. Making a Function Continuous Determine the values of b and c such that the function is continuous on the entire real number line.

$$f(x) = \begin{cases} x + 1, & 1 < x < 3 \\ x^2 + bx + c, & |x - 2| \ge 1 \end{cases}$$

Testing for Continuity In Exercises 57–64, describe the intervals on which the function is continuous.

57. $f(x) = -3x^2 + 7$ **58.** $f(x) = \dfrac{4x^2 + 7x - 2}{x + 2}$

59. $f(x) = \sqrt{x - 4}$ **60.** $f(x) = [[x + 3]]$

61. $g(x) = 2e^{[[x]]/4}$ **62.** $h(x) = -2\ln|5 - x|$

63. $f(x) = \begin{cases} \dfrac{3x^2 - x - 2}{x - 1}, & x \ne 1 \\ 0, & x = 1 \end{cases}$

64. $f(x) = \begin{cases} 5 - x, & x \le 2 \\ 2x - 3, & x > 2 \end{cases}$

65. Using the Intermediate Value Theorem Use the Intermediate Value Theorem to show that $f(x) = 2x^3 - 3$ has a zero in the interval $[1, 2]$.

66. Compound Interest A sum of \$5000 is deposited in a savings plan that pays 12% interest compounded semiannually. The account balance after t years is given by $A = 5000(1.06)^{[[2t]]}$. Use a graphing utility to graph the function, and discuss its continuity.

67. Finding Limits Let

$$f(x) = \frac{x^2 - 4}{|x - 2|}.$$

Find each limit (if it exists).

(a) $\lim\limits_{x \to 2^-} f(x)$ (b) $\lim\limits_{x \to 2^+} f(x)$ (c) $\lim\limits_{x \to 2} f(x)$

68. Finding Limits For $f(x) = \sqrt{x(x - 1)}$, find (a) the domain of f, (b) $\lim\limits_{x \to 0^-} f(x)$, and (c) $\lim\limits_{x \to 1^+} f(x)$.

Finding Vertical Asymptotes In Exercises 69–76, find the vertical asymptotes (if any) of the graph of the function.

69. $f(x) = \dfrac{3}{x}$ **70.** $f(x) = \dfrac{5}{(x - 2)^4}$

71. $f(x) = \dfrac{x^3}{x^2 - 9}$ **72.** $h(x) = \dfrac{6x}{36 - x^2}$

73. $g(x) = \dfrac{2x + 1}{x^2 - 64}$ **74.** $f(x) = \csc \pi x$

75. $g(x) = \ln(25 - x^2)$ **76.** $f(x) = 7e^{-3/x}$

Finding a One-Sided Limit In Exercises 77–88, find the one-sided limit (if it exists).

77. $\lim\limits_{x \to 1^-} \dfrac{x^2 + 2x + 1}{x - 1}$ **78.** $\lim\limits_{x \to (1/2)^+} \dfrac{x}{2x - 1}$

79. $\lim\limits_{x \to -1^+} \dfrac{x + 1}{x^3 + 1}$ **80.** $\lim\limits_{x \to -1^-} \dfrac{x + 1}{x^4 - 1}$

81. $\lim\limits_{x \to 0^+} \left(x - \dfrac{1}{x^3} \right)$ **82.** $\lim\limits_{x \to 2^-} \dfrac{1}{\sqrt[3]{x^2 - 4}}$

83. $\lim\limits_{x \to 0^+} \dfrac{\sin 4x}{5x}$ **84.** $\lim\limits_{x \to 0^+} \dfrac{\sec x}{x}$

85. $\lim\limits_{x \to 0^+} \dfrac{\csc 2x}{x}$ **86.** $\lim\limits_{x \to 0^-} \dfrac{\cos^2 x}{x}$

87. $\lim\limits_{x \to 0^+} \ln(\sin x)$ **88.** $\lim\limits_{x \to 0^-} 12e^{-2/x}$

89. Environment A utility company burns coal to generate electricity. The cost C in dollars of removing $p\%$ of the air pollutants in the stack emissions is

$$C = \frac{80,000p}{100 - p}, \quad 0 \le p < 100.$$

(a) Find the cost of removing 15% of the pollutants.

(b) Find the cost of removing 50% of the pollutants.

(c) Find the cost of removing 90% of the pollutants.

(d) Find the limit of C as p approaches 100 from the left and interpret its meaning.

90. Limits and Continuity The function f is defined as

$$f(x) = \frac{\tan 2x}{x}, \quad x \ne 0.$$

(a) Find $\lim\limits_{x \to 0} \dfrac{\tan 2x}{x}$ (if it exists).

(b) Can the function f be defined at $x = 0$ such that it is continuous at $x = 0$?

P.S. Problem Solving

See **CalcChat.com** for tutorial help and worked-out solutions to odd-numbered exercises.

1. Perimeter Let $P(x, y)$ be a point on the parabola $y = x^2$ in the first quadrant. Consider the triangle $\triangle PAO$ formed by P, $A(0, 1)$, and the origin $O(0, 0)$, and the triangle $\triangle PBO$ formed by P, $B(1, 0)$, and the origin.

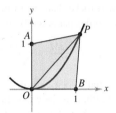

(a) Write the perimeter of each triangle in terms of x.

(b) Let $r(x)$ be the ratio of the perimeters of the two triangles,

$$r(x) = \frac{\text{Perimeter } \triangle PAO}{\text{Perimeter } \triangle PBO}.$$

Complete the table. Calculate $\lim\limits_{x \to 0^+} r(x)$.

x	4	2	1	0.1	0.01
Perimeter $\triangle PAO$					
Perimeter $\triangle PBO$					
$r(x)$					

2. Area Let $P(x, y)$ be a point on the parabola $y = x^2$ in the first quadrant. Consider the triangle $\triangle PAO$ formed by P, $A(0, 1)$, and the origin $O(0, 0)$, and the triangle $\triangle PBO$ formed by P, $B(1, 0)$, and the origin.

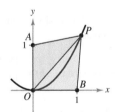

(a) Write the area of each triangle in terms of x.

(b) Let $a(x)$ be the ratio of the areas of the two triangles,

$$a(x) = \frac{\text{Area } \triangle PBO}{\text{Area } \triangle PAO}.$$

Complete the table. Calculate $\lim\limits_{x \to 0^+} a(x)$.

x	4	2	1	0.1	0.01
Area $\triangle PAO$					
Area $\triangle PBO$					
$a(x)$					

3. Area of a Circle

(a) Find the area of a regular hexagon inscribed in a circle of radius 1. How close is this area to that of the circle?

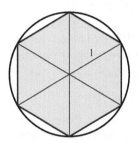

(b) Find the area A_n of an n-sided regular polygon inscribed in a circle of radius 1. Write your answer as a function of n.

(c) Complete the table. What number does A_n approach as n gets larger and larger?

n	6	12	24	48	96
A_n					

4. Tangent Line Let $P(3, 4)$ be a point on the circle $x^2 + y^2 = 25$.

(a) What is the slope of the line joining P and $O(0, 0)$?

(b) Find an equation of the tangent line to the circle at P.

(c) Let $Q(x, y)$ be another point on the circle in the first quadrant. Find the slope m_x of the line joining P and Q in terms of x.

(d) Calculate $\lim\limits_{x \to 3} m_x$. How does this number relate to your answer in part (b)?

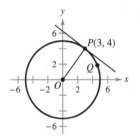

Figure for 4

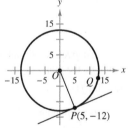

Figure for 5

5. Tangent Line Let $P(5, -12)$ be a point on the circle $x^2 + y^2 = 169$.

(a) What is the slope of the line joining P and $O(0, 0)$?

(b) Find an equation of the tangent line to the circle at P.

(c) Let $Q(x, y)$ be another point on the circle in the fourth quadrant. Find the slope m_x of the line joining P and Q in terms of x.

(d) Calculate $\lim\limits_{x \to 5} m_x$. How does this number relate to your answer in part (b)?

6. Finding Values Find the values of the constants a and b such that

$$\lim_{x \to 0} \frac{\sqrt{a + bx} - \sqrt{3}}{x} = \sqrt{3}.$$

7. Finding Limits Consider the function

$$f(x) = \frac{\sqrt{3 + x^{1/3}} - 2}{x - 1}.$$

(a) Find the domain of f.

(b) Use a graphing utility to graph the function.

(c) Calculate $\lim\limits_{x \to -27^+} f(x)$.

(d) Calculate $\lim\limits_{x \to 1} f(x)$.

8. Making a Function Continuous Determine all values of the constant a such that the following function is continuous for all real numbers.

$$f(x) = \begin{cases} \dfrac{ax}{\tan x}, & x \geq 0 \\ a^2 - 2, & x < 0 \end{cases}$$

9. Choosing Graphs Consider the graphs of the four functions g_1, g_2, g_3, and g_4.

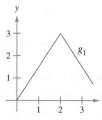
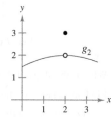
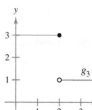
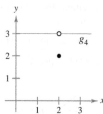

For each given condition of the function f, which of the graphs could be the graph of f?

(a) $\lim\limits_{x \to 2} f(x) = 3$

(b) f is continuous at 2.

(c) $\lim\limits_{x \to 2^-} f(x) = 3$

10. Limits and Continuity Sketch the graph of the function

$$f(x) = \left[\!\left[\frac{1}{x} \right]\!\right].$$

(a) Evaluate $f\left(\frac{1}{4}\right)$, $f(3)$, and $f(1)$.

(b) Evaluate the limits $\lim\limits_{x \to 1^-} f(x)$, $\lim\limits_{x \to 1^+} f(x)$, $\lim\limits_{x \to 0^-} f(x)$, and $\lim\limits_{x \to 0^+} f(x)$.

(c) Discuss the continuity of the function.

11. Limits and Continuity Sketch the graph of the function $f(x) = [\![x]\!] + [\![-x]\!]$.

(a) Evaluate $f(1)$, $f(0)$, $f\left(\frac{1}{2}\right)$, and $f(-2.7)$.

(b) Evaluate the limits $\lim\limits_{x \to 1^-} f(x)$, $\lim\limits_{x \to 1^+} f(x)$, and $\lim\limits_{x \to 1/2} f(x)$.

(c) Discuss the continuity of the function.

12. Escape Velocity To escape Earth's gravitational field, a rocket must be launched with an initial velocity called the **escape velocity.** A rocket launched from the surface of Earth has velocity v (in miles per second) given by

$$v = \sqrt{\frac{2GM}{r} + v_0^2 - \frac{2GM}{R}} \approx \sqrt{\frac{192{,}000}{r} + v_0^2 - 48}$$

where v_0 is the initial velocity, r is the distance from the rocket to the center of Earth, G is the gravitational constant, M is the mass of Earth, and R is the radius of Earth (approximately 4000 miles).

(a) Find the value of v_0 for which you obtain an infinite limit for r as v approaches zero. This value of v_0 is the escape velocity for Earth.

(b) A rocket launched from the surface of the moon has velocity v (in miles per second) given by

$$v = \sqrt{\frac{1920}{r} + v_0^2 - 2.17}.$$

Find the escape velocity for the moon.

(c) A rocket launched from the surface of a planet has velocity v (in miles per second) given by

$$v = \sqrt{\frac{10{,}600}{r} + v_0^2 - 6.99}.$$

Find the escape velocity for this planet. Is the mass of this planet larger or smaller than that of Earth? (Assume that the mean density of this planet is the same as that of Earth.)

13. Pulse Function For positive numbers $a < b$, the **pulse function** is defined as

$$P_{a,b}(x) = H(x - a) - H(x - b) = \begin{cases} 0, & x < a \\ 1, & a \leq x < b \\ 0, & x \geq b \end{cases}$$

where $H(x) = \begin{cases} 1, & x \geq 0 \\ 0, & x < 0 \end{cases}$ is the Heaviside function.

(a) Sketch the graph of the pulse function.

(b) Find the following limits:

(i) $\lim\limits_{x \to a^+} P_{a,b}(x)$ (ii) $\lim\limits_{x \to a^-} P_{a,b}(x)$

(iii) $\lim\limits_{x \to b^+} P_{a,b}(x)$ (iv) $\lim\limits_{x \to b^-} P_{a,b}(x)$

(c) Discuss the continuity of the pulse function.

(d) Why is $U(x) = \dfrac{1}{b - a} P_{a,b}(x)$ called the **unit pulse function?**

14. Proof Let a be a nonzero constant. Prove that if $\lim\limits_{x \to 0} f(x) = L$, then $\lim\limits_{x \to 0} f(ax) = L$. Show by means of an example that a must be nonzero.

3 Differentiation

3.1 The Derivative and the Tangent Line Problem

3.2 Basic Differentiation Rules and Rates of Change

3.3 Product and Quotient Rules and Higher-Order Derivatives

3.4 The Chain Rule

3.5 Implicit Differentiation

3.6 Derivatives of Inverse Functions

3.7 Related Rates

3.8 Newton's Method

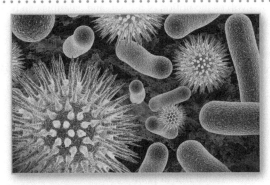

Bacteria *(Exercise 175, p. 164)*

Rate of Change
(Example 2, p. 182)

Acceleration Due to Gravity *(Example 10, p. 145)*

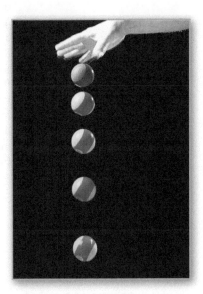

Velocity of a Falling Object
(Example 10, p. 133)

Stopping Distance *(Exercise 109, p.138)*

3.1 The Derivative and the Tangent Line Problem

■ Find the slope of the tangent line to a curve at a point.
■ Use the limit definition to find the derivative of a function.
■ Understand the relationship between differentiability and continuity.

The Tangent Line Problem

Calculus grew out of four major problems that European mathematicians were working on during the seventeenth century.

1. The tangent line problem (Section 2.1 and this section)
2. The velocity and acceleration problem (Sections 3.2 and 3.3)
3. The minimum and maximum problem (Section 4.1)
4. The area problem (Sections 2.1 and 5.2)

Each problem involves the notion of a limit, and calculus can be introduced with any of the four problems.

A brief introduction to the tangent line problem is given in Section 2.1. Although partial solutions to this problem were given by Pierre de Fermat (1601–1665), René Descartes (1596–1650), Christian Huygens (1629–1695), and Isaac Barrow (1630–1677), credit for the first general solution is usually given to Isaac Newton (1642–1727) and Gottfried Leibniz (1646–1716). Newton's work on this problem stemmed from his interest in optics and light refraction.

What does it mean to say that a line is tangent to a curve at a point? For a circle, the tangent line at a point P is the line that is perpendicular to the radial line at point P, as shown in Figure 3.1.

For a general curve, however, the problem is more difficult. For instance, how would you define the tangent lines shown in Figure 3.2? You might say that a line is tangent to a curve at a point P when it touches, but does not cross, the curve at point P. This definition would work for the first curve shown in Figure 3.2, but not for the second. *Or* you might say that a line is tangent to a curve when the line touches or intersects the curve at exactly one point. This definition would work for a circle, but not for more general curves, as the third curve in Figure 3.2 shows.

ISAAC NEWTON (1642–1727)

In addition to his work in calculus, Newton made revolutionary contributions to physics, including the Law of Universal Gravitation and his three laws of motion. *See LarsonCalculus.com to read more of this biography.*

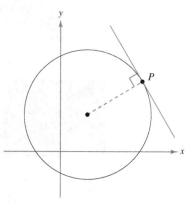

Tangent line to a circle
Figure 3.1

Mary Evans Picture Library/Alamy

Exploration

Use a graphing utility to graph $f(x) = 2x^3 - 4x^2 + 3x - 5$. On the same screen, graph $y = x - 5$, $y = 2x - 5$, and $y = 3x - 5$. Which of these lines, if any, appears to be tangent to the graph of f at the point $(0, -5)$? Explain your reasoning.

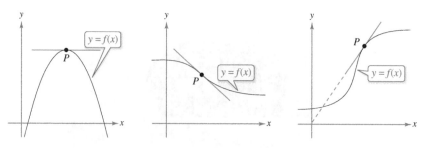

Tangent line to a curve at a point
Figure 3.2

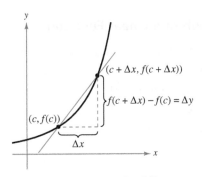

The secant line through $(c, f(c))$ and $(c + \Delta x, f(c + \Delta x))$
Figure 3.3

Essentially, the problem of finding the tangent line at a point P boils down to the problem of finding the *slope* of the tangent line at point P. You can approximate this slope using a **secant line*** through the point of tangency and a second point on the curve, as shown in Figure 3.3. If $(c, f(c))$ is the point of tangency and

$$(c + \Delta x, f(c + \Delta x))$$

is a second point on the graph of f, then the slope of the secant line through the two points is given by substitution into the slope formula

$$m = \frac{y_2 - y_1}{x_2 - x_1}$$

$$m_{\text{sec}} = \frac{f(c + \Delta x) - f(c)}{(c + \Delta x) - c} \qquad \text{Change in } y \atop \text{Change in } x$$

$$m_{\text{sec}} = \frac{f(c + \Delta x) - f(c)}{\Delta x}. \qquad \text{Slope of secant line}$$

The right-hand side of this equation is a **difference quotient.** The denominator Δx is the **change in x,** and the numerator

$$\Delta y = f(c + \Delta x) - f(c)$$

is the **change in y.**

The beauty of this procedure is that you can obtain more and more accurate approximations of the slope of the tangent line by choosing points closer and closer to the point of tangency, as shown in Figure 3.4.

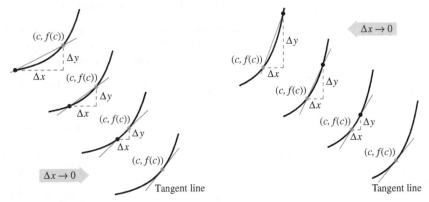

Tangent line approximations
Figure 3.4

Definition of Tangent Line with Slope m

If f is defined on an open interval containing c, and if the limit

$$\lim_{\Delta x \to 0} \frac{\Delta y}{\Delta x} = \lim_{\Delta x \to 0} \frac{f(c + \Delta x) - f(c)}{\Delta x} = m$$

exists, then the line passing through $(c, f(c))$ with slope m is the **tangent line** to the graph of f at the point $(c, f(c))$.

The slope of the tangent line to the graph of f at the point $(c, f(c))$ is also called the **slope of the graph of f at $x = c$.**

---

* This use of the word *secant* comes from the Latin *secare*, meaning to cut, and is not a reference to the trigonometric function of the same name.

EXAMPLE 1 **The Slope of the Graph of a Linear Function**

To find the slope of the graph of $f(x) = 2x - 3$ when $c = 2$, you can apply the definition of the slope of a tangent line, as shown.

$$\lim_{\Delta x \to 0} \frac{f(2 + \Delta x) - f(2)}{\Delta x} = \lim_{\Delta x \to 0} \frac{[2(2 + \Delta x) - 3] - [2(2) - 3]}{\Delta x}$$

$$= \lim_{\Delta x \to 0} \frac{4 + 2\Delta x - 3 - 4 + 3}{\Delta x}$$

$$= \lim_{\Delta x \to 0} \frac{2\Delta x}{\Delta x}$$

$$= \lim_{\Delta x \to 0} 2$$

$$= 2$$

The slope of f at $(c, f(c)) = (2, 1)$ is $m = 2$, as shown in Figure 3.5. Notice that the limit definition of the slope of f agrees with the definition of the slope of a line as discussed in Section 1.2.

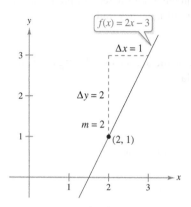

The slope of f at $(2, 1)$ is $m = 2$.
Figure 3.5

The graph of a linear function has the same slope at any point. This is not true of nonlinear functions, as shown in the next example.

EXAMPLE 2 **Tangent Lines to the Graph of a Nonlinear Function**

Find the slopes of the tangent lines to the graph of $f(x) = x^2 + 1$ at the points $(0, 1)$ and $(-1, 2)$, as shown in Figure 3.6.

Solution Let $(c, f(c))$ represent an arbitrary point on the graph of f. Then the slope of the tangent line at $(c, f(c))$ can be found as shown below. [Note in the limit process that c is held constant (as Δx approaches 0).]

$$\lim_{\Delta x \to 0} \frac{f(c + \Delta x) - f(c)}{\Delta x} = \lim_{\Delta x \to 0} \frac{[(c + \Delta x)^2 + 1] - (c^2 + 1)}{\Delta x}$$

$$= \lim_{\Delta x \to 0} \frac{c^2 + 2c(\Delta x) + (\Delta x)^2 + 1 - c^2 - 1}{\Delta x}$$

$$= \lim_{\Delta x \to 0} \frac{2c(\Delta x) + (\Delta x)^2}{\Delta x}$$

$$= \lim_{\Delta x \to 0} (2c + \Delta x)$$

$$= 2c$$

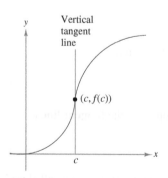

The slope of f at any point $(c, f(c))$ is $m = 2c$.
Figure 3.6

So, the slope at *any* point $(c, f(c))$ on the graph of f is $m = 2c$. At the point $(0, 1)$, the slope is $m = 2(0) = 0$, and at $(-1, 2)$, the slope is $m = 2(-1) = -2$.

The definition of a tangent line to a curve does not cover the possibility of a vertical tangent line. For vertical tangent lines, you can use the following definition. If f is continuous at c and

$$\lim_{\Delta x \to 0} \frac{f(c + \Delta x) - f(c)}{\Delta x} = \infty \quad \text{or} \quad \lim_{\Delta x \to 0} \frac{f(c + \Delta x) - f(c)}{\Delta x} = -\infty$$

then the vertical line $x = c$ passing through $(c, f(c))$ is a **vertical tangent line** to the graph of f. For example, the function shown in Figure 3.7 has a vertical tangent line at $(c, f(c))$. When the domain of f is the closed interval $[a, b]$, you can extend the definition of a vertical tangent line to include the endpoints by considering continuity and limits from the right (for $x = a$) and from the left (for $x = b$).

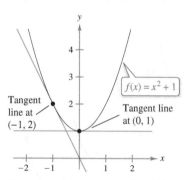

The graph of f has a vertical tangent line at $(c, f(c))$.
Figure 3.7

The Derivative of a Function

You have now arrived at a crucial point in the study of calculus. The limit used to define the slope of a tangent line is also used to define one of the two fundamental operations of calculus—**differentiation.**

> **Definition of the Derivative of a Function**
>
> The **derivative** of f at x is
>
> $$f'(x) = \lim_{\Delta x \to 0} \frac{f(x + \Delta x) - f(x)}{\Delta x}$$
>
> provided the limit exists. For all x for which this limit exists, f' is a function of x.

REMARK The notation $f'(x)$ is read as "f prime of x."

Be sure you see that the derivative of a function of x is also a function of x. This "new" function gives the slope of the tangent line to the graph of f at the point $(x, f(x))$, provided that the graph has a tangent line at this point. The derivative can also be used to determine the **instantaneous rate of change** (or simply the **rate of change**) of one variable with respect to another.

The process of finding the derivative of a function is called **differentiation.** A function is **differentiable** at x when its derivative exists at x and is **differentiable on an open interval** (a, b) when it is differentiable at every point in the interval.

In addition to $f'(x)$, other notations are used to denote the derivative of $y = f(x)$. The most common are

$$f'(x), \quad \frac{dy}{dx}, \quad y', \quad \frac{d}{dx}[f(x)], \quad D_x[y].$$

Notation for derivatives

FOR FURTHER INFORMATION For more information on the crediting of mathematical discoveries to the first "discoverers," see the article "Mathematical Firsts— Who Done It?" by Richard H. Williams and Roy D. Mazzagatti in *Mathematics Teacher.* To view this article, go to *MathArticles.com.*

The notation dy/dx is read as "the derivative of y *with respect to x*" or simply "dy, dx." Using limit notation, you can write

$$\frac{dy}{dx} = \lim_{\Delta x \to 0} \frac{\Delta y}{\Delta x} = \lim_{\Delta x \to 0} \frac{f(x + \Delta x) - f(x)}{\Delta x} = f'(x).$$

EXAMPLE 3 **Finding the Derivative by the Limit Process**

▷ *See LarsonCalculus.com for an interactive version of this type of example.*

To find the derivative of $f(x) = x^3 + 2x$, use the definition of the derivative as shown.

$$f'(x) = \lim_{\Delta x \to 0} \frac{f(x + \Delta x) - f(x)}{\Delta x}$$ Definition of derivative

$$= \lim_{\Delta x \to 0} \frac{(x + \Delta x)^3 + 2(x + \Delta x) - (x^3 + 2x)}{\Delta x}$$

$$= \lim_{\Delta x \to 0} \frac{x^3 + 3x^2 \Delta x + 3x(\Delta x)^2 + (\Delta x)^3 + 2x + 2\Delta x - x^3 - 2x}{\Delta x}$$

$$= \lim_{\Delta x \to 0} \frac{3x^2 \Delta x + 3x(\Delta x)^2 + (\Delta x)^3 + 2\Delta x}{\Delta x}$$

$$= \lim_{\Delta x \to 0} \frac{\Delta x[3x^2 + 3x \Delta x + (\Delta x)^2 + 2]}{\Delta x}$$

$$= \lim_{\Delta x \to 0} [3x^2 + 3x \Delta x + (\Delta x)^2 + 2]$$

$$= 3x^2 + 2$$

REMARK When using the definition to find a derivative of a function, the key is to rewrite the difference quotient so that Δx does not occur as a factor of the denominator.

EXAMPLE 4 **Using the Derivative to Find the Slope at a Point**

Find $f'(x)$ for $f(x) = \sqrt{x}$. Then find the slopes of the graph of f at the points $(1, 1)$ and $(4, 2)$. Discuss the behavior of f at $(0, 0)$.

Solution Use the procedure for rationalizing numerators, as discussed in Section 2.3.

$$
\begin{aligned}
f'(x) &= \lim_{\Delta x \to 0} \frac{f(x + \Delta x) - f(x)}{\Delta x} && \text{Definition of derivative} \\
&= \lim_{\Delta x \to 0} \frac{\sqrt{x + \Delta x} - \sqrt{x}}{\Delta x} \\
&= \lim_{\Delta x \to 0} \left(\frac{\sqrt{x + \Delta x} - \sqrt{x}}{\Delta x} \right)\left(\frac{\sqrt{x + \Delta x} + \sqrt{x}}{\sqrt{x + \Delta x} + \sqrt{x}} \right) \\
&= \lim_{\Delta x \to 0} \frac{(x + \Delta x) - x}{\Delta x(\sqrt{x + \Delta x} + \sqrt{x})} \\
&= \lim_{\Delta x \to 0} \frac{\Delta x}{\Delta x(\sqrt{x + \Delta x} + \sqrt{x})} \\
&= \lim_{\Delta x \to 0} \frac{1}{\sqrt{x + \Delta x} + \sqrt{x}} \\
&= \frac{1}{2\sqrt{x}}, \quad x > 0
\end{aligned}
$$

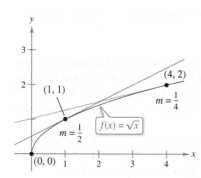

The slope of f at $(x, f(x))$, $x > 0$, is $m = 1/(2\sqrt{x})$.
Figure 3.8

At the point $(1, 1)$, the slope is $f'(1) = \frac{1}{2}$. At the point $(4, 2)$, the slope is $f'(4) = \frac{1}{4}$. See Figure 3.8. At the point $(0, 0)$, the slope is undefined. Moreover, the graph of f has a vertical tangent line at $(0, 0)$.

EXAMPLE 5 **Finding the Derivative of a Function**

••••▷ *See LarsonCalculus.com for an interactive version of this type of example.*

Find the derivative with respect to t for the function $y = 2/t$.

Solution Considering $y = f(t)$, you obtain

$$
\begin{aligned}
\frac{dy}{dt} &= \lim_{\Delta t \to 0} \frac{f(t + \Delta t) - f(t)}{\Delta t} && \text{Definition of derivative} \\
&= \lim_{\Delta t \to 0} \frac{\dfrac{2}{t + \Delta t} - \dfrac{2}{t}}{\Delta t} && f(t + \Delta t) = \frac{2}{t + \Delta t} \text{ and } f(t) = \frac{2}{t} \\
&= \lim_{\Delta t \to 0} \frac{\dfrac{2t - 2(t + \Delta t)}{t(t + \Delta t)}}{\Delta t} && \text{Combine fractions in numerator.} \\
&= \lim_{\Delta t \to 0} \frac{-2\Delta t}{\Delta t(t)(t + \Delta t)} && \text{Divide out common factor of } \Delta t. \\
&= \lim_{\Delta t \to 0} \frac{-2}{t(t + \Delta t)} && \text{Simplify.} \\
&= -\frac{2}{t^2}. && \text{Evaluate limit as } \Delta t \to 0.
\end{aligned}
$$

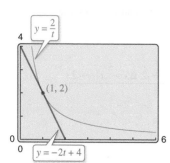

At the point $(1, 2)$, the line $y = -2t + 4$ is tangent to the graph of $y = 2/t$.
Figure 3.9

▷ **TECHNOLOGY** A graphing utility can be used to reinforce the result given in Example 5. For instance, using the formula $dy/dt = -2/t^2$, you know that the slope of the graph of $y = 2/t$ at the point $(1, 2)$ is $m = -2$. Using the point-slope form, you can find that the equation of the tangent line to the graph at $(1, 2)$ is

$$y - 2 = -2(t - 1) \quad \text{or} \quad y = -2t + 4$$

as shown in Figure 3.9.

Differentiability and Continuity

The alternative limit form of the derivative shown below is useful in investigating the relationship between differentiability and continuity. The derivative of f at c is

$$f'(c) = \lim_{x \to c} \frac{f(x) - f(c)}{x - c}$$ Alternative form of derivative

•••**REMARK** A proof of the equivalence of the alternative form of the derivative is given in Appendix A.

See LarsonCalculus.com for Bruce Edwards's video of this proof.

provided this limit exists (see Figure 3.10).

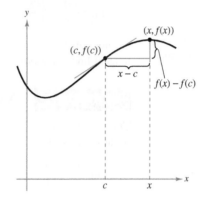

As x approaches c, the secant line approaches the tangent line.
Figure 3.10

Note that the existence of the limit in this alternative form requires that the one-sided limits

$$\lim_{x \to c^-} \frac{f(x) - f(c)}{x - c}$$

and

$$\lim_{x \to c^+} \frac{f(x) - f(c)}{x - c}$$

exist and are equal. These one-sided limits are called the **derivatives from the left and from the right,** respectively. It follows that f is **differentiable on the closed interval** $[a, b]$ when it is differentiable on (a, b) and when the derivative from the right at a and the derivative from the left at b both exist.

When a function is not continuous at $x = c$, it is also not differentiable at $x = c$. For instance, the greatest integer function

$$f(x) = [\![x]\!]$$

is not continuous at $x = 0$, and so it is not differentiable at $x = 0$ (see Figure 3.11 and Exercise 91). You can verify this by observing that

$$\lim_{x \to 0^-} \frac{f(x) - f(0)}{x - 0} = \lim_{x \to 0^-} \frac{[\![x]\!] - 0}{x} = \infty$$ Derivative from the left

and

$$\lim_{x \to 0^+} \frac{f(x) - f(0)}{x - 0} = \lim_{x \to 0^+} \frac{[\![x]\!] - 0}{x} = 0.$$ Derivative from the right

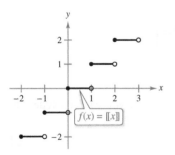

The greatest integer function is not differentiable at $x = 0$ because it is not continuous at $x = 0$.
Figure 3.11

Although it is true that differentiability implies continuity (as shown in Theorem 3.1 on the next page), the converse is not true. That is, it is possible for a function to be continuous at $x = c$ and *not* differentiable at $x = c$. Examples 6 and 7 illustrate this possibility.

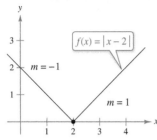

f is not differentiable at $x = 2$ because the derivatives from the left and from the right are not equal.
Figure 3.12

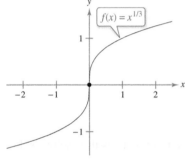

f is not differentiable at $x = 0$ because f has a vertical tangent line at $x = 0$.
Figure 3.13

▷ **TECHNOLOGY** Some graphing utilities, such as *Maple, Mathematica,* and the *TI-nspire,* perform symbolic differentiation. Others perform *numerical differentiation* by finding values of derivatives using the formula

$$f'(x) \approx \frac{f(x + \Delta x) - f(x - \Delta x)}{2\Delta x}$$

where Δx is a small number such as 0.001. Can you see any problems with this definition? For instance, using this definition, what is the value of the derivative of $f(x) = |x|$ when $x = 0$?

EXAMPLE 6 **A Graph with a Sharp Turn**

• • • ▷ *See LarsonCalculus.com for an interactive version of this type of example.*

The function $f(x) = |x - 2|$, shown in Figure 3.12, is continuous at $x = 2$. The one-sided limits, however,

$$\lim_{x \to 2^-} \frac{f(x) - f(2)}{x - 2} = \lim_{x \to 2^-} \frac{|x - 2| - 0}{x - 2} = -1 \qquad \text{Derivative from the left}$$

and

$$\lim_{x \to 2^+} \frac{f(x) - f(2)}{x - 2} = \lim_{x \to 2^+} \frac{|x - 2| - 0}{x - 2} = 1 \qquad \text{Derivative from the right}$$

are not equal. So, f is not differentiable at $x = 2$ and the graph of f does not have a tangent line at the point $(2, 0)$.

EXAMPLE 7 **A Graph with a Vertical Tangent Line**

The function $f(x) = x^{1/3}$ is continuous at $x = 0$, as shown in Figure 3.13. However, because the limit

$$\lim_{x \to 0} \frac{f(x) - f(0)}{x - 0} = \lim_{x \to 0} \frac{x^{1/3} - 0}{x} = \lim_{x \to 0} \frac{1}{x^{2/3}} = \infty$$

is infinite, you can conclude that the tangent line is vertical at $x = 0$. So, f is not differentiable at $x = 0$.

From Examples 6 and 7, you can see that a function is not differentiable at a point at which its graph has a sharp turn *or* a vertical tangent line.

THEOREM 3.1 **Differentiability Implies Continuity**

If f is differentiable at $x = c$, then f is continuous at $x = c$.

Proof You can prove that f is continuous at $x = c$ by showing that $f(x)$ approaches $f(c)$ as $x \to c$. To do this, use the differentiability of f at $x = c$ and consider the following limit.

$$\lim_{x \to c} [f(x) - f(c)] = \lim_{x \to c} \left[(x - c)\left(\frac{f(x) - f(c)}{x - c} \right) \right]$$

$$= \left[\lim_{x \to c} (x - c) \right]\left[\lim_{x \to c} \frac{f(x) - f(c)}{x - c} \right]$$

$$= (0)[f'(c)]$$

$$= 0$$

Because the difference $f(x) - f(c)$ approaches zero as $x \to c$, you can conclude that $\lim_{x \to c} f(x) = f(c)$. So, f is continuous at $x = c$.

See LarsonCalculus.com for Bruce Edwards's video of this proof.

The relationship between continuity and differentiability is summarized below.

1. If a function is differentiable at $x = c$, then it is continuous at $x = c$. So, differentiability implies continuity.

2. It is possible for a function to be continuous at $x = c$ and not be differentiable at $x = c$. So, continuity does not imply differentiability (see Example 6).

3.1 Exercises

See **CalcChat.com** for tutorial help and worked-out solutions to odd-numbered exercises.

Estimating Slope In Exercises 1 and 2, estimate the slope of the graph at the points (x_1, y_1) and (x_2, y_2).

1.
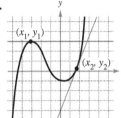

2.
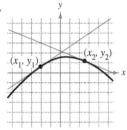

Slopes of Secant Lines In Exercises 3 and 4, use the graph shown in the figure. To print an enlarged copy of the graph, go to *MathGraphs.com*.

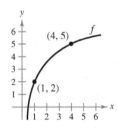

3. Identify or sketch each of the quantities on the figure.

(a) $f(1)$ and $f(4)$ (b) $f(4) - f(1)$

(c) $y = \dfrac{f(4) - f(1)}{4 - 1}(x - 1) + f(1)$

4. Insert the proper inequality symbol ($<$ or $>$) between the given quantities.

(a) $\dfrac{f(4) - f(1)}{4 - 1}$ ▭ $\dfrac{f(4) - f(3)}{4 - 3}$

(b) $\dfrac{f(4) - f(1)}{4 - 1}$ ▭ $f'(1)$

Finding the Slope of a Tangent Line In Exercises 5–10, find the slope of the tangent line to the graph of the function at the given point.

5. $f(x) = 3 - 5x$, $(-1, 8)$ **6.** $g(x) = \frac{3}{2}x + 1$, $(-2, -2)$

7. $g(x) = x^2 - 9$, $(2, -5)$ **8.** $f(x) = 5 - x^2$, $(3, -4)$

9. $f(t) = 3t - t^2$, $(0, 0)$ **10.** $h(t) = t^2 + 4t$, $(1, 5)$

Finding the Derivative by the Limit Process In Exercises 11–24, find the derivative of the function by the limit process.

11. $f(x) = 7$ **12.** $g(x) = -3$

13. $f(x) = -10x$ **14.** $f(x) = 7x - 3$

15. $h(s) = 3 + \frac{2}{3}s$ **16.** $f(x) = 5 - \frac{2}{3}x$

17. $f(x) = x^2 + x - 3$ **18.** $f(x) = x^2 - 5$

19. $f(x) = x^3 - 12x$ **20.** $f(x) = x^3 + x^2$

21. $f(x) = \dfrac{1}{x - 1}$ **22.** $f(x) = \dfrac{1}{x^2}$

23. $f(x) = \sqrt{x + 4}$ **24.** $f(x) = \dfrac{4}{\sqrt{x}}$

 Finding an Equation of a Tangent Line In Exercises 25–32, (a) find an equation of the tangent line to the graph of f at the given point, (b) use a graphing utility to graph the function and its tangent line at the point, and (c) use the *derivative* feature of a graphing utility to confirm your results.

25. $f(x) = x^2 + 3$, $(-1, 4)$ **26.** $f(x) = x^2 + 2x - 1$, $(1, 2)$

27. $f(x) = x^3$, $(2, 8)$ **28.** $f(x) = x^3 + 1$, $(-1, 0)$

29. $f(x) = \sqrt{x}$, $(1, 1)$ **30.** $f(x) = \sqrt{x - 1}$, $(5, 2)$

31. $f(x) = x + \dfrac{4}{x}$, $(-4, -5)$ **32.** $f(x) = \dfrac{6}{x + 2}$, $(0, 3)$

Finding an Equation of a Tangent Line In Exercises 33–38, find an equation of the line that is tangent to the graph of f *and* parallel to the given line.

Function	Line
33. $f(x) = x^2$	$2x - y + 1 = 0$
34. $f(x) = 2x^2$	$4x + y + 3 = 0$
35. $f(x) = x^3$	$3x - y + 1 = 0$
36. $f(x) = x^3 + 2$	$3x - y - 4 = 0$
37. $f(x) = \dfrac{1}{\sqrt{x}}$	$x + 2y - 6 = 0$
38. $f(x) = \dfrac{1}{\sqrt{x - 1}}$	$x + 2y + 7 = 0$

WRITING ABOUT CONCEPTS

Sketching a Derivative In Exercises 39–44, sketch the graph of f'. Explain how you found your answer.

39.
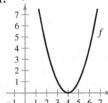

40.
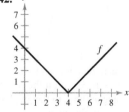

41.
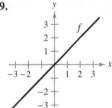

42.
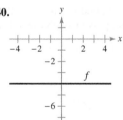

WRITING ABOUT CONCEPTS (continued)

43.

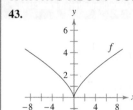

44.

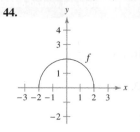

45. Sketching a Graph Sketch a graph of a function whose derivative is always negative. Explain how you found the answer.

46. Sketching a Graph Sketch a graph of a function whose derivative is always positive. Explain how you found the answer.

47. Using a Tangent Line The tangent line to the graph of $y = g(x)$ at the point $(4, 5)$ passes through the point $(7, 0)$. Find $g(4)$ and $g'(4)$.

48. Using a Tangent Line The tangent line to the graph of $y = h(x)$ at the point $(-1, 4)$ passes through the point $(3, 6)$. Find $h(-1)$ and $h'(-1)$.

Working Backwards **In Exercises 49–52, the limit represents $f'(c)$ for a function f and a number c. Find f and c.**

49. $\displaystyle\lim_{\Delta x \to 0} \frac{[5 - 3(1 + \Delta x)] - 2}{\Delta x}$

50. $\displaystyle\lim_{\Delta x \to 0} \frac{(-2 + \Delta x)^3 + 8}{\Delta x}$

51. $\displaystyle\lim_{x \to 6} \frac{-x^2 + 36}{x - 6}$

52. $\displaystyle\lim_{x \to 9} \frac{2\sqrt{x} - 6}{x - 9}$

Writing a Function Using Derivatives **In Exercises 53 and 54, identify a function f that has the given characteristics. Then sketch the function.**

53. $f(0) = 2; f'(x) = -3$ for $-\infty < x < \infty$

54. $f(0) = 4; f'(0) = 0; f'(x) < 0$ for $x < 0; f'(x) > 0$ for $x > 0$

Finding an Equation of a Tangent Line **In Exercises 55 and 56, find equations of the two tangent lines to the graph of f that pass through the indicated point.**

55. $f(x) = 4x - x^2$

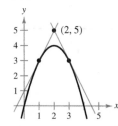

56. $f(x) = x^2$

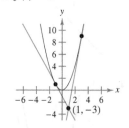

57. Graphical Reasoning Use a graphing utility to graph each function and its tangent lines at $x = -1$, $x = 0$, and $x = 1$. Based on the results, determine whether the slopes of tangent lines to the graph of a function at different values of x are always distinct.

(a) $f(x) = x^2$ (b) $g(x) = x^3$

58. HOW DO YOU SEE IT? The figure shows the graph of g'.

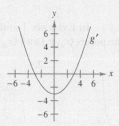

(a) $g'(0) = $ ▮

(b) $g'(3) = $ ▮

(c) What can you conclude about the graph of g knowing that $g'(1) = -\frac{8}{3}$?

(d) What can you conclude about the graph of g knowing that $g'(-4) = \frac{7}{3}$?

(e) Is $g(6) - g(4)$ positive or negative? Explain.

(f) Is it possible to find $g(2)$ from the graph? Explain.

59. Graphical Reasoning Consider the function $f(x) = \frac{1}{2}x^2$.

(a) Use a graphing utility to graph the function and estimate the values of $f'(0), f'\left(\frac{1}{2}\right), f'(1)$, and $f'(2)$.

(b) Use your results from part (a) to determine the values of $f'\left(-\frac{1}{2}\right), f'(-1)$, and $f'(-2)$.

(c) Sketch a possible graph of f'.

(d) Use the definition of derivative to find $f'(x)$.

60. Graphical Reasoning Consider the function $f(x) = \frac{1}{3}x^3$.

(a) Use a graphing utility to graph the function and estimate the values of $f'(0), f'\left(\frac{1}{2}\right), f'(1), f'(2)$, and $f'(3)$.

(b) Use your results from part (a) to determine the values of $f'\left(-\frac{1}{2}\right), f'(-1), f'(-2)$, and $f'(-3)$.

(c) Sketch a possible graph of f'.

(d) Use the definition of derivative to find $f'(x)$.

Graphical Reasoning **In Exercises 61 and 62, use a graphing utility to graph the functions f and g in the same viewing window, where**

$$g(x) = \frac{f(x + 0.01) - f(x)}{0.01}.$$

Label the graphs and describe the relationship between them.

61. $f(x) = 2x - x^2$

62. $f(x) = 3\sqrt{x}$

Approximating a Derivative **In Exercises 63 and 64, evaluate $f(2)$ and $f(2.1)$ and use the results to approximate $f'(2)$.**

63. $f(x) = x(4 - x)$

64. $f(x) = \frac{1}{4}x^3$

Using the Alternative Form of the Derivative **In Exercises 65–74, use the alternative form of the derivative to find the derivative at $x = c$ (if it exists).**

65. $f(x) = x^2 - 5$, $c = 3$

66. $g(x) = x^2 - x$, $c = 1$

67. $f(x) = x^3 + 2x^2 + 1$, $c = -2$

68. $f(x) = x^3 + 6x, \quad c = 2$

69. $g(x) = \sqrt{|x|}, \quad c = 0$ **70.** $f(x) = 3/x, \quad c = 4$

71. $f(x) = (x - 6)^{2/3}, \quad c = 6$

72. $g(x) = (x + 3)^{1/3}, \quad c = -3$

73. $h(x) = |x + 7|, \quad c = -7$ **74.** $f(x) = |x - 6|, \quad c = 6$

Determining Differentiability In Exercises 75–80, describe the *x*-values at which *f* is differentiable.

75. $f(x) = \dfrac{2}{x - 3}$ **76.** $f(x) = |x^2 - 9|$

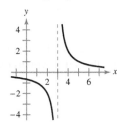 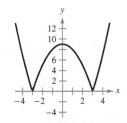

77. $f(x) = (x + 4)^{2/3}$ **78.** $f(x) = \dfrac{x^2}{x^2 - 4}$

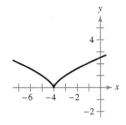 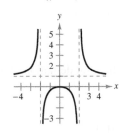

79. $f(x) = \sqrt{x - 1}$ **80.** $f(x) = \begin{cases} x^2 - 4, & x \le 0 \\ 4 - x^2, & x > 0 \end{cases}$

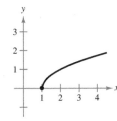 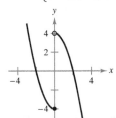

Graphical Reasoning In Exercises 81–84, use a graphing utility to graph the function and find the *x*-values at which *f* is differentiable.

81. $f(x) = |x - 5|$ **82.** $f(x) = \dfrac{4x}{x - 3}$

83. $f(x) = x^{2/5}$

84. $f(x) = \begin{cases} x^3 - 3x^2 + 3x, & x \le 1 \\ x^2 - 2x, & x > 1 \end{cases}$

Determining Differentiability In Exercises 85–88, find the derivatives from the left and from the right at $x = 1$ (if they exist). Is the function differentiable at $x = 1$?

85. $f(x) = |x - 1|$ **86.** $f(x) = \sqrt{1 - x^2}$

87. $f(x) = \begin{cases} (x - 1)^3, & x \le 1 \\ (x - 1)^2, & x > 1 \end{cases}$ **88.** $f(x) = \begin{cases} x, & x \le 1 \\ x^2, & x > 1 \end{cases}$

Determining Differentiability In Exercises 89 and 90, determine whether the function is differentiable at $x = 2$.

89. $f(x) = \begin{cases} x^2 + 1, & x \le 2 \\ 4x - 3, & x > 2 \end{cases}$ **90.** $f(x) = \begin{cases} \frac{1}{2}x + 1, & x < 2 \\ \sqrt{2x}, & x \ge 2 \end{cases}$

91. Greatest Integer Function and Differentiability Use a graphing utility to graph $g(x) = [\![x]\!]/x$. Then let $f(x) = [\![x]\!]$ and show that

$$\lim_{x \to 0^-} \frac{f(x) - f(0)}{x - 0} = \infty \quad \text{and} \quad \lim_{x \to 0^+} \frac{f(x) - f(0)}{x - 0} = 0.$$

Is *f* differentiable? Explain.

92. Conjecture Consider the functions $f(x) = x^2$ and $g(x) = x^3$.

(a) Graph *f* and *f'* on the same set of coordinate axes.

(b) Graph *g* and *g'* on the same set of coordinate axes.

(c) Identify a pattern between *f* and *g* and their respective derivatives. Use the pattern to make a conjecture about $h'(x)$ if $h(x) = x^n$, where *n* is an integer and $n \ge 2$.

(d) Find $f'(x)$ if $f(x) = x^4$. Compare the result with the conjecture in part (c). Is this a proof of your conjecture? Explain.

True or False? In Exercises 93–96, determine whether the statement is true or false. If it is false, explain why or give an example that shows it is false.

93. The slope of the tangent line to the differentiable function *f* at the point $(2, f(2))$ is

$$\frac{f(2 + \Delta x) - f(2)}{\Delta x}.$$

94. If a function is continuous at a point, then it is differentiable at that point.

95. If a function has derivatives from both the right and the left at a point, then it is differentiable at that point.

96. If a function is differentiable at a point, then it is continuous at that point.

97. Differentiability and Continuity Let

$$f(x) = \begin{cases} x \sin \dfrac{1}{x}, & x \ne 0 \\ 0, & x = 0 \end{cases}$$

and

$$g(x) = \begin{cases} x^2 \sin \dfrac{1}{x}, & x \ne 0 \\ 0, & x = 0 \end{cases}.$$

Show that *f* is continuous, but not differentiable, at $x = 0$. Show that *g* is differentiable at 0, and find $g'(0)$.

98. Writing Use a graphing utility to graph the two functions $f(x) = x^2 + 1$ and $g(x) = |x| + 1$ in the same viewing window. Use the *zoom* and *trace* features to analyze the graphs near the point $(0, 1)$. What do you observe? Which function is differentiable at this point? Write a short paragraph describing the geometric significance of differentiability at a point.

3.2 Basic Differentiation Rules and Rates of Change

- Find the derivative of a function using the Constant Rule.
- Find the derivative of a function using the Power Rule.
- Find the derivative of a function using the Constant Multiple Rule.
- Find the derivative of a function using the Sum and Difference Rules.
- Find the derivatives of the sine function and of the cosine function.
- Find the derivatives of exponential functions.
- Use derivatives to find rates of change.

The Constant Rule

In Section 3.1, you used the limit definition to find derivatives. In this and the next two sections, you will be introduced to several "differentiation rules" that allow you to find derivatives without the *direct* use of the limit definition.

THEOREM 3.2 The Constant Rule

The derivative of a constant function is 0. That is, if c is a real number, then

$$\frac{d}{dx}[c] = 0. \qquad \text{(See Figure 3.14.)}$$

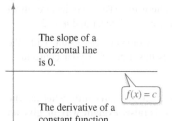

The slope of a horizontal line is 0.

$f(x) = c$

The derivative of a constant function is 0.

Notice that the Constant Rule is equivalent to saying that the slope of a horizontal line is 0. This demonstrates the relationship between slope and derivative.

Figure 3.14

Proof Let $f(x) = c$. Then, by the limit definition of the derivative,

$$\frac{d}{dx}[c] = f'(x)$$

$$= \lim_{\Delta x \to 0} \frac{f(x + \Delta x) - f(x)}{\Delta x}$$

$$= \lim_{\Delta x \to 0} \frac{c - c}{\Delta x}$$

$$= \lim_{\Delta x \to 0} 0$$

$$= 0.$$

See LarsonCalculus.com for Bruce Edwards's video of this proof.

EXAMPLE 1   **Using the Constant Rule**

Function	Derivative
a. $y = 7$	$dy/dx = 0$
b. $f(x) = 0$	$f'(x) = 0$
c. $s(t) = -3$	$s'(t) = 0$
d. $y = k\pi^2$, k is constant	$y' = 0$

Exploration

Writing a Conjecture   Use the definition of the derivative given in Section 3.1 to find the derivative of each function. What patterns do you see? Use your results to write a conjecture about the derivative of $f(x) = x^n$.

a. $f(x) = x^1$ **b.** $f(x) = x^2$ **c.** $f(x) = x^3$

d. $f(x) = x^4$ **e.** $f(x) = x^{1/2}$ **f.** $f(x) = x^{-1}$

The Power Rule

Before proving the next rule, it is important to review the procedure for expanding a binomial.

$$(x + \Delta x)^2 = x^2 + 2x\,\Delta x + (\Delta x)^2$$
$$(x + \Delta x)^3 = x^3 + 3x^2\,\Delta x + 3x(\Delta x)^2 + (\Delta x)^3$$
$$(x + \Delta x)^4 = x^4 + 4x^3\,\Delta x + 6x^2(\Delta x)^2 + 4x(\Delta x)^3 + (\Delta x)^4$$
$$(x + \Delta x)^5 = x^5 + 5x^4\,\Delta x + 10x^3(\Delta x)^2 + 10x^2(\Delta x)^3 + 5x(\Delta x)^4 + (\Delta x)^5$$

The general binomial expansion for a positive integer n is

$$(x + \Delta x)^n = x^n + nx^{n-1}(\Delta x) + \underbrace{\frac{n(n-1)x^{n-2}}{2}(\Delta x)^2 + \cdots + (\Delta x)^n}.$$

$(\Delta x)^2$ is a factor of these terms.

This binomial expansion is used in proving a special case of the Power Rule.

THEOREM 3.3   The Power Rule

If n is a rational number, then the function $f(x) = x^n$ is differentiable and

$$\frac{d}{dx}[x^n] = nx^{n-1}.$$

For f to be differentiable at $x = 0$, n must be a number such that x^{n-1} is defined on an interval containing 0.

• • • • • • • • • • • • • • • • • ▷

• • REMARK From Example 7 in Section 3.1, you know that the function $f(x) = x^{1/3}$ is defined at $x = 0$, but is not differentiable at $x = 0$. This is because $x^{-2/3}$ is not defined on an interval containing 0.

Proof   If n is a positive integer greater than 1, then the binomial expansion produces

$$\frac{d}{dx}[x^n] = \lim_{\Delta x \to 0} \frac{(x + \Delta x)^n - x^n}{\Delta x}$$

$$= \lim_{\Delta x \to 0} \frac{x^n + nx^{n-1}(\Delta x) + \dfrac{n(n-1)x^{n-2}}{2}(\Delta x)^2 + \cdots + (\Delta x)^n - x^n}{\Delta x}$$

$$= \lim_{\Delta x \to 0} \left[nx^{n-1} + \frac{n(n-1)x^{n-2}}{2}(\Delta x) + \cdots + (\Delta x)^{n-1} \right]$$

$$= nx^{n-1} + 0 + \cdots + 0$$

$$= nx^{n-1}.$$

This proves the case for which n is a positive integer greater than 1. It is left to you to prove the case for $n = 1$. Example 7 in Section 3.3 proves the case for which n is a negative integer. The cases for which n is rational and n is irrational are left as an exercise (see Section 3.5, Exercise 90). *See LarsonCalculus.com for Bruce Edwards's video of this proof.*

■

When using the Power Rule, the case for which $n = 1$ is best thought of as a separate differentiation rule. That is,

$$\frac{d}{dx}[x] = 1. \qquad \text{Power Rule when } n = 1$$

This rule is consistent with the fact that the slope of the line $y = x$ is 1, as shown in Figure 3.15.

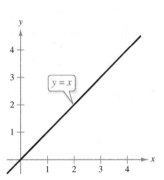

The slope of the line $y = x$ is 1.
Figure 3.15

EXAMPLE 2   **Using the Power Rule**

Function	Derivative
a. $f(x) = x^3$	$f'(x) = 3x^2$
b. $g(x) = \sqrt[3]{x}$	$g'(x) = \dfrac{d}{dx}[x^{1/3}] = \dfrac{1}{3}x^{-2/3} = \dfrac{1}{3x^{2/3}}$
c. $y = \dfrac{1}{x^2}$	$\dfrac{dy}{dx} = \dfrac{d}{dx}[x^{-2}] = (-2)x^{-3} = -\dfrac{2}{x^3}$

In Example 2(c), note that *before* differentiating, $1/x^2$ was rewritten as x^{-2}. Rewriting is the first step in *many* differentiation problems.

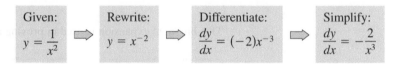

Given:	Rewrite:	Differentiate:	Simplify:
$y = \dfrac{1}{x^2}$	$y = x^{-2}$	$\dfrac{dy}{dx} = (-2)x^{-3}$	$\dfrac{dy}{dx} = -\dfrac{2}{x^3}$

EXAMPLE 3   **Finding the Slope of a Graph**

$\cdots\cdots\triangleright$ *See LarsonCalculus.com for an interactive version of this type of example.*

Find the slope of the graph of

$$f(x) = x^4$$

for each value of x.

a. $x = -1$ **b.** $x = 0$ **c.** $x = 1$

Solution   The slope of a graph at a point is the value of the derivative at that point. The derivative of f is $f'(x) = 4x^3$.

a. When $x = -1$, the slope is $f'(-1) = 4(-1)^3 = -4$.   Slope is negative.

b. When $x = 0$, the slope is $f'(0) = 4(0)^3 = 0$.   Slope is zero.

c. When $x = 1$, the slope is $f'(1) = 4(1)^3 = 4$.   Slope is positive.

See Figure 3.16.

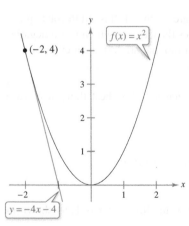

Note that the slope of the graph is negative at the point $(-1, 1)$, the slope is zero at the point $(0, 0)$, and the slope is positive at the point $(1, 1)$.
Figure 3.16

EXAMPLE 4   **Finding an Equation of a Tangent Line**

$\cdots\cdots\triangleright$ *See LarsonCalculus.com for an interactive version of this type of example.*

Find an equation of the tangent line to the graph of $f(x) = x^2$ when $x = -2$.

Solution   To find the *point* on the graph of f, evaluate the original function at $x = -2$.

$$(-2, f(-2)) = (-2, 4)$$ Point on graph

To find the *slope* of the graph when $x = -2$, evaluate the derivative, $f'(x) = 2x$, at $x = -2$.

$$m = f'(-2) = -4$$ Slope of graph at $(-2, 4)$

Now, using the point-slope form of the equation of a line, you can write

$$y - y_1 = m(x - x_1)$$ Point-slope form
$$y - 4 = -4[x - (-2)]$$ Substitute for y_1, m, and x_1.
$$y = -4x - 4.$$ Simplify.

The line $y = -4x - 4$ is tangent to the graph of $f(x) = x^2$ at the point $(-2, 4)$.
Figure 3.17

See Figure 3.17.

The Constant Multiple Rule

> **THEOREM 3.4   The Constant Multiple Rule**
>
> If f is a differentiable function and c is a real number, then cf is also differentiable and $\frac{d}{dx}[cf(x)] = cf'(x)$.

Proof

$$\frac{d}{dx}[cf(x)] = \lim_{\Delta x \to 0} \frac{cf(x + \Delta x) - cf(x)}{\Delta x} \qquad \text{Definition of derivative}$$

$$= \lim_{\Delta x \to 0} c\left[\frac{f(x + \Delta x) - f(x)}{\Delta x}\right]$$

$$= c\left[\lim_{\Delta x \to 0} \frac{f(x + \Delta x) - f(x)}{\Delta x}\right] \qquad \text{Apply Theorem 2.2.}$$

$$= cf'(x)$$

See LarsonCalculus.com for Bruce Edwards's video of this proof.

Informally, the Constant Multiple Rule states that constants can be factored out of the differentiation process, even when the constants appear in the denominator.

$$\frac{d}{dx}[cf(x)] = c\frac{d}{dx}[(\quad)f(x)] = cf'(x)$$

$$\frac{d}{dx}\left[\frac{f(x)}{c}\right] = \frac{d}{dx}\left[\left(\frac{1}{c}\right)f(x)\right] = \left(\frac{1}{c}\right)\frac{d}{dx}[(\quad)f(x)] = \left(\frac{1}{c}\right)f'(x)$$

EXAMPLE 5   Using the Constant Multiple Rule

Function	Derivative
a. $y = 5x^3$	$\dfrac{dy}{dx} = \dfrac{d}{dx}[5x^3] = 5\dfrac{d}{dx}[x^3] = 5(3)x^2 = 15x^2$
b. $y = \dfrac{2}{x}$	$\dfrac{dy}{dx} = \dfrac{d}{dx}[2x^{-1}] = 2\dfrac{d}{dx}[x^{-1}] = 2(-1)x^{-2} = -\dfrac{2}{x^2}$
c. $f(t) = \dfrac{4t^2}{5}$	$f'(t) = \dfrac{d}{dt}\left[\dfrac{4}{5}t^2\right] = \dfrac{4}{5}\dfrac{d}{dt}[t^2] = \dfrac{4}{5}(2t) = \dfrac{8}{5}t$
d. $y = 2\sqrt{x}$	$\dfrac{dy}{dx} = \dfrac{d}{dx}[2x^{1/2}] = 2\left(\dfrac{1}{2}x^{-1/2}\right) = x^{-1/2} = \dfrac{1}{\sqrt{x}}$
e. $y = \dfrac{1}{2\sqrt[3]{x^2}}$	$\dfrac{dy}{dx} = \dfrac{d}{dx}\left[\dfrac{1}{2}x^{-2/3}\right] = \dfrac{1}{2}\left(-\dfrac{2}{3}\right)x^{-5/3} = -\dfrac{1}{3x^{5/3}}$
f. $y = -\dfrac{3x}{2}$	$y' = \dfrac{d}{dx}\left[-\dfrac{3}{2}x\right] = -\dfrac{3}{2}(1) = -\dfrac{3}{2}$

• • • **REMARK** Before differentiating functions involving radicals, rewrite the function with rational exponents.

The Constant Multiple Rule and the Power Rule can be combined into one rule. The combination rule is

$$\frac{d}{dx}[cx^n] = cnx^{n-1}.$$

EXAMPLE 6 **Using Parentheses When Differentiating**

Original Function	Rewrite	Differentiate	Simplify
a. $y = \dfrac{5}{2x^3}$	$y = \dfrac{5}{2}(x^{-3})$	$y' = \dfrac{5}{2}(-3x^{-4})$	$y' = -\dfrac{15}{2x^4}$
b. $y = \dfrac{5}{(2x)^3}$	$y = \dfrac{5}{8}(x^{-3})$	$y' = \dfrac{5}{8}(-3x^{-4})$	$y' = -\dfrac{15}{8x^4}$
c. $y = \dfrac{7}{3x^{-2}}$	$y = \dfrac{7}{3}(x^2)$	$y' = \dfrac{7}{3}(2x)$	$y' = \dfrac{14x}{3}$
d. $y = \dfrac{7}{(3x)^{-2}}$	$y = 63(x^2)$	$y' = 63(2x)$	$y' = 126x$

The Sum and Difference Rules

> **THEOREM 3.5** **The Sum and Difference Rules**
>
> The sum (or difference) of two differentiable functions f and g is itself differentiable. Moreover, the derivative of $f + g$ (or $f - g$) is the sum (or difference) of the derivatives of f and g.
>
> $$\frac{d}{dx}[f(x) + g(x)] = f'(x) + g'(x) \qquad \text{Sum Rule}$$
>
> $$\frac{d}{dx}[f(x) - g(x)] = f'(x) - g'(x) \qquad \text{Difference Rule}$$

Proof A proof of the Sum Rule follows from Theorem 2.2. (The Difference Rule can be proved in a similar way.)

$$\frac{d}{dx}[f(x) + g(x)] = \lim_{\Delta x \to 0} \frac{[f(x + \Delta x) + g(x + \Delta x)] - [f(x) + g(x)]}{\Delta x}$$

$$= \lim_{\Delta x \to 0} \frac{f(x + \Delta x) + g(x + \Delta x) - f(x) - g(x)}{\Delta x}$$

$$= \lim_{\Delta x \to 0} \left[\frac{f(x + \Delta x) - f(x)}{\Delta x} + \frac{g(x + \Delta x) - g(x)}{\Delta x} \right]$$

$$= \lim_{\Delta x \to 0} \frac{f(x + \Delta x) - f(x)}{\Delta x} + \lim_{\Delta x \to 0} \frac{g(x + \Delta x) - g(x)}{\Delta x}$$

$$= f'(x) + g'(x)$$

See LarsonCalculus.com for Bruce Edwards's video of this proof.

The Sum and Difference Rules can be extended to any finite number of functions. For instance, if $F(x) = f(x) + g(x) - h(x)$, then $F'(x) = f'(x) + g'(x) - h'(x)$.

• • **REMARK** In Example 7(c), note that before differentiating,
$$\frac{3x^2 - x + 1}{x}$$
was rewritten as
$$3x - 1 + \frac{1}{x}.$$

EXAMPLE 7 **Using the Sum and Difference Rules**

Function	Derivative
a. $f(x) = x^3 - 4x + 5$	$f'(x) = 3x^2 - 4$
b. $g(x) = -\dfrac{x^4}{2} + 3x^3 - 2x$	$g'(x) = -2x^3 + 9x^2 - 2$
c. $y = \dfrac{3x^2 - x + 1}{x} = 3x - 1 + \dfrac{1}{x}$	$y' = 3 - \dfrac{1}{x^2} = \dfrac{3x^2 - 1}{x^2}$

■ **FOR FURTHER INFORMATION**
For the outline of a geometric proof of the derivatives of the sine and cosine functions, see the article "The Spider's Spacewalk Derivation of sin′ and cos′" by Tim Hesterberg in *The College Mathematics Journal*. To view this article, go to *MathArticles.com*.

Derivatives of the Sine and Cosine Functions

In Section 2.3, you studied the limits

$$\lim_{\Delta x \to 0} \frac{\sin \Delta x}{\Delta x} = 1 \quad \text{and} \quad \lim_{\Delta x \to 0} \frac{1 - \cos \Delta x}{\Delta x} = 0.$$

These two limits can be used to prove differentiation rules for the sine and cosine functions. (The derivatives of the other four trigonometric functions are discussed in Section 3.3.)

THEOREM 3.6 Derivatives of Sine and Cosine Functions

$$\frac{d}{dx}[\sin x] = \cos x \qquad \frac{d}{dx}[\cos x] = -\sin x$$

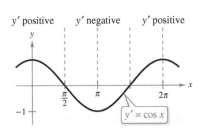

The derivative of the sine function is the cosine function.

Figure 3.18

Proof Here is a proof of the first rule. (The proof of the second rule is left as an exercise [see Exercise 120].)

$$\frac{d}{dx}[\sin x] = \lim_{\Delta x \to 0} \frac{\sin(x + \Delta x) - \sin x}{\Delta x} \qquad \text{Definition of derivative}$$

$$= \lim_{\Delta x \to 0} \frac{\sin x \cos \Delta x + \cos x \sin \Delta x - \sin x}{\Delta x}$$

$$= \lim_{\Delta x \to 0} \frac{\cos x \sin \Delta x - (\sin x)(1 - \cos \Delta x)}{\Delta x}$$

$$= \lim_{\Delta x \to 0} \left[(\cos x)\left(\frac{\sin \Delta x}{\Delta x}\right) - (\sin x)\left(\frac{1 - \cos \Delta x}{\Delta x}\right) \right]$$

$$= \cos x \left(\lim_{\Delta x \to 0} \frac{\sin \Delta x}{\Delta x} \right) - \sin x \left(\lim_{\Delta x \to 0} \frac{1 - \cos \Delta x}{\Delta x} \right)$$

$$= (\cos x)(1) - (\sin x)(0)$$

$$= \cos x$$

This differentiation rule is shown graphically in Figure 3.18. Note that for each x, the *slope* of the sine curve is equal to the value of the cosine.

See LarsonCalculus.com for Bruce Edwards's video of this proof.

EXAMPLE 8 **Derivatives Involving Sines and Cosines**

• • • • ▷ *See LarsonCalculus.com for an interactive version of this type of example.*

Function	Derivative
a. $y = 2 \sin x$	$y' = 2 \cos x$
b. $y = \dfrac{\sin x}{2} = \dfrac{1}{2} \sin x$	$y' = \dfrac{1}{2} \cos x = \dfrac{\cos x}{2}$
c. $y = x + \cos x$	$y' = 1 - \sin x$
d. $\cos x - \dfrac{\pi}{3} \sin x$	$-\sin x - \dfrac{\pi}{3} \cos x$

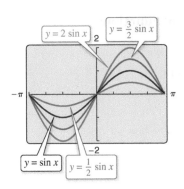

$$\frac{d}{dx}[a \sin x] = a \cos x$$

Figure 3.19

▷ **TECHNOLOGY** A graphing utility can provide insight into the interpretation of a derivative. For instance, Figure 3.19 shows the graphs of

$$y = a \sin x$$

for $a = \frac{1}{2}$, 1, $\frac{3}{2}$, and 2. Estimate the slope of each graph at the point $(0, 0)$. Then verify your estimates analytically by evaluating the derivative of each function when $x = 0$.

Derivatives of Exponential Functions

One of the most intriguing (and useful) characteristics of the natural exponential function is that *it is its own derivative*. Consider the following argument.

Let $f(x) = e^x$.

$$f'(x) = \lim_{\Delta x \to 0} \frac{f(x + \Delta x) - f(x)}{\Delta x}$$

$$= \lim_{\Delta x \to 0} \frac{e^{x + \Delta x} - e^x}{\Delta x}$$

$$= \lim_{\Delta x \to 0} \frac{e^x(e^{\Delta x} - 1)}{\Delta x}$$

The definition of e

$$\lim_{\Delta x \to 0} (1 + \Delta x)^{1/\Delta x} = e$$

tells you that for small values of Δx, you have $e \approx (1 + \Delta x)^{1/\Delta x}$, which implies that

$$e^{\Delta x} \approx 1 + \Delta x.$$

Replacing $e^{\Delta x}$ by this approximation produces the following.

$$f'(x) = \lim_{\Delta x \to 0} \frac{e^x[e^{\Delta x} - 1]}{\Delta x}$$

$$= \lim_{\Delta x \to 0} \frac{e^x[(1 + \Delta x) - 1]}{\Delta x}$$

$$= \lim_{\Delta x \to 0} \frac{e^x \Delta x}{\Delta x}$$

$$= e^x$$

This result is stated in the next theorem.

•• **REMARK** The key to the formula for the derivative of $f(x) = e^x$ is the limit

$$\lim_{x \to 0} (1 + x)^{1/x} = e.$$

This important limit was introduced on page 50 and formalized later on page 85. It is used to conclude that for $\Delta x \approx 0$,

$$(1 + \Delta x)^{1/\Delta x} \approx e.$$

> **THEOREM 3.7 Derivative of the Natural Exponential Function**
>
> $$\frac{d}{dx}[e^x] = e^x$$

You can interpret Theorem 3.7 graphically by saying that the slope of the graph of $f(x) = e^x$ at any point (x, e^x) is equal to the y-coordinate of the point, as shown in Figure 3.20.

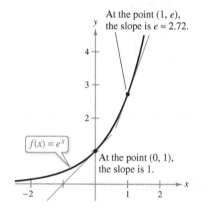

At the point $(1, e)$, the slope is $e \approx 2.72$.

$f(x) = e^x$

At the point $(0, 1)$, the slope is 1.

Figure 3.20

EXAMPLE 9   **Derivatives of Exponential Functions**

Find the derivative of each function.

a. $f(x) = 3e^x$ **b.** $f(x) = x^2 + e^x$ **c.** $f(x) = \sin x - e^x$

Solution

a. $f'(x) = 3 \dfrac{d}{dx}[e^x] = 3e^x$

b. $f'(x) = \dfrac{d}{dx}[x^2] + \dfrac{d}{dx}[e^x] = 2x + e^x$

c. $f'(x) = \dfrac{d}{dx}[\sin x] - \dfrac{d}{dx}[e^x] = \cos x - e^x$

Rates of Change

You have seen how the derivative is used to determine slope. The derivative can also be used to determine the rate of change of one variable with respect to another. Applications involving rates of change, sometimes referred to as instantaneous rates of change, occur in a wide variety of fields. A few examples are population growth rates, production rates, water flow rates, velocity, and acceleration.

A common use for rate of change is to describe the motion of an object moving in a straight line. In such problems, it is customary to use either a horizontal or a vertical line with a designated origin to represent the line of motion. On such lines, movement to the right (or upward) is considered to be in the positive direction, and movement to the left (or downward) is considered to be in the negative direction.

The function s that gives the position (relative to the origin) of an object as a function of time t is called a **position function.** If, over a period of time Δt, the object changes its position by the amount

$$\Delta s = s(t + \Delta t) - s(t)$$

then, by the familiar formula

$$\text{Rate} = \frac{\text{distance}}{\text{time}}$$

the **average velocity** is

$$\frac{\text{Change in distance}}{\text{Change in time}} = \frac{\Delta s}{\Delta t}. \qquad \text{Average velocity}$$

EXAMPLE 10 **Finding Average Velocity of a Falling Object**

A billiard ball is dropped from a height of 100 feet. The ball's height s at time t is the position function

$$s = -16t^2 + 100 \qquad \text{Position function}$$

where s is measured in feet and t is measured in seconds. Find the average velocity over each of the following time intervals.

a. $[1, 2]$ **b.** $[1, 1.5]$ **c.** $[1, 1.1]$

Solution

a. For the interval $[1, 2]$, the object falls from a height of $s(1) = -16(1)^2 + 100 = 84$ feet to a height of $s(2) = -16(2)^2 + 100 = 36$ feet. The average velocity is

$$\frac{\Delta s}{\Delta t} = \frac{36 - 84}{2 - 1} = \frac{-48}{1} = -48 \text{ feet per second.}$$

b. For the interval $[1, 1.5]$, the object falls from a height of 84 feet to a height of $s(1.5) = -16(1.5)^2 + 100 = 64$ feet. The average velocity is

$$\frac{\Delta s}{\Delta t} = \frac{64 - 84}{1.5 - 1} = \frac{-20}{0.5} = -40 \text{ feet per second.}$$

c. For the interval $[1, 1.1]$, the object falls from a height of 84 feet to a height of $s(1.1) = -16(1.1)^2 + 100 = 80.64$ feet. The average velocity is

$$\frac{\Delta s}{\Delta t} = \frac{80.64 - 84}{1.1 - 1} = \frac{-3.36}{0.1} = -33.6 \text{ feet per second.}$$

Note that the average velocities are *negative*, indicating that the object is moving downward.

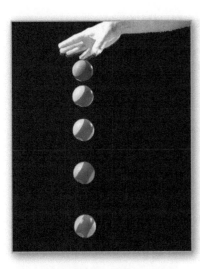

Time-lapse photograph of a free-falling billiard ball

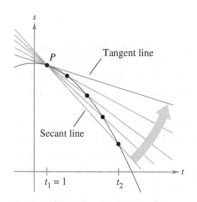

The average velocity between t_1 and t_2 is the slope of the secant line, and the instantaneous velocity at t_1 is the slope of the tangent line.

Figure 3.21

Suppose that in Example 10, you wanted to find the *instantaneous* velocity (or simply the velocity) of the object when $t = 1$. Just as you can approximate the slope of the tangent line by calculating the slope of the secant line, you can approximate the velocity at $t = 1$ by calculating the average velocity over a small interval $[1, 1 + \Delta t]$ (see Figure 3.21). By taking the limit as Δt approaches zero, you obtain the velocity when $t = 1$. Try doing this—you will find that the velocity when $t = 1$ is -32 feet per second.

In general, if $s = s(t)$ is the position function for an object moving along a straight line, then the **velocity** of the object at time t is

$$v(t) = \lim_{\Delta t \to 0} \frac{s(t + \Delta t) - s(t)}{\Delta t} = s\,'(t). \qquad \text{Velocity function}$$

In other words, the velocity function is the derivative of the position function. Velocity can be negative, zero, or positive. The **speed** of an object is the absolute value of its velocity. Speed cannot be negative.

The position of a free-falling object (neglecting air resistance) under the influence of gravity can be represented by the equation

$$s(t) = \frac{1}{2}gt^2 + v_0 t + s_0 \qquad \text{Position function}$$

where s_0 is the initial height of the object, v_0 is the initial velocity of the object, and g is the acceleration due to gravity. On Earth, the value of g is approximately -32 feet per second per second or -9.8 meters per second per second.

EXAMPLE 11 **Using the Derivative to Find Velocity**

At time $t = 0$, a diver jumps from a platform diving board that is 32 feet above the water (see Figure 3.22). Because the initial velocity of the diver is 16 feet per second, the position of the diver is

$$s(t) = -16t^2 + 16t + 32 \qquad \text{Position function}$$

where s is measured in feet and t is measured in seconds.

a. When does the diver hit the water?

b. What is the diver's velocity at impact?

Solution

a. To find the time t when the diver hits the water, let $s = 0$ and solve for t.

$$-16t^2 + 16t + 32 = 0 \qquad \text{Set position function equal to 0.}$$
$$-16(t + 1)(t - 2) = 0 \qquad \text{Factor.}$$
$$t = -1 \text{ or } 2 \qquad \text{Solve for } t.$$

Because $t \geq 0$, choose the positive value to conclude that the diver hits the water at $t = 2$ seconds.

b. The velocity at time t is given by the derivative

$$s\,'(t) = -32t + 16. \qquad \text{Velocity function}$$

So, the velocity at time $t = 2$ is

$$s\,'(2) = -32(2) + 16 = -48 \text{ feet per second.}$$

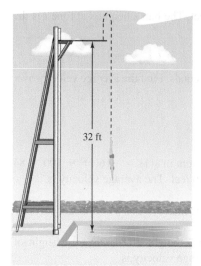

Velocity is positive when an object is rising, and is negative when an object is falling. Notice that the diver moves upward for the first half-second because the velocity is positive for $0 < t < \frac{1}{2}$. When the velocity is 0, the diver has reached the maximum height of the dive.

Figure 3.22

3.2 Exercises

See CalcChat.com for tutorial help and worked-out solutions to odd-numbered exercises.

Estimating Slope In Exercises 1 and 2, use the graph to estimate the slope of the tangent line to $y = x^n$ at the point $(1, 1)$. Verify your answer analytically. To print an enlarged copy of the graph, go to *MathGraphs.com*.

1. (a) $y = x^{1/2}$ (b) $y = x^3$

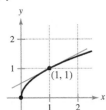 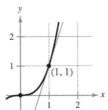

2. (a) $y = x^{-1/2}$ (b) $y = x^{-1}$

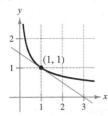 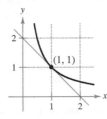

Finding a Derivative In Exercises 3–24, use the rules of differentiation to find the derivative of the function.

3. $y = 12$ **4.** $f(x) = -9$

5. $y = x^7$ **6.** $y = x^{12}$

7. $y = \dfrac{1}{x^5}$ **8.** $y = \dfrac{3}{x^7}$

9. $f(x) = \sqrt[5]{x}$ **10.** $g(x) = \sqrt[4]{x}$

11. $f(x) = x + 11$ **12.** $g(x) = 6x + 3$

13. $f(t) = -2t^2 + 3t - 6$ **14.** $y = t^2 - 3t + 1$

15. $g(x) = x^2 + 4x^3$ **16.** $y = 4x - 3x^3$

17. $s(t) = t^3 + 5t^2 - 3t + 8$ **18.** $y = 2x^3 + 6x^2 - 1$

19. $y = \dfrac{\pi}{2}\sin\theta - \cos\theta$ **20.** $g(t) = \pi\cos t$

21. $y = x^2 - \frac{1}{2}\cos x$ **22.** $y = 7 + \sin x$

23. $y = \frac{1}{2}e^x - 3\sin x$ **24.** $y = \frac{3}{4}e^x + 2\cos x$

Rewriting a Function Before Differentiating In Exercises 25–30, complete the table to find the derivative of the function.

Original Function	Rewrite	Differentiate	Simplify
25. $y = \dfrac{5}{2x^2}$			
26. $y = \dfrac{3}{2x^4}$			
27. $y = \dfrac{6}{(5x)^3}$			
28. $y = \dfrac{\pi}{(3x)^2}$			
29. $y = \dfrac{\sqrt{x}}{x}$			
30. $y = \dfrac{4}{x^{-3}}$			

Finding the Slope of a Graph In Exercises 31–38, find the slope of the graph of the function at the given point. Use the *derivative* feature of a graphing utility to confirm your results.

Function	Point
31. $f(x) = \dfrac{8}{x^2}$	$(2, 2)$
32. $f(t) = 2 - \dfrac{4}{t}$	$(4, 1)$
33. $y = 2x^4 - 3$	$(1, -1)$
34. $f(x) = 2(x - 4)^2$	$(2, 8)$
35. $f(\theta) = 4\sin\theta - \theta$	$(0, 0)$
36. $g(t) = -2\cos t + 5$	$(\pi, 7)$
37. $f(t) = \frac{3}{4}e^t$	$\left(0, \frac{3}{4}\right)$
38. $g(x) = -4e^x$	$(1, -4e)$

Finding a Derivative In Exercises 39–52, find the derivative of the function.

39. $g(t) = t^2 - \dfrac{4}{t^3}$ **40.** $f(x) = 8x + \dfrac{3}{x^2}$

41. $f(x) = \dfrac{4x^3 + 3x^2}{x}$ **42.** $f(x) = \dfrac{2x^4 - x}{x^3}$

43. $f(x) = \dfrac{x^3 - 3x^2 + 4}{x^2}$ **44.** $h(x) = \dfrac{4x^3 + 2x + 5}{x}$

45. $y = x(x^2 + 1)$ **46.** $y = x^2(2x^2 - 3x)$

47. $f(x) = \sqrt{x} - 6\sqrt[3]{x}$ **48.** $f(t) = t^{2/3} - t^{1/3} + 4$

49. $f(x) = 6\sqrt{x} + 5\cos x$ **50.** $f(x) = \dfrac{2}{\sqrt[3]{x}} + 3\cos x$

51. $f(x) = x^{-2} - 2e^x$ **52.** $g(x) = \sqrt{x} - 3e^x$

Finding an Equation of a Tangent Line In Exercises 53–56, (a) find an equation of the tangent line to the graph of f at the given point, (b) use a graphing utility to graph the function and its tangent line at the point, and (c) use the *derivative* feature of a graphing utility to confirm your results.

Function	Point
53. $y = x^4 - 3x^2 + 2$	$(1, 0)$
54. $f(x) = \dfrac{2}{\sqrt[4]{x^3}}$	$(1, 2)$
55. $g(x) = x + e^x$	$(0, 1)$
56. $h(t) = \sin t + \frac{1}{2}e^t$	$\left(\pi, \frac{1}{2}e^\pi\right)$

Horizontal Tangent Line In Exercises 57–64, determine the point(s) (if any) at which the graph of the function has a horizontal tangent line.

57. $y = x^4 - 2x^2 + 3$ **58.** $y = x^3 + x$

59. $y = \dfrac{1}{x^2}$ **60.** $y = x^2 + 9$

61. $y = -4x + e^x$ **62.** $y = x + 4e^x$

63. $y = x + \sin x, \quad 0 \le x < 2\pi$

64. $y = \sqrt{3}x + 2\cos x, \quad 0 \le x < 2\pi$

Finding a Value In Exercises 65–70, find k such that the line is tangent to the graph of the function.

Function	Line
65. $f(x) = k - x^2$	$y = -6x + 1$
66. $f(x) = kx^2$	$y = -2x + 3$
67. $f(x) = \dfrac{k}{x}$	$y = -\dfrac{3}{4}x + 3$
68. $f(x) = k\sqrt{x}$	$y = x + 4$
69. $f(x) = kx^3$	$y = x + 1$
70. $f(x) = kx^4$	$y = 4x - 1$

71. Sketching a Graph Sketch the graph of a function f such that $f' > 0$ for all x and the rate of change of the function is decreasing.

72. HOW DO YOU SEE IT? Use the graph of f to answer each question. To print an enlarged copy of the graph, go to *MathGraphs.com*.

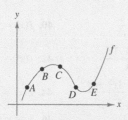

(a) Between which two consecutive points is the average rate of change of the function greatest?

(b) Is the average rate of change of the function between A and B greater than or less than the instantaneous rate of change at B?

(c) Sketch a tangent line to the graph between C and D such that the slope of the tangent line is the same as the average rate of change of the function between C and D.

WRITING ABOUT CONCEPTS

Exploring a Relationship In Exercises 73 and 74, the relationship between f and g is given. Explain the relationship between f' and g'.

73. $g(x) = f(x) + 6$ **74.** $g(x) = 3f(x) - 1$

WRITING ABOUT CONCEPTS (continued)

A Function and Its Derivative In Exercises 75 and 76, the graphs of a function f and its derivative f' are shown on the same set of coordinate axes. Label the graphs as f or f' and write a short paragraph stating the criteria you used in making your selection. To print an enlarged copy of the graph, go to *MathGraphs.com*.

75.
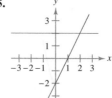

76.
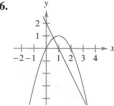

77. Finding Equations of Tangent Lines Sketch the graphs of $y = x^2$ and $y = -x^2 + 6x - 5$, and sketch the two lines that are tangent to both graphs. Find equations of these lines.

78. Tangent Lines Show that the graphs of the two equations

$$y = x \quad \text{and} \quad y = \frac{1}{x}$$

have tangent lines that are perpendicular to each other at their point of intersection.

79. Tangent Line Show that the graph of the function

$$f(x) = 3x + \sin x + 2$$

does not have a horizontal tangent line.

80. Tangent Line Show that the graph of the function

$$f(x) = x^5 + 3x^3 + 5x$$

does not have a tangent line with a slope of 3.

Finding an Equation of a Tangent Line In Exercises 81 and 82, find an equation of the tangent line to the graph of the function f through the point (x_0, y_0) not on the graph. To find the point of tangency (x, y) on the graph of f, solve the equation

$$f'(x) = \frac{y_0 - y}{x_0 - x}.$$

81. $f(x) = \sqrt{x}$ **82.** $f(x) = \dfrac{2}{x}$

$(x_0, y_0) = (-4, 0)$ $(x_0, y_0) = (5, 0)$

83. Linear Approximation Use a graphing utility with a square window setting to zoom in on the graph of

$$f(x) = 4 - \tfrac{1}{2}x^2$$

to approximate $f'(1)$. Use the derivative to find $f'(1)$.

84. Linear Approximation Use a graphing utility with a square window setting to zoom in on the graph of

$$f(x) = 4\sqrt{x} + 1$$

to approximate $f'(4)$. Use the derivative to find $f'(4)$.

85. Linear Approximation Consider the function $f(x) = x^{3/2}$ with the solution point $(4, 8)$.

(a) Use a graphing utility to graph f. Use the *zoom* feature to obtain successive magnifications of the graph in the neighborhood of the point $(4, 8)$. After zooming in a few times, the graph should appear nearly linear. Use the *trace* feature to determine the coordinates of a point near $(4, 8)$. Find an equation of the secant line $S(x)$ through the two points.

(b) Find the equation of the line $T(x) = f'(4)(x - 4) + f(4)$ tangent to the graph of f passing through the given point. Why are the linear functions S and T nearly the same?

(c) Use a graphing utility to graph f and T on the same set of coordinate axes. Note that T is a good approximation of f when x is close to 4. What happens to the accuracy of the approximation as you move farther away from the point of tangency?

(d) Demonstrate the conclusion in part (c) by completing the table.

Δx	-3	-2	-1	-0.5	-0.1	0
$f(4 + \Delta x)$						
$T(4 + \Delta x)$						

Δx	0.1	0.5	1	2	3
$f(4 + \Delta x)$					
$T(4 + \Delta x)$					

86. Linear Approximation Repeat Exercise 85 for the function $f(x) = x^3$, where $T(x)$ is the line tangent to the graph at the point $(1, 1)$. Explain why the accuracy of the linear approximation decreases more rapidly than in Exercise 85.

True or False? In Exercises 87–92, determine whether the statement is true or false. If it is false, explain why or give an example that shows it is false.

87. If $f'(x) = g'(x)$, then $f(x) = g(x)$.

88. If $f(x) = g(x) + c$, then $f'(x) = g'(x)$.

89. If $y = \pi^2$, then $dy/dx = 2\pi$.

90. If $y = x/\pi$, then $dy/dx = 1/\pi$.

91. If $g(x) = 3f(x)$, then $g'(x) = 3f'(x)$.

92. If $f(x) = \dfrac{1}{x^n}$, then $f'(x) = \dfrac{1}{nx^{n-1}}$.

Finding Rates of Change In Exercises 93–98, find the average rate of change of the function over the given interval. Compare this average rate of change with the instantaneous rates of change at the endpoints of the interval.

93. $f(t) = 4t + 5$, $[1, 2]$ **94.** $f(t) = t^2 - 7$, $[3, 3.1]$

95. $f(x) = \dfrac{-1}{x}$, $[1, 2]$ **96.** $f(x) = \sin x$, $\left[0, \dfrac{\pi}{6}\right]$

97. $g(x) = x^2 + e^x$, $[0, 1]$ **98.** $h(x) = x^3 - \frac{1}{2}e^x$, $[0, 2]$

Vertical Motion In Exercises 99 and 100, use the position function $s(t) = -16t^2 + v_0 t + s_0$ for free-falling objects.

99. A silver dollar is dropped from the top of a building that is 1362 feet tall.

(a) Determine the position and velocity functions for the coin.

(b) Determine the average velocity on the interval $[1, 2]$.

(c) Find the instantaneous velocities when $t = 1$ and $t = 2$.

(d) Find the time required for the coin to reach ground level.

(e) Find the velocity of the coin at impact.

100. A ball is thrown straight down from the top of a 220-foot building with an initial velocity of -22 feet per second. What is its velocity after 3 seconds? What is its velocity after falling 108 feet?

Vertical Motion In Exercises 101 and 102, use the position function $s(t) = -4.9t^2 + v_0 t + s_0$ for free-falling objects.

101. A projectile is shot upward from the surface of Earth with an initial velocity of 120 meters per second. What is its velocity after 5 seconds? After 10 seconds?

102. To estimate the height of a building, a stone is dropped from the top of the building into a pool of water at ground level. The splash is seen 5.6 seconds after the stone is dropped. What is the height of the building?

Think About It In Exercises 103 and 104, the graph of a position function is shown. It represents the distance in miles that a person drives during a 10-minute trip to work. Make a sketch of the corresponding velocity function.

103.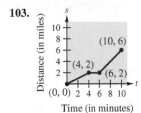

104.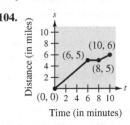

Think About It In Exercises 105 and 106, the graph of a velocity function is shown. It represents the velocity in miles per hour during a 10-minute trip to work. Make a sketch of the corresponding position function.

105.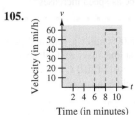

106.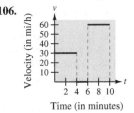

107. Volume The volume of a cube with sides of length s is given by $V = s^3$. Find the rate of change of the volume with respect to s when $s = 6$ centimeters.

108. Area The area of a square with sides of length s is given by $A = s^2$. Find the rate of change of the area with respect to s when $s = 6$ meters.

• • **109. Modeling Data** • • • • • • • • • • • • • • • • • •

The stopping distance of an automobile, on dry, level pavement, traveling at a speed v (in kilometers per hour) is the distance R (in meters) the car travels during the reaction time of the driver plus the distance B (in meters) the car travels after the brakes are applied (see figure). The table shows the results of an experiment.

	Reaction time		Braking distance	

Driver sees obstacle R Driver applies brakes B Car stops

Speed, v	20	40	60	80	100
Reaction Time Distance, R	8.3	16.7	25.0	33.3	41.7
Braking Time Distance, B	2.3	9.0	20.2	35.8	55.9

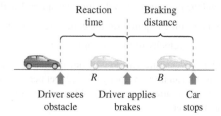

(a) Use the regression capabilities of a graphing utility to find a linear model for reaction time distance R.

(b) Use the regression capabilities of a graphing utility to find a quadratic model for braking time distance B.

(c) Determine the polynomial giving the total stopping distance T.

(d) Use a graphing utility to graph the functions R, B, and T in the same viewing window.

(e) Find the derivative of T and the rates of change of the total stopping distance for $v = 40$, $v = 80$, and $v = 100$.

(f) Use the results of this exercise to draw conclusions about the total stopping distance as speed increases.

110. Fuel Cost A car is driven 15,000 miles a year and gets x miles per gallon. Assume that the average fuel cost is $3.48 per gallon. Find the annual cost of fuel C as a function of x and use this function to complete the table.

x	10	15	20	25	30	35	40
C							
dC/dx							

Who would benefit more from a one-mile-per-gallon increase in fuel efficiency—the driver of a car that gets 15 miles per gallon, or the driver of a car that gets 35 miles per gallon? Explain.

111. Velocity Verify that the average velocity over the time interval $[t_0 - \Delta t, t_0 + \Delta t]$ is the same as the instantaneous velocity at $t = t_0$ for the position function

$$s(t) = -\frac{1}{2}at^2 + c.$$

112. Inventory Management The annual inventory cost C for a manufacturer is

$$C = \frac{1{,}008{,}000}{Q} + 6.3Q$$

where Q is the order size when the inventory is replenished. Find the change in annual cost when Q is increased from 350 to 351, and compare this with the instantaneous rate of change when $Q = 350$.

113. Finding an Equation of a Parabola Find an equation of the parabola $y = ax^2 + bx + c$ that passes through $(0, 1)$ and is tangent to the line $y = x - 1$ at $(1, 0)$.

114. Proof Let (a, b) be an arbitrary point on the graph of $y = 1/x$, $x > 0$. Prove that the area of the triangle formed by the tangent line through (a, b) and the coordinate axes is 2.

115. Finding Equation(s) of Tangent Line(s) Find the equation(s) of the tangent line(s) to the graph of the curve $y = x^3 - 9x$ through the point $(1, -9)$ not on the graph.

116. Finding Equation(s) of Tangent Line(s) Find the equation(s) of the tangent line(s) to the graph of the parabola $y = x^2$ through the given point not on the graph.

(a) $(0, a)$ (b) $(a, 0)$

Are there any restrictions on the constant a?

Making a Function Differentiable In Exercises 117 and 118, find a and b such that f is differentiable everywhere.

117. $f(x) = \begin{cases} ax^3, & x \le 2 \\ x^2 + b, & x > 2 \end{cases}$

118. $f(x) = \begin{cases} \cos x, & x < 0 \\ ax + b, & x \ge 0 \end{cases}$

119. Determining Differentiability Where are the functions $f_1(x) = |\sin x|$ and $f_2(x) = \sin|x|$ differentiable?

120. Proof Prove that $\dfrac{d}{dx}[\cos x] = -\sin x$.

■ **FOR FURTHER INFORMATION** For a geometric interpretation of the derivatives of trigonometric functions, see the article "Sines and Cosines of the Times" by Victor J. Katz in *Math Horizons*. To view this article, go to *MathArticles.com*.

PUTNAM EXAM CHALLENGE

121. Find all differentiable functions $f : \mathbb{R} \to \mathbb{R}$ such that

$$f'(x) = \frac{f(x + n) - f(x)}{n}$$

for all real numbers x and all positive integers n.

3.3 Product and Quotient Rules and Higher-Order Derivatives

■ Find the derivative of a function using the Product Rule.
■ Find the derivative of a function using the Quotient Rule.
■ Find the derivative of a trigonometric function.
■ Find a higher-order derivative of a function.

The Product Rule

In Section 3.2, you learned that the derivative of the sum of two functions is simply the sum of their derivatives. The rules for the derivatives of the product and quotient of two functions are not as simple.

> **• • REMARK** A version of the Product Rule that some people prefer is
> $$\frac{d}{dx}[f(x)g(x)] = f'(x)g(x) + f(x)g'(x).$$
> The advantage of this form is that it generalizes easily to products of three or more factors.

> **THEOREM 3.8 The Product Rule**
>
> The product of two differentiable functions f and g is itself differentiable. Moreover, the derivative of fg is the first function times the derivative of the second, plus the second function times the derivative of the first.
> $$\frac{d}{dx}[f(x)g(x)] = f(x)g'(x) + g(x)f'(x)$$

Proof Some mathematical proofs, such as the proof of the Sum Rule, are straightforward. Others involve clever steps that may appear unmotivated to a reader. This proof involves such a step—subtracting and adding the same quantity—which is shown in color.

$$\frac{d}{dx}[f(x)g(x)] = \lim_{\Delta x \to 0} \frac{f(x + \Delta x)g(x + \Delta x) - f(x)g(x)}{\Delta x}$$

$$= \lim_{\Delta x \to 0} \frac{f(x + \Delta x)g(x + \Delta x) - f(x + \Delta x)g(x) + f(x + \Delta x)g(x) - f(x)g(x)}{\Delta x}$$

$$= \lim_{\Delta x \to 0}\left[f(x + \Delta x)\frac{g(x + \Delta x) - g(x)}{\Delta x} + g(x)\frac{f(x + \Delta x) - f(x)}{\Delta x}\right]$$

$$= \lim_{\Delta x \to 0}\left[f(x + \Delta x)\frac{g(x + \Delta x) - g(x)}{\Delta x}\right] + \lim_{\Delta x \to 0}\left[g(x)\frac{f(x + \Delta x) - f(x)}{\Delta x}\right]$$

$$= \lim_{\Delta x \to 0} f(x + \Delta x) \cdot \lim_{\Delta x \to 0}\frac{g(x + \Delta x) - g(x)}{\Delta x} + \lim_{\Delta x \to 0} g(x) \cdot \lim_{\Delta x \to 0}\frac{f(x + \Delta x) - f(x)}{\Delta x}$$

$$= f(x)g'(x) + g(x)f'(x)$$

Note that $\lim_{\Delta x \to 0} f(x + \Delta x) = f(x)$ because f is given to be differentiable and therefore is continuous.

See LarsonCalculus.com for Bruce Edwards's video of this proof. ■

> **• • REMARK** The proof of the Product Rule for products of more than two factors is left as an exercise (see Exercise 145).

The Product Rule can be extended to cover products involving more than two factors. For example, if f, g, and h are differentiable functions of x, then

$$\frac{d}{dx}[f(x)g(x)h(x)] = f'(x)g(x)h(x) + f(x)g'(x)h(x) + f(x)g(x)h'(x).$$

So, the derivative of $y = x^2 \sin x \cos x$ is

$$\frac{dy}{dx} = 2x \sin x \cos x + x^2 \cos x \cos x + x^2 \sin x(-\sin x)$$

$$= 2x \sin x \cos x + x^2(\cos^2 x - \sin^2 x).$$

The derivative of a product of two functions is not (in general) given by the product of the derivatives of the two functions. To see this, try comparing the product of the derivatives of

$$f(x) = 3x - 2x^2$$

and

$$g(x) = 5 + 4x$$

with the derivative in Example 1.

EXAMPLE 1   Using the Product Rule

Find the derivative of $h(x) = (3x - 2x^2)(5 + 4x)$.

Solution

$$h'(x) = \overbrace{(3x - 2x^2)}^{\text{First}} \overbrace{\frac{d}{dx}[5 + 4x]}^{\substack{\text{Derivative} \\ \text{of second}}} + \overbrace{(5 + 4x)}^{\text{Second}} \overbrace{\frac{d}{dx}[3x - 2x^2]}^{\substack{\text{Derivative} \\ \text{of first}}}$$ Apply Product Rule.

$$= (3x - 2x^2)(4) + (5 + 4x)(3 - 4x)$$

$$= (12x - 8x^2) + (15 - 8x - 16x^2)$$

$$= -24x^2 + 4x + 15$$

In Example 1, you have the option of finding the derivative with or without the Product Rule. To find the derivative without the Product Rule, you can write

$$D_x[(3x - 2x^2)(5 + 4x)] = D_x[-8x^3 + 2x^2 + 15x]$$

$$= -24x^2 + 4x + 15.$$

In the next example, you must use the Product Rule.

EXAMPLE 2   Using the Product Rule

Find the derivative of $y = xe^x$.

Solution

$$\frac{d}{dx}[xe^x] = x\frac{d}{dx}[e^x] + e^x\frac{d}{dx}[x]$$ Apply Product Rule.

$$= xe^x + e^x(1)$$

$$= e^x(x + 1)$$

• • REMARK In Example 3, notice that you use the Product Rule when both factors of the product are variable, and you use the Constant Multiple Rule when one of the factors is a constant.

EXAMPLE 3   Using the Product Rule

Find the derivative of $y = 2x \cos x - 2 \sin x$.

Solution

$$\frac{dy}{dx} = \overbrace{(2x)\left(\frac{d}{dx}[\cos x]\right) + (\cos x)\left(\frac{d}{dx}[2x]\right)}^{\text{Product Rule}} - \overbrace{2\frac{d}{dx}[\sin x]}^{\text{Constant Multiple Rule}}$$

$$= (2x)(-\sin x) + (\cos x)(2) - 2(\cos x)$$

$$= -2x \sin x$$

The Quotient Rule

> **THEOREM 3.9   The Quotient Rule**
>
> The quotient f/g of two differentiable functions f and g is itself differentiable at all values of x for which $g(x) \neq 0$. Moreover, the derivative of f/g is given by the denominator times the derivative of the numerator minus the numerator times the derivative of the denominator, all divided by the square of the denominator.
>
> $$\frac{d}{dx}\left[\frac{f(x)}{g(x)}\right] = \frac{g(x)f'(x) - f(x)g'(x)}{[g(x)]^2}, \quad g(x) \neq 0$$

REMARK From the Quotient Rule, you can see that the derivative of a quotient is not (in general) the quotient of the derivatives.

Proof   As with the proof of Theorem 3.8, the key to this proof is subtracting and adding the same quantity.

$$\frac{d}{dx}\left[\frac{f(x)}{g(x)}\right] = \lim_{\Delta x \to 0}\frac{\dfrac{f(x + \Delta x)}{g(x + \Delta x)} - \dfrac{f(x)}{g(x)}}{\Delta x} \quad \text{Definition of derivative}$$

$$= \lim_{\Delta x \to 0}\frac{g(x)f(x + \Delta x) - f(x)g(x + \Delta x)}{\Delta x g(x)g(x + \Delta x)}$$

$$= \lim_{\Delta x \to 0}\frac{g(x)f(x + \Delta x) - f(x)g(x) + f(x)g(x) - f(x)g(x + \Delta x)}{\Delta x g(x)g(x + \Delta x)}$$

$$= \frac{\lim\limits_{\Delta x \to 0}\dfrac{g(x)[f(x + \Delta x) - f(x)]}{\Delta x} - \lim\limits_{\Delta x \to 0}\dfrac{f(x)[g(x + \Delta x) - g(x)]}{\Delta x}}{\lim\limits_{\Delta x \to 0}[g(x)g(x + \Delta x)]}$$

$$= \frac{g(x)\left[\lim\limits_{\Delta x \to 0}\dfrac{f(x + \Delta x) - f(x)}{\Delta x}\right] - f(x)\left[\lim\limits_{\Delta x \to 0}\dfrac{g(x + \Delta x) - g(x)}{\Delta x}\right]}{\lim\limits_{\Delta x \to 0}[g(x)g(x + \Delta x)]}$$

$$= \frac{g(x)f'(x) - f(x)g'(x)}{[g(x)]^2}$$

Note that $\lim\limits_{\Delta x \to 0} g(x + \Delta x) = g(x)$ because g is given to be differentiable and therefore is continuous.

See LarsonCalculus.com for Bruce Edwards's video of this proof.

EXAMPLE 4   **Using the Quotient Rule**

Find the derivative of $y = \dfrac{5x - 2}{x^2 + 1}$.

Solution

$$\frac{d}{dx}\left[\frac{5x - 2}{x^2 + 1}\right] = \frac{(x^2 + 1)\dfrac{d}{dx}[5x - 2] - (5x - 2)\dfrac{d}{dx}[x^2 + 1]}{(x^2 + 1)^2} \quad \text{Apply Quotient Rule.}$$

$$= \frac{(x^2 + 1)(5) - (5x - 2)(2x)}{(x^2 + 1)^2}$$

$$= \frac{(5x^2 + 5) - (10x^2 - 4x)}{(x^2 + 1)^2}$$

$$= \frac{-5x^2 + 4x + 5}{(x^2 + 1)^2}$$

▷ **TECHNOLOGY** A graphing utility can be used to compare the graph of a function with the graph of its derivative. For instance, in the figure below, the graph of the function in Example 4 appears to have two points that have horizontal tangent lines. What are the values of y' at these two points?

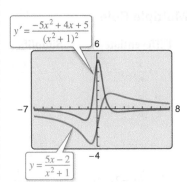

$$y' = \frac{-5x^2 + 4x + 5}{(x^2 + 1)^2}$$

$$y = \frac{5x - 2}{x^2 + 1}$$

Graphical comparison of a function and its derivative

Note the use of parentheses in Example 4. A liberal use of parentheses is recommended for *all* types of differentiation problems. For instance, with the Quotient Rule, it is a good idea to enclose all factors and derivatives in parentheses, and to pay special attention to the subtraction required in the numerator.

When differentiation rules were introduced in the preceding section, the need for rewriting *before* differentiating was emphasized. The next example illustrates this point with the Quotient Rule.

EXAMPLE 5   Rewriting Before Differentiating

Find an equation of the tangent line to the graph of $f(x) = \dfrac{3 - (1/x)}{x + 5}$ at $(-1, 1)$.

Solution   Begin by rewriting the function.

$$f(x) = \frac{3 - (1/x)}{x + 5} \qquad \text{Write original function.}$$

$$= \frac{x\left(3 - \dfrac{1}{x}\right)}{x(x + 5)} \qquad \text{Multiply numerator and denominator by } x.$$

$$= \frac{3x - 1}{x^2 + 5x} \qquad \text{Rewrite.}$$

Next, apply the Quotient Rule.

$$f'(x) = \frac{(x^2 + 5x)(3) - (3x - 1)(2x + 5)}{(x^2 + 5x)^2} \qquad \text{Quotient Rule}$$

$$= \frac{(3x^2 + 15x) - (6x^2 + 13x - 5)}{(x^2 + 5x)^2}$$

$$= \frac{-3x^2 + 2x + 5}{(x^2 + 5x)^2} \qquad \text{Simplify.}$$

To find the slope at $(-1, 1)$, evaluate $f'(-1)$.

$$f'(-1) = 0 \qquad \text{Slope of graph at } (-1, 1)$$

Then, using the point-slope form of the equation of a line, you can determine that the equation of the tangent line at $(-1, 1)$ is $y = 1$. See Figure 3.23.

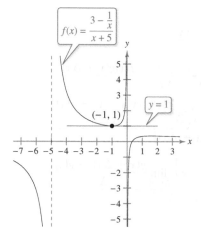

The line $y = 1$ is tangent to the graph of $f(x)$ at the point $(-1, 1)$.

Figure 3.23

Not every quotient needs to be differentiated by the Quotient Rule. For instance, each quotient in the next example can be considered as the product of a constant times a function of x. In such cases, it is more convenient to use the Constant Multiple Rule.

▷

·· REMARK   To see the benefit of using the Constant Multiple Rule for some quotients, try using the Quotient Rule to differentiate the functions in Example 6—you should obtain the same results, but with more work.

EXAMPLE 6   Using the Constant Multiple Rule

Original Function	Rewrite	Differentiate	Simplify
a. $y = \dfrac{x^2 + 3x}{6}$	$y = \dfrac{1}{6}(x^2 + 3x)$	$y' = \dfrac{1}{6}(2x + 3)$	$y' = \dfrac{2x + 3}{6}$
b. $y = \dfrac{5x^4}{8}$	$y = \dfrac{5}{8}x^4$	$y' = \dfrac{5}{8}(4x^3)$	$y' = \dfrac{5}{2}x^3$
c. $y = \dfrac{-3(3x - 2x^2)}{7x}$	$y = -\dfrac{3}{7}(3 - 2x)$	$y' = -\dfrac{3}{7}(-2)$	$y' = \dfrac{6}{7}$
d. $y = \dfrac{9}{5x^2}$	$y = \dfrac{9}{5}(x^{-2})$	$y' = \dfrac{9}{5}(-2x^{-3})$	$y' = -\dfrac{18}{5x^3}$

In Section 3.2, the Power Rule was proved only for the case in which the exponent n is a positive integer greater than 1. The next example extends the proof to include negative integer exponents.

EXAMPLE 7 Power Rule: Negative Integer Exponents

If n is a negative integer, then there exists a positive integer k such that $n = -k$. So, by the Quotient Rule, you can write

$$\frac{d}{dx}[x^n] = \frac{d}{dx}\left[\frac{1}{x^k}\right]$$

$$= \frac{x^k(0) - (1)(kx^{k-1})}{(x^k)^2} \qquad \text{Quotient Rule and Power Rule}$$

$$= \frac{0 - kx^{k-1}}{x^{2k}}$$

$$= -kx^{-k-1}$$

$$= nx^{n-1}. \qquad n = -k$$

So, the Power Rule

$$\frac{d}{dx}[x^n] = nx^{n-1} \qquad \text{Power Rule}$$

is valid for any integer. The cases for which n is rational and n is irrational are left as an exercise (see Section 3.5, Exercise 90).

Derivatives of Trigonometric Functions

Knowing the derivatives of the sine and cosine functions, you can use the Quotient Rule to find the derivatives of the four remaining trigonometric functions.

THEOREM 3.10 Derivatives of Trigonometric Functions

$$\frac{d}{dx}[\tan x] = \sec^2 x \qquad\qquad \frac{d}{dx}[\cot x] = -\csc^2 x$$

$$\frac{d}{dx}[\sec x] = \sec x \tan x \qquad\qquad \frac{d}{dx}[\csc x] = -\csc x \cot x$$

REMARK In the proof of Theorem 3.10, note the use of the trigonometric identities

$$\sin^2 x + \cos^2 x = 1$$

and

$$\sec x = \frac{1}{\cos x}.$$

These trigonometric identities and others are listed in Appendix C and on the formula cards for this text.

Proof Considering $\tan x = (\sin x)/(\cos x)$ and applying the Quotient Rule, you obtain

$$\frac{d}{dx}[\tan x] = \frac{d}{dx}\left[\frac{\sin x}{\cos x}\right]$$

$$= \frac{(\cos x)(\cos x) - (\sin x)(-\sin x)}{\cos^2 x} \qquad \text{Apply Quotient Rule.}$$

$$= \frac{\cos^2 x + \sin^2 x}{\cos^2 x}$$

$$= \frac{1}{\cos^2 x}$$

$$= \sec^2 x.$$

See LarsonCalculus.com for Bruce Edwards's video of this proof.

The proofs of the other three parts of the theorem are left as an exercise (see Exercise 93).

| EXAMPLE 8 | **Differentiating Trigonometric Functions** |

: • • • ▷ *See LarsonCalculus.com for an interactive version of this type of example.*

| **Function** | **Derivative** |

a. $y = x - \tan x$ $\dfrac{dy}{dx} = 1 - \sec^2 x$

b. $y = x \sec x$ $y' = x(\sec x \tan x) + (\sec x)(1)$
    $= (\sec x)(1 + x \tan x)$

• • • • • • • • • • • • • • • ▷

• • **REMARK** Because of trigonometric identities, the derivative of a trigonometric function can take many forms. This presents a challenge when you are trying to match your answers to those given in the back of the text.

| EXAMPLE 9 | **Different Forms of a Derivative** |

Differentiate both forms of

$$y = \frac{1 - \cos x}{\sin x} = \csc x - \cot x.$$

Solution

First form: $y = \dfrac{1 - \cos x}{\sin x}$

$y' = \dfrac{(\sin x)(\sin x) - (1 - \cos x)(\cos x)}{\sin^2 x}$

$\quad = \dfrac{\sin^2 x - \cos x + \cos^2 x}{\sin^2 x}$

$\quad = \dfrac{1 - \cos x}{\sin^2 x}$ $\sin^2 x + \cos^2 x = 1$

Second form: $y = \csc x - \cot x$

$y' = -\csc x \cot x + \csc^2 x$

To show that the two derivatives are equal, you can write

$\dfrac{1 - \cos x}{\sin^2 x} = \dfrac{1}{\sin^2 x} - \dfrac{\cos x}{\sin^2 x}$

$\qquad\qquad = \dfrac{1}{\sin^2 x} - \left(\dfrac{1}{\sin x}\right)\left(\dfrac{\cos x}{\sin x}\right)$

$\qquad\qquad = \csc^2 x - \csc x \cot x.$

The summary below shows that much of the work in obtaining a simplified form of a derivative occurs *after* differentiating. Note that two characteristics of a simplified form are the absence of negative exponents and the combining of like terms.

	$f'(x)$ After Differentiating	$f'(x)$ After Simplifying
Example 1	$(3x - 2x^2)(4) + (5 + 4x)(3 - 4x)$	$-24x^2 + 4x + 15$
Example 3	$(2x)(-\sin x) + (\cos x)(2) - 2(\cos x)$	$-2x \sin x$
Example 4	$\dfrac{(x^2 + 1)(5) - (5x - 2)(2x)}{(x^2 + 1)^2}$	$\dfrac{-5x^2 + 4x + 5}{(x^2 + 1)^2}$
Example 5	$\dfrac{(x^2 + 5x)(3) - (3x - 1)(2x + 5)}{(x^2 + 5x)^2}$	$\dfrac{-3x^2 + 2x + 5}{(x^2 + 5x)^2}$
Example 9	$\dfrac{(\sin x)(\sin x) - (1 - \cos x)(\cos x)}{\sin^2 x}$	$\dfrac{1 - \cos x}{\sin^2 x}$

Higher-Order Derivatives

Exploration

For which of the functions

$$y = e^x, \qquad y = \frac{1}{e^x}$$

$$y = \sin x, \qquad y = \cos x$$

are the equations below true?

a. $y = y'$ **b.** $y = y''$

c. $y = y'''$ **d.** $y = y^{(4)}$

Without determining the actual derivative, is $y = y^{(8)}$ for $y = \sin x$ true? What conclusion can you draw from this?

Just as you can obtain a velocity function by differentiating a position function, you can obtain an **acceleration** function by differentiating a velocity function. Another way of looking at this is that you can obtain an acceleration function by differentiating a position function *twice*.

$$s(t) \qquad \text{Position function}$$
$$v(t) = s'(t) \qquad \text{Velocity function}$$
$$a(t) = v'(t) = s''(t) \qquad \text{Acceleration function}$$

The function $a(t)$ is the **second derivative** of $s(t)$ and is denoted by $s''(t)$.

The second derivative is an example of a **higher-order derivative.** You can define derivatives of any positive integer order. For instance, the **third derivative** is the derivative of the second derivative. Higher-order derivatives are denoted as shown below.

First derivative: y', $f'(x)$, $\dfrac{dy}{dx}$, $\dfrac{d}{dx}[f(x)]$, $D_x[y]$

Second derivative: y'', $f''(x)$, $\dfrac{d^2y}{dx^2}$, $\dfrac{d^2}{dx^2}[f(x)]$, $D_x^2[y]$

Third derivative: y''', $f'''(x)$, $\dfrac{d^3y}{dx^3}$, $\dfrac{d^3}{dx^3}[f(x)]$, $D_x^3[y]$

Fourth derivative: $y^{(4)}$, $f^{(4)}(x)$, $\dfrac{d^4y}{dx^4}$, $\dfrac{d^4}{dx^4}[f(x)]$, $D_x^4[y]$

$$\vdots$$

nth derivative: $y^{(n)}$, $f^{(n)}(x)$, $\dfrac{d^ny}{dx^n}$, $\dfrac{d^n}{dx^n}[f(x)]$, $D_x^n[y]$

The moon's mass is 7.349×10^{22} kilograms, and Earth's mass is 5.976×10^{24} kilograms. The moon's radius is 1737 kilometers, and Earth's radius is 6378 kilometers. Because the gravitational force on the surface of a planet is directly proportional to its mass and inversely proportional to the square of its radius, the ratio of the gravitational force on Earth to the gravitational force on the moon is

$$\frac{(5.976 \times 10^{24})/6378^2}{(7.349 \times 10^{22})/1737^2} \approx 6.0.$$

NASA

| **EXAMPLE 10** | **Finding the Acceleration Due to Gravity** |

Because the moon has no atmosphere, a falling object on the moon encounters no air resistance. In 1971, astronaut David Scott demonstrated that a feather and a hammer fall at the same rate on the moon. The position function for each of these falling objects is

$$s(t) = -0.81t^2 + 2$$

where $s(t)$ is the height in meters and t is the time in seconds, as shown in the figure at the right. What is the ratio of Earth's gravitational force to the moon's?

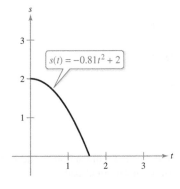

$s(t) = -0.81t^2 + 2$

Solution To find the acceleration, differentiate the position function twice.

$$s(t) = -0.81t^2 + 2 \qquad \text{Position function}$$
$$s'(t) = -1.62t \qquad \text{Velocity function}$$
$$s''(t) = -1.62 \qquad \text{Acceleration function}$$

So, the acceleration due to gravity on the moon is -1.62 meters per second per second. Because the acceleration due to gravity on Earth is -9.8 meters per second per second, the ratio of Earth's gravitational force to the moon's is

$$\frac{\text{Earth's gravitational force}}{\text{Moon's gravitational force}} = \frac{-9.8}{-1.62}$$

$$\approx 6.0.$$

3.3 Exercises

See **CalcChat.com** for tutorial help and worked-out solutions to odd-numbered exercises.

Using the Product Rule In Exercises 1–6, use the Product Rule to find the derivative of the function.

1. $g(x) = (x^2 + 3)(x^2 - 4x)$ 2. $y = (3x - 4)(x^3 + 5)$

3. $h(t) = \sqrt{t}(1 - t^2)$ 4. $g(s) = \sqrt{s}(s^2 + 8)$

5. $f(x) = e^x \cos x$ 6. $g(x) = \sqrt{x} \sin x$

Using the Quotient Rule In Exercises 7–12, use the Quotient Rule to find the derivative of the function.

7. $f(x) = \dfrac{x}{x^2 + 1}$ 8. $g(t) = \dfrac{3t^2 - 1}{2t + 5}$

9. $h(x) = \dfrac{\sqrt{x}}{x^3 + 1}$ 10. $f(x) = \dfrac{x^2}{2\sqrt{x} + 1}$

11. $g(x) = \dfrac{\sin x}{e^x}$ 12. $f(t) = \dfrac{\cos t}{t^3}$

Finding and Evaluating a Derivative In Exercises 13–20, find $f'(x)$ and $f'(c)$.

Function	Value of c
13. $f(x) = (x^3 + 4x)(3x^2 + 2x - 5)$	$c = 0$
14. $y = (x^2 - 3x + 2)(x^3 + 1)$	$c = 2$
15. $f(x) = \dfrac{x^2 - 4}{x - 3}$	$c = 1$
16. $f(x) = \dfrac{x - 4}{x + 4}$	$c = 3$
17. $f(x) = x \cos x$	$c = \dfrac{\pi}{4}$
18. $f(x) = \dfrac{\sin x}{x}$	$c = \dfrac{\pi}{6}$
19. $f(x) = e^x \sin x$	$c = 0$
20. $f(x) = \dfrac{\cos x}{e^x}$	$c = 0$

Using the Constant Multiple Rule In Exercises 21–26, complete the table to find the derivative of the function without using the Quotient Rule.

Function	Rewrite	Differentiate	Simplify
21. $y = \dfrac{x^2 + 3x}{7}$			
22. $y = \dfrac{5x^2 - 3}{4}$			
23. $y = \dfrac{6}{7x^2}$			
24. $y = \dfrac{10}{3x^3}$			
25. $y = \dfrac{4x^{3/2}}{x}$			
26. $y = \dfrac{2x}{x^{1/3}}$			

Finding a Derivative In Exercises 27–40, find the derivative of the algebraic function.

27. $f(x) = \dfrac{4 - 3x - x^2}{x^2 - 1}$ 28. $f(x) = \dfrac{x^2 + 5x + 6}{x^2 - 4}$

29. $f(x) = x\left(1 - \dfrac{4}{x + 3}\right)$ 30. $f(x) = x^4\left(1 - \dfrac{2}{x + 1}\right)$

31. $f(x) = \dfrac{3x - 1}{\sqrt{x}}$ 32. $f(x) = \sqrt[3]{x}(\sqrt{x} + 3)$

33. $h(s) = (s^3 - 2)^2$ 34. $h(x) = (x^2 + 3)^3$

35. $f(x) = \dfrac{2 - \dfrac{1}{x}}{x - 3}$ 36. $g(x) = x^2\left(\dfrac{2}{x} - \dfrac{1}{x + 1}\right)$

37. $f(x) = (2x^3 + 5x)(x - 3)(x + 2)$

38. $f(x) = (x^3 - x)(x^2 + 2)(x^2 + x - 1)$

39. $f(x) = \dfrac{x^2 + c^2}{x^2 - c^2}$, c is a constant

40. $f(x) = \dfrac{c^2 - x^2}{c^2 + x^2}$, c is a constant

Finding a Derivative of a Transcendental Function In Exercises 41–58, find the derivative of the transcendental function.

41. $f(t) = t^2 \sin t$ 42. $f(\theta) = (\theta + 1) \cos \theta$

43. $f(t) = \dfrac{\cos t}{t}$ 44. $f(x) = \dfrac{\sin x}{x^3}$

45. $f(x) = -e^x + \tan x$ 46. $y = e^x - \cot x$

47. $g(t) = \sqrt[4]{t} + 6 \csc t$ 48. $h(x) = \dfrac{1}{x} - 12 \sec x$

49. $y = \dfrac{3(1 - \sin x)}{2 \cos x}$ 50. $y = \dfrac{\sec x}{x}$

51. $y = -\csc x - \sin x$ 52. $y = x \sin x + \cos x$

53. $f(x) = x^2 \tan x$ 54. $f(x) = \sin x \cos x$

55. $y = 2x \sin x + x^2 e^x$ 56. $h(x) = 2e^x \cos x$

57. $y = \dfrac{e^x}{4\sqrt{x}}$ 58. $y = \dfrac{2e^x}{x^2 + 1}$

Finding a Derivative Using Technology In Exercises 59–62, use a computer algebra system to find the derivative of the function.

59. $g(x) = \left(\dfrac{x + 1}{x + 2}\right)(2x - 5)$

60. $f(x) = \left(\dfrac{x^2 - x - 3}{x^2 + 1}\right)(x^2 + x + 1)$

61. $g(\theta) = \dfrac{\theta}{1 - \sin \theta}$

62. $f(\theta) = \dfrac{\sin \theta}{1 - \cos \theta}$

Evaluating a Derivative In Exercises 63–66, evaluate the derivative of the function at the given point. Use a graphing utility to verify your result.

Function   Point

63. $y = \dfrac{1 + \csc x}{1 - \csc x}$ $\left(\dfrac{\pi}{6}, -3\right)$

64. $f(x) = \tan x \cot x$ $(1, 1)$

65. $h(t) = \dfrac{\sec t}{t}$ $\left(\pi, -\dfrac{1}{\pi}\right)$

66. $f(x) = \sin x(\sin x + \cos x)$ $\left(\dfrac{\pi}{4}, 1\right)$

Finding an Equation of a Tangent Line In Exercises 67–74, (a) find an equation of the tangent line to the graph of f at the given point, (b) use a graphing utility to graph the function and its tangent line at the point, and (c) use the *derivative* feature of a graphing utility to confirm your results.

67. $f(x) = (x^3 + 4x - 1)(x - 2)$, $(1, -4)$

68. $f(x) = (x - 2)(x^2 + 4)$, $(1, -5)$

69. $f(x) = \dfrac{x}{x + 4}$, $(-5, 5)$ **70.** $f(x) = \dfrac{x + 3}{x - 3}$, $(4, 7)$

71. $f(x) = \tan x$, $\left(\dfrac{\pi}{4}, 1\right)$ **72.** $f(x) = \sec x$, $\left(\dfrac{\pi}{3}, 2\right)$

73. $f(x) = (x - 1)e^x$, $(1, 0)$ **74.** $f(x) = \dfrac{e^x}{x + 4}$, $\left(0, \dfrac{1}{4}\right)$

Famous Curves In Exercises 75–78, find an equation of the tangent line to the graph at the given point. (The graphs in Exercises 75 and 76 are called *Witches of Agnesi*. The graphs in Exercises 77 and 78 are called *serpentines*.)

75.   **76.**

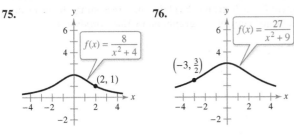

77.   **78.**

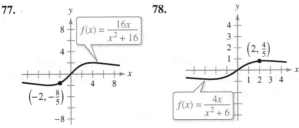

Horizontal Tangent Line In Exercises 79–82, determine the point(s) at which the graph of the function has a horizontal tangent line.

79. $f(x) = \dfrac{2x - 1}{x^2}$ **80.** $f(x) = \dfrac{x^2}{x^2 + 1}$

81. $g(x) = \dfrac{8(x - 2)}{e^x}$ **82.** $f(x) = e^x \sin x$, $[0, \pi]$

83. Tangent Lines Find equations of the tangent lines to the graph of $f(x) = (x + 1)/(x - 1)$ that are parallel to the line $2y + x = 6$. Then graph the function and the tangent lines.

84. Tangent Lines Find equations of the tangent lines to the graph of $f(x) = x/(x - 1)$ that pass through the point $(-1, 5)$. Then graph the function and the tangent lines.

Exploring a Relationship In Exercises 85 and 86, verify that $f'(x) = g'(x)$, and explain the relationship between f and g.

85. $f(x) = \dfrac{3x}{x + 2}$, $g(x) = \dfrac{5x + 4}{x + 2}$

86. $f(x) = \dfrac{\sin x - 3x}{x}$, $g(x) = \dfrac{\sin x + 2x}{x}$

Evaluating Derivatives In Exercises 87 and 88, use the graphs of f and g. Let $p(x) = f(x)g(x)$ and $q(x) = f(x)/g(x)$.

87. (a) Find $p'(1)$.   **88.** (a) Find $p'(4)$.

(b) Find $q'(4)$.   (b) Find $q'(7)$.

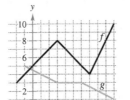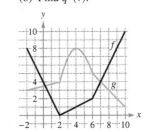

89. Area The length of a rectangle is given by $6t + 5$ and its height is $\sqrt{t}$, where t is time in seconds and the dimensions are in centimeters. Find the rate of change of the area with respect to time.

90. Volume The radius of a right circular cylinder is given by $\sqrt{t + 2}$ and its height is $\frac{1}{2}\sqrt{t}$, where t is time in seconds and the dimensions are in inches. Find the rate of change of the volume with respect to time.

91. Inventory Replenishment The ordering and transportation cost C for the components used in manufacturing a product is

$$C = 100\left(\dfrac{200}{x^2} + \dfrac{x}{x + 30}\right), \quad x \geq 1$$

where C is measured in thousands of dollars and x is the order size in hundreds. Find the rate of change of C with respect to x when (a) $x = 10$, (b) $x = 15$, and (c) $x = 20$. What do these rates of change imply about increasing order size?

92. Population Growth A population of 500 bacteria is introduced into a culture and grows in number according to the equation

$$P(t) = 500\left(1 + \dfrac{4t}{50 + t^2}\right)$$

where t is measured in hours. Find the rate at which the population is growing when $t = 2$.

93. Proof Prove each differentiation rule.

(a) $\dfrac{d}{dx}[\cot x] = -\csc^2 x$

(b) $\dfrac{d}{dx}[\sec x] = \sec x \tan x$

(c) $\dfrac{d}{dx}[\csc x] = -\csc x \cot x$

94. Rate of Change Determine whether there exist any values of x in the interval $[0, 2\pi)$ such that the rate of change of $f(x) = \sec x$ and the rate of change of $g(x) = \csc x$ are equal.

95. Modeling Data The table shows the health care expenditures h (in billions of dollars) in the United States and the population p (in millions) of the United States for the years 2004 through 2009. The year is represented by t, with $t = 4$ corresponding to 2004. (*Source: U.S. Centers for Medicare & Medicaid Services and U.S. Census Bureau*)

Year, t	4	5	6	7	8	9
h	1773	1890	2017	2135	2234	2330
p	293	296	299	302	305	307

(a) Use a graphing utility to find linear models for the health care expenditures $h(t)$ and the population $p(t)$.

(b) Use a graphing utility to graph each model found in part (a).

(c) Find $A = h(t)/p(t)$, then graph A using a graphing utility. What does this function represent?

(d) Find and interpret $A'(t)$ in the context of these data.

96. Satellites When satellites observe Earth, they can scan only part of Earth's surface. Some satellites have sensors that can measure the angle θ shown in the figure. Let h represent the satellite's distance from Earth's surface, and let r represent Earth's radius.

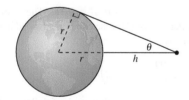

(a) Show that $h = r(\csc \theta - 1)$.

(b) Find the rate at which h is changing with respect to θ when $\theta = 30°$. (Assume $r = 3960$ miles.)

Finding a Second Derivative In Exercises 97–106, find the second derivative of the function.

97. $f(x) = x^4 + 2x^3 - 3x^2 - x$ **98.** $f(x) = 4x^5 - 2x^3 + 5x^2$

99. $f(x) = 4x^{3/2}$ **100.** $f(x) = x^2 + 3x^{-3}$

101. $f(x) = \dfrac{x}{x-1}$ **102.** $f(x) = \dfrac{x^2 + 3x}{x - 4}$

103. $f(x) = x \sin x$ **104.** $f(x) = \sec x$

105. $g(x) = \dfrac{e^x}{x}$ **106.** $h(t) = e^t \sin t$

Finding a Higher-Order Derivative In Exercises 107–110, find the given higher-order derivative.

107. $f'(x) = x^2$, $f''(x)$

108. $f''(x) = 2 - \dfrac{2}{x}$, $f'''(x)$

109. $f'''(x) = 2\sqrt{x}$, $f^{(4)}(x)$

110. $f^{(4)}(x) = 2x + 1$, $f^{(6)}(x)$

Using Relationships In Exercises 111–114, use the given information to find $f'(2)$.

$g(2) = 3$ and $g'(2) = -2$

$h(2) = -1$ and $h'(2) = 4$

111. $f(x) = 2g(x) + h(x)$

112. $f(x) = 4 - h(x)$

113. $f(x) = \dfrac{g(x)}{h(x)}$

114. $f(x) = g(x)h(x)$

WRITING ABOUT CONCEPTS

115. Sketching a Graph Sketch the graph of a differentiable function f such that $f(2) = 0$, $f' < 0$ for $-\infty < x < 2$, and $f' > 0$ for $2 < x < \infty$. Explain how you found your answer.

116. Sketching a Graph Sketch the graph of a differentiable function f such that $f > 0$ and $f' < 0$ for all real numbers x. Explain how you found your answer.

Identifying Graphs In Exercises 117 and 118, the graphs of f, f', and f'' are shown on the same set of coordinate axes. Identify each graph. Explain your reasoning. To print an enlarged copy of the graph, go to *MathGraphs.com*.

117.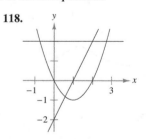

118.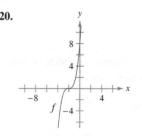

Sketching Graphs In Exercises 119–122, the graph of f is shown. Sketch the graphs of f' and f''. To print an enlarged copy of the graph, go to *MathGraphs.com*.

119.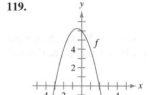

120.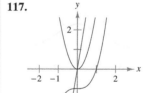

121.

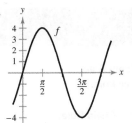

122.

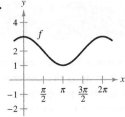

123. Acceleration The velocity of an object in meters per second is

$$v(t) = 36 - t^2$$

for $0 \le t \le 6$. Find the velocity and acceleration of the object when $t = 3$. What can be said about the speed of the object when the velocity and acceleration have opposite signs?

124. Acceleration The velocity of an automobile starting from rest is

$$v(t) = \frac{100t}{2t + 15}$$

where v is measured in feet per second. Find the acceleration at (a) 5 seconds, (b) 10 seconds, and (c) 20 seconds.

125. Stopping Distance A car is traveling at a rate of 66 feet per second (45 miles per hour) when the brakes are applied. The position function for the car is $s(t) = -8.25t^2 + 66t$, where s is measured in feet and t is measured in seconds. Use this function to complete the table, and find the average velocity during each time interval.

t	0	1	2	3	4
$s(t)$					
$v(t)$					
$a(t)$					

126. HOW DO YOU SEE IT? The figure shows the graphs of the position, velocity, and acceleration functions of a particle.

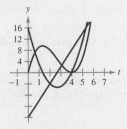

(a) Copy the graphs of the functions shown. Identify each graph. Explain your reasoning. To print an enlarged copy of the graph, go to *MathGraphs.com*.

(b) On your sketch, identify when the particle speeds up and when it slows down. Explain your reasoning.

Finding a Pattern In Exercises 127 and 128, develop a general rule for $f^{(n)}(x)$ given $f(x)$.

127. $f(x) = x^n$ **128.** $f(x) = \dfrac{1}{x}$

129. Finding a Pattern Consider the function $f(x) = g(x)h(x)$.

  (a) Use the Product Rule to generate rules for finding $f''(x)$, $f'''(x)$, and $f^{(4)}(x)$.

  (b) Use the results of part (a) to write a general rule for $f^{(n)}(x)$.

130. Finding a Pattern Develop a general rule for $[xf(x)]^{(n)}$, where f is a differentiable function of x.

Finding a Pattern In Exercises 131 and 132, find the derivatives of the function f for $n = 1, 2, 3,$ and 4. Use the results to write a general rule for $f'(x)$ in terms of n.

131. $f(x) = x^n \sin x$ **132.** $f(x) = \dfrac{\cos x}{x^n}$

Differential Equations In Exercises 133–136, verify that the function satisfies the differential equation.

Function	Differential Equation
133. $y = \dfrac{1}{x}, \; x > 0$	$x^3 y'' + 2x^2 y' = 0$
134. $y = 2x^3 - 6x + 10$	$-y''' - xy'' - 2y' = -24x^2$
135. $y = 2 \sin x + 3$	$y'' + y = 3$
136. $y = 3 \cos x + \sin x$	$y'' + y = 0$

True or False? In Exercises 137–142, determine whether the statement is true or false. If it is false, explain why or give an example that shows it is false.

137. If $y = f(x)g(x)$, then $\dfrac{dy}{dx} = f'(x)g'(x)$.

138. If $y = (x + 1)(x + 2)(x + 3)(x + 4)$, then $\dfrac{d^5 y}{dx^5} = 0$.

139. If $f'(c)$ and $g'(c)$ are zero and $h(x) = f(x)g(x)$, then $h'(c) = 0$.

140. If $f(x)$ is an nth-degree polynomial, then $f^{(n+1)}(x) = 0$.

141. The second derivative represents the rate of change of the first derivative.

142. If the velocity of an object is constant, then its acceleration is zero.

143. Absolute Value Find the derivative of $f(x) = x|x|$. Does $f''(0)$ exist? (*Hint:* Rewrite the function as a piecewise function and then differentiate each part.)

144. Think About It Let f and g be functions whose first and second derivatives exist on an interval I. Which of the following formulas is (are) true?

  (a) $fg'' - f''g = (fg' - f'g)'$ (b) $fg'' + f''g = (fg)''$

145. Proof Use the Product Rule twice to prove that if f, g, and h are differentiable functions of x, then

$$\frac{d}{dx}[f(x)g(x)h(x)] = f'(x)g(x)h(x) + f(x)g'(x)h(x) + f(x)g(x)h'(x).$$

3.4 The Chain Rule

- ◾ Find the derivative of a composite function using the Chain Rule.
- ◾ Find the derivative of a function using the General Power Rule.
- ◾ Simplify the derivative of a function using algebra.
- ◾ Find the derivative of a transcendental function using the Chain Rule.
- ◾ Find the derivative of a function involving the natural logarithmic function.
- ◾ Define and differentiate exponential functions that have bases other than *e*.

The Chain Rule

This text has yet to discuss one of the most powerful differentiation rules—the **Chain Rule.** This rule deals with composite functions and adds a surprising versatility to the rules discussed in the two previous sections. For example, compare the functions shown below. Those on the left can be differentiated without the Chain Rule, and those on the right are best differentiated with the Chain Rule.

Without the Chain Rule	**With the Chain Rule**
$y = x^2 + 1$	$y = \sqrt{x^2 + 1}$
$y = \sin x$	$y = \sin 6x$
$y = 3x + 2$	$y = (3x + 2)^5$
$y = e^x + \tan x$	$y = e^{5x} + \tan x^2$

Basically, the Chain Rule states that if y changes dy/du times as fast as u, and u changes du/dx times as fast as x, then y changes $(dy/du)(du/dx)$ times as fast as x.

EXAMPLE 1 **The Derivative of a Composite Function**

A set of gears is constructed so that the second and third gears are on the same axle (see Figure 3.24). As the first axle revolves, it drives the second axle, which in turn drives the third axle. Let y, u, and x represent the numbers of revolutions per minute of the first, second, and third axles, respectively. Find dy/du, du/dx, and dy/dx, and show that

$$\frac{dy}{dx} = \frac{dy}{du} \cdot \frac{du}{dx}.$$

Solution Because the circumference of the second gear is three times that of the first, the first axle must make three revolutions to turn the second axle once. Similarly, the second axle must make two revolutions to turn the third axle once, and you can write

$$\frac{dy}{du} = 3 \quad \text{and} \quad \frac{du}{dx} = 2.$$

Combining these two results, you know that the first axle must make six revolutions to turn the third axle once. So, you can write

$$\frac{dy}{dx} = \boxed{\begin{array}{c}\text{Rate of change of first axle}\\\text{with respect to second axle}\end{array}} \cdot \boxed{\begin{array}{c}\text{Rate of change of second axle}\\\text{with respect to third axle}\end{array}}$$

$$= \frac{dy}{du} \cdot \frac{du}{dx}$$

$$= 3 \cdot 2$$

$$= 6$$

$$= \boxed{\begin{array}{c}\text{Rate of change of first axle}\\\text{with respect to third axle}\end{array}} .$$

In other words, the rate of change of y with respect to x is the product of the rate of change of y with respect to u and the rate of change of u with respect to x. ◾

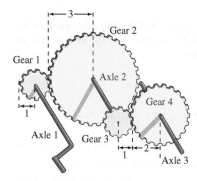

Axle 1: y revolutions per minute
Axle 2: u revolutions per minute
Axle 3: x revolutions per minute
Figure 3.24

Using the Chain Rule Each of the following functions can be differentiated using rules that you studied in Sections 3.2 and 3.3. For each function, find the derivative using those rules. Then find the derivative using the Chain Rule. Compare your results. Which method is simpler?

a. $\dfrac{2}{3x + 1}$

b. $(x + 2)^3$

c. $\sin 2x$

Example 1 illustrates a simple case of the Chain Rule. The general rule is stated in the next theorem.

THEOREM 3.11   The Chain Rule

If $y = f(u)$ is a differentiable function of u and $u = g(x)$ is a differentiable function of x, then $y = f(g(x))$ is a differentiable function of x and

$$\frac{dy}{dx} = \frac{dy}{du} \cdot \frac{du}{dx}$$

or, equivalently,

$$\frac{d}{dx}[f(g(x))] = f'(g(x))g'(x).$$

Proof   Let $h(x) = f(g(x))$. Then, using the alternative form of the derivative, you need to show that, for $x = c$,

$$h'(c) = f'(g(c))g'(c).$$

An important consideration in this proof is the behavior of g as x approaches c. A problem occurs when there are values of x, other than c, such that

$$g(x) = g(c).$$

Appendix A shows how to use the differentiability of f and g to overcome this problem. For now, assume that $g(x) \neq g(c)$ for values of x other than c. In the proofs of the Product Rule and the Quotient Rule, the same quantity was added and subtracted to obtain the desired form. This proof uses a similar technique—multiplying and dividing by the same (nonzero) quantity. Note that because g is differentiable, it is also continuous, and it follows that $g(x)$ approaches $g(c)$ as x approaches c.

$$h'(c) = \lim_{x \to c} \frac{f(g(x)) - f(g(c))}{x - c} \qquad \text{Alternative form of derivative}$$

$$= \lim_{x \to c} \left[\frac{f(g(x)) - f(g(c))}{x - c} \cdot \frac{g(x) - g(c)}{g(x) - g(c)} \right], \quad g(x) \neq g(c)$$

$$= \lim_{x \to c} \left[\frac{f(g(x)) - f(g(c))}{g(x) - g(c)} \cdot \frac{g(x) - g(c)}{x - c} \right]$$

$$= \left[\lim_{x \to c} \frac{f(g(x)) - f(g(c))}{g(x) - g(c)} \right] \left[\lim_{x \to c} \frac{g(x) - g(c)}{x - c} \right]$$

$$= f'(g(c))g'(c)$$

See LarsonCalculus.com for Bruce Edwards's video of this proof.

REMARK The alternative limit form of the derivative was given at the end of Section 3.1.

When applying the Chain Rule, it is helpful to think of the composite function $f \circ g$ as having two parts—an inner part and an outer part.

$$y = f(g(x)) = f(u)$$

Outer function / Inner function

The derivative of $y = f(u)$ is the derivative of the outer function (at the inner function u) times the derivative of the inner function.

$$y' = f'(u) \cdot u'$$

EXAMPLE 2 **Decomposition of a Composite Function**

$y = f(g(x))$	$u = g(x)$	$y = f(u)$
a. $y = \dfrac{1}{x + 1}$	$u = x + 1$	$y = \dfrac{1}{u}$
b. $y = \sin 2x$	$u = 2x$	$y = \sin u$
c. $y = \sqrt{3x^2 - x + 1}$	$u = 3x^2 - x + 1$	$y = \sqrt{u}$
d. $y = \tan^2 x$	$u = \tan x$	$y = u^2$

EXAMPLE 3 **Using the Chain Rule**

Find dy/dx for

$$y = (x^2 + 1)^3.$$

Solution For this function, you can consider the inside function to be $u = x^2 + 1$ and the outer function to be $y = u^3$. By the Chain Rule, you obtain

$$\frac{dy}{dx} = \underbrace{3(x^2 + 1)^2}_{\frac{dy}{du}}\underbrace{(2x)}_{\frac{du}{dx}} = 6x(x^2 + 1)^2.$$

REMARK You could also solve the problem in Example 3 without using the Chain Rule by observing that

$$y = x^6 + 3x^4 + 3x^2 + 1$$

and

$$y' = 6x^5 + 12x^3 + 6x.$$

Verify that this is the same as the derivative in Example 3. Which method would you use to find

$$\frac{d}{dx}(x^2 + 1)^{50}?$$

The General Power Rule

The function in Example 3 is an example of one of the most common types of composite functions, $y = [u(x)]^n$. The rule for differentiating such functions is called the **General Power Rule,** and it is a special case of the Chain Rule.

THEOREM 3.12 **The General Power Rule**

If $y = [u(x)]^n$, where u is a differentiable function of x and n is a rational number, then

$$\frac{dy}{dx} = n[u(x)]^{n-1}\frac{du}{dx}$$

or, equivalently,

$$\frac{d}{dx}[u^n] = nu^{n-1}u'.$$

Proof Because $y = [u(x)]^n = u^n$, you apply the Chain Rule to obtain

$$\frac{dy}{dx} = \left(\frac{dy}{du}\right)\left(\frac{du}{dx}\right)$$

$$= \frac{d}{du}[u^n]\frac{du}{dx}.$$

By the (Simple) Power Rule in Section 3.2, you have $D_u[u^n] = nu^{n-1}$, and it follows that

$$\frac{dy}{dx} = nu^{n-1}\frac{du}{dx}.$$

See LarsonCalculus.com for Bruce Edwards's video of this proof.

EXAMPLE 4 **Applying the General Power Rule**

Find the derivative of $f(x) = (3x - 2x^2)^3$.

Solution Let $u = 3x - 2x^2$. Then

$$f(x) = (3x - 2x^2)^3 = u^3$$

and, by the General Power Rule, the derivative is

$$f'(x) = \overset{n}{3}\overbrace{(3x - 2x^2)^2}^{u^{n-1}}\overbrace{\frac{d}{dx}[3x - 2x^2]}^{u'} \qquad \text{Apply General Power Rule.}$$

$$= 3(3x - 2x^2)^2(3 - 4x). \qquad \text{Differentiate } 3x - 2x^2.$$

EXAMPLE 5 **Differentiating Functions Involving Radicals**

Find all points on the graph of

$$f(x) = \sqrt[3]{(x^2 - 1)^2}$$

for which $f'(x) = 0$ and those for which $f'(x)$ does not exist.

Solution Begin by rewriting the function as

$$f(x) = (x^2 - 1)^{2/3}.$$

Then, applying the General Power Rule (with $u = x^2 - 1$) produces

$$f'(x) = \overset{n}{\frac{2}{3}}\overbrace{(x^2 - 1)^{-1/3}}^{u^{n-1}}\overbrace{(2x)}^{u'} \qquad \text{Apply General Power Rule.}$$

$$= \frac{4x}{3\sqrt[3]{x^2 - 1}}. \qquad \text{Write in radical form.}$$

So, $f'(x) = 0$ when $x = 0$, and $f'(x)$ does not exist when $x = \pm 1$, as shown in Figure 3.25.

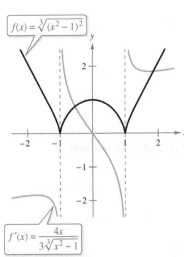

$$f(x) = \sqrt[3]{(x^2 - 1)^2}$$

$$f'(x) = \frac{4x}{3\sqrt[3]{x^2 - 1}}$$

The derivative of f is 0 at $x = 0$ and is undefined at $x = \pm 1$.
Figure 3.25

REMARK Try differentiating the function in Example 6 using the Quotient Rule. You should obtain the same result, but using the Quotient Rule is less efficient than using the General Power Rule.

EXAMPLE 6 **Differentiating Quotients: Constant Numerators**

Differentiate the function

$$g(t) = \frac{-7}{(2t - 3)^2}.$$

Solution Begin by rewriting the function as

$$g(t) = -7(2t - 3)^{-2}.$$

Then, applying the General Power Rule (with $u = 2t - 3$) produces

$$g'(t) = \underbrace{(-7)(-2)}_{\substack{\text{Constant} \\ \text{Multiple Rule}}}\overbrace{(2t - 3)^{-3}}^{u^{n-1}}\overbrace{(2)}^{u'} \qquad \text{Apply General Power Rule.}$$

$$= 28(2t - 3)^{-3} \qquad \text{Simplify.}$$

$$= \frac{28}{(2t - 3)^3}. \qquad \text{Write with positive exponent.}$$

Simplifying Derivatives

The next three examples demonstrate techniques for simplifying the "raw derivatives" of functions involving products, quotients, and composites.

EXAMPLE 7 Simplifying by Factoring Out the Least Powers

Find the derivative of $f(x) = x^2\sqrt{1 - x^2}$.

Solution

$$f(x) = x^2\sqrt{1 - x^2} \qquad \text{Write original function.}$$

$$= x^2(1 - x^2)^{1/2} \qquad \text{Rewrite.}$$

$$f'(x) = x^2\frac{d}{dx}[(1 - x^2)^{1/2}] + (1 - x^2)^{1/2}\frac{d}{dx}[x^2] \qquad \text{Product Rule}$$

$$= x^2\left[\frac{1}{2}(1 - x^2)^{-1/2}(-2x)\right] + (1 - x^2)^{1/2}(2x) \qquad \text{General Power Rule}$$

$$= -x^3(1 - x^2)^{-1/2} + 2x(1 - x^2)^{1/2} \qquad \text{Simplify.}$$

$$= x(1 - x^2)^{-1/2}[-x^2(1) + 2(1 - x^2)] \qquad \text{Factor.}$$

$$= \frac{x(2 - 3x^2)}{\sqrt{1 - x^2}} \qquad \text{Simplify.}$$

EXAMPLE 8 Simplifying the Derivative of a Quotient

▷ **TECHNOLOGY** Symbolic differentiation utilities are capable of differentiating very complicated functions. Often, however, the result is given in unsimplified form. If you have access to such a utility, use it to find the derivatives of the functions given in Examples 7, 8, and 9. Then compare the results with those given in these examples.

$$f(x) = \frac{x}{\sqrt[3]{x^2 + 4}} \qquad \text{Original function}$$

$$= \frac{x}{(x^2 + 4)^{1/3}} \qquad \text{Rewrite.}$$

$$f'(x) = \frac{(x^2 + 4)^{1/3}(1) - x(1/3)(x^2 + 4)^{-2/3}(2x)}{(x^2 + 4)^{2/3}} \qquad \text{Quotient Rule}$$

$$= \frac{1}{3}(x^2 + 4)^{-2/3}\left[\frac{3(x^2 + 4) - (2x^2)(1)}{(x^2 + 4)^{2/3}}\right] \qquad \text{Factor.}$$

$$= \frac{x^2 + 12}{3(x^2 + 4)^{4/3}} \qquad \text{Simplify.}$$

EXAMPLE 9 Simplifying the Derivative of a Power

•••▷ See LarsonCalculus.com for an interactive version of this type of example.

$$y = \left(\frac{3x - 1}{x^2 + 3}\right)^2 \qquad \text{Original function}$$

$$\overset{\displaystyle n}{\overset{\displaystyle |}{}}\ \overset{\displaystyle u^{n-1}}{\overbrace{\phantom{\left(\frac{3x-1}{x^2+3}\right)}}}\ \overset{\displaystyle u'}{\overbrace{\phantom{\frac{d}{dx}\left[\frac{3x-1}{x^2+3}\right]}}}$$

$$y' = 2\left(\frac{3x - 1}{x^2 + 3}\right)\frac{d}{dx}\left[\frac{3x - 1}{x^2 + 3}\right] \qquad \text{General Power Rule}$$

$$= \left[\frac{2(3x - 1)}{x^2 + 3}\right]\left[\frac{(x^2 + 3)(3) - (3x - 1)(2x)}{(x^2 + 3)^2}\right] \qquad \text{Quotient Rule}$$

$$= \frac{2(3x - 1)(3x^2 + 9 - 6x^2 + 2x)}{(x^2 + 3)^3} \qquad \text{Multiply.}$$

$$= \frac{2(3x - 1)(-3x^2 + 2x + 9)}{(x^2 + 3)^3} \qquad \text{Simplify.}$$

Transcendental Functions and the Chain Rule

The "Chain Rule versions" of the derivatives of the six trigonometric functions and the natural exponential function are shown below.

$$\frac{d}{dx}[\sin u] = (\cos u)u'$$ $$\frac{d}{dx}[\cos u] = -(\sin u)u'$$

$$\frac{d}{dx}[\tan u] = (\sec^2 u)u'$$ $$\frac{d}{dx}[\cot u] = -(\csc^2 u)u'$$

$$\frac{d}{dx}[\sec u] = (\sec u \tan u)u'$$ $$\frac{d}{dx}[\csc u] = -(\csc u \cot u)u'$$

$$\frac{d}{dx}[e^u] = e^u u'$$

•• **REMARK** Be sure you understand the mathematical conventions regarding parentheses and trigonometric functions. For instance, in Example 10(a), $\sin 2x$ is written to mean $\sin(2x)$.

EXAMPLE 10 The Chain Rule and Transcendental Functions

a. $y = \sin 2x$

$\overbrace{u}$

$y' = \overbrace{\cos 2x}^{\cos u} \overbrace{\frac{d}{dx}[2x]}^{u'} = (\cos 2x)(2) = 2 \cos 2x$

b. $y = \cos(x - 1)$

$\overbrace{u}$

$y' = \overbrace{-\sin(x - 1)}^{-(\sin u)} \overbrace{\frac{d}{dx}[x - 1]}^{u'} = -\sin(x - 1)$

c. $y = e^{3x}$

$\overbrace{u}$

$y' = \overbrace{e^{3x}}^{e^u} \overbrace{\frac{d}{dx}[3x]}^{u'} = 3e^{3x}$

EXAMPLE 11 Parentheses and Trigonometric Functions

a. $y = \cos 3x^2 = \cos(3x^2)$ $y' = (-\sin 3x^2)(6x) = -6x \sin 3x^2$
b. $y = (\cos 3)x^2$ $y' = (\cos 3)(2x) = 2x \cos 3$
c. $y = \cos(3x)^2 = \cos(9x^2)$ $y' = (-\sin 9x^2)(18x) = -18x \sin 9x^2$
d. $y = \cos^2 x = (\cos x)^2$ $y' = 2(\cos x)(-\sin x) = -2 \cos x \sin x$
e. $y = \sqrt{\cos x} = (\cos x)^{1/2}$ $y' = \frac{1}{2}(\cos x)^{-1/2}(-\sin x) = -\frac{\sin x}{2\sqrt{\cos x}}$

To find the derivative of a function of the form $k(x) = f(g(h(x)))$, you need to apply the Chain Rule twice, as shown in Example 12.

EXAMPLE 12 Repeated Application of the Chain Rule

$f(t) = \sin^3 4t$ Original function

$\quad = (\sin 4t)^3$ Rewrite.

$f'(t) = 3(\sin 4t)^2 \frac{d}{dt}[\sin 4t]$ Apply Chain Rule once.

$\quad = 3(\sin 4t)^2(\cos 4t)\frac{d}{dt}[4t]$ Apply Chain Rule a second time.

$\quad = 3(\sin 4t)^2(\cos 4t)(4)$

$\quad = 12 \sin^2 4t \cos 4t$ Simplify.

The Derivative of the Natural Logarithmic Function

Up to this point in the text, derivatives of algebraic functions have been algebraic and derivatives of transcendental functions have been transcendental. The next theorem looks at an unusual situation in which the derivative of a transcendental function is algebraic. Specifically, the derivative of the natural logarithmic function is the algebraic function $1/x$.

THEOREM 3.13   Derivative of the Natural Logarithmic Function

Let u be a differentiable function of x.

1. $\dfrac{d}{dx}[\ln x] = \dfrac{1}{x}, \quad x > 0$

2. $\dfrac{d}{dx}[\ln u] = \dfrac{1}{u}\dfrac{du}{dx} = \dfrac{u'}{u}, \quad u > 0$

Proof   To prove the first part, let $y = \ln x$, which implies that $e^y = x$. Differentiating both sides of this equation produces the following.

$$y = \ln x$$

$$e^y = x$$

$$\frac{d}{dx}[e^y] = \frac{d}{dx}[x]$$

$$e^y \frac{dy}{dx} = 1 \qquad\qquad \text{Chain Rule}$$

$$\frac{dy}{dx} = \frac{1}{e^y}$$

$$\frac{dy}{dx} = \frac{1}{x}$$

The second part of the theorem can be obtained by applying the Chain Rule to the first part.

See LarsonCalculus.com for Bruce Edwards's video of this proof.

EXAMPLE 13   **Differentiation of Logarithmic Functions**

$\cdots\triangleright$ *See LarsonCalculus.com for an interactive version of this type of example.*

a. $\dfrac{d}{dx}[\ln(2x)] = \dfrac{u'}{u} = \dfrac{2}{2x} = \dfrac{1}{x}$ $\qquad\qquad u = 2x$

b. $\dfrac{d}{dx}[\ln(x^2 + 1)] = \dfrac{u'}{u} = \dfrac{2x}{x^2 + 1}$ $\qquad\qquad u = x^2 + 1$

c. $\dfrac{d}{dx}[x \ln x] = x\left(\dfrac{d}{dx}[\ln x]\right) + (\ln x)\left(\dfrac{d}{dx}[x]\right)$ $\qquad$ Product Rule

$\qquad\qquad = x\left(\dfrac{1}{x}\right) + (\ln x)(1)$

$\qquad\qquad = 1 + \ln x$

d. $\dfrac{d}{dx}[(\ln x)^3] = 3(\ln x)^2 \dfrac{d}{dx}[\ln x]$ $\qquad\qquad$ Chain Rule

$\qquad\qquad = 3(\ln x)^2 \dfrac{1}{x}$

John Napier used logarithmic properties to simplify *calculations* involving products, quotients, and powers. Of course, given the availability of calculators, there is now little need for this particular application of logarithms. However, there is great value in using logarithmic properties to simplify *differentiation* involving products, quotients, and powers.

JOHN NAPIER (1550–1617)

Logarithms were invented by the Scottish mathematician John Napier. Although he did not introduce the *natural* logarithmic function, it is sometimes called the *Napierian* logarithm. *See LarsonCalculus.com to read more of this biography.*

EXAMPLE 14 Logarithmic Properties as Aids to Differentiation

Differentiate $f(x) = \ln\sqrt{x + 1}$.

Solution Because

$$f(x) = \ln\sqrt{x + 1} = \ln(x + 1)^{1/2} = \frac{1}{2}\ln(x + 1) \qquad \text{Rewrite before differentiating.}$$

you can write

$$f'(x) = \frac{1}{2}\left(\frac{1}{x + 1}\right) = \frac{1}{2(x + 1)}. \qquad \text{Differentiate.}$$

EXAMPLE 15 Logarithmic Properties as Aids to Differentiation

Differentiate $f(x) = \ln\dfrac{x(x^2 + 1)^2}{\sqrt{2x^3 - 1}}$.

Solution

$$f(x) = \ln\frac{x(x^2 + 1)^2}{\sqrt{2x^3 - 1}} \qquad \text{Write original function.}$$

$$= \ln x + 2\ln(x^2 + 1) - \frac{1}{2}\ln(2x^3 - 1) \qquad \text{Rewrite before differentiating.}$$

$$f'(x) = \frac{1}{x} + 2\left(\frac{2x}{x^2 + 1}\right) - \frac{1}{2}\left(\frac{6x^2}{2x^3 - 1}\right) \qquad \text{Differentiate.}$$

$$= \frac{1}{x} + \frac{4x}{x^2 + 1} - \frac{3x^2}{2x^3 - 1} \qquad \text{Simplify.}$$

• • • **REMARK** In Examples 14 and 15, be sure that you see the benefit of applying logarithmic properties *before* differentiation. Consider, for instance, the difficulty of direct differentiation of the function given in Example 15.

Because the natural logarithm is undefined for negative numbers, you will often encounter expressions of the form $\ln|u|$. Theorem 3.14 states that you can differentiate functions of the form $y = \ln|u|$ as though the absolute value notation was not present.

THEOREM 3.14 Derivative Involving Absolute Value

If u is a differentiable function of x such that $u \neq 0$, then

$$\frac{d}{dx}[\ln|u|] = \frac{u'}{u}.$$

Proof If $u > 0$, then $|u| = u$, and the result follows from Theorem 3.13. If $u < 0$, then $|u| = -u$, and you have

$$\frac{d}{dx}[\ln|u|] = \frac{d}{dx}[\ln(-u)] = \frac{-u'}{-u} = \frac{u'}{u}.$$

See LarsonCalculus.com for Bruce Edwards's video of this proof.

Bases Other than *e*

The **base** of the natural exponential function is *e*. This "natural" base can be used to assign a meaning to a general base *a*.

Definition of Exponential Function to Base *a*

If *a* is a positive real number ($a \neq 1$) and *x* is any real number, then the **exponential function to the base *a*** is denoted by a^x and is defined by

$$a^x = e^{(\ln a)x}.$$

If $a = 1$, then $y = 1^x = 1$ is a constant function.

Logarithmic functions to bases other than *e* can be defined in much the same way as exponential functions to other bases are defined.

Definition of Logarithmic Function to Base *a*

If *a* is a positive real number ($a \neq 1$) and *x* is any positive real number, then the **logarithmic function to the base *a*** is denoted by $\log_a x$ and is defined as

$$\log_a x = \frac{1}{\ln a} \ln x.$$

To differentiate exponential and logarithmic functions to other bases, you have two options: (1) use the definitions of a^x and $\log_a x$ and differentiate using the rules for the natural exponential and logarithmic functions, or (2) use the differentiation rules for bases other than *e* given in the next theorem.

REMARK These differentiation rules are similar to those for the natural exponential function and the natural logarithmic function. In fact, they differ only by the constant factors $\ln a$ and $1/\ln a$. This points out one reason why, for calculus, *e* is the most convenient base.

THEOREM 3.15 Derivatives for Bases Other than *e*

Let *a* be a positive real number ($a \neq 1$) and let *u* be a differentiable function of *x*.

1. $\dfrac{d}{dx}[a^x] = (\ln a)a^x$ **2.** $\dfrac{d}{dx}[a^u] = (\ln a)a^u \dfrac{du}{dx}$

3. $\dfrac{d}{dx}[\log_a x] = \dfrac{1}{(\ln a)x}$ **4.** $\dfrac{d}{dx}[\log_a u] = \dfrac{1}{(\ln a)u}\dfrac{du}{dx}$

Proof By definition, $a^x = e^{(\ln a)x}$. Therefore, you can prove the first rule by letting

$$u = (\ln a)x$$

and differentiating with base *e* to obtain

$$\frac{d}{dx}[a^x] = \frac{d}{dx}\left[e^{(\ln a)x}\right] = e^u \frac{du}{dx} = e^{(\ln a)x}(\ln a) = (\ln a)a^x.$$

To prove the third rule, you can write

$$\frac{d}{dx}[\log_a x] = \frac{d}{dx}\left[\frac{1}{\ln a}\ln x\right] = \frac{1}{\ln a}\left(\frac{1}{x}\right) = \frac{1}{(\ln a)x}.$$

The second and fourth rules are simply the Chain Rule versions of the first and third rules.

See LarsonCalculus.com for Bruce Edwards's video of this proof.

EXAMPLE 16 **Differentiating Functions to Other Bases**

•• REMARK Try writing 2^{3x} as 8^x and differentiating to see that you obtain the same result.

a. $y' = \dfrac{d}{dx}[2^x] = (\ln 2)2^x$

b. $y' = \dfrac{d}{dx}[2^{3x}] = (\ln 2)2^{3x}(3) = (3 \ln 2)2^{3x}$

c. $y' = \dfrac{d}{dx}[\log_{10} \cos x] = \dfrac{-\sin x}{(\ln 10) \cos x} = -\dfrac{1}{\ln 10} \tan x$

d. After rewriting the function below using logarithmic properties

$$y = \log_3 \frac{\sqrt{x}}{x + 5} = \frac{1}{2} \log_3 x - \log_3(x + 5)$$

you can apply Theorem 3.15 to find the derivative of the function.

$$y' = \frac{d}{dx}\left[\frac{1}{2} \log_3 x - \log_3(x + 5)\right] = \frac{1}{2(\ln 3)x} - \frac{1}{(\ln 3)(x + 5)} = \frac{5 - x}{2(\ln 3)x(x + 5)}$$

This section concludes with a summary of the differentiation rules studied so far. To become skilled at differentiation, you should memorize each rule in words, not symbols. As an aid to memorization, note that the cofunctions (cosine, cotangent, and cosecant) require a negative sign as part of their derivatives.

Summary of Differentiation Rules

General Differentiation Rules   Let u and v be differentiable functions of x.

Constant Rule:

$$\frac{d}{dx}[c] = 0$$

(Simple) Power Rule:

$$\frac{d}{dx}[x^n] = nx^{n-1}, \quad \frac{d}{dx}[x] = 1$$

Constant Multiple Rule:

$$\frac{d}{dx}[cu] = cu'$$

Sum or Difference Rule:

$$\frac{d}{dx}[u \pm v] = u' \pm v'$$

Product Rule:

$$\frac{d}{dx}[uv] = uv' + vu'$$

Quotient Rule:

$$\frac{d}{dx}\left[\frac{u}{v}\right] = \frac{vu' - uv'}{v^2}$$

Chain Rule:

$$\frac{d}{dx}[f(u)] = f'(u)\, u'$$

General Power Rule:

$$\frac{d}{dx}[u^n] = nu^{n-1}\, u'$$

Derivatives of Trigonometric Functions

$$\frac{d}{dx}[\sin x] = \cos x$$

$$\frac{d}{dx}[\cos x] = -\sin x$$

$$\frac{d}{dx}[\tan x] = \sec^2 x$$

$$\frac{d}{dx}[\cot x] = -\csc^2 x$$

$$\frac{d}{dx}[\sec x] = \sec x \tan x$$

$$\frac{d}{dx}[\csc x] = -\csc x \cot x$$

Derivatives of Exponential and Logarithmic Functions

$$\frac{d}{dx}[e^x] = e^x$$

$$\frac{d}{dx}[a^x] = (\ln a)a^x$$

$$\frac{d}{dx}[\ln x] = \frac{1}{x}$$

$$\frac{d}{dx}[\log_a x] = \frac{1}{(\ln a)x}$$

3.4 Exercises

See CalcChat.com for tutorial help and worked-out solutions to odd-numbered exercises.

Decomposition of a Composite Function In Exercises 1–6, complete the table.

$y = f(g(x))$	$u = g(x)$	$y = f(u)$
1. $y = (5x - 8)^4$		
2. $y = \dfrac{1}{\sqrt{x+1}}$		
3. $y = \csc^3 x$		
4. $y = 3\tan(\pi x^2)$		
5. $y = e^{-2x}$		
6. $y = (\ln x)^3$		

Finding a Derivative In Exercises 7–34, find the derivative of the function.

7. $y = (4x - 1)^3$

8. $y = 5(2 - x^3)^4$

9. $g(x) = 3(4 - 9x)^4$

10. $f(t) = (9t + 2)^{2/3}$

11. $f(t) = \sqrt{5 - t}$

12. $g(x) = \sqrt{4 - 3x^2}$

13. $y = \sqrt[3]{6x^2 + 1}$

14. $f(x) = \sqrt{x^2 - 4x + 2}$

15. $y = 2\sqrt[4]{9 - x^2}$

16. $f(x) = \sqrt[3]{12x - 5}$

17. $y = \dfrac{1}{x - 2}$

18. $s(t) = \dfrac{1}{4 - 5t - t^2}$

19. $f(t) = \left(\dfrac{1}{t - 3}\right)^2$

20. $y = -\dfrac{3}{(t - 2)^4}$

21. $y = \dfrac{1}{\sqrt{3x + 5}}$

22. $g(t) = \dfrac{1}{\sqrt{t^2 - 2}}$

23. $f(x) = x^2(x - 2)^4$

24. $f(x) = x(2x - 5)^3$

25. $y = x\sqrt{1 - x^2}$

26. $y = \frac{1}{2}x^2\sqrt{16 - x^2}$

27. $y = \dfrac{x}{\sqrt{x^2 + 1}}$

28. $y = \dfrac{x}{\sqrt{x^4 + 4}}$

29. $g(x) = \left(\dfrac{x + 5}{x^2 + 2}\right)^2$

30. $h(t) = \left(\dfrac{t^2}{t^3 + 2}\right)^2$

31. $f(v) = \left(\dfrac{1 - 2v}{1 + v}\right)^3$

32. $g(x) = \left(\dfrac{3x^2 - 2}{2x + 3}\right)^3$

33. $f(x) = ((x^2 + 3)^5 + x)^2$

34. $g(x) = (2 + (x^2 + 1)^4)^3$

Finding a Derivative Using Technology In Exercises 35–40, use a computer algebra system to find the derivative of the function. Then use the utility to graph the function and its derivative on the same set of coordinate axes. Describe the behavior of the function that corresponds to any zeros of the graph of the derivative.

35. $y = \dfrac{\sqrt{x + 1}}{x^2 + 1}$

36. $y = \sqrt{\dfrac{2x}{x + 1}}$

37. $y = \sqrt{\dfrac{x + 1}{x}}$

38. $g(x) = \sqrt{x - 1} + \sqrt{x + 1}$

39. $y = \dfrac{\cos \pi x + 1}{x}$

40. $y = x^2 \tan\dfrac{1}{x}$

Slope of a Tangent Line In Exercises 41 and 42, find the slope of the tangent line to the sine function at the origin. Compare this value with the number of complete cycles in the interval $[0, 2\pi]$. What can you conclude about the slope of the sine function $\sin ax$ at the origin?

41. (a) 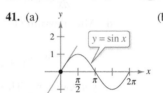   (b)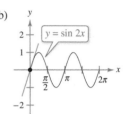

42. (a) 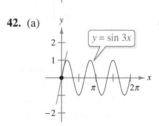   (b)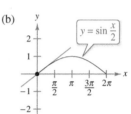

Slope of a Tangent Line In Exercises 43–46, find the slope of the tangent line to the graph of the function at the given point.

43. $y = e^{3x}$

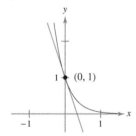

44. $y = e^{-3x}$

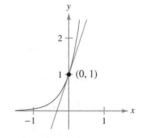

45. $y = \ln x^3$

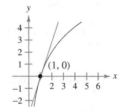

46. $y = \ln x^{3/2}$

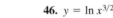
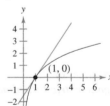

Finding a Derivative In Exercises 47–104, find the derivative of the function.

47. $y = \cos 4x$

48. $y = \sin \pi x$

49. $g(x) = 5\tan 3x$

50. $h(x) = \sec x^2$

51. $y = \sin(\pi x)^2$

52. $y = \cos(1 - 2x)^2$

53. $h(x) = \sin 2x \cos 2x$

54. $g(\theta) = \sec(\frac{1}{2}\theta)\tan(\frac{1}{2}\theta)$

55. $f(x) = \dfrac{\cot x}{\sin x}$

56. $g(v) = \dfrac{\cos v}{\csc v}$

57. $y = 4 \sec^2 x$

58. $g(t) = 5 \cos^2 \pi t$

59. $f(\theta) = \tan^2 5\theta$

60. $g(\theta) = \cos^2 8\theta$

61. $f(\theta) = \frac{1}{4} \sin^2 2\theta$

62. $h(t) = 2 \cot^2(\pi t + 2)$

63. $f(t) = 3 \sec^2(\pi t - 1)$

64. $y = 3x - 5 \cos(\pi x)^2$

65. $y = \sqrt{x} + \frac{1}{4} \sin(2x)^2$

66. $y = \sin \sqrt[3]{x} + \sqrt[3]{\sin x}$

67. $y = \sin(\tan 2x)$

68. $y = \cos\sqrt{\sin(\tan \pi x)}$

69. $f(x) = e^{2x}$

70. $y = e^{-x^2}$

71. $y = e^{\sqrt{x}}$

72. $y = x^2 e^{-x}$

73. $g(t) = (e^{-t} + e^t)^3$

74. $g(t) = e^{-3/t^2}$

75. $y = \ln(e^{x^2})$

76. $y = \ln\left(\dfrac{1 + e^x}{1 - e^x}\right)$

77. $y = \dfrac{2}{e^x + e^{-x}}$

78. $y = \dfrac{e^x - e^{-x}}{2}$

79. $y = x^2 e^x - 2xe^x + 2e^x$

80. $y = xe^x - e^x$

81. $f(x) = e^{-x} \ln x$

82. $f(x) = e^3 \ln x$

83. $y = e^x(\sin x + \cos x)$

84. $y = \ln e^x$

85. $g(x) = \ln x^2$

86. $h(x) = \ln(2x^2 + 3)$

87. $y = (\ln x)^4$

88. $y = x \ln x$

89. $y = \ln(x\sqrt{x^2 - 1})$

90. $y = \ln\sqrt{x^2 - 9}$

91. $f(x) = \ln\left(\dfrac{x}{x^2 + 1}\right)$

92. $f(x) = \ln\left(\dfrac{2x}{x + 3}\right)$

93. $g(t) = \dfrac{\ln t}{t^2}$

94. $h(t) = \dfrac{\ln t}{t}$

95. $y = \ln\sqrt{\dfrac{x + 1}{x - 1}}$

96. $y = \ln\sqrt[3]{\dfrac{x - 2}{x + 2}}$

97. $y = \dfrac{-\sqrt{x^2 + 1}}{x} + \ln\left(x + \sqrt{x^2 + 1}\right)$

98. $y = \dfrac{-\sqrt{x^2 + 4}}{2x^2} - \dfrac{1}{4}\ln\left(\dfrac{2 + \sqrt{x^2 + 4}}{x}\right)$

99. $y = \ln|\sin x|$

100. $y = \ln|\csc x|$

101. $y = \ln\left|\dfrac{\cos x}{\cos x - 1}\right|$

102. $y = \ln|\sec x + \tan x|$

103. $y = \ln\left|\dfrac{-1 + \sin x}{2 + \sin x}\right|$

104. $y = \ln\sqrt{1 + \sin^2 x}$

Evaluating a Derivative In Exercises 105–112, find and evaluate the derivative of the function at the given point. Use a graphing utility to verify your result.

105. $y = \sqrt{x^2 + 8x}, \quad (1, 3)$

106. $y = \sqrt[5]{3x^3 + 4x}, \quad (2, 2)$

107. $f(x) = \dfrac{5}{x^3 - 2}, \quad \left(-2, -\dfrac{1}{2}\right)$

108. $f(x) = \dfrac{1}{(x^2 - 3x)^2}, \quad \left(4, \dfrac{1}{16}\right)$

109. $f(t) = \dfrac{3t + 2}{t - 1}, \quad (0, -2)$

110. $f(x) = \dfrac{x + 4}{2x - 5}, \quad (9, 1)$

111. $y = 26 - \sec^3 4x, \quad (0, 25)$

112. $y = \dfrac{1}{x} + \sqrt{\cos x}, \quad \left(\dfrac{\pi}{2}, \dfrac{2}{\pi}\right)$

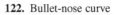 **Finding an Equation of a Tangent Line** In Exercises 113–120, (a) find an equation of the tangent line to the graph of f at the given point, (b) use a graphing utility to graph the function and its tangent line at the point, and (c) use the *derivative* feature of the graphing utility to confirm your results.

113. $f(x) = \sqrt{2x^2 - 7}, \quad (4, 5)$

114. $f(x) = (9 - x^2)^{2/3}, \quad (1, 4)$

115. $f(x) = \sin 2x, \quad (\pi, 0)$

116. $y = \cos 3x, \quad \left(\dfrac{\pi}{4}, -\dfrac{\sqrt{2}}{2}\right)$

117. $f(x) = \tan^2 x, \quad \left(\dfrac{\pi}{4}, 1\right)$

118. $y = 2 \tan^3 x, \quad \left(\dfrac{\pi}{4}, 2\right)$

119. $y = 4 - x^2 - \ln(\frac{1}{2}x + 1), \quad (0, 4)$

120. $y = 2e^{1-x^2}, \quad (1, 2)$

Famous Curves In Exercises 121 and 122, find an equation of the tangent line to the graph at the given point. Then use a graphing utility to graph the function and its tangent line in the same viewing window.

121. Top half of circle

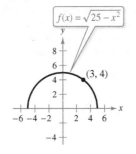

122. Bullet-nose curve

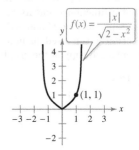

123. Horizontal Tangent Line Determine the point(s) in the interval $(0, 2\pi)$ at which the graph of

$$f(x) = 2 \cos x + \sin 2x$$

has a horizontal tangent.

124. Horizontal Tangent Line Determine the point(s) at which the graph of

$$f(x) = \dfrac{x}{\sqrt{2x - 1}}$$

has a horizontal tangent.

Finding a Second Derivative In Exercises 125–132, find the second derivative of the function.

125. $f(x) = 5(2 - 7x)^4$

126. $f(x) = 6(x^3 + 4)^3$

127. $f(x) = \dfrac{1}{x - 6}$

128. $f(x) = \dfrac{8}{(x - 2)^2}$

129. $f(x) = \sin x^2$

130. $f(x) = \sec^2 \pi x$

131. $f(x) = (3 + 2x)e^{-3x}$

132. $g(x) = \sqrt{x} + e^x \ln x$

Evaluating a Second Derivative In Exercises 133–136, evaluate the second derivative of the function at the given point. Use a computer algebra system to verify your result.

133. $h(x) = \dfrac{1}{9}(3x + 1)^3, \quad \left(1, \dfrac{64}{9}\right)$

134. $f(x) = \dfrac{1}{\sqrt{x + 4}}, \quad \left(0, \dfrac{1}{2}\right)$

135. $f(x) = \cos x^2, \quad (0, 1)$

136. $g(t) = \tan 2t, \quad \left(\dfrac{\pi}{6}, \sqrt{3}\right)$

Finding a Derivative In Exercises 137–152, find the derivative of the function.

137. $f(x) = 4^x$

138. $g(x) = 5^{-x}$

139. $y = 5^{x-2}$

140. $y = x(6^{-2x})$

141. $g(t) = t^2 2^t$

142. $f(t) = \dfrac{3^{2t}}{t}$

143. $h(\theta) = 2^{-\theta} \cos \pi\theta$

144. $g(\alpha) = 5^{-\alpha/2} \sin 2\alpha$

145. $y = \log_3 x$

146. $y = \log_{10} 2x$

147. $f(x) = \log_2 \dfrac{x^2}{x-1}$

148. $h(x) = \log_3 \dfrac{x\sqrt{x-1}}{2}$

149. $y = \log_5 \sqrt{x^2 - 1}$

150. $y = \log_{10} \dfrac{x^2 - 1}{x}$

151. $g(t) = \dfrac{10 \log_4 t}{t}$

152. $f(t) = t^{3/2} \log_2 \sqrt{t+1}$

WRITING ABOUT CONCEPTS

Identifying Graphs In Exercises 153–156, the graphs of a function f and its derivative f' are shown. Label the graphs as f or f' and write a short paragraph stating the criteria you used in making your selection. To print an enlarged copy of the graph, go to *MathGraphs.com.*

153.
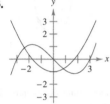

154.
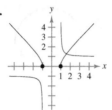

155.
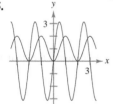

156.
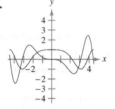

Describing a Relationship In Exercises 157 and 158, the relationship between f and g is given. Explain the relationship between f' and g'.

157. $g(x) = f(3x)$

158. $g(x) = f(x^2)$

Using Relationships In Exercises 159–162, given that

$$g(5) = -3, \quad g'(5) = 6, \quad h(5) = 3, \quad \text{and} \quad h'(5) = -2$$

find $f'(5)$, if possible. If it is not possible, state what additional information is required.

159. $f(x) = g(x)h(x)$

160. $f(x) = g(h(x))$

161. $f(x) = \dfrac{g(x)}{h(x)}$

162. $f(x) = [g(x)]^3$

Finding Derivatives In Exercises 163 and 164, the graphs of f and g are shown. Let $h(x) = f(g(x))$ and $s(x) = g(f(x))$. Find each derivative, if it exists. If the derivative does not exist, explain why.

163. (a) Find $h'(1)$.

(b) Find $s'(5)$.

164. (a) Find $h'(3)$.

(b) Find $s'(9)$.

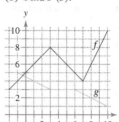

165. **Doppler Effect** The frequency F of a fire truck siren heard by a stationary observer is

$$F = \frac{132{,}400}{331 \pm v}$$

where $\pm v$ represents the velocity of the accelerating fire truck in meters per second (see figure). Find the rate of change of F with respect to v when

(a) the fire truck is approaching at a velocity of 30 meters per second (use $-v$).

(b) the fire truck is moving away at a velocity of 30 meters per second (use $+v$).

$$F = \frac{132{,}400}{331 + v} \qquad\qquad F = \frac{132{,}400}{331 - v}$$

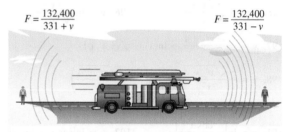

166. **Harmonic Motion** The displacement from equilibrium of an object in harmonic motion on the end of a spring is

$$y = \frac{1}{3} \cos 12t - \frac{1}{4} \sin 12t$$

where y is measured in feet and t is the time in seconds. Determine the position and velocity of the object when $t = \pi/8$.

167. **Pendulum** A 15-centimeter pendulum moves according to the equation $\theta = 0.2 \cos 8t$, where θ is the angular displacement from the vertical in radians and t is the time in seconds. Determine the maximum angular displacement and the rate of change of θ when $t = 3$ seconds.

168. **Wave Motion** A buoy oscillates in simple harmonic motion $y = A \cos \omega t$ as waves move past it. The buoy moves a total of 3.5 feet (vertically) from its low point to its high point. It returns to its high point every 10 seconds.

(a) Write an equation describing the motion of the buoy if it is at its high point at $t = 0$.

(b) Determine the velocity of the buoy as a function of t.

169. Modeling Data The normal daily maximum temperatures T (in degrees Fahrenheit) for Chicago, Illinois, are shown in the table. *(Source: National Oceanic and Atmospheric Administration)*

Month	Jan	Feb	Mar	Apr
Temperature	29.6	34.7	46.1	58.0

Month	May	Jun	Jul	Aug
Temperature	69.9	79.2	83.5	81.2

Month	Sep	Oct	Nov	Dec
Temperature	73.9	62.1	47.1	34.4

(a) Use a graphing utility to plot the data and find a model for the data of the form

$$T(t) = a + b \sin(ct - d)$$

where T is the temperature and t is the time in months, with $t = 1$ corresponding to January.

(b) Use a graphing utility to graph the model. How well does the model fit the data?

(c) Find T' and use a graphing utility to graph the derivative.

(d) Based on the graph of the derivative, during what times does the temperature change most rapidly? Most slowly? Do your answers agree with your observations of the temperature changes? Explain.

170. **HOW DO YOU SEE IT?** The cost C (in dollars) of producing x units of a product is $C = 60x + 1350$. For one week, management determined that the number of units produced x at the end of t hours can be modeled by $x = -1.6t^3 + 19t^2 - 0.5t - 1$. The graph shows the cost C in terms of the time t.

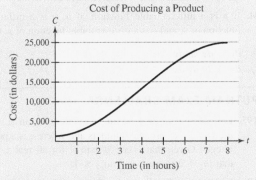

Cost of Producing a Product

(a) Using the graph, which is greater, the rate of change of the cost after 1 hour or the rate of change of the cost after 4 hours?

(b) Explain why the cost function is not increasing at a constant rate during the eight-hour shift.

171. Modeling Data The table shows the temperatures T (°F) at which water boils at selected pressures p (pounds per square inch). *(Source: Standard Handbook of Mechanical Engineers)*

p	5	10	14.696 (1 atm)	20
T	162.24°	193.21°	212.00°	227.96°

p	30	40	60	80	100
T	250.33°	267.25°	292.71°	312.03°	327.81°

A model that approximates the data is

$$T = 87.97 + 34.96 \ln p + 7.91 \sqrt{p}.$$

 (a) Use a graphing utility to plot the data and graph the model.

(b) Find the rates of change of T with respect to p when $p = 10$ and $p = 70$.

172. Think About It The table shows some values of the derivative of an unknown function f. Complete the table by finding the derivative of each transformation of f, if possible.

(a) $g(x) = f(x) - 2$ (b) $h(x) = 2f(x)$

(c) $r(x) = f(-3x)$ (d) $s(x) = f(x + 2)$

x	-2	-1	0	1	2	3
$f'(x)$	4	$\frac{2}{3}$	$-\frac{1}{3}$	-1	-2	-4
$g'(x)$						
$h'(x)$						
$r'(x)$						
$s'(x)$						

173. Circulatory System The speed S of blood that is r centimeters from the center of an artery is

$$S = C(R^2 - r^2)$$

where C is a constant, R is the radius of the artery, and S is measured in centimeters per second. After a drug is administered, the artery begins to dilate at a rate of dR/dt. At a constant distance r, find the rate at which S changes with respect to t for $C = 1.76 \times 10^5$, $R = 1.2 \times 10^{-2}$, and $dR/dt = 10^{-5}$.

174. Inflation If the annual rate of inflation averages 5% over the next 10 years, the approximate cost C of goods or services during any year in that decade is $C(t) = P(1.05)^t$, where t is the time in years and P is the present cost.

(a) If the price of an oil change for your car is presently $29.95, estimate the price 10 years from now.

(b) Find the rates of change of C with respect to t when $t = 1$ and $t = 8$.

(c) Verify that the rate of change of C is proportional to C. What is the constant of proportionality?

• • 175. **Biology** • • • • • • • • • • • • • • • • •

The number N of bacteria in a culture after t days is modeled by

$$N = 400\left[1 - \frac{3}{(t^2 + 2)^2}\right].$$

Find the rate of change of N with respect to t when (a) $t = 0$, (b) $t = 1$, (c) $t = 2$, (d) $t = 3$, and (e) $t = 4$. (f) What can you conclude?

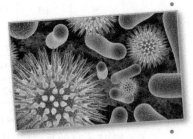

176. **Depreciation** The value V of a machine t years after it is purchased is inversely proportional to the square root of $t + 1$. The initial value of the machine is $10,000.

(a) Write V as a function of t.

(b) Find the rate of depreciation when $t = 1$.

(c) Find the rate of depreciation when $t = 3$.

177. **Finding a Pattern** Consider the function $f(x) = \sin \beta x$, where β is a constant.

(a) Find the first-, second-, third-, and fourth-order derivatives of the function.

(b) Verify that the function and its second derivative satisfy the equation $f''(x) + \beta^2 f(x) = 0$.

(c) Use the results of part (a) to write general rules for the even- and odd-order derivatives $f^{(2k)}(x)$ and $f^{(2k-1)}(x)$. [*Hint:* $(-1)^k$ is positive if k is even and negative if k is odd.]

178. **Conjecture** Let f be a differentiable function of period p.

(a) Is the function f' periodic? Verify your answer.

(b) Consider the function $g(x) = f(2x)$. Is the function $g'(x)$ periodic? Verify your answer.

179. **Think About It** Let $r(x) = f(g(x))$ and $s(x) = g(f(x))$, where f and g are shown in the figure. Find (a) $r'(1)$ and (b) $s'(4)$.

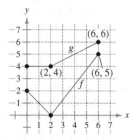

180. **Using Trigonometric Functions**

(a) Find the derivative of the function $g(x) = \sin^2 x + \cos^2 x$ in two ways.

(b) For $f(x) = \sec^2 x$ and $g(x) = \tan^2 x$, show that

$$f'(x) = g'(x).$$

181. **Even and Odd Functions**

(a) Show that the derivative of an odd function is even. That is, if $f(-x) = -f(x)$, then $f'(-x) = f'(x)$.

(b) Show that the derivative of an even function is odd. That is, if $f(-x) = f(x)$, then $f'(-x) = -f'(x)$.

182. **Proof** Let u be a differentiable function of x. Use the fact that $|u| = \sqrt{u^2}$ to prove that

$$\frac{d}{dx}[|u|] = u'\frac{u}{|u|}, \quad u \neq 0.$$

Using Absolute Value In Exercises 183–186, use the result of Exercise 182 to find the derivative of the function.

183. $g(x) = |3x - 5|$

184. $f(x) = |x^2 - 9|$

185. $h(x) = |x| \cos x$

186. $f(x) = |\sin x|$

Linear and Quadratic Approximations The linear and quadratic approximations of a function f at $x = a$ are

$$P_1(x) = f'(a)(x - a) + f(a) \quad \text{and}$$
$$P_2(x) = \tfrac{1}{2}f''(a)(x - a)^2 + f'(a)(x - a) + f(a).$$

In Exercises 187–190, (a) find the specified linear and quadratic approximations of f, (b) use a graphing utility to graph f and the approximations, (c) determine whether P_1 or P_2 is the better approximation, and (d) state how the accuracy changes as you move farther from $x = a$.

187. $f(x) = \tan x; \quad a = \dfrac{\pi}{4}$

188. $f(x) = \sec x; \quad a = \dfrac{\pi}{6}$

189. $f(x) = e^x; \quad a = 0$

190. $f(x) = \ln x; \quad a = 1$

True or False? In Exercises 191–194, determine whether the statement is true or false. If it is false, explain why or give an example that shows it is false.

191. If $y = (1 - x)^{1/2}$, then $y' = \tfrac{1}{2}(1 - x)^{-1/2}$.

192. If $f(x) = \sin^2(2x)$, then $f'(x) = 2(\sin 2x)(\cos 2x)$.

193. If y is a differentiable function of u, and u is a differentiable function of x, then y is a differentiable function of x.

194. If y is a differentiable function of u, u is a differentiable function of v, and v is a differentiable function of x, then

$$\frac{dy}{dx} = \frac{dy}{du}\frac{du}{dv}\frac{dv}{dx}.$$

PUTNAM EXAM CHALLENGE

195. Let $f(x) = a_1 \sin x + a_2 \sin 2x + \cdots + a_n \sin nx$, where $a_1, a_2, \ldots, a_n$ are real numbers and where n is a positive integer. Given that $|f(x)| \leq |\sin x|$ for all real x, prove that $|a_1 + 2a_2 + \cdots + na_n| \leq 1$.

196. Let k be a fixed positive integer. The nth derivative of $\dfrac{1}{x^k - 1}$ has the form $\dfrac{P_n(x)}{(x^k - 1)^{n+1}}$ where $P_n(x)$ is a polynomial. Find $P_n(1)$.

These problems were composed by the Committee on the Putnam Prize Competition.
© The Mathematical Association of America. All rights reserved.

3.5   Implicit Differentiation

■ Distinguish between functions written in implicit form and explicit form.
■ Use implicit differentiation to find the derivative of a function.
■ Find derivatives of functions using logarithmic differentiation.

Implicit and Explicit Functions

Up to this point in the text, most functions have been expressed in **explicit form.** For example, in the equation $y = 3x^2 - 5$, the variable y is explicitly written as a function of x. Some functions, however, are only implied by an equation. For instance, the function $y = 1/x$ is defined **implicitly** by the equation

$xy = 1$.   Implicit form

To find dy/dx for this equation, you can write y explicitly as a function of x and then differentiate.

Implicit Form	**Explicit Form**	**Derivative**
$xy = 1$	$y = \dfrac{1}{x} = x^{-1}$	$\dfrac{dy}{dx} = -x^{-2} = -\dfrac{1}{x^2}$

This strategy works whenever you can solve for the function explicitly. You cannot, however, use this procedure when you are unable to solve for y as a function of x. For instance, how would you find dy/dx for the equation

$x^2 - 2y^3 + 4y = 2$?

For this equation, it is difficult to express y as a function of x explicitly. To find dy/dx, you can use **implicit differentiation.**

To understand how to find dy/dx implicitly, you must realize that the differentiation is taking place *with respect to x*. This means that when you differentiate terms involving x alone, you can differentiate as usual. However, when you differentiate terms involving y, you must apply the Chain Rule, because you are assuming that y is defined implicitly as a differentiable function of x.

EXAMPLE 1   Differentiating with Respect to *x*

a. $\dfrac{d}{dx}[x^3] = 3x^2$ Variables agree: use Simple Power Rule.

Variables agree

b. $\dfrac{d}{dx}\overbrace{[y^3]}^{u^n} = \overbrace{3y^2}^{nu^{n-1}}\overbrace{\dfrac{dy}{dx}}^{u'}$ Variables disagree: use Chain Rule.

Variables disagree

c. $\dfrac{d}{dx}[x + 3y] = 1 + 3\dfrac{dy}{dx}$ Chain Rule: $\dfrac{d}{dx}[3y] = 3y'$

d. $\dfrac{d}{dx}[xy^2] = x\dfrac{d}{dx}[y^2] + y^2\dfrac{d}{dx}[x]$ Product Rule

$= x\left(2y\dfrac{dy}{dx}\right) + y^2(1)$ Chain Rule

$= 2xy\dfrac{dy}{dx} + y^2$ Simplify.

Implicit Differentiation

> **GUIDELINES FOR IMPLICIT DIFFERENTIATION**
>
> **1.** Differentiate both sides of the equation *with respect to x*.
> **2.** Collect all terms involving dy/dx on the left side of the equation and move all other terms to the right side of the equation.
> **3.** Factor dy/dx out of the left side of the equation.
> **4.** Solve for dy/dx.

In Example 2, note that implicit differentiation can produce an expression for dy/dx that contains both x and y.

EXAMPLE 2 **Implicit Differentiation**

Find dy/dx given that $y^3 + y^2 - 5y - x^2 = -4$.

Solution

1. Differentiate both sides of the equation with respect to x.

$$\frac{d}{dx}[y^3 + y^2 - 5y - x^2] = \frac{d}{dx}[-4]$$

$$\frac{d}{dx}[y^3] + \frac{d}{dx}[y^2] - \frac{d}{dx}[5y] - \frac{d}{dx}[x^2] = \frac{d}{dx}[-4]$$

$$3y^2\frac{dy}{dx} + 2y\frac{dy}{dx} - 5\frac{dy}{dx} - 2x = 0$$

2. Collect the dy/dx terms on the left side of the equation and move all other terms to the right side of the equation.

$$3y^2\frac{dy}{dx} + 2y\frac{dy}{dx} - 5\frac{dy}{dx} = 2x$$

3. Factor dy/dx out of the left side of the equation.

$$\frac{dy}{dx}(3y^2 + 2y - 5) = 2x$$

4. Solve for dy/dx by dividing by $(3y^2 + 2y - 5)$.

$$\frac{dy}{dx} = \frac{2x}{3y^2 + 2y - 5}$$

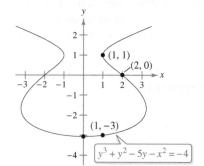

Point on Graph	Slope of Graph
$(2, 0)$	$-\frac{4}{5}$
$(1, -3)$	$\frac{1}{8}$
$x = 0$	0
$(1, 1)$	Undefined

The implicit equation

$$y^3 + y^2 - 5y - x^2 = -4$$

has the derivative

$$\frac{dy}{dx} = \frac{2x}{3y^2 + 2y - 5}.$$

Figure 3.26

To see how you can use an *implicit derivative*, consider the graph shown in Figure 3.26. From the graph, you can see that y is not a function of x. Even so, the derivative found in Example 2 gives a formula for the slope of the tangent line at a point on this graph. The slopes at several points on the graph are shown below the graph.

▷ **TECHNOLOGY** With most graphing utilities, it is easy to graph an equation that explicitly represents y as a function of x. Graphing other equations, however, can require some ingenuity. For instance, to graph the equation given in Example 2, use a graphing utility, set in *parametric* mode, to graph the parametric representations $x = \sqrt{t^3 + t^2 - 5t + 4}$, $y = t$, and $x = -\sqrt{t^3 + t^2 - 5t + 4}$, $y = t$, for $-5 \le t \le 5$. How does the result compare with the graph shown in Figure 3.26?

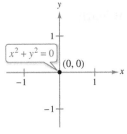

$x^2 + y^2 = 0$
$(0, 0)$

(a)

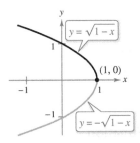

$y = \sqrt{1 - x^2}$
$(-1, 0)$ $(1, 0)$
$y = -\sqrt{1 - x^2}$

(b)

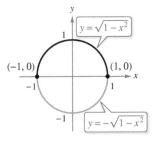

$y = \sqrt{1 - x}$
$(1, 0)$
$y = -\sqrt{1 - x}$

(c)

Some graph segments can be represented by differentiable functions.
Figure 3.27

It is meaningless to solve for dy/dx in an equation that has no solution points. (For example, $x^2 + y^2 = -4$ has no solution points.) If, however, a segment of a graph can be represented by a differentiable function, then dy/dx will have meaning as the slope at each point on the segment. Recall that a function is not differentiable at (a) points with vertical tangents and (b) points at which the function is not continuous.

EXAMPLE 3   **Graphs and Differentiable Functions**

If possible, represent y as a differentiable function of x.

a. $x^2 + y^2 = 0$ **b.** $x^2 + y^2 = 1$ **c.** $x + y^2 = 1$

Solution

a. The graph of this equation is a single point. So, it does not define y as a differentiable function of x. See Figure 3.27(a).

b. The graph of this equation is the unit circle centered at $(0, 0)$. The upper semicircle is given by the differentiable function

$$y = \sqrt{1 - x^2}, \quad -1 < x < 1$$

and the lower semicircle is given by the differentiable function

$$y = -\sqrt{1 - x^2}, \quad -1 < x < 1.$$

At the points $(-1, 0)$ and $(1, 0)$, the slope of the graph is undefined. See Figure 3.27(b).

c. The upper half of this parabola is given by the differentiable function

$$y = \sqrt{1 - x}, \quad x < 1$$

and the lower half of this parabola is given by the differentiable function

$$y = -\sqrt{1 - x}, \quad x < 1.$$

At the point $(1, 0)$, the slope of the graph is undefined. See Figure 3.27(c).

EXAMPLE 4   **Finding the Slope of a Graph Implicitly**

$\vdots \cdots \triangleright$ *See LarsonCalculus.com for an interactive version of this type of example.*

Determine the slope of the tangent line to the graph of $x^2 + 4y^2 = 4$ at the point $\left(\sqrt{2}, -1/\sqrt{2}\right)$. See Figure 3.28.

Solution

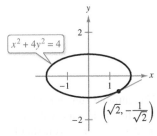

$x^2 + 4y^2 = 4$

Figure 3.28

$$x^2 + 4y^2 = 4 \qquad \text{Write original equation.}$$

$$2x + 8y\frac{dy}{dx} = 0 \qquad \text{Differentiate with respect to } x.$$

$$\frac{dy}{dx} = \frac{-2x}{8y} \qquad \text{Solve for } \frac{dy}{dx}.$$

$$= \frac{-x}{4y} \qquad \text{Simplify.}$$

So, at $\left(\sqrt{2}, -1/\sqrt{2}\right)$, the slope is

$\cdots \triangleright$ $\dfrac{dy}{dx} = \dfrac{-\sqrt{2}}{-4/\sqrt{2}} = \dfrac{1}{2}.$ Evaluate $\frac{dy}{dx}$ when $x = \sqrt{2}$ and $y = -\frac{1}{\sqrt{2}}$.   ■

$\cdots \cdots$ **REMARK**   To see the benefit of implicit differentiation, try doing Example 4 using the explicit function $y = -\frac{1}{2}\sqrt{4 - x^2}$.

| EXAMPLE 5 | **Finding the Slope of a Graph Implicitly** |

Determine the slope of the graph of

$$3(x^2 + y^2)^2 = 100xy$$

at the point $(3, 1)$.

Solution

$$\frac{d}{dx}[3(x^2 + y^2)^2] = \frac{d}{dx}[100xy]$$

$$3(2)(x^2 + y^2)\left(2x + 2y\frac{dy}{dx}\right) = 100\left[x\frac{dy}{dx} + y(1)\right]$$

$$12y(x^2 + y^2)\frac{dy}{dx} - 100x\frac{dy}{dx} = 100y - 12x(x^2 + y^2)$$

$$[12y(x^2 + y^2) - 100x]\frac{dy}{dx} = 100y - 12x(x^2 + y^2)$$

$$\frac{dy}{dx} = \frac{100y - 12x(x^2 + y^2)}{-100x + 12y(x^2 + y^2)}$$

$$= \frac{25y - 3x(x^2 + y^2)}{-25x + 3y(x^2 + y^2)}$$

At the point $(3, 1)$, the slope of the graph is

$$\frac{dy}{dx} = \frac{25(1) - 3(3)(3^2 + 1^2)}{-25(3) + 3(1)(3^2 + 1^2)} = \frac{25 - 90}{-75 + 30} = \frac{-65}{-45} = \frac{13}{9}$$

as shown in Figure 3.29. This graph is called a **lemniscate.**

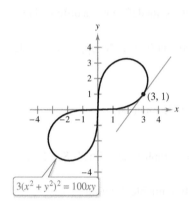

Lemniscate
Figure 3.29

| EXAMPLE 6 | **Determining a Differentiable Function** |

Find dy/dx implicitly for the equation $\sin y = x$. Then find the largest interval of the form $-a < y < a$ on which y is a differentiable function of x (see Figure 3.30).

Solution

$$\frac{d}{dx}[\sin y] = \frac{d}{dx}[x]$$

$$\cos y\frac{dy}{dx} = 1$$

$$\frac{dy}{dx} = \frac{1}{\cos y}$$

The largest interval about the origin for which y is a differentiable function of x is $-\pi/2 < y < \pi/2$. To see this, note that $\cos y$ is positive for all y in this interval and is 0 at the endpoints. When you restrict y to the interval $-\pi/2 < y < \pi/2$, you should be able to write dy/dx explicitly as a function of x. To do this, you can use

$$\cos y = \sqrt{1 - \sin^2 y}$$

$$= \sqrt{1 - x^2}, \quad -\frac{\pi}{2} < y < \frac{\pi}{2}$$

and conclude that

$$\frac{dy}{dx} = \frac{1}{\sqrt{1 - x^2}}.$$

You will study this example further when derivatives of inverse trigonometric functions are defined in Section 3.6.

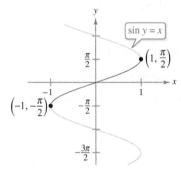

The derivative is $\dfrac{dy}{dx} = \dfrac{1}{\sqrt{1 - x^2}}$.

Figure 3.30

With implicit differentiation, the form of the derivative often can be simplified (as in Example 6) by an appropriate use of the *original* equation. A similar technique can be used to find and simplify higher-order derivatives obtained implicitly.

EXAMPLE 7   Finding the Second Derivative Implicitly

Given $x^2 + y^2 = 25$, find $\dfrac{d^2y}{dx^2}$.

Solution   Differentiating each term with respect to x produces

$$2x + 2y\frac{dy}{dx} = 0$$

$$2y\frac{dy}{dx} = -2x$$

$$\frac{dy}{dx} = \frac{-2x}{2y}$$

$$= -\frac{x}{y}.$$

Differentiating a second time with respect to x yields

$$\frac{d^2y}{dx^2} = -\frac{(y)(1) - (x)(dy/dx)}{y^2} \qquad \text{Quotient Rule}$$

$$= -\frac{y - (x)(-x/y)}{y^2} \qquad \text{Substitute } -\frac{x}{y} \text{ for } \frac{dy}{dx}.$$

$$= -\frac{y^2 + x^2}{y^3} \qquad \text{Simplify.}$$

$$= -\frac{25}{y^3}. \qquad \text{Substitute 25 for } x^2 + y^2.$$

EXAMPLE 8   Finding a Tangent Line to a Graph

Find the tangent line to the graph of $x^2(x^2 + y^2) = y^2$ at the point $\left(\sqrt{2}/2, \sqrt{2}/2\right)$, as shown in Figure 3.31.

Solution   By rewriting and differentiating implicitly, you obtain

$$x^4 + x^2y^2 - y^2 = 0$$

$$4x^3 + x^2\left(2y\frac{dy}{dx}\right) + 2xy^2 - 2y\frac{dy}{dx} = 0$$

$$2y(x^2 - 1)\frac{dy}{dx} = -2x(2x^2 + y^2)$$

$$\frac{dy}{dx} = \frac{x(2x^2 + y^2)}{y(1 - x^2)}.$$

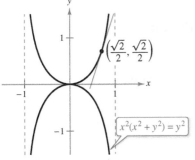

The kappa curve
Figure 3.31

At the point $\left(\sqrt{2}/2, \sqrt{2}/2\right)$, the slope is

$$\frac{dy}{dx} = \frac{\left(\sqrt{2}/2\right)[2(1/2) + (1/2)]}{\left(\sqrt{2}/2\right)[1 - (1/2)]} = \frac{3/2}{1/2} = 3$$

and the equation of the tangent line at this point is

$$y - \frac{\sqrt{2}}{2} = 3\left(x - \frac{\sqrt{2}}{2}\right)$$

$$y = 3x - \sqrt{2}.$$

Logarithmic Differentiation

On occasion, it is convenient to use logarithms as aids in differentiating nonlogarithmic functions. This procedure is called **logarithmic differentiation.**

EXAMPLE 9 **Logarithmic Differentiation**

Find the derivative of

$$y = \frac{(x-2)^2}{\sqrt{x^2+1}}, \quad x \neq 2.$$

Solution Note that $y > 0$ for all $x \neq 2$. So, $\ln y$ is defined. Begin by taking the natural logarithm of each side of the equation. Then apply logarithmic properties and differentiate implicitly. Finally, solve for y'.

$y = \dfrac{(x-2)^2}{\sqrt{x^2+1}}, \quad x \neq 2$	Write original equation.
$\ln y = \ln \dfrac{(x-2)^2}{\sqrt{x^2+1}}$	Take natural log of each side.
$\ln y = 2\ln(x-2) - \dfrac{1}{2}\ln(x^2+1)$	Logarithmic properties
$\dfrac{y'}{y} = 2\left(\dfrac{1}{x-2}\right) - \dfrac{1}{2}\left(\dfrac{2x}{x^2+1}\right)$	Differentiate.
$\dfrac{y'}{y} = \dfrac{x^2+2x+2}{(x-2)(x^2+1)}$	Simplify.
$y' = y\left[\dfrac{x^2+2x+2}{(x-2)(x^2+1)}\right]$	Solve for y'.
$y' = \dfrac{(x-2)^2}{\sqrt{x^2+1}}\left[\dfrac{x^2+2x+2}{(x-2)(x^2+1)}\right]$	Substitute for y.
$y' = \dfrac{(x-2)(x^2+2x+2)}{(x^2+1)^{3/2}}$	Simplify.

· · **REMARK** You could also solve the problem in Example 9 without using logarithmic differentiation by using the Power and Quotient Rules. Use these rules to find the derivative and show that the result is equivalent to the one in Example 9. Which method do you prefer?

EXAMPLE 10 **Logarithmic Differentiation**

Find the derivative of $y = x^{2x}$, $x > 0$.

Solution Note that $y > 0$ for all $x > 0$. So, $\ln y$ is defined.

$y = x^{2x}$	Write original equation.
$\ln y = \ln(x^{2x})$	Take natural log of each side.
$\ln y = (2x)(\ln x)$	Logarithmic property
$\dfrac{y'}{y} = 2x\left(\dfrac{1}{x}\right) + 2\ln x$	Differentiate.
$\dfrac{y'}{y} = 2(1 + \ln x)$	Simplify.
$y' = 2y(1 + \ln x)$	Solve for y'.
$y' = 2x^{2x}(1 + \ln x)$	Substitute for y.

Here are some guidelines for using logarithmic differentiation. In general, use logarithmic differentiation when differentiating (1) a function involving many factors or (2) a function having both a variable base and a variable exponent.

3.5 Exercises

See **CalcChat.com** for tutorial help and worked-out solutions to odd-numbered exercises.

Finding a Derivative In Exercises 1–20, find dy/dx by implicit differentiation.

1. $x^2 + y^2 = 9$

2. $x^2 - y^2 = 25$

3. $x^{1/2} + y^{1/2} = 16$

4. $2x^3 + 3y^3 = 64$

5. $x^3 - xy + y^2 = 7$

6. $x^2 y + y^2 x = -2$

7. $x^3 y^3 - y = x$

8. $\sqrt{xy} = x^2 y + 1$

9. $xe^y - 10x + 3y = 0$

10. $e^{xy} + x^2 - y^2 = 10$

11. $\sin x + 2 \cos 2y = 1$

12. $(\sin \pi x + \cos \pi y)^2 = 2$

13. $\sin x = x(1 + \tan y)$

14. $\cot y = x - y$

15. $y = \sin xy$

16. $x = \sec \dfrac{1}{y}$

17. $x^2 - 3 \ln y + y^2 = 10$

18. $\ln xy + 5x = 30$

19. $4x^3 + \ln y^2 + 2y = 2x$

20. $4xy + \ln x^2 y = 7$

Finding Derivatives Implicitly and Explicitly In Exercises 21–24, (a) find two explicit functions by solving the equation for y in terms of x, (b) sketch the graph of the equation and label the parts given by the corresponding explicit functions, (c) differentiate the explicit functions, and (d) find dy/dx implicitly and show that the result is equivalent to that of part (c).

21. $x^2 + y^2 = 64$

22. $25x^2 + 36y^2 = 300$

23. $16y^2 - x^2 = 16$

24. $x^2 + y^2 - 4x + 6y = -9$

Finding and Evaluating a Derivative In Exercises 25–32, find dy/dx by implicit differentiation and evaluate the derivative at the given point.

25. $xy = 6$, $(-6, -1)$

26. $y^3 - x^2 = 4$, $(2, 2)$

27. $y^2 = \dfrac{x^2 - 49}{x^2 + 49}$, $(7, 0)$

28. $x^{2/3} + y^{2/3} = 5$, $(8, 1)$

29. $\tan(x + y) = x$, $(0, 0)$

30. $x \cos y = 1$, $\left(2, \dfrac{\pi}{3}\right)$

31. $3e^{xy} - x = 0$, $(3, 0)$

32. $y^2 = \ln x$, $(e, 1)$

Famous Curves In Exercises 33–36, find the slope of the tangent line to the graph at the given point.

33. Witch of Agnesi:

$(x^2 + 4)y = 8$

Point: $(2, 1)$

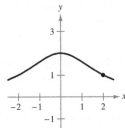

34. Cissoid:

$(4 - x)y^2 = x^3$

Point: $(2, 2)$

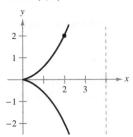

35. Bifolium:

$(x^2 + y^2)^2 = 4x^2 y$

Point: $(1, 1)$

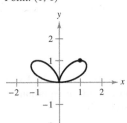

36. Folium of Descartes:

$x^3 + y^3 - 6xy = 0$

Point: $\left(\dfrac{4}{3}, \dfrac{8}{3}\right)$

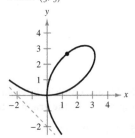

Famous Curves In Exercises 37–44, find an equation of the tangent line to the graph at the given point. To print an enlarged copy of the graph, go to *MathGraphs.com*.

37. Parabola

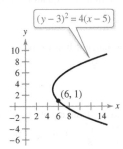
$(y - 3)^2 = 4(x - 5)$
$(6, 1)$

38. Circle

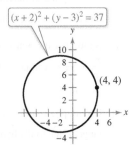
$(x + 2)^2 + (y - 3)^2 = 37$
$(4, 4)$

39. Rotated hyperbola

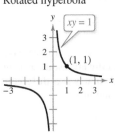
$xy = 1$
$(1, 1)$

40. Rotated ellipse

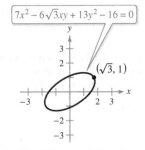
$7x^2 - 6\sqrt{3}xy + 13y^2 - 16 = 0$
$(\sqrt{3}, 1)$

41. Cruciform

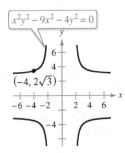
$x^2 y^2 - 9x^2 - 4y^2 = 0$
$(-4, 2\sqrt{3})$

42. Astroid

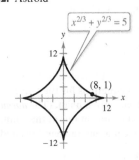
$x^{2/3} + y^{2/3} = 5$
$(8, 1)$

43. Lemniscate

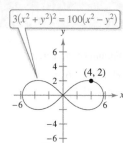

$$3(x^2 + y^2)^2 = 100(x^2 - y^2)$$

(4, 2)

44. Kappa curve

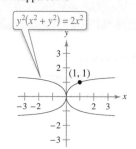

$$y^2(x^2 + y^2) = 2x^2$$

(1, 1)

Finding an Equation of a Tangent Line In Exercises 45–48, use implicit differentiation to find an equation of the tangent line to the graph at the given point.

45. $4xy = 9$, $\left(1, \frac{9}{4}\right)$ **46.** $x^2 + xy + y^2 = 4$, $(2, 0)$

47. $x + y - 1 = \ln(x^2 + y^2)$, $(1, 0)$

48. $y^2 + \ln xy = 2$, $(e, 1)$

49. Ellipse

(a) Use implicit differentiation to find an equation of the tangent line to the ellipse $\dfrac{x^2}{2} + \dfrac{y^2}{8} = 1$ at $(1, 2)$.

(b) Show that the equation of the tangent line to the ellipse $\dfrac{x^2}{a^2} + \dfrac{y^2}{b^2} = 1$ at (x_0, y_0) is $\dfrac{x_0 x}{a^2} + \dfrac{y_0 y}{b^2} = 1$.

50. Hyperbola

(a) Use implicit differentiation to find an equation of the tangent line to the hyperbola $\dfrac{x^2}{6} - \dfrac{y^2}{8} = 1$ at $(3, -2)$.

(b) Show that the equation of the tangent line to the hyperbola $\dfrac{x^2}{a^2} - \dfrac{y^2}{b^2} = 1$ at (x_0, y_0) is $\dfrac{x_0 x}{a^2} - \dfrac{y_0 y}{b^2} = 1$.

Determining a Differentiable Function In Exercises 51 and 52, find dy/dx implicitly and find the largest interval of the form $-a < y < a$ or $0 < y < a$ such that y is a differentiable function of x. Write dy/dx as a function of x.

51. $\tan y = x$ **52.** $\cos y = x$

Finding a Second Derivative In Exercises 53–58, find d^2y/dx^2 implicitly in terms of x and y.

53. $x^2 + y^2 = 4$ **54.** $x^2 y - 4x = 5$

55. $x^2 - y^2 = 36$ **56.** $xy - 1 = 2x + y^2$

57. $y^2 = x^3$ **58.** $y^3 = 4x$

Tangent Lines and Normal Lines In Exercises 59 and 60, find equations for the tangent line and normal line to the circle at each given point. (The *normal line* at a point is perpendicular to the tangent line at the point.) Use a graphing utility to graph the equation, tangent line, and normal line.

59. $x^2 + y^2 = 25$ **60.** $x^2 + y^2 = 36$

$(4, 3), (-3, 4)$ $(6, 0), (5, \sqrt{11})$

61. Normal Lines Show that the normal line at any point on the circle $x^2 + y^2 = r^2$ passes through the origin.

62. Circles Two circles of radius 4 are tangent to the graph of $y^2 = 4x$ at the point $(1, 2)$. Find equations of these two circles.

Vertical and Horizontal Tangent Lines In Exercises 63 and 64, find the points at which the graph of the equation has a vertical or horizontal tangent line.

63. $25x^2 + 16y^2 + 200x - 160y + 400 = 0$

64. $4x^2 + y^2 - 8x + 4y + 4 = 0$

Logarithmic Differentiation In Exercises 65–76, find dy/dx using logarithmic differentiation.

65. $y = x\sqrt{x^2 + 1}$, $x > 0$

66. $y = \sqrt{x^2(x + 1)(x + 2)}$, $x > 0$

67. $y = \dfrac{x^2\sqrt{3x - 2}}{(x + 1)^2}$, $x > \dfrac{2}{3}$ **68.** $y = \sqrt{\dfrac{x^2 - 1}{x^2 + 1}}$, $x > 1$

69. $y = \dfrac{x(x - 1)^{3/2}}{\sqrt{x + 1}}$, $x > 1$ **70.** $y = \dfrac{(x + 1)(x - 2)}{(x - 1)(x + 2)}$, $x > 2$

71. $y = x^{2/x}$, $x > 0$ **72.** $y = x^{x - 1}$, $x > 0$

73. $y = (x - 2)^{x + 1}$, $x > 2$ **74.** $y = (1 + x)^{1/x}$, $x > 0$

75. $y = x^{\ln x}$, $x > 0$ **76.** $y = (\ln x)^{\ln x}$, $x > 1$

Orthogonal Trajectories In Exercises 77–80, use a graphing utility to sketch the intersecting graphs of the equations and show that they are orthogonal. [Two graphs are *orthogonal* if at their point(s) of intersection, their tangent lines are perpendicular to each other.]

77. $2x^2 + y^2 = 6$ **78.** $y^2 = x^3$

$y^2 = 4x$ $2x^2 + 3y^2 = 5$

79. $x + y = 0$ **80.** $x^3 = 3(y - 1)$

$x = \sin y$ $x(3y - 29) = 3$

Orthogonal Trajectories In Exercises 81 and 82, verify that the two families of curves are orthogonal, where C and K are real numbers. Use a graphing utility to graph the two families for two values of C and two values of K.

81. $xy = C$, $x^2 - y^2 = K$ **82.** $x^2 + y^2 = C^2$, $y = Kx$

WRITING ABOUT CONCEPTS

83. Explicit and Implicit Functions Describe the difference between the explicit form of a function and an implicit equation. Give an example of each.

84. Implicit Differentiation In your own words, state the guidelines for implicit differentiation.

85. True or False? Determine whether the statement is true. If it is false, explain why and correct it. For each statement, assume y is a function of x.

(a) $\dfrac{d}{dx} \cos(x^2) = -2x \sin(x^2)$ (b) $\dfrac{d}{dy} \cos(y^2) = 2y \sin(y^2)$

(c) $\dfrac{d}{dx} \cos(y^2) = -2y \sin(y^2)$

86. **HOW DO YOU SEE IT?** Use the graph to answer the questions.

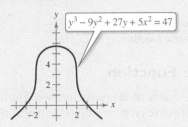

$$y^3 - 9y^2 + 27y + 5x^2 = 47$$

(a) Which is greater, the slope of the tangent line at $x = -3$ or the slope of the tangent line at $x = -1$?

(b) Estimate the point(s) where the graph has a vertical tangent line.

(c) Estimate the point(s) where the graph has a horizontal tangent line.

87. **Finding Equations of Tangent Lines** Consider the equation $x^4 = 4(4x^2 - y^2)$.

(a) Use a graphing utility to graph the equation.

(b) Find and graph the four tangent lines to the curve for $y = 3$.

(c) Find the exact coordinates of the point of intersection of the two tangent lines in the first quadrant.

88. **Tangent Lines and Intercepts** Let L be any tangent line to the curve

$$\sqrt{x} + \sqrt{y} = \sqrt{c}.$$

Show that the sum of the x- and y-intercepts of L is c.

89. **Slope** Find all points on the circle $x^2 + y^2 = 100$ where the slope is $\frac{3}{4}$.

90. **Proof**

(a) Prove (Theorem 3.3) that $d/dx[x^n] = nx^{n-1}$ for the case in which n is a rational number. (*Hint:* Write $y = x^{p/q}$ in the form $y^q = x^p$ and differentiate implicitly. Assume that p and q are integers, where $q > 0$.)

(b) Prove part (a) for the case in which n is an irrational number. (*Hint:* Let $y = x^r$, where r is a real number, and use logarithmic differentiation.)

91. **Tangent Lines** Find equations of both tangent lines to the graph of the ellipse $\dfrac{x^2}{4} + \dfrac{y^2}{9} = 1$ that pass through the point $(4, 0)$ not on the graph.

92. **Normals to a Parabola** The graph shows the normal lines from the point $(2, 0)$ to the graph of the parabola $x = y^2$. How many normal lines are there from the point $(x_0, 0)$ to the graph of the parabola if (a) $x_0 = \frac{1}{4}$, (b) $x_0 = \frac{1}{2}$, and (c) $x_0 = 1$? For what value of x_0 are two of the normal lines perpendicular to each other?

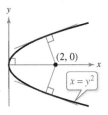

93. **Normal Lines** (a) Find an equation of the normal line to the ellipse $\dfrac{x^2}{32} + \dfrac{y^2}{8} = 1$ at the point $(4, 2)$. (b) Use a graphing utility to graph the ellipse and the normal line. (c) At what other point does the normal line intersect the ellipse?

SECTION PROJECT

Optical Illusions

In each graph below, an optical illusion is created by having lines intersect a family of curves. In each case, the lines appear to be curved. Find the value of dy/dx for the given values of x and y.

(a) Circles: $x^2 + y^2 = C^2$
$x = 3, y = 4, C = 5$

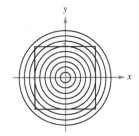

(b) Hyperbolas: $xy = C$
$x = 1, y = 4, C = 4$

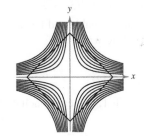

(c) Lines: $ax = by$
$x = \sqrt{3}, y = 3,$
$a = \sqrt{3}, b = 1$

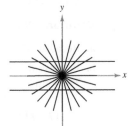

(d) Cosine curves: $y = C \cos x$
$x = \dfrac{\pi}{3}, y = \dfrac{1}{3}, C = \dfrac{2}{3}$

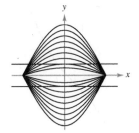

■ **FOR FURTHER INFORMATION** For more information on the mathematics of optical illusions, see the article "Descriptive Models for Perception of Optical Illusions" by David A. Smith in *The UMAP Journal.*

3.6 Derivatives of Inverse Functions

■ Find the derivative of an inverse function.
■ Differentiate an inverse trigonometric function.

Derivative of an Inverse Function

The next two theorems discuss the derivative of an inverse function. The reasonableness of Theorem 3.16 follows from the reflective property of inverse functions, as shown in Figure 3.32.

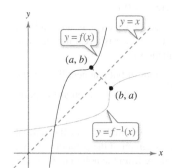

The graph of f^{-1} is a reflection of the graph of f in the line $y = x$.
Figure 3.32

> **THEOREM 3.16** **Continuity and Differentiability of Inverse Functions**
>
> Let f be a function whose domain is an interval I. If f has an inverse function, then the following statements are true.
>
> 1. If f is continuous on its domain, then f^{-1} is continuous on its domain.
> 2. If f is differentiable on an interval containing c and $f'(c) \neq 0$, then f^{-1} is differentiable at $f(c)$.
>
> A proof of this theorem is given in Appendix A.
> *See LarsonCalculus.com for Bruce Edwards's video of this proof.*

> **THEOREM 3.17** **The Derivative of an Inverse Function**
>
> Let f be a function that is differentiable on an interval I. If f has an inverse function g, then g is differentiable at any x for which $f'(g(x)) \neq 0$. Moreover,
>
> $$g'(x) = \frac{1}{f'(g(x))}, \quad f'(g(x)) \neq 0.$$
>
> A proof of this theorem is given in Appendix A.
> *See LarsonCalculus.com for Bruce Edwards's video of this proof.*

EXAMPLE 1 **Evaluating the Derivative of an Inverse Function**

Let $f(x) = \frac{1}{4}x^3 + x - 1$.

a. What is the value of $f^{-1}(x)$ when $x = 3$?

b. What is the value of $(f^{-1})'(x)$ when $x = 3$?

Solution Notice that f is one-to-one and therefore has an inverse function.

a. Because $f(2) = 3$, you know that $f^{-1}(3) = 2$.

b. Because the function f is differentiable and has an inverse function, you can apply Theorem 3.17 (with $g = f^{-1}$) to write

$$(f^{-1})'(3) = \frac{1}{f'(f^{-1}(3))} = \frac{1}{f'(2)}.$$

Moreover, using $f'(x) = \frac{3}{4}x^2 + 1$, you can conclude that

$$(f^{-1})'(3) = \frac{1}{f'(2)} = \frac{1}{\frac{3}{4}(2^2) + 1} = \frac{1}{4}.$$ (See Figure 3.33.)

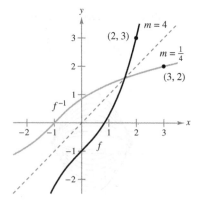

The graphs of the inverse functions f and f^{-1} have reciprocal slopes at points (a, b) and (b, a).
Figure 3.33

In Example 1, note that at the point $(2, 3)$ the slope of the graph of f is 4 and at the point $(3, 2)$ the slope of the graph of f^{-1} is $\frac{1}{4}$ (see Figure 3.33). This reciprocal relationship (which follows from Theorem 3.17) is sometimes written as

$$\frac{dy}{dx} = \frac{1}{dx/dy}.$$

EXAMPLE 2   Graphs of Functions Have Reciprocal Slopes

·····▷ *See LarsonCalculus.com for an interactive version of this type of example.*

Let $f(x) = x^2$ (for $x \geq 0$) and let $f^{-1}(x) = \sqrt{x}$. Show that the slopes of the graphs of f and f^{-1} are reciprocals at each of the following points.

a. $(2, 4)$ and $(4, 2)$ **b.** $(3, 9)$ and $(9, 3)$

Solution   The derivatives of f and f^{-1} are $f'(x) = 2x$ and $(f^{-1})'(x) = \dfrac{1}{2\sqrt{x}}$.

a. At $(2, 4)$, the slope of the graph of f is $f'(2) = 2(2) = 4$. At $(4, 2)$, the slope of the graph of f^{-1} is

$$(f^{-1})'(4) = \frac{1}{2\sqrt{4}} = \frac{1}{2(2)} = \frac{1}{4}.$$

b. At $(3, 9)$, the slope of the graph of f is $f'(3) = 2(3) = 6$. At $(9, 3)$, the slope of the graph of f^{-1} is

$$(f^{-1})'(9) = \frac{1}{2\sqrt{9}} = \frac{1}{2(3)} = \frac{1}{6}.$$

So, in both cases, the slopes are reciprocals, as shown in Figure 3.34.

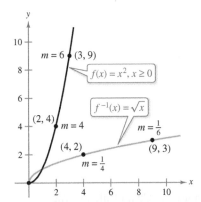

At $(0, 0)$, the derivative of f is 0 and the derivative of f^{-1} does not exist.
Figure 3.34

When determining the derivative of an inverse function, you have two options: (1) you can apply Theorem 3.17, or (2) you can use implicit differentiation. The first approach is illustrated in Example 3, and the second in the proof of Theorem 3.18.

■ **FOR FURTHER INFORMATION**
For more on the derivative of the arctangent function, see the article "Differentiating the Arctangent Directly" by Eric Key in *The College Mathematics Journal*. To view this article, go to *MathArticles.com*.

EXAMPLE 3   Finding the Derivative of an Inverse Function

Find the derivative of the inverse tangent function.

Solution   Let $f(x) = \tan x$, $-\pi/2 < x < \pi/2$. Then let $g(x) = \arctan x$ be the inverse tangent function. To find the derivative of $g(x)$, use the fact that $f'(x) = \sec^2 x = \tan^2 x + 1$, and apply Theorem 3.17 as follows.

$$g'(x) = \frac{1}{f'(g(x))} = \frac{1}{f'(\arctan x)} = \frac{1}{[\tan(\arctan x)]^2 + 1} = \frac{1}{x^2 + 1}$$

Derivatives of Inverse Trigonometric Functions

In Section 3.4, you saw that the derivative of the *transcendental* function $f(x) = \ln x$ is the *algebraic* function $f'(x) = 1/x$. You will now see that the derivatives of the inverse trigonometric functions also are algebraic (even though the inverse trigonometric functions are themselves transcendental).

The next theorem lists the derivatives of the six inverse trigonometric functions. Note that the derivatives of arccos u, arccot u, and arccsc u are the *negatives* of the derivatives of arcsin u, arctan u, and arcsec u, respectively.

> **THEOREM 3.18 Derivatives of Inverse Trigonometric Functions**
>
> Let u be a differentiable function of x.
>
> $$\frac{d}{dx}[\arcsin u] = \frac{u'}{\sqrt{1-u^2}} \qquad \frac{d}{dx}[\arccos u] = \frac{-u'}{\sqrt{1-u^2}}$$
>
> $$\frac{d}{dx}[\arctan u] = \frac{u'}{1+u^2} \qquad \frac{d}{dx}[\operatorname{arccot} u] = \frac{-u'}{1+u^2}$$
>
> $$\frac{d}{dx}[\operatorname{arcsec} u] = \frac{u'}{|u|\sqrt{u^2-1}} \qquad \frac{d}{dx}[\operatorname{arccsc} u] = \frac{-u'}{|u|\sqrt{u^2-1}}$$

Proof Let $y = \arcsin x$, $-\pi/2 \le y \le \pi/2$ (see Figure 3.35). So, $\sin y = x$, and you can use implicit differentiation as follows.

$$\sin y = x$$

$$(\cos y)\left(\frac{dy}{dx}\right) = 1$$

$$\frac{dy}{dx} = \frac{1}{\cos y}$$

$$\frac{dy}{dx} = \frac{1}{\sqrt{1 - \sin^2 y}}$$

$$\frac{dy}{dx} = \frac{1}{\sqrt{1 - x^2}}$$

Because u is a differentiable function of x, you can use the Chain Rule to write

$$\frac{d}{dx}[\arcsin u] = \frac{u'}{\sqrt{1-u^2}}, \quad \text{where} \quad u' = \frac{du}{dx}.$$

Proofs of the other differentiation rules are left as an exercise (see Exercise 79).

See LarsonCalculus.com for Bruce Edwards's video of this proof.

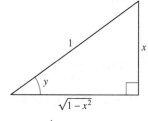

$y = \arcsin x$
Figure 3.35

There is no common agreement on the definition of $\operatorname{arcsec} x$ (or $\operatorname{arccsc} x$) for negative values of x. For this text, the range of arcsecant was defined to preserve the reciprocal identity $\operatorname{arcsec} x = \arccos(1/x)$. For example, to evaluate $\operatorname{arcsec}(-2)$, you can write

$$\operatorname{arcsec}(-2) = \arccos(-0.5) \approx 2.09.$$

One of the consequences of the definition of the inverse secant function given in this text is that its graph has a positive slope at every x-value in its domain. This accounts for the absolute value sign in the formula for the derivative of $\operatorname{arcsec} x$.

EXAMPLE 4 **Differentiating Inverse Trigonometric Functions**

a. $\dfrac{d}{dx}[\arcsin(2x)] = \dfrac{2}{\sqrt{1-(2x)^2}} = \dfrac{2}{\sqrt{1-4x^2}}$

b. $\dfrac{d}{dx}[\arctan(3x)] = \dfrac{3}{1+(3x)^2} = \dfrac{3}{1+9x^2}$

c. $\dfrac{d}{dx}[\arcsin \sqrt{x}] = \dfrac{(1/2)x^{-1/2}}{\sqrt{1-x}} = \dfrac{1}{2\sqrt{x}\sqrt{1-x}} = \dfrac{1}{2\sqrt{x-x^2}}$

d. $\dfrac{d}{dx}[\operatorname{arcsec} e^{2x}] = \dfrac{2e^{2x}}{e^{2x}\sqrt{(e^{2x})^2-1}} = \dfrac{2e^{2x}}{e^{2x}\sqrt{e^{4x}-1}} = \dfrac{2}{\sqrt{e^{4x}-1}}$

The absolute value sign is not necessary because $e^{2x} > 0$.

GALILEO GALILEI (1564–1642)

Galileo's approach to science departed from the accepted Aristotelian view that nature had describable *qualities*, such as "fluidity" and "potentiality." He chose to describe the physical world in terms of measurable *quantities*, such as time, distance, force, and mass.
See LarsonCalculus.com to read more of this biography.

EXAMPLE 5   **A Derivative That Can Be Simplified**

$$y = \arcsin x + x\sqrt{1 - x^2}$$

$$y' = \frac{1}{\sqrt{1 - x^2}} + x\left(\frac{1}{2}\right)(-2x)(1 - x^2)^{-1/2} + \sqrt{1 - x^2}$$

$$= \frac{1}{\sqrt{1 - x^2}} - \frac{x^2}{\sqrt{1 - x^2}} + \sqrt{1 - x^2}$$

$$= \sqrt{1 - x^2} + \sqrt{1 - x^2}$$

$$= 2\sqrt{1 - x^2}$$

In the 1600s, Europe was ushered into the scientific age by such great thinkers as Descartes, Galileo, Huygens, Newton, and Kepler. These men believed that nature is governed by basic laws—laws that can, for the most part, be written in terms of mathematical equations. One of the most influential publications of this period—*Dialogue on the Great World Systems*, by Galileo Galilei—has become a classic description of modern scientific thought.

As mathematics has developed during the past few hundred years, a small number of elementary functions has proven sufficient for modeling most* phenomena in physics, chemistry, biology, engineering, economics, and a variety of other fields. An **elementary function** is a function from the following list or one that can be formed as the sum, product, quotient, or composition of functions in the list.

Algebraic Functions	**Transcendental Functions**
Polynomial functions	Logarithmic functions
Rational functions	Exponential functions
Functions involving radicals	Trigonometric functions
	Inverse trigonometric functions

With the differentiation rules introduced so far in the text, you can differentiate any elementary function. For convenience, these differentiation rules are summarized below.

BASIC DIFFERENTIATION RULES FOR ELEMENTARY FUNCTIONS

1. $\dfrac{d}{dx}[cu] = cu'$

2. $\dfrac{d}{dx}[u \pm v] = u' \pm v'$

3. $\dfrac{d}{dx}[uv] = uv' + vu'$

4. $\dfrac{d}{dx}\left[\dfrac{u}{v}\right] = \dfrac{vu' - uv'}{v^2}$

5. $\dfrac{d}{dx}[c] = 0$

6. $\dfrac{d}{dx}[u^n] = nu^{n-1}u'$

7. $\dfrac{d}{dx}[x] = 1$

8. $\dfrac{d}{dx}[|u|] = \dfrac{u}{|u|}(u'), \quad u \neq 0$

9. $\dfrac{d}{dx}[\ln u] = \dfrac{u'}{u}$

10. $\dfrac{d}{dx}[e^u] = e^u u'$

11. $\dfrac{d}{dx}[\log_a u] = \dfrac{u'}{(\ln a)u}$

12. $\dfrac{d}{dx}[a^u] = (\ln a)a^u u'$

13. $\dfrac{d}{dx}[\sin u] = (\cos u)u'$

14. $\dfrac{d}{dx}[\cos u] = -(\sin u)u'$

15. $\dfrac{d}{dx}[\tan u] = (\sec^2 u)u'$

16. $\dfrac{d}{dx}[\cot u] = -(\csc^2 u)u'$

17. $\dfrac{d}{dx}[\sec u] = (\sec u \tan u)u'$

18. $\dfrac{d}{dx}[\csc u] = -(\csc u \cot u)u'$

19. $\dfrac{d}{dx}[\arcsin u] = \dfrac{u'}{\sqrt{1 - u^2}}$

20. $\dfrac{d}{dx}[\arccos u] = \dfrac{-u'}{\sqrt{1 - u^2}}$

21. $\dfrac{d}{dx}[\arctan u] = \dfrac{u'}{1 + u^2}$

22. $\dfrac{d}{dx}[\operatorname{arccot} u] = \dfrac{-u'}{1 + u^2}$

23. $\dfrac{d}{dx}[\operatorname{arcsec} u] = \dfrac{u'}{|u|\sqrt{u^2 - 1}}$

24. $\dfrac{d}{dx}[\operatorname{arccsc} u] = \dfrac{-u'}{|u|\sqrt{u^2 - 1}}$

---

* Some important functions used in engineering and science (such as Bessel functions and gamma functions) are not elementary functions.

3.6 Exercises

See **CalcChat.com** for tutorial help and worked-out solutions to odd-numbered exercises.

Evaluating the Derivative of an Inverse Function In Exercises 1–10, verify that f has an inverse. Then use the function f and the given real number a to find $(f^{-1})'(a)$. (*Hint:* See Example 1.)

Function	Real Number
1. $f(x) = x^3 - 1$	$a = 26$
2. $f(x) = 5 - 2x^3$	$a = 7$
3. $f(x) = x^3 + 2x - 1$	$a = 2$
4. $f(x) = \frac{1}{27}(x^5 + 2x^3)$	$a = -11$
5. $f(x) = \sin x,\ -\frac{\pi}{2} \le x \le \frac{\pi}{2}$	$a = \frac{1}{2}$
6. $f(x) = \cos 2x,\ 0 \le x \le \frac{\pi}{2}$	$a = 1$
7. $f(x) = \frac{x + 6}{x - 2},\ x > 2$	$a = 3$
8. $f(x) = \frac{x + 3}{x + 1},\ x > -1$	$a = 2$
9. $f(x) = x^3 - \frac{4}{x},\ x > 0$	$a = 6$
10. $f(x) = \sqrt{x - 4}$	$a = 2$

Graphs of Inverse Functions Have Reciprocal Slopes In Exercises 11–14, show that the slopes of the graphs of f and f^{-1} are reciprocals at the given points.

Function	Point
11. $f(x) = x^3$	$\left(\frac{1}{2}, \frac{1}{8}\right)$
$f^{-1}(x) = \sqrt[3]{x}$	$\left(\frac{1}{8}, \frac{1}{2}\right)$
12. $f(x) = 3 - 4x$	$(1, -1)$
$f^{-1}(x) = \frac{3 - x}{4}$	$(-1, 1)$
13. $f(x) = \sqrt{x - 4}$	$(5, 1)$
$f^{-1}(x) = x^2 + 4,\ x \ge 0$	$(1, 5)$
14. $f(x) = \frac{4}{1 + x^2},\ x \ge 0$	$(1, 2)$
$f^{-1}(x) = \sqrt{\dfrac{4 - x}{x}}$	$(2, 1)$

Finding an Equation of a Tangent Line In Exercises 15–18, (a) find an equation of the tangent line to the graph of f at the given point and (b) use a graphing utility to graph the function and its tangent line at the point.

15. $f(x) = \arccos x^2,\ \left(0, \frac{\pi}{2}\right)$ 16. $f(x) = \arctan x,\ \left(-1, -\frac{\pi}{4}\right)$

17. $f(x) = \arcsin 3x,\ \left(\frac{\sqrt{2}}{6}, \frac{\pi}{4}\right)$

18. $f(x) = \operatorname{arcsec} x,\ \left(\sqrt{2}, \frac{\pi}{4}\right)$

Finding dy/dx at a Point In Exercises 19–22, find dy/dx at the given point for the equation.

19. $x = y^3 - 7y^2 + 2,\ (-4, 1)$

20. $x = 2\ln(y^2 - 3),\ (0, 2)$

21. $x \arctan x = e^y,\ \left(1, \ln\frac{\pi}{4}\right)$

22. $\arcsin xy = \frac{2}{3}\arctan 2x,\ \left(\frac{1}{2}, 1\right)$

Finding a Derivative In Exercises 23–48, find the derivative of the function.

23. $f(x) = \arcsin(x + 1)$ 24. $f(t) = \arcsin t^2$

25. $g(x) = 3\arccos \frac{x}{2}$ 26. $f(x) = \operatorname{arcsec} 2x$

27. $f(x) = \arctan e^x$ 28. $f(x) = \arctan \sqrt{x}$

29. $g(x) = \dfrac{\arcsin 3x}{x}$ 30. $g(x) = \dfrac{\arccos x}{x + 1}$

31. $g(x) = e^{2x}\arcsin x$ 32. $h(x) = x^2 \arctan 5x$

33. $h(x) = \operatorname{arccot} 6x$ 34. $f(x) = \operatorname{arccsc} 3x$

35. $h(t) = \sin(\arccos t)$ 36. $f(x) = \arcsin x + \arccos x$

37. $y = 2x \arccos x - 2\sqrt{1 - x^2}$

38. $y = \ln(t^2 + 4) - \frac{1}{2}\arctan \frac{t}{2}$

39. $y = \frac{1}{2}\left(\frac{1}{2}\ln\frac{x + 1}{x - 1} + \arctan x\right)$

40. $y = \frac{1}{2}\left[x\sqrt{4 - x^2} + 4\arcsin\left(\frac{x}{2}\right)\right]$

41. $g(t) = \tan(\arcsin t)$ 42. $f(x) = \operatorname{arcsec} x + \operatorname{arccsc} x$

43. $y = x \arcsin x + \sqrt{1 - x^2}$

44. $y = x \arctan 2x - \frac{1}{4}\ln(1 + 4x^2)$

45. $y = 8\arcsin \frac{x}{4} - \dfrac{x\sqrt{16 - x^2}}{2}$

46. $y = 25\arcsin \frac{x}{5} - x\sqrt{25 - x^2}$

47. $y = \arctan x + \dfrac{x}{1 + x^2}$ 48. $y = \arctan \frac{x}{2} - \dfrac{1}{2(x^2 + 4)}$

Finding an Equation of a Tangent Line In Exercises 49–54, find an equation of the tangent line to the graph of the function at the given point.

49. $y = 2\arcsin x$ 50. $y = \frac{1}{2}\arccos x$

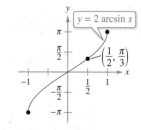

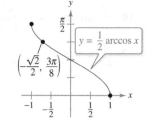

51. $y = \arctan \dfrac{x}{2}$

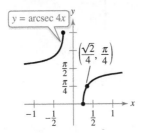

52. $y = \text{arcsec } 4x$

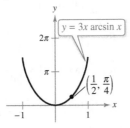

53. $y = 4x \arccos(x - 1)$

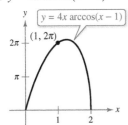

54. $y = 3x \arcsin x$

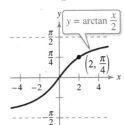

55. Tangent Lines Find equations of all tangent lines to the graph of $f(x) = \arccos x$ that have slope -2.

56. Tangent Lines Find an equation of the tangent line to the graph of $g(x) = \arctan x$ when $x = 1$.

Linear and Quadratic Approximations In Exercises 57–60, use a computer algebra system to find the linear approximation

$$P_1(x) = f(a) + f'(a)(x - a)$$

and the quadratic approximation

$$P_2(x) = f(a) + f'(a)(x - a) + \tfrac{1}{2}f''(a)(x - a)^2$$

to the function f at $x = a$. Sketch the graph of the function and its linear and quadratic approximations.

57. $f(x) = \arctan x, \quad a = 0$
58. $f(x) = \arccos x, \quad a = 0$
59. $f(x) = \arcsin x, \quad a = \tfrac{1}{2}$
60. $f(x) = \arctan x, \quad a = 1$

Implicit Differentiation In Exercises 61–64, find an equation of the tangent line to the graph of the equation at the given point.

61. $x^2 + x \arctan y = y - 1, \quad \left(-\dfrac{\pi}{4}, 1\right)$

62. $\arctan(xy) = \arcsin(x + y), \quad (0, 0)$

63. $\arcsin x + \arcsin y = \dfrac{\pi}{2}, \quad \left(\dfrac{\sqrt{2}}{2}, \dfrac{\sqrt{2}}{2}\right)$

64. $\arctan(x + y) = y^2 + \dfrac{\pi}{4}, \quad (1, 0)$

WRITING ABOUT CONCEPTS

Explaining Why a Function Is Not One-to-One In Exercises 65 and 66, the derivative of the function has the same sign for all x in its domain, but the function is not one-to-one. Explain.

65. $f(x) = \tan x$

66. $f(x) = \dfrac{x}{x^2 - 4}$

WRITING ABOUT CONCEPTS (CONTINUED)

67. Evaluating the Derivative of an Inverse Function Given $y_1 = f(x_1)$, explain how to find $(f^{-1})'(y_1)$. (Assume f^{-1} exists.)

68. Finding the Derivative of an Inverse Function State the theorem that gives the method for finding the derivative of an inverse function.

69. Inverse Trigonometric Functions Are the derivatives of the inverse trigonometric functions algebraic or transcendental functions? List the derivatives of the inverse trigonometric functions.

---

70. **HOW DO YOU SEE IT?** Use the information in the graph of f below.

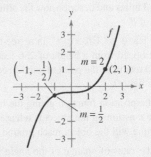

(a) What is the slope of the tangent line to the graph of f^{-1} at the point $\left(-\tfrac{1}{2}, -1\right)$? Explain.

(b) What is the slope of the tangent line to the graph of f^{-1} at the point $(1, 2)$? Explain.

---

71. Think About It The point $(1, 3)$ lies on the graph of f, and the slope of the tangent line through this point is $m = 2$. Assume f^{-1} exists. What is the slope of the tangent line to the graph of f^{-1} at the point $(3, 1)$?

72. Linear Approximation To find a linear approximation to the graph of the function in Example 5

$$y = \arcsin x + x\sqrt{1 - x^2}$$

you decide to use the tangent line at the origin, as shown below. Use a graphing utility to describe an interval about the origin where the tangent line is within 0.01 unit of the graph of the function. What might a person mean by saying that the original function is "locally linear"?

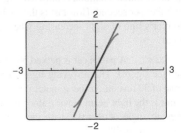

73. Angular Rate of Change An airplane flies at an altitude of 5 miles toward a point directly over an observer. Consider θ and x as shown in the figure.

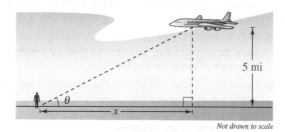

Not drawn to scale

(a) Write θ as a function of x.

(b) The speed of the plane is 400 miles per hour. Find $d\theta/dt$ when $x = 10$ miles and $x = 3$ miles.

74. Angular Rate of Change Repeat Exercise 73 for an altitude of 3 miles and describe how the altitude affects the rate of change of θ.

75. Angular Rate of Change In a free-fall experiment, an object is dropped from a height of 256 feet. A camera on the ground 500 feet from the point of impact records the fall of the object (see figure).

(a) Find the position function giving the height of the object at time t, assuming the object is released at time $t = 0$. At what time will the object reach ground level?

(b) Find the rates of change of the angle of elevation of the camera when $t = 1$ and $t = 2$.

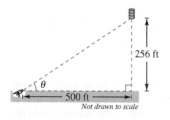

Not drawn to scale

Figure for 75

Figure for 76

76. Angular Rate of Change A television camera at ground level is filming the lift-off of a rocket at a point 800 meters from the launch pad. Let θ be the angle of elevation of the rocket and let s be the distance between the camera and the rocket (see figure). Write θ as a function of s for the period of time when the rocket is moving vertically. Differentiate the result to find $d\theta/dt$ in terms of s and ds/dt.

77. Angular Rate of Change An observer is standing 300 feet from the point at which a balloon is released. The balloon rises at a rate of 5 feet per second. How fast is the angle of elevation of the observer's line of sight increasing when the balloon is 100 feet high?

78. Angular Speed A patrol car is parked 50 feet from a long warehouse (see figure). The revolving light on top of the car turns at a rate of 30 revolutions per minute. Write θ as a function of x. How fast is the light beam moving along the wall when the beam makes an angle of $\theta = 45°$ with the line perpendicular from the light to the wall?

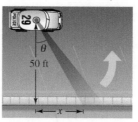

Figure for 78

79. Proof Prove each differentiation formula.

(a) $\dfrac{d}{dx}[\arccos u] = \dfrac{-u'}{\sqrt{1 - u^2}}$

(b) $\dfrac{d}{dx}[\arctan u] = \dfrac{u'}{1 + u^2}$

(c) $\dfrac{d}{dx}[\text{arcsec } u] = \dfrac{u'}{|u|\sqrt{u^2 - 1}}$

(d) $\dfrac{d}{dx}[\text{arccot } u] = \dfrac{-u'}{1 + u^2}$

(e) $\dfrac{d}{dx}[\text{arccsc } u] = \dfrac{-u'}{|u|\sqrt{u^2 - 1}}$

80. Existence of an Inverse Determine the values of k such that the function $f(x) = kx + \sin x$ has an inverse function.

True or False? In Exercises 81–84, determine whether the statement is true or false. If it is false, explain why or give an example that shows it is false.

81. The derivative of arccsc x is the negative of the derivative of arcsec x.

82. The slope of the graph of the inverse tangent function is positive for all x.

83. $\dfrac{d}{dx}[\arctan(\tan x)] = 1$ for all x in the domain.

84. If $y = \arcsin x$, then $\dfrac{dy}{dx} = \dfrac{1}{dx/dy}$ for all x in $[-1, 1]$.

85. Proof Prove that $\arcsin x = \arctan\left(\dfrac{x}{\sqrt{1 - x^2}}\right)$, $|x| < 1$.

86. Proof Prove that

$$\arccos x = \dfrac{\pi}{2} - \arctan\left(\dfrac{x}{\sqrt{1 - x^2}}\right), \quad |x| < 1.$$

87. Inverse Secant Function Some calculus textbooks define the inverse secant function using the range $[0, \pi/2) \cup [\pi, 3\pi/2)$.

(a) Sketch the graph of $y = \text{arcsec } x$ using this range.

(b) Show that $y' = \dfrac{1}{x\sqrt{x^2 - 1}}$.

88. Proof Show that the function

$$f(x) = \arcsin \dfrac{x - 2}{2} - 2\arcsin\left(\dfrac{\sqrt{x}}{2}\right)$$

is constant for $0 \le x \le 4$.

3.7   Related Rates

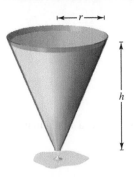

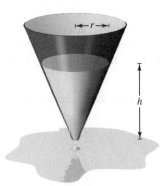

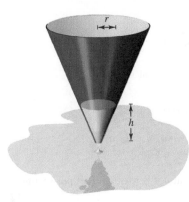

Volume is related to radius and height.
Figure 3.36

■ Find a related rate.
■ Use related rates to solve real-life problems.

Finding Related Rates

You have seen how the Chain Rule can be used to find dy/dx implicitly. Another important use of the Chain Rule is to find the rates of change of two or more related variables that are changing with respect to *time*.

For example, when water is drained out of a conical tank (see Figure 3.36), the volume V, the radius r, and the height h of the water level are all functions of time t. Knowing that these variables are related by the equation

$$V = \frac{\pi}{3}r^2 h \qquad \text{Original equation}$$

you can differentiate implicitly with respect to t to obtain the **related-rate** equation

$$\frac{d}{dt}[V] = \frac{d}{dt}\left[\frac{\pi}{3}r^2 h\right]$$

$$\frac{dV}{dt} = \frac{\pi}{3}\left[r^2\frac{dh}{dt} + h\left(2r\frac{dr}{dt}\right)\right] \qquad \text{Differentiate with respect to } t.$$

$$= \frac{\pi}{3}\left(r^2\frac{dh}{dt} + 2rh\frac{dr}{dt}\right).$$

From this equation, you can see that the rate of change of V is related to the rates of change of both h and r.

Exploration

Finding a Related Rate   In the conical tank shown in Figure 3.36, the height of the water level is changing at a rate of -0.2 foot per minute and the radius is changing at a rate of -0.1 foot per minute. What is the rate of change in the volume when the radius is $r = 1$ foot and the height is $h = 2$ feet? Does the rate of change in the volume depend on the values of r and h? Explain.

EXAMPLE 1   Two Rates That Are Related

The variables x and y are both differentiable functions of t and are related by the equation $y = x^2 + 3$. Find dy/dt when $x = 1$, given that $dx/dt = 2$ when $x = 1$.

Solution   Using the Chain Rule, you can differentiate both sides of the equation *with respect to t.*

$$y = x^2 + 3 \qquad \text{Write original equation.}$$

$$\frac{d}{dt}[y] = \frac{d}{dt}[x^2 + 3] \qquad \text{Differentiate with respect to } t.$$

$$\frac{dy}{dt} = 2x\frac{dx}{dt} \qquad \text{Chain Rule}$$

When $x = 1$ and $dx/dt = 2$, you have

$$\frac{dy}{dt} = 2(1)(2) = 4.$$

■

■ **FOR FURTHER INFORMATION**
To learn more about the history of related-rate problems, see the article "The Lengthening Shadow: The Story of Related Rates" by Bill Austin, Don Barry, and David Berman in *Mathematics Magazine*. To view this article, go to *MathArticles.com*.

Problem Solving with Related Rates

In Example 1, you were *given* an equation that related the variables x and y and were asked to find the rate of change of y when $x = 1$.

Equation: $\quad y = x^2 + 3$

Given rate: $\quad \dfrac{dx}{dt} = 2 \quad$ when $\quad x = 1$

Find: $\quad \dfrac{dy}{dt} \quad$ when $\quad x = 1$

In each of the remaining examples in this section, you must *create* a mathematical model from a verbal description.

EXAMPLE 2 Ripples in a Pond

A pebble is dropped into a calm pond, causing ripples in the form of concentric circles, as shown in Figure 3.37. The radius r of the outer ripple is increasing at a constant rate of 1 foot per second. When the radius is 4 feet, at what rate is the total area A of the disturbed water changing?

Solution The variables r and A are related by $A = \pi r^2$. The rate of change of the radius r is $dr/dt = 1$.

Equation: $\quad A = \pi r^2$

Given rate: $\quad \dfrac{dr}{dt} = 1$

Find: $\quad \dfrac{dA}{dt} \quad$ when $\quad r = 4$

With this information, you can proceed as in Example 1.

$$\frac{d}{dt}[A] = \frac{d}{dt}[\pi r^2] \qquad \text{Differentiate with respect to } t.$$

$$\frac{dA}{dt} = 2\pi r \frac{dr}{dt} \qquad \text{Chain Rule}$$

$$= 2\pi(4)(1) \qquad \text{Substitute 4 for } r \text{ and 1 for } \frac{dr}{dt}.$$

$$= 8\pi \text{ square feet per second} \qquad \text{Simplify.}$$

When the radius is 4 feet, the area is changing at a rate of 8π square feet per second.

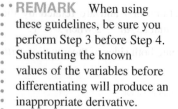

Total area increases as the outer radius increases.
Figure 3.37

· · REMARK When using these guidelines, be sure you perform Step 3 before Step 4. Substituting the known values of the variables before differentiating will produce an inappropriate derivative.

GUIDELINES FOR SOLVING RELATED-RATE PROBLEMS

1. Identify all *given* quantities and quantities *to be determined*. Make a sketch and label the quantities.

2. Write an equation involving the variables whose rates of change either are given or are to be determined.

3. Using the Chain Rule, implicitly differentiate both sides of the equation *with respect to time t.*

4. *After* completing Step 3, substitute into the resulting equation all known values for the variables and their rates of change. Then solve for the required rate of change.

The table below lists examples of mathematical models involving rates of change. For instance, the rate of change in the first example is the velocity of a car.

Verbal Statement	Mathematical Model
The velocity of a car after traveling for 1 hour is 50 miles per hour.	x = distance traveled $\dfrac{dx}{dt} = 50$ mi/h when $t = 1$
Water is being pumped into a swimming pool at a rate of 10 cubic meters per hour.	V = volume of water in pool $\dfrac{dV}{dt} = 10$ m³/h
A gear is revolving at a rate of 25 revolutions per minute (1 revolution = 2π rad).	θ = angle of revolution $\dfrac{d\theta}{dt} = 25(2\pi)$ rad/min
A population of bacteria is increasing at a rate of 2000 per hour.	x = number in population $\dfrac{dx}{dt} = 2000$ bacteria per hour

EXAMPLE 3 **An Inflating Balloon**

Air is being pumped into a spherical balloon (see Figure 3.38) at a rate of 4.5 cubic feet per minute. Find the rate of change of the radius when the radius is 2 feet.

Solution Let V be the volume of the balloon, and let r be its radius. Because the volume is increasing at a rate of 4.5 cubic feet per minute, you know that at time t the rate of change of the volume is $dV/dt = \frac{9}{2}$. So, the problem can be stated as shown.

Given rate: $\dfrac{dV}{dt} = \dfrac{9}{2}$ (constant rate)

Find: $\dfrac{dr}{dt}$ when $r = 2$

To find the rate of change of the radius, you must find an equation that relates the radius r to the volume V.

Equation: $V = \dfrac{4}{3}\pi r^3$ Volume of a sphere

Differentiating both sides of the equation with respect to t produces

$\dfrac{dV}{dt} = 4\pi r^2 \dfrac{dr}{dt}$ Differentiate with respect to t.

$\dfrac{dr}{dt} = \dfrac{1}{4\pi r^2}\left(\dfrac{dV}{dt}\right).$ Solve for $\frac{dr}{dt}$.

Finally, when $r = 2$, the rate of change of the radius is

$\dfrac{dr}{dt} = \dfrac{1}{4\pi(2)^2}\left(\dfrac{9}{2}\right) \approx 0.09$ foot per minute.   ∎

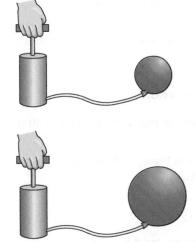

Inflating a balloon
Figure 3.38

In Example 3, note that the volume is increasing at a *constant* rate, but the radius is increasing at a *variable* rate. Just because two rates are related does not mean that they are proportional. In this particular case, the radius is growing more and more slowly as t increases. Do you see why?

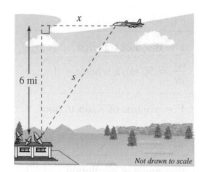

An airplane is flying at an altitude of 6 miles, s miles from the station.

Figure 3.39

EXAMPLE 4 **The Speed of an Airplane Tracked by Radar**

· · · ·▷ *See LarsonCalculus.com for an interactive version of this type of example.*

An airplane is flying on a flight path that will take it directly over a radar tracking station, as shown in Figure 3.39. The distance s is decreasing at a rate of 400 miles per hour when $s = 10$ miles. What is the speed of the plane?

Solution Let x be the horizontal distance from the station, as shown in Figure 3.39. Notice that when $s = 10$, $x = \sqrt{10^2 - 36} = 8$.

Given rate: $ds/dt = -400$ when $s = 10$

Find: dx/dt when $s = 10$ and $x = 8$

You can find the velocity of the plane as shown.

Equation: $x^2 + 6^2 = s^2$	Pythagorean Theorem
$2x\dfrac{dx}{dt} = 2s\dfrac{ds}{dt}$	Differentiate with respect to t.
$\dfrac{dx}{dt} = \dfrac{s}{x}\left(\dfrac{ds}{dt}\right)$	Solve for $\dfrac{dx}{dt}$.
$= \dfrac{10}{8}(-400)$	Substitute for s, x, and $\dfrac{ds}{dt}$.
$= -500$ miles per hour	Simplify.

· · ·▷ Because the velocity is -500 miles per hour, the *speed* is 500 miles per hour. ■

· · · · · ·**REMARK** The velocity in Example 4 is negative because x represents a distance that is decreasing.

EXAMPLE 5 **A Changing Angle of Elevation**

Find the rate of change in the angle of elevation of the camera shown in Figure 3.40 at 10 seconds after lift-off.

Solution Let θ be the angle of elevation, as shown in Figure 3.40. When $t = 10$, the height s of the rocket is $s = 50t^2 = 50(10)^2 = 5000$ feet.

Given rate: $ds/dt = 100t = $ velocity of rocket

Find: $d\theta/dt$ when $t = 10$ and $s = 5000$

Using Figure 3.40, you can relate s and θ by the equation $\tan \theta = s/2000$.

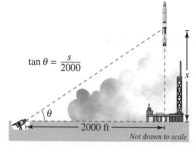

$\tan \theta = \dfrac{s}{2000}$

A television camera at ground level is filming the lift-off of a rocket that is rising vertically according to the position equation $s = 50t^2$, where s is measured in feet and t is measured in seconds. The camera is 2000 feet from the launch pad.

Figure 3.40

Equation: $\tan \theta = \dfrac{s}{2000}$	See Figure 3.40.
$(\sec^2 \theta)\dfrac{d\theta}{dt} = \dfrac{1}{2000}\left(\dfrac{ds}{dt}\right)$	Differentiate with respect to t.
$\dfrac{d\theta}{dt} = \cos^2 \theta \dfrac{100t}{2000}$	Substitute $100t$ for $\dfrac{ds}{dt}$.
$= \left(\dfrac{2000}{\sqrt{s^2 + 2000^2}}\right)^2 \dfrac{100t}{2000}$	$\cos \theta = \dfrac{2000}{\sqrt{s^2 + 2000^2}}$

When $t = 10$ and $s = 5000$, you have

$$\frac{d\theta}{dt} = \frac{2000(100)(10)}{5000^2 + 2000^2} = \frac{2}{29} \text{ radian per second.}$$

So, when $t = 10$, θ is changing at a rate of $\frac{2}{29}$ radian per second. ■

EXAMPLE 6   **The Velocity of a Piston**

In the engine shown in Figure 3.41, a 7-inch connecting rod is fastened to a crank of radius 3 inches. The crankshaft rotates counterclockwise at a constant rate of 200 revolutions per minute. Find the velocity of the piston when $\theta = \pi/3$.

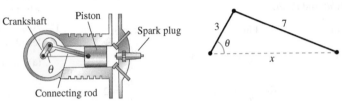

The velocity of a piston is related to the angle of the crankshaft.
Figure 3.41

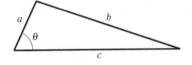

Law of Cosines:
$b^2 = a^2 + c^2 - 2ac \cos \theta$
Figure 3.42

Solution   Label the distances as shown in Figure 3.41. Because a complete revolution corresponds to 2π radians, it follows that $d\theta/dt = 200(2\pi) = 400\pi$ radians per minute.

Given rate: $\dfrac{d\theta}{dt} = 400\pi$ (constant rate)

Find: $\dfrac{dx}{dt}$ when $\theta = \dfrac{\pi}{3}$

You can use the Law of Cosines (see Figure 3.42) to find an equation that relates x and θ.

Equation:
$$7^2 = 3^2 + x^2 - 2(3)(x) \cos \theta$$
$$0 = 2x\frac{dx}{dt} - 6\left(-x \sin \theta \frac{d\theta}{dt} + \cos \theta \frac{dx}{dt}\right)$$
$$(6 \cos \theta - 2x)\frac{dx}{dt} = 6x \sin \theta \frac{d\theta}{dt}$$
$$\frac{dx}{dt} = \frac{6x \sin \theta}{6 \cos \theta - 2x}\left(\frac{d\theta}{dt}\right)$$

When $\theta = \pi/3$, you can solve for x as shown.

$$7^2 = 3^2 + x^2 - 2(3)(x) \cos \frac{\pi}{3}$$
$$49 = 9 + x^2 - 6x\left(\frac{1}{2}\right)$$
$$0 = x^2 - 3x - 40$$
$$0 = (x - 8)(x + 5)$$
$$x = 8 \qquad\qquad \text{Choose positive solution.}$$

So, when $x = 8$ and $\theta = \pi/3$, the velocity of the piston is

$$\frac{dx}{dt} = \frac{6(8)\left(\sqrt{3}/2\right)}{6(1/2) - 16}(400\pi)$$
$$= \frac{9600\pi\sqrt{3}}{-13}$$
$$\approx -4018 \text{ inches per minute.}$$

REMARK   The velocity in Example 6 is negative because x represents a distance that is decreasing.

3.7 Exercises

See CalcChat.com for tutorial help and worked-out solutions to odd-numbered exercises.

Using Related Rates In Exercises 1–4, assume that x and y are both differentiable functions of t and find the required values of dy/dt and dx/dt.

Equation	Find	Given
1. $y = \sqrt{x}$	(a) $\dfrac{dy}{dt}$ when $x = 4$	$\dfrac{dx}{dt} = 3$
	(b) $\dfrac{dx}{dt}$ when $x = 25$	$\dfrac{dy}{dt} = 2$
2. $y = 3x^2 - 5x$	(a) $\dfrac{dy}{dt}$ when $x = 3$	$\dfrac{dx}{dt} = 2$
	(b) $\dfrac{dx}{dt}$ when $x = 2$	$\dfrac{dy}{dt} = 4$
3. $xy = 4$	(a) $\dfrac{dy}{dt}$ when $x = 8$	$\dfrac{dx}{dt} = 10$
	(b) $\dfrac{dx}{dt}$ when $x = 1$	$\dfrac{dy}{dt} = -6$
4. $x^2 + y^2 = 25$	(a) $\dfrac{dy}{dt}$ when $x = 3, y = 4$	$\dfrac{dx}{dt} = 8$
	(b) $\dfrac{dx}{dt}$ when $x = 4, y = 3$	$\dfrac{dy}{dt} = -2$

Moving Point In Exercises 5–8, a point is moving along the graph of the given function at the rate dx/dt. Find dy/dt for the given values of x.

5. $y = 2x^2 + 1; \dfrac{dx}{dt} = 2$ centimeters per second

   (a) $x = -1$ (b) $x = 0$ (c) $x = 1$

6. $y = \dfrac{1}{1 + x^2}; \dfrac{dx}{dt} = 6$ inches per second

   (a) $x = -2$ (b) $x = 0$ (c) $x = 2$

7. $y = \tan x; \dfrac{dx}{dt} = 3$ feet per second

   (a) $x = -\dfrac{\pi}{3}$ (b) $x = -\dfrac{\pi}{4}$ (c) $x = 0$

8. $y = \cos x; \dfrac{dx}{dt} = 4$ centimeters per second

   (a) $x = \dfrac{\pi}{6}$ (b) $x = \dfrac{\pi}{4}$ (c) $x = \dfrac{\pi}{3}$

WRITING ABOUT CONCEPTS

9. Related Rates Consider the linear function

$$y = ax + b.$$

If x changes at a constant rate, does y change at a constant rate? If so, does it change at the same rate as x? Explain.

10. Related Rates In your own words, state the guidelines for solving related-rate problems.

11. Area The radius r of a circle is increasing at a rate of 4 centimeters per minute. Find the rates of change of the area when (a) $r = 8$ centimeters and (b) $r = 32$ centimeters.

12. Area The included angle of the two sides of constant equal length s of an isosceles triangle is θ.

   (a) Show that the area of the triangle is given by $A = \frac{1}{2}s^2 \sin \theta$.

   (b) The angle θ is increasing at the rate of $\frac{1}{2}$ radian per minute. Find the rates of change of the area when $\theta = \pi/6$ and $\theta = \pi/3$.

   (c) Explain why the rate of change of the area of the triangle is not constant even though $d\theta/dt$ is constant.

13. Volume The radius r of a sphere is increasing at a rate of 3 inches per minute.

   (a) Find the rates of change of the volume when $r = 9$ inches and $r = 36$ inches.

   (b) Explain why the rate of change of the volume of the sphere is not constant even though dr/dt is constant.

14. Volume A spherical balloon is inflated with gas at the rate of 800 cubic centimeters per minute. How fast is the radius of the balloon increasing at the instant the radius is (a) 30 centimeters and (b) 60 centimeters?

15. Volume All edges of a cube are expanding at a rate of 6 centimeters per second. How fast is the volume changing when each edge is (a) 2 centimeters and (b) 10 centimeters?

16. Surface Area All edges of a cube are expanding at a rate of 6 centimeters per second. How fast is the surface area changing when each edge is (a) 2 centimeters and (b) 10 centimeters?

17. Volume At a sand and gravel plant, sand is falling off a conveyor and onto a conical pile at a rate of 10 cubic feet per minute. The diameter of the base of the cone is approximately three times the altitude. At what rate is the height of the pile changing when the pile is 15 feet high? (*Hint:* The formula for the volume of a cone is $V = \frac{1}{3}\pi r^2 h$.)

18. Depth A conical tank (with vertex down) is 10 feet across the top and 12 feet deep. Water is flowing into the tank at a rate of 10 cubic feet per minute. Find the rate of change of the depth of the water when the water is 8 feet deep.

19. Depth A swimming pool is 12 meters long, 6 meters wide, 1 meter deep at the shallow end, and 3 meters deep at the deep end (see figure). Water is being pumped into the pool at $\frac{1}{4}$ cubic meter per minute, and there is 1 meter of water at the deep end.

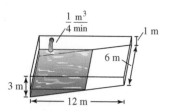

   (a) What percent of the pool is filled?

   (b) At what rate is the water level rising?

20. Depth A trough is 12 feet long and 3 feet across the top (see figure). Its ends are isosceles triangles with altitudes of 3 feet.

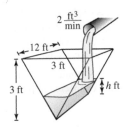

(a) Water is being pumped into the trough at 2 cubic feet per minute. How fast is the water level rising when the depth h is 1 foot?

(b) The water is rising at a rate of $\frac{3}{8}$ inch per minute when $h = 2$. Determine the rate at which water is being pumped into the trough.

21. Moving Ladder A ladder 25 feet long is leaning against the wall of a house (see figure). The base of the ladder is pulled away from the wall at a rate of 2 feet per second.

(a) How fast is the top of the ladder moving down the wall when its base is 7 feet, 15 feet, and 24 feet from the wall?

(b) Consider the triangle formed by the side of the house, the ladder, and the ground. Find the rate at which the area of the triangle is changing when the base of the ladder is 7 feet from the wall.

(c) Find the rate at which the angle between the ladder and the wall of the house is changing when the base of the ladder is 7 feet from the wall.

Figure for 21   Figure for 22

■ **FOR FURTHER INFORMATION** For more information on the mathematics of moving ladders, see the article "The Falling Ladder Paradox" by Paul Scholten and Andrew Simoson in *The College Mathematics Journal.* To view this article, go to *MathArticles.com.*

22. Construction A construction worker pulls a five-meter plank up the side of a building under construction by means of a rope tied to one end of the plank (see figure). Assume the opposite end of the plank follows a path perpendicular to the wall of the building and the worker pulls the rope at a rate of 0.15 meter per second. How fast is the end of the plank sliding along the ground when it is 2.5 meters from the wall of the building?

23. Construction A winch at the top of a 12-meter building pulls a pipe of the same length to a vertical position, as shown in the figure. The winch pulls in rope at a rate of -0.2 meter per second. Find the rate of vertical change and the rate of horizontal change at the end of the pipe when $y = 6$.

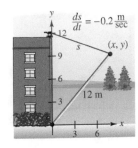

Figure for 23   Figure for 24

24. Boating A boat is pulled into a dock by means of a winch 12 feet above the deck of the boat (see figure).

(a) The winch pulls in rope at a rate of 4 feet per second. Determine the speed of the boat when there is 13 feet of rope out. What happens to the speed of the boat as it gets closer to the dock?

(b) Suppose the boat is moving at a constant rate of 4 feet per second. Determine the speed at which the winch pulls in rope when there is a total of 13 feet of rope out. What happens to the speed at which the winch pulls in rope as the boat gets closer to the dock?

25. Air Traffic Control An air traffic controller spots two planes at the same altitude converging on a point as they fly at right angles to each other (see figure). One plane is 225 miles from the point moving at 450 miles per hour. The other plane is 300 miles from the point moving at 600 miles per hour.

(a) At what rate is the distance between the planes decreasing?

(b) How much time does the air traffic controller have to get one of the planes on a different flight path?

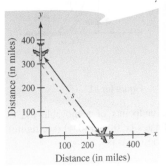

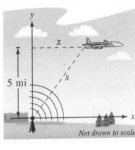

Figure for 25   Figure for 26

26. Air Traffic Control An airplane is flying at an altitude of 5 miles and passes directly over a radar antenna (see figure). When the plane is 10 miles away ($s = 10$), the radar detects that the distance s is changing at a rate of 240 miles per hour. What is the speed of the plane?

27. Sports A baseball diamond has the shape of a square with sides 90 feet long (see figure). A player running from second base to third base at a speed of 25 feet per second is 20 feet from third base. At what rate is the player's distance s from home plate changing?

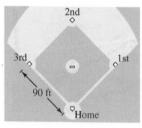

Figure for 27 and 28

28. Sports For the baseball diamond in Exercise 27, suppose the player is running from first base to second base at a speed of 25 feet per second. Find the rate at which the distance from home plate is changing when the player is 20 feet from second base.

29. Shadow Length A man 6 feet tall walks at a rate of 5 feet per second away from a light that is 15 feet above the ground (see figure).

(a) When he is 10 feet from the base of the light, at what rate is the tip of his shadow moving?

(b) When he is 10 feet from the base of the light, at what rate is the length of his shadow changing?

30. Shadow Length Repeat Exercise 29 for a man 6 feet tall walking at a rate of 5 feet per second *toward* a light that is 20 feet above the ground (see figure).

Figure for 30

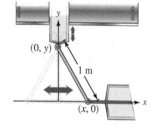

Figure for 31

31. Machine Design The endpoints of a movable rod of length 1 meter have coordinates $(x, 0)$ and $(0, y)$ (see figure). The position of the end on the x-axis is

$$x(t) = \frac{1}{2} \sin \frac{\pi t}{6}$$

where t is the time in seconds.

(a) Find the time of one complete cycle of the rod.

(b) What is the lowest point reached by the end of the rod on the y-axis?

(c) Find the speed of the y-axis endpoint when the x-axis endpoint is $\left(\frac{1}{4}, 0\right)$.

32. Machine Design Repeat Exercise 31 for a position function of $x(t) = \frac{3}{5} \sin \pi t$. Use the point $\left(\frac{3}{10}, 0\right)$ for part (c).

33. Evaporation As a spherical raindrop falls, it reaches a layer of dry air and begins to evaporate at a rate that is proportional to its surface area $(S = 4\pi r^2)$. Show that the radius of the raindrop decreases at a constant rate.

34. Electricity The combined electrical resistance R of two resistors R_1 and R_2, connected in parallel, is given by

$$\frac{1}{R} = \frac{1}{R_1} + \frac{1}{R_2}$$

where R, R_1, and R_2 are measured in ohms. R_1 and R_2 are increasing at rates of 1 and 1.5 ohms per second, respectively. At what rate is R changing when $R_1 = 50$ ohms and $R_2 = 75$ ohms?

35. Adiabatic Expansion When a certain polyatomic gas undergoes adiabatic expansion, its pressure p and volume V satisfy the equation

$$pV^{1.3} = k$$

where k is a constant. Find the relationship between the related rates dp/dt and dV/dt.

36. Roadway Design Cars on a certain roadway travel on a circular arc of radius r. In order not to rely on friction alone to overcome the centrifugal force, the road is banked at an angle of magnitude θ from the horizontal (see figure). The banking angle must satisfy the equation $rg \tan \theta = v^2$, where v is the velocity of the cars and $g = 32$ feet per second per second is the acceleration due to gravity. Find the relationship between the related rates dv/dt and $d\theta/dt$.

37. Angle of Elevation A balloon rises at a rate of 4 meters per second from a point on the ground 50 meters from an observer. Find the rate of change of the angle of elevation of the balloon from the observer when the balloon is 50 meters above the ground.

38. Angle of Elevation An airplane flies at an altitude of 5 miles toward a point directly over an observer (see figure). The speed of the plane is 600 miles per hour. Find the rates at which the angle of elevation θ is changing when the angle is (a) $\theta = 30°$, (b) $\theta = 60°$, and (c) $\theta = 75°$.

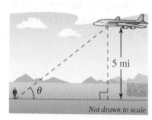

Not drawn to scale

39. Relative Humidity When the dewpoint is 65° Fahrenheit, the relative humidity H is

$$H = \frac{4347}{400,000,000} e^{369,444/(50t + 19,793)}$$

where t is the temperature in degrees Fahrenheit.

(a) Determine the relative humidity when $t = 65°$ and $t = 80°$.

(b) At 10 A.M., the temperature is 75° and increasing at the rate of 2° per hour. Find the rate at which the relative humidity is changing.

40. Linear vs. Angular Speed A patrol car is parked 50 feet from a long warehouse (see figure). The revolving light on top of the car turns at a rate of 30 revolutions per minute. How fast is the light beam moving along the wall when the beam makes angles of (a) $\theta = 30°$, (b) $\theta = 60°$, and (c) $\theta = 70°$ with the perpendicular line from the light to the wall?

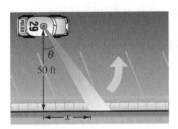

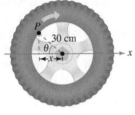

Figure for 40   Figure for 41

41. Linear vs. Angular Speed A wheel of radius 30 centimeters revolves at a rate of 10 revolutions per second. A dot is painted at a point P on the rim of the wheel (see figure).

(a) Find dx/dt as a function of θ.

(b) Use a graphing utility to graph the function in part (a).

(c) When is the absolute value of the rate of change of x greatest? When is it least?

(d) Find dx/dt when $\theta = 30°$ and $\theta = 60°$.

42. Flight Control An airplane is flying in still air with an airspeed of 275 miles per hour. The plane is climbing at an angle of 18°. Find the rate at which it is gaining altitude.

43. Security Camera A security camera is centered 50 feet above a 100-foot hallway (see figure). It is easiest to design the camera with a constant angular rate of rotation, but this results in recording the images of the surveillance area at a variable rate. So, it is desirable to design a system with a variable rate of rotation and a constant rate of movement of the scanning beam along the hallway. Find a model for the variable rate of rotation when $|dx/dt| = 2$ feet per second.

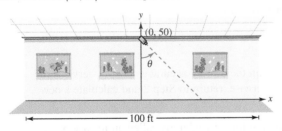

44. **HOW DO YOU SEE IT?** Using the graph of f, (a) determine whether dy/dt is positive or negative given that dx/dt is negative, and (b) determine whether dx/dt is positive or negative given that dy/dt is positive.

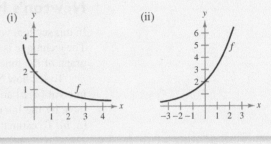

Acceleration In Exercises 45 and 46, find the acceleration of the specified object. (*Hint:* Recall that if a variable is changing at a constant rate, its acceleration is zero.)

45. Find the acceleration of the top of the ladder described in Exercise 21 when the base of the ladder is 7 feet from the wall.

46. Find the acceleration of the boat in Exercise 24(a) when there is a total of 13 feet of rope out.

47. Think About It Describe the relationship between the rate of change of y and the rate of change of x in each expression. Assume all variables and derivatives are positive.

(a) $\dfrac{dy}{dt} = 3\dfrac{dx}{dt}$ (b) $\dfrac{dy}{dt} = x(L - x)\dfrac{dx}{dt}, \quad 0 \le x \le L$

48. Moving Shadow A ball is dropped from a height of 20 meters, 12 meters away from the top of a 20-meter lamppost (see figure). The ball's shadow, caused by the light at the top of the lamppost, is moving along the level ground. How fast is the shadow moving 1 second after the ball is released? (*Submitted by Dennis Gittinger, St. Philips College, San Antonio, TX*)

49. Geometry Consider the rectangle shown in the figure.

(a) Find the area of the rectangle as a function of x.

(b) Find the rate of change of the area when $x = 4$ centimeters if $dx/dt = 4$ centimeters per minute.

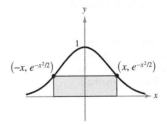

3.8 Newton's Method

■ Approximate a zero of a function using Newton's Method.

Newton's Method

In this section, you will study a technique for approximating the real zeros of a function. The technique is called **Newton's Method,** and it uses tangent lines to approximate the graph of the function near its x-intercepts.

To see how Newton's Method works, consider a function f that is continuous on the interval $[a, b]$ and differentiable on the interval (a, b). If $f(a)$ and $f(b)$ differ in sign, then, by the Intermediate Value Theorem, f must have at least one zero in the interval (a, b). To estimate this zero, you choose

$$x = x_1 \qquad \text{First estimate}$$

as shown in Figure 3.43(a). Newton's Method is based on the assumption that the graph of f and the tangent line at $(x_1, f(x_1))$ both cross the x-axis at *about* the same point. Because you can easily calculate the x-intercept for this tangent line, you can use it as a second (and, usually, better) estimate of the zero of f. The tangent line passes through the point $(x_1, f(x_1))$ with a slope of $f'(x_1)$. In point-slope form, the equation of the tangent line is

$$y - f(x_1) = f'(x_1)(x - x_1)$$
$$y = f'(x_1)(x - x_1) + f(x_1).$$

Letting $y = 0$ and solving for x produces

$$x = x_1 - \frac{f(x_1)}{f'(x_1)}.$$

So, from the initial estimate x_1, you obtain a new estimate

$$x_2 = x_1 - \frac{f(x_1)}{f'(x_1)}. \qquad \text{Second estimate [See Figure 3.43(b).]}$$

You can improve on x_2 and calculate yet a third estimate

$$x_3 = x_2 - \frac{f(x_2)}{f'(x_2)}. \qquad \text{Third estimate}$$

Repeated application of this process is called Newton's Method.

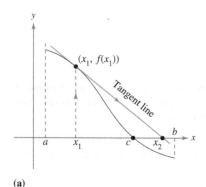

(a)

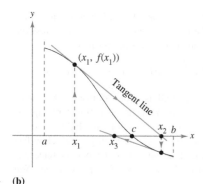

(b)

The x-intercept of the tangent line approximates the zero of f.

Figure 3.43

Newton's Method for Approximating the Zeros of a Function

Let $f(c) = 0$, where f is differentiable on an open interval containing c. Then, to approximate c, use these steps.

1. Make an initial estimate x_1 that is close to c. (A graph is helpful.)
2. Determine a new approximation

$$x_{n+1} = x_n - \frac{f(x_n)}{f'(x_n)}.$$

3. When $|x_n - x_{n+1}|$ is within the desired accuracy, let x_{n+1} serve as the final approximation. Otherwise, return to Step 2 and calculate a new approximation.

Each successive application of this procedure is called an **iteration.**

. . . . ▷

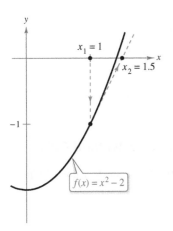

The first iteration of Newton's Method
Figure 3.44

EXAMPLE 1 **Using Newton's Method**

Calculate three iterations of Newton's Method to approximate a zero of $f(x) = x^2 - 2$. Use $x_1 = 1$ as the initial guess.

Solution Because $f(x) = x^2 - 2$, you have $f'(x) = 2x$, and the iterative formula is

$$x_{n+1} = x_n - \frac{f(x_n)}{f'(x_n)} = x_n - \frac{x_n^2 - 2}{2x_n}.$$

The calculations for three iterations are shown in the table.

n	x_n	$f(x_n)$	$f'(x_n)$	$\dfrac{f(x_n)}{f'(x_n)}$	$x_n - \dfrac{f(x_n)}{f'(x_n)}$
1	1.000000	-1.000000	2.000000	-0.500000	1.500000
2	1.500000	0.250000	3.000000	0.083333	1.416667
3	1.416667	0.006945	2.833334	0.002451	1.414216
4	1.414216				

Of course, in this case you know that the two zeros of the function are $\pm\sqrt{2}$. To six decimal places, $\sqrt{2} = 1.414214$. So, after only three iterations of Newton's Method, you have obtained an approximation that is within 0.000002 of an actual root. The first iteration of this process is shown in Figure 3.44.

EXAMPLE 2 **Using Newton's Method**

· · · ·▷ *See LarsonCalculus.com for an interactive version of this type of example.*

Use Newton's Method to approximate the zero(s) of

$$f(x) = e^x + x.$$

Continue the iterations until two successive approximations differ by less than 0.0001.

Solution Begin by sketching a graph of f, as shown in Figure 3.45. From the graph, you can observe that the function has only one zero, which occurs near $x = -0.6$. Next, differentiate f and form the iterative formula

$$x_{n+1} = x_n - \frac{f(x_n)}{f'(x_n)} = x_n - \frac{e^{x_n} + x_n}{e^{x_n} + 1}.$$

The calculations are shown in the table.

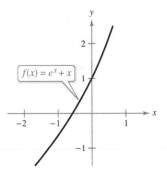

After three iterations of Newton's Method, the zero of f is approximated to the desired accuracy.
Figure 3.45

n	x_n	$f(x_n)$	$f'(x_n)$	$\dfrac{f(x_n)}{f'(x_n)}$	$x_n - \dfrac{f(x_n)}{f'(x_n)}$
1	-0.60000	-0.05119	1.54881	-0.03305	-0.56695
2	-0.56695	0.00030	1.56725	0.00019	-0.56714
3	-0.56714	0.00000	1.56714	0.00000	-0.56714
4	-0.56714				

Because two successive approximations differ by less than the required 0.0001, you can estimate the zero of f to be -0.56714.

When, as in Examples 1 and 2, the approximations approach a limit, the sequence $x_1, x_2, x_3, \ldots, x_n, \ldots$ is said to **converge**. Moreover, when the limit is c, it can be shown that c must be a zero of f.

Newton's Method does not always yield a convergent sequence. One way it can fail to do so is shown in Figure 3.46. Because Newton's Method involves division by $f'(x_n)$, it is clear that the method will fail when the derivative is zero for any x_n in the sequence. When you encounter this problem, you can usually overcome it by choosing a different value for x_1. Another way Newton's Method can fail is shown in the next example.

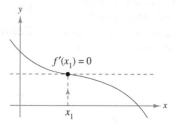

Newton's Method fails to converge when $f'(x_n) = 0$.

Figure 3.46

■ **FOR FURTHER INFORMATION** For more on when Newton's Method fails, see the article "No Fooling! Newton's Method Can Be Fooled" by Peter Horton in *Mathematics Magazine*. To view this article, go to *MathArticles.com*.

EXAMPLE 3   **An Example in Which Newton's Method Fails**

The function $f(x) = x^{1/3}$ is not differentiable at $x = 0$. Show that Newton's Method fails to converge using $x_1 = 0.1$.

Solution   Because $f'(x) = \frac{1}{3}x^{-2/3}$, the iterative formula is

$$x_{n+1} = x_n - \frac{f(x_n)}{f'(x_n)} = x_n - \frac{x_n^{1/3}}{\frac{1}{3}x_n^{-2/3}} = x_n - 3x_n = -2x_n.$$

The calculations are shown in the table. This table and Figure 3.47 indicate that x_n continues to increase in magnitude as $n \to \infty$, and so the limit of the sequence does not exist.

n	x_n	$f(x_n)$	$f'(x_n)$	$\dfrac{f(x_n)}{f'(x_n)}$	$x_n - \dfrac{f(x_n)}{f'(x_n)}$
1	0.10000	0.46416	1.54720	0.30000	-0.20000
2	-0.20000	-0.58480	0.97467	-0.60000	0.40000
3	0.40000	0.73681	0.61401	1.20000	-0.80000
4	-0.80000	-0.92832	0.3680	-2.40000	1.60000

•• **REMARK**   In Example 3, the initial estimate $x_1 = 0.1$ fails to produce a convergent sequence. Try showing that Newton's Method also fails for every other choice of x_1 (other than the actual zero).

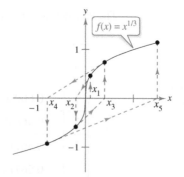

Newton's Method fails to converge for every x-value other than the actual zero of f.

Figure 3.47

It can be shown that a condition sufficient to produce convergence of Newton's Method to a zero of f is that

$$\left| \frac{f(x)f''(x)}{[f'(x)]^2} \right| < 1 \qquad \text{Condition for convergence}$$

on an open interval containing the zero. For instance, in Example 1, this test would yield

$$f(x) = x^2 - 2, \quad f'(x) = 2x, \quad f''(x) = 2,$$

and

$$\left| \frac{f(x)f''(x)}{[f'(x)]^2} \right| = \left| \frac{(x^2-2)(2)}{4x^2} \right| = \left| \frac{1}{2} - \frac{1}{x^2} \right|. \qquad \text{Example 1}$$

On the interval $(1, 3)$, this quantity is less than 1 and therefore the convergence of Newton's Method is guaranteed. On the other hand, in Example 3, you have

$$f(x) = x^{1/3}, \quad f'(x) = \frac{1}{3}x^{-2/3}, \quad f''(x) = -\frac{2}{9}x^{-5/3}$$

and

$$\left| \frac{f(x)f''(x)}{[f'(x)]^2} \right| = \left| \frac{x^{1/3}(-2/9)(x^{-5/3})}{(1/9)(x^{-4/3})} \right| = 2 \qquad \text{Example 3}$$

which is not less than 1 for any value of x, so you cannot conclude that Newton's Method will converge.

You have learned several techniques for finding the zeros of functions. The zeros of some functions, such as

$$f(x) = x^3 - 2x^2 - x + 2$$

can be found by simple algebraic techniques, such as factoring. The zeros of other functions, such as

$$f(x) = x^3 - x + 1$$

cannot be found by *elementary* algebraic methods. This particular function has only one real zero, and by using more advanced algebraic techniques, you can determine the zero to be

$$x = -\sqrt[3]{\frac{3 - \sqrt{23/3}}{6}} - \sqrt[3]{\frac{3 + \sqrt{23/3}}{6}}.$$

Because the *exact* solution is written in terms of square roots and cube roots, it is called a **solution by radicals.**

The determination of radical solutions of a polynomial equation is one of the fundamental problems of algebra. The earliest such result is the Quadratic Formula, which dates back at least to Babylonian times. The general formula for the zeros of a cubic function was developed much later. In the sixteenth century, an Italian mathematician, Jerome Cardan, published a method for finding radical solutions to cubic and quartic equations. Then, for 300 years, the problem of finding a general quintic formula remained open. Finally, in the nineteenth century, the problem was answered independently by two young mathematicians. Niels Henrik Abel, a Norwegian mathematician, and Evariste Galois, a French mathematician, proved that it is not possible to solve a *general* fifth- (or higher-) degree polynomial equation by radicals. Of course, you can solve particular fifth-degree equations, such as

$$x^5 - 1 = 0$$

but Abel and Galois were able to show that no general *radical* solution exists.

NIELS HENRIK ABEL (1802–1829)

EVARISTE GALOIS (1811–1832)

Although the lives of both Abel and Galois were brief, their work in the fields of analysis and abstract algebra was far-reaching.
See LarsonCalculus.com to read a biography about each of these mathematicians.

3.8 Exercises

See **CalcChat.com** for tutorial help and worked-out solutions to odd-numbered exercises.

Using Newton's Method In Exercises 1–4, complete two iterations of Newton's Method to approximate a zero of the function using the given initial guess.

1. $f(x) = x^2 - 5$, $x_1 = 2.2$

2. $f(x) = x^3 - 3$, $x_1 = 1.4$

3. $f(x) = \cos x$, $x_1 = 1.6$

4. $f(x) = \tan x$, $x_1 = 0.1$

Using Newton's Method In Exercises 5–16, approximate the zero(s) of the function. Use Newton's Method and continue the process until two successive approximations differ by less than 0.001. Then find the zero(s) using a graphing utility and compare the results.

5. $f(x) = x^3 + 4$　　　　**6.** $f(x) = 2 - x^3$

7. $f(x) = x^3 + x - 1$　　**8.** $f(x) = x^5 + x - 1$

9. $f(x) = 5\sqrt{x - 1} - 2x$　**10.** $f(x) = x - 2\sqrt{x + 1}$

11. $f(x) = x - e^{-x}$　　　**12.** $f(x) = x - 3 + \ln x$

13. $f(x) = x^3 - 3.9x^2 + 4.79x - 1.881$

14. $f(x) = x^4 + x^3 - 1$

15. $f(x) = 1 - x + \sin x$　**16.** $f(x) = x^3 - \cos x$

Finding Point(s) of Intersection In Exercises 17–20, apply Newton's Method to approximate the x-value(s) of the indicated point(s) of intersection of the two graphs. Continue the process until two successive approximations differ by less than 0.001. [*Hint:* Let $h(x) = f(x) - g(x)$.]

17. $f(x) = 2x + 1$　　　　**18.** $f(x) = 2 - x^2$

　　$g(x) = \sqrt{x + 4}$　　　　　$g(x) = e^{x/2}$

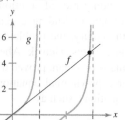　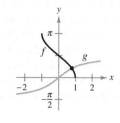

19. $f(x) = x$　　　　　　**20.** $f(x) = \arccos x$

　　$g(x) = \tan x$　　　　　　$g(x) = \arctan x$

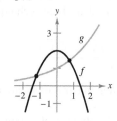

21. Mechanic's Rule The Mechanic's Rule for approximating $\sqrt{a}$, $a > 0$, is

$$x_{n+1} = \frac{1}{2}\left(x_n + \frac{a}{x_n}\right), \quad n = 1, 2, 3 \ldots$$

where x_1 is an approximation of $\sqrt{a}$.

(a) Use Newton's Method and the function $f(x) = x^2 - a$ to derive the Mechanic's Rule.

(b) Use the Mechanic's Rule to approximate $\sqrt{5}$ and $\sqrt{7}$ to three decimal places.

22. Approximating Radicals

(a) Use Newton's Method and the function $f(x) = x^n - a$ to obtain a general rule for approximating $x = \sqrt[n]{a}$.

(b) Use the general rule found in part (a) to approximate $\sqrt[4]{6}$ and $\sqrt[3]{15}$ to three decimal places.

Failure of Newton's Method In Exercises 23 and 24, apply Newton's Method using the given initial guess, and explain why the method fails.

23. $y = 2x^3 - 6x^2 + 6x - 1$, $x_1 = 1$

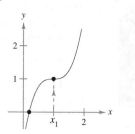

Figure for 23　　　　　Figure for 24

24. $y = x^3 - 2x - 2$, $x_1 = 0$

Fixed Point In Exercises 25–28, approximate the fixed point of the function to two decimal places. [A *fixed point* x_0 of a function f is a value of x such that $f(x_0) = x_0$.]

25. $f(x) = \cos x$　　　　**26.** $f(x) = \cot x$, $0 < x < \pi$

27. $f(x) = e^{x/10}$　　　　**28.** $f(x) = -\ln x$

29. Approximating Reciprocals Use Newton's Method to show that the equation

$$x_{n+1} = x_n(2 - ax_n)$$

can be used to approximate $1/a$ when x_1 is an initial guess of the reciprocal of a. Note that this method of approximating reciprocals uses only the operations of multiplication and subtraction. (*Hint:* Consider

$$f(x) = \frac{1}{x} - a.)$$

30. Approximating Reciprocals Use the result of Exercise 29 to approximate (a) $\frac{1}{3}$ and (b) $\frac{1}{11}$ to three decimal places.

31. Using Newton's Method Consider the function $f(x) = x^3 - 3x^2 + 3$.

 (a) Use a graphing utility to graph f.

(b) Use Newton's Method to approximate a zero with $x_1 = 1$ as an initial guess.

(c) Repeat part (b) using $x_1 = \frac{1}{4}$ as an initial guess and observe that the result is different.

(d) To understand why the results in parts (b) and (c) are different, sketch the tangent lines to the graph of f at the points $(1, f(1))$ and $\left(\frac{1}{4}, f\left(\frac{1}{4}\right)\right)$. Find the x-intercept of each tangent line and compare the intercepts with the first iteration of Newton's Method using the respective initial guesses.

(e) Write a short paragraph summarizing how Newton's Method works. Use the results of this exercise to describe why it is important to select the initial guess carefully.

32. Using Newton's Method Repeat the steps in Exercise 31 for the function $f(x) = \sin x$ with initial guesses of $x_1 = 1.8$ and $x_1 = 3$.

33. Newton's Method In your own words and using a sketch, describe Newton's Method for approximating the zeros of a function.

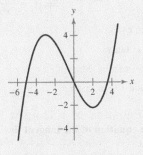

34. HOW DO YOU SEE IT? For what value(s) will Newton's Method fail to converge for the function shown in the graph? Explain your reasoning.

Using Newton's Method Exercises 35–37 present problems similar to exercises from the previous sections of this chapter. In each case, use Newton's Method to approximate the solution.

35. Minimum Distance Find the point on the graph of $f(x) = 4 - x^2$ that is closest to the point $(1, 0)$.

36. Medicine The concentration C of a chemical in the bloodstream t hours after injection into muscle tissue is given by

$$C = \frac{3t^2 + t}{50 + t^3}.$$

When is the concentration the greatest?

37. Minimum Time You are in a boat 2 miles from the nearest point on the coast (see figure). You are to go to a point Q that is 3 miles down the coast and 1 mile inland. You can row at 3 miles per hour and walk at 4 miles per hour. Toward what point on the coast should you row in order to reach Q in the least time?

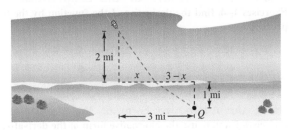

38. Crime The total number of arrests T (in thousands) for all males ages 15 to 24 in 2010 is approximated by the model

$$T = 0.2988x^4 - 22.625x^3 + 628.49x^2 - 7565.9x + 33,478$$

for $15 \le x \le 24$, where x is the age in years (see figure). Approximate the two ages that had total arrests of 300 thousand. *(Source: U.S. Department of Justice)*

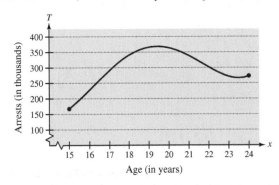

True or False? In Exercises 39–42, determine whether the statement is true or false. If it is false, explain why or give an example that shows it is false.

39. The zeros of $f(x) = \dfrac{p(x)}{q(x)}$ coincide with the zeros of $p(x)$.

40. If the coefficients of a polynomial function are all positive, then the polynomial has no positive zeros.

41. If $f(x)$ is a cubic polynomial such that $f'(x)$ is never zero, then any initial guess will force Newton's Method to converge to the zero of f.

42. The roots of $\sqrt{f(x)} = 0$ coincide with the roots of $f(x) = 0$.

43. Tangent Lines The graph of $f(x) = -\sin x$ has infinitely many tangent lines that pass through the origin. Use Newton's Method to approximate to three decimal places the slope of the tangent line having the greatest slope.

44. Point of Tangency The graph of $f(x) = \cos x$ and a tangent line to f through the origin are shown. Find the coordinates of the point of tangency to three decimal places.

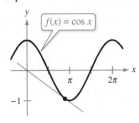

Review Exercises   See CalcChat.com for tutorial help and worked-out solutions to odd-numbered exercises.

Finding the Derivative by the Limit Process In Exercises 1–4, find the derivative of the function by the limit process.

1. $f(x) = 12$

2. $f(x) = 5x - 4$

3. $f(x) = x^2 - 4x + 5$

4. $f(x) = \dfrac{6}{x}$

Using the Alternative Form of the Derivative In Exercises 5 and 6, use the alternative form of the derivative to find the derivative at $x = c$ (if it exists).

5. $g(x) = 2x^2 - 3x,\quad c = 2$ 6. $f(x) = \dfrac{1}{x + 4},\quad c = 3$

Determining Differentiability In Exercises 7 and 8, describe the x-values at which f is differentiable.

7. $f(x) = (x - 3)^{2/5}$

8. $f(x) = \dfrac{3x}{x + 1}$

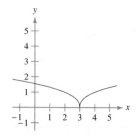
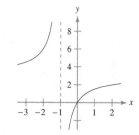

Finding a Derivative In Exercises 9–20, use the rules of differentiation to find the derivative of the function.

9. $y = 25$

10. $f(t) = 4t^4$

11. $f(x) = x^3 - 11x^2$

12. $g(s) = 3s^5 - 2s^4$

13. $h(x) = 6\sqrt{x} + 3\sqrt[3]{x}$

14. $f(x) = x^{1/2} - x^{-1/2}$

15. $g(t) = \dfrac{2}{3t^2}$

16. $h(x) = \dfrac{8}{5x^4}$

17. $f(\theta) = 4\theta - 5\sin\theta$

18. $g(\alpha) = 4\cos\alpha + 6$

19. $f(t) = 3\cos t - 4e^t$

20. $g(s) = \frac{5}{3}\sin s - 2e^s$

Finding the Slope of a Graph In Exercises 21–24, find the slope of the graph of the functions at the given point.

21. $f(x) = \dfrac{27}{x^3},\quad (3, 1)$

22. $f(x) = 3x^2 - 4x,\quad (1, -1)$

23. $f(x) = 2x^4 - 8,\quad (0, -8)$

24. $f(\theta) = 3\cos\theta - 2\theta,\quad (0, 3)$

25. **Vibrating String** When a guitar string is plucked, it vibrates with a frequency of $F = 200\sqrt{T}$, where F is measured in vibrations per second and the tension T is measured in pounds. Find the rates of change of F when (a) $T = 4$ and (b) $T = 9$.

26. **Volume** The surface area of a cube with sides of length s is given by $S = 6s^2$. Find the rates of change of the surface area with respect to s when (a) $s = 3$ inches and (b) $s = 5$ inches.

Vertical Motion In Exercises 27 and 28, use the position function $s(t) = -16t^2 + v_0 t + s_0$ for free-falling objects.

27. A ball is thrown straight down from the top of a 600-foot building with an initial velocity of -30 feet per second.

   (a) Determine the position and velocity functions for the ball.

   (b) Determine the average velocity on the interval $[1, 3]$.

   (c) Find the instantaneous velocities when $t = 1$ and $t = 3$.

   (d) Find the time required for the ball to reach ground level.

   (e) Find the velocity of the ball at impact.

28. To estimate the height of a building, a weight is dropped from the top of the building into a pool at ground level. The splash is seen 9.2 seconds after the weight is dropped. What is the height (in feet) of the building?

Finding a Derivative In Exercises 29–40, find the derivative of the function.

29. $f(x) = (5x^2 + 8)(x^2 - 4x - 6)$

30. $g(x) = (2x^3 + 5x)(3x - 4)$

31. $h(x) = \sqrt{x}\sin x$ 32. $f(t) = 2t^5\cos t$

33. $f(x) = \dfrac{x^2 + x - 1}{x^2 - 1}$ 34. $f(x) = \dfrac{2x + 7}{x^2 + 4}$

35. $y = \dfrac{x^4}{\cos x}$ 36. $y = \dfrac{\sin x}{x^4}$

37. $y = 3x^2\sec x$

38. $y = 2x - x^2\tan x$

39. $y = 4xe^x - \cot x$

40. $g(x) = 3x\sin x + x^2\cos x$

Finding an Equation of a Tangent Line In Exercises 41–44, find an equation of the tangent line to the graph of f at the given point.

41. $f(x) = (x + 2)(x^2 + 5),\quad (-1, 6)$

42. $f(x) = (x - 4)(x^2 + 6x - 1),\quad (0, 4)$

43. $f(x) = \dfrac{x + 1}{x - 1},\quad \left(\dfrac{1}{2}, -3\right)$

44. $f(x) = \dfrac{1 + \cos x}{1 - \cos x},\quad \left(\dfrac{\pi}{2}, 1\right)$

Finding a Second Derivative In Exercises 45–50, find the second derivative of the function.

45. $g(t) = -8t^3 - 5t + 12$ 46. $h(x) = 6x^{-2} + 7x^2$

47. $f(x) = 15x^{5/2}$ 48. $f(x) = 20\sqrt[5]{x}$

49. $f(\theta) = 3\tan\theta$ 50. $h(t) = 10\cos t - 15\sin t$

51. Acceleration The velocity of an object in meters per second is $v(t) = 20 - t^2$, $0 \le t \le 6$. Find the velocity and acceleration of the object when $t = 3$.

52. Acceleration The velocity of an automobile starting from rest is

$$v(t) = \frac{90t}{4t + 10}$$

where v is measured in feet per second. Find the acceleration at (a) 1 second, (b) 5 seconds, and (c) 10 seconds.

Finding a Derivative **In Exercises 53–78, find the derivative of the function.**

53. $y = (7x + 3)^4$

54. $y = (x^2 - 6)^3$

55. $y = \dfrac{1}{x^2 + 4}$

56. $f(x) = \dfrac{1}{(5x + 1)^2}$

57. $y = 5\cos(9x + 1)$

58. $y = 1 - \cos 2x + 2\cos^2 x$

59. $y = \dfrac{x}{2} - \dfrac{\sin 2x}{4}$

60. $y = \dfrac{\sec^7 x}{7} - \dfrac{\sec^5 x}{5}$

61. $y = x(6x + 1)^5$

62. $f(s) = (s^2 - 1)^{5/2}(s^3 + 5)$

63. $f(x) = \dfrac{3x}{\sqrt{x^2 + 1}}$

64. $h(x) = \left(\dfrac{x + 5}{x^2 + 3}\right)^2$

65. $g(t) = t^2 e^{t/4}$

66. $h(z) = e^{-z^2/2}$

67. $y = \sqrt{e^{2x} + e^{-2x}}$

68. $y = 3e^{-3/t}$

69. $g(x) = \dfrac{x^2}{e^x}$

70. $f(\theta) = \dfrac{1}{2}e^{\sin 2\theta}$

71. $g(x) = \ln\sqrt{x}$

72. $h(x) = \ln\dfrac{x(x - 1)}{x - 2}$

73. $f(x) = x\sqrt{\ln x}$

74. $f(x) = \ln[x(x^2 - 2)^{2/3}]$

75. $y = \dfrac{1}{b^2}\left[\ln(a + bx) + \dfrac{a}{a + bx}\right]$

76. $y = \dfrac{1}{b^2}[a + bx - a\ln(a + bx)]$

77. $y = -\dfrac{1}{a}\ln\dfrac{a + bx}{x}$

78. $y = -\dfrac{1}{ax} + \dfrac{b}{a^2}\ln\dfrac{a + bx}{x}$

Evaluating a Derivative **In Exercises 79–84, find and evaluate the derivative of the function at the given point.**

79. $f(x) = \sqrt{1 - x^3}$, $(-2, 3)$

80. $f(x) = \sqrt[3]{x^2 - 1}$, $(3, 2)$

81. $f(x) = \dfrac{4}{x^2 + 1}$, $(-1, 2)$

82. $f(x) = \dfrac{3x + 1}{4x - 3}$, $(4, 1)$

83. $y = \dfrac{1}{2}\csc 2x$, $\left(\dfrac{\pi}{4}, \dfrac{1}{2}\right)$

84. $y = \csc 3x + \cot 3x$, $\left(\dfrac{\pi}{6}, 1\right)$

Finding a Second Derivative **In Exercises 85–88, find the second derivative of the function.**

85. $y = (8x + 5)^3$

86. $y = \dfrac{1}{5x + 1}$

87. $f(x) = \cot x$

88. $y = \sin^2 x$

89. Refrigeration The temperature T (in degrees Fahrenheit) of food in a freezer is

$$T = \frac{700}{t^2 + 4t + 10}$$

where t is the time in hours. Find the rate of change of T with respect to t at each of the following times.

(a) $t = 1$ (b) $t = 3$ (c) $t = 5$ (d) $t = 10$

90. Harmonic Motion The displacement from equilibrium of an object in harmonic motion on the end of a spring is

$$y = \frac{1}{4}\cos 8t - \frac{1}{4}\sin 8t$$

where y is measured in feet and t is the time in seconds. Determine the position and velocity of the object when $t = \pi/4$.

91. Modeling Data The atmospheric pressure decreases with increasing altitude. At sea level, the average air pressure is one atmosphere (1.033227 kilograms per square centimeter). The table gives the pressures p (in atmospheres) at various altitudes h (in kilometers).

h	0	5	10	15	20	25
p	1	0.55	0.25	0.12	0.06	0.02

(a) Use a graphing utility to find a model of the form $p = a + b\ln h$ for the data. Explain why the result is an error message.

(b) Use a graphing utility to find the logarithmic model $h = a + b\ln p$ for the data.

(c) Use a graphing utility to plot the data and graph the logarithmic model.

(d) Use the model to estimate the altitude at which the pressure is 0.75 atmosphere.

(e) Use the model to estimate the pressure at an altitude of 13 kilometers.

(f) Find the rates of change of pressure when $h = 5$ and $h = 20$. Interpret the results in the context of the problem.

92. Tractrix A person walking along a dock drags a boat by a 10-meter rope. The boat travels along a path known as a *tractrix* (see figure). The equation of this path is

$$y = 10\ln\left(\frac{10 + \sqrt{100 - x^2}}{x}\right) - \sqrt{100 - x^2}.$$

(a) Use a graphing utility to graph the function.

(b) What is the slope of the path when $x = 5$ and $x = 9$?

(c) What does the slope of the path approach as $x \to 10$?

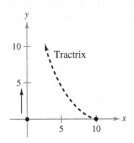
Tractrix

Finding a Derivative In Exercises 93–98, find dy/dx by implicit differentiation.

93. $x^2 + y^2 = 64$

94. $x^2 + 4xy - y^3 = 6$

95. $x^3y - xy^3 = 4$

96. $\sqrt{xy} = x - 4y$

97. $x \sin y = y \cos x$

98. $\cos(x + y) = x$

Tangent Lines and Normal Lines In Exercises 99–102, find equations for the tangent line and the normal line to the graph of the equation at the given point. (The *normal line* at a point is perpendicular to the tangent line at the point.) Use a graphing utility to graph the equation, the tangent line, and the normal line.

99. $x^2 + y^2 = 10$, $(3, 1)$

100. $x^2 - y^2 = 20$, $(6, 4)$

101. $y \ln x + y^2 = 0$, $(e, -1)$

102. $\ln(x + y) = x$, $(0, 1)$

Logarithmic Differentiation In Exercises 103 and 104, use logarithmic differentiation to find dy/dx.

103. $y = \dfrac{x\sqrt{x^2 + 1}}{x + 4}$

104. $y = \dfrac{(2x + 1)^3(x^2 - 1)^2}{x + 3}$

Evaluating the Derivative of an Inverse Function In Exercises 105–108, verify that f has an inverse. Then use the function f and the given real number a to find $(f^{-1})'(a)$. (*Hint:* Use Theorem 3.17.)

Function	Real Number
105. $f(x) = x^3 + 2$	$a = -1$
106. $f(x) = x\sqrt{x - 3}$	$a = 4$
107. $f(x) = \tan x,\ -\dfrac{\pi}{4} \le x \le \dfrac{\pi}{4}$	$a = \dfrac{\sqrt{3}}{3}$
108. $f(x) = \cos x,\ 0 \le x \le \pi$	$a = 0$

Finding a Derivative In Exercises 109–114, find the derivative of the function.

109. $y = \tan(\arcsin x)$

110. $y = \arctan(2x^2 - 3)$

111. $y = x \operatorname{arcsec} x$

112. $y = \frac{1}{2} \arctan e^{2x}$

113. $y = x(\arcsin x)^2 - 2x + 2\sqrt{1 - x^2}\arcsin x$

114. $y = \sqrt{x^2 - 4} - 2\operatorname{arcsec}\dfrac{x}{2}$, $2 < x < 4$

115. **Rate of Change** A point moves along the curve $y = \sqrt{x}$ in such a way that the y-value is increasing at a rate of 2 units per second. At what rate is x changing for each of the following values?

(a) $x = \frac{1}{2}$ (b) $x = 1$ (c) $x = 4$

116. **Surface Area** All edges of a cube are expanding at a rate of 8 centimeters per second. How fast is the surface area changing when each edge is 6.5 centimeters?

117. **Linear vs. Angular Speed** A rotating beacon is located 1 kilometer off a straight shoreline (see figure). The beacon rotates at a rate of 3 revolutions per minute. How fast (in kilometers per hour) does the beam of light appear to be moving to a viewer who is $\frac{1}{2}$ kilometer down the shoreline?

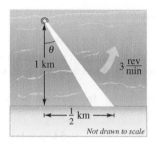

Not drawn to scale

118. **Moving Shadow** A sandbag is dropped from a balloon at a height of 60 meters when the angle of elevation to the sun is 30° (see figure). The position of the sandbag is

$$s(t) = 60 - 4.9t^2.$$

Find the rate at which the shadow of the sandbag is traveling along the ground when the sandbag is at a height of 35 meters.

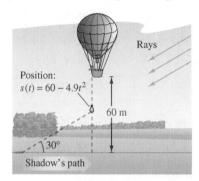

Position: $s(t) = 60 - 4.9t^2$

Rays

60 m

30°

Shadow's path

Using Newton's Method In Exercises 119–124, use Newton's Method to approximate any real zeros of the function accurate to three decimal places. Use the root-finding capabilities of a graphing utility to verify your results.

119. $f(x) = x^3 - 3x - 1$

120. $f(x) = x^3 + 2x + 1$

121. $g(x) = xe^x - 4$

122. $f(x) = 3 - x \ln x$

123. $f(x) = x^4 + x^3 - 3x^2 + 2$

124. $f(x) = 3\sqrt{x - 1} - x$

Finding Point(s) of Intersection In Exercises 125–128, use Newton's Method to approximate, to three decimal places, the x-values of any points of intersection of the graphs of the equations. Use a graphing utility to verify your results.

125. $y = x^4$

$y = x + 3$

126. $y = \sin \pi x$

$y = 1 - x$

127. $y = -x$

$y = \ln x$

128. $y = 1 - x$

$y = \arcsin x$

P.S. Problem Solving

See **CalcChat.com** for tutorial help and worked-out solutions to odd-numbered exercises.

1. Finding Equations of Circles Consider the graph of the parabola $y = x^2$.

(a) Find the radius r of the largest possible circle centered on the y-axis that is tangent to the parabola at the origin, as shown in the figure. This circle is called the **circle of curvature** (see Section 12.5). Find the equation of this circle. Use a graphing utility to graph the circle and parabola in the same viewing window to verify your answer.

(b) Find the center $(0, b)$ of the circle of radius 1 centered on the y-axis that is tangent to the parabola at two points, as shown in the figure. Find the equation of this circle. Use a graphing utility to graph the circle and parabola in the same viewing window to verify your answer.

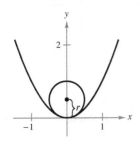

Figure for 1(a)   Figure for 1(b)

2. Finding Equations of Tangent Lines Graph the two parabolas

$$y = x^2 \quad \text{and} \quad y = -x^2 + 2x - 5$$

in the same coordinate plane. Find equations of the two lines that are simultaneously tangent to both parabolas.

3. Finding a Polynomial Find a third-degree polynomial $p(x)$ that is tangent to the line $y = 14x - 13$ at the point $(1, 1)$, and tangent to the line $y = -2x - 5$ at the point $(-1, -3)$.

4. Finding a Function Find a function of the form $f(x) = a + b \cos cx$ that is tangent to the line $y = 1$ at the point $(0, 1)$, and tangent to the line

$$y = x + \frac{3}{2} - \frac{\pi}{4}$$

at the point $\left(\frac{\pi}{4}, \frac{3}{2}\right)$.

5. Tangent Lines and Normal Lines

(a) Find an equation of the tangent line to the parabola $y = x^2$ at the point $(2, 4)$.

(b) Find an equation of the normal line to $y = x^2$ at the point $(2, 4)$. (The *normal line* at a point is perpendicular to the tangent line at the point.) Where does this line intersect the parabola a second time?

(c) Find equations of the tangent line and normal line to $y = x^2$ at the point $(0, 0)$.

(d) Prove that for any point $(a, b) \neq (0, 0)$ on the parabola $y = x^2$, the normal line intersects the graph a second time.

6. Finding Polynomials

(a) Find the polynomial $P_1(x) = a_0 + a_1 x$ whose value and slope agree with the value and slope of $f(x) = \cos x$ at the point $x = 0$.

(b) Find the polynomial $P_2(x) = a_0 + a_1 x + a_2 x^2$ whose value and first two derivatives agree with the value and first two derivatives of $f(x) = \cos x$ at the point $x = 0$. This polynomial is called the second-degree Taylor polynomial of $f(x) = \cos x$ at $x = 0$.

(c) Complete the table comparing the values of $f(x) = \cos x$ and $P_2(x)$. What do you observe?

x	-1.0	-0.1	-0.001	0	0.001	0.1	1.0
$\cos x$							
$P_2(x)$							

(d) Find the third-degree Taylor polynomial of $f(x) = \sin x$ at $x = 0$.

7. Famous Curve The graph of the **eight curve**

$$x^4 = a^2(x^2 - y^2), \quad a \neq 0$$

is shown below.

(a) Explain how you could use a graphing utility to graph this curve.

(b) Use a graphing utility to graph the curve for various values of the constant a. Describe how a affects the shape of the curve.

(c) Determine the points on the curve at which the tangent line is horizontal.

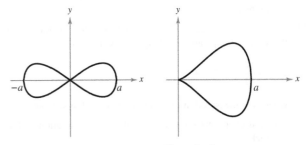

Figure for 7   Figure for 8

8. Famous Curve The graph of the **pear-shaped quartic**

$$b^2 y^2 = x^3(a - x), \quad a, b > 0$$

is shown above.

(a) Explain how you could use a graphing utility to graph this curve.

(b) Use a graphing utility to graph the curve for various values of the constants a and b. Describe how a and b affect the shape of the curve.

(c) Determine the points on the curve at which the tangent line is horizontal.

9. Shadow Length A man 6 feet tall walks at a rate of 5 feet per second toward a streetlight that is 30 feet high (see figure). The man's 3-foot-tall child follows at the same speed, but 10 feet behind the man. At times, the shadow behind the child is caused by the man, and at other times, by the child.

(a) Suppose the man is 90 feet from the streetlight. Show that the man's shadow extends beyond the child's shadow.

(b) Suppose the man is 60 feet from the streetlight. Show that the child's shadow extends beyond the man's shadow.

(c) Determine the distance d from the man to the streetlight at which the tips of the two shadows are exactly the same distance from the streetlight.

(d) Determine how fast the tip of the man's shadow is moving as a function of x, the distance between the man and the streetlight. Discuss the continuity of this shadow speed function.

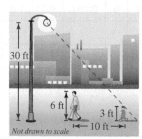

Figure for 9   Figure for 10

10. Moving Point A particle is moving along the graph of $y = \sqrt[3]{x}$ (see figure). When $x = 8$, the y-component of the position of the particle is increasing at the rate of 1 centimeter per second.

(a) How fast is the x-component changing at this moment?

(b) How fast is the distance from the origin changing at this moment?

(c) How fast is the angle of inclination θ changing at this moment?

11. Projectile Motion An astronaut standing on the moon throws a rock upward. The height of the rock is

$$s = -\frac{27}{10}t^2 + 27t + 6$$

where s is measured in feet and t is measured in seconds.

(a) Find expressions for the velocity and acceleration of the rock.

(b) Find the time when the rock is at its highest point by finding the time when the velocity is zero. What is the height of the rock at this time?

(c) How does the acceleration of the rock compare with the acceleration due to gravity on Earth?

12. Proof Let E be a function satisfying $E(0) = E'(0) = 1$. Prove that if

$$E(a + b) = E(a)E(b)$$

for all a and b, then E is differentiable and $E'(x) = E(x)$ for all x. Find an example of a function satisfying $E(a + b) = E(a)E(b)$.

13. Padé Approximation To approximate e^x, you can use a function of the form $f(x) = \dfrac{a + bx}{1 + cx}$. (This function is known as a **Padé approximation.**) The values of $f(0), f'(0)$, and $f''(0)$ are equal to the corresponding values of e^x. Show that these values are equal to 1 and find the values of a, b, and c such that $f(0) = f'(0) = f''(0) = 1$. Then use a graphing utility to compare the graphs of f and e^x.

14. Radians and Degrees The fundamental limit

$$\lim_{x \to 0} \frac{\sin x}{x} = 1$$

assumes that x is measured in radians. Suppose you assume that x is measured in degrees instead of radians.

(a) Set your calculator to *degree* mode and complete the table.

z (in degrees)	0.1	0.01	0.0001
$\dfrac{\sin z}{z}$			

(b) Use the table to estimate

$$\lim_{z \to 0} \frac{\sin z}{z}$$

for z in degrees. What is the exact value of this limit? *(Hint: $180° = \pi$ radians)*

(c) Use the limit definition of the derivative to find $D_z[\sin z]$ for z in degrees.

(d) Define the new functions $S(z) = \sin(cz)$ and $C(z) = \cos(cz)$, where $c = \pi/180$. Find $S(90)$ and $C(180)$. Use the Chain Rule to calculate $D_z[S(z)]$.

(e) Explain why calculus is made easier by using radians instead of degrees.

15. Acceleration and Jerk If a is the acceleration of an object, then the *jerk* j is defined by $j = a'(t)$.

(a) Use this definition to give a physical interpretation of j.

(b) Find j for the slowing vehicle in Exercise 125 in Section 3.3 and interpret the result.

(c) The figure shows the graphs of the position, velocity, acceleration, and jerk functions of a vehicle. Identify each graph and explain your reasoning.

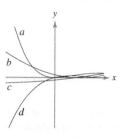   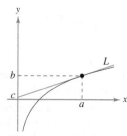

Figure for 15   Figure for 16

16. Finding a Distance The figure shows the graph of the function $y = \ln x$ and its tangent line L at the point (a, b). Show that the distance between b and c is always equal to 1.

4 Applications of Differentiation

4.1 Extrema on an Interval
4.2 Rolle's Theorem and the Mean Value Theorem
4.3 Increasing and Decreasing Functions and the First Derivative Test
4.4 Concavity and the Second Derivative Test
4.5 Limits at Infinity
4.6 A Summary of Curve Sketching
4.7 Optimization Problems
4.8 Differentials

Estimation of Error
(Example 3, p. 269)

Offshore Oil Well (Exercise 39, p. 264)

Engine Efficiency (Exercise 91, p. 244)

Path of a Projectile
(Example 5, p. 222)

Speed (Exercise 65, p. 215)

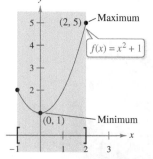

(a) f is continuous, $[-1, 2]$ is closed.

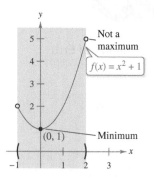

(b) f is continuous, $(-1, 2)$ is open.

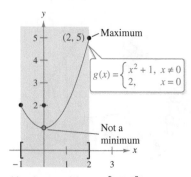

(c) g is not continuous, $[-1, 2]$ is closed.
Figure 4.1

4.1 Extrema on an Interval

■ Understand the definition of extrema of a function on an interval.
■ Understand the definition of relative extrema of a function on an open interval.
■ Find extrema on a closed interval.

Extrema of a Function

In calculus, much effort is devoted to determining the behavior of a function f on an interval I. Does f have a maximum value on I? Does it have a minimum value? Where is the function increasing? Where is it decreasing? In this chapter, you will learn how derivatives can be used to answer these questions. You will also see why these questions are important in real-life applications.

Definition of Extrema

Let f be defined on an interval I containing c.

1. $f(c)$ is the **minimum of f on I** when $f(c) \le f(x)$ for all x in I.
2. $f(c)$ is the **maximum of f on I** when $f(c) \ge f(x)$ for all x in I.

The minimum and maximum of a function on an interval are the **extreme values,** or **extrema** (the singular form of extrema is extremum), of the function on the interval. The minimum and maximum of a function on an interval are also called the **absolute minimum** and **absolute maximum,** or the **global minimum** and **global maximum,** on the interval. Extrema can occur at interior points or endpoints of an interval (see Figure 4.1). Extrema that occur at the endpoints are called **endpoint extrema.**

A function need not have a minimum or a maximum on an interval. For instance, in Figure 4.1(a) and (b), you can see that the function $f(x) = x^2 + 1$ has both a minimum and a maximum on the closed interval $[-1, 2]$, but does not have a maximum on the open interval $(-1, 2)$. Moreover, in Figure 4.1(c), you can see that continuity (or the lack of it) can affect the existence of an extremum on the interval. This suggests the theorem below. (Although the Extreme Value Theorem is intuitively plausible, a proof of this theorem is not within the scope of this text.)

THEOREM 4.1 The Extreme Value Theorem

If f is continuous on a closed interval $[a, b]$, then f has both a minimum and a maximum on the interval.

Exploration

Finding Minimum and Maximum Values   The Extreme Value Theorem (like the Intermediate Value Theorem) is an *existence theorem* because it tells of the existence of minimum and maximum values but does not show how to find these values. Use the *minimum* and *maximum* features of a graphing utility to find the extrema of each function. In each case, do you think the x-values are exact or approximate? Explain your reasoning.

a. $f(x) = x^2 - 4x + 5$ on the closed interval $[-1, 3]$
b. $f(x) = x^3 - 2x^2 - 3x - 2$ on the closed interval $[-1, 3]$

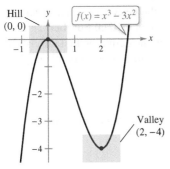

f has a relative maximum at $(0, 0)$ and a relative minimum at $(2, -4)$.

Figure 4.2

Relative Extrema and Critical Numbers

In Figure 4.2, the graph of $f(x) = x^3 - 3x^2$ has a **relative maximum** at the point $(0, 0)$ and a **relative minimum** at the point $(2, -4)$. Informally, for a continuous function, you can think of a relative maximum as occurring on a "hill" on the graph, and a relative minimum as occurring in a "valley" on the graph. Such a hill and valley can occur in two ways. When the hill (or valley) is smooth and rounded, the graph has a horizontal tangent line at the high point (or low point). When the hill (or valley) is sharp and peaked, the graph represents a function that is not differentiable at the high point (or low point).

Definition of Relative Extrema

1. If there is an open interval containing c on which $f(c)$ is a maximum, then $f(c)$ is called a **relative maximum** of f, or you can say that f has a **relative maximum at $(c, f(c))$**.

2. If there is an open interval containing c on which $f(c)$ is a minimum, then $f(c)$ is called a **relative minimum** of f, or you can say that f has a **relative minimum at $(c, f(c))$**.

The plural of relative maximum is relative maxima, and the plural of relative minimum is relative minima. Relative maximum and relative minimum are sometimes called **local maximum** and **local minimum,** respectively.

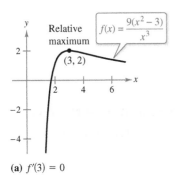

(a) $f'(3) = 0$

Example 1 examines the derivatives of functions at *given* relative extrema. (Much more is said about *finding* the relative extrema of a function in Section 4.3.)

EXAMPLE 1 **The Value of the Derivative at Relative Extrema**

Find the value of the derivative at each relative extremum shown in Figure 4.3.

Solution

a. The derivative of $f(x) = \dfrac{9(x^2 - 3)}{x^3}$ is

$$f'(x) = \frac{x^3(18x) - (9)(x^2 - 3)(3x^2)}{(x^3)^2} \qquad \text{Differentiate using Quotient Rule.}$$

$$= \frac{9(9 - x^2)}{x^4}. \qquad \text{Simplify.}$$

At the point $(3, 2)$, the value of the derivative is $f'(3) = 0$ [see Figure 4.3(a)].

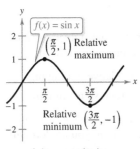

(b) $f'(0)$ does not exist.

b. At $x = 0$, the derivative of $f(x) = |x|$ *does not exist* because the following one-sided limits differ [see Figure 4.3(b)].

$$\lim_{x \to 0^-} \frac{f(x) - f(0)}{x - 0} = \lim_{x \to 0^-} \frac{|x|}{x} = -1 \qquad \text{Limit from the left}$$

$$\lim_{x \to 0^+} \frac{f(x) - f(0)}{x - 0} = \lim_{x \to 0^+} \frac{|x|}{x} = 1 \qquad \text{Limit from the right}$$

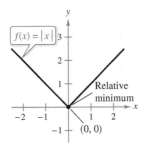

(c) $f'\left(\dfrac{\pi}{2}\right) = 0; f'\left(\dfrac{3\pi}{2}\right) = 0$

Figure 4.3

c. The derivative of $f(x) = \sin x$ is

$$f'(x) = \cos x.$$

At the point $(\pi/2, 1)$, the value of the derivative is $f'(\pi/2) = \cos(\pi/2) = 0$. At the point $(3\pi/2, -1)$, the value of the derivative is $f'(3\pi/2) = \cos(3\pi/2) = 0$ [see Figure 4.3(c)].

Note in Example 1 that at each relative extremum, the derivative either is zero or does not exist. The x-values at these special points are called **critical numbers.** Figure 4.4 illustrates the two types of critical numbers. Notice in the definition that the critical number c has to be in the domain of f, but c does not have to be in the domain of f'.

Definition of a Critical Number

Let f be defined at c. If $f'(c) = 0$ or if f is not differentiable at c, then c is a **critical number** of f.

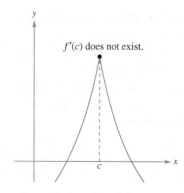
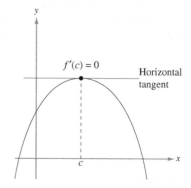

c is a critical number of f.
Figure 4.4

THEOREM 4.2 Relative Extrema Occur Only at Critical Numbers

If f has a relative minimum or relative maximum at $x = c$, then c is a critical number of f.

PIERRE DE FERMAT (1601–1665)

For Fermat, who was trained as a lawyer, mathematics was more of a hobby than a profession. Nevertheless, Fermat made many contributions to analytic geometry, number theory, calculus, and probability. In letters to friends, he wrote of many of the fundamental ideas of calculus, long before Newton or Leibniz. For instance, Theorem 4.2 is sometimes attributed to Fermat. *See LarsonCalculus.com to read more of this biography.*

Proof

Case 1: If f is *not* differentiable at $x = c$, then, by definition, c is a critical number of f and the theorem is valid.

Case 2: If f is differentiable at $x = c$, then $f'(c)$ must be positive, negative, or 0. Suppose $f'(c)$ is positive. Then

$$f'(c) = \lim_{x \to c} \frac{f(x) - f(c)}{x - c} > 0$$

which implies that there exists an interval (a, b) containing c such that

$$\frac{f(x) - f(c)}{x - c} > 0, \text{ for all } x \neq c \text{ in } (a, b). \qquad \text{[See Exercise 80(b), Section 2.2.]}$$

Because this quotient is positive, the signs of the denominator and numerator must agree. This produces the following inequalities for x-values in the interval (a, b).

Left of c: $x < c$ and $f(x) < f(c)$ ⟹ $f(c)$ is not a relative minimum.

Right of c: $x > c$ and $f(x) > f(c)$ ⟹ $f(c)$ is not a relative maximum.

So, the assumption that $f'(c) > 0$ contradicts the hypothesis that $f(c)$ is a relative extremum. Assuming that $f'(c) < 0$ produces a similar contradiction, you are left with only one possibility—namely, $f'(c) = 0$. So, by definition, c is a critical number of f and the theorem is valid.

See LarsonCalculus.com for Bruce Edwards's video of this proof.

Finding Extrema on a Closed Interval

Theorem 4.2 states that the relative extrema of a function can occur *only* at the critical numbers of the function. Knowing this, you can use the following guidelines to find extrema on a closed interval.

GUIDELINES FOR FINDING EXTREMA ON A CLOSED INTERVAL

To find the extrema of a continuous function f on a closed interval $[a, b]$, use these steps.

1. Find the critical numbers of f in (a, b).
2. Evaluate f at each critical number in (a, b).
3. Evaluate f at each endpoint of $[a, b]$.
4. The least of these values is the minimum. The greatest is the maximum.

The next three examples show how to apply these guidelines. Be sure you see that finding the critical numbers of the function is only part of the procedure. Evaluating the function at the critical numbers *and* the endpoints is the other part.

EXAMPLE 2   **Finding Extrema on a Closed Interval**

Find the extrema of

$$f(x) = 3x^4 - 4x^3$$

on the interval $[-1, 2]$.

Solution   Begin by differentiating the function.

$$f(x) = 3x^4 - 4x^3 \quad \text{Write original function.}$$
$$f'(x) = 12x^3 - 12x^2 \quad \text{Differentiate.}$$

To find the critical numbers of f in the interval $(-1, 2)$, you must find all x-values for which $f'(x) = 0$ and all x-values for which $f'(x)$ does not exist.

$$12x^3 - 12x^2 = 0 \quad \text{Set } f'(x) \text{ equal to 0.}$$
$$12x^2(x - 1) = 0 \quad \text{Factor.}$$
$$x = 0, 1 \quad \text{Critical numbers}$$

Because f' is defined for all x, you can conclude that these are the only critical numbers of f. By evaluating f at these two critical numbers and at the endpoints of $[-1, 2]$, you can determine that the maximum is $f(2) = 16$ and the minimum is $f(1) = -1$, as shown in the table. The graph of f is shown in Figure 4.5.

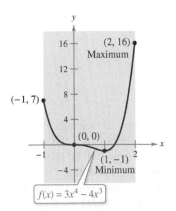

On the closed interval $[-1, 2]$, f has a minimum at $(1, -1)$ and a maximum at $(2, 16)$.
Figure 4.5

Left Endpoint	Critical Number	Critical Number	Right Endpoint
$f(-1) = 7$	$f(0) = 0$	$f(1) = -1$ Minimum	$f(2) = 16$ Maximum

In Figure 4.5, note that the critical number $x = 0$ does not yield a relative minimum or a relative maximum. This tells you that the converse of Theorem 4.2 is not true. In other words, *the critical numbers of a function need not produce relative extrema.*

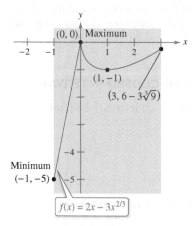

On the closed interval $[-1, 3]$, f has a minimum at $(-1, -5)$ and a maximum at $(0, 0)$.
Figure 4.6

EXAMPLE 3 **Finding Extrema on a Closed Interval**

Find the extrema of $f(x) = 2x - 3x^{2/3}$ on the interval $[-1, 3]$.

Solution Begin by differentiating the function.

$$f(x) = 2x - 3x^{2/3} \qquad \text{Write original function.}$$

$$f'(x) = 2 - \frac{2}{x^{1/3}} \qquad \text{Differentiate.}$$

$$= 2\left(\frac{x^{1/3} - 1}{x^{1/3}}\right) \qquad \text{Simplify.}$$

From this derivative, you can see that the function has two critical numbers in the interval $(-1, 3)$. The number 1 is a critical number because $f'(1) = 0$, and the number 0 is a critical number because $f'(0)$ does not exist. By evaluating f at these two numbers and at the endpoints of the interval, you can conclude that the minimum is $f(-1) = -5$ and the maximum is $f(0) = 0$, as shown in the table. The graph of f is shown in Figure 4.6.

Left Endpoint	Critical Number	Critical Number	Right Endpoint
$f(-1) = -5$ Minimum	$f(0) = 0$ Maximum	$f(1) = -1$	$f(3) = 6 - 3\sqrt[3]{9} \approx -0.24$

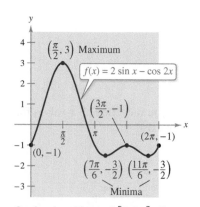

On the closed interval $[0, 2\pi]$, f has two minima at $(7\pi/6, -3/2)$ and $(11\pi/6, -3/2)$ and a maximum at $(\pi/2, 3)$.
Figure 4.7

EXAMPLE 4 **Finding Extrema on a Closed Interval**

$\cdots \triangleright$ *See LarsonCalculus.com for an interactive version of this type of example.*

Find the extrema of

$$f(x) = 2 \sin x - \cos 2x$$

on the interval $[0, 2\pi]$.

Solution Begin by differentiating the function.

$$f(x) = 2 \sin x - \cos 2x \qquad \text{Write original function.}$$

$$f'(x) = 2 \cos x + 2 \sin 2x \qquad \text{Differentiate.}$$

$$= 2 \cos x + 4 \cos x \sin x \qquad \sin 2x = 2 \cos x \sin x$$

$$= 2(\cos x)(1 + 2 \sin x) \qquad \text{Factor.}$$

Because f is differentiable for all real x, you can find all critical numbers of f by finding the zeros of its derivative. Considering $2(\cos x)(1 + 2 \sin x) = 0$ in the interval $(0, 2\pi)$, the factor $\cos x$ is zero when $x = \pi/2$ and when $x = 3\pi/2$. The factor $(1 + 2 \sin x)$ is zero when $x = 7\pi/6$ and when $x = 11\pi/6$. By evaluating f at these four critical numbers and at the endpoints of the interval, you can conclude that the maximum is $f(\pi/2) = 3$ and the minimum occurs at *two* points, $f(7\pi/6) = -3/2$ and $f(11\pi/6) = -3/2$, as shown in the table. The graph is shown in Figure 4.7.

Left Endpoint	Critical Number	Critical Number	Critical Number	Critical Number	Right Endpoint
$f(0) = -1$	$f\left(\dfrac{\pi}{2}\right) = 3$ Maximum	$f\left(\dfrac{7\pi}{6}\right) = -\dfrac{3}{2}$ Minimum	$f\left(\dfrac{3\pi}{2}\right) = -1$	$f\left(\dfrac{11\pi}{6}\right) = -\dfrac{3}{2}$ Minimum	$f(2\pi) = -1$

4.1 Exercises See **CalcChat.com** for tutorial help and worked-out solutions to odd-numbered exercises.

Finding the Value of the Derivative at Relative Extrema
In Exercises 1–6, find the value of the derivative (if it exists) at each indicated extremum.

1. $f(x) = \dfrac{x^2}{x^2 + 4}$

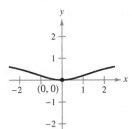

2. $f(x) = \cos \dfrac{\pi x}{2}$

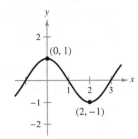

3. $g(x) = x + \dfrac{4}{x^2}$

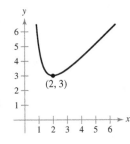

4. $f(x) = -3x\sqrt{x + 1}$

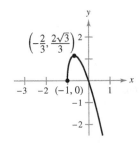

5. $f(x) = (x + 2)^{2/3}$

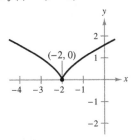

6. $f(x) = 4 - |x|$

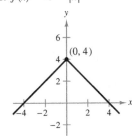

Approximating Critical Numbers In Exercises 7–10, approximate the critical numbers of the function shown in the graph. Determine whether the function has a relative maximum, a relative minimum, an absolute maximum, an absolute minimum, or none of these at each critical number on the interval shown.

7.

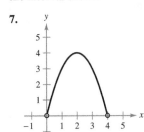

8.

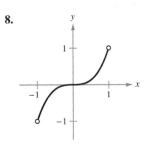

9.

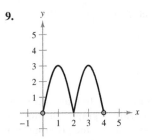

10.

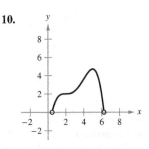

Finding Critical Numbers In Exercises 11–20, find the critical numbers of the function.

11. $f(x) = x^3 - 3x^2$

12. $g(x) = x^4 - 8x^2$

13. $g(t) = t\sqrt{4 - t}, \ t < 3$

14. $f(x) = \dfrac{4x}{x^2 + 1}$

15. $h(x) = \sin^2 x + \cos x$
$0 < x < 2\pi$

16. $f(\theta) = 2 \sec \theta + \tan \theta$
$0 < \theta < 2\pi$

17. $f(t) = te^{-2t}$

18. $g(x) = 4x^2(3^x)$

19. $f(x) = x^2 \log_2(x^2 + 1)$

20. $g(t) = 2t \ln t$

Finding Extrema on a Closed Interval In Exercises 21–44, find the absolute extrema of the function on the closed interval.

21. $f(x) = 3 - x, \ [-1, 2]$

22. $f(x) = \tfrac{3}{4}x + 2, \ [0, 4]$

23. $g(x) = 2x^2 - 8x, \ [0, 6]$

24. $h(x) = 5 - x^2, \ [-3, 1]$

25. $f(x) = x^3 - \dfrac{3}{2}x^2, \ [-1, 2]$

26. $f(x) = 2x^3 - 6x, \ [0, 3]$

27. $y = 3x^{2/3} - 2x, \ [-1, 1]$

28. $g(x) = \sqrt[3]{x}, \ [-8, 8]$

29. $h(s) = \dfrac{1}{s - 2}, \ [0, 1]$

30. $h(t) = \dfrac{t}{t + 3}, \ [-1, 6]$

31. $y = 3 - |t - 3|, \ [-1, 5]$

32. $g(x) = |x + 4|, \ [-7, 1]$

33. $f(x) = [\![x]\!], \ [-2, 2]$

34. $h(x) = [\![2 - x]\!], \ [-2, 2]$

35. $f(x) = \sin x, \ \left[\dfrac{5\pi}{6}, \dfrac{11\pi}{6}\right]$

36. $g(x) = \sec x, \ \left[-\dfrac{\pi}{6}, \dfrac{\pi}{3}\right]$

37. $y = 3 \cos x, \ [0, 2\pi]$

38. $y = \tan\left(\dfrac{\pi x}{8}\right), \ [0, 2]$

39. $f(x) = \arctan x^2, \ [-2, 1]$

40. $g(x) = \dfrac{\ln x}{x}, \ [1, 4]$

41. $h(x) = 5e^x - e^{2x}, \ [-1, 2]$

42. $y = x^2 - 8 \ln x, \ [1, 5]$

43. $y = e^x \sin x, \ [0, \pi]$

44. $y = x \ln(x + 3), \ [0, 3]$

Finding Extrema on an Interval In Exercises 45 and 46, find the absolute extrema of the function (if any exist) on each interval.

45. $f(x) = 2x - 3$
(a) $[0, 2]$ (b) $[0, 2)$
(c) $(0, 2]$ (d) $(0, 2)$

46. $f(x) = \sqrt{4 - x^2}$
(a) $[-2, 2]$ (b) $[-2, 0)$
(c) $(-2, 2)$ (d) $[1, 2)$

Finding Absolute Extrema In Exercises 47–50, use a graphing utility to graph the function and find the absolute extrema of the function on the given interval.

47. $f(x) = \dfrac{3}{x-1}$, $(1, 4]$ **48.** $f(x) = \dfrac{2}{2-x}$, $[0, 2)$

49. $f(x) = \sqrt{x+4}\,e^{x^2/10}$, $[-2, 2]$

50. $f(x) = \sqrt{x} + \cos\dfrac{x}{2}$, $[0, 2\pi]$

Finding Extrema Using Technology In Exercises 51–54, (a) use a computer algebra system to graph the function and approximate any absolute extrema on the given interval. (b) Use the utility to find any critical numbers, and use them to find any absolute extrema not located at the endpoints. Compare the results with those in part (a).

51. $f(x) = 3.2x^5 + 5x^3 - 3.5x$, $[0, 1]$

52. $f(x) = \dfrac{4}{3}x\sqrt{3-x}$, $[0, 3]$

53. $f(x) = (x^2 - 2x)\ln(x+3)$, $[0, 3]$

54. $f(x) = (x-4)\arcsin\dfrac{x}{4}$, $[-2, 4]$

Finding Maximum Values Using Technology In Exercises 55–58, use a computer algebra system to find the maximum value of $|f''(x)|$ on the closed interval. (This value is used in the error estimate for the Trapezoidal Rule, as discussed in Section 5.6.)

55. $f(x) = \sqrt{1+x^3}$, $[0, 2]$ **56.** $f(x) = \dfrac{1}{x^2+1}$, $\left[\dfrac{1}{2}, 3\right]$

57. $f(x) = e^{-x^2/2}$, $[0, 1]$ **58.** $f(x) = x\ln(x+1)$, $[0, 2]$

Finding Maximum Values Using Technology In Exercises 59 and 60, use a computer algebra system to find the maximum value of $|f^{(4)}(x)|$ on the closed interval. (This value is used in the error estimate for Simpson's Rule, as discussed in Section 5.6.)

59. $f(x) = (x+1)^{2/3}$, $[0, 2]$ **60.** $f(x) = \dfrac{1}{x^2+1}$, $[-1, 1]$

61. Think About It Explain why the function $f(x) = \tan x$ has a maximum on $[0, \pi/4]$ but not on $[0, \pi]$.

62. HOW DO YOU SEE IT? Determine whether each labeled point is an absolute maximum or minimum, a relative maximum or minimum, or none of these.

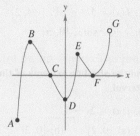

WRITING ABOUT CONCEPTS

Creating the Graph of a Function In Exercises 63 and 64, graph a function on the interval $[-2, 5]$ having the given characteristics.

63. Absolute maximum at $x = -2$
Absolute minimum at $x = 1$
Relative maximum at $x = 3$

64. Relative minimum at $x = -1$
Critical number (but no extremum) at $x = 0$
Absolute maximum at $x = 2$
Absolute minimum at $x = 5$

Using Graphs In Exercises 65–68, determine from the graph whether f has a minimum in the open interval (a, b).

65. (a)   (b)

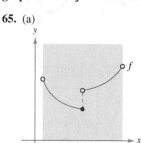   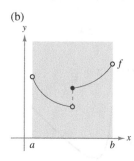

66. (a)   (b)

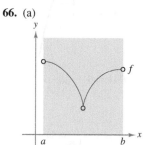   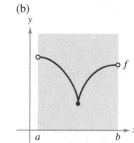

67. (a)   (b)

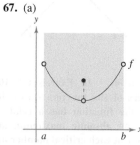   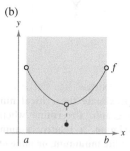

68. (a)   (b)

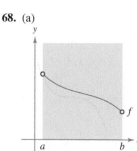   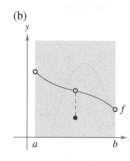

69. Power The formula for the power output P of a battery is

$$P = VI - RI^2$$

where V is the electromotive force in volts, R is the resistance in ohms, and I is the current in amperes. Find the current that corresponds to a maximum value of P in a battery for which $V = 12$ volts and $R = 0.5$ ohm. Assume that a 15-ampere fuse bounds the output in the interval $0 \leq I \leq 15$. Could the power output be increased by replacing the 15-ampere fuse with a 20-ampere fuse? Explain.

70. Lawn Sprinkler A lawn sprinkler is constructed in such a way that $d\theta/dt$ is constant, where θ ranges between $45°$ and $135°$ (see figure). The distance the water travels horizontally is

$$x = \frac{v^2 \sin 2\theta}{32}, \quad 45° \leq \theta \leq 135°$$

where v is the speed of the water. Find dx/dt and explain why this lawn sprinkler does not water evenly. What part of the lawn receives the most water?

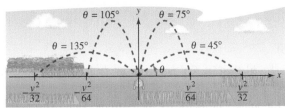

Water sprinkler: $45° \leq \theta \leq 135°$

■ **FOR FURTHER INFORMATION** For more information on the "calculus of lawn sprinklers," see the article "Design of an Oscillating Sprinkler" by Bart Braden in *Mathematics Magazine*. To view this article, go to *MathArticles.com*.

71. Honeycomb The surface area of a cell in a honeycomb is

$$S = 6hs + \frac{3s^2}{2}\left(\frac{\sqrt{3} - \cos \theta}{\sin \theta}\right)$$

where h and s are positive constants and θ is the angle at which the upper faces meet the altitude of the cell (see figure). Find the angle θ $(\pi/6 \leq \theta \leq \pi/2)$ that minimizes the surface area S.

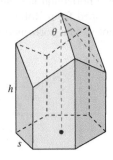

■ **FOR FURTHER INFORMATION** For more information on the geometric structure of a honeycomb cell, see the article "The Design of Honeycombs" by Anthony L. Peressini in UMAP Module 502, published by COMAP, Inc., Suite 210, 57 Bedford Street, Lexington, MA.

72. Highway Design In order to build a highway, it is necessary to fill a section of a valley where the grades (slopes) of the sides are 9% and 6% (see figure). The top of the filled region will have the shape of a parabolic arc that is tangent to the two slopes at the points A and B. The horizontal distances from A to the y-axis and from B to the y-axis are both 500 feet.

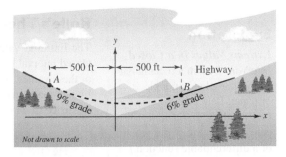

(a) Find the coordinates of A and B.

(b) Find a quadratic function $y = ax^2 + bx + c$ for $-500 \leq x \leq 500$ that describes the top of the filled region.

(c) Construct a table giving the depths d of the fill for $x = -500, -400, -300, -200, -100, 0, 100, 200, 300, 400,$ and 500.

(d) What will be the lowest point on the completed highway? Will it be directly over the point where the two hillsides come together?

True or False? In Exercises 73–76, determine whether the statement is true or false. If it is false, explain why or give an example that shows it is false.

73. The maximum of a function that is continuous on a closed interval can occur at two different values in the interval.

74. If a function is continuous on a closed interval, then it must have a minimum on the interval.

75. If $x = c$ is a critical number of the function f, then it is also a critical number of the function $g(x) = f(x) + k$, where k is a constant.

76. If $x = c$ is a critical number of the function f, then it is also a critical number of the function $g(x) = f(x - k)$, where k is a constant.

77. Functions Let the function f be differentiable on an interval I containing c. If f has a maximum value at $x = c$, show that $-f$ has a minimum value at $x = c$.

78. Critical Numbers Consider the cubic function $f(x) = ax^3 + bx^2 + cx + d$, where $a \neq 0$. Show that f can have zero, one, or two critical numbers and give an example of each case.

PUTNAM EXAM CHALLENGE

79. Determine all real numbers $a > 0$ for which there exists a nonnegative continuous function $f(x)$ defined on $[0, a]$ with the property that the region $R = \{(x, y); 0 \leq x \leq a, 0 \leq y \leq f(x)\}$ has perimeter k units and area k square units for some real number k.

4.2 Rolle's Theorem and the Mean Value Theorem

■ Understand and use Rolle's Theorem.
■ Understand and use the Mean Value Theorem.

Rolle's Theorem

The Extreme Value Theorem (see Section 4.1) states that a continuous function on a closed interval $[a, b]$ must have both a minimum and a maximum on the interval. Both of these values, however, can occur at the endpoints. **Rolle's Theorem,** named after the French mathematician Michel Rolle (1652–1719), gives conditions that guarantee the existence of an extreme value in the *interior* of a closed interval.

THEOREM 4.3 Rolle's Theorem

Let f be continuous on the closed interval $[a, b]$ and differentiable on the open interval (a, b). If $f(a) = f(b)$, then there is at least one number c in (a, b) such that $f'(c) = 0$.

Proof Let $f(a) = d = f(b)$.

Case 1: If $f(x) = d$ for all x in $[a, b]$, then f is constant on the interval and, by Theorem 3.2, $f'(x) = 0$ for all x in (a, b).

Case 2: Consider $f(x) > d$ for some x in (a, b). By the Extreme Value Theorem, you know that f has a maximum at some c in the interval. Moreover, because $f(c) > d$, this maximum does not occur at either endpoint. So, f has a maximum in the *open* interval (a, b). This implies that $f(c)$ is a *relative* maximum and, by Theorem 4.2, c is a critical number of f. Finally, because f is differentiable at c, you can conclude that $f'(c) = 0$.

Case 3: When $f(x) < d$ for some x in (a, b), you can use an argument similar to that in Case 2, but involving the minimum instead of the maximum.

See LarsonCalculus.com for Bruce Edwards's video of this proof. ■

From Rolle's Theorem, you can see that if a function f is continuous on $[a, b]$ and differentiable on (a, b), and if $f(a) = f(b)$, then there must be at least one x-value between a and b at which the graph of f has a horizontal tangent [see Figure 4.8(a)]. When the differentiability requirement is dropped from Rolle's Theorem, f will still have a critical number in (a, b), but it may not yield a horizontal tangent. Such a case is shown in Figure 4.8(b).

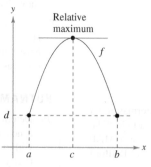

(a) f is continuous on $[a, b]$ and differentiable on (a, b).

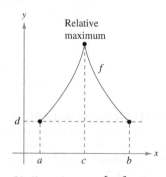

(b) f is continuous on $[a, b]$.

Figure 4.8

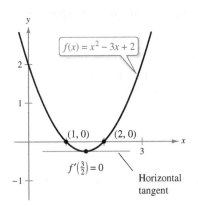

The x-value for which $f'(x) = 0$ is between the two x-intercepts.
Figure 4.9

EXAMPLE 1 **Illustrating Rolle's Theorem**

Find the two x-intercepts of

$$f(x) = x^2 - 3x + 2$$

and show that $f'(x) = 0$ at some point between the two x-intercepts.

Solution Note that f is differentiable on the entire real number line. Setting $f(x)$ equal to 0 produces

$$\begin{array}{ll} x^2 - 3x + 2 = 0 & \text{Set } f(x) \text{ equal to 0.} \\ (x - 1)(x - 2) = 0 & \text{Factor.} \\ x = 1, 2. & \text{Solve for } x. \end{array}$$

So, $f(1) = f(2) = 0$, and from Rolle's Theorem you know that there *exists* at least one c in the interval $(1, 2)$ such that $f'(c) = 0$. To *find* such a c, differentiate f to obtain

$$f'(x) = 2x - 3 \qquad \text{Differentiate.}$$

and then determine that $f'(x) = 0$ when $x = \frac{3}{2}$. Note that this x-value lies in the open interval $(1, 2)$, as shown in Figure 4.9.

Rolle's Theorem states that when f satisfies the conditions of the theorem, there must be *at least* one point between a and b at which the derivative is 0. There may, of course, be more than one such point, as shown in the next example.

EXAMPLE 2 **Illustrating Rolle's Theorem**

Let $f(x) = x^4 - 2x^2$. Find all values of c in the interval $(-2, 2)$ such that $f'(c) = 0$.

Solution To begin, note that the function satisfies the conditions of Rolle's Theorem. That is, f is continuous on the interval $[-2, 2]$ and differentiable on the interval $(-2, 2)$. Moreover, because $f(-2) = f(2) = 8$, you can conclude that there exists at least one c in $(-2, 2)$ such that $f'(c) = 0$. Because

$$f'(x) = 4x^3 - 4x \qquad \text{Differentiate.}$$

setting the derivative equal to 0 produces

$$\begin{array}{ll} 4x^3 - 4x = 0 & \text{Set } f'(x) \text{ equal to 0.} \\ 4x(x - 1)(x + 1) = 0 & \text{Factor.} \\ x = 0, 1, -1. & x\text{-values for which } f'(x) = 0 \end{array}$$

So, in the interval $(-2, 2)$, the derivative is zero at three different values of x, as shown in Figure 4.10.

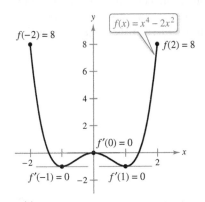

$f'(x) = 0$ for more than one x-value in the interval $(-2, 2)$.
Figure 4.10

▷ **TECHNOLOGY PITFALL** A graphing utility can be used to indicate whether the points on the graphs in Examples 1 and 2 are relative minima or relative maxima of the functions. When using a graphing utility, however, you should keep in mind that it can give misleading pictures of graphs. For example, use a graphing utility to graph

$$f(x) = 1 - (x - 1)^2 - \frac{1}{1000(x - 1)^{1/7} + 1}.$$

With most viewing windows, it appears that the function has a maximum of 1 when $x = 1$ (see Figure 4.11). By evaluating the function at $x = 1$, however, you can see that $f(1) = 0$. To determine the behavior of this function near $x = 1$, you need to examine the graph analytically to get the complete picture.

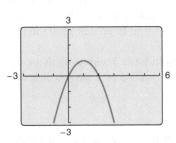

Figure 4.11

The Mean Value Theorem

Rolle's Theorem can be used to prove another theorem—the **Mean Value Theorem.**

··REMARK The "mean" in the Mean Value Theorem refers to the mean (or average) rate of change of f on the interval $[a, b]$.

> **THEOREM 4.4   The Mean Value Theorem**
>
> If f is continuous on the closed interval $[a, b]$ and differentiable on the open interval (a, b), then there exists a number c in (a, b) such that
>
> $$f'(c) = \frac{f(b) - f(a)}{b - a}.$$

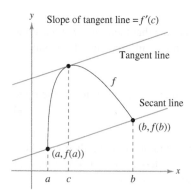

Figure 4.12

Proof   Refer to Figure 4.12. The equation of the secant line that passes through the points $(a, f(a))$ and $(b, f(b))$ is

$$y = \left[\frac{f(b) - f(a)}{b - a} \right](x - a) + f(a).$$

Let $g(x)$ be the difference between $f(x)$ and y. Then

$$g(x) = f(x) - y$$
$$= f(x) - \left[\frac{f(b) - f(a)}{b - a} \right](x - a) - f(a).$$

By evaluating g at a and b, you can see that

$$g(a) = 0 = g(b).$$

Because f is continuous on $[a, b]$, it follows that g is also continuous on $[a, b]$. Furthermore, because f is differentiable, g is also differentiable, and you can apply Rolle's Theorem to the function g. So, there exists a number c in (a, b) such that $g'(c) = 0$, which implies that

$$g'(c) = 0$$
$$f'(c) - \frac{f(b) - f(a)}{b - a} = 0.$$

So, there exists a number c in (a, b) such that

$$f'(c) = \frac{f(b) - f(a)}{b - a}.$$

See LarsonCalculus.com for Bruce Edwards's video of this proof. ■

**JOSEPH-LOUIS LAGRANGE
(1736–1813)**

The Mean Value Theorem was first proved by the famous mathematician Joseph-Louis Lagrange. Born in Italy, Lagrange held a position in the court of Frederick the Great in Berlin for 20 years. *See LarsonCalculus.com to read more of this biography.*

Although the Mean Value Theorem can be used directly in problem solving, it is used more often to prove other theorems. In fact, some people consider this to be the most important theorem in calculus—it is closely related to the Fundamental Theorem of Calculus discussed in Section 5.4. For now, you can get an idea of the versatility of the Mean Value Theorem by looking at the results stated in Exercises 85–93 in this section.

The Mean Value Theorem has implications for both basic interpretations of the derivative. Geometrically, the theorem guarantees the existence of a tangent line that is parallel to the secant line through the points

$$(a, f(a)) \quad \text{and} \quad (b, f(b)),$$

as shown in Figure 4.12. Example 3 illustrates this geometric interpretation of the Mean Value Theorem. In terms of rates of change, the Mean Value Theorem implies that there must be a point in the open interval (a, b) at which the instantaneous rate of change is equal to the average rate of change over the interval $[a, b]$. This is illustrated in Example 4.

EXAMPLE 3 **Finding a Tangent Line**

⊳ *See LarsonCalculus.com for an interactive version of this type of example.*

For $f(x) = 5 - (4/x)$, find all values of c in the open interval $(1, 4)$ such that

$$f'(c) = \frac{f(4) - f(1)}{4 - 1}.$$

Solution The slope of the secant line through $(1, f(1))$ and $(4, f(4))$ is

$$\frac{f(4) - f(1)}{4 - 1} = \frac{4 - 1}{4 - 1} = 1. \qquad \text{Slope of secant line}$$

Note that the function satisfies the conditions of the Mean Value Theorem. That is, f is continuous on the interval $[1, 4]$ and differentiable on the interval $(1, 4)$. So, there exists at least one number c in $(1, 4)$ such that $f'(c) = 1$. Solving the equation $f'(x) = 1$ yields

$$\frac{4}{x^2} = 1 \qquad \text{Set } f'(x) \text{ equal to 1.}$$

which implies that

$$x = \pm 2.$$

So, in the interval $(1, 4)$, you can conclude that $c = 2$, as shown in Figure 4.13.

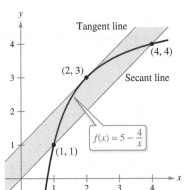

The tangent line at $(2, 3)$ is parallel to the secant line through $(1, 1)$ and $(4, 4)$.
Figure 4.13

EXAMPLE 4 **Finding an Instantaneous Rate of Change**

Two stationary patrol cars equipped with radar are 5 miles apart on a highway, as shown in Figure 4.14. As a truck passes the first patrol car, its speed is clocked at 55 miles per hour. Four minutes later, when the truck passes the second patrol car, its speed is clocked at 50 miles per hour. Prove that the truck must have exceeded the speed limit (of 55 miles per hour) at some time during the 4 minutes.

Solution Let $t = 0$ be the time (in hours) when the truck passes the first patrol car. The time when the truck passes the second patrol car is

$$t = \frac{4}{60} = \frac{1}{15} \text{ hour.}$$

By letting $s(t)$ represent the distance (in miles) traveled by the truck, you have $s(0) = 0$ and $s\left(\frac{1}{15}\right) = 5$. So, the average velocity of the truck over the five-mile stretch of highway is

$$\text{Average velocity} = \frac{s(1/15) - s(0)}{(1/15) - 0} = \frac{5}{1/15} = 75 \text{ miles per hour.}$$

Assuming that the position function is differentiable, you can apply the Mean Value Theorem to conclude that the truck must have been traveling at a rate of 75 miles per hour sometime during the 4 minutes.

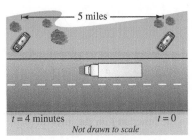

At some time t, the instantaneous velocity is equal to the average velocity over 4 minutes.
Figure 4.14

A useful alternative form of the Mean Value Theorem is: If f is continuous on $[a, b]$ and differentiable on (a, b), then there exists a number c in (a, b) such that

$$f(b) = f(a) + (b - a)f'(c). \qquad \text{Alternative form of Mean Value Theorem}$$

When doing the exercises for this section, keep in mind that polynomial functions, rational functions, and trigonometric functions are differentiable at all points in their domains.

4.2 Exercises

See **CalcChat.com** for tutorial help and worked-out solutions to odd-numbered exercises.

Writing In Exercises 1–4, explain why Rolle's Theorem does not apply to the function even though there exist a and b such that $f(a) = f(b)$.

1. $f(x) = \left|\dfrac{1}{x}\right|$, $[-1, 1]$ 2. $f(x) = \cot\dfrac{x}{2}$, $[\pi, 3\pi]$

3. $f(x) = 1 - |x - 1|$, $[0, 2]$ 4. $f(x) = \sqrt{(2 - x^{2/3})^3}$, $[-1, 1]$

Intercepts and Derivatives In Exercises 5–8, find the two x-intercepts of the function f and show that $f'(x) = 0$ at some point between the two x-intercepts.

5. $f(x) = x^2 - x - 2$ 6. $f(x) = x^2 + 6x$

7. $f(x) = x\sqrt{x + 4}$ 8. $f(x) = -3x\sqrt{x + 1}$

Using Rolle's Theorem In Exercises 9–22, determine whether Rolle's Theorem can be applied to f on the closed interval $[a, b]$. If Rolle's Theorem can be applied, find all values of c in the open interval (a, b) such that $f'(c) = 0$. If Rolle's Theorem cannot be applied, explain why not.

9. $f(x) = -x^2 + 3x$, $[0, 3]$

10. $f(x) = x^2 - 8x + 5$, $[2, 6]$

11. $f(x) = (x - 1)(x - 2)(x - 3)$, $[1, 3]$

12. $f(x) = (x - 4)(x + 2)^2$, $[-2, 4]$

13. $f(x) = x^{2/3} - 1$, $[-8, 8]$ 14. $f(x) = 3 - |x - 3|$, $[0, 6]$

15. $f(x) = \dfrac{x^2 - 2x}{x + 2}$, $[-1, 6]$ 16. $f(x) = \dfrac{x^2 - 1}{x}$, $[-1, 1]$

17. $f(x) = \sin x$, $[0, 2\pi]$ 18. $f(x) = \cos 2x$, $[-\pi, \pi]$

19. $f(x) = \tan x$, $[0, \pi]$ 20. $f(x) = \sec x$, $[\pi, 2\pi]$

21. $f(x) = (x^2 - 2x)e^x$, $[0, 2]$ 22. $f(x) = x - 2\ln x$, $[1, 3]$

Using Rolle's Theorem In Exercises 23–28, use a graphing utility to graph the function on the closed interval $[a, b]$. Determine whether Rolle's Theorem can be applied to f on the interval and, if so, find all values of c in the open interval (a, b) such that $f'(c) = 0$.

23. $f(x) = |x| - 1$, $[-1, 1]$ 24. $f(x) = x - x^{1/3}$, $[0, 1]$

25. $f(x) = x - \tan \pi x$, $\left[-\dfrac{1}{4}, \dfrac{1}{4}\right]$

26. $f(x) = \dfrac{x}{2} - \sin\dfrac{\pi x}{6}$, $[-1, 0]$

27. $f(x) = 2 + \arcsin(x^2 - 1)$, $[-1, 1]$

28. $f(x) = 2 + (x^2 - 4x)(2^{-x/4})$, $[0, 4]$

29. **Vertical Motion** The height of a ball t seconds after it is thrown upward from a height of 6 feet and with an initial velocity of 48 feet per second is $f(t) = -16t^2 + 48t + 6$.

   (a) Verify that $f(1) = f(2)$.

   (b) According to Rolle's Theorem, what must the velocity be at some time in the interval $(1, 2)$? Find that time.

30. **Reorder Costs** The ordering and transportation cost C for components used in a manufacturing process is approximated by

$$C(x) = 10\left(\dfrac{1}{x} + \dfrac{x}{x + 3}\right)$$

where C is measured in thousands of dollars and x is the order size in hundreds.

   (a) Verify that $C(3) = C(6)$.

   (b) According to Rolle's Theorem, the rate of change of the cost must be 0 for some order size in the interval $(3, 6)$. Find that order size.

Mean Value Theorem In Exercises 31 and 32, copy the graph and sketch the secant line to the graph through the points $(a, f(a))$ and $(b, f(b))$. Then sketch any tangent lines to the graph for each value of c guaranteed by the Mean Value Theorem. To print an enlarged copy of the graph, go to *MathGraphs.com*.

31. 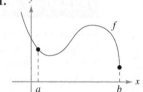   32.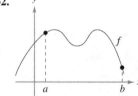

Writing In Exercises 33–36, explain why the Mean Value Theorem does not apply to the function f on the interval $[0, 6]$.

33. 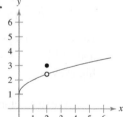   34.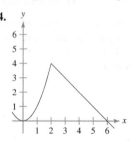

35. $f(x) = \dfrac{1}{x - 3}$ 36. $f(x) = |x - 3|$

37. **Mean Value Theorem** Consider the graph of the function $f(x) = -x^2 + 5$ (see figure on next page).

   (a) Find the equation of the secant line joining the points $(-1, 4)$ and $(2, 1)$.

   (b) Use the Mean Value Theorem to determine a point c in the interval $(-1, 2)$ such that the tangent line at c is parallel to the secant line.

   (c) Find the equation of the tangent line through c.

   (d) Use a graphing utility to graph f, the secant line, and the tangent line.

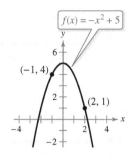

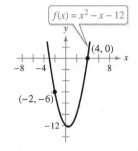

Figure for 37   Figure for 38

38. Mean Value Theorem   Consider the graph of the function $f(x) = x^2 - x - 12$ (see figure).

(a) Find the equation of the secant line joining the points $(-2, -6)$ and $(4, 0)$.

(b) Use the Mean Value Theorem to determine a point c in the interval $(-2, 4)$ such that the tangent line at c is parallel to the secant line.

(c) Find the equation of the tangent line through c.

(d) Use a graphing utility to graph f, the secant line, and the tangent line.

Using the Mean Value Theorem   In Exercises 39–52, determine whether the Mean Value Theorem can be applied to f on the closed interval $[a, b]$. If the Mean Value Theorem can be applied, find all values of c in the open interval (a, b) such that

$$f'(c) = \frac{f(b) - f(a)}{b - a}.$$

If the Mean Value Theorem cannot be applied, explain why not.

39. $f(x) = x^2,\quad [-2, 1]$ **40.** $f(x) = 2x^3,\quad [0, 6]$

41. $f(x) = x^3 + 2x,\quad [-1, 1]$ **42.** $f(x) = x^4 - 8x,\quad [0, 2]$

43. $f(x) = x^{2/3},\quad [0, 1]$ **44.** $f(x) = \dfrac{x + 1}{x},\quad [-1, 2]$

45. $f(x) = |2x + 1|,\quad [-1, 3]$ **46.** $f(x) = \sqrt{2 - x},\quad [-7, 2]$

47. $f(x) = \sin x,\quad [0, \pi]$ **48.** $f(x) = e^{-3x},\quad [0, 2]$

49. $f(x) = \cos x + \tan x,\quad [0, \pi]$

50. $f(x) = (x + 3)\ln(x + 3),\quad [-2, -1]$

51. $f(x) = x\log_2 x,\quad [1, 2]$ **52.** $f(x) = \arctan(1 - x),\quad [0, 1]$

Using the Mean Value Theorem   In Exercises 53–58, use a graphing utility to (a) graph the function f on the given interval, (b) find and graph the secant line through points on the graph of f at the endpoints of the given interval, and (c) find and graph any tangent lines to the graph of f that are parallel to the secant line.

53. $f(x) = \dfrac{x}{x + 1},\quad \left[-\dfrac{1}{2}, 2\right]$ **54.** $f(x) = \sqrt{x},\quad [1, 9]$

55. $f(x) = x - 2\sin x,\quad [-\pi, \pi]$

56. $f(x) = x^4 - 2x^3 + x^2,\quad [0, 6]$

57. $f(x) = 2e^{x/4}\cos\dfrac{\pi x}{4},\ [0, 2]$ **58.** $f(x) = \ln|\sec \pi x|,\ \left[0, \tfrac{1}{4}\right]$

59. Vertical Motion   The height of an object t seconds after it is dropped from a height of 300 meters is

$$s(t) = -4.9t^2 + 300.$$

(a) Find the average velocity of the object during the first 3 seconds.

(b) Use the Mean Value Theorem to verify that at some time during the first 3 seconds of fall, the instantaneous velocity equals the average velocity. Find that time.

60. Sales   A company introduces a new product for which the number of units sold S is

$$S(t) = 200\left(5 - \frac{9}{2 + t}\right)$$

where t is the time in months.

(a) Find the average rate of change of $S(t)$ during the first year.

(b) During what month of the first year does $S'(t)$ equal the average rate of change?

WRITING ABOUT CONCEPTS

61. Converse of Rolle's Theorem   Let f be continuous on $[a, b]$ and differentiable on (a, b). If there exists c in (a, b) such that $f'(c) = 0$, does it follow that $f(a) = f(b)$? Explain.

62. Rolle's Theorem   Let f be continuous on $[a, b]$ and differentiable on (a, b). Also, suppose that $f(a) = f(b)$ and that c is a real number in the interval such that $f'(c) = 0$. Find an interval for the function g over which Rolle's Theorem can be applied, and find the corresponding critical number of g (k is a constant).

(a) $g(x) = f(x) + k$ (b) $g(x) = f(x - k)$

(c) $g(x) = f(kx)$

63. Rolle's Theorem   The function

$$f(x) = \begin{cases} 0, & x = 0 \\ 1 - x, & 0 < x \le 1 \end{cases}$$

is differentiable on $(0, 1)$ and satisfies $f(0) = f(1)$. However, its derivative is never zero on $(0, 1)$. Does this contradict Rolle's Theorem? Explain.

64. Mean Value Theorem   Can you find a function f such that $f(-2) = -2$, $f(2) = 6$, and $f'(x) < 1$ for all x? Why or why not?

---

65. Speed

A plane begins its takeoff at 2:00 P.M. on a 2500-mile flight. After 5.5 hours, the plane arrives at its destination. Explain why there are at least two times during the flight when the speed of the plane is 400 miles per hour.

66. Temperature   When an object is removed from a furnace and placed in an environment with a constant temperature of 90°F, its core temperature is 1500°F. Five hours later, the core temperature is 390°F. Explain why there must exist a time in the interval when the temperature is decreasing at a rate of 222°F per hour.

67. Velocity   Two bicyclists begin a race at 8:00 A.M. They both finish the race 2 hours and 15 minutes later. Prove that at some time during the race, the bicyclists are traveling at the same velocity.

68. Acceleration   At 9:13 A.M., a sports car is traveling 35 miles per hour. Two minutes later, the car is traveling 85 miles per hour. Prove that at some time during this two-minute interval, the car's acceleration is exactly 1500 miles per hour squared.

69. Using a Function   Consider the function

$$f(x) = 3 \cos^2\left(\frac{\pi x}{2}\right).$$

(a) Use a graphing utility to graph f and f'.

(b) Is f a continuous function? Is f' a continuous function?

(c) Does Rolle's Theorem apply on the interval $[-1, 1]$? Does it apply on the interval $[1, 2]$? Explain.

(d) Evaluate, if possible, $\lim\limits_{x \to 3^-} f'(x)$ and $\lim\limits_{x \to 3^+} f'(x)$.

70. HOW DO YOU SEE IT?   The figure shows two parts of the graph of a continuous differentiable function f on $[-10, 4]$. The derivative f' is also continuous. To print an enlarged copy of the graph, go to *MathGraphs.com*.

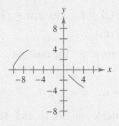

(a) Explain why f must have at least one zero in $[-10, 4]$.

(b) Explain why f' must also have at least one zero in the interval $[-10, 4]$. What are these zeros called?

(c) Make a possible sketch of the function with one zero of f' on the interval $[-10, 4]$.

Think About It   In Exercises 71 and 72, sketch the graph of an arbitrary function f that satisfies the given condition but does not satisfy the conditions of the Mean Value Theorem.

71. f is continuous on $[-5, 5]$.

72. f is not continuous on $[-5, 5]$.

Finding a Solution   In Exercises 73–76, use the Intermediate Value Theorem and Rolle's Theorem to prove that the equation has exactly one real solution.

73. $x^5 + x^3 + x + 1 = 0$ **74.** $2x^5 + 7x - 1 = 0$

75. $3x + 1 - \sin x = 0$ **76.** $2x - 2 - \cos x = 0$

Differential Equation   In Exercises 77–80, find a function f that has the derivative $f'(x)$ and whose graph passes through the given point. Explain your reasoning.

77. $f'(x) = 0$, $(2, 5)$ **78.** $f'(x) = 4$, $(0, 1)$

79. $f'(x) = 2x$, $(1, 0)$ **80.** $f'(x) = 6x - 1$, $(2, 7)$

True or False?   In Exercises 81–84, determine whether the statement is true or false. If it is false, explain why or give an example that shows it is false.

81. The Mean Value Theorem can be applied to

$$f(x) = \frac{1}{x}$$

on the interval $[-1, 1]$.

82. If the graph of a function has three x-intercepts, then it must have at least two points at which its tangent line is horizontal.

83. If the graph of a polynomial function has three x-intercepts, then it must have at least two points at which its tangent line is horizontal.

84. If $f'(x) = 0$ for all x in the domain of f, then f is a constant function.

85. Proof   Prove that if $a > 0$ and n is any positive integer, then the polynomial function $p(x) = x^{2n+1} + ax + b$ cannot have two real roots.

86. Proof   Prove that if $f'(x) = 0$ for all x in an interval (a, b), then f is constant on (a, b).

87. Proof   Let $p(x) = Ax^2 + Bx + C$. Prove that for any interval $[a, b]$, the value c guaranteed by the Mean Value Theorem is the midpoint of the interval.

88. Using Rolle's Theorem

(a) Let $f(x) = x^2$ and $g(x) = -x^3 + x^2 + 3x + 2$. Then $f(-1) = g(-1)$ and $f(2) = g(2)$. Show that there is at least one value c in the interval $(-1, 2)$ where the tangent line to f at $(c, f(c))$ is parallel to the tangent line to g at $(c, g(c))$. Identify c.

(b) Let f and g be differentiable functions on $[a, b]$ where $f(a) = g(a)$ and $f(b) = g(b)$. Show that there is at least one value c in the interval (a, b) where the tangent line to f at $(c, f(c))$ is parallel to the tangent line to g at $(c, g(c))$.

89. Proof   Prove that if f is differentiable on $(-\infty, \infty)$ and $f'(x) < 1$ for all real numbers, then f has at most one fixed point. A fixed point of a function f is a real number c such that $f(c) = c$.

90. Fixed Point   Use the result of Exercise 89 to show that $f(x) = \frac{1}{2} \cos x$ has at most one fixed point.

91. Proof   Prove that $|\cos a - \cos b| \le |a - b|$ for all a and b.

92. Proof   Prove that $|\sin a - \sin b| \le |a - b|$ for all a and b.

93. Using the Mean Value Theorem   Let $0 < a < b$. Use the Mean Value Theorem to show that

$$\sqrt{b} - \sqrt{a} < \frac{b - a}{2\sqrt{a}}.$$

4.3 Increasing and Decreasing Functions and the First Derivative Test

■ Determine intervals on which a function is increasing or decreasing.
■ Apply the First Derivative Test to find relative extrema of a function.

Increasing and Decreasing Functions

In this section, you will learn how derivatives can be used to *classify* relative extrema as either relative minima or relative maxima. First, it is important to define increasing and decreasing functions.

> ### Definitions of Increasing and Decreasing Functions
>
> A function f is **increasing** on an interval when, for any two numbers x_1 and x_2 in the interval, $x_1 < x_2$ implies $f(x_1) < f(x_2)$.
>
> A function f is **decreasing** on an interval when, for any two numbers x_1 and x_2 in the interval, $x_1 < x_2$ implies $f(x_1) > f(x_2)$.

A function is increasing when, *as x moves to the right*, its graph moves up, and is decreasing when its graph moves down. For example, the function in Figure 4.15 is decreasing on the interval $(-\infty, a)$, is constant on the interval (a, b), and is increasing on the interval (b, ∞). As shown in Theorem 4.5 below, a positive derivative implies that the function is increasing, a negative derivative implies that the function is decreasing, and a zero derivative on an entire interval implies that the function is constant on that interval.

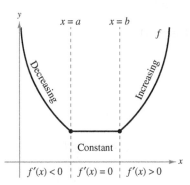

The derivative is related to the slope of a function.
Figure 4.15

> ### THEOREM 4.5 Test for Increasing and Decreasing Functions
>
> Let f be a function that is continuous on the closed interval $[a, b]$ and differentiable on the open interval (a, b).
>
> 1. If $f'(x) > 0$ for all x in (a, b), then f is increasing on $[a, b]$.
> 2. If $f'(x) < 0$ for all x in (a, b), then f is decreasing on $[a, b]$.
> 3. If $f'(x) = 0$ for all x in (a, b), then f is constant on $[a, b]$.

• • REMARK The conclusions in the first two cases of Theorem 4.5 are valid even when $f'(x) = 0$ at a finite number of x-values in (a, b).

Proof To prove the first case, assume that $f'(x) > 0$ for all x in the interval (a, b) and let $x_1 < x_2$ be any two points in the interval. By the Mean Value Theorem, you know that there exists a number c such that $x_1 < c < x_2$, and

$$f'(c) = \frac{f(x_2) - f(x_1)}{x_2 - x_1}.$$

Because $f'(c) > 0$ and $x_2 - x_1 > 0$, you know that $f(x_2) - f(x_1) > 0$, which implies that $f(x_1) < f(x_2)$. So, f is increasing on the interval. The second case has a similar proof (see Exercise 117), and the third case is a consequence of Exercise 86 in Section 4.2.

See LarsonCalculus.com for Bruce Edwards's video of this proof. ■

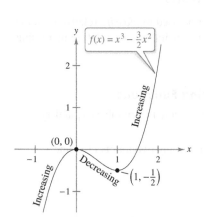

Figure 4.16

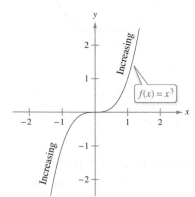

(a) Strictly monotonic function

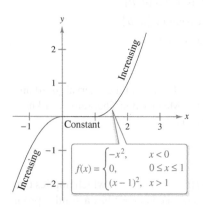

(b) Not strictly monotonic
Figure 4.17

| EXAMPLE 1 | **Intervals on Which f Is Increasing or Decreasing** |

Find the open intervals on which $f(x) = x^3 - \frac{3}{2}x^2$ is increasing or decreasing.

Solution Note that f is differentiable on the entire real number line and the derivative of f is

$$f(x) = x^3 - \tfrac{3}{2}x^2 \qquad \text{Write original function.}$$
$$f'(x) = 3x^2 - 3x. \qquad \text{Differentiate.}$$

To determine the critical numbers of f, set $f'(x)$ equal to zero.

$$3x^2 - 3x = 0 \qquad \text{Set } f'(x) \text{ equal to 0.}$$
$$3(x)(x - 1) = 0 \qquad \text{Factor.}$$
$$x = 0, 1 \qquad \text{Critical numbers}$$

Because there are no points for which f' does not exist, you can conclude that $x = 0$ and $x = 1$ are the only critical numbers. The table summarizes the testing of the three intervals determined by these two critical numbers.

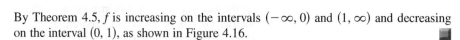

Interval	$-\infty < x < 0$	$0 < x < 1$	$1 < x < \infty$
Test Value	$x = -1$	$x = \frac{1}{2}$	$x = 2$
Sign of $f'(x)$	$f'(-1) = 6 > 0$	$f'\left(\frac{1}{2}\right) = -\frac{3}{4} < 0$	$f'(2) = 6 > 0$
Conclusion	Increasing	Decreasing	Increasing

By Theorem 4.5, f is increasing on the intervals $(-\infty, 0)$ and $(1, \infty)$ and decreasing on the interval $(0, 1)$, as shown in Figure 4.16.

Example 1 gives you one instance of how to find intervals on which a function is increasing or decreasing. The guidelines below summarize the steps followed in that example.

GUIDELINES FOR FINDING INTERVALS ON WHICH A FUNCTION IS INCREASING OR DECREASING

Let f be continuous on the interval (a, b). To find the open intervals on which f is increasing or decreasing, use the following steps.

1. Locate the critical numbers of f in (a, b), and use these numbers to determine test intervals.
2. Determine the sign of $f'(x)$ at one test value in each of the intervals.
3. Use Theorem 4.5 to determine whether f is increasing or decreasing on each interval.

These guidelines are also valid when the interval (a, b) is replaced by an interval of the form $(-\infty, b)$, (a, ∞), or $(-\infty, \infty)$.

A function is **strictly monotonic** on an interval when it is either increasing on the entire interval or decreasing on the entire interval. For instance, the function $f(x) = x^3$ is strictly monotonic on the entire real number line because it is increasing on the entire real number line, as shown in Figure 4.17(a). The function shown in Figure 4.17(b) is not strictly monotonic on the entire real number line because it is constant on the interval $[0, 1]$.

The First Derivative Test

After you have determined the intervals on which a function is increasing or decreasing, it is not difficult to locate the relative extrema of the function. For instance, in Figure 4.18 (from Example 1), the function

$$f(x) = x^3 - \frac{3}{2}x^2$$

has a relative maximum at the point $(0, 0)$ because f is increasing immediately to the left of $x = 0$ and decreasing immediately to the right of $x = 0$. Similarly, f has a relative minimum at the point $\left(1, -\frac{1}{2}\right)$ because f is decreasing immediately to the left of $x = 1$ and increasing immediately to the right of $x = 1$. The next theorem makes this more explicit.

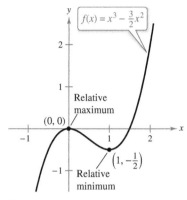

Relative extrema of f
Figure 4.18

THEOREM 4.6   The First Derivative Test

Let c be a critical number of a function f that is continuous on an open interval I containing c. If f is differentiable on the interval, except possibly at c, then $f(c)$ can be classified as follows.

1. If $f'(x)$ changes from negative to positive at c, then f has a *relative minimum* at $(c, f(c))$.

2. If $f'(x)$ changes from positive to negative at c, then f has a *relative maximum* at $(c, f(c))$.

3. If $f'(x)$ is positive on both sides of c or negative on both sides of c, then $f(c)$ is neither a relative minimum nor a relative maximum.

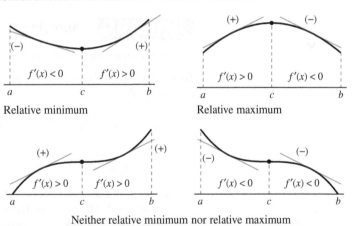

Proof   Assume that $f'(x)$ changes from negative to positive at c. Then there exist a and b in I such that

$$f'(x) < 0 \text{ for all } x \text{ in } (a, c) \quad \text{and} \quad f'(x) > 0 \text{ for all } x \text{ in } (c, b).$$

By Theorem 4.5, f is decreasing on $[a, c]$ and increasing on $[c, b]$. So, $f(c)$ is a minimum of f on the open interval (a, b) and, consequently, a relative minimum of f. This proves the first case of the theorem. The second case can be proved in a similar way (see Exercise 118).

See LarsonCalculus.com for Bruce Edwards's video of this proof.

Applying the First Derivative Test

Find the relative extrema of $f(x) = \frac{1}{2}x - \sin x$ in the interval $(0, 2\pi)$.

Solution Note that f is continuous on the interval $(0, 2\pi)$. The derivative of f is $f'(x) = \frac{1}{2} - \cos x$. To determine the critical numbers of f in this interval, set $f'(x)$ equal to 0.

$$\frac{1}{2} - \cos x = 0 \qquad \text{Set } f'(x) \text{ equal to 0.}$$

$$\cos x = \frac{1}{2}$$

$$x = \frac{\pi}{3}, \frac{5\pi}{3} \qquad \text{Critical numbers}$$

Because there are no points for which f' does not exist, you can conclude that $x = \pi/3$ and $x = 5\pi/3$ are the only critical numbers. The table summarizes the testing of the three intervals determined by these two critical numbers. By applying the First Derivative Test, you can conclude that f has a relative minimum at the point where $x = \pi/3$ and a relative maximum at the point where $x = 5\pi/3$, as shown in Figure 4.19.

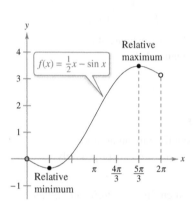

A relative minimum occurs where f changes from decreasing to increasing, and a relative maximum occurs where f changes from increasing to decreasing.
Figure 4.19

Interval	$0 < x < \frac{\pi}{3}$	$\frac{\pi}{3} < x < \frac{5\pi}{3}$	$\frac{5\pi}{3} < x < 2\pi$
Test Value	$x = \frac{\pi}{4}$	$x = \pi$	$x = \frac{7\pi}{4}$
Sign of $f'(x)$	$f'\left(\frac{\pi}{4}\right) < 0$	$f'(\pi) > 0$	$f'\left(\frac{7\pi}{4}\right) < 0$
Conclusion	Decreasing	Increasing	Decreasing

Applying the First Derivative Test

Find the relative extrema of $f(x) = (x^2 - 4)^{2/3}$.

Solution Begin by noting that f is continuous on the entire real number line. The derivative of f

$$f'(x) = \frac{2}{3}(x^2 - 4)^{-1/3}(2x) \qquad \text{General Power Rule}$$

$$= \frac{4x}{3(x^2 - 4)^{1/3}} \qquad \text{Simplify.}$$

is 0 when $x = 0$ and does not exist when $x = \pm 2$. So, the critical numbers are $x = -2$, $x = 0$, and $x = 2$. The table summarizes the testing of the four intervals determined by these three critical numbers. By applying the First Derivative Test, you can conclude that f has a relative minimum at the point $(-2, 0)$, a relative maximum at the point $\left(0, \sqrt[3]{16}\right)$, and another relative minimum at the point $(2, 0)$, as shown in Figure 4.20.

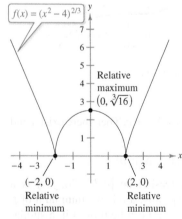

Figure 4.20

Interval	$-\infty < x < -2$	$-2 < x < 0$	$0 < x < 2$	$2 < x < \infty$
Test Value	$x = -3$	$x = -1$	$x = 1$	$x = 3$
Sign of $f'(x)$	$f'(-3) < 0$	$f'(-1) > 0$	$f'(1) < 0$	$f'(3) > 0$
Conclusion	Decreasing	Increasing	Decreasing	Increasing

Note that in Examples 1 and 2, the given functions are differentiable on the entire real number line. For such functions, the only critical numbers are those for which $f'(x) = 0$. Example 3 concerns a function that has two types of critical numbers—those for which $f'(x) = 0$ and those for which f is not differentiable.

When using the First Derivative Test, be sure to consider the domain of the function. For instance, in the next example, the function

$$f(x) = \frac{x^4 + 1}{x^2}$$

is not defined when $x = 0$. This x-value must be used with the critical numbers to determine the test intervals.

EXAMPLE 4   Applying the First Derivative Test

$\cdots\cdots\triangleright$ *See LarsonCalculus.com for an interactive version of this type of example.*

Find the relative extrema of $f(x) = \dfrac{x^4 + 1}{x^2}$.

Solution   Note that f is not defined when $x = 0$.

$$f(x) = x^2 + x^{-2} \qquad \text{Rewrite original function.}$$

$$f'(x) = 2x - 2x^{-3} \qquad \text{Differentiate.}$$

$$= 2x - \frac{2}{x^3} \qquad \text{Rewrite with positive exponent.}$$

$$= \frac{2(x^4 - 1)}{x^3} \qquad \text{Simplify.}$$

$$= \frac{2(x^2 + 1)(x - 1)(x + 1)}{x^3} \qquad \text{Factor.}$$

So, $f'(x)$ is zero at $x = \pm 1$. Moreover, because $x = 0$ is not in the domain of f, you should use this x-value along with the critical numbers to determine the test intervals.

$$x = \pm 1 \qquad \text{Critical numbers, } f'(\pm 1) = 0$$

$$x = 0 \qquad \text{0 is not in the domain of } f.$$

The table summarizes the testing of the four intervals determined by these three x-values. By applying the First Derivative Test, you can conclude that f has one relative minimum at the point $(-1, 2)$ and another at the point $(1, 2)$, as shown in Figure 4.21.

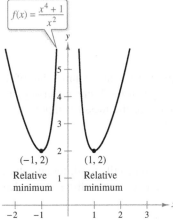

x-values that are not in the domain of f, as well as critical numbers, determine test intervals for f'.

Figure 4.21

Interval	$-\infty < x < -1$	$-1 < x < 0$	$0 < x < 1$	$1 < x < \infty$
Test Value	$x = -2$	$x = -\frac{1}{2}$	$x = \frac{1}{2}$	$x = 2$
Sign of $f'(x)$	$f'(-2) < 0$	$f'\left(-\frac{1}{2}\right) > 0$	$f'\left(\frac{1}{2}\right) < 0$	$f'(2) > 0$
Conclusion	Decreasing	Increasing	Decreasing	Increasing

$\triangleright$ **TECHNOLOGY**   The most difficult step in applying the First Derivative Test is finding the values for which the derivative is equal to 0. For instance, the values of x for which the derivative of

$$f(x) = \frac{x^4 + 1}{x^2 + 1}$$

is equal to zero are $x = 0$ and $x = \pm\sqrt{\sqrt{2} - 1}$. If you have access to technology that can perform symbolic differentiation and solve equations, use it to apply the First Derivative Test to this function.

When a projectile is propelled from ground level and air resistance is neglected, the object will travel farthest with an initial angle of 45°. When, however, the projectile is propelled from a point above ground level, the angle that yields a maximum horizontal distance is not 45° (see Example 5).

EXAMPLE 5 **The Path of a Projectile**

Neglecting air resistance, the path of a projectile that is propelled at an angle θ is

$$y = \frac{g \sec^2 \theta}{2v_0^2}x^2 + (\tan \theta)x + h, \quad 0 \le \theta \le \frac{\pi}{2}$$

where y is the height, x is the horizontal distance, g is the acceleration due to gravity, v_0 is the initial velocity, and h is the initial height. (This equation is derived in Section 12.3.) Let $g = -32$ feet per second per second, $v_0 = 24$ feet per second, and $h = 9$ feet. What value of θ will produce a maximum horizontal distance?

Solution To find the distance the projectile travels, let $y = 0$, $g = -32$, $v_0 = 24$, and $h = 9$. Then substitute these values in the given equation as shown.

$$\frac{g \sec^2 \theta}{2v_0^2}x^2 + (\tan \theta)x + h = y$$

$$\frac{-32 \sec^2 \theta}{2(24^2)}x^2 + (\tan \theta)x + 9 = 0$$

$$-\frac{\sec^2 \theta}{36}x^2 + (\tan \theta)x + 9 = 0$$

Next, solve for x using the Quadratic Formula with $a = -\sec^2 \theta/36$, $b = \tan \theta$, and $c = 9$.

$$x = \frac{-b \pm \sqrt{b^2 - 4ac}}{2a}$$

$$x = \frac{-\tan \theta \pm \sqrt{(\tan \theta)^2 - 4(-\sec^2 \theta/36)(9)}}{2(-\sec^2 \theta/36)}$$

$$x = \frac{-\tan \theta \pm \sqrt{\tan^2 \theta + \sec^2 \theta}}{-\sec^2 \theta/18}$$

$$x = 18 \cos \theta \left(\sin \theta + \sqrt{\sin^2 \theta + 1}\right), \quad x \ge 0$$

At this point, you need to find the value of θ that produces a maximum value of x. Applying the First Derivative Test by hand would be very tedious. Using technology to solve the equation $dx/d\theta = 0$, however, eliminates most of the messy computations. The result is that the maximum value of x occurs when

$$\theta \approx 0.61548 \text{ radian}, \quad \text{or} \quad 35.3°.$$

This conclusion is reinforced by sketching the path of the projectile for different values of θ, as shown in Figure 4.22. Of the three paths shown, note that the distance traveled is greatest for $\theta = 35°$.

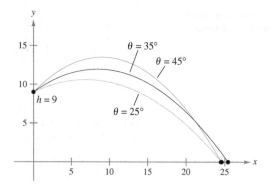

The path of a projectile with initial angle θ
Figure 4.22

4.3 Exercises

See **CalcChat.com** for tutorial help and worked-out solutions to odd-numbered exercises.

Using a Graph In Exercises 1 and 2, use the graph of f to find (a) the largest open interval on which f is increasing, and (b) the largest open interval on which f is decreasing.

1.

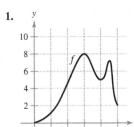

2.

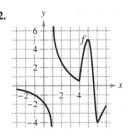

Using a Graph In Exercises 3–8, use the graph to estimate the open intervals on which the function is increasing or decreasing. Then find the open intervals analytically.

3. $f(x) = x^2 - 6x + 8$

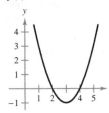

4. $y = -(x + 1)^2$

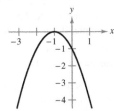

5. $y = \dfrac{x^3}{4} - 3x$

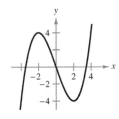

6. $f(x) = x^4 - 2x^2$

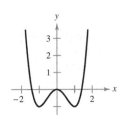

7. $f(x) = \dfrac{1}{(x + 1)^2}$

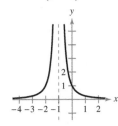

8. $y = \dfrac{x^2}{2x - 1}$

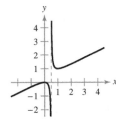

Intervals on Which f Is Increasing or Decreasing In Exercises 9–20, identify the open intervals on which the function is increasing or decreasing.

9. $g(x) = x^2 - 2x - 8$

10. $h(x) = 12x - x^3$

11. $y = x\sqrt{16 - x^2}$

12. $y = x + \dfrac{9}{x}$

13. $f(x) = \sin x - 1, \quad 0 < x < 2\pi$

14. $h(x) = \cos \dfrac{x}{2}, \quad 0 < x < 2\pi$

15. $y = x - 2 \cos x, \quad 0 < x < 2\pi$

16. $f(x) = \sin^2 x + \sin x, \quad 0 < x < 2\pi$

17. $g(x) = e^{-x} + e^{3x}$

18. $h(x) = \sqrt{x}e^{-x}$

19. $f(x) = x^2 \ln\left(\dfrac{x}{2}\right)$

20. $f(x) = \dfrac{\ln x}{\sqrt{x}}$

Applying the First Derivative Test In Exercises 21–56, (a) find the critical numbers of f (if any), (b) find the open interval(s) on which the function is increasing or decreasing, (c) apply the First Derivative Test to identify all relative extrema, and (d) use a graphing utility to confirm your results.

21. $f(x) = x^2 - 4x$

22. $f(x) = x^2 + 6x + 10$

23. $f(x) = -2x^2 + 4x + 3$

24. $f(x) = -3x^2 - 4x - 2$

25. $f(x) = 2x^3 + 3x^2 - 12x$

26. $f(x) = x^3 - 6x^2 + 15$

27. $f(x) = (x - 1)^2(x + 3)$

28. $f(x) = (x + 2)^2(x - 1)$

29. $f(x) = \dfrac{x^5 - 5x}{5}$

30. $f(x) = x^4 - 32x + 4$

31. $f(x) = x^{1/3} + 1$

32. $f(x) = x^{2/3} - 4$

33. $f(x) = (x + 2)^{2/3}$

34. $f(x) = (x - 3)^{1/3}$

35. $f(x) = 5 - |x - 5|$

36. $f(x) = |x + 3| - 1$

37. $f(x) = 2x + \dfrac{1}{x}$

38. $f(x) = \dfrac{x}{x - 5}$

39. $f(x) = \dfrac{x^2}{x^2 - 9}$

40. $f(x) = \dfrac{x^2 - 2x + 1}{x + 1}$

41. $f(x) = \begin{cases} 4 - x^2, & x \le 0 \\ -2x, & x > 0 \end{cases}$

42. $f(x) = \begin{cases} 2x + 1, & x \le -1 \\ x^2 - 2, & x > -1 \end{cases}$

43. $f(x) = \begin{cases} 3x + 1, & x \le 1 \\ 5 - x^2, & x > 1 \end{cases}$

44. $f(x) = \begin{cases} -x^3 + 1, & x \le 0 \\ -x^2 + 2x, & x > 0 \end{cases}$

45. $f(x) = (3 - x)e^{x-3}$

46. $f(x) = (x - 1)e^x$

47. $f(x) = 4(x - \arcsin x)$

48. $f(x) = x \arctan x$

49. $f(x) = (x)3^{-x}$

50. $f(x) = 2^{x^2 - 3}$

51. $f(x) = x - \log_4 x$

52. $f(x) = \dfrac{x^3}{3} - \ln x$

53. $f(x) = \dfrac{e^{2x}}{e^{2x} + 1}$

54. $f(x) = \ln(2 - \ln x)$

55. $f(x) = e^{-1/(x-2)}$

56. $f(x) = e^{\arctan x}$

Applying the First Derivative Test In Exercises 57–64, consider the function on the interval $(0, 2\pi)$. For each function, (a) find the open interval(s) on which the function is increasing or decreasing, (b) apply the First Derivative Test to identify all relative extrema, and (c) use a graphing utility to confirm your results.

57. $f(x) = \dfrac{x}{2} + \cos x$

58. $f(x) = \sin x \cos x + 5$

59. $f(x) = \sin x + \cos x$

60. $f(x) = x + 2 \sin x$

61. $f(x) = \cos^2(2x)$ **62.** $f(x) = \sin x - \sqrt{3} \cos x$

63. $f(x) = \sin^2 x + \sin x$ **64.** $f(x) = \dfrac{\sin x}{1 + \cos^2 x}$

Finding and Analyzing Derivatives Using Technology In Exercises 65–72, (a) use a computer algebra system to differentiate the function, (b) sketch the graphs of f and f' on the same set of coordinate axes over the given interval, (c) find the critical numbers of f in the open interval, and (d) find the interval(s) on which f' is positive and the interval(s) on which it is negative. Compare the behavior of f and the sign of f'.

65. $f(x) = 2x\sqrt{9 - x^2}$, $[-3, 3]$

66. $f(x) = 10\left(5 - \sqrt{x^2 - 3x + 16}\right)$, $[0, 5]$

67. $f(t) = t^2 \sin t$, $[0, 2\pi]$

68. $f(x) = \dfrac{x}{2} + \cos \dfrac{x}{2}$, $[0, 4\pi]$

69. $f(x) = -3 \sin \dfrac{x}{3}$, $[0, 6\pi]$

70. $f(x) = 2 \sin 3x + 4 \cos 3x$, $[0, \pi]$

71. $f(x) = \frac{1}{2}(x^2 - \ln x)$, $(0, 3]$

72. $f(x) = (4 - x^2)e^x$, $[0, 2]$

Comparing Functions In Exercises 73 and 74, use symmetry, extrema, and zeros to sketch the graph of f. How do the functions f and g differ?

73. $f(x) = \dfrac{x^5 - 4x^3 + 3x}{x^2 - 1}$ **74.** $f(t) = \cos^2 t - \sin^2 t$

       $g(x) = x(x^2 - 3)$ $g(t) = 1 - 2\sin^2 t$

Think About It In Exercises 75–80, the graph of f is shown in the figure. Sketch a graph of the derivative of f. To print an enlarged copy of the graph, go to *MathGraphs.com*.

75.
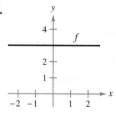

76.
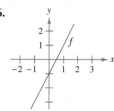

77.
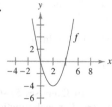

78.
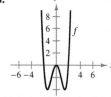

79.
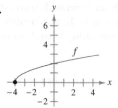

80.
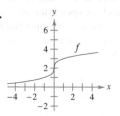

Transformations of Functions In Exercises 81–86, assume that f is differentiable for all x, where $f'(x) > 0$ on $(-\infty, -4)$, $f'(x) < 0$ on $(-4, 6)$, and $f'(x) > 0$ on $(6, \infty)$. Supply the appropriate inequality symbol for the given value of c.

Function	Sign of $g'(c)$
81. $g(x) = f(x) + 5$	$g'(0)$ ▢ 0
82. $g(x) = 3f(x) - 3$	$g'(-5)$ ▢ 0
83. $g(x) = -f(x)$	$g'(-6)$ ▢ 0
84. $g(x) = -f(x)$	$g'(0)$ ▢ 0
85. $g(x) = f(x - 10)$	$g'(0)$ ▢ 0
86. $g(x) = f(x - 10)$	$g'(8)$ ▢ 0

87. Think About It Consider a function f that is continuous and differentiable on an open interval I. Given $f'(c) = 0$ and c is in I, must f have a local maximum or minimum at $x = c$? Why or why not?

88. Think About It Is it possible to find a differentiable function f where $f(x) > 0$ and $f'(x) < 0$? If so, give an example. If not, explain why not.

89. Sketching a Graph Sketch the graph of the arbitrary function f such that

$$f'(x) \begin{cases} > 0, & x < 4 \\ \text{undefined}, & x = 4 \\ < 0, & x > 4 \end{cases}.$$

90. HOW DO YOU SEE IT? Use the graph of f' to (a) identify the critical numbers of f, (b) identify the open interval(s) on which f is increasing or decreasing, and (c) determine whether f has a relative maximum, a relative minimum, or neither at each critical number.

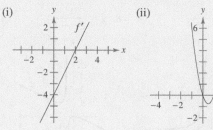

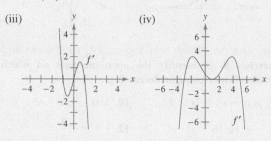

91. Analyzing a Critical Number   A differentiable function f has one critical number at $x = 5$. Identify the relative extrema of f at the critical number when $f'(4) = -2.5$ and $f'(6) = 3$.

92. Analyzing a Critical Number   A differentiable function f has one critical number at $x = 2$. Identify the relative extrema of f at the critical number when $f'(1) = 2$ and $f'(3) = 6$.

Think About It   In Exercises 93 and 94, the function f is differentiable on the indicated interval. The table shows $f'(x)$ for selected values of x. (a) Sketch the graph of f, (b) approximate the critical numbers, and (c) identify the relative extrema.

93. f is differentiable on $[-1, 1]$.

x	-1	-0.75	-0.50	-0.25	0
$f'(x)$	-10	-3.2	-0.5	0.8	5.6

x	0.25	0.50	0.75	1
$f'(x)$	3.6	-0.2	-6.7	-20.1

94. f is differentiable on $[0, \pi]$.

x	0	$\pi/6$	$\pi/4$	$\pi/3$	$\pi/2$
$f'(x)$	3.14	-0.23	-2.45	-3.11	0.69

x	$2\pi/3$	$3\pi/4$	$5\pi/6$	π
$f'(x)$	3.00	1.37	-1.14	-2.84

95. Rolling a Ball Bearing   A ball bearing is placed on an inclined plane and begins to roll. The angle of elevation of the plane is θ. The distance (in meters) the ball bearing rolls in t seconds is $s(t) = 4.9(\sin\theta)t^2$.

(a) Determine the speed of the ball bearing after t seconds.

(b) Complete the table and use it to determine the value of θ that produces the maximum speed at a particular time.

θ	0	$\pi/4$	$\pi/3$	$\pi/2$	$2\pi/3$	$3\pi/4$	π
$s'(t)$							

96. Modeling Data   The end-of-year assets of the Medicare Hospital Insurance Trust Fund (in billions of dollars) for the years 1999 through 2010 are shown.

1999: 141.4; 2000: 177.5; 2001: 208.7; 2002: 234.8; 2003: 256.0; 2004: 269.3; 2005: 285.8; 2006: 305.4 2007: 326.0; 2008: 321.3; 2009: 304.2; 2010: 271.9

(Source: U.S. Centers for Medicare and Medicaid Services)

(a) Use the regression capabilities of a graphing utility to find a model of the form $M = at^4 + bt^3 + ct^2 + dt + e$ for the data. (Let $t = 9$ represent 1999.)

(b) Use a graphing utility to plot the data and graph the model.

(c) Find the maximum value of the model and compare the result with the actual data.

97. Numerical, Graphical, and Analytic Analysis   The concentration C of a chemical in the bloodstream t hours after injection into muscle tissue is

$$C(t) = \frac{3t}{27 + t^3}, \quad t \geq 0.$$

(a) Complete the table and use it to approximate the time when the concentration is greatest.

t	0	0.5	1	1.5	2	2.5	3
$C(t)$							

(b) Use a graphing utility to graph the concentration function and use the graph to approximate the time when the concentration is greatest.

(c) Use calculus to determine analytically the time when the concentration is greatest.

98. Numerical, Graphical, and Analytic Analysis   Consider the functions

$$f(x) = x \quad \text{and} \quad g(x) = \sin x$$

on the interval $(0, \pi)$.

(a) Complete the table and make a conjecture about which is the greater function on the interval $(0, \pi)$.

x	0.5	1	1.5	2	2.5	3
$f(x)$						
$g(x)$						

(b) Use a graphing utility to graph the functions and use the graphs to make a conjecture about which is the greater function on the interval $(0, \pi)$.

(c) Prove that $f(x) > g(x)$ on the interval $(0, \pi)$. [*Hint*: Show that $h'(x) > 0$, where $h = f - g$.]

99. Trachea Contraction   Coughing forces the trachea (windpipe) to contract, which affects the velocity v of the air passing through the trachea. The velocity of the air during coughing is

$$v = k(R - r)r^2, \quad 0 \leq r < R$$

where k is a constant, R is the normal radius of the trachea, and r is the radius during coughing. What radius will produce the maximum air velocity?

100. Electrical Resistance   The resistance R of a certain type of resistor is

$$R = \sqrt{0.001T^4 - 4T + 100}$$

where R is measured in ohms and the temperature T is measured in degrees Celsius.

(a) Use a computer algebra system to find dR/dT and the critical number of the function. Determine the minimum resistance for this type of resistor.

(b) Use a graphing utility to graph the function R and use the graph to approximate the minimum resistance for this type of resistor.

Motion Along a Line In Exercises 101–104, the function $s(t)$ describes the motion of a particle along a line. For each function, (a) find the velocity function of the particle at any time $t \geq 0$, (b) identify the time interval(s) in which the particle is moving in a positive direction, (c) identify the time interval(s) in which the particle is moving in a negative direction, and (d) identify the time(s) at which the particle changes direction.

101. $s(t) = 6t - t^2$

102. $s(t) = t^2 - 7t + 10$

103. $s(t) = t^3 - 5t^2 + 4t$

104. $s(t) = t^3 - 20t^2 + 128t - 280$

Motion Along a Line In Exercises 105 and 106, the graph shows the position of a particle moving along a line. Describe how the particle's position changes with respect to time.

105.
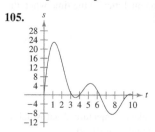

106.
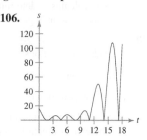

Creating Polynomial Functions In Exercises 107–110, find a polynomial function

$$f(x) = a_n x^n + a_{n-1} x^{n-1} + \cdots + a_2 x^2 + a_1 x + a_0$$

that has only the specified extrema. (a) Determine the minimum degree of the function and give the criteria you used in determining the degree. (b) Using the fact that the coordinates of the extrema are solution points of the function, and that the x-coordinates are critical numbers, determine a system of linear equations whose solution yields the coefficients of the required function. (c) Use a graphing utility to solve the system of equations and determine the function. (d) Use a graphing utility to confirm your result graphically.

107. Relative minimum: $(0, 0)$; Relative maximum: $(2, 2)$

108. Relative minimum: $(0, 0)$; Relative maximum: $(4, 1000)$

109. Relative minima: $(0, 0)$, $(4, 0)$; Relative maximum: $(2, 4)$

110. Relative minimum: $(1, 2)$; Relative maxima: $(-1, 4)$, $(3, 4)$

True or False? In Exercises 111–116, determine whether the statement is true or false. If it is false, explain why or give an example that shows it is false.

111. The sum of two increasing functions is increasing.

112. The product of two increasing functions is increasing.

113. Every nth-degree polynomial has $(n - 1)$ critical numbers.

114. An nth-degree polynomial has at most $(n - 1)$ critical numbers.

115. There is a relative maximum or minimum at each critical number.

116. The relative maxima of the function f are $f(1) = 4$ and $f(3) = 10$. Therefore, f has at least one minimum for some x in the interval $(1, 3)$.

117. Proof Prove the second case of Theorem 4.5.

118. Proof Prove the second case of Theorem 4.6.

119. Proof Let $x > 0$ and $n > 1$ be real numbers. Prove that $(1 + x)^n > 1 + nx$.

120. Proof Use the definitions of increasing and decreasing functions to prove that $f(x) = x^3$ is increasing on $(-\infty, \infty)$.

121. Proof Use the definitions of increasing and decreasing functions to prove that $f(x) = 1/x$ is decreasing on $(0, \infty)$.

122. Finding Values Consider $f(x) = axe^{bx^2}$. Find a and b such that the relative maximum of f is $f(4) = 2$.

PUTNAM EXAM CHALLENGE

123. Find the minimum value of

$$|\sin x + \cos x + \tan x + \cot x + \sec x + \csc x|$$

for real numbers x.

This problem was composed by the Committee on the Putnam Prize Competition.
© The Mathematical Association of America. All rights reserved.

SECTION PROJECT

Rainbows

Rainbows are formed when light strikes raindrops and is reflected and refracted, as shown in the figure. (This figure shows a cross section of a spherical raindrop.) The Law of Refraction states that

$$\frac{\sin \alpha}{\sin \beta} = k$$

where $k \approx 1.33$ (for water). The angle of deflection is given by $D = \pi + 2\alpha - 4\beta$.

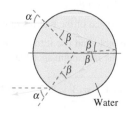

Water

(a) Use a graphing utility to graph

$$D = \pi + 2\alpha - 4\sin^{-1}\left(\frac{\sin \alpha}{k}\right), \quad 0 \leq \alpha \leq \frac{\pi}{2}.$$

(b) Prove that the minimum angle of deflection occurs when

$$\cos \alpha = \sqrt{\frac{k^2 - 1}{3}}.$$

For water, what is the minimum angle of deflection $D_{\min}$? (The angle $\pi - D_{\min}$ is called the *rainbow angle*.) What value of α produces this minimum angle? (A ray of sunlight that strikes a raindrop at this angle, α, is called a *rainbow ray*.)

■ **FOR FURTHER INFORMATION** For more information about the mathematics of rainbows, see the article "Somewhere Within the Rainbow" by Steven Janke in *The UMAP Journal*.

4.4 Concavity and the Second Derivative Test

- Determine intervals on which a function is concave upward or concave downward.
- Find any points of inflection of the graph of a function.
- Apply the Second Derivative Test to find relative extrema of a function.

Concavity

You have already seen that locating the intervals in which a function f increases or decreases helps to describe its graph. In this section, you will see how locating the intervals in which f' increases or decreases can be used to determine where the graph of f is *curving upward* or *curving downward*.

> **Definition of Concavity**
>
> Let f be differentiable on an open interval I. The graph of f is **concave upward** on I when f' is increasing on the interval and **concave downward** on I when f' is decreasing on the interval.

The following graphical interpretation of concavity is useful. (See Appendix A for a proof of these results.)

See LarsonCalculus.com for Bruce Edwards's video of this proof.

1. Let f be differentiable on an open interval I. If the graph of f is concave *upward* on I, then the graph of f lies *above* all of its tangent lines on I. [See Figure 4.23(a).]
2. Let f be differentiable on an open interval I. If the graph of f is concave *downward* on I, then the graph of f lies *below* all of its tangent lines on I. [See Figure 4.23(b).]

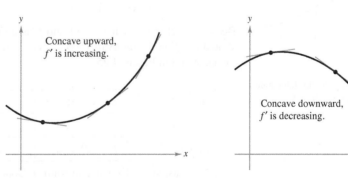

(a) The graph of f lies above its tangent lines.   (b) The graph of f lies below its tangent lines.
Figure 4.23

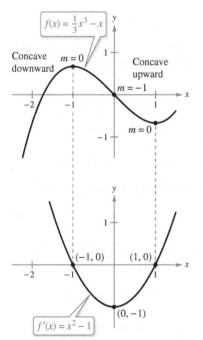

f' is decreasing. f' is increasing.

The concavity of f is related to the slope of the derivative.
Figure 4.24

To find the open intervals on which the graph of a function f is concave upward or concave downward, you need to find the intervals on which f' is increasing or decreasing. For instance, the graph of

$$f(x) = \frac{1}{3}x^3 - x$$

is concave downward on the open interval $(-\infty, 0)$ because

$$f'(x) = x^2 - 1$$

is decreasing there. (See Figure 4.24.) Similarly, the graph of f is concave upward on the interval $(0, \infty)$ because f' is increasing on $(0, \infty)$.

The next theorem shows how to use the *second* derivative of a function f to determine intervals on which the graph of f is concave upward or concave downward. A proof of this theorem follows directly from Theorem 4.5 and the definition of concavity.

· · · · · · · · · · · · · · · · · · ▷

· · REMARK A third case of Theorem 4.7 could be that if $f''(x) = 0$ for all x in I, then f is linear. Note, however, that concavity is not defined for a line. In other words, a straight line is neither concave upward nor concave downward.

THEOREM 4.7 Test for Concavity

Let f be a function whose second derivative exists on an open interval I.

1. If $f''(x) > 0$ for all x in I, then the graph of f is concave upward on I.
2. If $f''(x) < 0$ for all x in I, then the graph of f is concave downward on I.

A proof of this theorem is given in Appendix A.
See LarsonCalculus.com for Bruce Edwards's video of this proof.

To apply Theorem 4.7, locate the x-values at which $f''(x) = 0$ or f'' does not exist. Use these x-values to determine test intervals. Finally, test the sign of $f''(x)$ in each of the test intervals.

EXAMPLE 1   Determining Concavity

Determine the open intervals on which the graph of

$$f(x) = e^{-x^2/2}$$

is concave upward or concave downward.

Solution Begin by observing that f is continuous on the entire real number line. Next, find the second derivative of f.

$$f'(x) = -xe^{-x^2/2} \qquad \text{First derivative}$$
$$f''(x) = (-x)(-x)e^{-x^2/2} + e^{-x^2/2}(-1) \qquad \text{Differentiate.}$$
$$= e^{-x^2/2}(x^2 - 1) \qquad \text{Second derivative}$$

Because $f''(x) = 0$ when $x = \pm 1$ and f'' is defined on the entire real number line, you should test f'' in the intervals $(-\infty, -1)$, $(-1, 1)$, and $(1, \infty)$. The results are shown in the table and in Figure 4.25.

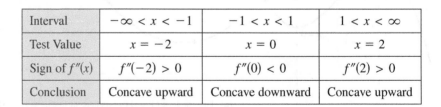

Interval	$-\infty < x < -1$	$-1 < x < 1$	$1 < x < \infty$
Test Value	$x = -2$	$x = 0$	$x = 2$
Sign of $f''(x)$	$f''(-2) > 0$	$f''(0) < 0$	$f''(2) > 0$
Conclusion	Concave upward	Concave downward	Concave upward

Note that the function in Example 1 is similar to the **normal probability density function,** whose general form is

$$f(x) = \frac{1}{\sigma\sqrt{2\pi}} e^{-x^2/(2\sigma^2)} \qquad \text{Normal probability density function}$$

where σ is the **standard deviation** (σ is the lowercase Greek letter sigma). This "bell-shaped" curve is concave downward on the interval $(-\sigma, \sigma)$.

The function given in Example 1 is continuous on the entire real number line. When there are x-values at which the function is not continuous, these values should be used, along with the points at which $f''(x) = 0$ or $f''(x)$ does not exist, to form the test intervals.

From the sign of f'', you can determine the concavity of the graph of f.
Figure 4.25

EXAMPLE 2 **Determining Concavity**

Determine the open intervals on which the graph of

$$f(x) = \frac{x^2 + 1}{x^2 - 4}$$

is concave upward or concave downward.

Solution   Differentiating twice produces the following.

$$f(x) = \frac{x^2 + 1}{x^2 - 4}$$ Write original function.

$$f'(x) = \frac{(x^2 - 4)(2x) - (x^2 + 1)(2x)}{(x^2 - 4)^2}$$ Differentiate.

$$= \frac{-10x}{(x^2 - 4)^2}$$ First derivative

$$f''(x) = \frac{(x^2 - 4)^2(-10) - (-10x)(2)(x^2 - 4)(2x)}{(x^2 - 4)^4}$$ Differentiate.

$$= \frac{10(3x^2 + 4)}{(x^2 - 4)^3}$$ Second derivative

There are no points at which $f''(x) = 0$, but at $x = \pm 2$, the function f is not continuous. So, test for concavity in the intervals $(-\infty, -2)$, $(-2, 2)$, and $(2, \infty)$, as shown in the table. The graph of f is shown in Figure 4.26.

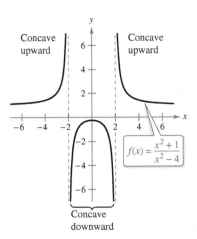

Figure 4.26

Interval	$-\infty < x < -2$	$-2 < x < 2$	$2 < x < \infty$
Test Value	$x = -3$	$x = 0$	$x = 3$
Sign of $f''(x)$	$f''(-3) > 0$	$f''(0) < 0$	$f''(3) > 0$
Conclusion	Concave upward	Concave downward	Concave upward

Points of Inflection

The graph in Figure 4.25 has two points at which the concavity changes. If the tangent line to the graph exists at such a point, then that point is a **point of inflection.** Three types of points of inflection are shown in Figure 4.27.

> ### Definition of Point of Inflection
>
> Let f be a function that is continuous on an open interval, and let c be a point in the interval. If the graph of f has a tangent line at this point $(c, f(c))$, then this point is a **point of inflection** of the graph of f when the concavity of f changes from upward to downward (or downward to upward) at the point.

This definition of *point of inflection* requires that the tangent line exists at the point of inflection. Some texts do not require this. For instance, using this definition, the function

$$f(x) = \begin{cases} x^3, & x < 0 \\ x^2 + 2x, & x \ge 0 \end{cases}$$

does *not* have a point of inflection at the origin, even though the concavity of the graph changes from concave downward to concave upward.

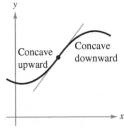

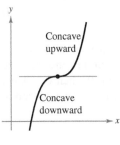

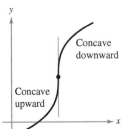

The concavity of f changes at a point of inflection. Note that the graph crosses its tangent line at a point of inflection.

Figure 4.27

To locate *possible* points of inflection, you can determine the values of x for which $f''(x) = 0$ or $f''(x)$ does not exist. This is similar to the procedure for locating relative extrema of f.

THEOREM 4.8   Points of Inflection

If $(c, f(c))$ is a point of inflection of the graph of f, then either $f''(c) = 0$ or f'' does not exist at $x = c$.

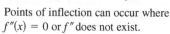

Figure 4.28 — left margin figure

$f(x) = x^4 - 4x^3$

Points of inflection

Concave upward   Concave downward   Concave upward

Points of inflection can occur where $f''(x) = 0$ or f'' does not exist.
Figure 4.28

EXAMPLE 3   **Finding Points of Inflection**

Determine the points of inflection and discuss the concavity of the graph of

$$f(x) = x^4 - 4x^3.$$

Solution   Differentiating twice produces the following.

$f(x) = x^4 - 4x^3$ Write original function.

$f'(x) = 4x^3 - 12x^2$ Find first derivative.

$f''(x) = 12x^2 - 24x = 12x(x - 2)$ Find second derivative.

Setting $f''(x) = 0$, you can determine that the possible points of inflection occur at $x = 0$ and $x = 2$. By testing the intervals determined by these x-values, you can conclude that they both yield points of inflection. A summary of this testing is shown in the table, and the graph of f is shown in Figure 4.28.

Interval	$-\infty < x < 0$	$0 < x < 2$	$2 < x < \infty$
Test Value	$x = -1$	$x = 1$	$x = 3$
Sign of $f''(x)$	$f''(-1) > 0$	$f''(1) < 0$	$f''(3) > 0$
Conclusion	Concave upward	Concave downward	Concave upward

The converse of Theorem 4.8 is not generally true. That is, it is possible for the second derivative to be 0 at a point that is *not* a point of inflection. For instance, the graph of $f(x) = x^4$ is shown in Figure 4.29. The second derivative is 0 when $x = 0$, but the point $(0, 0)$ is not a point of inflection because the graph of f is concave upward in both intervals $-\infty < x < 0$ and $0 < x < \infty$.

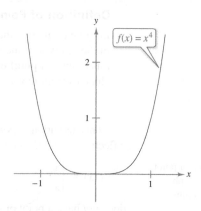

$f''(x) = 0$, but $(0, 0)$ is not a point of inflection.
Figure 4.29

The Second Derivative Test

In addition to testing for concavity, the second derivative can be used to perform a simple test for relative maxima and minima. The test is based on the fact that if the graph of a function f is concave upward on an open interval containing c, and $f'(c) = 0$, then $f(c)$ must be a relative minimum of f. Similarly, if the graph of a function f is concave downward on an open interval containing c, and $f'(c) = 0$, then $f(c)$ must be a relative maximum of f (see Figure 4.30).

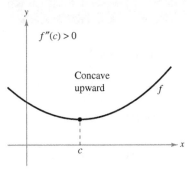

If $f'(c) = 0$ and $f''(c) > 0$, then $f(c)$ is a relative minimum.

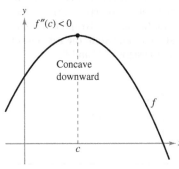

If $f'(c) = 0$ and $f''(c) < 0$, then $f(c)$ is a relative maximum.
Figure 4.30

THEOREM 4.9   Second Derivative Test

Let f be a function such that $f'(c) = 0$ and the second derivative of f exists on an open interval containing c.

1. If $f''(c) > 0$, then f has a relative minimum at $(c, f(c))$.
2. If $f''(c) < 0$, then f has a relative maximum at $(c, f(c))$.

If $f''(c) = 0$, then the test fails. That is, f may have a relative maximum, a relative minimum, or neither. In such cases, you can use the First Derivative Test.

Proof   If $f'(c) = 0$ and $f''(c) > 0$, then there exists an open interval I containing c for which

$$\frac{f'(x) - f'(c)}{x - c} = \frac{f'(x)}{x - c} > 0$$

for all $x \neq c$ in I. If $x < c$, then $x - c < 0$ and $f'(x) < 0$. Also, if $x > c$, then $x - c > 0$ and $f'(x) > 0$. So, $f'(x)$ changes from negative to positive at c, and the First Derivative Test implies that $f(c)$ is a relative minimum. A proof of the second case is left to you.

See LarsonCalculus.com for Bruce Edwards's video of this proof.

EXAMPLE 4   **Using the Second Derivative Test**

• • • • ▷ *See LarsonCalculus.com for an interactive version of this type of example.*

Find the relative extrema of

$$f(x) = -3x^5 + 5x^3.$$

Solution   Begin by finding the first derivative of f.

$$f'(x) = -15x^4 + 15x^2 = 15x^2(1 - x^2)$$

From this derivative, you can see that $x = -1, 0,$ and 1 are the only critical numbers of f. By finding the second derivative

$$f''(x) = -60x^3 + 30x = 30x(1 - 2x^2)$$

you can apply the Second Derivative Test as shown below.

Point	$(-1, -2)$	$(0, 0)$	$(1, 2)$
Sign of $f''(x)$	$f''(-1) > 0$	$f''(0) = 0$	$f''(1) < 0$
Conclusion	Relative minimum	Test fails	Relative maximum

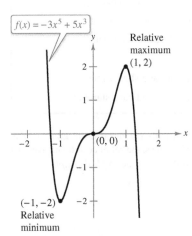

$(0, 0)$ is neither a relative minimum nor a relative maximum.
Figure 4.31

Because the Second Derivative Test fails at $(0, 0)$, you can use the First Derivative Test and observe that f increases to the left and right of $x = 0$. So, $(0, 0)$ is neither a relative minimum nor a relative maximum (even though the graph has a horizontal tangent line at this point). The graph of f is shown in Figure 4.31.

4.4 Exercises

Determining Concavity In Exercises 1–12, determine the open intervals on which the graph is concave upward or concave downward.

1. $y = x^2 - x - 2$

2. $g(x) = 3x^2 - x^3$

3. $f(x) = -x^3 + 6x^2 - 9x - 1$

4. $h(x) = x^5 - 5x + 2$

5. $f(x) = \dfrac{24}{x^2 + 12}$

6. $f(x) = \dfrac{2x^2}{3x^2 + 1}$

7. $f(x) = \dfrac{x^2 + 1}{x^2 - 1}$

8. $y = \dfrac{-3x^5 + 40x^3 + 135x}{270}$

9. $g(x) = \dfrac{x^2 + 4}{4 - x^2}$

10. $h(x) = \dfrac{x^2 - 1}{2x - 1}$

11. $y = 2x - \tan x, \quad \left(-\dfrac{\pi}{2}, \dfrac{\pi}{2}\right)$

12. $y = x + \dfrac{2}{\sin x}, \quad (-\pi, \pi)$

Finding Points of Inflection In Exercises 13–34, find the points of inflection and discuss the concavity of the graph of the function.

13. $f(x) = x^3 - 6x^2 + 12x$

14. $f(x) = -x^3 + 6x^2 - 5$

15. $f(x) = \frac{1}{2}x^4 + 2x^3$

16. $f(x) = 4 - x - 3x^4$

17. $f(x) = x(x - 4)^3$

18. $f(x) = (x - 2)^3(x - 1)$

19. $f(x) = x\sqrt{x + 3}$

20. $f(x) = x\sqrt{9 - x}$

21. $f(x) = \dfrac{4}{x^2 + 1}$

22. $f(x) = \dfrac{x + 3}{\sqrt{x}}$

23. $f(x) = \sin \dfrac{x}{2}, \quad [0, 4\pi]$

24. $f(x) = 2 \csc \dfrac{3x}{2}, \quad (0, 2\pi)$

25. $f(x) = \sec\left(x - \dfrac{\pi}{2}\right), \quad (0, 4\pi)$

26. $f(x) = \sin x + \cos x, \quad [0, 2\pi]$

27. $f(x) = 2 \sin x + \sin 2x, \quad [0, 2\pi]$

28. $f(x) = x + 2 \cos x, \quad [0, 2\pi]$

29. $y = e^{-3/x}$

30. $y = \frac{1}{2}(e^x - e^{-x})$

31. $y = x - \ln x$

32. $y = \ln\sqrt{x^2 + 9}$

33. $f(x) = \arcsin x^{4/5}$

34. $f(x) = \arctan(x^2)$

Using the Second Derivative Test In Exercises 35–58, find all relative extrema. Use the Second Derivative Test where applicable.

35. $f(x) = 6x - x^2$

36. $f(x) = x^2 + 3x - 8$

37. $f(x) = x^3 - 3x^2 + 3$

38. $f(x) = -x^3 + 7x^2 - 15x$

39. $f(x) = x^4 - 4x^3 + 2$

40. $f(x) = -x^4 + 4x^3 + 8x^2$

41. $f(x) = x^{2/3} - 3$

42. $f(x) = \sqrt{x^2 + 1}$

43. $f(x) = x + \dfrac{4}{x}$

44. $f(x) = \dfrac{x}{x - 1}$

45. $f(x) = \cos x - x, \quad [0, 4\pi]$

46. $f(x) = 2 \sin x + \cos 2x, \quad [0, 2\pi]$

47. $y = 8x^2 - \ln x$

48. $y = x \ln x$

49. $y = \dfrac{x}{\ln x}$

50. $y = x^2 \ln \dfrac{x}{4}$

51. $f(x) = \dfrac{e^x + e^{-x}}{2}$

52. $g(x) = \dfrac{1}{\sqrt{2\pi}} e^{-(x-3)^2/2}$

53. $f(x) = x^2 e^{-x}$

54. $f(x) = xe^{-x}$

55. $f(x) = 8x(4^{-x})$

56. $y = x^2 \log_3 x$

57. $f(x) = \text{arcsec } x - x$

58. $f(x) = \arcsin x - 2x$

Finding Extrema and Points of Inflection Using Technology In Exercises 59–62, use a computer algebra system to analyze the function over the given interval. (a) Find the first and second derivatives of the function. (b) Find any relative extrema and points of inflection. (c) Graph f, f', and f'' on the same set of coordinate axes and state the relationship between the behavior of f and the signs of f' and f''.

59. $f(x) = 0.2x^2(x - 3)^3, \quad [-1, 4]$

60. $f(x) = x^2\sqrt{6 - x^2}, \quad [-\sqrt{6}, \sqrt{6}]$

61. $f(x) = \sin x - \frac{1}{3}\sin 3x + \frac{1}{5}\sin 5x, \quad [0, \pi]$

62. $f(x) = \sqrt{2x}\sin x, \quad [0, 2\pi]$

WRITING ABOUT CONCEPTS

63. Sketching a Graph Consider a function f such that f' is increasing. Sketch graphs of f for (a) $f' < 0$ and (b) $f' > 0$.

64. Sketching a Graph Consider a function f such that f' is decreasing. Sketch graphs of f for (a) $f' < 0$ and (b) $f' > 0$.

65. Sketching a Graph Sketch the graph of a function f that does *not* have a point of inflection at $(c, f(c))$ even though $f''(c) = 0$.

66. Think About It S represents weekly sales of a product. What can be said of S' and S'' for each of the following statements?

(a) The rate of change of sales is increasing.

(b) Sales are increasing at a slower rate.

(c) The rate of change of sales is constant.

(d) Sales are steady.

(e) Sales are declining, but at a slower rate.

(f) Sales have bottomed out and have started to rise.

---

67. Sketching Graphs In parts (a) and (b), the graph of f is shown. Graph f, f', and f'' on the same set of coordinate axes. To print an enlarged copy of the graph, go to *MathGraphs.com*.

(a)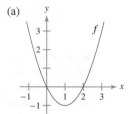

(b)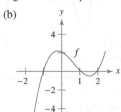

68. **HOW DO YOU SEE IT?** Using the graph of f, state the signs of f' and f'' on the interval $(0, 2)$.

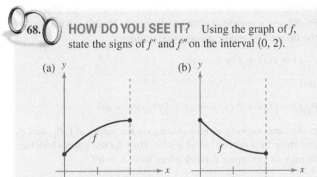

(a)

(b)

Think About It In Exercises 69–72, sketch the graph of a function f having the given characteristics.

69. $f(2) = f(4) = 0$
$f'(x) < 0$ for $x < 3$
$f'(3)$ does not exist.
$f'(x) > 0$ for $x > 3$
$f''(x) < 0, x \neq 3$

70. $f(0) = f(2) = 0$
$f'(x) > 0$ for $x < 1$
$f'(1) = 0$
$f'(x) < 0$ for $x > 1$
$f''(x) < 0$

71. $f(2) = f(4) = 0$
$f'(x) > 0$ for $x < 3$
$f'(3)$ does not exist.
$f'(x) < 0$ for $x > 3$
$f''(x) > 0, x \neq 3$

72. $f(0) = f(2) = 0$
$f'(x) < 0$ for $x < 1$
$f'(1) = 0$
$f'(x) > 0$ for $x > 1$
$f''(x) > 0$

73. **Think About It** The figure shows the graph of f''. Sketch a graph of f. (The answer is not unique.) To print an enlarged copy of the graph, go to *MathGraphs.com*.

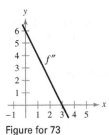

Figure for 73

Figure for 74

74. **Think About It** Water is running into the vase shown in the figure at a constant rate.

(a) Graph the depth d of water in the vase as a function of time.

(b) Does the function have any extrema? Explain.

(c) Interpret the inflection points of the graph of d.

75. **Conjecture** Consider the function $f(x) = (x - 2)^n$.

(a) Use a graphing utility to graph f for $n = 1, 2, 3,$ and 4. Use the graphs to make a conjecture about the relationship between n and any inflection points of the graph of f.

(b) Verify your conjecture in part (a).

76. **Inflection Point** Consider the function $f(x) = \sqrt[3]{x}$.

(a) Graph the function and identify the inflection point.

(b) Does $f''(x)$ exist at the inflection point? Explain.

Finding a Cubic Function In Exercises 77 and 78, find a, b, c, and d such that the cubic

$$f(x) = ax^3 + bx^2 + cx + d$$

satisfies the given conditions.

77. Relative maximum: $(3, 3)$
Relative minimum: $(5, 1)$
Inflection point: $(4, 2)$

78. Relative maximum: $(2, 4)$
Relative minimum: $(4, 2)$
Inflection point: $(3, 3)$

79. **Aircraft Glide Path** A small aircraft starts its descent from an altitude of 1 mile, 4 miles west of the runway (see figure).

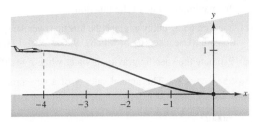

(a) Find the cubic $f(x) = ax^3 + bx^2 + cx + d$ on the interval $[-4, 0]$ that describes a smooth glide path for the landing.

(b) The function in part (a) models the glide path of the plane. When would the plane be descending at the greatest rate?

FOR FURTHER INFORMATION For more information on this type of modeling, see the article "How Not to Land at Lake Tahoe!" by Richard Barshinger in *The American Mathematical Monthly*. To view this article, go to *MathArticles.com*.

80. **Highway Design** A section of highway connecting two hillsides with grades of 6% and 4% is to be built between two points that are separated by a horizontal distance of 2000 feet (see figure). At the point where the two hillsides come together, there is a 50-foot difference in elevation.

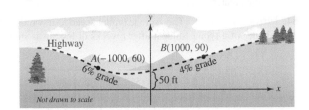

(a) Design a section of highway connecting the hillsides modeled by the function

$$f(x) = ax^3 + bx^2 + cx + d, \quad -1000 \le x \le 1000.$$

At points A and B, the slope of the model must match the grade of the hillside.

(b) Use a graphing utility to graph the model.

(c) Use a graphing utility to graph the derivative of the model.

(d) Determine the grade at the steepest part of the transitional section of the highway.

81. Average Cost A manufacturer has determined that the total cost C of operating a factory is

$$C = 0.5x^2 + 15x + 5000$$

where x is the number of units produced. At what level of production will the average cost per unit be minimized? (The average cost per unit is C/x.)

82. Specific Gravity A model for the specific gravity of water S is

$$S = \frac{5.755}{10^8}T^3 - \frac{8.521}{10^6}T^2 + \frac{6.540}{10^5}T + 0.99987, \ 0 < T < 25$$

where T is the water temperature in degrees Celsius.

(a) Use the second derivative to determine the concavity of S.

(b) Use a computer algebra system to find the coordinates of the maximum value of the function.

(c) Use a graphing utility to graph the function over the specified domain. (Use a setting in which $0.996 \le S \le 1.001$.)

(d) Estimate the specific gravity of water when $T = 20°$.

83. Sales Growth The annual sales S of a new product are given by

$$S = \frac{5000t^2}{8 + t^2}, \quad 0 \le t \le 3$$

where t is time in years.

(a) Complete the table. Then use it to estimate when the annual sales are increasing at the greatest rate.

t	0.5	1	1.5	2	2.5	3
S						

(b) Use a graphing utility to graph the function S. Then use the graph to estimate when the annual sales are increasing at the greatest rate.

(c) Find the exact time when the annual sales are increasing at the greatest rate.

84. Modeling Data The average typing speed S (in words per minute) of a typing student after t weeks of lessons is shown in the table.

t	5	10	15	20	25	30
S	38	56	79	90	93	94

A model for the data is

$$S = \frac{100t^2}{65 + t^2}, \quad t > 0.$$

(a) Use a graphing utility to plot the data and graph the model.

(b) Use the second derivative to determine the concavity of S. Compare the result with the graph in part (a).

(c) What is the sign of the first derivative for $t > 0$? By combining this information with the concavity of the model, what inferences can be made about the typing speed as t increases?

Linear and Quadratic Approximations In Exercises 85–88, use a graphing utility to graph the function. Then graph the linear and quadratic approximations

$$P_1(x) = f(a) + f'(a)(x - a)$$

and

$$P_2(x) = f(a) + f'(a)(x - a) + \tfrac{1}{2}f''(a)(x - a)^2$$

in the same viewing window. Compare the values of f, P_1, and P_2 and their first derivatives at $x = a$. How do the approximations change as you move farther away from $x = a$?

Function	Value of a
85. $f(x) = 2(\sin x + \cos x)$	$a = \dfrac{\pi}{4}$
86. $f(x) = 2(\sin x + \cos x)$	$a = 0$
87. $f(x) = \arctan x$	$a = -1$
88. $f(x) = \dfrac{\sqrt{x}}{x - 1}$	$a = 2$

89. Determining Concavity Use a graphing utility to graph

$$y = x \sin \frac{1}{x}.$$

Show that the graph is concave downward to the right of

$$x = \frac{1}{\pi}.$$

90. Point of Inflection and Extrema Show that the point of inflection of

$$f(x) = x(x - 6)^2$$

lies midway between the relative extrema of f.

True or False? In Exercises 91–94, determine whether the statement is true or false. If it is false, explain why or give an example that shows it is false.

91. The graph of every cubic polynomial has precisely one point of inflection.

92. The graph of

$$f(x) = \frac{1}{x}$$

is concave downward for $x < 0$ and concave upward for $x > 0$, and thus it has a point of inflection at $x = 0$.

93. If $f'(c) > 0$, then f is concave upward at $x = c$.

94. If $f''(2) = 0$, then the graph of f must have a point of inflection at $x = 2$.

Proof In Exercises 95 and 96, let f and g represent differentiable functions such that $f'' \ne 0$ and $g'' \ne 0$.

95. Show that if f and g are concave upward on the interval (a, b), then $f + g$ is also concave upward on (a, b).

96. Prove that if f and g are positive, increasing, and concave upward on the interval (a, b), then fg is also concave upward on (a, b).

4.5   Limits at Infinity

■ Determine (finite) limits at infinity.
■ Determine the horizontal asymptotes, if any, of the graph of a function.
■ Determine infinite limits at infinity.

Limits at Infinity

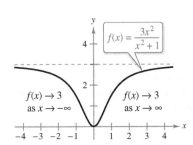

The limit of $f(x)$ as x approaches $-\infty$ or ∞ is 3.
Figure 4.32

This section discusses the "end behavior" of a function on an *infinite* interval. Consider the graph of

$$f(x) = \frac{3x^2}{x^2 + 1}$$

as shown in Figure 4.32. Graphically, you can see that the values of $f(x)$ appear to approach 3 as x increases without bound or decreases without bound. You can come to the same conclusions numerically, as shown in the table.

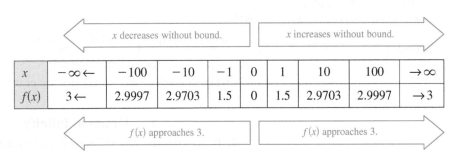

	x decreases without bound.					x increases without bound.			
x	$-\infty \leftarrow$	-100	-10	-1	0	1	10	100	$\rightarrow \infty$
$f(x)$	$3 \leftarrow$	2.9997	2.9703	1.5	0	1.5	2.9703	2.9997	$\rightarrow 3$
	$f(x)$ approaches 3.					$f(x)$ approaches 3.			

The table suggests that the value of $f(x)$ approaches 3 as x increases without bound ($x \to \infty$). Similarly, $f(x)$ approaches 3 as x decreases without bound ($x \to -\infty$). These **limits at infinity** are denoted by

$$\lim_{x \to -\infty} f(x) = 3 \qquad \text{Limit at negative infinity}$$

and

$$\lim_{x \to \infty} f(x) = 3. \qquad \text{Limit at positive infinity}$$

To say that a statement is true as x increases *without bound* means that for some (large) real number M, the statement is true for *all* x in the interval $\{x : x > M\}$. The next definition uses this concept.

> **·· REMARK**   The statement $\lim_{x \to -\infty} f(x) = L$ or $\lim_{x \to \infty} f(x) = L$ means that the limit exists *and* the limit is equal to L.

Definition of Limits at Infinity

Let L be a real number.

1. The statement $\lim_{x \to \infty} f(x) = L$ means that for each $\varepsilon > 0$ there exists an $M > 0$ such that $|f(x) - L| < \varepsilon$ whenever $x > M$.
2. The statement $\lim_{x \to -\infty} f(x) = L$ means that for each $\varepsilon > 0$ there exists an $N < 0$ such that $|f(x) - L| < \varepsilon$ whenever $x < N$.

The definition of a limit at infinity is shown in Figure 4.33. In this figure, note that for a given positive number ε, there exists a positive number M such that, for $x > M$, the graph of f will lie between the horizontal lines

$$y = L + \varepsilon \quad \text{and} \quad y = L - \varepsilon.$$

$f(x)$ is within ε units of L as $x \to \infty$.
Figure 4.33

Exploration

Use a graphing utility to graph

$$f(x) = \frac{2x^2 + 4x - 6}{3x^2 + 2x - 16}.$$

Describe all the important features of the graph. Can you find a single viewing window that shows all of these features clearly? Explain your reasoning.

What are the horizontal asymptotes of the graph? How far to the right do you have to move on the graph so that the graph is within 0.001 unit of its horizontal asymptote? Explain your reasoning.

Horizontal Asymptotes

In Figure 4.33, the graph of f approaches the line $y = L$ as x increases without bound. The line $y = L$ is called a **horizontal asymptote** of the graph of f.

Definition of a Horizontal Asymptote

The line $y = L$ is a **horizontal asymptote** of the graph of f when

$$\lim_{x \to -\infty} f(x) = L \quad \text{or} \quad \lim_{x \to \infty} f(x) = L.$$

Note that from this definition, it follows that the graph of a *function* of x can have at most two horizontal asymptotes—one to the right and one to the left.

Limits at infinity have many of the same properties of limits discussed in Section 2.3. For example, if $\lim\limits_{x \to \infty} f(x)$ and $\lim\limits_{x \to \infty} g(x)$ both exist, then

$$\lim_{x \to \infty} [f(x) + g(x)] = \lim_{x \to \infty} f(x) + \lim_{x \to \infty} g(x)$$

and

$$\lim_{x \to \infty} [f(x)g(x)] = \left[\lim_{x \to \infty} f(x)\right]\left[\lim_{x \to \infty} g(x)\right].$$

Similar properties hold for limits at $-\infty$.

When evaluating limits at infinity, the next theorem is helpful.

THEOREM 4.10   Limits at Infinity

1. If r is a positive rational number and c is any real number, then

$$\lim_{x \to \infty} \frac{c}{x^r} = 0 \quad \text{and} \quad \lim_{x \to -\infty} \frac{c}{x^r} = 0.$$

The second limit is valid only if x^r is defined when $x < 0$.

2. $\lim\limits_{x \to -\infty} e^x = 0 \quad \text{and} \quad \lim\limits_{x \to \infty} e^{-x} = 0$

A proof of the first part of this theorem is given in Appendix A.
See LarsonCalculus.com for Bruce Edwards's video of this proof.

EXAMPLE 1   Evaluating a Limit at Infinity

Find the limit.

a. $\lim\limits_{x \to \infty} \left(5 - \dfrac{2}{x^2}\right)$ **b.** $\lim\limits_{x \to \infty} \dfrac{3}{e^x}$

Solution

a. $\lim\limits_{x \to \infty} \left(5 - \dfrac{2}{x^2}\right) = \lim\limits_{x \to \infty} 5 - \lim\limits_{x \to \infty} \dfrac{2}{x^2}$ Property of limits

$$= 5 - 0$$

$$= 5$$

b. $\lim\limits_{x \to \infty} \dfrac{3}{e^x} = \lim\limits_{x \to \infty} 3e^{-x}$

$$= 3 \lim_{x \to \infty} e^{-x} \qquad \text{Property of limits}$$

$$= 3(0)$$

$$= 0$$

EXAMPLE 2   **Finding a Limit at Infinity**

Find the limit: $\displaystyle\lim_{x \to \infty} \frac{2x - 1}{x + 1}$.

Solution   Note that both the numerator and the denominator approach infinity as x approaches infinity.

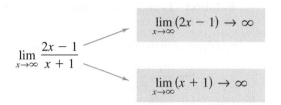

$$\lim_{x \to \infty} \frac{2x - 1}{x + 1} \qquad \lim_{x \to \infty} (2x - 1) \to \infty$$
$$\lim_{x \to \infty} (x + 1) \to \infty$$

This results in $\dfrac{\infty}{\infty}$, an **indeterminate form.** To resolve this problem, you can divide both the numerator and the denominator by x. After dividing, the limit may be evaluated as shown.

$$\lim_{x \to \infty} \frac{2x - 1}{x + 1} = \lim_{x \to \infty} \frac{\dfrac{2x - 1}{x}}{\dfrac{x + 1}{x}} \qquad \text{Divide numerator and denominator by } x.$$

$$= \lim_{x \to \infty} \frac{2 - \dfrac{1}{x}}{1 + \dfrac{1}{x}} \qquad \text{Simplify.}$$

$$= \frac{\displaystyle\lim_{x \to \infty} 2 - \lim_{x \to \infty} \dfrac{1}{x}}{\displaystyle\lim_{x \to \infty} 1 + \lim_{x \to \infty} \dfrac{1}{x}} \qquad \text{Take limits of numerator and denominator.}$$

$$= \frac{2 - 0}{1 + 0} \qquad \text{Apply Theorem 4.10.}$$

$$= 2$$

So, the line $y = 2$ is a horizontal asymptote to the right. By taking the limit as $x \to -\infty$, you can see that $y = 2$ is also a horizontal asymptote to the left. The graph of the function is shown in Figure 4.34.

▷ **REMARK**   When you encounter an indeterminate form such as the one in Example 2, you should divide the numerator and denominator by the highest power of x in the *denominator*.

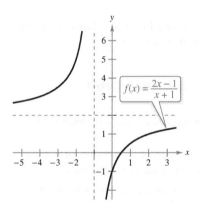

$y = 2$ is a horizontal asymptote.
Figure 4.34

▷ **TECHNOLOGY**   You can test the reasonableness of the limit found in Example 2 by evaluating $f(x)$ for a few large positive values of x. For instance,

$$f(100) \approx 1.9703, \quad f(1000) \approx 1.9970,$$
$$\text{and} \quad f(10{,}000) \approx 1.9997.$$

Another way to test the reasonableness of the limit is to use a graphing utility. For instance, in Figure 4.35, the graph of

$$f(x) = \frac{2x - 1}{x + 1}$$

is shown with the horizontal line $y = 2$. Note that as x increases, the graph of f moves closer and closer to its horizontal asymptote.

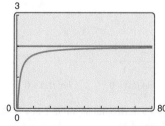

As x increases, the graph of f moves closer and closer to the line $y = 2$.
Figure 4.35

**MARIA GAETANA AGNESI
(1718–1799)**

Agnesi was one of a handful of women to receive credit for significant contributions to mathematics before the twentieth century. In her early twenties, she wrote the first text that included both differential and integral calculus. By age 30, she was an honorary member of the faculty at the University of Bologna. *See LarsonCalculus.com to read more of this biography.* For more information on the contributions of women to mathematics, see the article "Why Women Succeed in Mathematics" by Mona Fabricant, Sylvia Svitak, and Patricia Clark Kenschaft in *Mathematics Teacher.* To view this article, go to *MathArticles.com.*

EXAMPLE 3 **A Comparison of Three Rational Functions**

⋮ • • ▷ *See LarsonCalculus.com for an interactive version of this type of example.*

Find each limit.

a. $\lim\limits_{x \to \infty} \dfrac{2x + 5}{3x^2 + 1}$ **b.** $\lim\limits_{x \to \infty} \dfrac{2x^2 + 5}{3x^2 + 1}$ **c.** $\lim\limits_{x \to \infty} \dfrac{2x^3 + 5}{3x^2 + 1}$

Solution In each case, attempting to evaluate the limit produces the indeterminate form ∞/∞.

a. Divide both the numerator and the denominator by x^2.

$$\lim_{x \to \infty} \frac{2x + 5}{3x^2 + 1} = \lim_{x \to \infty} \frac{(2/x) + (5/x^2)}{3 + (1/x^2)} = \frac{0 + 0}{3 + 0} = \frac{0}{3} = 0$$

b. Divide both the numerator and the denominator by x^2.

$$\lim_{x \to \infty} \frac{2x^2 + 5}{3x^2 + 1} = \lim_{x \to \infty} \frac{2 + (5/x^2)}{3 + (1/x^2)} = \frac{2 + 0}{3 + 0} = \frac{2}{3}$$

c. Divide both the numerator and the denominator by x^2.

$$\lim_{x \to \infty} \frac{2x^3 + 5}{3x^2 + 1} = \lim_{x \to \infty} \frac{2x + (5/x^2)}{3 + (1/x^2)} = \frac{\infty}{3}$$

You can conclude that the limit *does not exist* because the numerator increases without bound while the denominator approaches 3. ∎

Example 3 suggests the guidelines below for finding limits at infinity of rational functions. Use these guidelines to check the results in Example 3.

GUIDELINES FOR FINDING LIMITS AT $\pm\infty$ OF RATIONAL FUNCTIONS

1. If the degree of the numerator is *less than* the degree of the denominator, then the limit of the rational function is 0.

2. If the degree of the numerator is *equal to* the degree of the denominator, then the limit of the rational function is the ratio of the leading coefficients.

3. If the degree of the numerator is *greater than* the degree of the denominator, then the limit of the rational function does not exist.

The guidelines for finding limits at infinity of rational functions seem reasonable when you consider that for large values of x, the highest-power term of the rational function is the most "influential" in determining the limit. For instance,

$$\lim_{x \to \infty} \frac{1}{x^2 + 1}$$

is 0 because the denominator overpowers the numerator as x increases or decreases without bound, as shown in Figure 4.36.

The function shown in Figure 4.36 is a special case of a type of curve studied by the Italian mathematician Maria Gaetana Agnesi. The general form of this function is

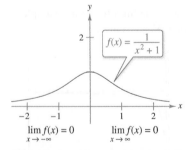

$\lim\limits_{x \to -\infty} f(x) = 0$ $\qquad$ $\lim\limits_{x \to \infty} f(x) = 0$

f has a horizontal asymptote at $y = 0$.
Figure 4.36

$$f(x) = \frac{8a^3}{x^2 + 4a^2} \qquad \text{Witch of Agnesi}$$

and, through a mistranslation of the Italian word *vertéré*, the curve has come to be known as the Witch of Agnesi. Agnesi's work with this curve first appeared in a comprehensive text on calculus that was published in 1748.

In Figure 4.36, you can see that the function

$$f(x) = \frac{1}{x^2 + 1}$$

approaches the same horizontal asymptote to the right and to the left. This is always true of rational functions. Functions that are not rational, however, may approach different horizontal asymptotes to the right and to the left. A common example of such a function is the **logistic function** shown in the next example.

> ### EXAMPLE 4   A Function with Two Horizontal Asymptotes

Show that the *logistic function*

$$f(x) = \frac{1}{1 + e^{-x}}$$

has different horizontal asymptotes to the left and to the right.

Solution   Begin by sketching a graph of the function. From Figure 4.37, it appears that

$$y = 0 \quad \text{and} \quad y = 1$$

are horizontal asymptotes to the left and to the right, respectively. The table shows the same results numerically.

x	-10	-5	-2	-1	1	2	5	10
$f(x)$	0.000	0.007	0.119	0.269	0.731	0.881	0.9933	1.0000

You can obtain the same results analytically, as follows.

$$\lim_{x \to \infty} \frac{1}{1 + e^{-x}} = \frac{\displaystyle\lim_{x \to \infty} 1}{\displaystyle\lim_{x \to \infty}(1 + e^{-x})}$$

$$= \frac{1}{1 + 0}$$

$$= 1 \qquad\qquad\qquad \text{\small $y = 1$ is a horizontal asymptote to the right.}$$

For the horizontal asymptote to the left, note that as $x \to -\infty$ the denominator of

$$\frac{1}{1 + e^{-x}}$$

approaches infinity. So, the quotient approaches 0 and thus the limit is 0. You can conclude that $y = 0$ is a horizontal asymptote to the left. ∎

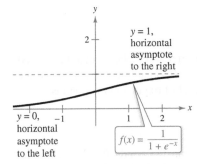

Functions that are not rational may have different right and left horizontal asymptotes.
Figure 4.37

▷ **TECHNOLOGY PITFALL**   If you use a graphing utility to estimate a limit, be sure that you also confirm the estimate analytically—the pictures shown by a graphing utility can be misleading. For instance, Figure 4.38 shows one view of the graph of

$$y = \frac{2x^3 + 1000x^2 + x}{x^3 + 1000x^2 + x + 1000}.$$

From this view, one could be convinced that the graph has $y = 1$ as a horizontal asymptote. An analytical approach shows that the horizontal asymptote is actually $y = 2$. Confirm this by enlarging the viewing window on the graphing utility.

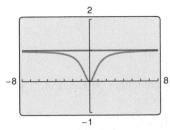

The horizontal asymptote appears to be the line $y = 1$, but it is actually the line $y = 2$.
Figure 4.38

In Section 2.4, Example 7(c), you saw how the Squeeze Theorem can be used to evaluate a limit involving a trigonometric function. This theorem is also valid for limits at infinity.

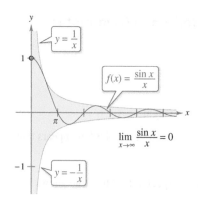

$y = \dfrac{1}{x}$

$f(x) = \dfrac{\sin x}{x}$

$\displaystyle\lim_{x\to\infty}\frac{\sin x}{x} = 0$

$y = -\dfrac{1}{x}$

As x increases without bound, $f(x)$ approaches 0.
Figure 4.39

EXAMPLE 5   Limits Involving Trigonometric Functions

Find each limit.

a. $\displaystyle\lim_{x\to\infty}\sin x$ **b.** $\displaystyle\lim_{x\to\infty}\frac{\sin x}{x}$

Solution

a. As x approaches infinity, the sine function oscillates between 1 and -1. So, this limit does not exist.

b. Because $-1 \le \sin x \le 1$, it follows that for $x > 0$,

$$-\frac{1}{x} \le \frac{\sin x}{x} \le \frac{1}{x}$$

where

$$\lim_{x\to\infty}\left(-\frac{1}{x}\right) = 0 \quad \text{and} \quad \lim_{x\to\infty}\frac{1}{x} = 0.$$

So, by the Squeeze Theorem, you can obtain

$$\lim_{x\to\infty}\frac{\sin x}{x} = 0$$

as shown in Figure 4.39.

EXAMPLE 6   Oxygen Level in a Pond

Let $f(t)$ measure the level of oxygen in a pond, where $f(t) = 1$ is the normal (unpolluted) level and the time t is measured in weeks. When $t = 0$, organic waste is dumped into the pond, and as the waste material oxidizes, the level of oxygen in the pond is

$$f(t) = \frac{t^2 - t + 1}{t^2 + 1}.$$

What percent of the normal level of oxygen exists in the pond after 1 week? After 2 weeks? After 10 weeks? What is the limit as t approaches infinity?

Solution   When $t = 1, 2,$ and 10, the levels of oxygen are as shown.

$$f(1) = \frac{1^2 - 1 + 1}{1^2 + 1} = \frac{1}{2} = 50\% \qquad \text{1 week}$$

$$f(2) = \frac{2^2 - 2 + 1}{2^2 + 1} = \frac{3}{5} = 60\% \qquad \text{2 weeks}$$

$$f(10) = \frac{10^2 - 10 + 1}{10^2 + 1} = \frac{91}{101} \approx 90.1\% \qquad \text{10 weeks}$$

To find the limit as t approaches infinity, you can use the guidelines on page 238, or you can divide the numerator and the denominator by t^2 to obtain

$$\lim_{t\to\infty}\frac{t^2 - t + 1}{t^2 + 1} = \lim_{t\to\infty}\frac{1 - (1/t) + (1/t^2)}{1 + (1/t^2)} = \frac{1 - 0 + 0}{1 + 0} = 1 = 100\%.$$

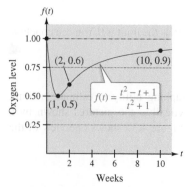

$f(t) = \dfrac{t^2 - t + 1}{t^2 + 1}$

$(2, 0.6)$ $(10, 0.9)$

$(1, 0.5)$

Weeks

The level of oxygen in a pond approaches the normal level of 1 as t approaches ∞.
Figure 4.40

See Figure 4.40.

Infinite Limits at Infinity

Many functions do not approach a finite limit as x increases (or decreases) without bound. For instance, no polynomial function has a finite limit at infinity. The next definition is used to describe the behavior of polynomial and other functions at infinity.

$\triangleright$ **REMARK** Determining whether a function has an infinite limit at infinity is useful in analyzing the "end behavior" of its graph. You will see examples of this in Section 4.6 on curve sketching.

Definition of Infinite Limits at Infinity

Let f be a function defined on the interval (a, ∞).

1. The statement $\lim\limits_{x \to \infty} f(x) = \infty$ means that for each positive number M, there is a corresponding number $N > 0$ such that $f(x) > M$ whenever $x > N$.
2. The statement $\lim\limits_{x \to \infty} f(x) = -\infty$ means that for each negative number M, there is a corresponding number $N > 0$ such that $f(x) < M$ whenever $x > N$.

Similar definitions can be given for the statements

$$\lim_{x \to -\infty} f(x) = \infty \quad \text{and} \quad \lim_{x \to -\infty} f(x) = -\infty.$$

EXAMPLE 7   **Finding Infinite Limits at Infinity**

Find each limit.

a. $\lim\limits_{x \to \infty} x^3$ **b.** $\lim\limits_{x \to -\infty} x^3$

Solution

a. As x increases without bound, x^3 also increases without bound. So, you can write

$$\lim_{x \to \infty} x^3 = \infty.$$

b. As x decreases without bound, x^3 also decreases without bound. So, you can write

$$\lim_{x \to -\infty} x^3 = -\infty.$$

The graph of $f(x) = x^3$ in Figure 4.41 illustrates these two results. These results agree with the Leading Coefficient Test for polynomial functions as described in Section 1.3.

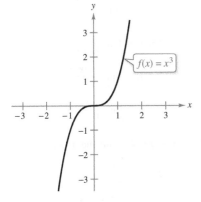

Figure 4.41

EXAMPLE 8   **Finding Infinite Limits at Infinity**

Find each limit.

a. $\lim\limits_{x \to \infty} \dfrac{2x^2 - 4x}{x + 1}$ **b.** $\lim\limits_{x \to -\infty} \dfrac{2x^2 - 4x}{x + 1}$

Solution   One way to evaluate each of these limits is to use long division to rewrite the improper rational function as the sum of a polynomial and a rational function.

a. $\lim\limits_{x \to \infty} \dfrac{2x^2 - 4x}{x + 1} = \lim\limits_{x \to \infty} \left(2x - 6 + \dfrac{6}{x + 1} \right) = \infty$

b. $\lim\limits_{x \to -\infty} \dfrac{2x^2 - 4x}{x + 1} = \lim\limits_{x \to -\infty} \left(2x - 6 + \dfrac{6}{x + 1} \right) = -\infty$

The statements above can be interpreted as saying that as x approaches $\pm\infty$, the function $f(x) = (2x^2 - 4x)/(x + 1)$ behaves like the function $g(x) = 2x - 6$. In Section 4.6, you will see that this is graphically described by saying that the line $y = 2x - 6$ is a *slant asymptote* of the graph of f, as shown in Figure 4.42.

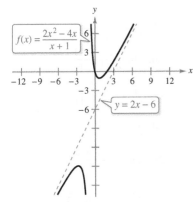

Figure 4.42

4.5 Exercises

See **CalcChat.com** for tutorial help and worked-out solutions to odd-numbered exercises.

Matching In Exercises 1–6, match the function with one of the graphs [(a), (b), (c), (d), (e), or (f)] using horizontal asymptotes as an aid.

(a)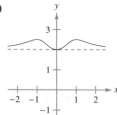

(b)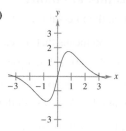

(c)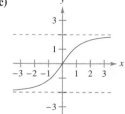

(d)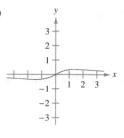

(e)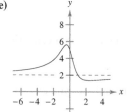

(f)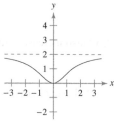

1. $f(x) = \dfrac{2x^2}{x^2 + 2}$

2. $f(x) = \dfrac{2x}{\sqrt{x^2 + 2}}$

3. $f(x) = \dfrac{x}{x^2 + 2}$

4. $f(x) = 2 + \dfrac{x^2}{x^4 + 1}$

5. $f(x) = \dfrac{4 \sin x}{x^2 + 1}$

6. $f(x) = \dfrac{2x^2 - 3x + 5}{x^2 + 1}$

Numerical and Graphical Analysis In Exercises 7–12, use a graphing utility to complete the table and estimate the limit as x approaches infinity. Then use a graphing utility to graph the function and estimate the limit graphically.

x	10^0	10^1	10^2	10^3	10^4	10^5	10^6
$f(x)$							

7. $f(x) = \dfrac{4x + 3}{2x - 1}$

8. $f(x) = \dfrac{2x^2}{x + 1}$

9. $f(x) = \dfrac{-6x}{\sqrt{4x^2 + 5}}$

10. $f(x) = \dfrac{10}{\sqrt{2x^2 - 1}}$

11. $f(x) = 5 - \dfrac{1}{x^2 + 1}$

12. $f(x) = 4 + \dfrac{3}{x^2 + 2}$

Finding Limits at Infinity In Exercises 13 and 14, find $\lim\limits_{x \to \infty} h(x)$, if possible.

13. $f(x) = 5x^3 - 3x^2 + 10x$

(a) $h(x) = \dfrac{f(x)}{x^2}$

(b) $h(x) = \dfrac{f(x)}{x^3}$

(c) $h(x) = \dfrac{f(x)}{x^4}$

14. $f(x) = -4x^2 + 2x - 5$

(a) $h(x) = \dfrac{f(x)}{x}$

(b) $h(x) = \dfrac{f(x)}{x^2}$

(c) $h(x) = \dfrac{f(x)}{x^3}$

Finding Limits at Infinity In Exercises 15–18, find each limit, if possible.

15. (a) $\lim\limits_{x \to \infty} \dfrac{x^2 + 2}{x^3 - 1}$

(b) $\lim\limits_{x \to \infty} \dfrac{x^2 + 2}{x^2 - 1}$

(c) $\lim\limits_{x \to \infty} \dfrac{x^2 + 2}{x - 1}$

16. (a) $\lim\limits_{x \to \infty} \dfrac{3 - 2x}{3x^3 - 1}$

(b) $\lim\limits_{x \to \infty} \dfrac{3 - 2x}{3x - 1}$

(c) $\lim\limits_{x \to \infty} \dfrac{3 - 2x^2}{3x - 1}$

17. (a) $\lim\limits_{x \to \infty} \dfrac{5 - 2x^{3/2}}{3x^2 - 4}$

(b) $\lim\limits_{x \to \infty} \dfrac{5 - 2x^{3/2}}{3x^{3/2} - 4}$

(c) $\lim\limits_{x \to \infty} \dfrac{5 - 2x^{3/2}}{3x - 4}$

18. (a) $\lim\limits_{x \to \infty} \dfrac{5x^{3/2}}{4x^2 + 1}$

(b) $\lim\limits_{x \to \infty} \dfrac{5x^{3/2}}{4x^{3/2} + 1}$

(c) $\lim\limits_{x \to \infty} \dfrac{5x^{3/2}}{4\sqrt{x} + 1}$

Finding a Limit In Exercises 19–42, find the limit.

19. $\lim\limits_{x \to \infty} \left(4 + \dfrac{3}{x} \right)$

20. $\lim\limits_{x \to -\infty} \left(\dfrac{5}{x} - \dfrac{x}{3} \right)$

21. $\lim\limits_{x \to \infty} \dfrac{2x - 1}{3x + 2}$

22. $\lim\limits_{x \to -\infty} \dfrac{4x^2 + 5}{x^2 + 3}$

23. $\lim\limits_{x \to \infty} \dfrac{x}{x^2 - 1}$

24. $\lim\limits_{x \to \infty} \dfrac{5x^3 + 1}{10x^3 - 3x^2 + 7}$

25. $\lim\limits_{x \to -\infty} \dfrac{x}{\sqrt{x^2 - x}}$

26. $\lim\limits_{x \to -\infty} \dfrac{x}{\sqrt{x^2 + 1}}$

27. $\lim\limits_{x \to -\infty} \dfrac{2x + 1}{\sqrt{x^2 - x}}$

28. $\lim\limits_{x \to \infty} \dfrac{5x^2 + 2}{\sqrt{x^2 + 3}}$

29. $\lim\limits_{x \to \infty} \dfrac{\sqrt{x^2 - 1}}{2x - 1}$

30. $\lim\limits_{x \to -\infty} \dfrac{\sqrt{x^4 - 1}}{x^3 - 1}$

31. $\lim\limits_{x \to \infty} \dfrac{x + 1}{(x^2 + 1)^{1/3}}$

32. $\lim\limits_{x \to -\infty} \dfrac{2x}{(x^6 - 1)^{1/3}}$

33. $\lim\limits_{x \to \infty} \dfrac{1}{2x + \sin x}$

34. $\lim\limits_{x \to \infty} \cos \dfrac{1}{x}$

35. $\lim\limits_{x \to \infty} \dfrac{\sin 2x}{x}$

36. $\lim\limits_{x \to \infty} \dfrac{x - \cos x}{x}$

37. $\lim\limits_{x \to \infty} (2 - 5e^{-x})$

38. $\lim\limits_{x \to \infty} \dfrac{8}{4 - 10^{-x/2}}$

39. $\lim\limits_{x \to \infty} \log_{10}(1 + 10^{-x})$

40. $\lim\limits_{x \to \infty} \left[\dfrac{5}{2} + \ln\left(\dfrac{x^2 + 1}{x^2} \right) \right]$

41. $\lim\limits_{t \to \infty} (8t^{-1} - \arctan t)$

42. $\lim\limits_{u \to \infty} \operatorname{arcsec}(u + 1)$

Horizontal Asymptotes In Exercises 43–46, use a graphing utility to graph the function and identify any horizontal asymptotes.

43. $f(x) = \dfrac{|x|}{x+1}$

44. $f(x) = \dfrac{|3x+2|}{x-2}$

45. $f(x) = \dfrac{3x}{\sqrt{x^2+2}}$

46. $f(x) = \dfrac{\sqrt{9x^2-2}}{2x+1}$

Finding a Limit In Exercises 47 and 48, find the limit. (*Hint:* Let $x = 1/t$ and find the limit as $t \to 0^+$.)

47. $\displaystyle\lim_{x\to\infty} x \sin \dfrac{1}{x}$

48. $\displaystyle\lim_{x\to\infty} x \tan \dfrac{1}{x}$

Finding a Limit In Exercises 49–52, find the limit. (*Hint:* Treat the expression as a fraction whose denominator is 1, and rationalize the numerator.) Use a graphing utility to verify your result.

49. $\displaystyle\lim_{x\to-\infty} \left(x + \sqrt{x^2+3}\right)$

50. $\displaystyle\lim_{x\to\infty} \left(x - \sqrt{x^2+x}\right)$

51. $\displaystyle\lim_{x\to-\infty} \left(3x + \sqrt{9x^2-x}\right)$

52. $\displaystyle\lim_{x\to\infty} \left(4x - \sqrt{16x^2-x}\right)$

Numerical, Graphical, and Analytic Analysis In Exercises 53–56, use a graphing utility to complete the table and estimate the limit as x approaches infinity. Then use a graphing utility to graph the function and estimate the limit. Finally, find the limit analytically and compare your results with the estimates.

x	10^0	10^1	10^2	10^3	10^4	10^5	10^6
$f(x)$							

53. $f(x) = x - \sqrt{x(x-1)}$

54. $f(x) = x^2 - x\sqrt{x(x-1)}$

55. $f(x) = x \sin \dfrac{1}{2x}$

56. $f(x) = \dfrac{x+1}{x\sqrt{x}}$

WRITING ABOUT CONCEPTS

57. **Writing** Describe in your own words what is meant by the statements (a) $\displaystyle\lim_{x\to\infty} f(x) = 4$ and (b) $\displaystyle\lim_{x\to-\infty} f(x) = 2$.

58. **Writing** In your own words, state the guidelines for finding the limit of a rational function. Give examples.

59. **Sketching a Graph** Sketch a graph of a differentiable function f that satisfies the following conditions and has $x = 2$ as its only critical number.

$f'(x) < 0$ for $x < 2$

$f'(x) > 0$ for $x > 2$

$\displaystyle\lim_{x\to-\infty} f(x) = 6$

$\displaystyle\lim_{x\to\infty} f(x) = 6$

60. **Points of Inflection** Is it possible to sketch a graph of a function that satisfies the conditions of Exercise 59 and has *no* points of inflection? Explain.

WRITING ABOUT CONCEPTS (continued)

61. **Writing** Consider the function $f(x) = \dfrac{2}{1 + e^{1/x}}$.

(a) Use a graphing utility to graph f.

(b) Write a short paragraph explaining why the graph has a horizontal asymptote at $y = 1$ and why the function has a nonremovable discontinuity at $x = 0$.

62. **A Function and Its Derivative** The graph of a function f is shown below. To print an enlarged copy of the graph, go to *MathGraphs.com*.

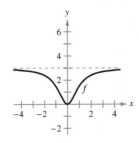

(a) Sketch f'.

(b) Use the graphs to estimate $\displaystyle\lim_{x\to\infty} f(x)$ and $\displaystyle\lim_{x\to\infty} f'(x)$.

(c) Explain the answers you gave in part (b).

Sketching a Graph In Exercises 63–78, sketch the graph of the equation using extrema, intercepts, symmetry, and asymptotes. Then use a graphing utility to verify your result.

63. $y = \dfrac{x}{1-x}$

64. $y = \dfrac{x-4}{x-3}$

65. $y = \dfrac{x+1}{x^2-4}$

66. $y = \dfrac{2x}{9-x^2}$

67. $y = \dfrac{x^2}{x^2+16}$

68. $y = \dfrac{2x^2}{x^2-4}$

69. $xy^2 = 9$

70. $x^2y = 9$

71. $y = \dfrac{3x}{x-1}$

72. $y = \dfrac{3x}{1-x^2}$

73. $y = 2 - \dfrac{3}{x^2}$

74. $y = 1 - \dfrac{1}{x}$

75. $y = 3 + \dfrac{2}{x}$

76. $y = \dfrac{4}{x^2} + 1$

77. $y = \dfrac{x^3}{\sqrt{x^2-4}}$

78. $y = \dfrac{x}{\sqrt{x^2-4}}$

Analyzing a Graph Using Technology In Exercises 79–88, use a computer algebra system to analyze the graph of the function. Label any extrema and/or asymptotes that exist.

79. $f(x) = 9 - \dfrac{5}{x^2}$

80. $f(x) = \dfrac{1}{x^2-x-2}$

81. $f(x) = \dfrac{x-2}{x^2-4x+3}$

82. $f(x) = \dfrac{x+1}{x^2+x+1}$

83. $f(x) = \dfrac{3x}{\sqrt{4x^2+1}}$

84. $g(x) = \dfrac{2x}{\sqrt{3x^2+1}}$

85. $g(x) = \sin\left(\dfrac{x}{x-2}\right), \quad x > 3$ **86.** $f(x) = \dfrac{2\sin 2x}{x}$

87. $f(x) = 2 + (x^2 - 3)e^{-x}$ **88.** $f(x) = \dfrac{10\ln x}{x^2\sqrt{x}}$

Comparing Functions **In Exercises 89 and 90, (a) use a graphing utility to graph f and g in the same viewing window, (b) verify algebraically that f and g represent the same function, and (c) zoom out sufficiently far so that the graph appears as a line. What equation does this line appear to have? (Note that the points at which the function is not continuous are not readily seen when you zoom out.)**

89. $f(x) = \dfrac{x^3 - 3x^2 + 2}{x(x-3)}$

$g(x) = x + \dfrac{2}{x(x-3)}$

90. $f(x) = -\dfrac{x^3 - 2x^2 + 2}{2x^2}$

$g(x) = -\dfrac{1}{2}x + 1 - \dfrac{1}{x^2}$

• • 91. Engine Efficiency • • • • • • • • • • • • • •

The efficiency of an internal combustion engine is

Efficiency (%) $= 100\left[1 - \dfrac{1}{(v_1/v_2)^c}\right]$

where v_1/v_2 is the ratio of the uncompressed gas to the compressed gas and c is a positive constant dependent on the engine design. Find the limit of the efficiency as the compression ratio approaches infinity.

92. Average Cost A business has a cost of $C = 0.5x + 500$ for producing x units. The average cost per unit is

$\overline{C} = \dfrac{C}{x}.$

Find the limit of $\overline{C}$ as x approaches infinity.

93. Physics Newton's First Law of Motion and Einstein's Special Theory of Relativity differ concerning a particle's behavior as its velocity approaches the speed of light c. In the graph, functions N and E represent the velocity v, with respect to time t, of a particle accelerated by a constant force as predicted by Newton and Einstein, respectively. Write limit statements that describe these two theories.

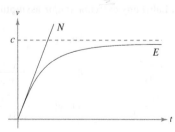

94. **HOW DO YOU SEE IT?** The graph shows the temperature T, in degrees Fahrenheit, of molten glass t seconds after it is removed from a kiln.

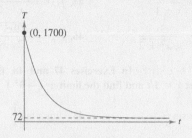

(a) Find $\lim\limits_{t\to 0^+} T$. What does this limit represent?

(b) Find $\lim\limits_{t\to\infty} T$. What does this limit represent?

(c) Will the temperature of the glass ever actually reach room temperature? Why?

95. Learning Theory In a group project in learning theory, a mathematical model for the proportion P of correct responses after n trials was found to be

$P = \dfrac{0.83}{1 + e^{-0.2n}}.$

(a) Find the limiting proportion of correct responses as n approaches infinity.

(b) Find the rates at which P is changing after $n = 3$ trials and $n = 10$ trials.

96. Modeling Data A heat probe is attached to the heat exchanger of a heating system. The temperature T (in degrees Celsius) is recorded t seconds after the furnace is started. The results for the first 2 minutes are recorded in the table.

t	0	15	30	45	60
T	25.2°	36.9°	45.5°	51.4°	56.0°

t	75	90	105	120
T	59.6°	62.0°	64.0°	65.2°

(a) Use the regression capabilities of a graphing utility to find a model of the form $T_1 = at^2 + bt + c$ for the data.

(b) Use a graphing utility to graph T_1.

(c) A rational model for the data is

$T_2 = \dfrac{1451 + 86t}{58 + t}.$

Use a graphing utility to graph T_2.

(d) Find $T_1(0)$ and $T_2(0)$.

(e) Find $\lim\limits_{t\to\infty} T_2$.

(f) Interpret the result in part (e) in the context of the problem. Is it possible to do this type of analysis using T_1? Explain.

97. Using the Definition of Limits at Infinity The graph of

$$f(x) = \frac{2x^2}{x^2 + 2}$$

is shown.

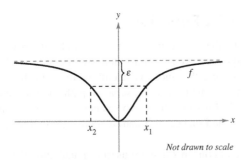

Not drawn to scale

(a) Find $L = \lim\limits_{x \to \infty} f(x)$.

(b) Determine x_1 and x_2 in terms of ε.

(c) Determine M, where $M > 0$, such that $|f(x) - L| < \varepsilon$ for $x > M$.

(d) Determine N, where $N < 0$, such that $|f(x) - L| < \varepsilon$ for $x < N$.

98. Using the Definition of Limits at Infinity The graph of

$$f(x) = \frac{6x}{\sqrt{x^2 + 2}}$$

is shown.

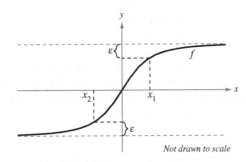

Not drawn to scale

(a) Find $L = \lim\limits_{x \to \infty} f(x)$ and $K = \lim\limits_{x \to -\infty} f(x)$.

(b) Determine x_1 and x_2 in terms of ε.

(c) Determine M, where $M > 0$, such that $|f(x) - L| < \varepsilon$ for $x > M$.

(d) Determine N, where $N < 0$, such that $|f(x) - K| < \varepsilon$ for $x < N$.

99. Using the Definition of Limits at Infinity Consider

$$\lim_{x \to \infty} \frac{3x}{\sqrt{x^2 + 3}}.$$

(a) Use the definition of limits at infinity to find values of M that correspond to $\varepsilon = 0.5$.

(b) Use the definition of limits at infinity to find values of M that correspond to $\varepsilon = 0.1$.

100. Using the Definition of Limits at Infinity Consider

$$\lim_{x \to -\infty} \frac{3x}{\sqrt{x^2 + 3}}.$$

(a) Use the definition of limits at infinity to find values of N that correspond to $\varepsilon = 0.5$.

(b) Use the definition of limits at infinity to find values of N that correspond to $\varepsilon = 0.1$.

Proof In Exercises 101–104, use the definition of limits at infinity to prove the limit.

101. $\lim\limits_{x \to \infty} \dfrac{1}{x^2} = 0$

102. $\lim\limits_{x \to \infty} \dfrac{2}{\sqrt{x}} = 0$

103. $\lim\limits_{x \to -\infty} \dfrac{1}{x^3} = 0$

104. $\lim\limits_{x \to -\infty} \dfrac{1}{x - 2} = 0$

105. Distance A line with slope m passes through the point $(0, 4)$.

(a) Write the shortest distance d between the line and the point $(3, 1)$ as a function of m.

(b) Use a graphing utility to graph the equation in part (a).

(c) Find $\lim\limits_{m \to \infty} d(m)$ and $\lim\limits_{m \to -\infty} d(m)$. Interpret the results geometrically.

106. Distance A line with slope m passes through the point $(0, -2)$.

(a) Write the shortest distance d between the line and the point $(4, 2)$ as a function of m.

(b) Use a graphing utility to graph the equation in part (a).

(c) Find $\lim\limits_{m \to \infty} d(m)$ and $\lim\limits_{m \to -\infty} d(m)$. Interpret the results geometrically.

107. Proof Prove that if

$$p(x) = a_n x^n + \cdots + a_1 x + a_0$$

and

$$q(x) = b_m x^m + \cdots + b_1 x + b_0$$

where $a_n \neq 0$ and $b_m \neq 0$, then

$$\lim_{x \to \infty} \frac{p(x)}{q(x)} = \begin{cases} 0, & n < m \\ \dfrac{a_n}{b_m}, & n = m. \\ \pm\infty, & n > m \end{cases}$$

108. Proof Use the definition of infinite limits at infinity to prove that $\lim\limits_{x \to \infty} x^3 = \infty$.

True or False? In Exercises 109 and 110, determine whether the statement is true or false. If it is false, explain why or give an example that shows it is false.

109. If $f'(x) > 0$ for all real numbers x, then f increases without bound.

110. If $f''(x) < 0$ for all real numbers x, then f decreases without bound.

4.6 A Summary of Curve Sketching

■ Analyze and sketch the graph of a function.

Analyzing the Graph of a Function

It would be difficult to overstate the importance of using graphs in mathematics. Descartes's introduction of analytic geometry contributed significantly to the rapid advances in calculus that began during the mid-seventeenth century. In the words of Lagrange, "As long as algebra and geometry traveled separate paths their advance was slow and their applications limited. But when these two sciences joined company, they drew from each other fresh vitality and thenceforth marched on at a rapid pace toward perfection."

So far, you have studied several concepts that are useful in analyzing the graph of a function.

• x-intercepts and y-intercepts	(Section 1.1)
• Symmetry	(Section 1.1)
• Domain and range	(Section 1.3)
• Continuity	(Section 2.4)
• Vertical asymptotes	(Section 2.5)
• Differentiability	(Section 3.1)
• Relative extrema	(Section 4.1)
• Concavity	(Section 4.4)
• Points of inflection	(Section 4.4)
• Horizontal asymptotes	(Section 4.5)
• Infinite limits at infinity	(Section 4.5)

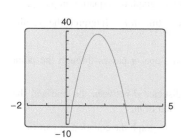

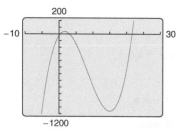

Different viewing windows for the graph of $f(x) = x^3 - 25x^2 + 74x - 20$
Figure 4.43

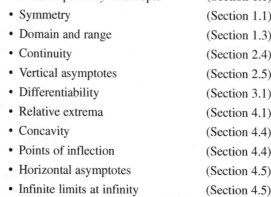

When you are sketching the graph of a function, either by hand or with a graphing utility, remember that normally you cannot show the *entire* graph. The decision as to which part of the graph you choose to show is often crucial. For instance, which of the viewing windows in Figure 4.43 better represents the graph of

$$f(x) = x^3 - 25x^2 + 74x - 20?$$

By seeing both views, it is clear that the second viewing window gives a more complete representation of the graph. But would a third viewing window reveal other interesting portions of the graph? To answer this, you need to use calculus to interpret the first and second derivatives. Here are some guidelines for determining a good viewing window for the graph of a function.

····▷

GUIDELINES FOR ANALYZING THE GRAPH OF A FUNCTION

1. Determine the domain and range of the function.

2. Determine the intercepts, asymptotes, and symmetry of the graph.

3. Locate the x-values for which $f'(x)$ and $f''(x)$ either are zero or do not exist. Use the results to determine relative extrema and points of inflection.

······**REMARK** In these guidelines, note the importance of *algebra* (as well as calculus) for solving the equations

$$f(x) = 0, \quad f'(x) = 0, \quad \text{and} \quad f''(x) = 0.$$

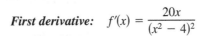
EXAMPLE 1   Sketching the Graph of a Rational Function

Analyze and sketch the graph of

$$f(x) = \frac{2(x^2 - 9)}{x^2 - 4}.$$

Solution

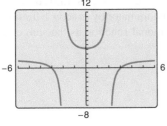

$$f(x) = \frac{2(x^2 - 9)}{x^2 - 4}$$

Vertical asymptote: $x = -2$

Vertical asymptote: $x = 2$

Horizontal asymptote: $y = 2$

Relative minimum $\left(0, \frac{9}{2}\right)$

$(-3, 0)$ $(3, 0)$

Using calculus, you can be certain that you have determined all characteristics of the graph of f.
Figure 4.44

First derivative:	$f'(x) = \dfrac{20x}{(x^2 - 4)^2}$
Second derivative:	$f''(x) = \dfrac{-20(3x^2 + 4)}{(x^2 - 4)^3}$
x-intercepts:	$(-3, 0), (3, 0)$
y-intercept:	$\left(0, \frac{9}{2}\right)$
Vertical asymptotes:	$x = -2, x = 2$
Horizontal asymptote:	$y = 2$
Critical number:	$x = 0$
Possible points of inflection:	None
Domain:	All real numbers except $x = \pm 2$
Symmetry:	With respect to y-axis
Test intervals:	$(-\infty, -2), (-2, 0), (0, 2), (2, \infty)$

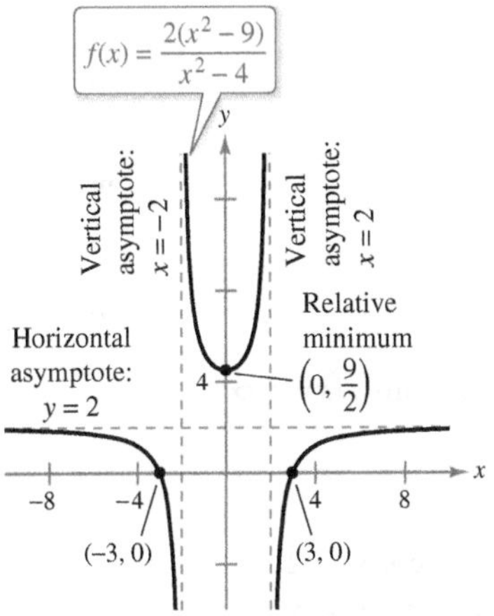

The table shows how the test intervals are used to determine several characteristics of the graph. The graph of f is shown in Figure 4.44.

	$f(x)$	$f'(x)$	$f''(x)$	Characteristic of Graph
$-\infty < x < -2$		$-$	$-$	Decreasing, concave downward
$x = -2$	Undef.	Undef.	Undef.	Vertical asymptote
$-2 < x < 0$		$-$	$+$	Decreasing, concave upward
$x = 0$	$\frac{9}{2}$	0	$+$	Relative minimum
$0 < x < 2$		$+$	$+$	Increasing, concave upward
$x = 2$	Undef.	Undef.	Undef.	Vertical asymptote
$2 < x < \infty$		$+$	$-$	Increasing, concave downward

■ **FOR FURTHER INFORMATION**
For more information on the use of technology to graph rational functions, see the article "Graphs of Rational Functions for Computer Assisted Calculus" by Stan Byrd and Terry Walters in *The College Mathematics Journal*. To view this article, go to *MathArticles.com*.

Be sure you understand all of the implications of creating a table such as that shown in Example 1. By using calculus, you can be *sure* that the graph has no relative extrema or points of inflection other than those shown in Figure 4.44.

▷ TECHNOLOGY PITFALL   Without using the type of analysis outlined in Example 1, it is easy to obtain an incomplete view of a graph's basic characteristics. For instance, Figure 4.45 shows a view of the graph of

$$g(x) = \frac{2(x^2 - 9)(x - 20)}{(x^2 - 4)(x - 21)}.$$

From this view, it appears that the graph of g is about the same as the graph of f shown in Figure 4.44. The graphs of these two functions, however, differ significantly. Try enlarging the viewing window to see the differences.

12

-6 6

-8

By not using calculus, you may overlook important characteristics of the graph of g.
Figure 4.45

EXAMPLE 2 **Sketching the Graph of a Rational Function**

Analyze and sketch the graph of $f(x) = \dfrac{x^2 - 2x + 4}{x - 2}$.

Solution

First derivative:	$f'(x) = \dfrac{x(x - 4)}{(x - 2)^2}$
Second derivative:	$f''(x) = \dfrac{8}{(x - 2)^3}$
x-intercepts:	None
y-intercept:	$(0, -2)$
Vertical asymptote:	$x = 2$
Horizontal asymptotes:	None
End behavior:	$\displaystyle\lim_{x \to -\infty} f(x) = -\infty, \ \lim_{x \to \infty} f(x) = \infty$
Critical numbers:	$x = 0, x = 4$
Possible points of inflection:	None
Domain:	All real numbers except $x = 2$
Test intervals:	$(-\infty, 0), (0, 2), (2, 4), (4, \infty)$

The analysis of the graph of f is shown in the table, and the graph is shown in Figure 4.46.

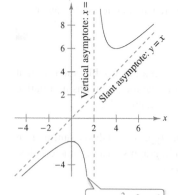

Figure 4.46

	$f(x)$	$f'(x)$	$f''(x)$	Characteristic of Graph
$-\infty < x < 0$		$+$	$-$	Increasing, concave downward
$x = 0$	-2	0	$-$	Relative maximum
$0 < x < 2$		$-$	$-$	Decreasing, concave downward
$x = 2$	Undef.	Undef.	Undef.	Vertical asymptote
$2 < x < 4$		$-$	$+$	Decreasing, concave upward
$x = 4$	6	0	$+$	Relative minimum
$4 < x < \infty$		$+$	$+$	Increasing, concave upward

Although the graph of the function in Example 2 has no horizontal asymptote, it does have a slant asymptote. The graph of a rational function (having no common factors and whose denominator is of degree 1 or greater) has a **slant asymptote** when the degree of the numerator exceeds the degree of the denominator by exactly 1. To find the slant asymptote, use long division to rewrite the rational function as the sum of a first-degree polynomial and another rational function.

$$f(x) = \frac{x^2 - 2x + 4}{x - 2} \qquad \text{Write original equation.}$$

$$= x + \frac{4}{x - 2} \qquad \text{Rewrite using long division.}$$

In Figure 4.47, note that the graph of f approaches the slant asymptote $y = x$ as x approaches $-\infty$ or ∞.

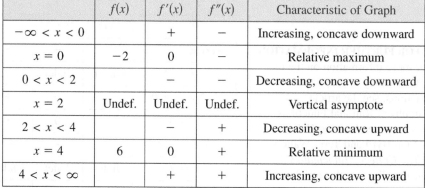

A slant asymptote
Figure 4.47

EXAMPLE 3   **Sketching the Graph of a Logistic Function**

Analyze and sketch the graph of the *logistic function* $f(x) = \dfrac{1}{1 + e^{-x}}$.

Solution

$$f'(x) = \frac{e^{-x}}{(1 + e^{-x})^2} \qquad \text{Find first derivative.}$$

$$f''(x) = -\frac{e^{-x}(e^{-x} - 1)}{(1 + e^{-x})^3} \qquad \text{Find second derivative.}$$

The graph has only one intercept, $\left(0, \frac{1}{2}\right)$. It has no vertical asymptotes, but it has two horizontal asymptotes: $y = 1$ (to the right) and $y = 0$ (to the left). The function has no critical numbers and one possible point of inflection (at $x = 0$). The domain of the function is all real numbers. The analysis of the graph of f is shown in the table, and the graph is shown in Figure 4.48.

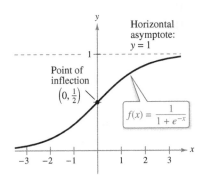

Figure 4.48

	$f(x)$	$f'(x)$	$f''(x)$	Characteristic of Graph
$-\infty < x < 0$		$+$	$+$	Increasing, concave upward
$x = 0$	$\dfrac{1}{2}$	$\dfrac{1}{4}$	0	Point of inflection
$0 < x < \infty$		$+$	$-$	Increasing, concave downward

EXAMPLE 4   **Sketching the Graph of a Radical Function**

Analyze and sketch the graph of $f(x) = 2x^{5/3} - 5x^{4/3}$.

Solution

$$f'(x) = \frac{10}{3}x^{1/3}(x^{1/3} - 2) \qquad \text{Find first derivative.}$$

$$f''(x) = \frac{20(x^{1/3} - 1)}{9x^{2/3}} \qquad \text{Find second derivative.}$$

The function has two intercepts: $(0, 0)$ and $\left(\frac{125}{8}, 0\right)$. There are no horizontal or vertical asymptotes. The function has two critical numbers ($x = 0$ and $x = 8$) and two possible points of inflection ($x = 0$ and $x = 1$). The domain is all real numbers. The analysis of the graph of f is shown in the table, and the graph is shown in Figure 4.49.

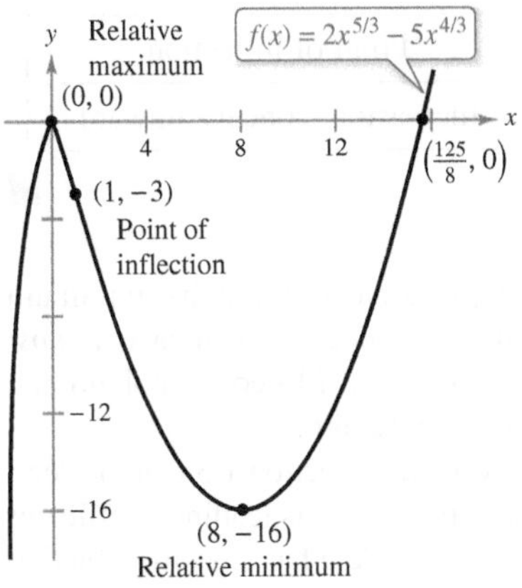

$f(x) = 2x^{5/3} - 5x^{4/3}$

Figure 4.49

	$f(x)$	$f'(x)$	$f''(x)$	Characteristic of Graph
$-\infty < x < 0$		$+$	$-$	Increasing, concave downward
$x = 0$	0	0	Undef.	Relative maximum
$0 < x < 1$		$-$	$-$	Decreasing, concave downward
$x = 1$	-3	$-$	0	Point of inflection
$1 < x < 8$		$-$	$+$	Decreasing, concave upward
$x = 8$	-16	0	$+$	Relative minimum
$8 < x < \infty$		$+$	$+$	Increasing, concave upward

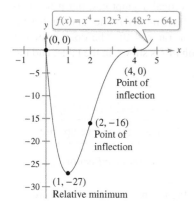

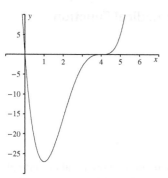

(a)

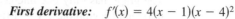

(b)

A polynomial function of even degree must have at least one relative extremum.

Figure 4.50

EXAMPLE 5 **Sketching the Graph of a Polynomial Function**

• • • • ▷ *See LarsonCalculus.com for an interactive version of this type of example.*

Analyze and sketch the graph of

$$f(x) = x^4 - 12x^3 + 48x^2 - 64x.$$

Solution Begin by factoring to obtain

$$f(x) = x^4 - 12x^3 + 48x^2 - 64x$$
$$= x(x - 4)^3.$$

Then, using the factored form of $f(x)$, you can perform the following analysis.

First derivative:	$f'(x) = 4(x - 1)(x - 4)^2$
Second derivative:	$f''(x) = 12(x - 4)(x - 2)$
x-intercepts:	$(0, 0), (4, 0)$
y-intercept:	$(0, 0)$
Vertical asymptotes:	None
Horizontal asymptotes:	None
End behavior:	$\lim\limits_{x \to -\infty} f(x) = \infty, \ \lim\limits_{x \to \infty} f(x) = \infty$
Critical numbers:	$x = 1, x = 4$
Possible points of inflection:	$x = 2, x = 4$
Domain:	All real numbers
Test intervals:	$(-\infty, 1), (1, 2), (2, 4), (4, \infty)$

The analysis of the graph of f is shown in the table, and the graph is shown in Figure 4.50(a). Using a computer algebra system such as *Maple* [see Figure 4.50(b)] can help you verify your analysis.

	$f(x)$	$f'(x)$	$f''(x)$	Characteristic of Graph
$-\infty < x < 1$		$-$	$+$	Decreasing, concave upward
$x = 1$	-27	0	$+$	Relative minimum
$1 < x < 2$		$+$	$+$	Increasing, concave upward
$x = 2$	-16	$+$	0	Point of inflection
$2 < x < 4$		$+$	$-$	Increasing, concave downward
$x = 4$	0	0	0	Point of inflection
$4 < x < \infty$		$+$	$+$	Increasing, concave upward

The fourth-degree polynomial function in Example 5 has one relative minimum and no relative maxima. In general, a polynomial function of degree n can have *at most* $n - 1$ relative extrema, and *at most* $n - 2$ points of inflection. Moreover, polynomial functions of even degree must have *at least* one relative extremum.

Remember from the Leading Coefficient Test described in Section 1.3 that the "end behavior" of the graph of a polynomial function is determined by its leading coefficient and its degree. For instance, because the polynomial in Example 5 has a positive leading coefficient, the graph rises to the right. Moreover, because the degree is even, the graph also rises to the left.

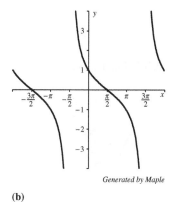

(a)

Generated by Maple

(b)

Figure 4.51

> **EXAMPLE 6**   **Sketching the Graph of a Trigonometric Function**

Analyze and sketch the graph of $f(x) = (\cos x)/(1 + \sin x)$.

Solution   Because the function has a period of 2π, you can restrict the analysis of the graph to any interval of length 2π. For convenience, choose $(-\pi/2, 3\pi/2)$.

$$\textit{First derivative:} \quad f'(x) = -\frac{1}{1 + \sin x}$$

$$\textit{Second derivative:} \quad f''(x) = \frac{\cos x}{(1 + \sin x)^2}$$

$$\textit{Period:} \quad 2\pi$$

$$\textit{x-intercept:} \quad \left(\frac{\pi}{2}, 0\right)$$

$$\textit{y-intercept:} \quad (0, 1)$$

$$\textit{Vertical asymptotes:} \quad x = -\frac{\pi}{2}, x = \frac{3\pi}{2} \qquad \text{See Remark below.}$$

$$\textit{Horizontal asymptotes:} \quad \text{None}$$

$$\textit{Critical numbers:} \quad \text{None}$$

$$\textit{Possible points of inflection:} \quad x = \frac{\pi}{2}$$

$$\textit{Domain:} \quad \text{All real numbers except } x = \frac{3 + 4n}{2}\pi$$

$$\textit{Test intervals:} \quad \left(-\frac{\pi}{2}, \frac{\pi}{2}\right), \left(\frac{\pi}{2}, \frac{3\pi}{2}\right)$$

The analysis of the graph of f on the interval $(-\pi/2, 3\pi/2)$ is shown in the table, and the graph is shown in Figure 4.51(a). Compare this with the graph generated by the computer algebra system *Maple* in Figure 4.51(b).

	$f(x)$	$f'(x)$	$f''(x)$	Characteristic of Graph
$x = -\dfrac{\pi}{2}$	Undef.	Undef.	Undef.	Vertical asymptote
$-\dfrac{\pi}{2} < x < \dfrac{\pi}{2}$		$-$	$+$	Decreasing, concave upward
$x = \dfrac{\pi}{2}$	0	$-\dfrac{1}{2}$	0	Point of inflection
$\dfrac{\pi}{2} < x < \dfrac{3\pi}{2}$		$-$	$-$	Decreasing, concave downward
$x = \dfrac{3\pi}{2}$	Undef.	Undef.	Undef.	Vertical asymptote

REMARK   By substituting $-\pi/2$ or $3\pi/2$ into the function, you obtain the form $0/0$. This is called an indeterminate form, which you will study in Section 8.7. To determine that the function has vertical asymptotes at these two values, rewrite f as

$$f(x) = \frac{\cos x}{1 + \sin x} = \frac{(\cos x)(1 - \sin x)}{(1 + \sin x)(1 - \sin x)} = \frac{(\cos x)(1 - \sin x)}{\cos^2 x} = \frac{1 - \sin x}{\cos x}.$$

In this form, it is clear that the graph of f has vertical asymptotes at $x = -\pi/2$ and $3\pi/2$.

EXAMPLE 7   **Analyzing an Inverse Trigonometric Graph**

Analyze the graph of $y = (\arctan x)^2$.

Solution   From the derivative

$$y' = 2(\arctan x)\left(\frac{1}{1 + x^2}\right)$$

$$= \frac{2 \arctan x}{1 + x^2}$$

you can see that the only critical number is $x = 0$. By the First Derivative Test, this value corresponds to a relative minimum. From the second derivative

$$y'' = \frac{(1 + x^2)\left(\dfrac{2}{1 + x^2}\right) - (2 \arctan x)(2x)}{(1 + x^2)^2}$$

$$= \frac{2(1 - 2x \arctan x)}{(1 + x^2)^2}$$

it follows that points of inflection occur when

$$2x \arctan x = 1.$$

Using Newton's Method, these points occur when $x \approx \pm 0.765$. Finally, because

$$\lim_{x \to \pm\infty} (\arctan x)^2 = \frac{\pi^2}{4}$$

it follows that the graph has a horizontal asymptote at

$$y = \frac{\pi^2}{4}.$$

The graph is shown in Figure 4.52.

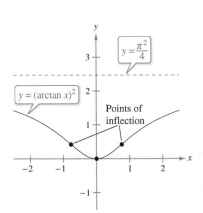

The graph of $y = (\arctan x)^2$ has a horizontal asymptote at $y = \pi^2/4$.
Figure 4.52

EXAMPLE 8   **Analyzing a Logarithmic Graph**

Analyze the graph of $f(x) = \ln(x^2 + 2x + 3)$.

Solution   Note that the domain of f is all real numbers. The graph of f has no x-intercepts, but it does have a y-intercept at $(0, \ln 3)$. From the derivative

$$f'(x) = \frac{2x + 2}{x^2 + 2x + 3}$$

you can see that the only critical number is $x = -1$. By the First Derivative Test, this value corresponds to a relative minimum at $(-1, \ln 2)$. You can use the first derivative to conclude that the graph of f is decreasing on the interval $(-\infty, -1)$ and increasing on $(-1, \infty)$. From the second derivative

$$f''(x) = \frac{(x^2 + 2x + 3)(2) - (2x + 2)(2x + 2)}{(x^2 + 2x + 3)^2}$$

$$= \frac{-2(x^2 + 2x - 1)}{(x^2 + 2x + 3)^2}$$

it follows that points of inflection occur when $x^2 + 2x - 1 = 0$. Using the Quadratic Formula, these points occur when $x = -1 \pm \sqrt{2}$. Also, the graph of f is concave downward on the intervals $\left(-\infty, -1 - \sqrt{2}\right)$ and $\left(-1 + \sqrt{2}, \infty\right)$, and concave upward on $\left(-1 - \sqrt{2}, -1 + \sqrt{2}\right)$. The graph of f is shown in Figure 4.53. ∎

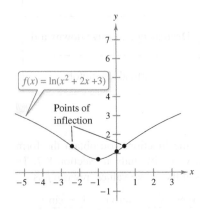

Figure 4.53

4.6 Exercises

See CalcChat.com for tutorial help and worked-out solutions to odd-numbered exercises.

Analyzing the Graph of a Function In Exercises 1–34, analyze and sketch a graph of the function. Label any intercepts, relative extrema, points of inflection, and asymptotes. Use a graphing utility to verify your results.

1. $y = \dfrac{1}{x-2} - 3$

2. $y = \dfrac{x}{x^2 + 1}$

3. $y = \dfrac{x^2}{x^2 + 3}$

4. $y = \dfrac{x^2 + 1}{x^2 - 4}$

5. $y = \dfrac{3x}{x^2 - 1}$

6. $f(x) = \dfrac{x-3}{x}$

7. $f(x) = x + \dfrac{32}{x^2}$

8. $f(x) = \dfrac{x^3}{x^2 - 9}$

9. $y = \dfrac{x^2 - 6x + 12}{x - 4}$

10. $y = \dfrac{-x^2 - 4x - 7}{x + 3}$

11. $y = x\sqrt{4 - x}$

12. $g(x) = x\sqrt{9 - x^2}$

13. $y = 3x^{2/3} - 2x$

14. $y = (x + 1)^2 - 3(x + 1)^{2/3}$

15. $y = 2 - x - x^3$

16. $y = -\frac{1}{3}(x^3 - 3x + 2)$

17. $y = 3x^4 + 4x^3$

18. $y = -2x^4 + 3x^2$

19. $y = x^5 - 5x$

20. $y = (x - 1)^5$

21. $y = |2x - 3|$

22. $y = |x^2 - 6x + 5|$

23. $f(x) = e^{3x}(2 - x)$

24. $f(x) = -2 + e^{3x}(4 - 2x)$

25. $g(t) = \dfrac{10}{1 + 4e^{-t}}$

26. $h(x) = \dfrac{8}{2 + 3e^{-x/2}}$

27. $y = (x - 1)\ln(x - 1)$

28. $y = \frac{1}{24}x^3 - \ln x$

29. $g(x) = 6\arcsin\left(\dfrac{x-2}{2}\right)^2$

30. $h(x) = 7\arctan(x + 1) - \ln(x^2 + 2x + 2)$

31. $f(x) = \dfrac{x}{3^{x-3}}$

32. $g(t) = (5 - t)5^t$

33. $g(x) = \log_4(x - x^2)$

34. $f(x) = \log_2|x^2 - 4x|$

Analyzing the Graph of a Function Using Technology In Exercises 35–40, use a computer algebra system to analyze and graph the function. Identify any relative extrema, points of inflection, and asymptotes.

35. $f(x) = \dfrac{20x}{x^2 + 1} - \dfrac{1}{x}$

36. $f(x) = x + \dfrac{4}{x^2 + 1}$

37. $f(x) = \dfrac{-2x}{\sqrt{x^2 + 7}}$

38. $f(x) = \dfrac{4x}{\sqrt{x^2 + 15}}$

39. $y = \dfrac{x}{2} + \ln\left(\dfrac{x}{x + 3}\right)$

40. $y = \dfrac{3x}{2}(1 + 4e^{-x/3})$

Sketching a Graph In Exercises 41–50, sketch a graph of the function over the given interval. Use a graphing utility to verify your graph.

Function	Interval
41. $f(x) = 2x - 4\sin x$	$0 \le x \le 2\pi$
42. $f(x) = -x + 2\cos x$	$0 \le x \le 2\pi$
43. $y = \sin x - \frac{1}{18}\sin 3x$	$0 \le x \le 2\pi$
44. $y = \cos x - \frac{1}{4}\cos 2x$	$0 \le x \le 2\pi$
45. $y = 2x - \tan x$	$-\dfrac{\pi}{2} < x < \dfrac{\pi}{2}$
46. $y = 2(x - 2) + \cot x$	$0 < x < \pi$
47. $y = 2(\csc x + \sec x)$	$0 < x < \dfrac{\pi}{2}$
48. $y = \sec^2\left(\dfrac{\pi x}{8}\right) - 2\tan\left(\dfrac{\pi x}{8}\right) - 1$	$-3 < x < 3$
49. $g(x) = x\tan x$	$-\dfrac{3\pi}{2} < x < \dfrac{3\pi}{2}$
50. $g(x) = x\cot x$	$-2\pi < x < 2\pi$

WRITING ABOUT CONCEPTS

51. Using a Derivative Let $f'(t) < 0$ for all t in the interval $(2, 8)$. Explain why $f(3) > f(5)$.

52. Using a Derivative Let $f(0) = 3$ and $2 \le f'(x) \le 4$ for all x in the interval $[-5, 5]$. Determine the greatest and least possible values of $f(2)$.

Identifying Graphs In Exercises 53 and 54, the graphs of f, f', and f'' are shown on the same set of coordinate axes. Which is which? Explain your reasoning. To print an enlarged copy of the graph, go to *MathGraphs.com*.

53.

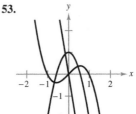

54.

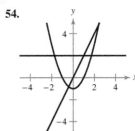

Horizontal and Vertical Asymptotes In Exercises 55–58, use a graphing utility to graph the function. Use the graph to determine whether it is possible for the graph of a function to cross its horizontal asymptote. Do you think it is possible for the graph of a function to cross its vertical asymptote? Why or why not?

55. $f(x) = \dfrac{4(x - 1)^2}{x^2 - 4x + 5}$

56. $g(x) = \dfrac{3x^4 - 5x + 3}{x^4 + 1}$

57. $h(x) = \dfrac{\sin 2x}{x}$

58. $f(x) = \dfrac{\cos 3x}{4x}$

WRITING ABOUT CONCEPTS (continued)

Examining a Function In Exercises 59 and 60, use a graphing utility to graph the function. Explain why there is no vertical asymptote when a superficial examination of the function may indicate that there should be one.

59. $h(x) = \dfrac{6 - 2x}{3 - x}$ **60.** $g(x) = \dfrac{x^2 + x - 2}{x - 1}$

Slant Asymptote In Exercises 61–64, use a graphing utility to graph the function and determine the slant asymptote of the graph. Zoom out repeatedly and describe how the graph on the display appears to change. Why does this occur?

61. $f(x) = -\dfrac{x^2 - 3x - 1}{x - 2}$

62. $g(x) = \dfrac{2x^2 - 8x - 15}{x - 5}$

63. $f(x) = \dfrac{2x^3}{x^2 + 1}$

64. $h(x) = \dfrac{-x^3 + x^2 + 4}{x^2}$

Graphical Reasoning In Exercises 65–68, use the graph of f' to sketch a graph of f and the graph of f''. To print an enlarged copy of the graph, go to MathGraphs.com.

65.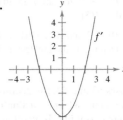

66.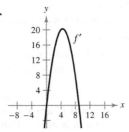

67.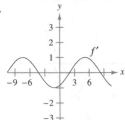

68.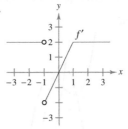

(Submitted by Bill Fox, Moberly Area Community College, Moberly, MO)

69. Graphical Reasoning Consider the function

$$f(x) = \frac{\cos^2 \pi x}{\sqrt{x^2 + 1}}, \quad 0 < x < 4.$$

(a) Use a computer algebra system to graph the function and use the graph to approximate the critical numbers visually.

(b) Use a computer algebra system to find f' and approximate the critical numbers. Are the results the same as the visual approximation in part (a)? Explain.

70. Graphical Reasoning Consider the function

$$f(x) = \tan(\sin \pi x).$$

(a) Use a graphing utility to graph the function.

(b) Identify any symmetry of the graph.

(c) Is the function periodic? If so, what is the period?

(d) Identify any extrema on $(-1, 1)$.

(e) Use a graphing utility to determine the concavity of the graph on $(0, 1)$.

Think About It In Exercises 71–74, create a function whose graph has the given characteristics. (There is more than one correct answer.)

71. Vertical asymptote: $x = 3$

Horizontal asymptote: $y = 0$

72. Vertical asymptote: $x = -5$

Horizontal asymptote: None

73. Vertical asymptote: $x = 3$

Slant asymptote: $y = 3x + 2$

74. Vertical asymptote: $x = 2$

Slant asymptote: $y = -x$

75. Conjecture Use a graphing utility to graph f and g in the same viewing window and determine which is increasing at the faster rate for "large" values of x. What can you conclude about the rate of growth of the natural logarithmic function?

(a) $f(x) = \ln x, \quad g(x) = \sqrt{x}$

(b) $f(x) = \ln x, \quad g(x) = \sqrt[4]{x}$

76. Comparing Functions Let f be a function that is positive and differentiable on the entire real number line. Let $g(x) = \ln f(x)$.

(a) If g is increasing, must f be increasing? Explain.

(b) If the graph of f is concave upward, must the graph of g be concave upward? Explain.

77. Graphical Reasoning Identify the real numbers x_0, x_1, x_2, x_3, and x_4 in the figure that satisfy each statement.

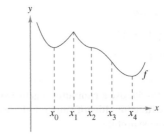

(a) $f'(x) = 0$

(b) $f''(x) = 0$

(c) $f'(x)$ does not exist.

(d) f has a relative maximum.

(e) f has a point of inflection.

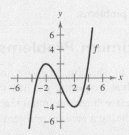

78. **HOW DO YOU SEE IT?**   The graph of f is shown in the figure.

(a) For which values of x is $f'(x)$ zero? Positive? Negative? What do these values mean?

(b) For which values of x is $f''(x)$ zero? Positive? Negative? What do these values mean?

(c) On what open interval is f' an increasing function?

(d) For which value of x is $f'(x)$ minimum? For this value of x, how does the rate of change of f compare with the rates of change of f for other values of x? Explain.

79. Investigation   Let $P(x_0, y_0)$ be an arbitrary point on the graph of f such that $f'(x_0) \neq 0$, as shown in the figure. Verify each statement.

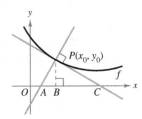

(a) The x-intercept of the tangent line is

$$\left(x_0 - \frac{f(x_0)}{f'(x_0)}, 0 \right).$$

(b) The y-intercept of the tangent line is

$$(0, f(x_0) - x_0 f'(x_0)).$$

(c) The x-intercept of the normal line is

$$(x_0 + f(x_0) f'(x_0), 0).$$

(d) The y-intercept of the normal line is

$$\left(0, y_0 + \frac{x_0}{f'(x_0)} \right).$$

(e) $|BC| = \left| \dfrac{f(x_0)}{f'(x_0)} \right|$

(f) $|PC| = \left| \dfrac{f(x_0) \sqrt{1 + [f'(x_0)]^2}}{f'(x_0)} \right|$

(g) $|AB| = |f(x_0) f'(x_0)|$

(h) $|AP| = |f(x_0)| \sqrt{1 + [f'(x_0)]^2}$

80. Investigation   Consider the function

$$f(x) = \frac{2x^n}{x^4 + 1}$$

for nonnegative integer values of n.

(a) Discuss the relationship between the value of n and the symmetry of the graph.

(b) For which values of n will the x-axis be the horizontal asymptote?

(c) For which value of n will $y = 2$ be the horizontal asymptote?

(d) What is the asymptote of the graph when $n = 5$?

(e) Use a graphing utility to graph f for the indicated values of n in the table. Use the graph to determine the number of extrema M and the number of inflection points N of the graph.

n	0	1	2	3	4	5
M						
N						

81. Graphical Reasoning   Consider the function

$$f(x) = \frac{ax}{(x - b)^2}.$$

Determine the effect on the graph of f as a and b are changed. Consider cases where a and b are both positive or both negative, and cases where a and b have opposite signs.

82. Graphical Reasoning   Consider the function

$$f(x) = \frac{1}{2}(ax)^2 - ax, \quad a \neq 0.$$

(a) Determine the changes (if any) in the intercepts, extrema, and concavity of the graph of f when a is varied.

(b) In the same viewing window, use a graphing utility to graph the function for four different values of a.

Slant Asymptotes   In Exercises 83 and 84, the graph of the function has two slant asymptotes. Identify each slant asymptote. Then graph the function and its asymptotes.

83. $y = \sqrt{4 + 16x^2}$ **84.** $y = \sqrt{x^2 + 6x}$

PUTNAM EXAM CHALLENGE

85. Let $f(x)$ be defined for $a \leq x \leq b$. Assuming appropriate properties of continuity and derivability, prove for $a < x < b$ that

$$\frac{\dfrac{f(x) - f(a)}{x - a} - \dfrac{f(b) - f(a)}{b - a}}{x - b} = \frac{1}{2} f''(\varepsilon),$$

where ε is some number between a and b.

4.7 Optimization Problems

■ Solve applied minimum and maximum problems.

Applied Minimum and Maximum Problems

One of the most common applications of calculus involves the determination of minimum and maximum values. Consider how frequently you hear or read terms such as greatest profit, least cost, least time, greatest voltage, optimum size, least size, greatest strength, and greatest distance. Before outlining a general problem-solving strategy for such problems, consider the next example.

EXAMPLE 1 Finding Maximum Volume

A manufacturer wants to design an open box having a square base and a surface area of 108 square inches, as shown in Figure 4.54. What dimensions will produce a box with maximum volume?

Solution Because the box has a square base, its volume is

$$V = x^2h. \qquad \text{Primary equation}$$

This equation is called the **primary equation** because it gives a formula for the quantity to be optimized. The surface area of the box is

$$S = (\text{area of base}) + (\text{area of four sides})$$
$$108 = x^2 + 4xh. \qquad \text{Secondary equation}$$

Because V is to be maximized, you want to write V as a function of just one variable. To do this, you can solve the equation $x^2 + 4xh = 108$ for h in terms of x to obtain $h = (108 - x^2)/(4x)$. Substituting into the primary equation produces

$$V = x^2h \qquad \text{Function of two variables}$$
$$= x^2\left(\frac{108 - x^2}{4x}\right) \qquad \text{Substitute for } h.$$
$$= 27x - \frac{x^3}{4}. \qquad \text{Function of one variable}$$

Before finding which x-value will yield a maximum value of V, you should determine the *feasible domain*. That is, what values of x make sense in this problem? You know that $V \geq 0$. You also know that x must be nonnegative and that the area of the base ($A = x^2$) is at most 108. So, the feasible domain is

$$0 \leq x \leq \sqrt{108}. \qquad \text{Feasible domain}$$

To maximize V, find the critical numbers of the volume function on the interval $\left(0, \sqrt{108}\right)$.

$$\frac{dV}{dx} = 27 - \frac{3x^2}{4} \qquad \text{Differentiate with respect to } x.$$
$$27 - \frac{3x^2}{4} = 0 \qquad \text{Set derivative equal to 0.}$$
$$3x^2 = 108 \qquad \text{Simplify.}$$
$$x = \pm 6 \qquad \text{Critical numbers}$$

So, the critical numbers are $x = \pm 6$. You do not need to consider $x = -6$ because it is outside the domain. Evaluating V at the critical number $x = 6$ and at the endpoints of the domain produces $V(0) = 0$, $V(6) = 108$, and $V\left(\sqrt{108}\right) = 0$. So, V is maximum when $x = 6$, and the dimensions of the box are 6 inches by 6 inches by 3 inches. ■

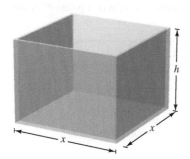

Open box with square base:
$S = x^2 + 4xh = 108$

Figure 4.54

▷ TECHNOLOGY You can verify your answer in Example 1 by using a graphing utility to graph the volume function

$$V = 27x - \frac{x^3}{4}.$$

Use a viewing window in which $0 \leq x \leq \sqrt{108} \approx 10.4$ and $0 \leq y \leq 120$, and use the *maximum* or *trace* feature to determine the maximum value of V.

In Example 1, you should realize that there are infinitely many open boxes having 108 square inches of surface area. To begin solving the problem, you might ask yourself which basic shape would seem to yield a maximum volume. Should the box be tall, squat, or nearly cubical?

You might even try calculating a few volumes, as shown in Figure 4.55, to see if you can get a better feeling for what the optimum dimensions should be. Remember that you are not ready to begin solving a problem until you have clearly identified what the problem is.

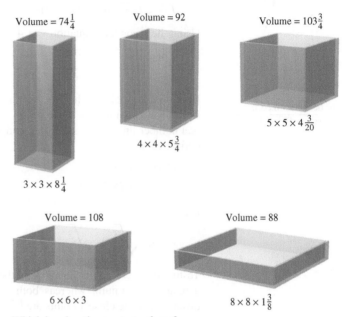

Which box has the greatest volume?
Figure 4.55

Example 1 illustrates the following guidelines for solving applied minimum and maximum problems.

GUIDELINES FOR SOLVING APPLIED MINIMUM AND MAXIMUM PROBLEMS

1. Identify all *given* quantities and all quantities *to be determined*. If possible, make a sketch.

2. Write a **primary equation** for the quantity that is to be maximized or minimized. (A review of several useful formulas from geometry is presented inside the back cover.)

3. Reduce the primary equation to one having a *single independent variable*. This may involve the use of **secondary equations** relating the independent variables of the primary equation.

4. Determine the feasible domain of the primary equation. That is, determine the values for which the stated problem makes sense.

5. Determine the desired maximum or minimum value by the calculus techniques discussed in Sections 4.1 through 4.4.

REMARK   For Step 5, recall that to determine the maximum or minimum value of a continuous function f on a closed interval, you should compare the values of f at its critical numbers with the values of f at the endpoints of the interval.

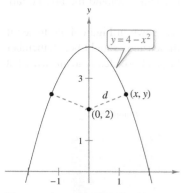

The quantity to be minimized is distance: $d = \sqrt{(x-0)^2 + (y-2)^2}$.
Figure 4.56

EXAMPLE 2 **Finding Minimum Distance**

••••▷ *See LarsonCalculus.com for an interactive version of this type of example.*

Which points on the graph of $y = 4 - x^2$ are closest to the point $(0, 2)$?

Solution Figure 4.56 shows that there are two points at a minimum distance from the point $(0, 2)$. The distance between the point $(0, 2)$ and a point (x, y) on the graph of $y = 4 - x^2$ is

$$d = \sqrt{(x-0)^2 + (y-2)^2}. \qquad \text{Primary equation}$$

Using the secondary equation $y = 4 - x^2$, you can rewrite the primary equation as

$$d = \sqrt{x^2 + (4 - x^2 - 2)^2}$$
$$= \sqrt{x^4 - 3x^2 + 4}.$$

Because d is smallest when the expression inside the radical is smallest, you need only find the critical numbers of $f(x) = x^4 - 3x^2 + 4$. Note that the domain of f is the entire real number line. So, there are no endpoints of the domain to consider. Moreover, the derivative of f

$$f'(x) = 4x^3 - 6x$$
$$= 2x(2x^2 - 3)$$

is zero when

$$x = 0, \ \sqrt{\frac{3}{2}}, \ -\sqrt{\frac{3}{2}}.$$

Testing these critical numbers using the First Derivative Test verifies that $x = 0$ yields a relative maximum, whereas both $x = \sqrt{3/2}$ and $x = -\sqrt{3/2}$ yield a minimum distance. So, the closest points are $\left(\sqrt{3/2}, 5/2\right)$ and $\left(-\sqrt{3/2}, 5/2\right)$.

EXAMPLE 3 **Finding Minimum Area**

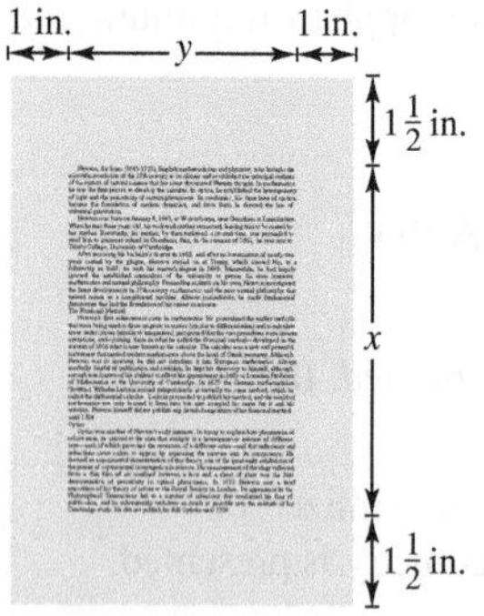

A rectangular page is to contain 24 square inches of print. The margins at the top and bottom of the page are to be $1\frac{1}{2}$ inches, and the margins on the left and right are to be 1 inch (see Figure 4.57). What should the dimensions of the page be so that the least amount of paper is used?

Solution Let A be the area to be minimized.

$$A = (x + 3)(y + 2) \qquad \text{Primary equation}$$

The printed area inside the margins is

$$24 = xy. \qquad \text{Secondary equation}$$

Solving this equation for y produces $y = 24/x$. Substitution into the primary equation produces

$$A = (x + 3)\left(\frac{24}{x} + 2\right) = 30 + 2x + \frac{72}{x}. \qquad \text{Function of one variable}$$

Because x must be positive, you are interested only in values of A for $x > 0$. To find the critical numbers, differentiate with respect to x

$$\frac{dA}{dx} = 2 - \frac{72}{x^2}$$

and note that the derivative is zero when $x^2 = 36$, or $x = \pm 6$. So, the critical numbers are $x = \pm 6$. You do not have to consider $x = -6$ because it is outside the domain. The First Derivative Test confirms that A is a minimum when $x = 6$. So, $y = \frac{24}{6} = 4$ and the dimensions of the page should be $x + 3 = 9$ inches by $y + 2 = 6$ inches.

The quantity to be minimized is area: $A = (x + 3)(y + 2)$.
Figure 4.57

EXAMPLE 4   **Finding Minimum Length**

Two posts, one 12 feet high and the other 28 feet high, stand 30 feet apart. They are to be stayed by two wires, attached to a single stake, running from ground level to the top of each post. Where should the stake be placed to use the least amount of wire?

Solution   Let W be the wire length to be minimized. Using the figure at the right, you can write

$$W = y + z. \qquad \text{Primary equation}$$

In this problem, rather than solving for y in terms of z (or vice versa), you can solve for both y and z in terms of a third variable x, as shown in the figure at the right. From the Pythagorean Theorem, you obtain

$$x^2 + 12^2 = y^2$$
$$(30 - x)^2 + 28^2 = z^2$$

which implies that

$$y = \sqrt{x^2 + 144}$$
$$z = \sqrt{x^2 - 60x + 1684}.$$

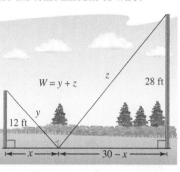

The quantity to be minimized is length. From the diagram, you can see that x varies between 0 and 30.

So, you can rewrite the primary equation as

$$\begin{aligned} W &= y + z \\ &= \sqrt{x^2 + 144} + \sqrt{x^2 - 60x + 1684}, \quad 0 \le x \le 30. \end{aligned}$$

Differentiating W with respect to x yields

$$\frac{dW}{dx} = \frac{x}{\sqrt{x^2 + 144}} + \frac{x - 30}{\sqrt{x^2 - 60x + 1684}}.$$

By letting $dW/dx = 0$, you obtain

$$\frac{x}{\sqrt{x^2 + 144}} + \frac{x - 30}{\sqrt{x^2 - 60x + 1684}} = 0$$
$$x\sqrt{x^2 - 60x + 1684} = (30 - x)\sqrt{x^2 + 144}$$
$$x^2(x^2 - 60x + 1684) = (30 - x)^2(x^2 + 144)$$
$$x^4 - 60x^3 + 1684x^2 = x^4 - 60x^3 + 1044x^2 - 8640x + 129{,}600$$
$$640x^2 + 8640x - 129{,}600 = 0$$
$$320(x - 9)(2x + 45) = 0$$
$$x = 9, \; -22.5.$$

Because $x = -22.5$ is not in the domain and

$$W(0) \approx 53.04, \quad W(9) = 50, \quad \text{and} \quad W(30) \approx 60.31$$

you can conclude that the wire should be staked at 9 feet from the 12-foot pole.   ■

▷ **TECHNOLOGY**   From Example 4, you can see that applied optimization problems can involve a lot of algebra. If you have access to a graphing utility, you can confirm that $x = 9$ yields a minimum value of W by graphing

$$W = \sqrt{x^2 + 144} + \sqrt{x^2 - 60x + 1684}$$

as shown in Figure 4.58.

60
45
0   30
Minimum
X=9   Y=50

You can confirm the minimum value of W with a graphing utility.
Figure 4.58

In each of the first four examples, the extreme value occurred at a critical number. Although this happens often, remember that an extreme value can also occur at an endpoint of an interval, as shown in Example 5.

EXAMPLE 5   An Endpoint Maximum

Four feet of wire is to be used to form a square and a circle. How much of the wire should be used for the square and how much should be used for the circle to enclose the maximum total area?

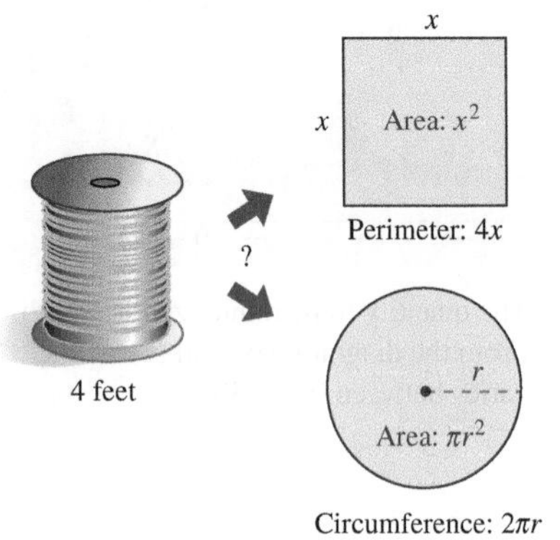

Solution   The total area (see Figure 4.59) is

$$A = (\text{area of square}) + (\text{area of circle})$$

$$A = x^2 + \pi r^2. \qquad \text{Primary equation}$$

Because the total length of wire is 4 feet, you obtain

$$4 = (\text{perimeter of square}) + (\text{circumference of circle})$$

$$4 = 4x + 2\pi r.$$

So, $r = 2(1 - x)/\pi$, and by substituting into the primary equation you have

$$A = x^2 + \pi \left[\frac{2(1 - x)}{\pi} \right]^2$$

$$= x^2 + \frac{4(1 - x)^2}{\pi}$$

$$= \frac{1}{\pi}[(\pi + 4)x^2 - 8x + 4].$$

The feasible domain is $0 \le x \le 1$, restricted by the square's perimeter. Because

$$\frac{dA}{dx} = \frac{2(\pi + 4)x - 8}{\pi}$$

the only critical number in $(0, 1)$ is $x = 4/(\pi + 4) \approx 0.56$. So, using

$$A(0) \approx 1.273, \quad A(0.56) \approx 0.56, \quad \text{and} \quad A(1) = 1$$

you can conclude that the maximum area occurs when $x = 0$. That is, *all* the wire is used for the circle.   ∎

The quantity to be maximized is area:
$A = x^2 + \pi r^2$.

Figure 4.59

Exploration

What would the answer be if Example 5 asked for the dimensions needed to enclose the *minimum* total area?

Before doing the section exercises, review the primary equations developed in the first five examples. As applications go, these five examples are fairly simple, and yet the resulting primary equations are quite complicated.

$$V = 27x - \frac{x^3}{4} \qquad \text{Example 1}$$

$$d = \sqrt{x^4 - 3x^2 + 4} \qquad \text{Example 2}$$

$$A = 30 + 2x + \frac{72}{x} \qquad \text{Example 3}$$

$$W = \sqrt{x^2 + 144} + \sqrt{x^2 - 60x + 1684} \qquad \text{Example 4}$$

$$A = \frac{1}{\pi}[(\pi + 4)x^2 - 8x + 4] \qquad \text{Example 5}$$

You must expect that real-life applications often involve equations that are *at least as complicated* as these five. Remember that one of the main goals of this course is to learn to use calculus to analyze equations that initially seem formidable.

EXAMPLE 6 **Maximizing an Angle**

⋮ ⋯▷ *See LarsonCalculus.com for an interactive version of this type of example.*

A photographer is taking a picture of a 4-foot painting hung in an art gallery. The camera lens is 1 foot below the lower edge of the painting, as shown in Figure 4.60. How far should the camera be from the painting to maximize the angle subtended by the camera lens?

Solution In Figure 4.60, let β be the angle to be maximized.

$$\beta = \theta - \alpha \qquad \text{Primary equation}$$

From Figure 4.60, you can see that $\cot \theta = \dfrac{x}{5}$ and $\cot \alpha = \dfrac{x}{1}$. Therefore, $\theta = \text{arccot}\,\dfrac{x}{5}$ and $\alpha = \text{arccot}\,x$. So,

$$\beta = \text{arccot}\,\frac{x}{5} - \text{arccot}\,x.$$

Differentiating β with respect to x produces

$$\frac{d\beta}{dx} = \frac{-1/5}{1 + (x^2/25)} - \frac{-1}{1 + x^2}$$

$$= \frac{-5}{25 + x^2} + \frac{1}{1 + x^2}$$

$$= \frac{4(5 - x^2)}{(25 + x^2)(1 + x^2)}.$$

Because $d\beta/dx = 0$ when $x = \sqrt{5}$, you can conclude from the First Derivative Test that this distance yields a maximum value of β. So, the distance is $x \approx 2.236$ feet and the angle is $\beta \approx 0.7297$ radian $\approx 41.81°$.

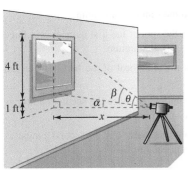

The camera should be 2.236 feet from the painting to maximize the angle β.
Figure 4.60

EXAMPLE 7 **Finding a Maximum Revenue**

The demand function for a product is modeled by

$$p = 56e^{-0.000012x} \qquad \text{Demand function}$$

where p is the price per unit (in dollars) and x is the number of units. What price will yield a maximum revenue?

Solution The revenue function is given by

$$R = xp. \qquad \text{Revenue function}$$

Substituting for p (from the demand function) produces

$$R = 56xe^{-0.000012x}. \qquad \text{Primary equation}$$

The rate of change of revenue R with respect to the number of units sold x is called the *marginal revenue* and is given by

$$\frac{dR}{dx} = 56x(e^{-0.000012x})(-0.000012) + e^{-0.000012x}(56).$$

Setting the marginal revenue equal to zero,

$$56x(e^{-0.000012x})(-0.000012) + e^{-0.000012x}(56) = 0$$

yields $x \approx 83{,}333$ units. From this, you can conclude that the maximum revenue occurs when the price is

$$p = 56e^{-0.000012(83{,}333)} \approx \$20.60.$$

So, a price of about \$20.60 will yield a maximum revenue (see Figure 4.61). ◼

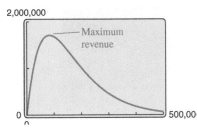

Figure 4.61

4.7 Exercises

See CalcChat.com for tutorial help and worked-out solutions to odd-numbered exercises.

1. **Numerical, Graphical, and Analytic Analysis** Find two positive numbers whose sum is 110 and whose product is a maximum.

   (a) Analytically complete six rows of a table such as the one below. (The first two rows are shown.)

First Number, x	Second Number	Product, P
10	$110 - 10$	$10(110 - 10) = 1000$
20	$110 - 20$	$20(110 - 20) = 1800$

   (b) Use a graphing utility to generate additional rows of the table. Use the table to estimate the solution. (*Hint:* Use the *table* feature of the graphing utility.)

   (c) Write the product P as a function of x.

   (d) Use a graphing utility to graph the function in part (c) and estimate the solution from the graph.

   (e) Use calculus to find the critical number of the function in part (c). Then find the two numbers.

2. **Numerical, Graphical, and Analytic Analysis** An open box of maximum volume is to be made from a square piece of material, 24 inches on a side, by cutting equal squares from the corners and turning up the sides (see figure).

   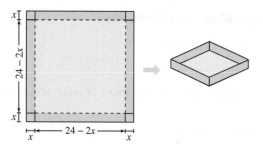

   (a) Analytically complete six rows of a table such as the one below. (The first two rows are shown.) Use the table to guess the maximum volume.

Height, x	Length and Width	Volume, V
1	$24 - 2(1)$	$1[24 - 2(1)]^2 = 484$
2	$24 - 2(2)$	$2[24 - 2(2)]^2 = 800$

   (b) Write the volume V as a function of x.

   (c) Use calculus to find the critical number of the function in part (b) and find the maximum value.

   (d) Use a graphing utility to graph the function in part (b) and verify the maximum volume from the graph.

Finding Numbers In Exercises 3–8, find two positive numbers that satisfy the given requirements.

3. The sum is S and the product is a maximum.

4. The product is 185 and the sum is a minimum.

5. The product is 147 and the sum of the first number plus three times the second number is a minimum.

6. The second number is the reciprocal of the first number and the sum is a minimum.

7. The sum of the first number and twice the second number is 108 and the product is a maximum.

8. The sum of the first number squared and the second number is 54 and the product is a maximum.

Maximum Area In Exercises 9 and 10, find the length and width of a rectangle that has the given perimeter and a maximum area.

9. Perimeter: 80 meters
10. Perimeter: P units

Minimum Perimeter In Exercises 11 and 12, find the length and width of a rectangle that has the given area and a minimum perimeter.

11. Area: 32 square feet
12. Area: A square centimeters

Minimum Distance In Exercises 13–16, find the point on the graph of the function that is closest to the given point.

13. $f(x) = x^2$, $\left(2, \frac{1}{2}\right)$
14. $f(x) = (x - 1)^2$, $(-5, 3)$
15. $f(x) = \sqrt{x}$, $(4, 0)$
16. $f(x) = \sqrt{x - 8}$, $(12, 0)$

17. **Minimum Area** A rectangular page is to contain 30 square inches of print. The margins on each side are 1 inch. Find the dimensions of the page such that the least amount of paper is used.

18. **Minimum Area** A rectangular page is to contain 36 square inches of print. The margins on each side are $1\frac{1}{2}$ inches. Find the dimensions of the page such that the least amount of paper is used.

19. **Minimum Length** A farmer plans to fence a rectangular pasture adjacent to a river (see figure). The pasture must contain 245,000 square meters in order to provide enough grass for the herd. No fencing is needed along the river. What dimensions will require the least amount of fencing?

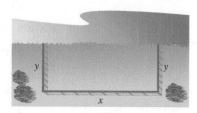

20. Maximum Volume A rectangular solid (with a square base) has a surface area of 337.5 square centimeters. Find the dimensions that will result in a solid with maximum volume.

21. Maximum Area A Norman window is constructed by adjoining a semicircle to the top of an ordinary rectangular window (see figure). Find the dimensions of a Norman window of maximum area when the total perimeter is 16 feet.

22. Maximum Area A rectangle is bounded by the x- and y-axes and the graph of $y = (6 - x)/2$ (see figure). What length and width should the rectangle have so that its area is a maximum?

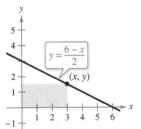

Figure for 22   Figure for 23

23. Minimum Length and Minimum Area A right triangle is formed in the first quadrant by the x- and y-axes and a line through the point $(1, 2)$ (see figure).

(a) Write the length L of the hypotenuse as a function of x.

(b) Use a graphing utility to approximate x graphically such that the length of the hypotenuse is a minimum.

(c) Find the vertices of the triangle such that its area is a minimum.

24. Maximum Area Find the area of the largest isosceles triangle that can be inscribed in a circle of radius 6 (see figure).

(a) Solve by writing the area as a function of h.

(b) Solve by writing the area as a function of α.

(c) Identify the type of triangle of maximum area.

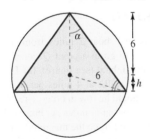

Figure for 24

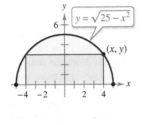

Figure for 25

25. Maximum Area A rectangle is bounded by the x-axis and the semicircle

$$y = \sqrt{25 - x^2}$$

(see figure). What length and width should the rectangle have so that its area is a maximum?

26. Maximum Area Find the dimensions of the largest rectangle that can be inscribed in a semicircle of radius r (see Exercise 25).

27. Numerical, Graphical, and Analytic Analysis An exercise room consists of a rectangle with a semicircle on each end. A 200-meter running track runs around the outside of the room.

(a) Draw a figure to represent the problem. Let x and y represent the length and width of the rectangle.

(b) Analytically complete six rows of a table such as the one below. (The first two rows are shown.) Use the table to guess the maximum area of the rectangular region.

Length, x	Width, y	Area, xy
10	$\frac{2}{\pi}(100 - 10)$	$(10)\frac{2}{\pi}(100 - 10) \approx 573$
20	$\frac{2}{\pi}(100 - 20)$	$(20)\frac{2}{\pi}(100 - 20) \approx 1019$

(c) Write the area A as a function of x.

(d) Use calculus to find the critical number of the function in part (c) and find the maximum value.

(e) Use a graphing utility to graph the function in part (c) and verify the maximum area from the graph.

28. Numerical, Graphical, and Analytic Analysis A right circular cylinder is designed to hold 22 cubic inches of a soft drink (approximately 12 fluid ounces).

(a) Analytically complete six rows of a table such as the one below. (The first two rows are shown.)

Radius, r	Height	Surface Area, S
0.2	$\frac{22}{\pi(0.2)^2}$	$2\pi(0.2)\left[0.2 + \frac{22}{\pi(0.2)^2}\right] \approx 220.3$
0.4	$\frac{22}{\pi(0.4)^2}$	$2\pi(0.4)\left[0.4 + \frac{22}{\pi(0.4)^2}\right] \approx 111.0$

(b) Use a graphing utility to generate additional rows of the table. Use the table to estimate the minimum surface area. (*Hint:* Use the *table* feature of the graphing utility.)

(c) Write the surface area S as a function of r.

(d) Use a graphing utility to graph the function in part (c) and estimate the minimum surface area from the graph.

(e) Use calculus to find the critical number of the function in part (c) and find dimensions that will yield the minimum surface area.

29. Maximum Volume A rectangular package to be sent by a postal service can have a maximum combined length and girth (perimeter of a cross section) of 108 inches (see figure). Find the dimensions of the package of maximum volume that can be sent. (Assume the cross section is square.)

30. Maximum Volume Rework Exercise 29 for a cylindrical package. (The cross section is circular.)

WRITING ABOUT CONCEPTS

31. Surface Area and Volume A shampoo bottle is a right circular cylinder. Because the surface area of the bottle does not change when it is squeezed, is it true that the volume remains the same? Explain.

32. Area and Perimeter The perimeter of a rectangle is 20 feet. Of all possible dimensions, the maximum area is 25 square feet when its length and width are both 5 feet. Are there dimensions that yield a minimum area? Explain.

---

33. Minimum Surface Area A solid is formed by adjoining two hemispheres to the ends of a right circular cylinder. The total volume of the solid is 14 cubic centimeters. Find the radius of the cylinder that produces the minimum surface area.

34. Minimum Cost An industrial tank of the shape described in Exercise 33 must have a volume of 4000 cubic feet. The hemispherical ends cost twice as much per square foot of surface area as the sides. Find the dimensions that will minimize cost.

35. Minimum Area The sum of the perimeters of an equilateral triangle and a square is 10. Find the dimensions of the triangle and the square that produce a minimum total area.

36. Maximum Area Twenty feet of wire is to be used to form two figures. In each of the following cases, how much wire should be used for each figure so that the total enclosed area is maximum?

(a) Equilateral triangle and square

(b) Square and regular pentagon

(c) Regular pentagon and regular hexagon

(d) Regular hexagon and circle

What can you conclude from this pattern? {*Hint:* The area of a regular polygon with n sides of length x is $A = (n/4)[\cot(\pi/n)]x^2$.}

37. Beam Strength A wooden beam has a rectangular cross section of height h and width w (see figure). The strength S of the beam is directly proportional to the width and the square of the height. What are the dimensions of the strongest beam that can be cut from a round log of diameter 20 inches? (*Hint:* $S = kh^2w$, where k is the proportionality constant.)

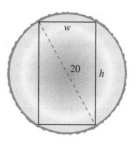

Figure for 37

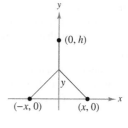

Figure for 38

38. Minimum Length Two factories are located at the coordinates $(-x, 0)$ and $(x, 0)$, and their power supply is at $(0, h)$ (see figure). Find y such that the total length of power line from the power supply to the factories is a minimum.

39. Minimum Cost

An offshore oil well is 2 kilometers off the coast. The refinery is 4 kilometers down the coast. Laying pipe in the ocean is twice as expensive as laying it on land. What path should the pipe follow in order to minimize the cost?

40. Illumination A light source is located over the center of a circular table of diameter 4 feet (see figure). Find the height h of the light source such that the illumination I at the perimeter of the table is maximum when

$$I = \frac{k \sin \alpha}{s^2}$$

where s is the slant height, α is the angle at which the light strikes the table, and k is a constant.

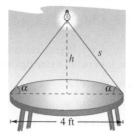

Figure for 40

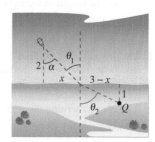

Figure for 41

41. Minimum Time A man is in a boat 2 miles from the nearest point on the coast. He is to go to a point Q, located 3 miles down the coast and 1 mile inland (see figure). (a) The man rows at 2 miles per hour and walks at 4 miles per hour. Toward what point on the coast should he row in order to reach Q in the least time? (b) The man rows at v_1 miles per hour and walks at v_2 miles per hour. Let θ_1 and θ_2 be the magnitudes of the angles. Show that the man will reach Q in the least time when $(\sin \theta_1)/v_1 = (\sin \theta_2)/v_2$.

42. Population Growth Fifty elk are introduced into a game preserve. It is estimated that their population will increase according to the model $p(t) = 250/(1 + 4e^{-t/3})$, where t is measured in years. At what rate is the population increasing when $t = 2$? After how many years is the population increasing most rapidly?

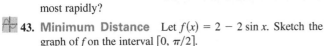

43. Minimum Distance Let $f(x) = 2 - 2\sin x$. Sketch the graph of f on the interval $[0, \pi/2]$.

(a) Find the distance from the origin to the y-intercept and the distance from the origin to the x-intercept.

(b) Write the distance d from the origin to a point on the graph of f as a function of x. Use your graphing utility to graph d and find the minimum distance.

(c) Use calculus and the *zero* or *root* feature of a graphing utility to find the value of x that minimizes the function d on the interval $[0, \pi/2]$. What is the minimum distance?

(Submitted by Tim Chapell, Penn Valley Community College, Kansas City, MO)

44. Minimum Time When light waves traveling in a transparent medium strike the surface of a second transparent medium, they change direction. This change of direction is called *refraction* and is defined by **Snell's Law of Refraction,**

$$\frac{\sin\theta_1}{v_1} = \frac{\sin\theta_2}{v_2}$$

where θ_1 and θ_2 are the magnitudes of the angles shown in the figure and v_1 and v_2 are the velocities of light in the two media. Show that this problem is equivalent to that in Exercise 41(b), and that light waves traveling from P to Q follow the path of minimum time.

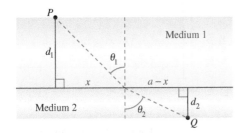

45. Maximum Volume A sector with central angle θ is cut from a circle of radius 12 inches (see figure), and the edges of the sector are brought together to form a cone. Find the magnitude of θ such that the volume of the cone is a maximum.

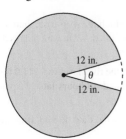

Figure for 45

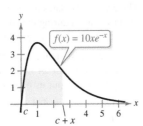

Figure for 46

46. Area Perform the following steps to find the maximum area of the rectangle shown in the figure.

(a) Solve for c in the equation $f(c) = f(c + x)$.

(b) Use the result in part (a) to write the area A as a function of x. [*Hint:* $A = xf(c)$]

(c) Use a graphing utility to graph the area function. Use the graph to approximate the dimensions of the rectangle of maximum area. Determine the required area.

(d) Use a graphing utility to graph the expression for c found in part (a). Use the graph to approximate

$$\lim_{x\to 0^+} c \quad \text{and} \quad \lim_{x\to\infty} c.$$

Use this result to describe the changes in the dimensions and position of the rectangle for $0 < x < \infty$.

47. Maximum Profit Assume that the amount of money deposited in a bank is proportional to the square of the interest rate the bank pays on this money. Furthermore, the bank can reinvest this money at 12%. Find the interest rate the bank should pay to maximize profit. (Use the simple interest formula.)

48. HOW DO YOU SEE IT? The graph shows the profit P (in thousands of dollars) of a company in terms of its advertising cost x (in thousands of dollars).

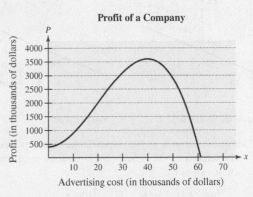

Profit of a Company

(a) Estimate the interval on which the profit is increasing.

(b) Estimate the interval on which the profit is decreasing.

(c) Estimate the amount of money the company should spend on advertising in order to yield a maximum profit.

(d) The *point of diminishing returns* is the point at which the rate of growth of the profit function begins to decline. Estimate the point of diminishing returns.

49. Maximum Rate Verify that the function

$$y = \frac{L}{1 + ae^{-x/b}}, \quad a > 0, \ b > 0, \ L > 0$$

increases at the maximum rate when $y = L/2$.

50. Area Find the area of the largest rectangle that can be inscribed under the curve $y = e^{-x^2}$ in the first and second quadrants.

Minimum Distance In Exercises 51–53, consider a fuel distribution center located at the origin of the rectangular coordinate system (units in miles; see figures). The center supplies three factories with coordinates $(4, 1)$, $(5, 6)$, and $(10, 3)$. A trunk line will run from the distribution center along the line $y = mx$, and feeder lines will run to the three factories. The objective is to find m such that the lengths of the feeder lines are minimized.

51. Minimize the sum of the squares of the lengths of the vertical feeder lines (see figure) given by

    $$S_1 = (4m - 1)^2 + (5m - 6)^2 + (10m - 3)^2.$$

    Find the equation of the trunk line by this method and then determine the sum of the lengths of the feeder lines.

52. Minimize the sum of the absolute values of the lengths of the vertical feeder lines (see figure) given by

    $$S_2 = |4m - 1| + |5m - 6| + |10m - 3|.$$

    Find the equation of the trunk line by this method and then determine the sum of the lengths of the feeder lines. (*Hint:* Use a graphing utility to graph the function S_2 and approximate the required critical number.)

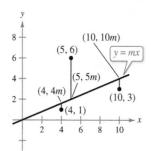

Figure for 51 and 52   Figure for 53

53. Minimize the sum of the perpendicular distances (see figure and Exercises 83–86 in Section 1.2) from the trunk line to the factories given by

    $$S_3 = \frac{|4m - 1|}{\sqrt{m^2 + 1}} + \frac{|5m - 6|}{\sqrt{m^2 + 1}} + \frac{|10m - 3|}{\sqrt{m^2 + 1}}.$$

    Find the equation of the trunk line by this method and then determine the sum of the lengths of the feeder lines. (*Hint:* Use a graphing utility to graph the function S_3 and approximate the required critical number.)

54. **Maximum Area** Consider a symmetric cross inscribed in a circle of radius r (see figure).

    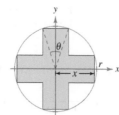

    (a) Write the area A of the cross as a function of x and find the value of x that maximizes the area.

    (b) Write the area A of the cross as a function of θ and find the value of θ that maximizes the area.

    (c) Show that the critical numbers of parts (a) and (b) yield the same maximum area. What is that area?

PUTNAM EXAM CHALLENGE

55. Find, with explanation, the maximum value of $f(x) = x^3 - 3x$ on the set of all real numbers x satisfying $x^4 + 36 \leq 13x^2$.

56. Find the minimum value of

    $$\frac{(x + 1/x)^6 - (x^6 + 1/x^6) - 2}{(x + 1/x)^3 + (x^3 + 1/x^3)} \quad \text{for} \quad x > 0.$$

SECTION PROJECT

Connecticut River

Whenever the Connecticut River reaches a level of 105 feet above sea level, two Northampton, Massachusetts, flood control station operators begin a round-the-clock river watch. Every 2 hours, they check the height of the river, using a scale marked off in tenths of a foot, and record the data in a log book. In the spring of 1996, the flood watch lasted from April 4, when the river reached 105 feet and was rising at 0.2 foot per hour, until April 25, when the level subsided again to 105 feet. Between those dates, their log shows that the river rose and fell several times, at one point coming close to the 115-foot mark. If the river had reached 115 feet, the city would have closed down Mount Tom Road (Route 5, south of Northampton).

The graph below shows the rate of change of the level of the river during one portion of the flood watch. Use the graph to answer each question.

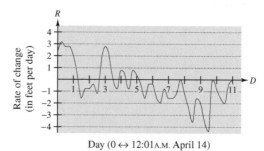

Day (0 ↔ 12:01A.M. April 14)

(a) On what date was the river rising most rapidly? How do you know?

(b) On what date was the river falling most rapidly? How do you know?

(c) There were two dates in a row on which the river rose, then fell, then rose again during the course of the day. On which days did this occur, and how do you know?

(d) At 1 minute past midnight, April 14, the river level was 111.0 feet. Estimate its height 24 hours later and 48 hours later. Explain how you made your estimates.

(e) The river crested at 114.4 feet. On what date do you think this occurred?

(Submitted by Mary Murphy, Smith College, Northampton, MA)

4.8 Differentials

■ Understand the concept of a tangent line approximation.
■ Compare the value of the differential, *dy*, with the actual change in *y*, Δ*y*.
■ Estimate a propagated error using a differential.
■ Find the differential of a function using differentiation formulas.

Exploration

Tangent Line Approximation
Use a graphing utility to graph $f(x) = x^2$. In the same viewing window, graph the tangent line to the graph of *f* at the point $(1, 1)$. Zoom in twice on the point of tangency. Does your graphing utility distinguish between the two graphs? Use the *trace* feature to compare the two graphs. As the *x*-values get closer to 1, what can you say about the *y*-values?

Tangent Line Approximations

Newton's Method (Section 3.8) is an example of the use of a tangent line to approximate the graph of a function. In this section, you will study other situations in which the graph of a function can be approximated by a straight line.

To begin, consider a function *f* that is differentiable at *c*. The equation for the tangent line at the point $(c, f(c))$ is

$$y - f(c) = f'(c)(x - c)$$

$$y = f(c) + f'(c)(x - c)$$

and is called the **tangent line approximation** (or **linear approximation**) of *f* at *c*. Because *c* is a constant, *y* is a linear function of *x*. Moreover, by restricting the values of *x* to those sufficiently close to *c*, the values of *y* can be used as approximations (to any desired degree of accuracy) of the values of the function *f*. In other words, as *x* approaches *c*, the limit of *y* is $f(c)$.

EXAMPLE 1   Using a Tangent Line Approximation

····▷ *See LarsonCalculus.com for an interactive version of this type of example.*

Find the tangent line approximation of $f(x) = 1 + \sin x$ at the point $(0, 1)$. Then use a table to compare the *y*-values of the linear function with those of $f(x)$ on an open interval containing $x = 0$.

Solution   The derivative of *f* is

$$f'(x) = \cos x. \qquad \text{First derivative}$$

So, the equation of the tangent line to the graph of *f* at the point $(0, 1)$ is

$$y = f(0) + f'(0)(x - 0)$$
$$y = 1 + (1)(x - 0)$$
$$y = 1 + x. \qquad \text{Tangent line approximation}$$

The table compares the values of *y* given by this linear approximation with the values of $f(x)$ near $x = 0$. Notice that the closer *x* is to 0, the better the approximation. This conclusion is reinforced by the graph shown in Figure 4.62.

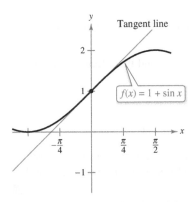

Tangent line

$f(x) = 1 + \sin x$

The tangent line approximation of *f* at the point $(0, 1)$
Figure 4.62

x	-0.5	-0.1	-0.01	0	0.01	0.1	0.5
$f(x) = 1 + \sin x$	0.521	0.9002	0.9900002	1	1.0099998	1.0998	1.479
$y = 1 + x$	0.5	0.9	0.99	1	1.01	1.1	1.5

REMARK   Be sure you see that this linear approximation of $f(x) = 1 + \sin x$ depends on the point of tangency. At a different point on the graph of *f*, you would obtain a different tangent line approximation.

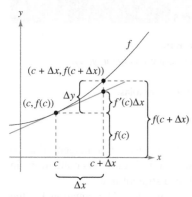

When Δx is small,
$\Delta y = f(c + \Delta x) - f(c)$ is
approximated by $f'(c)\Delta x$.
Figure 4.63

Differentials

When the tangent line to the graph of f at the point $(c, f(c))$

$$y = f(c) + f'(c)(x - c)$$ Tangent line at $(c, f(c))$

is used as an approximation of the graph of f, the quantity $x - c$ is called the change in x, and is denoted by Δx, as shown in Figure 4.63. When Δx is small, the change in y (denoted by Δy) can be approximated as shown.

$$\Delta y = f(c + \Delta x) - f(c)$$ Actual change in y

$$\approx f'(c)\Delta x$$ Approximate change in y

For such an approximation, the quantity Δx is traditionally denoted by dx, and is called the **differential of x**. The expression $f'(x)\,dx$ is denoted by dy, and is called the **differential of y**.

Definition of Differentials

Let $y = f(x)$ represent a function that is differentiable on an open interval containing x. The **differential of x** (denoted by dx) is any nonzero real number. The **differential of y** (denoted by dy) is

$$dy = f'(x)\,dx.$$

In many types of applications, the differential of y can be used as an approximation of the change in y. That is,

$$\Delta y \approx dy \quad \text{or} \quad \Delta y \approx f'(x)\,dx.$$

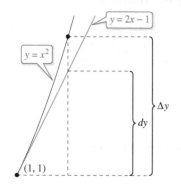

The change in y, Δy, is approximated by the differential of y, dy.
Figure 4.64

EXAMPLE 2   **Comparing Δy and dy**

Let $y = x^2$. Find dy when $x = 1$ and $dx = 0.01$. Compare this value with Δy for $x = 1$ and $\Delta x = 0.01$.

Solution   Because $y = f(x) = x^2$, you have $f'(x) = 2x$, and the differential dy is

$$dy = f'(x)\,dx = f'(1)(0.01) = 2(0.01) = 0.02.$$ Differential of y

Now, using $\Delta x = 0.01$, the change in y is

$$\Delta y = f(x + \Delta x) - f(x) = f(1.01) - f(1) = (1.01)^2 - 1^2 = 0.0201.$$

Figure 4.64 shows the geometric comparison of dy and Δy. Try comparing other values of dy and Δy. You will see that the values become closer to each other as dx (or Δx) approaches 0.

In Example 2, the tangent line to the graph of $f(x) = x^2$ at $x = 1$ is

$$y = 2x - 1.$$ Tangent line to the graph of f at $x = 1$.

For x-values near 1, this line is close to the graph of f, as shown in Figure 4.64 and in the table.

x	0.5	0.9	0.99	1	1.01	1.1	1.5
$f(x) = x^2$	0.25	0.81	0.9801	1	1.0201	1.21	2.25
$y = 2x - 1$	0	0.8	0.98	1	1.02	1.2	2

Error Propagation

Physicists and engineers tend to make liberal use of the approximation of Δy by dy. One way this occurs in practice is in the estimation of errors propagated by physical measuring devices. For example, if you let x represent the measured value of a variable and let $x + \Delta x$ represent the exact value, then Δx is the *error in measurement*. Finally, if the measured value x is used to compute another value $f(x)$, then the difference between $f(x + \Delta x)$ and $f(x)$ is the **propagated error.**

$$\underbrace{f(\overbrace{x + \Delta x}^{\text{Measurement error}}) - \overbrace{f(x)}^{} }_{} = \overbrace{\Delta y}^{\text{Propagated error}}$$

Exact value   Measured value

EXAMPLE 3   **Estimation of Error**

The measured radius of a ball bearing is 0.7 inch, as shown in the figure. The measurement is correct to within 0.01 inch. Estimate the propagated error in the volume V of the ball bearing.

Solution   The formula for the volume of a sphere is

$$V = \frac{4}{3}\pi r^3$$

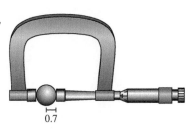

Ball bearing with measured radius that is correct to within 0.01 inch.

where r is the radius of the sphere. So, you can write

$$r = 0.7 \qquad \text{Measured radius}$$

and

$$-0.01 \leq \Delta r \leq 0.01. \qquad \text{Possible error}$$

To approximate the propagated error in the volume, differentiate V to obtain $dV/dr = 4\pi r^2$ and write

$$\begin{aligned} \Delta V &\approx dV && \text{Approximate } \Delta V \text{ by } dV.\\ &= 4\pi r^2\, dr\\ &= 4\pi(0.7)^2(\pm 0.01) && \text{Substitute for } r \text{ and } dr.\\ &\approx \pm 0.06158 \text{ cubic inch.} \end{aligned}$$

So, the volume has a propagated error of about 0.06 cubic inch.

Would you say that the propagated error in Example 3 is large or small? The answer is best given in *relative* terms by comparing dV with V. The ratio

$$\begin{aligned} \frac{dV}{V} &= \frac{4\pi r^2\, dr}{\frac{4}{3}\pi r^3} && \text{Ratio of } dV \text{ to } V\\ &= \frac{3\, dr}{r} && \text{Simplify.}\\ &\approx \frac{3}{0.7}(\pm 0.01) && \text{Substitute for } dr \text{ and } r.\\ &\approx \pm 0.0429 \end{aligned}$$

is called the **relative error.** The corresponding **percent error** is approximately 4.29%.

Calculating Differentials

Each of the differentiation rules that you studied in Chapter 3 can be written in **differential form.** For example, let u and v be differentiable functions of x. By the definition of differentials, you have

$$du = u' \, dx$$

and

$$dv = v' \, dx.$$

So, you can write the differential form of the Product Rule as shown below.

$$
\begin{aligned}
d[uv] &= \frac{d}{dx}[uv] \, dx && \text{Differential of } uv.\\
&= [uv' + vu'] \, dx && \text{Product Rule}\\
&= uv' \, dx + vu' \, dx\\
&= u \, dv + v \, du
\end{aligned}
$$

Differential Formulas

Let u and v be differentiable functions of x.

Constant multiple: $\quad d[cu] = c \, du$

Sum or difference: $\quad d[u \pm v] = du \pm dv$

Product: $\quad\quad\quad\ d[uv] = u \, dv + v \, du$

Quotient: $\quad\quad\quad d\left[\dfrac{u}{v}\right] = \dfrac{v \, du - u \, dv}{v^2}$

EXAMPLE 4 **Finding Differentials**

	Function	Derivative	Differential
a.	$y = x^2$	$\dfrac{dy}{dx} = 2x$	$dy = 2x \, dx$
b.	$y = \sqrt{x}$	$\dfrac{dy}{dx} = \dfrac{1}{2\sqrt{x}}$	$dy = \dfrac{dx}{2\sqrt{x}}$
c.	$y = 2 \sin x$	$\dfrac{dy}{dx} = 2 \cos x$	$dy = 2 \cos x \, dx$
d.	$y = xe^x$	$\dfrac{dy}{dx} = e^x(x + 1)$	$dy = e^x(x + 1) \, dx$
e.	$y = \dfrac{1}{x}$	$\dfrac{dy}{dx} = -\dfrac{1}{x^2}$	$dy = -\dfrac{dx}{x^2}$

GOTTFRIED WILHELM LEIBNIZ (1646–1716)

Both Leibniz and Newton are credited with creating calculus. It was Leibniz, however, who tried to broaden calculus by developing rules and formal notation. He often spent days choosing an appropriate notation for a new concept.
See LarsonCalculus.com to read more of this biography.

The notation in Example 4 is called the **Leibniz notation** for derivatives and differentials, named after the German mathematician Gottfried Wilhelm Leibniz. The beauty of this notation is that it provides an easy way to remember several important calculus formulas by making it seem as though the formulas were derived from algebraic manipulations of differentials. For instance, in Leibniz notation, the *Chain Rule*

$$\frac{dy}{dx} = \frac{dy}{du}\frac{du}{dx}$$

would appear to be true because the du's divide out. Even though this reasoning is *incorrect*, the notation does help one remember the Chain Rule.

EXAMPLE 5   **Finding the Differential of a Composite Function**

$$y = f(x) = \sin 3x$$ Original function

$$f'(x) = 3\cos 3x$$ Apply Chain Rule.

$$dy = f'(x)\, dx = 3\cos 3x\, dx$$ Differential form

EXAMPLE 6   **Finding the Differential of a Composite Function**

$$y = f(x) = (x^2 + 1)^{1/2}$$ Original function

$$f'(x) = \frac{1}{2}(x^2 + 1)^{-1/2}(2x) = \frac{x}{\sqrt{x^2 + 1}}$$ Apply Chain Rule.

$$dy = f'(x)\, dx = \frac{x}{\sqrt{x^2 + 1}}\, dx$$ Differential form

Differentials can be used to approximate function values. To do this for the function given by $y = f(x)$, use the formula

$$f(x + \Delta x) \approx f(x) + dy = f(x) + f'(x)\, dx$$

• REMARK This formula is equivalent to the tangent line approximation given earlier in this section.

which is derived from the approximation

$$\Delta y = f(x + \Delta x) - f(x) \approx dy.$$

The key to using this formula is to choose a value for x that makes the calculations easier, as shown in Example 7.

EXAMPLE 7   **Approximating Function Values**

Use differentials to approximate $\sqrt{16.5}$.

Solution   Using $f(x) = \sqrt{x}$, you can write

$$f(x + \Delta x) \approx f(x) + f'(x)\, dx = \sqrt{x} + \frac{1}{2\sqrt{x}}\, dx.$$

Now, choosing $x = 16$ and $dx = 0.5$, you obtain the following approximation.

$$f(x + \Delta x) = \sqrt{16.5} \approx \sqrt{16} + \frac{1}{2\sqrt{16}}(0.5) = 4 + \left(\frac{1}{8}\right)\left(\frac{1}{2}\right) = 4.0625$$

The tangent line approximation to $f(x) = \sqrt{x}$ at $x = 16$ is the line $g(x) = \frac{1}{8}x + 2$. For x-values near 16, the graphs of f and g are close together, as shown in Figure 4.65. For instance,

$$f(16.5) = \sqrt{16.5} \approx 4.0620$$

and

$$g(16.5) = \frac{1}{8}(16.5) + 2 = 4.0625.$$

In fact, if you use a graphing utility to zoom in near the point of tangency $(16, 4)$, you will see that the two graphs appear to coincide. Notice also that as you move farther away from the point of tangency, the linear approximation becomes less accurate.

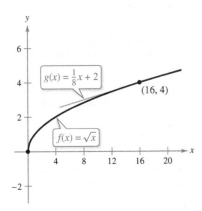

Figure 4.65

4.8 Exercises

See **CalcChat.com** for tutorial help and worked-out solutions to odd-numbered exercises.

Using a Tangent Line Approximation In Exercises 1–6, find the tangent line approximation T to the graph of f at the given point. Use this linear approximation to complete the table.

x	1.9	1.99	2	2.01	2.1
$f(x)$					
$T(x)$					

1. $f(x) = x^2$, $(2, 4)$
2. $f(x) = \dfrac{6}{x^2}$, $\left(2, \dfrac{3}{2}\right)$
3. $f(x) = x^5$, $(2, 32)$
4. $f(x) = \sqrt{x}$, $\left(2, \sqrt{2}\right)$
5. $f(x) = \sin x$, $(2, \sin 2)$
6. $f(x) = \log_2 x$, $(2, 1)$

Comparing Δy and dy In Exercises 7–10, use the information to evaluate and compare Δy and dy.

Function	x-Value	Differential of x
7. $y = x^3$	$x = 1$	$\Delta x = dx = 0.1$
8. $y = 6 - 2x^2$	$x = -2$	$\Delta x = dx = 0.1$
9. $y = x^4 + 1$	$x = -1$	$\Delta x = dx = 0.01$
10. $y = 2 - x^4$	$x = 2$	$\Delta x = dx = 0.01$

Finding a Differential In Exercises 11–24, find the differential dy of the given function.

11. $y = 3x^2 - 4$
12. $y = 3x^{2/3}$
13. $y = x \tan x$
14. $y = \csc 2x$
15. $y = \dfrac{x + 1}{2x - 1}$
16. $y = \sqrt{x} + \dfrac{1}{\sqrt{x}}$
17. $y = \sqrt{9 - x^2}$
18. $y = x\sqrt{1 - x^2}$
19. $y = 3x - \sin^2 x$
20. $y = \dfrac{\sec^2 x}{x^2 + 1}$
21. $y = \ln\sqrt{4 - x^2}$
22. $y = e^{-0.5x} \cos 4x$
23. $y = x \arcsin x$
24. $y = \arctan(x - 2)$

Using Differentials In Exercises 25 and 26, use differentials and the graph of f to approximate (a) $f(1.9)$ and (b) $f(2.04)$. To print an enlarged copy of the graph, go to *MathGraphs.com*.

25.
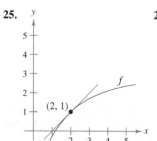

26.
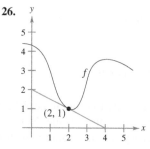

Using Differentials In Exercises 27 and 28, use differentials and the graph of g' to approximate (a) $g(2.93)$ and (b) $g(3.1)$ given that $g(3) = 8$.

27.
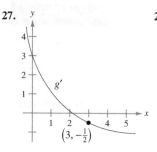

28.
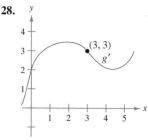

29. Area The measurement of the side of a square floor tile is 10 inches, with a possible error of $\frac{1}{32}$ inch.

(a) Use differentials to approximate the possible propagated error in computing the area of the square.

(b) Approximate the percent error in computing the area of the square.

30. Area The measurement of the radius of a circle is 16 inches, with a possible error of $\frac{1}{4}$ inch.

(a) Use differentials to approximate the possible propagated error in computing the area of the circle.

(b) Approximate the percent error in computing the area of the circle.

31. Area The measurements of the base and altitude of a triangle are found to be 36 and 50 centimeters, respectively. The possible error in each measurement is 0.25 centimeter.

(a) Use differentials to approximate the possible propagated error in computing the area of the triangle.

(b) Approximate the percent error in computing the area of the triangle.

32. Circumference The measurement of the circumference of a circle is found to be 64 centimeters, with a possible error of 0.9 centimeter.

(a) Approximate the percent error in computing the area of the circle.

(b) Estimate the maximum allowable percent error in measuring the circumference if the error in computing the area cannot exceed 3%.

33. Volume and Surface Area The measurement of the edge of a cube is found to be 15 inches, with a possible error of 0.03 inch.

(a) Use differentials to approximate the possible propagated error in computing the volume of the cube.

(b) Use differentials to approximate the possible propagated error in computing the surface area of the cube.

(c) Approximate the percent errors in parts (a) and (b).

34. Volume and Surface Area The radius of a spherical balloon is measured as 8 inches, with a possible error of 0.02 inch.

(a) Use differentials to approximate the possible propagated error in computing the volume of the sphere.

(b) Use differentials to approximate the possible propagated error in computing the surface area of the sphere.

(c) Approximate the percent errors in parts (a) and (b).

35. Stopping Distance The total stopping distance T of a vehicle is

$$T = 2.5x + 0.5x^2$$

where T is in feet and x is the speed in miles per hour. Approximate the change and percent change in total stopping distance as speed changes from $x = 25$ to $x = 26$ miles per hour.

36. HOW DO YOU SEE IT? The graph shows the profit P (in dollars) from selling x units of an item. Use the graph to determine which is greater, the change in profit when the production level changes from 400 to 401 units or the change in profit when the production level changes from 900 to 901 units. Explain your reasoning

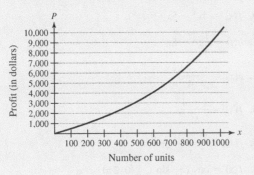

Number of units

37. Pendulum The period of a pendulum is given by

$$T = 2\pi\sqrt{\frac{L}{g}}$$

where L is the length of the pendulum in feet, g is the acceleration due to gravity, and T is the time in seconds. The pendulum has been subjected to an increase in temperature such that the length has increased by $\frac{1}{2}\%$.

(a) Find the approximate percent change in the period.

(b) Using the result in part (a), find the approximate error in this pendulum clock in 1 day.

38. Ohm's Law A current of I amperes passes through a resistor of R ohms. **Ohm's Law** states that the voltage E applied to the resistor is

$$E = IR.$$

The voltage is constant. Show that the magnitude of the relative error in R caused by a change in I is equal in magnitude to the relative error in I.

39. Relative Humidity When the dewpoint is 65° Fahrenheit, the relative humidity H is modeled by

$$H = \frac{4347}{400,000,000} e^{369,444/(50t + 19,793)}$$

where t is the air temperature in degrees Fahrenheit. Use differentials to approximate the change in relative humidity at $t = 72$ for a 1-degree change in the air temperature.

40. Surveying A surveyor standing 50 feet from the base of a large tree measures the angle of elevation to the top of the tree as 71.5°. How accurately must the angle be measured for the percent error in estimating the height of the tree to be less than 6%?

Approximating Function Values In Exercises 41–44, use differentials to approximate the value of the expression. Compare your answer with that of a calculator.

41. $\sqrt{99.4}$

42. $\sqrt[3]{26}$

43. $\sqrt[4]{624}$

44. $(2.99)^3$

Verifying a Tangent Line Approximation In Exercises 45 and 46, verify the tangent line approximation of the function at the given point. Then use a graphing utility to graph the function and its approximation in the same viewing window.

Function	Approximation	Point
45. $f(x) = \sqrt{x + 4}$	$y = 2 + \dfrac{x}{4}$	$(0, 2)$
46. $f(x) = \tan x$	$y = x$	$(0, 0)$

WRITING ABOUT CONCEPTS

47. Comparing Δy **and** dy Describe the change in accuracy of dy as an approximation for Δy when Δx is decreased.

48. Describing Terms When using differentials, what is meant by the terms *propagated error*, *relative error*, and *percent error*?

49. Think About It Give a short explanation of why the approximation is valid.

(a) $\sqrt{4.02} \approx 2 + \frac{1}{4}(0.02)$ (b) $\tan 0.05 \approx 0 + 1(0.05)$

50. Think About It Would you use $y = x$ to approximate $f(x) = \sin x$ near $x = 0$? Why or why not?

True or False? In Exercises 51–54, determine whether the statement is true or false. If it is false, explain why or give an example that shows it is false.

51. If $y = x + c$, then $dy = dx$.

52. If $y = ax + b$, then $\dfrac{\Delta y}{\Delta x} = \dfrac{dy}{dx}$.

53. If y is differentiable, then $\lim\limits_{\Delta x \to 0} (\Delta y - dy) = 0$.

54. If $y = f(x)$, f is increasing and differentiable, and $\Delta x > 0$, then $\Delta y \geq dy$.

Review Exercises

Finding Extrema on a Closed Interval In Exercises 1–8, find the absolute extrema of the function on the closed interval.

1. $f(x) = x^2 + 5x$, $[-4, 0]$

2. $f(x) = x^3 + 6x^2$, $[-6, 1]$

3. $f(x) = \sqrt{x} - 2$, $[0, 4]$

4. $h(x) = 3\sqrt{x} - x$, $[0, 9]$

5. $f(x) = \dfrac{4x}{x^2 + 9}$, $[-4, 4]$

6. $f(x) = \dfrac{x}{\sqrt{x^2 + 1}}$, $[0, 2]$

7. $g(x) = 2x + 5\cos x$, $[0, 2\pi]$

8. $f(x) = \sin 2x$, $[0, 2\pi]$

Using Rolle's Theorem In Exercises 9–12, determine whether Rolle's Theorem can be applied to f on the closed interval $[a, b]$. If Rolle's Theorem can be applied, find all values of c in the open interval (a, b) such that $f'(c) = 0$. If Rolle's Theorem cannot be applied, explain why not.

9. $f(x) = 2x^2 - 7$, $[0, 4]$

10. $f(x) = (x - 2)(x + 3)^2$, $[-3, 2]$

11. $f(x) = \dfrac{x^2}{1 - x^2}$, $[-2, 2]$

12. $f(x) = \sin 2x$, $[-\pi, \pi]$

Using the Mean Value Theorem In Exercises 13–18, determine whether the Mean Value Theorem can be applied to f on the closed interval $[a, b]$. If the Mean Value Theorem can be applied, find all values of c in the open interval (a, b) such that

$$f'(c) = \frac{f(b) - f(a)}{b - a}.$$

If the Mean Value Theorem cannot be applied, explain why not.

13. $f(x) = x^{2/3}$, $[1, 8]$

14. $f(x) = \dfrac{1}{x}$, $[1, 4]$

15. $f(x) = |5 - x|$, $[2, 6]$

16. $f(x) = 2x - 3\sqrt{x}$, $[-1, 1]$

17. $f(x) = x - \cos x$, $\left[-\dfrac{\pi}{2}, \dfrac{\pi}{2}\right]$

18. $f(x) = x \log_2 x$, $[1, 2]$

19. **Mean Value Theorem** Can the Mean Value Theorem be applied to the function

$$f(x) = \frac{1}{x^2}$$

on the interval $[-2, 1]$? Explain.

20. **Using the Mean Value Theorem**

(a) For the function $f(x) = Ax^2 + Bx + C$, determine the value of c guaranteed by the Mean Value Theorem on the interval $[x_1, x_2]$.

(b) Demonstrate the result of part (a) for $f(x) = 2x^2 - 3x + 1$ on the interval $[0, 4]$.

Intervals on Which f Is Increasing or Decreasing In Exercises 21–28, identify the open intervals on which the function is increasing or decreasing.

21. $f(x) = x^2 + 3x - 12$

22. $h(x) = (x + 2)^{1/3} + 8$

23. $f(x) = (x - 1)^2(x - 3)$

24. $g(x) = (x + 1)^3$

25. $h(x) = \sqrt{x}(x - 3)$, $x > 0$

26. $f(x) = \sin x + \cos x$, $[0, 2\pi]$

27. $f(t) = (2 - t)2^t$

28. $g(x) = 2x \ln x$

Applying the First Derivative Test In Exercises 29–36, (a) find the critical numbers of f (if any), (b) find the open interval(s) on which the function is increasing or decreasing, (c) apply the First Derivative Test to identify all relative extrema, and (d) use a graphing utility to confirm your results.

29. $f(x) = x^2 - 6x + 5$

30. $f(x) = 4x^3 - 5x$

31. $h(t) = \dfrac{1}{4}t^4 - 8t$

32. $g(x) = \dfrac{x^3 - 8x}{4}$

33. $f(x) = \dfrac{x + 4}{x^2}$

34. $f(x) = \dfrac{x^2 - 3x - 4}{x - 2}$

35. $f(x) = \cos x - \sin x$, $(0, 2\pi)$

36. $g(x) = \dfrac{3}{2}\sin\left(\dfrac{\pi x}{2} - 1\right)$, $[0, 4]$

Finding Points of Inflection In Exercises 37–42, find the points of inflection and discuss the concavity of the graph of the function.

37. $f(x) = x^3 - 9x^2$

38. $f(x) = 6x^4 - x^2$

39. $g(x) = x\sqrt{x + 5}$

40. $f(x) = 3x - 5x^3$

41. $f(x) = x + \cos x$, $[0, 2\pi]$

42. $f(x) = \tan\dfrac{x}{4}$, $(0, 2\pi)$

Using the Second Derivative Test In Exercises 43–48, find all relative extrema. Use the Second Derivative Test where applicable.

43. $f(x) = (x + 9)^2$

44. $f(x) = 2x^3 + 11x^2 - 8x - 12$

45. $g(x) = 2x^2(1 - x^2)$

46. $h(t) = t - 4\sqrt{t + 1}$

47. $f(x) = 2x + \dfrac{18}{x}$

48. $h(x) = x - 2\cos x, \quad [0, 4\pi]$

Think About It In Exercises 49 and 50, sketch the graph of a function f having the given characteristics.

49. $f(0) = f(6) = 0$
$f'(3) = f'(5) = 0$
$f'(x) > 0$ for $x < 3$
$f'(x) > 0$ for $3 < x < 5$
$f'(x) < 0$ for $x > 5$
$f''(x) < 0$ for $x < 3$ or $x > 4$
$f''(x) > 0$ for $3 < x < 4$

50. $f(0) = 4, \ f(6) = 0$
$f'(x) < 0$ for $x < 2$ or $x > 4$
$f'(2)$ does not exist.
$f'(4) = 0$
$f'(x) > 0$ for $2 < x < 4$
$f''(x) < 0$ for $x \ne 2$

51. Writing A newspaper headline states that "The rate of growth of the national deficit is decreasing." What does this mean? What does it imply about the graph of the deficit as a function of time?

52. Inventory Cost The cost of inventory C depends on the ordering and storage costs according to the inventory model

$$C = \left(\dfrac{Q}{x}\right)s + \left(\dfrac{x}{2}\right)r.$$

Determine the order size that will minimize the cost, assuming that sales occur at a constant rate, Q is the number of units sold per year, r is the cost of storing one unit for one year, s is the cost of placing an order, and x is the number of units per order.

53. Modeling Data Outlays for national defense D (in billions of dollars) for selected years from 1970 through 2010 are shown in the table, where t is time in years, with $t = 0$ corresponding to 1970. (Source: U.S. Office of Management and Budget)

t	0	5	10	15	20
D	81.7	86.5	134.0	252.7	299.3

t	25	30	35	40
D	272.1	294.4	495.3	693.6

(a) Use the regression capabilities of a graphing utility to find a model of the form

$$D = at^4 + bt^3 + ct^2 + dt + e$$

for the data.

(b) Use a graphing utility to plot the data and graph the model.

(c) For the years shown in the table, when does the model indicate that the outlay for national defense was at a maximum? When was it at a minimum?

(d) For the years shown in the table, when does the model indicate that the outlay for national defense was increasing at the greatest rate?

54. Climb Rate The time t (in minutes) for a small plane to climb to an altitude of h feet is

$$t = 50 \log_{10} \dfrac{18{,}000}{18{,}000 - h}$$

where 18,000 feet is the plane's absolute ceiling.

(a) Determine the domain of the function appropriate for the context of the problem.

(b) Use a graphing utility to graph the time function and identify any asymptotes.

(c) Find the time when the altitude is increasing at the greatest rate.

Finding a Limit In Exercises 55–64, find the limit.

55. $\displaystyle\lim_{x\to\infty}\left(8 + \dfrac{1}{x}\right)$

56. $\displaystyle\lim_{x\to-\infty}\dfrac{1 - 4x}{x + 1}$

57. $\displaystyle\lim_{x\to\infty}\dfrac{2x^2}{3x^2 + 5}$

58. $\displaystyle\lim_{x\to\infty}\dfrac{4x^3}{x^4 + 3}$

59. $\displaystyle\lim_{x\to-\infty}\dfrac{3x^2}{x + 5}$

60. $\displaystyle\lim_{x\to-\infty}\dfrac{\sqrt{x^2 + x}}{-2x}$

61. $\displaystyle\lim_{x\to\infty}\dfrac{5\cos x}{x}$

62. $\displaystyle\lim_{x\to\infty}\dfrac{x^3}{\sqrt{x^2 + 2}}$

63. $\displaystyle\lim_{x\to-\infty}\dfrac{6x}{x + \cos x}$

64. $\displaystyle\lim_{x\to-\infty}\dfrac{x}{2\sin x}$

Horizontal Asymptotes In Exercises 65–72, use a graphing utility to graph the function and identify any horizontal asymptotes.

65. $f(x) = \dfrac{3}{x} - 2$

66. $g(x) = \dfrac{5x^2}{x^2 + 2}$

67. $h(x) = \dfrac{2x + 3}{x - 4}$

68. $f(x) = \dfrac{3x}{\sqrt{x^2 + 2}}$

69. $f(x) = \dfrac{5}{3 + 2e^{-x}}$

70. $g(x) = 30xe^{-2x}$

71. $g(x) = 3\ln(1 + e^{-x/4})$

72. $h(x) = 10\ln\left(\dfrac{x}{x + 1}\right)$

Analyzing the Graph of a Function In Exercises 73–82, analyze and sketch a graph of the function. Label any intercepts, relative extrema, points of inflection, and asymptotes. Use a graphing utility to verify your results.

73. $f(x) = 4x - x^2$

74. $f(x) = 4x^3 - x^4$

75. $f(x) = x\sqrt{16 - x^2}$

76. $f(x) = (x^2 - 4)^2$

77. $f(x) = x^{1/3}(x + 3)^{2/3}$

78. $f(x) = (x - 3)(x + 2)^3$

79. $f(x) = \dfrac{5 - 3x}{x - 2}$

80. $f(x) = \dfrac{2x}{1 + x^2}$

81. $f(x) = x^3 + x + \dfrac{4}{x}$ **82.** $f(x) = x^2 + \dfrac{1}{x}$

83. Maximum Area   A rancher has 400 feet of fencing with which to enclose two adjacent rectangular corrals (see figure). What dimensions should be used so that the enclosed area will be a maximum?

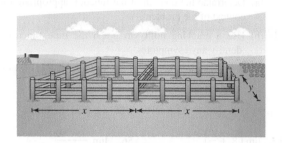

84. Maximum Area   Find the dimensions of the rectangle of maximum area, with sides parallel to the coordinate axes, that can be inscribed in the ellipse given by

$$\frac{x^2}{144} + \frac{y^2}{16} = 1.$$

85. Minimum Length   A right triangle in the first quadrant has the coordinate axes as sides, and the hypotenuse passes through the point $(1, 8)$. Find the vertices of the triangle such that the length of the hypotenuse is minimum.

86. Minimum Length   The wall of a building is to be braced by a beam that must pass over a parallel fence 5 feet high and 4 feet from the building. Find the length of the shortest beam that can be used.

87. Modeling Data   A meteorologist measures the atmospheric pressure P (in kilograms per square meter) at altitude h (in kilometers). The data are shown below.

h	0	5	10	15	20
P	10,332	5583	2376	1240	517

(a) Use a graphing utility to plot the points $(h, \ln P)$. Use the regression capabilities of the graphing utility to find a linear model for the revised data points.

(b) The line in part (a) has the form

$\ln P = ah + b.$

Write the equation in exponential form.

(c) Use a graphing utility to plot the original data and graph the exponential model in part (b).

(d) Find the rate of change of the pressure when $h = 5$ and $h = 18$.

88. Using a Function   Consider the function $f(x) = x^n$ for positive integer values of n.

(a) For what values of n does the function have a relative minimum at the origin?

(b) For what values of n does the function have a point of inflection at the origin?

89. Maximum Length   Find the length of the longest pipe that can be carried level around a right-angle corner at the intersection of two corridors of widths 4 feet and 6 feet.

90. Maximum Length   A hallway of width 6 feet meets a hallway of width 9 feet at right angles. Find the length of the longest pipe that can be carried level around this corner. [*Hint:* If L is the length of the pipe, show that

$$L = 6 \csc \theta + 9 \csc\left(\frac{\pi}{2} - \theta\right)$$

where θ is the angle between the pipe and the wall of the narrower hallway.]

91. Maximum Volume   Find the volume of the largest right circular cone that can be inscribed in a sphere of radius r.

92. Maximum Volume   Find the volume of the largest right circular cylinder that can be inscribed in a sphere of radius r.

Comparing Δy and dy   In Exercises 93 and 94, use the information to evaluate and compare Δy and dy.

Function	x-Value	Differential of x
93. $y = 0.5x^2$	$x = 3$	$\Delta x = dx = 0.01$
94. $y = x^3 - 6x$	$x = 2$	$\Delta x = dx = 0.1$

Finding a Differential   In Exercises 95 and 96, find the differential dy of the given function.

95. $y = x(1 - \cos x)$ **96.** $y = \sqrt{36 - x^2}$

97. Volume and Surface Area   The radius of a sphere is measured as 9 centimeters, with a possible error of 0.025 centimeter.

(a) Use differentials to approximate the possible propagated error in computing the volume of the sphere.

(b) Use differentials to approximate the possible propagated error in computing the surface area of the sphere.

(c) Approximate the percent errors in parts (a) and (b).

98. Demand Function   A company finds that the demand for its commodity is

$$p = 75 - \frac{1}{4}x$$

where p is the price in dollars and x is the number of units. Find and compare the values of Δp and dp as x changes from 7 to 8.

99. Profit   The profit P for a company is $P = 100xe^{-x/400}$, where x is sales. Approximate the change and percent change in profit as sales increase from $x = 115$ to $x = 120$ units.

P.S. Problem Solving

See **CalcChat.com** for tutorial help and worked-out solutions to odd-numbered exercises.

1. Relative Extrema Graph the fourth-degree polynomial

$$p(x) = x^4 + ax^2 + 1$$

for various values of the constant a.

(a) Determine the values of a for which p has exactly one relative minimum.

(b) Determine the values of a for which p has exactly one relative maximum.

(c) Determine the values of a for which p has exactly two relative minima.

(d) Show that the graph of p cannot have exactly two relative extrema.

2. Relative Extrema

(a) Graph the fourth-degree polynomial $p(x) = ax^4 - 6x^2$ for $a = -3, -2, -1, 0, 1, 2,$ and 3. For what values of the constant a does p have a relative minimum or relative maximum?

(b) Show that p has a relative maximum for all values of the constant a.

(c) Determine analytically the values of a for which p has a relative minimum.

(d) Let $(x, y) = (x, p(x))$ be a relative extremum of p. Show that (x, y) lies on the graph of $y = -3x^2$. Verify this result graphically by graphing $y = -3x^2$ together with the seven curves from part (a).

3. Relative Minimum Let

$$f(x) = \frac{c}{x} + x^2.$$

Determine all values of the constant c such that f has a relative minimum, but no relative maximum.

4. Points of Inflection

(a) Let $f(x) = ax^2 + bx + c$, $a \neq 0$, be a quadratic polynomial. How many points of inflection does the graph of f have?

(b) Let $f(x) = ax^3 + bx^2 + cx + d$, $a \neq 0$, be a cubic polynomial. How many points of inflection does the graph of f have?

(c) Suppose the function $y = f(x)$ satisfies the equation

$$\frac{dy}{dx} = ky\left(1 - \frac{y}{L}\right)$$

where k and L are positive constants. Show that the graph of f has a point of inflection at the point where $y = L/2$. (This equation is called the **logistic differential equation.**)

5. Extended Mean Value Theorem Prove the following **Extended Mean Value Theorem.** If f and f' are continuous on the closed interval $[a, b]$, and if f'' exists in the open interval (a, b), then there exists a number c in (a, b) such that

$$f(b) = f(a) + f'(a)(b - a) + \frac{1}{2}f''(c)(b - a)^2.$$

6. Illumination The amount of illumination of a surface is proportional to the intensity of the light source, inversely proportional to the square of the distance from the light source, and proportional to sin θ, where θ is the angle at which the light strikes the surface. A rectangular room measures 10 feet by 24 feet, with a 10-foot ceiling (see figure). Determine the height at which the light should be placed to allow the corners of the floor to receive as much light as possible.

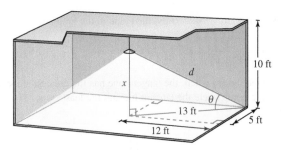

7. Minimum Distance Consider a room in the shape of a cube, 4 meters on each side. A bug at point P wants to walk to point Q at the opposite corner, as shown in the figure. Use calculus to determine the shortest path. Explain how you can solve this problem without calculus. (*Hint:* Consider the two walls as one wall.)

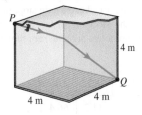

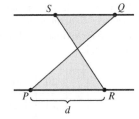

Figure for 7   Figure for 8

8. Areas of Triangles The line joining P and Q crosses the two parallel lines, as shown in the figure. The point R is d units from P. How far from Q should the point S be positioned so that the sum of the areas of the two shaded triangles is a minimum? So that the sum is a maximum?

9. Mean Value Theorem Determine the values a, b, and c such that the function f satisfies the hypotheses of the Mean Value Theorem on the interval $[0, 3]$.

$$f(x) = \begin{cases} 1, & x = 0 \\ ax + b, & 0 < x \leq 1 \\ x^2 + 4x + c, & 1 < x \leq 3 \end{cases}$$

10. Mean Value Theorem Determine the values a, b, c, and d such that the function f satisfies the hypotheses of the Mean Value Theorem on the interval $[-1, 2]$.

$$f(x) = \begin{cases} a, & x = -1 \\ 2, & -1 < x \leq 0 \\ bx^2 + c, & 0 < x \leq 1 \\ dx + 4, & 1 < x \leq 2 \end{cases}$$

11. Proof Let f and g be functions that are continuous on $[a, b]$ and differentiable on (a, b). Prove that if $f(a) = g(a)$ and $g'(x) > f'(x)$ for all x in (a, b), then $g(b) > f(b)$.

12. Proof

(a) Prove that $\lim\limits_{x \to \infty} x^2 = \infty$.

(b) Prove that $\lim\limits_{x \to \infty}\left(\dfrac{1}{x^2}\right) = 0$.

(c) Let L be a real number. Prove that if $\lim\limits_{x \to \infty} f(x) = L$, then

$$\lim_{y \to 0^+} f\left(\frac{1}{y}\right) = L.$$

13. Tangent Lines Find the point on the graph of

$$y = \frac{1}{1 + x^2}$$

(see figure) where the tangent line has the greatest slope, and the point where the tangent line has the least slope.

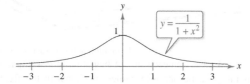

14. Stopping Distance The police department must determine the speed limit on a bridge such that the flow rate of cars is maximum per unit time. The greater the speed limit, the farther apart the cars must be in order to keep a safe stopping distance. Experimental data on the stopping distances d (in meters) for various speeds v (in kilometers per hour) are shown in the table.

v	20	40	60	80	100
d	5.1	13.7	27.2	44.2	66.4

(a) Convert the speeds v in the table to speeds s in meters per second. Use the regression capabilities of a graphing utility to find a model of the form $d(s) = as^2 + bs + c$ for the data.

(b) Consider two consecutive vehicles of average length 5.5 meters, traveling at a safe speed on the bridge. Let T be the difference between the times (in seconds) when the front bumpers of the vehicles pass a given point on the bridge. Verify that this difference in times is given by

$$T = \frac{d(s)}{s} + \frac{5.5}{s}.$$

(c) Use a graphing utility to graph the function T and estimate the speed s that minimizes the time between vehicles.

(d) Use calculus to determine the speed that minimizes T. What is the minimum value of T? Convert the required speed to kilometers per hour.

(e) Find the optimal distance between vehicles for the posted speed limit determined in part (d).

15. Darboux's Theorem Prove Darboux's Theorem: Let f be differentiable on the closed interval $[a, b]$ such that $f'(a) = y_1$ and $f'(b) = y_2$. If d lies between y_1 and y_2, then there exists c in (a, b) such that $f'(c) = d$.

16. Maximum Area The figures show a rectangle, a circle, and a semicircle inscribed in a triangle bounded by the coordinate axes and the first-quadrant portion of the line with intercepts $(3, 0)$ and $(0, 4)$. Find the dimensions of each inscribed figure such that its area is maximum. State whether calculus was helpful in finding the required dimensions. Explain your reasoning.

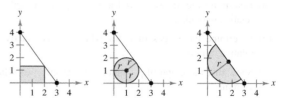

17. Point of Inflection Show that the cubic polynomial $p(x) = ax^3 + bx^2 + cx + d$ has exactly one point of inflection (x_0, y_0), where

$$x_0 = \frac{-b}{3a} \quad \text{and} \quad y_0 = \frac{2b^3}{27a^2} - \frac{bc}{3a} + d.$$

Use this formula to find the point of inflection of $p(x) = x^3 - 3x^2 + 2$.

18. Minimum Length A legal-sized sheet of paper (8.5 inches by 14 inches) is folded so that corner P touches the opposite 14-inch edge at R (see figure). $\left(\text{Note: } PQ = \sqrt{C^2 - x^2}.\right)$

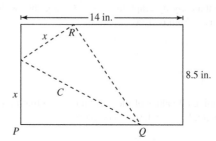

(a) Show that $C^2 = \dfrac{2x^3}{2x - 8.5}$.

(b) What is the domain of C?

(c) Determine the x-value that minimizes C.

(d) Determine the minimum length C.

19. Using a Function Let $f(x) = \sin(\ln x)$.

(a) Determine the domain of the function f.

(b) Find two values of x satisfying $f(x) = 1$.

(c) Find two values of x satisfying $f(x) = -1$.

(d) What is the range of the function f?

(e) Calculate $f'(x)$ and use calculus to find the maximum value of f on the interval $[1, 10]$.

(f) Use a graphing utility to graph f in the viewing window $[0, 5] \times [-2, 2]$ and estimate $\lim\limits_{x \to 0^+} f(x)$, if it exists.

(g) Determine $\lim\limits_{x \to 0^+} f(x)$ analytically, if it exists.

5 Integration

5.1 Antiderivatives and Indefinite Integration
5.2 Area
5.3 Riemann Sums and Definite Integrals
5.4 The Fundamental Theorem of Calculus
5.5 Integration by Substitution
5.6 Numerical Integration
5.7 The Natural Logarithmic Function: Integration
5.8 Inverse Trigonometric Functions: Integration
5.9 Hyperbolic Functions

Surveying *(Exercise 41, p. 347)*

Heat Transfer *(Exercise 101, p. 356)*

The Speed of Sound *(Example 5, p. 318)*

Amount of Chemical
Flowing into a Tank
(Example 9, p. 322)

Grand Canyon *(Exercise 58, p. 288)*

5.1 Antiderivatives and Indefinite Integration

■ Write the general solution of a differential equation and use indefinite integral notation for antiderivatives.
■ Use basic integration rules to find antiderivatives.
■ Find a particular solution of a differential equation.

Antiderivatives

To find a function F whose derivative is $f(x) = 3x^2$, you might use your knowledge of derivatives to conclude that

$$F(x) = x^3 \quad \text{because} \quad \frac{d}{dx}[x^3] = 3x^2.$$

The function F is an *antiderivative* of f.

> **Definition of Antiderivative**
>
> A function F is an **antiderivative** of f on an interval I when $F'(x) = f(x)$ for all x in I.

Note that F is called *an* antiderivative of f, rather than *the* antiderivative of f. To see why, observe that

$$F_1(x) = x^3, \quad F_2(x) = x^3 - 5, \quad \text{and} \quad F_3(x) = x^3 + 97$$

are all antiderivatives of $f(x) = 3x^2$. In fact, for any constant C, the function $F(x) = x^3 + C$ is an antiderivative of f.

> **THEOREM 5.1 Representation of Antiderivatives**
>
> If F is an antiderivative of f on an interval I, then G is an antiderivative of f on the interval I if and only if G is of the form $G(x) = F(x) + C$, for all x in I where C is a constant.

Proof The proof of Theorem 5.1 in one direction is straightforward. That is, if $G(x) = F(x) + C$, $F'(x) = f(x)$, and C is a constant, then

$$G'(x) = \frac{d}{dx}[F(x) + C] = F'(x) + 0 = f(x).$$

To prove this theorem in the other direction, assume that G is an antiderivative of f. Define a function H such that

$$H(x) = G(x) - F(x).$$

For any two points a and b ($a < b$) in the interval, H is continuous on $[a, b]$ and differentiable on (a, b). By the Mean Value Theorem,

$$H'(c) = \frac{H(b) - H(a)}{b - a}$$

for some c in (a, b). However, $H'(c) = 0$, so $H(a) = H(b)$. Because a and b are arbitrary points in the interval, you know that H is a constant function C. So, $G(x) - F(x) = C$ and it follows that $G(x) = F(x) + C$.

See LarsonCalculus.com for Bruce Edwards's video of this proof.

Using Theorem 5.1, you can represent the entire family of antiderivatives of a function by adding a constant to a *known* antiderivative. For example, knowing that

$$D_x[x^2] = 2x$$

you can represent the family of *all* antiderivatives of $f(x) = 2x$ by

$$G(x) = x^2 + C \qquad \text{Family of all antiderivatives of } f(x) = 2x$$

where C is a constant. The constant C is called the **constant of integration.** The family of functions represented by G is the **general antiderivative** of f, and $G(x) = x^2 + C$ is the **general solution** of the *differential equation*

$$G'(x) = 2x. \qquad \text{Differential equation}$$

A **differential equation** in x and y is an equation that involves x, y, and derivatives of y. For instance,

$$y' = 3x \quad \text{and} \quad y' = x^2 + 1$$

are examples of differential equations.

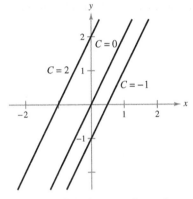

Functions of the form $y = 2x + C$
Figure 5.1

EXAMPLE 1   **Solving a Differential Equation**

Find the general solution of the differential equation $y' = 2$.

Solution   To begin, you need to find a function whose derivative is 2. One such function is

$$y = 2x. \qquad \text{2x is an antiderivative of 2.}$$

Now, you can use Theorem 5.1 to conclude that the general solution of the differential equation is

$$y = 2x + C. \qquad \text{General solution}$$

The graphs of several functions of the form $y = 2x + C$ are shown in Figure 5.1.   ■

When solving a differential equation of the form

$$\frac{dy}{dx} = f(x)$$

it is convenient to write it in the equivalent differential form

$$dy = f(x)\,dx.$$

The operation of finding all solutions of this equation is called **antidifferentiation** (or **indefinite integration**) and is denoted by an integral sign $\int$. The general solution is denoted by

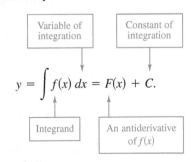

> **REMARK**   In this text, the notation $\int f(x)\,dx = F(x) + C$ means that F is an antiderivative of f on an interval.

The expression $\int f(x)\,dx$ is read as the *antiderivative of f with respect to x.* So, the differential dx serves to identify x as the variable of integration. The term **indefinite integral** is a synonym for antiderivative.

Basic Integration Rules

The inverse nature of integration and differentiation can be verified by substituting $F'(x)$ for $f(x)$ in the indefinite integration definition to obtain

$$\int F'(x)\, dx = F(x) + C.$$

Integration is the "inverse" of differentiation.

Moreover, if $\int f(x)\, dx = F(x) + C$, then

$$\frac{d}{dx}\left[\int f(x)\, dx\right] = f(x).$$

Differentiation is the "inverse" of integration.

REMARK   The Power Rule for Integration has the restriction that $n \neq -1$. To evaluate $\int x^{-1}\, dx$, you must use the natural log rule. (See Exercise 75.)

These two equations allow you to obtain integration formulas directly from differentiation formulas, as shown in the following summary.

Basic Integration Rules

Differentiation Formula	Integration Formula
$\frac{d}{dx}[C] = 0$	$\int 0\, dx = C$
$\frac{d}{dx}[kx] = k$	$\int k\, dx = kx + C$
$\frac{d}{dx}[kf(x)] = kf'(x)$	$\int kf(x)\, dx = k\int f(x)\, dx$
$\frac{d}{dx}[f(x) \pm g(x)] = f'(x) \pm g'(x)$	$\int [f(x) \pm g(x)]\, dx = \int f(x)\, dx \pm \int g(x)\, dx$
$\frac{d}{dx}[x^n] = nx^{n-1}$	$\int x^n\, dx = \frac{x^{n+1}}{n+1} + C, \quad n \neq -1$ Power Rule
$\frac{d}{dx}[\sin x] = \cos x$	$\int \cos x\, dx = \sin x + C$
$\frac{d}{dx}[\cos x] = -\sin x$	$\int \sin x\, dx = -\cos x + C$
$\frac{d}{dx}[\tan x] = \sec^2 x$	$\int \sec^2 x\, dx = \tan x + C$
$\frac{d}{dx}[\sec x] = \sec x \tan x$	$\int \sec x \tan x\, dx = \sec x + C$
$\frac{d}{dx}[\cot x] = -\csc^2 x$	$\int \csc^2 x\, dx = -\cot x + C$
$\frac{d}{dx}[\csc x] = -\csc x \cot x$	$\int \csc x \cot x\, dx = -\csc x + C$
$\frac{d}{dx}[e^x] = e^x$	$\int e^x\, dx = e^x + C$
$\frac{d}{dx}[a^x] = (\ln a)a^x$	$\int a^x\, dx = \left(\frac{1}{\ln a}\right)a^x + C$
$\frac{d}{dx}[\ln x] = \frac{1}{x}, \; x > 0$	$\int \frac{1}{x}\, dx = \ln|x| + C$

· · · · · · · · · · · · · · · · · ▷
•• **REMARK** In Example 2, note that the general pattern of integration is similar to that of differentiation.

Original integral

Rewrite

Integrate

⬇

Simplify

EXAMPLE 2 **Describing Antiderivatives**

$$\int 3x \, dx = 3 \int x \, dx \qquad\qquad \text{Constant Multiple Rule}$$

$$= 3 \int x^1 \, dx \qquad\qquad \text{Rewrite } x \text{ as } x^1.$$

$$= 3 \left(\frac{x^2}{2} \right) + C \qquad\qquad \text{Power Rule } (n = 1)$$

$$= \frac{3}{2} x^2 + C \qquad\qquad \text{Simplify.}$$

The antiderivatives of $3x$ are of the form $\frac{3}{2} x^2 + C$, where C is any constant.

When indefinite integrals are evaluated, a strict application of the basic integration rules tends to produce complicated constants of integration. For instance, in Example 2, the solution could have been written as

$$\int 3x \, dx = 3 \int x \, dx = 3 \left(\frac{x^2}{2} + C \right) = \frac{3}{2} x^2 + 3C.$$

Because C represents *any* constant, it is both cumbersome and unnecessary to write $3C$ as the constant of integration. So, $\frac{3}{2} x^2 + 3C$ is written in the simpler form $\frac{3}{2} x^2 + C$.

EXAMPLE 3 **Rewriting Before Integrating**

· · · ▷ *See LarsonCalculus.com for an interactive version of this type of example.*

•• **REMARK** The properties of logarithms presented on page 52 can be used to rewrite antiderivatives in different forms. For instance, the antiderivative in Example 3(d) can be rewritten as

$$3 \ln|x| + C = \ln|x|^3 + C.$$

· · · · · · · · · · · · · · · ▷

	Original Integral	Rewrite	Integrate	Simplify
a.	$\int \dfrac{1}{x^3} \, dx$	$\int x^{-3} \, dx$	$\dfrac{x^{-2}}{-2} + C$	$-\dfrac{1}{2x^2} + C$
b.	$\int \sqrt{x} \, dx$	$\int x^{1/2} \, dx$	$\dfrac{x^{3/2}}{3/2} + C$	$\dfrac{2}{3} x^{3/2} + C$
c.	$\int 2 \sin x \, dx$	$2 \int \sin x \, dx$	$2(-\cos x) + C$	$-2 \cos x + C$
d.	$\int \dfrac{3}{x} \, dx$	$3 \int \dfrac{1}{x} \, dx$	$3 (\ln|x|) + C$	$3 \ln|x| + C$

EXAMPLE 4 **Integrating Polynomial Functions**

•• **REMARK** The basic integration rules allow you to integrate any polynomial function.

a. $\displaystyle\int dx = \int 1 \, dx$ \qquad\qquad Integrand is understood to be 1.

$$= x + C \qquad\qquad \text{Integrate.}$$

b. $\displaystyle\int (x + 2) \, dx = \int x \, dx + \int 2 \, dx$

$$= \frac{x^2}{2} + C_1 + 2x + C_2 \qquad \text{Integrate.}$$

$$= \frac{x^2}{2} + 2x + C \qquad\qquad C = C_1 + C_2$$

The second line in the solution is usually omitted.

c. $\displaystyle\int (3x^4 - 5x^2 + x) \, dx = 3 \left(\frac{x^5}{5} \right) - 5 \left(\frac{x^3}{3} \right) + \frac{x^2}{2} + C = \frac{3}{5} x^5 - \frac{5}{3} x^3 + \frac{1}{2} x^2 + C$

· · · · · · · · · · · · · · · · · · · ▷

REMARK Before you begin the exercise set, be sure you realize that one of the most important steps in integration is *rewriting the integrand* in a form that fits one of the basic integration rules.

EXAMPLE 5 **Rewriting Before Integrating**

$$\int \frac{x+1}{\sqrt{x}}\, dx = \int \left(\frac{x}{\sqrt{x}} + \frac{1}{\sqrt{x}} \right) dx \qquad \text{Rewrite as two fractions.}$$

$$= \int (x^{1/2} + x^{-1/2})\, dx \qquad \text{Rewrite with fractional exponents.}$$

$$= \frac{x^{3/2}}{3/2} + \frac{x^{1/2}}{1/2} + C \qquad \text{Integrate.}$$

$$= \frac{2}{3}x^{3/2} + 2x^{1/2} + C \qquad \text{Simplify.}$$

$$= \frac{2}{3}\sqrt{x}(x+3) + C$$

When integrating quotients, do not integrate the numerator and denominator separately. This is no more valid in integration than it is in differentiation. For instance, in Example 5, be sure you understand that

$$\int \frac{x+1}{\sqrt{x}}\, dx = \frac{2}{3}\sqrt{x}(x+3) + C$$

is not the same as

$$\frac{\int (x+1)\, dx}{\int \sqrt{x}\, dx} = \frac{\frac{1}{2}x^2 + x + C_1}{\frac{2}{3}x\sqrt{x} + C_2}.$$

EXAMPLE 6 **Rewriting Before Integrating**

$$\int \frac{\sin x}{\cos^2 x}\, dx = \int \left(\frac{1}{\cos x} \right)\left(\frac{\sin x}{\cos x} \right) dx \qquad \text{Rewrite as a product.}$$

$$= \int \sec x \tan x\, dx \qquad \text{Rewrite using trigonometric identities.}$$

$$= \sec x + C \qquad \text{Integrate.}$$

▷ **TECHNOLOGY** Some software programs, such as *Maple* and *Mathematica*, are capable of performing integration symbolically. If you have access to such a symbolic integration utility, try using it to evaluate the indefinite integrals in Example 7.

EXAMPLE 7 **Rewriting Before Integrating**

Original Integral	Rewrite	Integrate	Simplify
a. $\displaystyle\int \frac{2}{\sqrt{x}}\, dx$	$2\displaystyle\int x^{-1/2}\, dx$	$2\left(\dfrac{x^{1/2}}{1/2}\right) + C$	$4x^{1/2} + C$
b. $\displaystyle\int (t^2 + 1)^2\, dt$	$\displaystyle\int (t^4 + 2t^2 + 1)\, dt$	$\dfrac{t^5}{5} + 2\left(\dfrac{t^3}{3}\right) + t + C$	$\dfrac{1}{5}t^5 + \dfrac{2}{3}t^3 + t + C$
c. $\displaystyle\int \frac{x^3 + 3}{x^2}\, dx$	$\displaystyle\int (x + 3x^{-2})\, dx$	$\dfrac{x^2}{2} + 3\left(\dfrac{x^{-1}}{-1}\right) + C$	$\dfrac{1}{2}x^2 - \dfrac{3}{x} + C$
d. $\displaystyle\int \sqrt[3]{x}(x-4)\, dx$	$\displaystyle\int (x^{4/3} - 4x^{1/3})\, dx$	$\dfrac{x^{7/3}}{7/3} - 4\left(\dfrac{x^{4/3}}{4/3}\right) + C$	$\dfrac{3}{7}x^{7/3} - 3x^{4/3} + C$

As you do the exercises, note that you can check your answer to an antidifferentiation problem by differentiating. For instance, in Example 7(a), you can check that $4x^{1/2} + C$ is the correct antiderivative by differentiating the answer to obtain

$$D_x[4x^{1/2} + C] = 4\left(\frac{1}{2}\right)x^{-1/2} = \frac{2}{\sqrt{x}}. \qquad \text{Use differentiation to check antiderivative.}$$

Initial Conditions and Particular Solutions

You have already seen that the equation $y = \int f(x)\,dx$ has many solutions (each differing from the others by a constant). This means that the graphs of any two antiderivatives of f are vertical translations of each other. For example, Figure 5.2 shows the graphs of several antiderivatives of the form

$$y = \int (3x^2 - 1)\,dx = x^3 - x + C \qquad \text{General solution}$$

for various integer values of C. Each of these antiderivatives is a solution of the differential equation

$$\frac{dy}{dx} = 3x^2 - 1.$$

In many applications of integration, you are given enough information to determine a **particular solution.** To do this, you need only know the value of $y = F(x)$ for one value of x. This information is called an **initial condition.** For example, in Figure 5.2, only one curve passes through the point $(2, 4)$. To find this curve, you can use the general solution

$$F(x) = x^3 - x + C \qquad \text{General solution}$$

and the initial condition

$$F(2) = 4. \qquad \text{Initial condition}$$

By using the initial condition in the general solution, you can determine that

$$F(2) = 8 - 2 + C = 4$$

which implies that $C = -2$. So, you obtain

$$F(x) = x^3 - x - 2. \qquad \text{Particular solution}$$

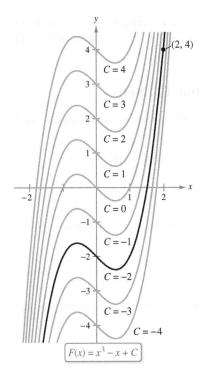

The particular solution that satisfies the initial condition $F(2) = 4$ is $F(x) = x^3 - x - 2$.
Figure 5.2

EXAMPLE 8   **Finding a Particular Solution**

Find the general solution of

$$F'(x) = e^x \qquad \text{Differential equation}$$

and find the particular solution that satisfies the initial condition

$$F(0) = 3. \qquad \text{Initial condition}$$

Solution   To find the general solution, integrate to obtain

$$F(x) = \int e^x\,dx$$

$$= e^x + C. \qquad \text{General solution}$$

Using the initial condition $F(0) = 3$, you can solve for C as follows.

$$F(0) = e^0 + C$$
$$3 = 1 + C$$
$$2 = C$$

So, the particular solution is

$$F(x) = e^x + 2 \qquad \text{Particular solution}$$

as shown in Figure 5.3. Note that Figure 5.3 also shows the solution curves that correspond to $C = -3, -2, -1, 0, 1,$ and 3.

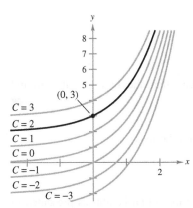

The particular solution that satisfies the initial condition $F(0) = 3$ is $F(x) = e^x + 2$.
Figure 5.3

So far in this section, you have been using x as the variable of integration. In applications, it is often convenient to use a different variable. For instance, in the next example, involving *time*, the variable of integration is t.

EXAMPLE 9 **Solving a Vertical Motion Problem**

A ball is thrown upward with an initial velocity of 64 feet per second from an initial height of 80 feet.

a. Find the position function giving the height s as a function of the time t.

b. When does the ball hit the ground?

Solution

a. Let $t = 0$ represent the initial time. The two given initial conditions can be written as follows.

$$s(0) = 80 \qquad \text{Initial height is 80 feet.}$$
$$s'(0) = 64 \qquad \text{Initial velocity is 64 feet per second.}$$

Using -32 feet per second per second as the acceleration due to gravity, you can write

$$s''(t) = -32$$
$$s'(t) = \int s''(t)\, dt = \int -32\, dt = -32t + C_1.$$

Using the initial velocity, you obtain $s'(0) = 64 = -32(0) + C_1$, which implies that $C_1 = 64$. Next, by integrating $s'(t)$, you obtain

$$s(t) = \int s'(t)\, dt = \int (-32t + 64)\, dt = -16t^2 + 64t + C_2.$$

Using the initial height, you obtain

$$s(0) = 80 = -16(0^2) + 64(0) + C_2$$

which implies that $C_2 = 80$. So, the position function is

$$s(t) = -16t^2 + 64t + 80. \qquad \text{See Figure 5.4.}$$

b. Using the position function found in part (a), you can find the time at which the ball hits the ground by solving the equation $s(t) = 0$.

$$-16t^2 + 64t + 80 = 0$$
$$-16(t + 1)(t - 5) = 0$$
$$t = -1, 5$$

Because t must be positive, you can conclude that the ball hits the ground 5 seconds after it was thrown.

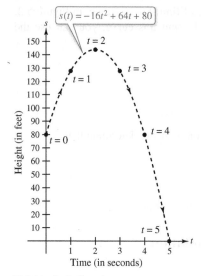

Height of a ball at time t
Figure 5.4

In Example 9, note that the position function has the form

$$s(t) = \frac{1}{2}gt^2 + v_0 t + s_0$$

where $g = -32$, v_0 is the initial velocity, and s_0 is the initial height, as presented in Section 3.2.

Example 9 shows how to use calculus to analyze vertical motion problems in which the acceleration is determined by a gravitational force. You can use a similar strategy to analyze other linear motion problems (vertical or horizontal) in which the acceleration (or deceleration) is the result of some other force, as you will see in Exercises 61–68.

5.1 Exercises

See **CalcChat.com** for tutorial help and worked-out solutions to odd-numbered exercises.

Integration and Differentiation In Exercises 1 and 2, verify the statement by showing that the derivative of the right side equals the integrand of the left side.

1. $\int \left(-\dfrac{6}{x^4}\right) dx = \dfrac{2}{x^3} + C$

2. $\int \left(8x^3 + \dfrac{1}{2x^2}\right) dx = 2x^4 - \dfrac{1}{2x} + C$

Solving a Differential Equation In Exercises 3–6, find the general solution of the differential equation and check the result by differentiation.

3. $\dfrac{dy}{dt} = 9t^2$

4. $\dfrac{dy}{dt} = 5$

5. $\dfrac{dy}{dx} = x^{3/2}$

6. $\dfrac{dy}{dx} = 2x^{-3}$

Rewriting Before Integrating In Exercises 7–10, complete the table to find the indefinite integral.

Original Integral	Rewrite	Integrate	Simplify
7. $\int \sqrt[3]{x}\, dx$			
8. $\int \dfrac{1}{4x^2}\, dx$			
9. $\int \dfrac{1}{x\sqrt{x}}\, dx$			
10. $\int \dfrac{1}{(3x)^2}\, dx$			

Finding an Indefinite Integral In Exercises 11–32, find the indefinite integral and check the result by differentiation.

11. $\int (x + 7)\, dx$

12. $\int (8x^3 - 9x^2 + 4)\, dx$

13. $\int (x^{3/2} + 2x + 1)\, dx$

14. $\int \left(\sqrt{x} + \dfrac{1}{2\sqrt{x}}\right) dx$

15. $\int \sqrt[3]{x^2}\, dx$

16. $\int (\sqrt[4]{x^3} + 1)\, dx$

17. $\int \dfrac{1}{x^5}\, dx$

18. $\int \dfrac{3}{x^7}\, dx$

19. $\int \dfrac{x + 6}{\sqrt{x}}\, dx$

20. $\int \dfrac{x^4 - 3x^2 + 5}{x^4}\, dx$

21. $\int (x + 1)(3x - 2)\, dx$

22. $\int (4t^2 + 3)^2\, dt$

23. $\int (5 \cos x + 4 \sin x)\, dx$

24. $\int (\theta^2 + \sec^2 \theta)\, d\theta$

25. $\int (2 \sin x - 5e^x)\, dx$

26. $\int \sec y (\tan y - \sec y)\, dy$

27. $\int (\tan^2 y + 1)\, dy$

28. $\int (4x - \csc^2 x)\, dx$

29. $\int (2x - 4^x)\, dx$

30. $\int (\cos x + 3^x)\, dx$

31. $\int \left(x - \dfrac{5}{x}\right) dx$

32. $\int \left(\dfrac{4}{x} + \sec^2 x\right) dx$

Sketching a Graph In Exercises 33 and 34, the graph of the derivative of a function is given. Sketch the graphs of *two* functions that have the given derivative. (There is more than one correct answer.) To print an enlarged copy of the graph, go to *MathGraphs.com*.

33.
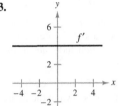

34.
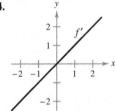

Finding a Particular Solution In Exercises 35–42, find the particular solution that satisfies the differential equation and the initial condition.

35. $f'(x) = 6x$, $f(0) = 8$

36. $f'(s) = 10s - 12s^3$, $f(3) = 2$

37. $f''(x) = 2$, $f'(2) = 5$, $f(2) = 10$

38. $f''(x) = x^2$, $f'(0) = 8$, $f(0) = 4$

39. $f''(x) = x^{-3/2}$, $f'(4) = 2$, $f(0) = 0$

40. $f''(x) = \sin x$, $f'(0) = 1$, $f(0) = 6$

41. $f''(x) = e^x$, $f'(0) = 2$, $f(0) = 5$

42. $f''(x) = \dfrac{2}{x^2}$, $f'(1) = 4$, $f(1) = 3$

Slope Field In Exercises 43 and 44, a differential equation, a point, and a slope field are given. A *slope field* (or *direction field*) consists of line segments with slopes given by the differential equation. These line segments give a visual perspective of the slopes of the solutions of the differential equation. (a) Sketch two approximate solutions of the differential equation on the slope field, one of which passes through the indicated point. (To print an enlarged copy of the graph, go to *MathGraphs.com*.) (b) Use integration to find the particular solution of the differential equation and use a graphing utility to graph the solution. Compare the result with the sketches in part (a).

43. $\dfrac{dy}{dx} = x^2 - 1$, $(-1, 3)$

44. $\dfrac{dy}{dx} = -\dfrac{1}{x^2}$, $x > 0$, $(1, 3)$

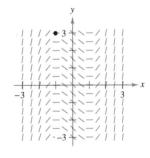

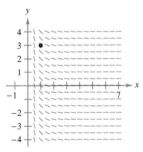

Slope Field In Exercises 45 and 46, (a) use a graphing utility to graph a slope field for the differential equation, (b) use integration and the given point to find the particular solution of the differential equation, and (c) graph the solution and the slope field in the same viewing window.

45. $\dfrac{dy}{dx} = 2x,\ (-2, -2)$ **46.** $\dfrac{dy}{dx} = 2\sqrt{x},\ (4, 12)$

WRITING ABOUT CONCEPTS

47. Antiderivatives and Indefinite Integrals What is the difference, if any, between finding the antiderivative of $f(x)$ and evaluating the integral $\int f(x)\,dx$?

48. Comparing Functions Consider $f(x) = \tan^2 x$ and $g(x) = \sec^2 x$. What do you notice about the derivatives of $f(x)$ and $g(x)$? What can you conclude about the relationship between $f(x)$ and $g(x)$?

49. Sketching Graphs The graphs of f and f' each pass through the origin. Use the graph of f'' shown in the figure to sketch the graphs of f and f'. To print an enlarged copy of the graph, go to *MathGraphs.com*.

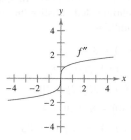

50. HOW DO YOU SEE IT? Use the graph of f' shown in the figure to answer the following.

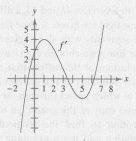

(a) Approximate the slope of f at $x = 4$. Explain.

(b) Is it possible that $f(2) = -1$? Explain.

(c) Is $f(5) - f(4) > 0$? Explain.

(d) Approximate the value of x where f is maximum. Explain.

(e) Approximate any open intervals in which the graph of f is concave upward and any open intervals in which it is concave downward. Approximate the x-coordinates of any points of inflection.

51. Tree Growth An evergreen nursery usually sells a certain type of shrub after 6 years of growth and shaping. The growth rate during those 6 years is approximated by $dh/dt = 1.5t + 5$, where t is the time in years and h is the height in centimeters. The seedlings are 12 centimeters tall when planted ($t = 0$).

(a) Find the height after t years.

(b) How tall are the shrubs when they are sold?

52. Population Growth The rate of growth dP/dt of a population of bacteria is proportional to the square root of t, where P is the population size and t is the time in days ($0 \le t \le 10$). That is,

$$\frac{dP}{dt} = k\sqrt{t}.$$

The initial size of the population is 500. After 1 day the population has grown to 600. Estimate the population after 7 days.

Vertical Motion In Exercises 53–55, use $a(t) = -32$ feet per second per second as the acceleration due to gravity. (Neglect air resistance.)

53. A ball is thrown vertically upward from a height of 6 feet with an initial velocity of 60 feet per second. How high will the ball go?

54. With what initial velocity must an object be thrown upward (from ground level) to reach the top of the Washington Monument (approximately 550 feet)?

55. A balloon, rising vertically with a velocity of 16 feet per second, releases a sandbag at the instant it is 64 feet above the ground.

(a) How many seconds after its release will the bag strike the ground?

(b) At what velocity will it hit the ground?

Vertical Motion In Exercises 56–58, use $a(t) = -9.8$ meters per second per second as the acceleration due to gravity. (Neglect air resistance.)

56. A baseball is thrown upward from a height of 2 meters with an initial velocity of 10 meters per second. Determine its maximum height.

57. With what initial velocity must an object be thrown upward (from a height of 2 meters) to reach a maximum height of 200 meters?

58. Grand Canyon

The Grand Canyon is 1800 meters deep at its deepest point. A rock is dropped from the rim above this point. Write the height of the rock as a function of the time t in seconds. How long will it take the rock to hit the canyon floor?

59. Lunar Gravity On the moon, the acceleration due to gravity is -1.6 meters per second per second. A stone is dropped from a cliff on the moon and hits the surface of the moon 20 seconds later. How far did it fall? What was its velocity at impact?

60. Escape Velocity The minimum velocity required for an object to escape Earth's gravitational pull is obtained from the solution of the equation

$$\int v \, dv = -GM \int \frac{1}{y^2} \, dy$$

where v is the velocity of the object projected from Earth, y is the distance from the center of Earth, G is the gravitational constant, and M is the mass of Earth. Show that v and y are related by the equation

$$v^2 = v_0^2 + 2GM\left(\frac{1}{y} - \frac{1}{R}\right)$$

where v_0 is the initial velocity of the object and R is the radius of Earth.

Rectilinear Motion In Exercises 61–64, consider a particle moving along the x-axis where $x(t)$ is the position of the particle at time t, $x'(t)$ is its velocity, and $x''(t)$ is its acceleration.

61. $x(t) = t^3 - 6t^2 + 9t - 2$, $0 \le t \le 5$

(a) Find the velocity and acceleration of the particle.

(b) Find the open t-intervals on which the particle is moving to the right.

(c) Find the velocity of the particle when the acceleration is 0.

62. Repeat Exercise 61 for the position function

$$x(t) = (t - 1)(t - 3)^2, \quad 0 \le t \le 5.$$

63. A particle moves along the x-axis at a velocity of $v(t) = 1/\sqrt{t}$, $t > 0$. At time $t = 1$, its position is $x = 4$. Find the acceleration and position functions for the particle.

64. A particle, initially at rest, moves along the x-axis such that its acceleration at time $t > 0$ is given by $a(t) = \cos t$. At the time $t = 0$, its position is $x = 3$.

(a) Find the velocity and position functions for the particle.

(b) Find the values of t for which the particle is at rest.

65. Acceleration The maker of an automobile advertises that it takes 13 seconds to accelerate from 25 kilometers per hour to 80 kilometers per hour. Assume the acceleration is constant.

(a) Find the acceleration in meters per second per second.

(b) Find the distance the car travels during the 13 seconds.

66. Deceleration A car traveling at 45 miles per hour is brought to a stop, at constant deceleration, 132 feet from where the brakes are applied.

(a) How far has the car moved when its speed has been reduced to 30 miles per hour?

(b) How far has the car moved when its speed has been reduced to 15 miles per hour?

(c) Draw the real number line from 0 to 132. Plot the points found in parts (a) and (b). What can you conclude?

67. Acceleration At the instant the traffic light turns green, a car that has been waiting at an intersection starts with a constant acceleration of 6 feet per second per second. At the same instant, a truck traveling with a constant velocity of 30 feet per second passes the car.

(a) How far beyond its starting point will the car pass the truck?

(b) How fast will the car be traveling when it passes the truck?

68. Acceleration Assume that a fully loaded plane starting from rest has a constant acceleration while moving down a runway. The plane requires 0.7 mile of runway and a speed of 160 miles per hour in order to lift off. What is the plane's acceleration?

True or False? In Exercises 69 and 70, determine whether the statement is true or false. If it is false, explain why or give an example that shows it is false.

69. The antiderivative of $f(x)$ is unique.

70. Each antiderivative of an nth-degree polynomial function is an $(n + 1)$th-degree polynomial function.

71. Horizontal Tangent Find a function f such that the graph of f has a horizontal tangent at $(2, 0)$ and $f''(x) = 2x$.

72. Finding a Function The graph of f' is shown. Find and sketch the graph of f given that f is continuous and $f(0) = 1$.

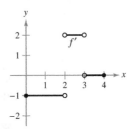

73. Proof Let $s(x)$ and $c(x)$ be two functions satisfying $s'(x) = c(x)$ and $c'(x) = -s(x)$ for all x. If $s(0) = 0$ and $c(0) = 1$, prove that $[s(x)]^2 + [c(x)]^2 = 1$.

74. Verification Verify the natural log rule $\int \frac{1}{x} \, dx = \ln|Cx|$, $C \ne 0$, by showing that the derivative of $\ln|Cx|$ is $1/x$.

75. Verification Verify the natural log rule $\int \frac{1}{x} \, dx = \ln|x| + C$ by showing that the derivative of $\ln|x| + C$ is $1/x$.

PUTNAM EXAM CHALLENGE

76. Suppose f and g are non-constant, differentiable, real-valued functions defined on $(-\infty, \infty)$. Furthermore, suppose that for each pair of real numbers x and y,

$$f(x + y) = f(x)f(y) - g(x)g(y) \quad \text{and}$$
$$g(x + y) = f(x)g(y) + g(x)f(y).$$

If $f'(0) = 0$, prove that $(f(x))^2 + (g(x))^2 = 1$ for all x.

5.2 Area

■ Use sigma notation to write and evaluate a sum.
■ Understand the concept of area.
■ Approximate the area of a plane region.
■ Find the area of a plane region using limits.

Sigma Notation

In the preceding section, you studied antidifferentiation. In this section, you will look further into a problem introduced in Section 2.1—that of finding the area of a region in the plane. At first glance, these two ideas may seem unrelated, but you will discover in Section 5.4 that they are closely related by an extremely important theorem called the Fundamental Theorem of Calculus.

This section begins by introducing a concise notation for sums. This notation is called **sigma notation** because it uses the uppercase Greek letter sigma, written as Σ.

Sigma Notation

The sum of n terms $a_1, a_2, a_3, \ldots, a_n$ is written as

$$\sum_{i=1}^{n} a_i = a_1 + a_2 + a_3 + \cdots + a_n$$

where i is the **index of summation,** a_i is the **ith term** of the sum, and the **upper and lower bounds of summation** are n and 1.

REMARK The upper and lower bounds must be constant with respect to the index of summation. However, the lower bound doesn't have to be 1. Any integer less than or equal to the upper bound is legitimate.

EXAMPLE 1 **Examples of Sigma Notation**

a. $\displaystyle\sum_{i=1}^{6} i = 1 + 2 + 3 + 4 + 5 + 6$

b. $\displaystyle\sum_{i=0}^{5} (i + 1) = 1 + 2 + 3 + 4 + 5 + 6$

c. $\displaystyle\sum_{j=3}^{7} j^2 = 3^2 + 4^2 + 5^2 + 6^2 + 7^2$

d. $\displaystyle\sum_{j=1}^{5} \frac{1}{\sqrt{j}} = \frac{1}{\sqrt{1}} + \frac{1}{\sqrt{2}} + \frac{1}{\sqrt{3}} + \frac{1}{\sqrt{4}} + \frac{1}{\sqrt{5}}$

e. $\displaystyle\sum_{k=1}^{n} \frac{1}{n}(k^2 + 1) = \frac{1}{n}(1^2 + 1) + \frac{1}{n}(2^2 + 1) + \cdots + \frac{1}{n}(n^2 + 1)$

f. $\displaystyle\sum_{i=1}^{n} f(x_i)\,\Delta x = f(x_1)\,\Delta x + f(x_2)\,\Delta x + \cdots + f(x_n)\,\Delta x$

From parts (a) and (b), notice that the same sum can be represented in different ways using sigma notation.

■ FOR FURTHER INFORMATION
For a geometric interpretation of summation formulas, see the article "Looking at $\displaystyle\sum_{k=1}^{n} k$ and $\displaystyle\sum_{k=1}^{n} k^2$ Geometrically" by Eric Hegblom in *Mathematics Teacher*. To view this article, go to *MathArticles.com*.

Although any variable can be used as the index of summation, $i, j,$ and k are often used. Notice in Example 1 that the index of summation does not appear in the terms of the expanded sum.

The properties of summation shown below can be derived using the Associative and Commutative Properties of Addition and the Distributive Property of Addition over Multiplication. (In the first property, k is a constant.)

1. $\displaystyle\sum_{i=1}^{n} ka_i = k\sum_{i=1}^{n} a_i$ $\qquad\qquad$ **2.** $\displaystyle\sum_{i=1}^{n} (a_i \pm b_i) = \sum_{i=1}^{n} a_i \pm \sum_{i=1}^{n} b_i$

The next theorem lists some useful formulas for sums of powers.

THEOREM 5.2 **Summation Formulas**

1. $\displaystyle\sum_{i=1}^{n} c = cn, \ c$ is a constant $\qquad$ **2.** $\displaystyle\sum_{i=1}^{n} i = \frac{n(n + 1)}{2}$

3. $\displaystyle\sum_{i=1}^{n} i^2 = \frac{n(n + 1)(2n + 1)}{6}$ $\qquad$ **4.** $\displaystyle\sum_{i=1}^{n} i^3 = \frac{n^2(n + 1)^2}{4}$

A proof of this theorem is given in Appendix A.
See LarsonCalculus.com for Bruce Edwards's video of this proof.

EXAMPLE 2 **Evaluating a Sum**

Evaluate $\displaystyle\sum_{i=1}^{n} \frac{i + 1}{n^2}$ for $n = 10, 100, 1000,$ and $10,000.$

Solution

$$\sum_{i=1}^{n} \frac{i + 1}{n^2} = \frac{1}{n^2}\sum_{i=1}^{n} (i + 1) \qquad \text{Factor the constant } \tfrac{1}{n^2} \text{ out of sum.}$$

$$= \frac{1}{n^2}\left(\sum_{i=1}^{n} i + \sum_{i=1}^{n} 1\right) \qquad \text{Write as two sums.}$$

$$= \frac{1}{n^2}\left[\frac{n(n + 1)}{2} + n\right] \qquad \text{Apply Theorem 5.2.}$$

$$= \frac{1}{n^2}\left[\frac{n^2 + 3n}{2}\right] \qquad \text{Simplify.}$$

$$= \frac{n + 3}{2n} \qquad \text{Simplify.}$$

Now you can evaluate the sum by substituting the appropriate values of n, as shown in the table below.

n	10	100	1000	10,000
$\displaystyle\sum_{i=1}^{n} \frac{i + 1}{n^2} = \frac{n + 3}{2n}$	0.65000	0.51500	0.50150	0.50015

In the table, note that the sum appears to approach a limit as n increases. Although the discussion of limits at infinity in Section 4.5 applies to a variable x, where x can be any real number, many of the same results hold true for limits involving the variable n, where n is restricted to positive integer values. So, to find the limit of $(n + 3)/2n$ as n approaches infinity, you can write

$$\lim_{n \to \infty} \frac{n + 3}{2n} = \lim_{n \to \infty}\left(\frac{n}{2n} + \frac{3}{2n}\right) = \lim_{n \to \infty}\left(\frac{1}{2} + \frac{3}{2n}\right) = \frac{1}{2} + 0 = \frac{1}{2}.$$

Area

In Euclidean geometry, the simplest type of plane region is a rectangle. Although people often say that the *formula* for the area of a rectangle is

$$A = bh$$

it is actually more proper to say that this is the *definition* of the **area of a rectangle.**

From this definition, you can develop formulas for the areas of many other plane regions. For example, to determine the area of a triangle, you can form a rectangle whose area is twice that of the triangle, as shown in Figure 5.5. Once you know how to find the area of a triangle, you can determine the area of any polygon by subdividing the polygon into triangular regions, as shown in Figure 5.6.

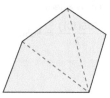

Triangle: $A = \frac{1}{2}bh$
Figure 5.5

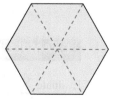

Parallelogram
Figure 5.6

Hexagon

Polygon

Finding the areas of regions other than polygons is more difficult. The ancient Greeks were able to determine formulas for the areas of some general regions (principally those bounded by conics) by the *exhaustion* method. The clearest description of this method was given by Archimedes. Essentially, the method is a limiting process in which the area is squeezed between two polygons—one inscribed in the region and one circumscribed about the region.

For instance, in Figure 5.7, the area of a circular region is approximated by an n-sided inscribed polygon and an n-sided circumscribed polygon. For each value of n, the area of the inscribed polygon is less than the area of the circle, and the area of the circumscribed polygon is greater than the area of the circle. Moreover, as n increases, the areas of both polygons become better and better approximations of the area of the circle.

ARCHIMEDES (287–212 B.C.)

Archimedes used the method of exhaustion to derive formulas for the areas of ellipses, parabolic segments, and sectors of a spiral. He is considered to have been the greatest applied mathematician of antiquity.
See LarsonCalculus.com to read more of this biography.

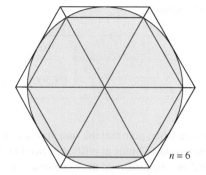
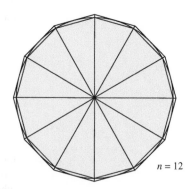

$n = 6$

$n = 12$

The exhaustion method for finding the area of a circular region
Figure 5.7

■ **FOR FURTHER INFORMATION**
For an alternative development of the formula for the area of a circle, see the article "Proof Without Words: Area of a Disk is πR^2" by Russell Jay Hendel in *Mathematics Magazine*. To view this article, go to *MathArticles.com*.

A process that is similar to that used by Archimedes to determine the area of a plane region is used in the remaining examples in this section.

The Area of a Plane Region

Recall from Section 2.1 that the origins of calculus are connected to two classic problems: the tangent line problem and the area problem. Example 3 begins the investigation of the area problem.

EXAMPLE 3 Approximating the Area of a Plane Region

Use the five rectangles in Figure 5.8(a) and (b) to find *two* approximations of the area of the region lying between the graph of

$$f(x) = -x^2 + 5$$

and the *x*-axis between $x = 0$ and $x = 2$.

Solution

a. The right endpoints of the five intervals are

$$\frac{2}{5}i \qquad \text{Right endpoints}$$

where $i = 1, 2, 3, 4, 5$. The width of each rectangle is $\frac{2}{5}$, and the height of each rectangle can be obtained by evaluating f at the right endpoint of each interval.

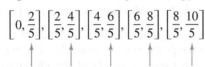

Evaluate f at the right endpoints of these intervals.

The sum of the areas of the five rectangles is

$$\sum_{i=1}^{5} \overbrace{f\left(\frac{2i}{5}\right)}^{\text{Height}} \overbrace{\left(\frac{2}{5}\right)}^{\text{Width}} = \sum_{i=1}^{5} \left[-\left(\frac{2i}{5}\right)^2 + 5 \right]\left(\frac{2}{5}\right) = \frac{162}{25} = 6.48.$$

Because each of the five rectangles lies inside the parabolic region, you can conclude that the area of the parabolic region is greater than 6.48.

b. The left endpoints of the five intervals are

$$\frac{2}{5}(i - 1) \qquad \text{Left endpoints}$$

where $i = 1, 2, 3, 4, 5$. The width of each rectangle is $\frac{2}{5}$, and the height of each rectangle can be obtained by evaluating f at the left endpoint of each interval. So, the sum is

$$\sum_{i=1}^{5} \overbrace{f\left(\frac{2i - 2}{5}\right)}^{\text{Height}} \overbrace{\left(\frac{2}{5}\right)}^{\text{Width}} = \sum_{i=1}^{5} \left[-\left(\frac{2i - 2}{5}\right)^2 + 5 \right]\left(\frac{2}{5}\right) = \frac{202}{25} = 8.08.$$

Because the parabolic region lies within the union of the five rectangular regions, you can conclude that the area of the parabolic region is less than 8.08.

By combining the results in parts (a) and (b), you can conclude that

$$6.48 < (\text{Area of region}) < 8.08.$$

By increasing the number of rectangles used in Example 3, you can obtain closer and closer approximations of the area of the region. For instance, using 25 rectangles of width $\frac{2}{25}$ each, you can conclude that

$$7.1712 < (\text{Area of region}) < 7.4912.$$

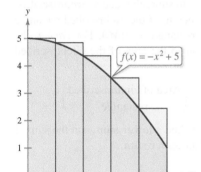

(a) The area of the parabolic region is greater than the area of the rectangles.

(b) The area of the parabolic region is less than the area of the rectangles.

Figure 5.8

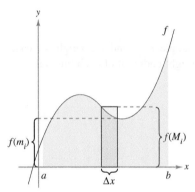

The region under a curve
Figure 5.9

Upper and Lower Sums

The procedure used in Example 3 can be generalized as follows. Consider a plane region bounded above by the graph of a nonnegative, continuous function

$$y = f(x)$$

as shown in Figure 5.9. The region is bounded below by the x-axis, and the left and right boundaries of the region are the vertical lines $x = a$ and $x = b$.

To approximate the area of the region, begin by subdividing the interval $[a, b]$ into n subintervals, each of width

$$\Delta x = \frac{b - a}{n}$$

as shown in Figure 5.10. The endpoints of the intervals are

$$\overbrace{a = x_0}\quad \overbrace{x_1}\quad \overbrace{x_2}\quad \cdots \quad \overbrace{x_n = b}$$
$$a + 0(\Delta x) < a + 1(\Delta x) < a + 2(\Delta x) < \cdots < a + n(\Delta x).$$

Because f is continuous, the Extreme Value Theorem guarantees the existence of a minimum and a maximum value of $f(x)$ in *each* subinterval.

$$f(m_i) = \text{Minimum value of } f(x) \text{ in } i\text{th subinterval}$$
$$f(M_i) = \text{Maximum value of } f(x) \text{ in } i\text{th subinterval}$$

Next, define an **inscribed rectangle** lying *inside* the ith subregion and a **circumscribed rectangle** extending *outside* the ith subregion. The height of the ith inscribed rectangle is $f(m_i)$ and the height of the ith circumscribed rectangle is $f(M_i)$. For *each* i, the area of the inscribed rectangle is less than or equal to the area of the circumscribed rectangle.

$$\left(\begin{array}{c}\text{Area of inscribed} \\ \text{rectangle}\end{array}\right) = f(m_i)\,\Delta x \leq f(M_i)\,\Delta x = \left(\begin{array}{c}\text{Area of circumscribed} \\ \text{rectangle}\end{array}\right)$$

The sum of the areas of the inscribed rectangles is called a **lower sum,** and the sum of the areas of the circumscribed rectangles is called an **upper sum.**

$$\text{Lower sum} = s(n) = \sum_{i=1}^{n} f(m_i)\,\Delta x \qquad \text{Area of inscribed rectangles}$$

$$\text{Upper sum} = S(n) = \sum_{i=1}^{n} f(M_i)\,\Delta x \qquad \text{Area of circumscribed rectangles}$$

From Figure 5.11, you can see that the lower sum $s(n)$ is less than or equal to the upper sum $S(n)$. Moreover, the actual area of the region lies between these two sums.

$$s(n) \leq (\text{Area of region}) \leq S(n)$$

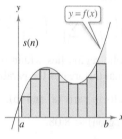

Area of inscribed rectangles is less than area of region.

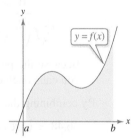

Area of region

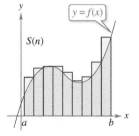

Area of circumscribed rectangles is greater than area of region.

Figure 5.11

The interval $[a, b]$ is divided into n subintervals of width $\Delta x = \dfrac{b - a}{n}$.

Figure 5.10

EXAMPLE 4   **Finding Upper and Lower Sums for a Region**

Find the upper and lower sums for the region bounded by the graph of $f(x) = x^2$ and the x-axis between $x = 0$ and $x = 2$.

Solution   To begin, partition the interval $[0, 2]$ into n subintervals, each of width

$$\Delta x = \frac{b - a}{n} = \frac{2 - 0}{n} = \frac{2}{n}.$$

Figure 5.12 shows the endpoints of the subintervals and several inscribed and circumscribed rectangles. Because f is increasing on the interval $[0, 2]$, the minimum value on each subinterval occurs at the left endpoint, and the maximum value occurs at the right endpoint.

Left Endpoints

$$m_i = 0 + (i - 1)\left(\frac{2}{n}\right) = \frac{2(i - 1)}{n}$$

Right Endpoints

$$M_i = 0 + i\left(\frac{2}{n}\right) = \frac{2i}{n}$$

Using the left endpoints, the lower sum is

$$
\begin{aligned}
s(n) &= \sum_{i=1}^{n} f(m_i)\, \Delta x \\
&= \sum_{i=1}^{n} f\left[\frac{2(i - 1)}{n}\right]\left(\frac{2}{n}\right) \\
&= \sum_{i=1}^{n} \left[\frac{2(i - 1)}{n}\right]^2\left(\frac{2}{n}\right) \\
&= \sum_{i=1}^{n} \left(\frac{8}{n^3}\right)(i^2 - 2i + 1) \\
&= \frac{8}{n^3}\left(\sum_{i=1}^{n} i^2 - 2\sum_{i=1}^{n} i + \sum_{i=1}^{n} 1\right) \\
&= \frac{8}{n^3}\left\{\frac{n(n + 1)(2n + 1)}{6} - 2\left[\frac{n(n + 1)}{2}\right] + n\right\} \\
&= \frac{4}{3n^3}(2n^3 - 3n^2 + n) \\
&= \frac{8}{3} - \frac{4}{n} + \frac{4}{3n^2}. \qquad \text{Lower sum}
\end{aligned}
$$

Using the right endpoints, the upper sum is

$$
\begin{aligned}
S(n) &= \sum_{i=1}^{n} f(M_i)\, \Delta x \\
&= \sum_{i=1}^{n} f\left(\frac{2i}{n}\right)\left(\frac{2}{n}\right) \\
&= \sum_{i=1}^{n} \left(\frac{2i}{n}\right)^2\left(\frac{2}{n}\right) \\
&= \sum_{i=1}^{n} \left(\frac{8}{n^3}\right)i^2 \\
&= \frac{8}{n^3}\left[\frac{n(n + 1)(2n + 1)}{6}\right] \\
&= \frac{4}{3n^3}(2n^3 + 3n^2 + n) \\
&= \frac{8}{3} + \frac{4}{n} + \frac{4}{3n^2}. \qquad \text{Upper sum}
\end{aligned}
$$

Inscribed rectangles

Circumscribed rectangles
Figure 5.12

Exploration

For the region given in Example 4, evaluate the lower sum

$$s(n) = \frac{8}{3} - \frac{4}{n} + \frac{4}{3n^2}$$

and the upper sum

$$S(n) = \frac{8}{3} + \frac{4}{n} + \frac{4}{3n^2}$$

for $n = 10$, 100, and 1000. Use your results to determine the area of the region.

Example 4 illustrates some important things about lower and upper sums. First, notice that for any value of n, the lower sum is less than (or equal to) the upper sum.

$$s(n) = \frac{8}{3} - \frac{4}{n} + \frac{4}{3n^2} < \frac{8}{3} + \frac{4}{n} + \frac{4}{3n^2} = S(n)$$

Second, the difference between these two sums lessens as n increases. In fact, when you take the limits as $n \to \infty$, both the lower sum and the upper sum approach $\frac{8}{3}$.

$$\lim_{n \to \infty} s(n) = \lim_{n \to \infty} \left(\frac{8}{3} - \frac{4}{n} + \frac{4}{3n^2} \right) = \frac{8}{3} \qquad \text{Lower sum limit}$$

and

$$\lim_{n \to \infty} S(n) = \lim_{n \to \infty} \left(\frac{8}{3} + \frac{4}{n} + \frac{4}{3n^2} \right) = \frac{8}{3} \qquad \text{Upper sum limit}$$

The next theorem shows that the equivalence of the limits (as $n \to \infty$) of the upper and lower sums is not mere coincidence. It is true for all functions that are continuous and nonnegative on the closed interval $[a, b]$. The proof of this theorem is best left to a course in advanced calculus.

THEOREM 5.3 Limits of the Lower and Upper Sums

Let f be continuous and nonnegative on the interval $[a, b]$. The limits as $n \to \infty$ of both the lower and upper sums exist and are equal to each other. That is,

$$\lim_{n \to \infty} s(n) = \lim_{n \to \infty} \sum_{i=1}^{n} f(m_i) \, \Delta x$$

$$= \lim_{n \to \infty} \sum_{i=1}^{n} f(M_i) \, \Delta x$$

$$= \lim_{n \to \infty} S(n)$$

where $\Delta x = (b - a)/n$ and $f(m_i)$ and $f(M_i)$ are the minimum and maximum values of f on the subinterval.

In Theorem 5.3, the same limit is attained for both the minimum value $f(m_i)$ and the maximum value $f(M_i)$. So, it follows from the Squeeze Theorem (Theorem 2.8) that the choice of x in the ith subinterval does not affect the limit. This means that you are free to choose an *arbitrary* x-value in the ith subinterval, as shown in the *definition of the area of a region in the plane*.

Definition of the Area of a Region in the Plane

Let f be continuous and nonnegative on the interval $[a, b]$. (See Figure 5.13.) The area of the region bounded by the graph of f, the x-axis, and the vertical lines $x = a$ and $x = b$ is

$$\text{Area} = \lim_{n \to \infty} \sum_{i=1}^{n} f(c_i) \, \Delta x$$

where $x_{i-1} \le c_i \le x_i$ and

$$\Delta x = \frac{b - a}{n}.$$

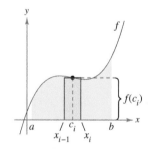

The width of the ith subinterval is $\Delta x = x_i - x_{i-1}$.

Figure 5.13

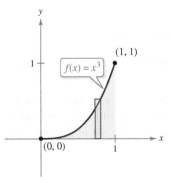

The area of the region bounded by the graph of f, the x-axis, $x = 0$, and $x = 1$ is $\frac{1}{4}$.

Figure 5.14

EXAMPLE 5   Finding Area by the Limit Definition

Find the area of the region bounded by the graph $f(x) = x^3$, the x-axis, and the vertical lines $x = 0$ and $x = 1$, as shown in Figure 5.14.

Solution   Begin by noting that f is continuous and nonnegative on the interval $[0, 1]$. Next, partition the interval $[0, 1]$ into n subintervals, each of width $\Delta x = 1/n$. According to the definition of area, you can choose any x-value in the ith subinterval. For this example, the right endpoints $c_i = i/n$ are convenient.

$$\text{Area} = \lim_{n \to \infty} \sum_{i=1}^{n} f(c_i)\, \Delta x$$

$$= \lim_{n \to \infty} \sum_{i=1}^{n} \left(\frac{i}{n}\right)^3 \left(\frac{1}{n}\right) \qquad \text{Right endpoints: } c_i = \frac{i}{n}$$

$$= \lim_{n \to \infty} \frac{1}{n^4} \sum_{i=1}^{n} i^3$$

$$= \lim_{n \to \infty} \frac{1}{n^4} \left[\frac{n^2(n+1)^2}{4}\right]$$

$$= \lim_{n \to \infty} \left(\frac{1}{4} + \frac{1}{2n} + \frac{1}{4n^2}\right)$$

$$= \frac{1}{4}$$

The area of the region is $\frac{1}{4}$.

EXAMPLE 6   Finding Area by the Limit Definition

• • • ▷ *See LarsonCalculus.com for an interactive version of this type of example.*

Find the area of the region bounded by the graph of $f(x) = 4 - x^2$, the x-axis, and the vertical lines $x = 1$ and $x = 2$, as shown in Figure 5.15.

Solution   Note that the function f is continuous and nonnegative on the interval $[1, 2]$. So, begin by partitioning the interval into n subintervals, each of width $\Delta x = 1/n$. Choosing the right endpoint

$$c_i = a + i\Delta x = 1 + \frac{i}{n} \qquad \text{Right endpoints}$$

of each subinterval, you obtain

$$\text{Area} = \lim_{n \to \infty} \sum_{i=1}^{n} f(c_i)\, \Delta x$$

$$= \lim_{n \to \infty} \sum_{i=1}^{n} \left[4 - \left(1 + \frac{i}{n}\right)^2\right]\left(\frac{1}{n}\right)$$

$$= \lim_{n \to \infty} \sum_{i=1}^{n} \left(3 - \frac{2i}{n} - \frac{i^2}{n^2}\right)\left(\frac{1}{n}\right)$$

$$= \lim_{n \to \infty} \left(\frac{1}{n} \sum_{i=1}^{n} 3 - \frac{2}{n^2} \sum_{i=1}^{n} i - \frac{1}{n^3} \sum_{i=1}^{n} i^2\right)$$

$$= \lim_{n \to \infty} \left[3 - \left(1 + \frac{1}{n}\right) - \left(\frac{1}{3} + \frac{1}{2n} + \frac{1}{6n^2}\right)\right]$$

$$= 3 - 1 - \frac{1}{3}$$

$$= \frac{5}{3}.$$

The area of the region is $\frac{5}{3}$.

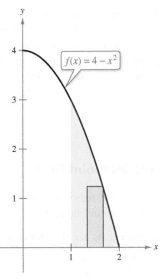

The area of the region bounded by the graph of f, the x-axis, $x = 1$, and $x = 2$ is $\frac{5}{3}$.

Figure 5.15

The next example looks at a region that is bounded by the *y*-axis (rather than by the *x*-axis).

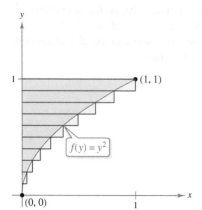

The area of the region bounded by the graph of *f* and the *y*-axis for $0 \leq y \leq 1$ is $\frac{1}{3}$.

Figure 5.16

EXAMPLE 7   A Region Bounded by the *y*-axis

Find the area of the region bounded by the graph of $f(y) = y^2$ and the *y*-axis for $0 \leq y \leq 1$, as shown in Figure 5.16.

Solution   When *f* is a continuous, nonnegative function of *y*, you can still use the same basic procedure shown in Examples 5 and 6. Begin by partitioning the interval $[0, 1]$ into *n* subintervals, each of width $\Delta y = 1/n$. Then, using the upper endpoints $c_i = i/n$, you obtain

$$\text{Area} = \lim_{n \to \infty} \sum_{i=1}^{n} f(c_i)\, \Delta y$$

$$= \lim_{n \to \infty} \sum_{i=1}^{n} \left(\frac{i}{n}\right)^2 \left(\frac{1}{n}\right) \qquad \text{Upper endpoints: } c_i = \frac{i}{n}$$

$$= \lim_{n \to \infty} \frac{1}{n^3} \sum_{i=1}^{n} i^2$$

$$= \lim_{n \to \infty} \frac{1}{n^3} \left[\frac{n(n+1)(2n+1)}{6} \right]$$

$$= \lim_{n \to \infty} \left(\frac{1}{3} + \frac{1}{2n} + \frac{1}{6n^2} \right)$$

$$= \frac{1}{3}.$$

The area of the region is $\frac{1}{3}$.

• •REMARK   You will learn about other approximation methods in Section 5.6. One of the methods, the Trapezoidal Rule, is similar to the Midpoint Rule.

In Examples 5, 6, and 7, c_i is chosen to be a value that is convenient for calculating the limit. Because each limit gives the exact area for *any* c_i, there is no need to find values that give good approximations when *n* is small. For an *approximation*, however, you should try to find a value of c_i that gives a good approximation of the area of the *i*th subregion. In general, a good value to choose is the midpoint of the interval, $c_i = (x_i + x_{i-1})/2$, and apply the **Midpoint Rule.**

$$\text{Area} \approx \sum_{i=1}^{n} f\left(\frac{x_i + x_{i-1}}{2} \right) \Delta x. \qquad \text{Midpoint Rule}$$

EXAMPLE 8   Approximating Area with the Midpoint Rule

Use the Midpoint Rule with $n = 4$ to approximate the area of the region bounded by the graph of $f(x) = \sin x$ and the *x*-axis for $0 \leq x \leq \pi$, as shown in Figure 5.17.

Solution   For $n = 4$, $\Delta x = \pi/4$. The midpoints of the subregions are shown below.

$$c_1 = \frac{0 + (\pi/4)}{2} = \frac{\pi}{8} \qquad\qquad c_2 = \frac{(\pi/4) + (\pi/2)}{2} = \frac{3\pi}{8}$$

$$c_3 = \frac{(\pi/2) + (3\pi/4)}{2} = \frac{5\pi}{8} \qquad\qquad c_4 = \frac{(3\pi/4) + \pi}{2} = \frac{7\pi}{8}$$

So, the area is approximated by

$$\text{Area} \approx \sum_{i=1}^{n} f(c_i)\, \Delta x = \sum_{i=1}^{4} (\sin c_i)\left(\frac{\pi}{4} \right) = \frac{\pi}{4}\left(\sin \frac{\pi}{8} + \sin \frac{3\pi}{8} + \sin \frac{5\pi}{8} + \sin \frac{7\pi}{8} \right)$$

which is about 2.052.

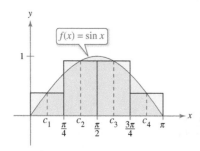

The area of the region bounded by the graph of $f(x) = \sin x$ and the *x*-axis for $0 \leq x \leq \pi$ is about 2.052.

Figure 5.17

5.2 Exercises

See **CalcChat.com** for tutorial help and worked-out solutions to odd-numbered exercises.

Finding a Sum In Exercises 1–6, find the sum. Use the summation capabilities of a graphing utility to verify your result.

1. $\displaystyle\sum_{i=1}^{6} (3i + 2)$

2. $\displaystyle\sum_{k=3}^{9} (k^2 + 1)$

3. $\displaystyle\sum_{k=0}^{4} \frac{1}{k^2 + 1}$

4. $\displaystyle\sum_{j=4}^{6} \frac{3}{j}$

5. $\displaystyle\sum_{k=1}^{4} c$

6. $\displaystyle\sum_{i=1}^{4} [(i - 1)^2 + (i + 1)^3]$

Using Sigma Notation In Exercises 7–12, use sigma notation to write the sum.

7. $\dfrac{1}{5(1)} + \dfrac{1}{5(2)} + \dfrac{1}{5(3)} + \cdots + \dfrac{1}{5(11)}$

8. $\dfrac{9}{1 + 1} + \dfrac{9}{1 + 2} + \dfrac{9}{1 + 3} + \cdots + \dfrac{9}{1 + 14}$

9. $\left[7\left(\dfrac{1}{6}\right) + 5\right] + \left[7\left(\dfrac{2}{6}\right) + 5\right] + \cdots + \left[7\left(\dfrac{6}{6}\right) + 5\right]$

10. $\left[1 - \left(\dfrac{1}{4}\right)^2\right] + \left[1 - \left(\dfrac{2}{4}\right)^2\right] + \cdots + \left[1 - \left(\dfrac{4}{4}\right)^2\right]$

11. $\left[\left(\dfrac{2}{n}\right)^3 - \dfrac{2}{n}\right]\left(\dfrac{2}{n}\right) + \cdots + \left[\left(\dfrac{2n}{n}\right)^3 - \dfrac{2n}{n}\right]\left(\dfrac{2}{n}\right)$

12. $\left[2\left(1 + \dfrac{3}{n}\right)^2\right]\left(\dfrac{3}{n}\right) + \cdots + \left[2\left(1 + \dfrac{3n}{n}\right)^2\right]\left(\dfrac{3}{n}\right)$

Evaluating a Sum In Exercises 13–20, use the properties of summation and Theorem 5.2 to evaluate the sum. Use the summation capabilities of a graphing utility to verify your result.

13. $\displaystyle\sum_{i=1}^{12} 7$

14. $\displaystyle\sum_{i=1}^{30} -18$

15. $\displaystyle\sum_{i=1}^{24} 4i$

16. $\displaystyle\sum_{i=1}^{16} (5i - 4)$

17. $\displaystyle\sum_{i=1}^{20} (i - 1)^2$

18. $\displaystyle\sum_{i=1}^{10} (i^2 - 1)$

19. $\displaystyle\sum_{i=1}^{15} i(i - 1)^2$

20. $\displaystyle\sum_{i=1}^{25} (i^3 - 2i)$

Evaluating a Sum In Exercises 21–24, use the summation formulas to rewrite the expression without the summation notation. Use the result to find the sums for $n = 10$, 100, 1000, and 10,000.

21. $\displaystyle\sum_{i=1}^{n} \frac{2i + 1}{n^2}$

22. $\displaystyle\sum_{j=1}^{n} \frac{7j + 4}{n^2}$

23. $\displaystyle\sum_{k=1}^{n} \frac{6k(k - 1)}{n^3}$

24. $\displaystyle\sum_{i=1}^{n} \frac{2i^3 - 3i}{n^4}$

Approximating the Area of a Plane Region In Exercises 25–30, use left and right endpoints and the given number of rectangles to find two approximations of the area of the region between the graph of the function and the x-axis over the given interval.

25. $f(x) = 2x + 5$, $[0, 2]$, 4 rectangles

26. $f(x) = 9 - x$, $[2, 4]$, 6 rectangles

27. $g(x) = 2x^2 - x - 1$, $[2, 5]$, 6 rectangles

28. $g(x) = x^2 + 1$, $[1, 3]$, 8 rectangles

29. $f(x) = \cos x$, $\left[0, \dfrac{\pi}{2}\right]$, 4 rectangles

30. $g(x) = \sin x$, $[0, \pi]$, 6 rectangles

Using Upper and Lower Sums In Exercises 31 and 32, bound the area of the shaded region by approximating the upper and lower sums. Use rectangles of width 1.

31.

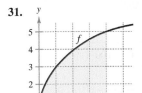

32.

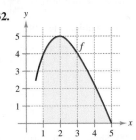

Finding Upper and Lower Sums for a Region In Exercises 33–36, use upper and lower sums to approximate the area of the region using the given number of subintervals (of equal width).

33. $y = \sqrt{x}$

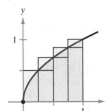

34. $y = 4e^{-x}$

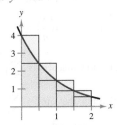

35. $y = \dfrac{1}{x}$

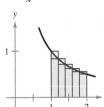

36. $y = \sqrt{1 - x^2}$

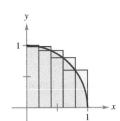

Finding a Limit In Exercises 37–42, find a formula for the sum of n terms. Use the formula to find the limit as $n \to \infty$.

37. $\displaystyle \lim_{n \to \infty} \sum_{i=1}^{n} \frac{24i}{n^2}$

38. $\displaystyle \lim_{n \to \infty} \sum_{i=1}^{n} \left(\frac{3i}{n}\right)\left(\frac{3}{n}\right)$

39. $\displaystyle \lim_{n \to \infty} \sum_{i=1}^{n} \frac{1}{n^3}(i-1)^2$

40. $\displaystyle \lim_{n \to \infty} \sum_{i=1}^{n} \left(1 + \frac{2i}{n}\right)^2\left(\frac{2}{n}\right)$

41. $\displaystyle \lim_{n \to \infty} \sum_{i=1}^{n} \left(1 + \frac{i}{n}\right)\left(\frac{2}{n}\right)$

42. $\displaystyle \lim_{n \to \infty} \sum_{i=1}^{n} \left(2 + \frac{3i}{n}\right)^3\left(\frac{3}{n}\right)$

43. Numerical Reasoning Consider a triangle of area 2 bounded by the graphs of $y = x$, $y = 0$, and $x = 2$.

(a) Sketch the region.

(b) Divide the interval $[0, 2]$ into n subintervals of equal width and show that the endpoints are

$$0 < 1\left(\frac{2}{n}\right) < \cdots < (n-1)\left(\frac{2}{n}\right) < n\left(\frac{2}{n}\right).$$

(c) Show that $\displaystyle s(n) = \sum_{i=1}^{n} \left[(i-1)\left(\frac{2}{n}\right)\right]\left(\frac{2}{n}\right)$.

(d) Show that $\displaystyle S(n) = \sum_{i=1}^{n} \left[i\left(\frac{2}{n}\right)\right]\left(\frac{2}{n}\right)$.

(e) Complete the table.

n	5	10	50	100
$s(n)$				
$S(n)$				

(f) Show that $\displaystyle \lim_{n \to \infty} s(n) = \lim_{n \to \infty} S(n) = 2$.

44. Numerical Reasoning Consider a trapezoid of area 4 bounded by the graphs of $y = x$, $y = 0$, $x = 1$, and $x = 3$.

(a) Sketch the region.

(b) Divide the interval $[1, 3]$ into n subintervals of equal width and show that the endpoints are

$$1 < 1 + 1\left(\frac{2}{n}\right) < \cdots < 1 + (n-1)\left(\frac{2}{n}\right) < 1 + n\left(\frac{2}{n}\right).$$

(c) Show that $\displaystyle s(n) = \sum_{i=1}^{n} \left[1 + (i-1)\left(\frac{2}{n}\right)\right]\left(\frac{2}{n}\right)$.

(d) Show that $\displaystyle S(n) = \sum_{i=1}^{n} \left[1 + i\left(\frac{2}{n}\right)\right]\left(\frac{2}{n}\right)$.

(e) Complete the table.

n	5	10	50	100
$s(n)$				
$S(n)$				

(f) Show that $\displaystyle \lim_{n \to \infty} s(n) = \lim_{n \to \infty} S(n) = 4$.

Finding Area by the Limit Definition In Exercises 45–54, use the limit process to find the area of the region bounded by the graph of the function and the x-axis over the given interval. Sketch the region.

45. $y = -4x + 5$, $[0, 1]$ **46.** $y = 3x - 2$, $[2, 5]$

47. $y = x^2 + 2$, $[0, 1]$ **48.** $y = 3x^2 + 1$, $[0, 2]$

49. $y = 25 - x^2$, $[1, 4]$ **50.** $y = 4 - x^2$, $[-2, 2]$

51. $y = 27 - x^3$, $[1, 3]$ **52.** $y = 2x - x^3$, $[0, 1]$

53. $y = x^2 - x^3$, $[-1, 1]$ **54.** $y = 2x^3 - x^2$, $[1, 2]$

Finding Area by the Limit Definition In Exercises 55–60, use the limit process to find the area of the region bounded by the graph of the function and the y-axis over the given y-interval. Sketch the region.

55. $f(y) = 4y$, $0 \le y \le 2$

56. $g(y) = \frac{1}{2}y$, $2 \le y \le 4$

57. $f(y) = y^2$, $0 \le y \le 5$

58. $f(y) = 4y - y^2$, $1 \le y \le 2$

59. $g(y) = 4y^2 - y^3$, $1 \le y \le 3$

60. $h(y) = y^3 + 1$, $1 \le y \le 2$

Approximating Area with the Midpoint Rule In Exercises 61–66, use the Midpoint Rule with $n = 4$ to approximate the area of the region bounded by the graph of the function and the x-axis over the given interval.

61. $f(x) = x^2 + 3$, $[0, 2]$ **62.** $f(x) = x^2 + 4x$, $[0, 4]$

63. $f(x) = \tan x$, $\left[0, \frac{\pi}{4}\right]$

64. $f(x) = \cos x$, $\left[0, \frac{\pi}{2}\right]$

65. $f(x) = \ln x$, $[1, 5]$ **66.** $f(x) = xe^x$, $[0, 2]$

WRITING ABOUT CONCEPTS

Approximation In Exercises 67 and 68, determine which value best approximates the area of the region between the x-axis and the graph of the function over the given interval. (Make your selection on the basis of a sketch of the region, not by performing calculations.)

67. $f(x) = 4 - x^2$, $[0, 2]$

   (a) -2 (b) 6   (c) 10   (d) 3   (e) 8

68. $f(x) = \sin \frac{\pi x}{4}$, $[0, 4]$

   (a) 3   (b) 1   (c) -2 (d) 8   (e) 6

69. Upper and Lower Sums In your own words and using appropriate figures, describe the methods of upper sums and lower sums in approximating the area of a region.

70. Area of a Region in the Plane Give the definition of the area of a region in the plane.

71. Graphical Reasoning Consider the region bounded by the graphs of $f(x) = 8x/(x + 1)$, $x = 0$, $x = 4$, and $y = 0$, as shown in the figure. To print an enlarged copy of the graph, go to *MathGraphs.com*.

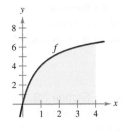

(a) Redraw the figure, and complete and shade the rectangles representing the lower sum when $n = 4$. Find this lower sum.

(b) Redraw the figure, and complete and shade the rectangles representing the upper sum when $n = 4$. Find this upper sum.

(c) Redraw the figure, and complete and shade the rectangles whose heights are determined by the functional values at the midpoint of each subinterval when $n = 4$. Find this sum using the Midpoint Rule.

(d) Verify the following formulas for approximating the area of the region using n subintervals of equal width.

Lower sum: $s(n) = \sum_{i=1}^{n} f\left[(i - 1)\dfrac{4}{n}\right]\left(\dfrac{4}{n}\right)$

Upper sum: $S(n) = \sum_{i=1}^{n} f\left[(i)\dfrac{4}{n}\right]\left(\dfrac{4}{n}\right)$

Midpoint Rule: $M(n) = \sum_{i=1}^{n} f\left[\left(i - \dfrac{1}{2}\right)\dfrac{4}{n}\right]\left(\dfrac{4}{n}\right)$

 (e) Use a graphing utility to create a table of values of $s(n)$, $S(n)$, and $M(n)$ for $n = 4, 8, 20, 100$, and 200.

(f) Explain why $s(n)$ increases and $S(n)$ decreases for increasing values of n, as shown in the table in part (e).

72. HOW DO YOU SEE IT? The function shown in the graph below is increasing on the interval $[1, 4]$. The interval will be divided into 12 subintervals.

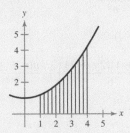

(a) What are the left endpoints of the first and last subintervals?

(b) What are the right endpoints of the first two subintervals?

(c) When using the right endpoints, do the rectangles lie above or below the graph of the function?

(d) What can you conclude about the heights of the rectangles when the function is constant on the given interval?

True or False? In Exercises 73 and 74, determine whether the statement is true or false. If it is false, explain why or give an example that shows it is false.

73. The sum of the first n positive integers is $n(n + 1)/2$.

74. If f is continuous and nonnegative on $[a, b]$, then the limits as $n \to \infty$ of its lower sum $s(n)$ and upper sum $S(n)$ both exist and are equal.

75. Writing Use the figure to write a short paragraph explaining why the formula $1 + 2 + \cdots + n = \frac{1}{2}n(n + 1)$ is valid for all positive integers n.

Figure for 75   Figure for 76

76. Graphical Reasoning Consider an n-sided regular polygon inscribed in a circle of radius r. Join the vertices of the polygon to the center of the circle, forming n congruent triangles (see figure).

(a) Determine the central angle θ in terms of n.

(b) Show that the area of each triangle is $\frac{1}{2}r^2 \sin \theta$.

(c) Let A_n be the sum of the areas of the n triangles. Find $\lim\limits_{n \to \infty} A_n$.

77. Building Blocks A child places n cubic building blocks in a row to form the base of a triangular design (see figure). Each successive row contains two fewer blocks than the preceding row. Find a formula for the number of blocks used in the design. (*Hint:* The number of building blocks in the design depends on whether n is odd or even.)

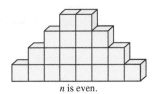

n is even.

78. Proof Prove each formula by mathematical induction. (You may need to review the method of proof by induction from a precalculus text.)

(a) $\sum_{i=1}^{n} 2i = n(n + 1)$ (b) $\sum_{i=1}^{n} i^3 = \dfrac{n^2(n + 1)^2}{4}$

PUTNAM EXAM CHALLENGE

79. A dart, thrown at random, hits a square target. Assuming that any two parts of the target of equal area are equally likely to be hit, find the probability that the point hit is nearer to the center than to any edge. Write your answer in the form $(a\sqrt{b} + c)/d$, where a, b, c, and d are integers.

5.3 Riemann Sums and Definite Integrals

■ Understand the definition of a Riemann sum.
■ Evaluate a definite integral using limits.
■ Evaluate a definite integral using properties of definite integrals.

Riemann Sums

In the definition of area given in Section 5.2, the partitions have subintervals of *equal width*. This was done only for computational convenience. The next example shows that it is not necessary to have subintervals of equal width.

EXAMPLE 1 **A Partition with Subintervals of Unequal Widths**

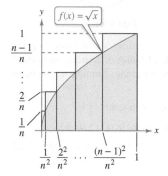

The subintervals do not have equal widths.
Figure 5.18

Consider the region bounded by the graph of

$$f(x) = \sqrt{x}$$

and the x-axis for $0 \le x \le 1$, as shown in Figure 5.18. Evaluate the limit

$$\lim_{n \to \infty} \sum_{i=1}^{n} f(c_i) \, \Delta x_i$$

where c_i is the right endpoint of the partition given by $c_i = i^2/n^2$ and Δx_i is the width of the ith interval.

Solution The width of the ith interval is

$$\Delta x_i = \frac{i^2}{n^2} - \frac{(i-1)^2}{n^2}$$

$$= \frac{i^2 - i^2 + 2i - 1}{n^2}$$

$$= \frac{2i - 1}{n^2}.$$

So, the limit is

$$\lim_{n \to \infty} \sum_{i=1}^{n} f(c_i) \, \Delta x_i = \lim_{n \to \infty} \sum_{i=1}^{n} \sqrt{\frac{i^2}{n^2}} \left(\frac{2i - 1}{n^2} \right)$$

$$= \lim_{n \to \infty} \frac{1}{n^3} \sum_{i=1}^{n} (2i^2 - i)$$

$$= \lim_{n \to \infty} \frac{1}{n^3} \left[2 \left(\frac{n(n+1)(2n+1)}{6} \right) - \frac{n(n+1)}{2} \right]$$

$$= \lim_{n \to \infty} \frac{4n^3 + 3n^2 - n}{6n^3}$$

$$= \frac{2}{3}.$$

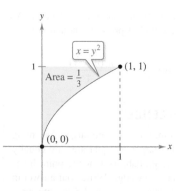

The area of the region bounded by the graph of $x = y^2$ and the y-axis for $0 \le y \le 1$ is $\frac{1}{3}$.
Figure 5.19

From Example 7 in Section 5.2, you know that the region shown in Figure 5.19 has an area of $\frac{1}{3}$. Because the square bounded by $0 \le x \le 1$ and $0 \le y \le 1$ has an area of 1, you can conclude that the area of the region shown in Figure 5.18 has an area of $\frac{2}{3}$. This agrees with the limit found in Example 1, even though that example used a partition having subintervals of unequal widths. The reason this particular partition gave the proper area is that as n increases, the *width of the largest subinterval approaches zero*. This is a key feature of the development of definite integrals.

In Section 5.2, the limit of a sum was used to define the area of a region in the plane. Finding area by this means is only one of *many* applications involving the limit of a sum. A similar approach can be used to determine quantities as diverse as arc lengths, average values, centroids, volumes, work, and surface areas. The next definition is named after Georg Friedrich Bernhard Riemann. Although the definite integral had been defined and used long before Riemann's time, he generalized the concept to cover a broader category of functions.

In the definition of a Riemann sum below, note that the function f has no restrictions other than being defined on the interval $[a, b]$. (In Section 5.2, the function f was assumed to be continuous and nonnegative because you were finding the area under a curve.)

GEORG FRIEDRICH BERNHARD RIEMANN (1826-1866)

German mathematician Riemann did his most famous work in the areas of non-Euclidean geometry, differential equations, and number theory. It was Riemann's results in physics and mathematics that formed the structure on which Einstein's General Theory of Relativity is based.
See LarsonCalculus.com to read more of this biography.

Definition of Riemann Sum

Let f be defined on the closed interval $[a, b]$, and let Δ be a partition of $[a, b]$ given by

$$a = x_0 < x_1 < x_2 < \ldots < x_{n-1} < x_n = b$$

where Δx_i is the width of the ith subinterval

$$[x_{i-1}, x_i]. \qquad i\text{th subinterval}$$

If c_i is *any* point in the ith subinterval, then the sum

$$\sum_{i=1}^{n} f(c_i)\, \Delta x_i, \quad x_{i-1} \le c_i \le x_i$$

is called a **Riemann sum** of f for the partition Δ. (The sums in Section 5.2 are examples of Riemann sums, but there are more general Riemann sums than those covered there.)

The width of the largest subinterval of a partition Δ is the **norm** of the partition and is denoted by $\|\Delta\|$. If every subinterval is of equal width, then the partition is **regular** and the norm is denoted by

$$\|\Delta\| = \Delta x = \frac{b - a}{n}. \qquad \text{Regular partition}$$

For a general partition, the norm is related to the number of subintervals of $[a, b]$ in the following way.

$$\frac{b - a}{\|\Delta\|} \le n \qquad \text{General partition}$$

So, the number of subintervals in a partition approaches infinity as the norm of the partition approaches 0. That is, $\|\Delta\| \to 0$ implies that $n \to \infty$.

The converse of this statement is not true. For example, let Δ_n be the partition of the interval $[0, 1]$ given by

$$0 < \frac{1}{2^n} < \frac{1}{2^{n-1}} < \cdots < \frac{1}{8} < \frac{1}{4} < \frac{1}{2} < 1.$$

As shown in Figure 5.20, for any positive value of n, the norm of the partition Δ_n is $\frac{1}{2}$. So, letting n approach infinity does not force $\|\Delta\|$ to approach 0. In a regular partition, however, the statements

$$\|\Delta\| \to 0 \quad \text{and} \quad n \to \infty$$

are equivalent.

$$\|\Delta\| = \tfrac{1}{2}$$

$n \to \infty$ does not imply that $\|\Delta\| \to 0$.

Figure 5.20

■ **FOR FURTHER INFORMATION**
For insight into the history of the
definite integral, see the article
"The Evolution of Integration" by
A. Shenitzer and J. Stepr̄ans in *The
American Mathematical Monthly.*
To view this article, go to
MathArticles.com.

·············▷
·· REMARK   Later in this
chapter, you will learn
convenient methods for
calculating $\int_a^b f(x)\, dx$ for
continuous functions. For now,
you must use the limit definition.

Definite Integrals

To define the definite integral, consider the limit

$$\lim_{\|\Delta\|\to 0} \sum_{i=1}^{n} f(c_i)\,\Delta x_i = L.$$

To say that this limit exists means there exists a real number L such that for each $\varepsilon > 0$,
there exists a $\delta > 0$ such that for every partition with $\|\Delta\| < \delta$, it follows that

$$\left| L - \sum_{i=1}^{n} f(c_i)\,\Delta x_i \right| < \varepsilon$$

regardless of the choice of c_i in the ith subinterval of each partition Δ.

Definition of Definite Integral

If f is defined on the closed interval $[a, b]$ and the limit of Riemann sums over
partitions Δ

$$\lim_{\|\Delta\|\to 0} \sum_{i=1}^{n} f(c_i)\,\Delta x_i$$

exists (as described above), then f is said to be **integrable** on $[a, b]$ and the
limit is denoted by

$$\lim_{\|\Delta\|\to 0} \sum_{i=1}^{n} f(c_i)\,\Delta x_i = \int_a^b f(x)\, dx.$$

The limit is called the **definite integral** of f from a to b. The number a is the
lower limit of integration, and the number b is the **upper limit** of integration.

It is not a coincidence that the notation for definite integrals is similar to that used
for indefinite integrals. You will see why in the next section when the Fundamental
Theorem of Calculus is introduced. For now, it is important to see that definite integrals
and indefinite integrals are different concepts. A definite integral is a *number*, whereas
an indefinite integral is a *family of functions*.

Though Riemann sums were defined for functions with very few restrictions, a
sufficient condition for a function f to be integrable on $[a, b]$ is that it is continuous on
$[a, b]$. A proof of this theorem is beyond the scope of this text.

THEOREM 5.4   Continuity Implies Integrability

If a function f is continuous on the closed interval $[a, b]$, then f is integrable
on $[a, b]$. That is, $\int_a^b f(x)\, dx$ exists.

Exploration

The Converse of Theorem 5.4   Is the converse of Theorem 5.4 true? That is,
when a function is integrable, does it have to be continuous? Explain your
reasoning and give examples.

Describe the relationships among continuity, differentiability, and integrability.
Which is the strongest condition? Which is the weakest? Which conditions imply
other conditions?

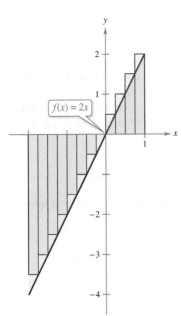

Because the definite integral is negative, it does not represent the area of the region.
Figure 5.21

| EXAMPLE 2 | **Evaluating a Definite Integral as a Limit** |

Evaluate the definite integral $\displaystyle\int_{-2}^{1} 2x \, dx$.

Solution The function $f(x) = 2x$ is integrable on the interval $[-2, 1]$ because it is continuous on $[-2, 1]$. Moreover, the definition of integrability implies that any partition whose norm approaches 0 can be used to determine the limit. For computational convenience, define Δ by subdividing $[-2, 1]$ into n subintervals of equal width

$$\Delta x_i = \Delta x = \frac{b - a}{n} = \frac{3}{n}.$$

Choosing c_i as the right endpoint of each subinterval produces

$$c_i = a + i(\Delta x) = -2 + \frac{3i}{n}.$$

So, the definite integral is

$$\int_{-2}^{1} 2x \, dx = \lim_{\|\Delta\| \to 0} \sum_{i=1}^{n} f(c_i) \, \Delta x_i$$

$$= \lim_{n \to \infty} \sum_{i=1}^{n} f(c_i) \, \Delta x$$

$$= \lim_{n \to \infty} \sum_{i=1}^{n} 2\left(-2 + \frac{3i}{n}\right)\left(\frac{3}{n}\right)$$

$$= \lim_{n \to \infty} \frac{6}{n} \sum_{i=1}^{n} \left(-2 + \frac{3i}{n}\right)$$

$$= \lim_{n \to \infty} \frac{6}{n}\left(-2 \sum_{i=1}^{n} 1 + \frac{3}{n} \sum_{i=1}^{n} i\right)$$

$$= \lim_{n \to \infty} \frac{6}{n}\left\{-2n + \frac{3}{n}\left[\frac{n(n + 1)}{2}\right]\right\}$$

$$= \lim_{n \to \infty}\left(-12 + 9 + \frac{9}{n}\right)$$

$$= -3.$$

Because the definite integral in Example 2 is negative, it *does not* represent the area of the region shown in Figure 5.21. Definite integrals can be positive, negative, or zero. For a definite integral to be interpreted as an area (as defined in Section 5.2), the function f must be continuous and nonnegative on $[a, b]$, as stated in the next theorem. The proof of this theorem is straightforward—you simply use the definition of area given in Section 5.2, because it is a Riemann sum.

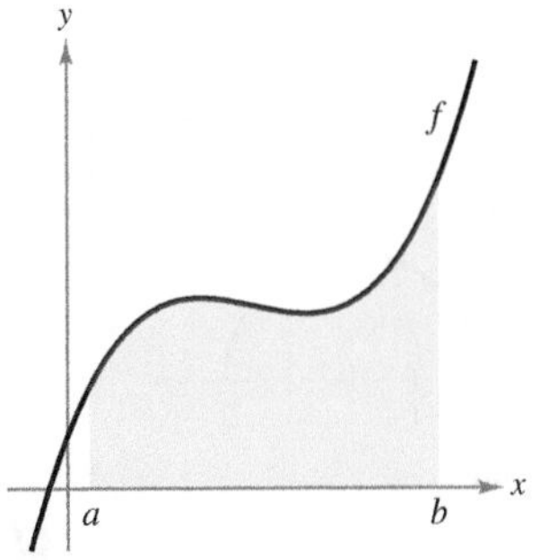

You can use a definite integral to find the area of the region bounded by the graph of f, the x-axis, $x = a$, and $x = b$.
Figure 5.22

THEOREM 5.5   The Definite Integral as the Area of a Region

If f is continuous and nonnegative on the closed interval $[a, b]$, then the area of the region bounded by the graph of f, the x-axis, and the vertical lines $x = a$ and $x = b$ is

$$\text{Area} = \int_{a}^{b} f(x) \, dx.$$

(See Figure 5.22.)

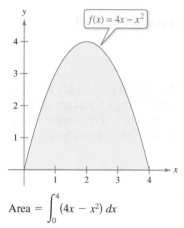

$$\text{Area} = \int_0^4 (4x - x^2)\, dx$$

Figure 5.23

As an example of Theorem 5.5, consider the region bounded by the graph of

$$f(x) = 4x - x^2$$

and the x-axis, as shown in Figure 5.23. Because f is continuous and nonnegative on the closed interval $[0, 4]$, the area of the region is

$$\text{Area} = \int_0^4 (4x - x^2)\, dx.$$

A straightforward technique for evaluating a definite integral such as this will be discussed in Section 5.4. For now, however, you can evaluate a definite integral in two ways—you can use the limit definition *or* you can check to see whether the definite integral represents the area of a common geometric region, such as a rectangle, triangle, or semicircle.

EXAMPLE 3 **Areas of Common Geometric Figures**

Sketch the region corresponding to each definite integral. Then evaluate each integral using a geometric formula.

a. $\displaystyle\int_1^3 4\, dx$ **b.** $\displaystyle\int_0^3 (x + 2)\, dx$ **c.** $\displaystyle\int_{-2}^2 \sqrt{4 - x^2}\, dx$

Solution A sketch of each region is shown in Figure 5.24.

a. This region is a rectangle of height 4 and width 2.

$$\int_1^3 4\, dx = (\text{Area of rectangle}) = 4(2) = 8$$

b. This region is a trapezoid with an altitude of 3 and parallel bases of lengths 2 and 5. The formula for the area of a trapezoid is $\frac{1}{2}h(b_1 + b_2)$.

$$\int_0^3 (x + 2)\, dx = (\text{Area of trapezoid}) = \frac{1}{2}(3)(2 + 5) = \frac{21}{2}$$

c. This region is a semicircle of radius 2. The formula for the area of a semicircle is $\frac{1}{2}\pi r^2$.

$$\int_{-2}^2 \sqrt{4 - x^2}\, dx = (\text{Area of semicircle}) = \frac{1}{2}\pi(2^2) = 2\pi$$

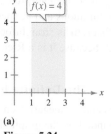

(a)

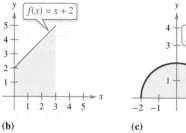

(b)   (c)

Figure 5.24

The variable of integration in a definite integral is sometimes called a *dummy variable* because it can be replaced by any other variable without changing the value of the integral. For instance, the definite integrals

$$\int_0^3 (x + 2)\, dx \quad \text{and} \quad \int_0^3 (t + 2)\, dt$$

have the same value.

Properties of Definite Integrals

The definition of the definite integral of f on the interval $[a, b]$ specifies that $a < b$. Now, however, it is convenient to extend the definition to cover cases in which $a = b$ or $a > b$. Geometrically, the next two definitions seem reasonable. For instance, it makes sense to define the area of a region of zero width and finite height to be 0.

Definitions of Two Special Definite Integrals

1. If f is defined at $x = a$, then $\displaystyle\int_a^a f(x)\, dx = 0$.

2. If f is integrable on $[a, b]$, then $\displaystyle\int_b^a f(x)\, dx = -\int_a^b f(x)\, dx$.

EXAMPLE 4 **Evaluating Definite Integrals**

•••▷ *See LarsonCalculus.com for an interactive version of this type of example.*

Evaluate each definite integral.

a. $\displaystyle\int_\pi^\pi \sin x\, dx$ **b.** $\displaystyle\int_3^0 (x + 2)\, dx$

Solution

a. Because the sine function is defined at $x = \pi$, and the upper and lower limits of integration are equal, you can write

$$\int_\pi^\pi \sin x\, dx = 0.$$

b. The integral $\int_3^0 (x + 2)\, dx$ is the same as that given in Example 3(b) except that the upper and lower limits are interchanged. Because the integral in Example 3(b) has a value of $\frac{21}{2}$, you can write

$$\int_3^0 (x + 2)\, dx = -\int_0^3 (x + 2)\, dx = -\frac{21}{2}.$$

In Figure 5.25, the larger region can be divided at $x = c$ into two subregions whose intersection is a line segment. Because the line segment has zero area, it follows that the area of the larger region is equal to the sum of the areas of the two smaller regions.

THEOREM 5.6 **Additive Interval Property**

If f is integrable on the three closed intervals determined by a, b, and c, then

$$\int_a^b f(x)\, dx = \int_a^c f(x)\, dx + \int_c^b f(x)\, dx.$$

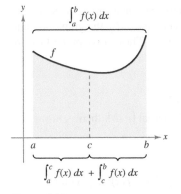

Figure 5.25

EXAMPLE 5 **Using the Additive Interval Property**

$$\int_{-1}^1 |x|\, dx = \int_{-1}^0 -x\, dx + \int_0^1 x\, dx \qquad \text{Theorem 5.6}$$

$$= \frac{1}{2} + \frac{1}{2} \qquad \text{Area of a triangle}$$

$$= 1$$

Because the definite integral is defined as the limit of a sum, it inherits the properties of summation given at the top of page 291.

THEOREM 5.7 Properties of Definite Integrals

If f and g are integrable on $[a, b]$ and k is a constant, then the functions kf and $f \pm g$ are integrable on $[a, b]$, and

1. $\displaystyle\int_{a}^{b} kf(x)\,dx = k\int_{a}^{b} f(x)\,dx$

2. $\displaystyle\int_{a}^{b} [f(x) \pm g(x)]\,dx = \int_{a}^{b} f(x)\,dx \pm \int_{a}^{b} g(x)\,dx.$

▷

•• **REMARK** Property 2 of Theorem 5.7 can be extended to cover any finite number of functions (see Example 6).

EXAMPLE 6 **Evaluation of a Definite Integral**

Evaluate $\displaystyle\int_{1}^{3} (-x^2 + 4x - 3)\,dx$ using each of the following values.

$$\int_{1}^{3} x^2\,dx = \frac{26}{3}, \qquad \int_{1}^{3} x\,dx = 4, \qquad \int_{1}^{3} dx = 2$$

Solution

$$\int_{1}^{3} (-x^2 + 4x - 3)\,dx = \int_{1}^{3} (-x^2)\,dx + \int_{1}^{3} 4x\,dx + \int_{1}^{3} (-3)\,dx$$

$$= -\int_{1}^{3} x^2\,dx + 4\int_{1}^{3} x\,dx - 3\int_{1}^{3} dx$$

$$= -\left(\frac{26}{3}\right) + 4(4) - 3(2)$$

$$= \frac{4}{3}$$

If f and g are continuous on the closed interval $[a, b]$ and $0 \le f(x) \le g(x)$ for $a \le x \le b$, then the following properties are true. First, the area of the region bounded by the graph of f and the x-axis (between a and b) must be nonnegative. Second, this area must be less than or equal to the area of the region bounded by the graph of g and the x-axis (between a and b), as shown in Figure 5.26. These two properties are generalized in Theorem 5.8.

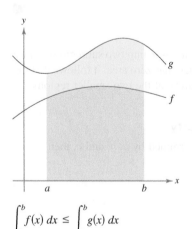

$$\int_{a}^{b} f(x)\,dx \le \int_{a}^{b} g(x)\,dx$$

Figure 5.26

THEOREM 5.8 Preservation of Inequality

1. If f is integrable and nonnegative on the closed interval $[a, b]$, then

$$0 \le \int_{a}^{b} f(x)\,dx.$$

2. If f and g are integrable on the closed interval $[a, b]$ and $f(x) \le g(x)$ for every x in $[a, b]$, then

$$\int_{a}^{b} f(x)\,dx \le \int_{a}^{b} g(x)\,dx.$$

A proof of this theorem is given in Appendix A.
See LarsonCalculus.com for Bruce Edwards's video of this proof.

5.3 Exercises

Evaluating a Limit In Exercises 1 and 2, use Example 1 as a model to evaluate the limit

$$\lim_{n \to \infty} \sum_{i=1}^{n} f(c_i)\,\Delta x_i$$

over the region bounded by the graphs of the equations.

1. $f(x) = \sqrt{x}, \quad y = 0, \quad x = 0, \quad x = 3$

$\left(\text{Hint : Let } c_i = \dfrac{3i^2}{n^2}.\right)$

2. $f(x) = \sqrt[3]{x}, \quad y = 0, \quad x = 0, \quad x = 1$

$\left(\text{Hint : Let } c_i = \dfrac{i^3}{n^3}.\right)$

Evaluating a Definite Integral as a Limit In Exercises 3–8, evaluate the definite integral by the limit definition.

3. $\displaystyle\int_{2}^{6} 8\,dx$

4. $\displaystyle\int_{-2}^{3} x\,dx$

5. $\displaystyle\int_{-1}^{1} x^3\,dx$

6. $\displaystyle\int_{1}^{4} 4x^2\,dx$

7. $\displaystyle\int_{1}^{2} (x^2 + 1)\,dx$

8. $\displaystyle\int_{-2}^{1} (2x^2 + 3)\,dx$

Writing a Limit as a Definite Integral In Exercises 9–14, write the limit as a definite integral on the interval $[a, b]$, where c_i is any point in the ith subinterval.

9. $\displaystyle\lim_{\|\Delta\| \to 0} \sum_{i=1}^{n} (3c_i + 10)\,\Delta x_i, \quad [-1, 5]$

10. $\displaystyle\lim_{\|\Delta\| \to 0} \sum_{i=1}^{n} 6c_i(4 - c_i)^2\,\Delta x_i, \quad [0, 4]$

11. $\displaystyle\lim_{\|\Delta\| \to 0} \sum_{i=1}^{n} \sqrt{c_i^2 + 4}\,\Delta x_i, \quad [0, 3]$

12. $\displaystyle\lim_{\|\Delta\| \to 0} \sum_{i=1}^{n} \left(\dfrac{3}{c_i^2}\right)\Delta x_i, \quad [1, 3]$

13. $\displaystyle\lim_{\|\Delta\| \to 0} \sum_{i=1}^{n} \left(1 + \dfrac{3}{c_i}\right)\Delta x_i, \quad [1, 5]$

14. $\displaystyle\lim_{\|\Delta\| \to 0} \sum_{i=1}^{n} (2^{-c_i} \sin c_i)\,\Delta x_i, \quad [0, \pi]$

Writing a Definite Integral In Exercises 15–26, set up a definite integral that yields the area of the region. (Do not evaluate the integral.)

15. $f(x) = 5$

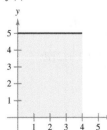

16. $f(x) = 6 - 3x$

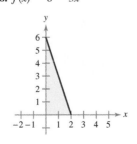

17. $f(x) = 4 - |x|$

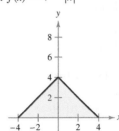

18. $f(x) = x^2$

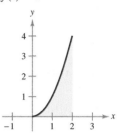

19. $f(x) = 25 - x^2$

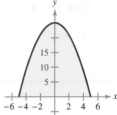

20. $f(x) = \dfrac{4}{x^2 + 2}$

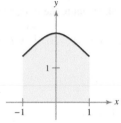

21. $f(x) = \cos x$

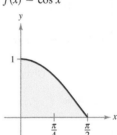

22. $f(x) = \tan x$

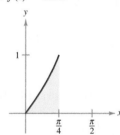

23. $g(y) = y^3$

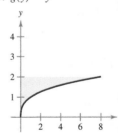

24. $f(y) = (y - 2)^2$

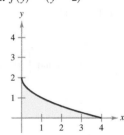

25. $f(x) = \dfrac{2}{x}$

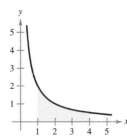

26. $f(x) = 2e^{-x}$

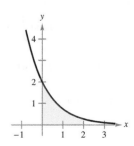

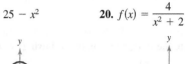

Evaluating a Definite Integral Using a Geometric Formula In Exercises 27–36, sketch the region whose area is given by the definite integral. Then use a geometric formula to evaluate the integral ($a > 0, r > 0$).

27. $\displaystyle\int_0^3 4\,dx$

28. $\displaystyle\int_{-4}^6 6\,dx$

29. $\displaystyle\int_0^4 x\,dx$

30. $\displaystyle\int_0^8 \frac{x}{4}\,dx$

31. $\displaystyle\int_0^2 (3x + 4)\,dx$

32. $\displaystyle\int_0^3 (8 - 2x)\,dx$

33. $\displaystyle\int_{-1}^1 \left(1 - |x|\right)\,dx$

34. $\displaystyle\int_{-a}^a \left(a - |x|\right)\,dx$

35. $\displaystyle\int_{-7}^7 \sqrt{49 - x^2}\,dx$

36. $\displaystyle\int_{-r}^r \sqrt{r^2 - x^2}\,dx$

Using Properties of Definite Integrals In Exercises 37–44, evaluate the integral using the following values.

$$\int_2^4 x^3\,dx = 60, \qquad \int_2^4 x\,dx = 6, \qquad \int_2^4 dx = 2$$

37. $\displaystyle\int_4^2 x\,dx$

38. $\displaystyle\int_2^2 x^3\,dx$

39. $\displaystyle\int_2^4 8x\,dx$

40. $\displaystyle\int_2^4 25\,dx$

41. $\displaystyle\int_2^4 (x - 9)\,dx$

42. $\displaystyle\int_2^4 (x^3 + 4)\,dx$

43. $\displaystyle\int_2^4 \left(\tfrac{1}{2}x^3 - 3x + 2\right)\,dx$

44. $\displaystyle\int_2^4 (10 + 4x - 3x^3)\,dx$

45. **Using Properties of Definite Integrals** Given $\displaystyle\int_0^5 f(x)\,dx = 10$ and $\displaystyle\int_5^7 f(x)\,dx = 3$, evaluate

(a) $\displaystyle\int_0^7 f(x)\,dx.$

(b) $\displaystyle\int_5^0 f(x)\,dx.$

(c) $\displaystyle\int_5^5 f(x)\,dx.$

(d) $\displaystyle\int_0^5 3f(x)\,dx.$

46. **Using Properties of Definite Integrals** Given $\displaystyle\int_0^3 f(x)\,dx = 4$ and $\displaystyle\int_3^6 f(x)\,dx = -1$, evaluate

(a) $\displaystyle\int_0^6 f(x)\,dx.$

(b) $\displaystyle\int_6^3 f(x)\,dx.$

(c) $\displaystyle\int_3^3 f(x)\,dx.$

(d) $\displaystyle\int_3^6 -5f(x)\,dx.$

47. **Using Properties of Definite Integrals** Given $\displaystyle\int_2^6 f(x)\,dx = 10$ and $\displaystyle\int_2^6 g(x)\,dx = -2$, evaluate

(a) $\displaystyle\int_2^6 [f(x) + g(x)]\,dx.$

(b) $\displaystyle\int_2^6 [g(x) - f(x)]\,dx.$

(c) $\displaystyle\int_2^6 2g(x)\,dx.$

(d) $\displaystyle\int_2^6 3f(x)\,dx.$

48. **Using Properties of Definite Integrals** Given

$$\int_{-1}^1 f(x)\,dx = 0 \quad \text{and} \quad \int_0^1 f(x)\,dx = 5$$

evaluate

(a) $\displaystyle\int_{-1}^0 f(x)\,dx.$

(b) $\displaystyle\int_0^1 f(x)\,dx - \int_{-1}^0 f(x)\,dx.$

(c) $\displaystyle\int_{-1}^1 3f(x)\,dx.$

(d) $\displaystyle\int_0^1 3f(x)\,dx.$

49. **Estimating a Definite Integral** Use the table of values to find lower and upper estimates of

$$\int_0^{10} f(x)\,dx.$$

Assume that f is a decreasing function.

x	0	2	4	6	8	10
$f(x)$	32	24	12	-4	-20	-36

50. **Estimating a Definite Integral** Use the table of values to estimate

$$\int_0^6 f(x)\,dx.$$

Use three equal subintervals and the (a) left endpoints, (b) right endpoints, and (c) midpoints. When f is an increasing function, how does each estimate compare with the actual value? Explain your reasoning.

x	0	1	2	3	4	5	6
$f(x)$	-6	0	8	18	30	50	80

51. **Think About It** The graph of f consists of line segments and a semicircle, as shown in the figure. Evaluate each definite integral by using geometric formulas.

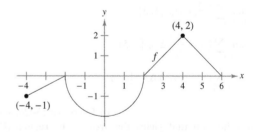

(a) $\displaystyle\int_0^2 f(x)\,dx$

(b) $\displaystyle\int_2^6 f(x)\,dx$

(c) $\displaystyle\int_{-4}^2 f(x)\,dx$

(d) $\displaystyle\int_{-4}^6 f(x)\,dx$

(e) $\displaystyle\int_{-4}^6 |f(x)|\,dx$

(f) $\displaystyle\int_{-4}^6 [f(x) + 2]\,dx$

52. Think About It The graph of f consists of line segments, as shown in the figure. Evaluate each definite integral by using geometric formulas.

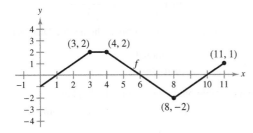

(a) $\int_0^1 -f(x)\, dx$

(b) $\int_3^4 3f(x)\, dx$

(c) $\int_0^7 f(x)\, dx$

(d) $\int_5^{11} f(x)\, dx$

(e) $\int_0^{11} f(x)\, dx$

(f) $\int_4^{10} f(x)\, dx$

53. Think About It Consider the function f that is continuous on the interval $[-5, 5]$ and for which

$$\int_0^5 f(x)\, dx = 4.$$

Evaluate each integral.

(a) $\int_0^5 [f(x) + 2]\, dx$

(b) $\int_{-2}^3 f(x + 2)\, dx$

(c) $\int_{-5}^5 f(x)\, dx$ (f is even.)

(d) $\int_{-5}^5 f(x)\, dx$ (f is odd.)

54. **HOW DO YOU SEE IT?** Use the figure to fill in the blank with the symbol $<$, $>$, or $=$. Explain your reasoning.

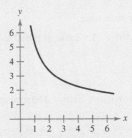

(a) The interval $[1, 5]$ is partitioned into n subintervals of equal width Δx, and x_i is the left endpoint of the ith subinterval.

$$\sum_{i=1}^n f(x_i)\, \Delta x \quad\rule{1cm}{0.4pt}\quad \int_1^5 f(x)\, dx$$

(b) The interval $[1, 5]$ is partitioned into n subintervals of equal width Δx, and x_i is the right endpoint of the ith subinterval.

$$\sum_{i=1}^n f(x_i)\, \Delta x \quad\rule{1cm}{0.4pt}\quad \int_1^5 f(x)\, dx$$

55. Think About It A function f is defined below. Use geometric formulas to find $\int_0^8 f(x)\, dx$.

$$f(x) = \begin{cases} 4, & x < 4 \\ x, & x \geq 4 \end{cases}$$

56. Think About It A function f is defined below. Use geometric formulas to find $\int_0^{12} f(x)\, dx$.

$$f(x) = \begin{cases} 6, & x > 6 \\ -\frac{1}{2}x + 9, & x \leq 6 \end{cases}$$

WRITING ABOUT CONCEPTS

Approximation In Exercises 57–60, determine which value best approximates the definite integral. Make your selection on the basis of a sketch.

57. $\int_0^4 \sqrt{x}\, dx$

(a) 5 (b) -3 (c) 10 (d) 2 (e) 8

58. $\int_0^{1/2} 4\cos \pi x\, dx$

(a) 4 (b) $\frac{4}{3}$ (c) 16 (d) 2π (e) -6

59. $\int_0^2 2e^{-x^2}\, dx$

(a) $\frac{1}{3}$ (b) 6 (c) 2 (d) 4

60. $\int_1^2 \ln x\, dx$

(a) $\frac{1}{3}$ (b) 1 (c) 4 (d) 3

61. Determining Integrability Determine whether the function

$$f(x) = \frac{1}{x - 4}$$

is integrable on the interval $[3, 5]$. Explain.

62. Finding a Function Give an example of a function that is integrable on the interval $[-1, 1]$, but not continuous on $[-1, 1]$.

Finding Values In Exercises 63–66, find possible values of a and b that make the statement true. If possible, use a graph to support your answer. (There may be more than one correct answer.)

63. $\int_{-2}^1 f(x)\, dx + \int_1^5 f(x)\, dx = \int_a^b f(x)\, dx$

64. $\int_{-3}^3 f(x)\, dx + \int_3^6 f(x)\, dx - \int_a^b f(x)\, dx = \int_{-1}^6 f(x)\, dx$

65. $\int_a^b \sin x\, dx < 0$

66. $\int_a^b \cos x\, dx = 0$

True or False? In Exercises 67–72, determine whether the statement is true or false. If it is false, explain why or give an example that shows it is false.

67. $\displaystyle\int_a^b [f(x) + g(x)]\,dx = \int_a^b f(x)\,dx + \int_a^b g(x)\,dx$

68. $\displaystyle\int_a^b f(x)g(x)\,dx = \left[\int_a^b f(x)\,dx\right]\left[\int_a^b g(x)\,dx\right]$

69. If the norm of a partition approaches zero, then the number of subintervals approaches infinity.

70. If f is increasing on $[a, b]$, then the minimum value of $f(x)$ on $[a, b]$ is $f(a)$.

71. The value of

$$\int_a^b f(x)\,dx$$

must be positive.

72. The value of

$$\int_2^2 \sin(x^2)\,dx$$

is 0.

73. Finding a Riemann Sum Find the Riemann sum for $f(x) = x^2 + 3x$ over the interval $[0, 8]$, where

$$x_0 = 0, \quad x_1 = 1, \quad x_2 = 3, \quad x_3 = 7, \quad \text{and} \quad x_4 = 8$$

and where

$$c_1 = 1, \quad c_2 = 2, \quad c_3 = 5, \quad \text{and} \quad c_4 = 8.$$

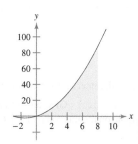

74. Finding a Riemann Sum Find the Riemann sum for $f(x) = \sin x$ over the interval $[0, 2\pi]$, where

$$x_0 = 0, \quad x_1 = \frac{\pi}{4}, \quad x_2 = \frac{\pi}{3}, \quad x_3 = \pi, \quad \text{and} \quad x_4 = 2\pi,$$

and where

$$c_1 = \frac{\pi}{6}, \quad c_2 = \frac{\pi}{3}, \quad c_3 = \frac{2\pi}{3}, \quad \text{and} \quad c_4 = \frac{3\pi}{2}.$$

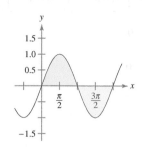

75. Proof Prove that $\displaystyle\int_a^b x\,dx = \frac{b^2 - a^2}{2}$.

76. Proof Prove that $\displaystyle\int_a^b x^2\,dx = \frac{b^3 - a^3}{3}$.

77. Think About It Determine whether the Dirichlet function

$$f(x) = \begin{cases} 1, & x \text{ is rational} \\ 0, & x \text{ is irrational} \end{cases}$$

is integrable on the interval $[0, 1]$. Explain.

78. Finding a Definite Integral The function

$$f(x) = \begin{cases} 0, & x = 0 \\ \dfrac{1}{x}, & 0 < x \le 1 \end{cases}$$

is defined on $[0, 1]$, as shown in the figure. Show that

$$\int_0^1 f(x)\,dx$$

does not exist. Why doesn't this contradict Theorem 5.4?

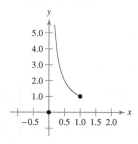

79. Finding Values Find the constants a and b that maximize the value of

$$\int_a^b (1 - x^2)\,dx.$$

Explain your reasoning.

80. Step Function Evaluate, if possible, the integral

$$\int_0^2 [\![x]\!]\,dx.$$

81. Using a Riemann Sum Determine

$$\lim_{n\to\infty} \frac{1}{n^3}[1^2 + 2^2 + 3^2 + \cdots + n^2]$$

by using an appropriate Riemann sum.

PUTNAM EXAM CHALLENGE

82. For each continuous function $f: [0, 1] \to \mathbb{R}$, let

$$I(f) = \int_0^1 x^2 f(x)\,dx \quad \text{and} \quad J(x) = \int_0^1 x(f(x))^2\,dx.$$

Find the maximum value of $I(f) - J(f)$ over all such functions f.

5.4 The Fundamental Theorem of Calculus

- ◾ Evaluate a definite integral using the Fundamental Theorem of Calculus.
- ◾ Understand and use the Mean Value Theorem for Integrals.
- ◾ Find the average value of a function over a closed interval.
- ◾ Understand and use the Second Fundamental Theorem of Calculus.
- ◾ Understand and use the Net Change Theorem.

The Fundamental Theorem of Calculus

You have now been introduced to the two major branches of calculus: differential calculus (introduced with the tangent line problem) and integral calculus (introduced with the area problem). So far, these two problems might seem unrelated—but there is a very close connection. The connection was discovered independently by Isaac Newton and Gottfried Leibniz and is stated in the **Fundamental Theorem of Calculus.**

Informally, the theorem states that differentiation and (definite) integration are inverse operations, in the same sense that division and multiplication are inverse operations. To see how Newton and Leibniz might have anticipated this relationship, consider the approximations shown in Figure 5.27. The slope of the tangent line was defined using the *quotient* $\Delta y/\Delta x$ (the slope of the secant line). Similarly, the area of a region under a curve was defined using the *product* $\Delta y \Delta x$ (the area of a rectangle). So, at least in the primitive approximation stage, the operations of differentiation and definite integration appear to have an inverse relationship in the same sense that division and multiplication are inverse operations. The Fundamental Theorem of Calculus states that the limit processes (used to define the derivative and definite integral) preserve this inverse relationship.

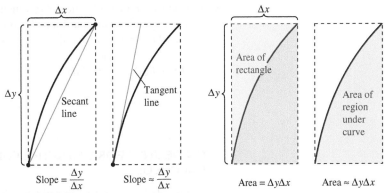

(a) Differentiation   (b) Definite integration

Differentiation and definite integration have an "inverse" relationship.

Figure 5.27

ANTIDIFFERENTIATION AND DEFINITE INTEGRATION

Throughout this chapter, you have been using the integral sign to denote an antiderivative (a family of functions) and a definite integral (a number).

$$\text{Antidifferentiation: } \int f(x)\, dx \qquad \text{Definite integration: } \int_a^b f(x)\, dx$$

The use of the same symbol for both operations makes it appear that they are related. In the early work with calculus, however, it was not known that the two operations were related. The symbol $\int$ was first applied to the definite integral by Leibniz and was derived from the letter S. (Leibniz calculated area as an infinite sum, thus, the letter S.)

THEOREM 5.9 **The Fundamental Theorem of Calculus**

If a function f is continuous on the closed interval $[a, b]$ and F is an antiderivative of f on the interval $[a, b]$, then

$$\int_a^b f(x)\, dx = F(b) - F(a).$$

Proof The key to the proof is writing the difference $F(b) - F(a)$ in a convenient form. Let Δ be any partition of $[a, b]$.

$$a = x_0 < x_1 < x_2 < \cdots < x_{n-1} < x_n = b$$

By pairwise subtraction and addition of like terms, you can write

$$F(b) - F(a) = F(x_n) - F(x_{n-1}) + F(x_{n-1}) - \cdots - F(x_1) + F(x_1) - F(x_0)$$

$$= \sum_{i=1}^{n} [F(x_i) - F(x_{i-1})].$$

By the Mean Value Theorem, you know that there exists a number c_i in the ith subinterval such that

$$F'(c_i) = \frac{F(x_i) - F(x_{i-1})}{x_i - x_{i-1}}.$$

Because $F'(c_i) = f(c_i)$, you can let $\Delta x_i = x_i - x_{i-1}$ and obtain

$$F(b) - F(a) = \sum_{i=1}^{n} f(c_i)\, \Delta x_i.$$

This important equation tells you that by repeatedly applying the Mean Value Theorem, you can always find a collection of c_i's such that the *constant* $F(b) - F(a)$ is a Riemann sum of f on $[a, b]$ for any partition. Theorem 5.4 guarantees that the limit of Riemann sums over the partition with $\|\Delta\| \to 0$ exists. So, taking the limit (as $\|\Delta\| \to 0$) produces

$$F(b) - F(a) = \int_a^b f(x)\, dx.$$

See LarsonCalculus.com for Bruce Edwards's video of this proof. ◼

GUIDELINES FOR USING THE FUNDAMENTAL THEOREM OF CALCULUS

1. *Provided you can find* an antiderivative of f, you now have a way to evaluate a definite integral without having to use the limit of a sum.

2. When applying the Fundamental Theorem of Calculus, the notation shown below is convenient.

$$\int_a^b f(x)\, dx = F(x) \Big]_a^b = F(b) - F(a)$$

For instance, to evaluate $\int_1^3 x^3\, dx$, you can write

$$\int_1^3 x^3\, dx = \frac{x^4}{4} \Big]_1^3 = \frac{3^4}{4} - \frac{1^4}{4} = \frac{81}{4} - \frac{1}{4} = 20.$$

3. It is not necessary to include a constant of integration C in the antiderivative.

$$\int_a^b f(x)\, dx = \left[F(x) + C \right]_a^b = [F(b) + C] - [F(a) + C] = F(b) - F(a)$$

EXAMPLE 1   **Evaluating a Definite Integral**

· · · · ▷ *See LarsonCalculus.com for an interactive version of this type of example.*

Evaluate each definite integral.

a. $\displaystyle\int_1^2 (x^2 - 3)\, dx$ **b.** $\displaystyle\int_1^4 3\sqrt{x}\, dx$ **c.** $\displaystyle\int_0^{\pi/4} \sec^2 x\, dx$

Solution

a. $\displaystyle\int_1^2 (x^2 - 3)\, dx = \left[\frac{x^3}{3} - 3x\right]_1^2 = \left(\frac{8}{3} - 6\right) - \left(\frac{1}{3} - 3\right) = -\frac{2}{3}$

b. $\displaystyle\int_1^4 3\sqrt{x}\, dx = 3\int_1^4 x^{1/2}\, dx = 3\left[\frac{x^{3/2}}{3/2}\right]_1^4 = 2(4)^{3/2} - 2(1)^{3/2} = 14$

c. $\displaystyle\int_0^{\pi/4} \sec^2 x\, dx = \tan x\Big]_0^{\pi/4} = 1 - 0 = 1$

EXAMPLE 2   **A Definite Integral Involving Absolute Value**

Evaluate $\displaystyle\int_0^2 |2x - 1|\, dx$.

Solution Using Figure 5.28 and the definition of absolute value, you can rewrite the integrand as shown.

$$|2x - 1| = \begin{cases} -(2x - 1), & x < \frac{1}{2} \\ 2x - 1, & x \geq \frac{1}{2} \end{cases}$$

From this, you can rewrite the integral in two parts.

$$\int_0^2 |2x - 1|\, dx = \int_0^{1/2} -(2x - 1)\, dx + \int_{1/2}^2 (2x - 1)\, dx$$

$$= \left[-x^2 + x\right]_0^{1/2} + \left[x^2 - x\right]_{1/2}^2$$

$$= \left(-\frac{1}{4} + \frac{1}{2}\right) - (0 + 0) + (4 - 2) - \left(\frac{1}{4} - \frac{1}{2}\right)$$

$$= \frac{5}{2}$$

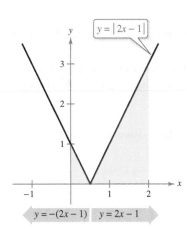

$y = |2x - 1|$

$y = -(2x - 1)$ $y = 2x - 1$

The definite integral of y on $[0, 2]$ is $\frac{5}{2}$.
Figure 5.28

EXAMPLE 3   **Using the Fundamental Theorem to Find Area**

Find the area of the region bounded by the graph of

$$y = \frac{1}{x}$$

the x-axis, and the vertical lines $x = 1$ and $x = e$, as shown in Figure 5.29.

Solution Note that $y > 0$ on the interval $[1, e]$.

$$\text{Area} = \int_1^e \frac{1}{x}\, dx \qquad \text{Integrate between } x = 1 \text{ and } x = e.$$

$$= \Big[\ln x\Big]_1^e \qquad \text{Find antiderivative.}$$

$$= \ln e - \ln 1 \qquad \text{Apply Fundamental Theorem of Calculus.}$$

$$= 1 \qquad \text{Simplify.}$$

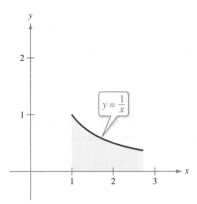

$y = \frac{1}{x}$

The area of the region bounded by the graph of $y = 1/x$, the x-axis, $x = 1$, and $x = e$ is 1.
Figure 5.29

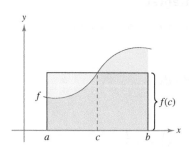

Mean value rectangle:

$$f(c)(b - a) = \int_a^b f(x)\, dx$$

Figure 5.30

The Mean Value Theorem for Integrals

In Section 5.2, you saw that the area of a region under a curve is greater than the area of an inscribed rectangle and less than the area of a circumscribed rectangle. The Mean Value Theorem for Integrals states that somewhere "between" the inscribed and circumscribed rectangles, there is a rectangle whose area is precisely equal to the area of the region under the curve, as shown in Figure 5.30.

THEOREM 5.10   Mean Value Theorem for Integrals

If f is continuous on the closed interval $[a, b]$, then there exists a number c in the closed interval $[a, b]$ such that

$$\int_a^b f(x)\, dx = f(c)(b - a).$$

Proof

Case 1: If f is constant on the interval $[a, b]$, then the theorem is clearly valid because c can be any point in $[a, b]$.

Case 2: If f is not constant on $[a, b]$, then, by the Extreme Value Theorem, you can choose $f(m)$ and $f(M)$ to be the minimum and maximum values of f on $[a, b]$. Because

$$f(m) \le f(x) \le f(M)$$

for all x in $[a, b]$, you can apply Theorem 5.8 to write the following.

$$\int_a^b f(m)\, dx \le \int_a^b f(x)\, dx \le \int_a^b f(M)\, dx \qquad \text{See Figure 5.31.}$$

$$f(m)(b - a) \le \int_a^b f(x)\, dx \le f(M)(b - a) \qquad \text{Apply Fundamental Theorem.}$$

$$f(m) \le \frac{1}{b - a}\int_a^b f(x)\, dx \le f(M) \qquad \text{Divide by } b - a.$$

From the third inequality, you can apply the Intermediate Value Theorem to conclude that there exists some c in $[a, b]$ such that

$$f(c) = \frac{1}{b - a}\int_a^b f(x)\, dx \quad \text{or} \quad f(c)(b - a) = \int_a^b f(x)\, dx.$$

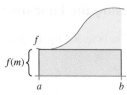

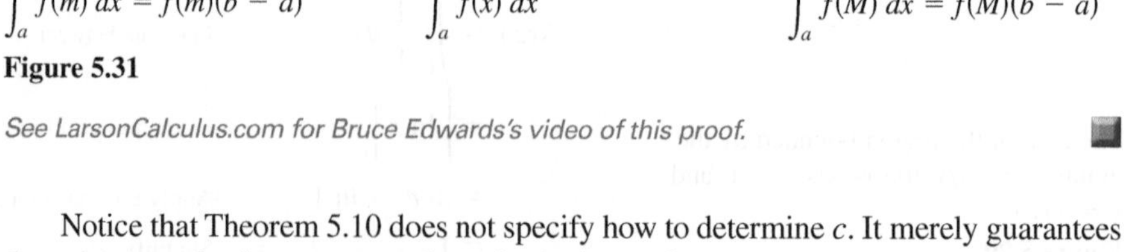

Inscribed rectangle
(less than actual area)

$$\int_a^b f(m)\, dx = f(m)(b - a)$$

Mean value rectangle
(equal to actual area)

$$\int_a^b f(x)\, dx$$

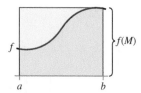

Circumscribed rectangle
(greater than actual area)

$$\int_a^b f(M)\, dx = f(M)(b - a)$$

Figure 5.31

See LarsonCalculus.com for Bruce Edwards's video of this proof.

Notice that Theorem 5.10 does not specify how to determine c. It merely guarantees the existence of at least one number c in the interval.

Average Value of a Function

The value of $f(c)$ given in the Mean Value Theorem for Integrals is called the **average value** of f on the interval $[a, b]$.

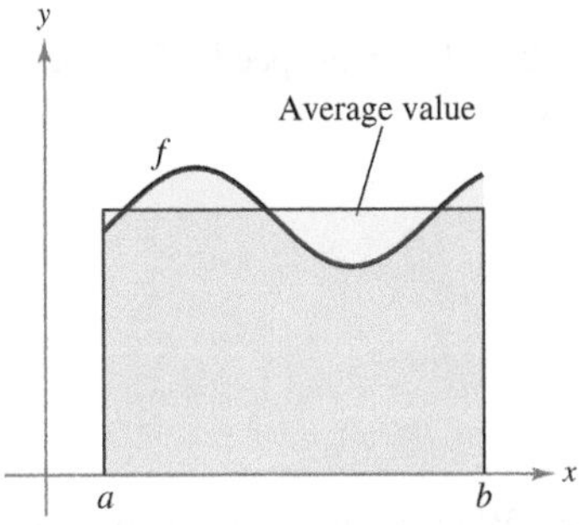

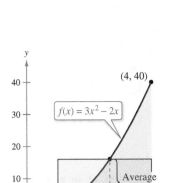

Average value $= \dfrac{1}{b-a}\displaystyle\int_a^b f(x)\,dx$

Figure 5.32

Definition of the Average Value of a Function on an Interval

If f is integrable on the closed interval $[a, b]$, then the **average value** of f on the interval is

$$\frac{1}{b-a}\int_a^b f(x)\,dx. \qquad \text{See Figure 5.32.}$$

To see why the average value of f is defined in this way, partition $[a, b]$ into n subintervals of equal width

$$\Delta x = \frac{b-a}{n}.$$

If c_i is any point in the ith subinterval, then the arithmetic average (or mean) of the function values at the c_i's is

$$a_n = \frac{1}{n}[f(c_1) + f(c_2) + \cdots + f(c_n)]. \qquad \text{Average of } f(c_1),\dots,f(c_n)$$

By multiplying and dividing by $(b - a)$, you can write the average as

$$a_n = \frac{1}{n}\sum_{i=1}^{n} f(c_i)\left(\frac{b-a}{b-a}\right)$$

$$= \frac{1}{b-a}\sum_{i=1}^{n} f(c_i)\left(\frac{b-a}{n}\right)$$

$$= \frac{1}{b-a}\sum_{i=1}^{n} f(c_i)\,\Delta x.$$

Finally, taking the limit as $n \to \infty$ produces the average value of f on the interval $[a, b]$, as given in the definition above. In Figure 5.32, notice that the area of the region under the graph of f is equal to the area of the rectangle whose height is the average value.

This development of the average value of a function on an interval is only one of many practical uses of definite integrals to represent summation processes. In Chapter 7, you will study other applications, such as volume, arc length, centers of mass, and work.

EXAMPLE 4 **Finding the Average Value of a Function**

Find the average value of $f(x) = 3x^2 - 2x$ on the interval $[1, 4]$.

Solution The average value is

$$\frac{1}{b-a}\int_a^b f(x)\,dx = \frac{1}{4-1}\int_1^4 (3x^2 - 2x)\,dx$$

$$= \frac{1}{3}\left[x^3 - x^2\right]_1^4$$

$$= \frac{1}{3}[64 - 16 - (1 - 1)]$$

$$= \frac{48}{3}$$

$$= 16. \qquad \text{See Figure 5.33.}$$

$f(x) = 3x^2 - 2x$

(4, 40)

(1, 1)

Average value = 16

Figure 5.33

The first person to fly at a speed greater than the speed of sound was Charles Yeager. On October 14, 1947, Yeager was clocked at 295.9 meters per second at an altitude of 12.2 kilometers. If Yeager had been flying at an altitude below 11.275 kilometers, this speed would not have "broken the sound barrier." The photo shows an F/A-18F Super Hornet, a supersonic twin-engine strike fighter. A "green Hornet" using a 50/50 mixture of biofuel made from camelina oil became the first U.S. naval tactical aircraft to exceed 1 mach.

EXAMPLE 5   **The Speed of Sound**

At different altitudes in Earth's atmosphere, sound travels at different speeds. The speed of sound $s(x)$ (in meters per second) can be modeled by

$$s(x) = \begin{cases} -4x + 341, & 0 \le x < 11.5 \\ 295, & 11.5 \le x < 22 \\ \frac{3}{4}x + 278.5, & 22 \le x < 32 \\ \frac{3}{2}x + 254.5, & 32 \le x < 50 \\ -\frac{3}{2}x + 404.5, & 50 \le x \le 80 \end{cases}$$

where x is the altitude in kilometers (see Figure 5.34). What is the average speed of sound over the interval $[0, 80]$?

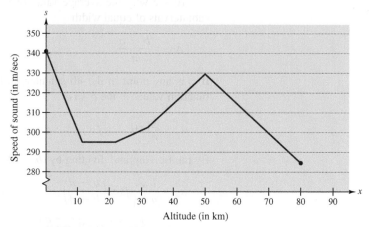

Speed of sound depends on altitude.
Figure 5.34

Solution   Begin by integrating $s(x)$ over the interval $[0, 80]$. To do this, you can break the integral into five parts.

$$\int_0^{11.5} s(x)\, dx = \int_0^{11.5} (-4x + 341)\, dx = \left[-2x^2 + 341x \right]_0^{11.5} = 3657$$

$$\int_{11.5}^{22} s(x)\, dx = \int_{11.5}^{22} 295\, dx = \left[295x \right]_{11.5}^{22} = 3097.5$$

$$\int_{22}^{32} s(x)\, dx = \int_{22}^{32} \left(\tfrac{3}{4}x + 278.5\right) dx = \left[\tfrac{3}{8}x^2 + 278.5x \right]_{22}^{32} = 2987.5$$

$$\int_{32}^{50} s(x)\, dx = \int_{32}^{50} \left(\tfrac{3}{2}x + 254.5\right) dx = \left[\tfrac{3}{4}x^2 + 254.5x \right]_{32}^{50} = 5688$$

$$\int_{50}^{80} s(x)\, dx = \int_{50}^{80} \left(-\tfrac{3}{2}x + 404.5\right) dx = \left[-\tfrac{3}{4}x^2 + 404.5x \right]_{50}^{80} = 9210$$

By adding the values of the five integrals, you have

$$\int_0^{80} s(x)\, dx = 24{,}640.$$

So, the average speed of sound from an altitude of 0 kilometers to an altitude of 80 kilometers is

$$\text{Average speed} = \frac{1}{80} \int_0^{80} s(x)\, dx = \frac{24{,}640}{80} = 308 \text{ meters per second.}$$

The Second Fundamental Theorem of Calculus

Earlier you saw that the definite integral of f on the interval $[a, b]$ was defined using the constant b as the upper limit of integration and x as the variable of integration. However, a slightly different situation may arise in which the variable x is used in the upper limit of integration. To avoid the confusion of using x in two different ways, t is temporarily used as the variable of integration. (Remember that the definite integral is *not* a function of its variable of integration.)

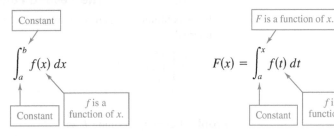

The Definite Integral as a Number   The Definite Integral as a Function of x

Exploration

Use a graphing utility to graph the function

$$F(x) = \int_0^x \cos t \, dt$$

for $0 \le x \le \pi$. Do you recognize this graph? Explain.

EXAMPLE 6   **The Definite Integral as a Function**

Evaluate the function

$$F(x) = \int_0^x \cos t \, dt$$

at $x = 0, \dfrac{\pi}{6}, \dfrac{\pi}{4}, \dfrac{\pi}{3},$ and $\dfrac{\pi}{2}$.

Solution You could evaluate five different definite integrals, one for each of the given upper limits. However, it is much simpler to fix x (as a constant) temporarily to obtain

$$\int_0^x \cos t \, dt = \sin t \Big]_0^x$$
$$= \sin x - \sin 0$$
$$= \sin x.$$

Now, using $F(x) = \sin x$, you can obtain the results shown in Figure 5.35.

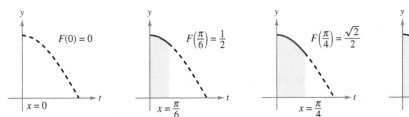

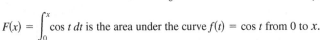

$F(x) = \displaystyle\int_0^x \cos t \, dt$ is the area under the curve $f(t) = \cos t$ from 0 to x.

Figure 5.35

You can think of the function $F(x)$ as *accumulating* the area under the curve $f(t) = \cos t$ from $t = 0$ to $t = x$. For $x = 0$, the area is 0 and $F(0) = 0$. For $x = \pi/2$, $F(\pi/2) = 1$ gives the accumulated area under the cosine curve on the entire interval $[0, \pi/2]$. This interpretation of an integral as an **accumulation function** is used often in applications of integration.

In Example 6, note that the derivative of F is the original integrand (with only the variable changed). That is,

$$\frac{d}{dx}[F(x)] = \frac{d}{dx}[\sin x] = \frac{d}{dx}\left[\int_0^x \cos t\, dt\right] = \cos x.$$

This result is generalized in the next theorem, called the **Second Fundamental Theorem of Calculus.**

THEOREM 5.11   The Second Fundamental Theorem of Calculus

If f is continuous on an open interval I containing a, then, for every x in the interval,

$$\frac{d}{dx}\left[\int_a^x f(t)\, dt\right] = f(x).$$

Proof   Begin by defining F as

$$F(x) = \int_a^x f(t)\, dt.$$

Then, by the definition of the derivative, you can write

$$
\begin{aligned}
F'(x) &= \lim_{\Delta x \to 0} \frac{F(x + \Delta x) - F(x)}{\Delta x} \\
&= \lim_{\Delta x \to 0} \frac{1}{\Delta x}\left[\int_a^{x+\Delta x} f(t)\, dt - \int_a^x f(t)\, dt\right] \\
&= \lim_{\Delta x \to 0} \frac{1}{\Delta x}\left[\int_a^{x+\Delta x} f(t)\, dt + \int_x^a f(t)\, dt\right] \\
&= \lim_{\Delta x \to 0} \frac{1}{\Delta x}\left[\int_x^{x+\Delta x} f(t)\, dt\right].
\end{aligned}
$$

From the Mean Value Theorem for Integrals (assuming $\Delta x > 0$), you know there exists a number c in the interval $[x, x + \Delta x]$ such that the integral in the expression above is equal to $f(c)\,\Delta x$. Moreover, because $x \le c \le x + \Delta x$, it follows that $c \to x$ as $\Delta x \to 0$. So, you obtain

$$F'(x) = \lim_{\Delta x \to 0}\left[\frac{1}{\Delta x} f(c)\, \Delta x\right] = \lim_{\Delta x \to 0} f(c) = f(x).$$

A similar argument can be made for $\Delta x < 0$.

See LarsonCalculus.com for Bruce Edwards's video of this proof.

Using the area model for definite integrals, the approximation

$$f(x)\,\Delta x \approx \int_x^{x+\Delta x} f(t)\, dt$$

can be viewed as saying that the area of the rectangle of height $f(x)$ and width Δx is approximately equal to the area of the region lying between the graph of f and the x-axis on the interval

$$[x, x + \Delta x]$$

as shown in the figure at the right.

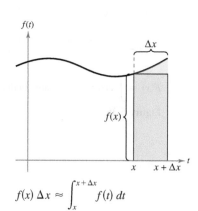

$$f(x)\,\Delta x \approx \int_x^{x+\Delta x} f(t)\, dt$$

Note that the Second Fundamental Theorem of Calculus tells you that when a function is continuous, you can be sure that it has an antiderivative. This antiderivative need not, however, be an elementary function. (Recall the discussion of elementary functions in Section 1.3.)

EXAMPLE 7   **The Second Fundamental Theorem of Calculus**

Evaluate $\dfrac{d}{dx}\left[\displaystyle\int_0^x \sqrt{t^2 + 1}\, dt\right]$.

Solution   Note that $f(t) = \sqrt{t^2 + 1}$ is continuous on the entire real number line. So, using the Second Fundamental Theorem of Calculus, you can write

$$\frac{d}{dx}\left[\int_0^x \sqrt{t^2 + 1}\, dt\right] = \sqrt{x^2 + 1}.$$

The differentiation shown in Example 7 is a straightforward application of the Second Fundamental Theorem of Calculus. The next example shows how this theorem can be combined with the Chain Rule to find the derivative of a function.

EXAMPLE 8   **The Second Fundamental Theorem of Calculus**

Find the derivative of $F(x) = \displaystyle\int_{\pi/2}^{x^3} \cos t\, dt$.

Solution   Using $u = x^3$, you can apply the Second Fundamental Theorem of Calculus with the Chain Rule as shown.

$$
\begin{aligned}
F'(x) &= \frac{dF}{du}\frac{du}{dx} && \text{Chain Rule}\\[2mm]
&= \frac{d}{du}[F(x)]\frac{du}{dx} && \text{Definition of } \frac{dF}{du}\\[2mm]
&= \frac{d}{du}\left[\int_{\pi/2}^{x^3}\cos t\, dt\right]\frac{du}{dx} && \text{Substitute } \int_{\pi/2}^{x^3}\cos t\, dt \text{ for } F(x).\\[2mm]
&= \frac{d}{du}\left[\int_{\pi/2}^{u}\cos t\, dt\right]\frac{du}{dx} && \text{Substitute } u \text{ for } x^3.\\[2mm]
&= (\cos u)(3x^2) && \text{Apply Second Fundamental Theorem of Calculus.}\\[2mm]
&= (\cos x^3)(3x^2) && \text{Rewrite as function of } x.
\end{aligned}
$$

Because the integrand in Example 8 is easily integrated, you can verify the derivative as follows.

$$
\begin{aligned}
F(x) &= \int_{\pi/2}^{x^3}\cos t\, dt\\[2mm]
&= \sin t \Big]_{\pi/2}^{x^3}\\[2mm]
&= \sin x^3 - \sin\frac{\pi}{2}\\[2mm]
&= \sin x^3 - 1
\end{aligned}
$$

In this form, you can apply the Power Rule to verify that the derivative of F is the same as that obtained in Example 8.

$$\frac{d}{dx}[\sin x^3 - 1] = (\cos x^3)(3x^2) \qquad \text{Derivative of } F$$

Net Change Theorem

The Fundamental Theorem of Calculus (Theorem 5.9) states that if f is continuous on the closed interval $[a, b]$ and F is an antiderivative of f on $[a, b]$, then

$$\int_a^b f(x)\, dx = F(b) - F(a).$$

But because $F'(x) = f(x)$, this statement can be rewritten as

$$\int_a^b F'(x)\, dx = F(b) - F(a)$$

where the quantity $F(b) - F(a)$ represents the *net change of F* on the interval $[a, b]$.

THEOREM 5.12   The Net Change Theorem

The definite integral of the rate of change of quantity $F'(x)$ gives the total change, or **net change,** in that quantity on the interval $[a, b]$.

$$\int_a^b F'(x)\, dx = F(b) - F(a) \qquad \text{Net change of } F$$

EXAMPLE 9   **Using the Net Change Theorem**

A chemical flows into a storage tank at a rate of $(180 + 3t)$ liters per minute, where t is the time in minutes and $0 \le t \le 60$. Find the amount of the chemical that flows into the tank during the first 20 minutes.

Solution   Let $c(t)$ be the amount of the chemical in the tank at time t. Then $c'(t)$ represents the rate at which the chemical flows into the tank at time t. During the first 20 minutes, the amount that flows into the tank is

$$\int_0^{20} c'(t)\, dt = \int_0^{20} (180 + 3t)\, dt$$
$$= \left[180t + \frac{3}{2}t^2 \right]_0^{20}$$
$$= 3600 + 600$$
$$= 4200.$$

So, the amount that flows into the tank during the first 20 minutes is 4200 liters.

Another way to illustrate the Net Change Theorem is to examine the velocity of a particle moving along a straight line, where $s(t)$ is the position at time t. Then its velocity is $v(t) = s'(t)$ and

$$\int_a^b v(t)\, dt = s(b) - s(a).$$

This definite integral represents the net change in position, or **displacement,** of the particle.

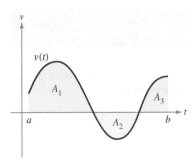

$A_1, A_2,$ and A_3 are the areas of the shaded regions.
Figure 5.36

When calculating the *total* distance traveled by the particle, you must consider the intervals where $v(t) \leq 0$ and the intervals where $v(t) \geq 0$. When $v(t) \leq 0$, the particle moves to the left, and when $v(t) \geq 0$, the particle moves to the right. To calculate the total distance traveled, integrate the absolute value of velocity $|v(t)|$. So, the **displacement** of the particle on the interval $[a, b]$ is

$$\text{Displacement on } [a, b] = \int_a^b v(t) \, dt = A_1 - A_2 + A_3$$

and the **total distance traveled** by the particle on $[a, b]$ is

$$\text{Total distance traveled on } [a, b] = \int_a^b |v(t)| \, dt = A_1 + A_2 + A_3.$$

(See Figure 5.36.)

EXAMPLE 10 **Solving a Particle Motion Problem**

The velocity (in feet per second) of a particle moving along a line is

$$v(t) = t^3 - 10t^2 + 29t - 20$$

where t is the time in seconds.

a. What is the displacement of the particle on the time interval $1 \leq t \leq 5$?

b. What is the total distance traveled by the particle on the time interval $1 \leq t \leq 5$?

Solution

a. By definition, you know that the displacement is

$$\int_1^5 v(t) \, dt = \int_1^5 (t^3 - 10t^2 + 29t - 20) \, dt$$

$$= \left[\frac{t^4}{4} - \frac{10}{3}t^3 + \frac{29}{2}t^2 - 20t \right]_1^5$$

$$= \frac{25}{12} - \left(-\frac{103}{12} \right)$$

$$= \frac{128}{12}$$

$$= \frac{32}{3}.$$

So, the particle moves $\frac{32}{3}$ feet to the right.

b. To find the total distance traveled, calculate $\int_1^5 |v(t)| \, dt$. Using Figure 5.37 and the fact that $v(t)$ can be factored as $(t - 1)(t - 4)(t - 5)$, you can determine that $v(t) \geq 0$ on $[1, 4]$ and $v(t) \leq 0$ on $[4, 5]$. So, the total distance traveled is

$$\int_1^5 |v(t)| \, dt = \int_1^4 v(t) \, dt - \int_4^5 v(t) \, dt$$

$$= \int_1^4 (t^3 - 10t^2 + 29t - 20) \, dt - \int_4^5 (t^3 - 10t^2 + 29t - 20) \, dt$$

$$= \left[\frac{t^4}{4} - \frac{10}{3}t^3 + \frac{29}{2}t^2 - 20t \right]_1^4 - \left[\frac{t^4}{4} - \frac{10}{3}t^3 + \frac{29}{2}t^2 - 20t \right]_4^5$$

$$= \frac{45}{4} - \left(-\frac{7}{12} \right)$$

$$= \frac{71}{6} \text{ feet.}$$

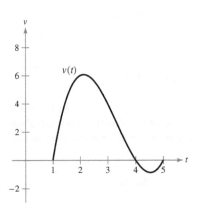

Figure 5.37

5.4 Exercises

See CalcChat.com for tutorial help and worked-out solutions to odd-numbered exercises.

Graphical Reasoning In Exercises 1–4, use a graphing utility to graph the integrand. Use the graph to determine whether the definite integral is positive, negative, or zero.

1. $\displaystyle\int_0^\pi \frac{4}{x^2+1}\, dx$

2. $\displaystyle\int_0^\pi \cos x\, dx$

3. $\displaystyle\int_{-2}^2 x\sqrt{x^2+1}\, dx$

4. $\displaystyle\int_{-2}^2 x\sqrt{2-x}\, dx$

Evaluating a Definite Integral In Exercises 5–38, evaluate the definite integral. Use a graphing utility to verify your result.

5. $\displaystyle\int_0^2 6x\, dx$

6. $\displaystyle\int_{-3}^1 8\, dt$

7. $\displaystyle\int_{-1}^0 (2x-1)\, dx$

8. $\displaystyle\int_{-1}^2 (7-3t)\, dt$

9. $\displaystyle\int_{-1}^1 (t^2-2)\, dt$

10. $\displaystyle\int_1^2 (6x^2-3x)\, dx$

11. $\displaystyle\int_0^1 (2t-1)^2\, dt$

12. $\displaystyle\int_1^3 (4x^3-3x^2)\, dx$

13. $\displaystyle\int_1^2 \left(\frac{3}{x^2}-1\right)dx$

14. $\displaystyle\int_{-2}^{-1}\left(u-\frac{1}{u^2}\right)du$

15. $\displaystyle\int_1^4 \frac{u-2}{\sqrt{u}}\, du$

16. $\displaystyle\int_{-8}^8 x^{1/3}\, dx$

17. $\displaystyle\int_{-1}^1 (\sqrt[3]{t}-2)\, dt$

18. $\displaystyle\int_1^8 \sqrt{\frac{2}{x}}\, dx$

19. $\displaystyle\int_0^1 \frac{x-\sqrt{x}}{3}\, dx$

20. $\displaystyle\int_0^2 (2-t)\sqrt{t}\, dt$

21. $\displaystyle\int_{-1}^0 (t^{1/3}-t^{2/3})\, dt$

22. $\displaystyle\int_{-8}^{-1} \frac{x-x^2}{2\sqrt[3]{x}}\, dx$

23. $\displaystyle\int_0^5 |2x-5|\, dx$

24. $\displaystyle\int_1^4 (3-|x-3|)\, dx$

25. $\displaystyle\int_0^4 |x^2-9|\, dx$

26. $\displaystyle\int_0^4 |x^2-4x+3|\, dx$

27. $\displaystyle\int_0^\pi (1+\sin x)\, dx$

28. $\displaystyle\int_0^\pi (2+\cos x)\, dx$

29. $\displaystyle\int_0^{\pi/4} \frac{1-\sin^2\theta}{\cos^2\theta}\, d\theta$

30. $\displaystyle\int_0^{\pi/4} \frac{\sec^2\theta}{\tan^2\theta+1}\, d\theta$

31. $\displaystyle\int_{-\pi/6}^{\pi/6} \sec^2 x\, dx$

32. $\displaystyle\int_{\pi/4}^{\pi/2} (2-\csc^2 x)\, dx$

33. $\displaystyle\int_{-\pi/3}^{\pi/3} 4\sec\theta\tan\theta\, d\theta$

34. $\displaystyle\int_{-\pi/2}^{\pi/2} (2t+\cos t)\, dt$

35. $\displaystyle\int_0^2 (2^x+6)\, dx$

36. $\displaystyle\int_0^3 (t-5^t)\, dt$

37. $\displaystyle\int_{-1}^1 (e^\theta+\sin\theta)\, d\theta$

38. $\displaystyle\int_e^{2e}\left(\cos x-\frac{1}{x}\right)dx$

Finding the Area of a Region In Exercises 39–42, determine the area of the given region.

39. $y=x-x^2$

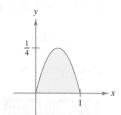

40. $y=\dfrac{1}{x^2}$

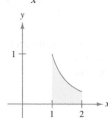

41. $y=\cos x$

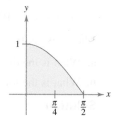

42. $y=x+\sin x$

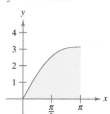

Finding the Area of a Region In Exercises 43–48, find the area of the region bounded by the graphs of the equations.

43. $y=5x^2+2,\quad x=0,\quad x=2,\quad y=0$

44. $y=x^3+x,\quad x=2,\quad y=0$

45. $y=1+\sqrt[3]{x},\quad x=0,\quad x=8,\quad y=0$

46. $y=-x^2+4x,\quad y=0$

47. $y=\dfrac{4}{x},\quad x=1,\quad x=e,\quad y=0$

48. $y=e^x,\quad x=0,\quad x=2,\quad y=0$

Using the Mean Value Theorem for Integrals In Exercises 49–54, find the value(s) of c guaranteed by the Mean Value Theorem for Integrals for the function over the given interval.

49. $f(x)=x^3,\quad [0,3]$

50. $f(x)=\sqrt{x},\quad [4,9]$

51. $f(x)=5-\dfrac{1}{x},\quad [1,4]$

52. $f(x)=10-2^x,\quad [0,3]$

53. $f(x)=2\sec^2 x,\quad \left[-\dfrac{\pi}{4},\dfrac{\pi}{4}\right]$

54. $f(x)=\cos x,\quad \left[-\dfrac{\pi}{3},\dfrac{\pi}{3}\right]$

Finding the Average Value of a Function In Exercises 55–60, find the average value of the function over the given interval and all values of x in the interval for which the function equals its average value.

55. $f(x)=9-x^2,\quad [-3,3]$

56. $f(x)=\dfrac{4(x^2+1)}{x^2},\quad [1,3]$

57. $f(x)=2e^x,\quad [-1,1]$

58. $f(x)=\dfrac{1}{2x},\quad [1,4]$

59. $f(x)=\sin x,\quad [0,\pi]$

60. $f(x)=\cos x,\quad \left[0,\dfrac{\pi}{2}\right]$

61. Velocity The graph shows the velocity, in feet per second, of a car accelerating from rest. Use the graph to estimate the distance the car travels in 8 seconds.

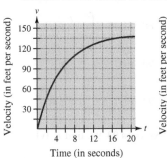

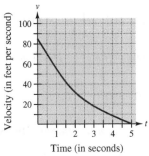

Figure for 61   Figure for 62

62. Velocity The graph shows the velocity, in feet per second, of a decelerating car after the driver applies the brakes. Use the graph to estimate how far the car travels before it comes to a stop.

WRITING ABOUT CONCEPTS

63. Using a Graph The graph of f is shown in the figure.

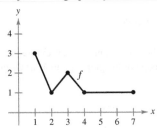

(a) Evaluate $\int_1^7 f(x)\, dx$.

(b) Determine the average value of f on the interval $[1, 7]$.

(c) Determine the answers to parts (a) and (b) when the graph is translated two units upward.

64. Rate of Growth Let $r'(t)$ represent the rate of growth of a dog, in pounds per year. What does $r(t)$ represent? What does $\int_2^6 r'(t)\, dt$ represent about the dog?

---

65. Force The force F (in newtons) of a hydraulic cylinder in a press is proportional to the square of $\sec x$, where x is the distance (in meters) that the cylinder is extended in its cycle. The domain of F is $[0, \pi/3]$, and $F(0) = 500$.

(a) Find F as a function of x.

(b) Find the average force exerted by the press over the interval $[0, \pi/3]$.

66. Blood Flow The velocity v of the flow of blood at a distance r from the central axis of an artery of radius R is

$$v = k(R^2 - r^2)$$

where k is the constant of proportionality. Find the average rate of flow of blood along a radius of the artery. (Use 0 and R as the limits of integration.)

67. Respiratory Cycle The volume V, in liters, of air in the lungs during a five-second respiratory cycle is approximated by the model $V = 0.1729t + 0.1522t^2 - 0.0374t^3$, where t is the time in seconds. Approximate the average volume of air in the lungs during one cycle.

68. Average Sales A company fits a model to the monthly sales data for a seasonal product. The model is

$$S(t) = \frac{t}{4} + 1.8 + 0.5 \sin\left(\frac{\pi t}{6}\right), \quad 0 \le t \le 24$$

where S is sales (in thousands) and t is time in months.

(a) Use a graphing utility to graph $f(t) = 0.5 \sin(\pi t/6)$ for $0 \le t \le 24$. Use the graph to explain why the average value of $f(t)$ is 0 over the interval.

(b) Use a graphing utility to graph $S(t)$ and the line $g(t) = t/4 + 1.8$ in the same viewing window. Use the graph and the result of part (a) to explain why g is called the *trend line*.

69. Modeling Data An experimental vehicle is tested on a straight track. It starts from rest, and its velocity v (in meters per second) is recorded every 10 seconds for 1 minute (see table).

t	0	10	20	30	40	50	60
v	0	5	21	40	62	78	83

(a) Use a graphing utility to find a model of the form $v = at^3 + bt^2 + ct + d$ for the data.

(b) Use a graphing utility to plot the data and graph the model.

(c) Use the Fundamental Theorem of Calculus to approximate the distance traveled by the vehicle during the test.

70. HOW DO YOU SEE IT? The graph of f is shown in the figure. The shaded region A has an area of 1.5, and $\int_0^6 f(x)\, dx = 3.5$. Use this information to fill in the blanks.

(a) $\int_0^2 f(x)\, dx = $ ▨

(b) $\int_2^6 f(x)\, dx = $ ▨

(c) $\int_0^6 |f(x)|\, dx = $ ▨

(d) $\int_0^2 -2f(x)\, dx = $ ▨

(e) $\int_0^6 [2 + f(x)]\, dx = $ ▨

(f) The average value of f over the interval $[0, 6]$ is ▨.

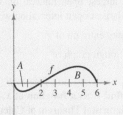

Evaluating a Definite Integral In Exercises 71–76, find F as a function of x and evaluate it at $x = 2$, $x = 5$, and $x = 8$.

71. $F(x) = \displaystyle\int_0^x (4t - 7)\, dt$

72. $F(x) = \displaystyle\int_2^x (t^3 + 2t - 2)\, dt$

73. $F(x) = \displaystyle\int_1^x \frac{20}{v^2}\, dv$

74. $F(x) = \displaystyle\int_2^x -\frac{2}{t^3}\, dt$

75. $F(x) = \displaystyle\int_1^x \cos\theta\, d\theta$

76. $F(x) = \displaystyle\int_0^x \sin\theta\, d\theta$

77. Analyzing a Function Let

$$g(x) = \int_0^x f(t)\, dt$$

where f is the function whose graph is shown in the figure.

(a) Estimate $g(0)$, $g(2)$, $g(4)$, $g(6)$, and $g(8)$.

(b) Find the largest open interval on which g is increasing. Find the largest open interval on which g is decreasing.

(c) Identify any extrema of g.

(d) Sketch a rough graph of g.

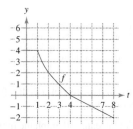

Figure for 77

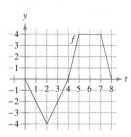

Figure for 78

78. Analyzing a Function Let

$$g(x) = \int_0^x f(t)\, dt$$

where f is the function whose graph is shown in the figure.

(a) Estimate $g(0)$, $g(2)$, $g(4)$, $g(6)$, and $g(8)$.

(b) Find the largest open interval on which g is increasing. Find the largest open interval on which g is decreasing.

(c) Identify any extrema of g.

(d) Sketch a rough graph of g.

Finding and Checking an Integral In Exercises 79–86, (a) integrate to find F as a function of x, and (b) demonstrate the Second Fundamental Theorem of Calculus by differentiating the result in part (a).

79. $F(x) = \displaystyle\int_0^x (t + 2)\, dt$

80. $F(x) = \displaystyle\int_0^x t(t^2 + 1)\, dt$

81. $F(x) = \displaystyle\int_8^x \sqrt[3]{t}\, dt$

82. $F(x) = \displaystyle\int_4^x \sqrt{t}\, dt$

83. $F(x) = \displaystyle\int_{\pi/4}^x \sec^2 t\, dt$

84. $F(x) = \displaystyle\int_{\pi/3}^x \sec t \tan t\, dt$

85. $F(x) = \displaystyle\int_{-1}^x e^t\, dt$

86. $F(x) = \displaystyle\int_1^x \frac{1}{t}\, dt$

Using the Second Fundamental Theorem of Calculus In Exercises 87–92, use the Second Fundamental Theorem of Calculus to find $F'(x)$.

87. $F(x) = \displaystyle\int_{-2}^x (t^2 - 2t)\, dt$

88. $F(x) = \displaystyle\int_1^x \frac{t^2}{t^2 + 1}\, dt$

89. $F(x) = \displaystyle\int_{-1}^x \sqrt{t^4 + 1}\, dt$

90. $F(x) = \displaystyle\int_1^x \sqrt[4]{t}\, dt$

91. $F(x) = \displaystyle\int_0^x t \cos t\, dt$

92. $F(x) = \displaystyle\int_0^x \sec^3 t\, dt$

Finding a Derivative In Exercises 93–98, find $F'(x)$.

93. $F(x) = \displaystyle\int_x^{x+2} (4t + 1)\, dt$

94. $F(x) = \displaystyle\int_{-x}^x t^3\, dt$

95. $F(x) = \displaystyle\int_0^{\sin x} \sqrt{t}\, dt$

96. $F(x) = \displaystyle\int_2^{x^2} \frac{1}{t^3}\, dt$

97. $F(x) = \displaystyle\int_0^{x^3} \sin t^2\, dt$

98. $F(x) = \displaystyle\int_0^{x^2} \sin\theta^2\, d\theta$

99. Graphical Analysis Sketch an approximate graph of g on the interval $0 \le x \le 4$, where

$$g(x) = \int_0^x f(t)\, dt.$$

Identify the x-coordinate of an extremum of g. To print an enlarged copy of the graph, go to *MathGraphs.com*.

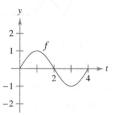

100. Area The area A between the graph of the function

$$g(t) = 4 - \frac{4}{t^2}$$

and the t-axis over the interval $[1, x]$ is

$$A(x) = \int_1^x \left(4 - \frac{4}{t^2}\right) dt.$$

(a) Find the horizontal asymptote of the graph of g.

(b) Integrate to find A as a function of x. Does the graph of A have a horizontal asymptote? Explain.

Particle Motion In Exercises 101–106, the velocity function, in feet per second, is given for a particle moving along a straight line. Find (a) the displacement and (b) the total distance that the particle travels over the given interval.

101. $v(t) = 5t - 7$, $\quad 0 \le t \le 3$

102. $v(t) = t^2 - t - 12$, $\quad 1 \le t \le 5$

103. $v(t) = t^3 - 10t^2 + 27t - 18$, $\quad 1 \le t \le 7$

104. $v(t) = t^3 - 8t^2 + 15t$, $\quad 0 \le t \le 5$

105. $v(t) = \dfrac{1}{\sqrt{t}}, \quad 1 \le t \le 4$

106. $v(t) = \cos t, \quad 0 \le t \le 3\pi$

107. Particle Motion A particle is moving along the x-axis. The position of the particle at time t is given by

$$x(t) = t^3 - 6t^2 + 9t - 2, \quad 0 \le t \le 5.$$

Find the total distance the particle travels in 5 units of time.

108. Particle Motion Repeat Exercise 107 for the position function given by

$$x(t) = (t - 1)(t - 3)^2, \quad 0 \le t \le 5.$$

109. Water Flow Water flows from a storage tank at a rate of $(500 - 5t)$ liters per minute. Find the amount of water that flows out of the tank during the first 18 minutes.

110. Oil Leak At 1:00 P.M., oil begins leaking from a tank at a rate of $(4 + 0.75t)$ gallons per hour.

(a) How much oil is lost from 1:00 P.M. to 4:00 P.M.?

(b) How much oil is lost from 4:00 P.M. to 7:00 P.M.?

(c) Compare your answers to parts (a) and (b). What do you notice?

Error Analysis In Exercises 111–114, describe why the statement is incorrect.

111. $\displaystyle \int_{-1}^{1} x^{-2}\, dx = \left[-x^{-1} \right]_{-1}^{1} = (-1) - 1 = -2$

112. $\displaystyle \int_{-2}^{1} \frac{2}{x^3}\, dx = \left[\frac{1}{x^2} \right]_{-2}^{1} = -\frac{3}{4}$

113. $\displaystyle \int_{\pi/4}^{3\pi/4} \sec^2 x\, dx = \left[\tan x \right]_{\pi/4}^{3\pi/4} = -2$

114. $\displaystyle \int_{\pi/2}^{3\pi/2} \csc x \cot x\, dx = \left[-\csc x \right]_{\pi/2}^{3\pi/2} = 2$

115. Buffon's Needle Experiment A horizontal plane is ruled with parallel lines 2 inches apart. A two-inch needle is tossed randomly onto the plane. The probability that the needle will touch a line is

$$P = \frac{2}{\pi} \int_{0}^{\pi/2} \sin \theta\, d\theta$$

where θ is the acute angle between the needle and any one of the parallel lines. Find this probability.

116. Proof Prove that

$$\frac{d}{dx}\left[\int_{u(x)}^{v(x)} f(t)\, dt \right] = f(v(x))v'(x) - f(u(x))u'(x).$$

True or False? In Exercises 117 and 118, determine whether the statement is true or false. If it is false, explain why or give an example that shows it is false.

117. If $F'(x) = G'(x)$ on the interval $[a, b]$, then

$$F(b) - F(a) = G(b) - G(a).$$

118. If f is continuous on $[a, b]$, then f is integrable on $[a, b]$.

119. Analyzing a Function Show that the function

$$f(x) = \int_{0}^{1/x} \frac{1}{t^2 + 1}\, dt + \int_{0}^{x} \frac{1}{t^2 + 1}\, dt$$

is constant for $x > 0$.

120. Finding a Function Find the function $f(x)$ and all values of c such that

$$\int_{c}^{x} f(t)\, dt = x^2 + x - 2.$$

121. Finding Values Let

$$G(x) = \int_{0}^{x} \left[s \int_{0}^{s} f(t)\, dt \right] ds$$

where f is continuous for all real t. Find (a) $G(0)$, (b) $G'(0)$, (c) $G''(x)$, and (d) $G''(0)$.

SECTION PROJECT

Demonstrating the Fundamental Theorem

Use a graphing utility to graph the function

$$y_1 = \sin^2 t$$

on the interval $0 \le t \le \pi$. Let $F(x)$ be the following function of x.

$$F(x) = \int_{0}^{x} \sin^2 t\, dt$$

(a) Complete the table. Explain why the values of F are increasing.

x	0	$\dfrac{\pi}{6}$	$\dfrac{\pi}{3}$	$\dfrac{\pi}{2}$	$\dfrac{2\pi}{3}$	$\dfrac{5\pi}{6}$	π
$F(x)$							

(b) Use the integration capabilities of a graphing utility to graph F.

(c) Use the differentiation capabilities of a graphing utility to graph $F'(x)$. How is this graph related to the graph in part (b)?

(d) Verify that the derivative of

$$y = \frac{1}{2}t - \frac{1}{4}\sin 2t$$

is $\sin^2 t$. Graph y and write a short paragraph about how this graph is related to those in parts (b) and (c).

5.5 Integration by Substitution

- Use pattern recognition to find an indefinite integral.
- Use a change of variables to find an indefinite integral.
- Use the General Power Rule for Integration to find an indefinite integral.
- Use a change of variables to evaluate a definite integral.
- Evaluate a definite integral involving an even or odd function.

Pattern Recognition

In this section, you will study techniques for integrating composite functions. The discussion is split into two parts—*pattern recognition* and *change of variables.* Both techniques involve a *u*-**substitution.** With pattern recognition, you perform the substitution mentally, and with change of variables, you write the substitution steps.

The role of substitution in integration is comparable to the role of the Chain Rule in differentiation. Recall that for the differentiable functions

$$y = F(u) \quad \text{and} \quad u = g(x)$$

the Chain Rule states that

$$\frac{d}{dx}[F(g(x))] = F'(g(x))g'(x).$$

From the definition of an antiderivative, it follows that

$$\int F'(g(x))g'(x)\, dx = F(g(x)) + C.$$

These results are summarized in the next theorem.

THEOREM 5.13 Antidifferentiation of a Composite Function

Let g be a function whose range is an interval I, and let f be a function that is continuous on I. If g is differentiable on its domain and F is an antiderivative of f on I, then

$$\int f(g(x))g'(x)\, dx = F(g(x)) + C.$$

Letting $u = g(x)$ gives $du = g'(x)\, dx$ and

$$\int f(u)\, du = F(u) + C.$$

Examples 1 and 2 show how to apply Theorem 5.13 *directly*, by recognizing the presence of $f(g(x))$ and $g'(x)$. Note that the composite function in the integrand has an *outside function f* and an *inside function g.* Moreover, the derivative $g'(x)$ is present as a factor of the integrand.

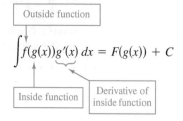

EXAMPLE 1   Recognizing the $f(g(x))g'(x)$ Pattern

Find $\displaystyle\int (x^2 + 1)^2(2x)\, dx$.

Solution   Letting $g(x) = x^2 + 1$, you obtain

$$g'(x) = 2x$$

and

$$f(g(x)) = f(x^2 + 1) = (x^2 + 1)^2.$$

From this, you can recognize that the integrand follows the $f(g(x))g'(x)$ pattern. Using the Power Rule for Integration and Theorem 5.13, you can write

$$\int \overbrace{(x^2 + 1)^2}^{f(g(x))}\overbrace{(2x)}^{g'(x)}\, dx = \frac{1}{3}(x^2 + 1)^3 + C.$$

Try using the Chain Rule to check that the derivative of $\frac{1}{3}(x^2 + 1)^3 + C$ is the integrand of the original integral.

EXAMPLE 2   Recognizing the $f(g(x))g'(x)$ Pattern

Find $\displaystyle\int 5e^{5x}\, dx$.

Solution   Letting $g(x) = 5x$, you obtain

$$g'(x) = 5$$

and

$$f(g(x)) = f(5x) = e^{5x}.$$

From this, you can recognize that the integrand follows the $f(g(x))g'(x)$ pattern. Using the Exponential Rule for Integration and Theorem 5.13, you can write

$$\int \overset{f(g(x))}{e^{5x}}\overset{g'(x)}{(5)}\, dx = e^{5x} + C.$$

You can check this by differentiating $e^{5x} + C$ to obtain the original integrand. ■

▷ **TECHNOLOGY** Try using a computer algebra system, such as *Maple, Mathematica*, or the *TI-Nspire*, to solve the integrals given in Examples 1 and 2. Do you obtain the same antiderivatives that are listed in the examples?

Exploration

Recognizing Patterns   The integrand in each of the integrals labeled (a)–(c) fits the pattern $f(g(x))g'(x)$. Identify the pattern and use the result to evaluate the integral.

a. $\displaystyle\int 2x(x^2 + 1)^4\, dx$ **b.** $\displaystyle\int 3x^2\sqrt{x^3 + 1}\, dx$ **c.** $\displaystyle\int \sec^2 x(\tan x + 3)\, dx$

The integrals labeled (d)–(f) are similar to (a)–(c). Show how you can multiply and divide by a constant to evaluate these integrals.

d. $\displaystyle\int x(x^2 + 1)^4\, dx$ **e.** $\displaystyle\int x^2\sqrt{x^3 + 1}\, dx$ **f.** $\displaystyle\int 2\sec^2 x(\tan x + 3)\, dx$

The integrands in Examples 1 and 2 fit the $f(g(x))g'(x)$ pattern exactly—you only had to recognize the pattern. You can extend this technique considerably with the Constant Multiple Rule

$$\int kf(x)\, dx = k\int f(x)\, dx.$$

Many integrands contain the essential part (the variable part) of $g'(x)$ but are missing a constant multiple. In such cases, you can multiply and divide by the necessary constant multiple, as shown in Example 3.

EXAMPLE 3 **Multiplying and Dividing by a Constant**

Find the indefinite integral.

$$\int x(x^2 + 1)^2\, dx$$

Solution This is similar to the integral given in Example 1, except that the integrand is missing a factor of 2. Recognizing that $2x$ is the derivative of $x^2 + 1$, you can let

$$g(x) = x^2 + 1$$

and supply the $2x$ as shown.

$$\int x(x^2 + 1)^2\, dx = \int (x^2 + 1)^2\left(\frac{1}{2}\right)(2x)\, dx \qquad \text{Multiply and divide by 2.}$$

$$= \frac{1}{2}\int \overbrace{(x^2 + 1)^2}^{f(g(x))}\overbrace{(2x)}^{g'(x)}\, dx \qquad \text{Constant Multiple Rule}$$

$$= \frac{1}{2}\left[\frac{(x^2 + 1)^3}{3}\right] + C \qquad \text{Integrate.}$$

$$= \frac{1}{6}(x^2 + 1)^3 + C \qquad \text{Simplify.}$$

In practice, most people would not write as many steps as are shown in Example 3. For instance, you could evaluate the integral by simply writing

$$\int x(x^2 + 1)^2\, dx = \frac{1}{2}\int (x^2 + 1)^2(2x)\, dx$$

$$= \frac{1}{2}\left[\frac{(x^2 + 1)^3}{3}\right] + C$$

$$= \frac{1}{6}(x^2 + 1)^3 + C.$$

Be sure you see that the *Constant* Multiple Rule applies only to *constants*. You cannot multiply and divide by a variable and then move the variable outside the integral sign. For instance,

$$\int (x^2 + 1)^2\, dx \neq \frac{1}{2x}\int (x^2 + 1)^2(2x)\, dx.$$

After all, if it were legitimate to move variable quantities outside the integral sign, you could move the entire integrand out and simplify the whole process. But the result would be incorrect.

Change of Variables

With a formal **change of variables,** you completely rewrite the integral in terms of u and du (or any other convenient variable). Although this procedure can involve more written steps than the pattern recognition illustrated in Examples 1 to 3, it is useful for complicated integrands. The change of variables technique uses the Leibniz notation for the differential. That is, if $u = g(x)$, then $du = g'(x)\,dx$, and the integral in Theorem 5.13 takes the form

$$\int f(g(x))g'(x)\,dx = \int f(u)\,du = F(u) + C.$$

EXAMPLE 4   **Change of Variables**

Find $\displaystyle\int \sqrt{2x-1}\,dx$.

Solution   First, let u be the inner function, $u = 2x - 1$. Then calculate the differential du to be $du = 2\,dx$. Now, using $\sqrt{2x-1} = \sqrt{u}$ and $dx = du/2$, substitute to obtain

$$\begin{aligned}
\int \sqrt{2x-1}\,dx &= \int \sqrt{u}\left(\frac{du}{2}\right) && \text{Integral in terms of } u \\
&= \frac{1}{2}\int u^{1/2}\,du && \text{Constant Multiple Rule} \\
&= \frac{1}{2}\left(\frac{u^{3/2}}{3/2}\right) + C && \text{Antiderivative in terms of } u \\
&= \frac{1}{3}u^{3/2} + C && \text{Simplify.} \\
&= \frac{1}{3}(2x-1)^{3/2} + C. && \text{Antiderivative in terms of } x
\end{aligned}$$

> **•• REMARK** Because integration is usually more difficult than differentiation, you should always check your answer to an integration problem by differentiating. For instance, in Example 4, you should differentiate $\frac{1}{3}(2x-1)^{3/2} + C$ to verify that you obtain the original integrand.

EXAMPLE 5   **Change of Variables**

⋯▷ *See LarsonCalculus.com for an interactive version of this type of example.*

Find $\displaystyle\int x\sqrt{2x-1}\,dx$.

Solution   As in the previous example, let $u = 2x - 1$ and obtain $dx = du/2$. Because the integrand contains a factor of x, you must also solve for x in terms of u, as shown.

$$u = 2x - 1 \implies x = \frac{u+1}{2} \qquad \text{Solve for } x \text{ in terms of } u.$$

Now, using substitution, you obtain

$$\begin{aligned}
\int x\sqrt{2x-1}\,dx &= \int \left(\frac{u+1}{2}\right)u^{1/2}\left(\frac{du}{2}\right) \\
&= \frac{1}{4}\int (u^{3/2} + u^{1/2})\,du \\
&= \frac{1}{4}\left(\frac{u^{5/2}}{5/2} + \frac{u^{3/2}}{3/2}\right) + C \\
&= \frac{1}{10}(2x-1)^{5/2} + \frac{1}{6}(2x-1)^{3/2} + C.
\end{aligned}$$

To complete the change of variables in Example 5, you solved for x in terms of u. Sometimes this is very difficult. Fortunately, it is not always necessary, as shown in the next example.

EXAMPLE 6 **Change of Variables**

Find $\int \sin^2 3x \cos 3x \, dx$.

Solution Because $\sin^2 3x = (\sin 3x)^2$, you can let $u = \sin 3x$. Then

$$du = (\cos 3x)(3) \, dx.$$

Now, because $\cos 3x \, dx$ is part of the original integral, you can write

$$\frac{du}{3} = \cos 3x \, dx.$$

Substituting u and $du/3$ in the original integral yields

$$\int \sin^2 3x \cos 3x \, dx = \int u^2 \frac{du}{3}$$

$$= \frac{1}{3} \int u^2 \, du$$

$$= \frac{1}{3}\left(\frac{u^3}{3}\right) + C$$

$$= \frac{1}{9} \sin^3 3x + C.$$

• • • • • • • • • • • • • • • ▷
• •**REMARK** When making a change of variables, be sure that your answer is written using the same variables as in the original integrand. For instance, in Example 6, you should not leave your answer as

$$\frac{1}{9}u^3 + C$$

but rather, you should replace u by $\sin 3x$.

You can check this by differentiating.

$$\frac{d}{dx}\left[\frac{1}{9} \sin^3 3x + C\right] = \left(\frac{1}{9}\right)(3)(\sin 3x)^2(\cos 3x)(3)$$

$$= \sin^2 3x \cos 3x$$

Because differentiation produces the original integrand, you know that you have obtained the correct antiderivative.

The steps used for integration by substitution are summarized in the following guidelines.

GUIDELINES FOR MAKING A CHANGE OF VARIABLES

1. Choose a substitution $u = g(x)$. Usually, it is best to choose the *inner* part of a composite function, such as a quantity raised to a power.
2. Compute $du = g'(x) \, dx$.
3. Rewrite the integral in terms of the variable u.
4. Find the resulting integral in terms of u.
5. Replace u by $g(x)$ to obtain an antiderivative in terms of x.
6. Check your answers by differentiating.

So far, you have seen two techniques for applying substitution, and you will see more techniques in the remainder of this section. Each technique differs slightly from the others. You should remember, however, that the goal is the same with each technique—*you are trying to find an antiderivative of the integrand.*

The General Power Rule for Integration

One of the most common u-substitutions involves quantities in the integrand that are raised to a power. Because of the importance of this type of substitution, it is given a special name—the **General Power Rule for Integration.** A proof of this rule follows directly from the (simple) Power Rule for Integration, together with Theorem 5.13.

THEOREM 5.14   The General Power Rule for Integration

If g is a differentiable function of x, then

$$\int [g(x)]^n g'(x)\, dx = \frac{[g(x)]^{n+1}}{n+1} + C, \quad n \neq -1.$$

Equivalently, if $u = g(x)$, then

$$\int u^n\, du = \frac{u^{n+1}}{n+1} + C, \quad n \neq -1.$$

EXAMPLE 7   **Substitution and the General Power Rule**

a. $\displaystyle \int 3(3x - 1)^4\, dx = \int \overbrace{(3x-1)^4}^{u^4}\overbrace{(3)\, dx}^{du} = \overbrace{\frac{(3x-1)^5}{5}}^{u^5/5} + C$

b. $\displaystyle \int (e^x + 1)(e^x + x)\, dx = \int \overbrace{(e^x + x)}^{u^1}\overbrace{(e^x + 1)\, dx}^{du} = \overbrace{\frac{(e^x + x)^2}{2}}^{u^2/2} + C$

c. $\displaystyle \int 3x^2\sqrt{x^3 - 2}\, dx = \int \overbrace{(x^3 - 2)^{1/2}}^{u^{1/2}}\overbrace{(3x^2)\, dx}^{du} = \overbrace{\frac{(x^3 - 2)^{3/2}}{3/2}}^{u^{3/2}/(3/2)} + C = \frac{2}{3}(x^3 - 2)^{3/2} + C$

d. $\displaystyle \int \frac{-4x}{(1 - 2x^2)^2}\, dx = \int \overbrace{(1 - 2x^2)^{-2}}^{u^{-2}}\overbrace{(-4x)\, dx}^{du} = \overbrace{\frac{(1 - 2x^2)^{-1}}{-1}}^{u^{-1}/(-1)} + C = -\frac{1}{1 - 2x^2} + C$

e. $\displaystyle \int \cos^2 x \sin x\, dx = -\int \overbrace{(\cos x)^2}^{u^2}\overbrace{(-\sin x)\, dx}^{du} = -\overbrace{\frac{(\cos x)^3}{3}}^{u^3/3} + C$ ∎

Some integrals whose integrands involve quantities raised to powers cannot be found by the General Power Rule. Consider the two integrals

$$\int x(x^2 + 1)^2\, dx \quad \text{and} \quad \int (x^2 + 1)^2\, dx.$$

The substitution

$$u = x^2 + 1$$

works in the first integral, but not in the second. In the second, the substitution fails because the integrand lacks the factor x needed for du. Fortunately, *for this particular integral,* you can expand the integrand as

$$(x^2 + 1)^2 = x^4 + 2x^2 + 1$$

and use the (simple) Power Rule to integrate each term.

Change of Variables for Definite Integrals

When using u-substitution with a definite integral, it is often convenient to determine the limits of integration for the variable u rather than to convert the antiderivative back to the variable x and evaluate at the original limits. This change of variables is stated explicitly in the next theorem. The proof follows from Theorem 5.13 combined with the Fundamental Theorem of Calculus.

THEOREM 5.15   Change of Variables for Definite Integrals

If the function $u = g(x)$ has a continuous derivative on the closed interval $[a, b]$ and f is continuous on the range of g, then

$$\int_a^b f(g(x))g'(x)\, dx = \int_{g(a)}^{g(b)} f(u)\, du.$$

EXAMPLE 8   Change of Variables

Evaluate $\displaystyle\int_0^1 x(x^2 + 1)^3\, dx$.

Solution   To evaluate this integral, let $u = x^2 + 1$. Then, you obtain

$$u = x^2 + 1 \implies du = 2x\, dx.$$

Before substituting, determine the new upper and lower limits of integration.

Lower Limit

When $x = 0, u = 0^2 + 1 = 1$.

Upper Limit

When $x = 1, u = 1^2 + 1 = 2$.

Now, you can substitute to obtain

$$\int_0^1 x(x^2 + 1)^3\, dx = \frac{1}{2}\int_0^1 (x^2 + 1)^3(2x)\, dx \qquad \text{Integration limits for } x$$

$$= \frac{1}{2}\int_1^2 u^3\, du \qquad \text{Integration limits for } u$$

$$= \frac{1}{2}\left[\frac{u^4}{4}\right]_1^2$$

$$= \frac{1}{2}\left(4 - \frac{1}{4}\right)$$

$$= \frac{15}{8}.$$

Notice that you obtain the same result when you rewrite the antiderivative $\frac{1}{2}(u^4/4)$ in terms of the variable x and evaluate the definite integral at the original limits of integration, as shown below.

$$\frac{1}{2}\left[\frac{u^4}{4}\right]_1^2 = \frac{1}{2}\left[\frac{(x^2 + 1)^4}{4}\right]_0^1$$

$$= \frac{1}{2}\left(4 - \frac{1}{4}\right)$$

$$= \frac{15}{8}$$

EXAMPLE 9   **Change of Variables**

Evaluate the definite integral.

$$\int_1^5 \frac{x}{\sqrt{2x - 1}} \, dx$$

Solution   To evaluate this integral, let $u = \sqrt{2x - 1}$. Then, you obtain

$$u^2 = 2x - 1$$
$$u^2 + 1 = 2x$$
$$\frac{u^2 + 1}{2} = x$$
$$u \, du = dx. \qquad \text{Differentiate each side.}$$

Before substituting, determine the new upper and lower limits of integration.

Lower Limit   **Upper Limit**

When $x = 1, u = \sqrt{2 - 1} = 1$.   When $x = 5, u = \sqrt{10 - 1} = 3$.

Now, substitute to obtain

$$\int_1^5 \frac{x}{\sqrt{2x - 1}} \, dx = \int_1^3 \frac{1}{u}\left(\frac{u^2 + 1}{2}\right) u \, du$$

$$= \frac{1}{2} \int_1^3 (u^2 + 1) \, du$$

$$= \frac{1}{2}\left[\frac{u^3}{3} + u\right]_1^3$$

$$= \frac{1}{2}\left(9 + 3 - \frac{1}{3} - 1\right)$$

$$= \frac{16}{3}.$$

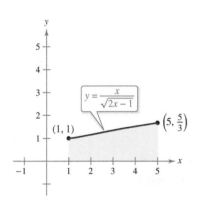

The region before substitution has an area of $\frac{16}{3}$.
Figure 5.38

Geometrically, you can interpret the equation

$$\int_1^5 \frac{x}{\sqrt{2x - 1}} \, dx = \int_1^3 \frac{u^2 + 1}{2} \, du$$

to mean that the two *different* regions shown in Figures 5.38 and 5.39 have the *same* area.

When evaluating definite integrals by substitution, it is possible for the upper limit of integration of the u-variable form to be smaller than the lower limit. When this happens, do not rearrange the limits. Simply evaluate as usual. For example, after substituting $u = \sqrt{1 - x}$ in the integral

$$\int_0^1 x^2(1 - x)^{1/2} \, dx$$

you obtain $u = \sqrt{1 - 1} = 0$ when $x = 1$, and $u = \sqrt{1 - 0} = 1$ when $x = 0$. So, the correct u-variable form of this integral is

$$-2\int_1^0 (1 - u^2)^2 u^2 \, du.$$

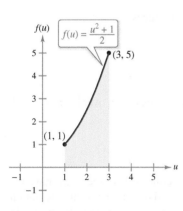

The region after substitution has an area of $\frac{16}{3}$.
Figure 5.39

Expanding the integrand, you can evaluate this integral as shown.

$$-2\int_1^0 (u^2 - 2u^4 + u^6) \, du = -2\left[\frac{u^3}{3} - \frac{2u^5}{5} + \frac{u^7}{7}\right]_1^0 = -2\left(-\frac{1}{3} + \frac{2}{5} - \frac{1}{7}\right) = \frac{16}{105}$$

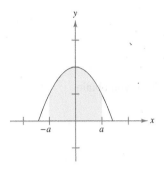

Even function

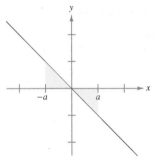

Odd function
Figure 5.40

Integration of Even and Odd Functions

Even with a change of variables, integration can be difficult. Occasionally, you can simplify the evaluation of a definite integral over an interval that is symmetric about the y-axis or about the origin by recognizing the integrand to be an even or odd function (see Figure 5.40).

THEOREM 5.16   Integration of Even and Odd Functions

Let f be integrable on the closed interval $[a, -a]$.

1. If f is an *even* function, then $\displaystyle\int_{-a}^{a} f(x)\, dx = 2\int_{0}^{a} f(x)\, dx.$

2. If f is an *odd* function, then $\displaystyle\int_{-a}^{a} f(x)\, dx = 0.$

Proof   Here is the proof of the first property. (The proof of the second property is left to you [see Exercise 119].) Because f is even, you know that $f(x) = f(-x)$. Using Theorem 5.13 with the substitution $u = -x$ produces

$$\int_{-a}^{0} f(x)\, dx = \int_{a}^{0} f(-u)(du) = -\int_{a}^{0} f(u)\, du = \int_{0}^{a} f(u)\, du = \int_{0}^{a} f(x)\, dx.$$

Finally, using Theorem 5.6, you obtain

$$\int_{-a}^{a} f(x)\, dx = \int_{-a}^{0} f(x)\, dx + \int_{0}^{a} f(x)\, dx$$

$$= \int_{0}^{a} f(x)\, dx + \int_{0}^{a} f(x)\, dx$$

$$= 2\int_{0}^{a} f(x)\, dx.$$

See LarsonCalculus.com for Bruce Edwards's video of this proof.

EXAMPLE 10   **Integration of an Odd Function**

Evaluate the definite integral.

$$\int_{-\pi/2}^{\pi/2} (\sin^3 x \cos x + \sin x \cos x)\, dx$$

Solution   Letting $f(x) = \sin^3 x \cos x + \sin x \cos x$ produces

$$f(-x) = \sin^3(-x) \cos(-x) + \sin(-x) \cos(-x)$$

$$= -\sin^3 x \cos x - \sin x \cos x$$

$$= -f(x).$$

So, f is an odd function, and because f is symmetric about the origin over $[-\pi/2, \pi/2]$, you can apply Theorem 5.16 to conclude that

$$\int_{-\pi/2}^{\pi/2} (\sin^3 x \cos x + \sin x \cos x)\, dx = 0.$$

From Figure 5.41, you can see that the two regions on either side of the y-axis have the same area. However, because one lies below the x-axis and one lies above it, integration produces a cancellation effect. (More will be said about areas below the x-axis in Section 7.1.)

$f(x) = \sin^3 x \cos x + \sin x \cos x$

Because f is an odd function,
$$\int_{-\pi/2}^{\pi/2} f(x)\, dx = 0.$$
Figure 5.41

5.5 Exercises

Finding u and du In Exercises 1–4, complete the table by identifying u and du for the integral.

$\int f(g(x))g'(x)\,dx$	$u = g(x)$	$du = g'(x)\,dx$
1. $\int (8x^2 + 1)^2(16x)\,dx$		
2. $\int x^2\sqrt{x^3 + 1}\,dx$		
3. $\int \tan^2 x \sec^2 x\,dx$		
4. $\int \dfrac{\cos x}{\sin^2 x}\,dx$		

Finding an Indefinite Integral In Exercises 5–26, find the indefinite integral and check the result by differentiation.

5. $\int (1 + 6x)^4(6)\,dx$

6. $\int (x^2 - 9)^3(2x)\,dx$

7. $\int \sqrt{25 - x^2}\,(-2x)\,dx$

8. $\int \sqrt[3]{3 - 4x^2}\,(-8x)\,dx$

9. $\int x^3(x^4 + 3)^2\,dx$

10. $\int x^2(6 - x^3)^5\,dx$

11. $\int x^2(x^3 - 1)^4\,dx$

12. $\int x(5x^2 + 4)^3\,dx$

13. $\int t\sqrt{t^2 + 2}\,dt$

14. $\int t^3\sqrt{2t^4 + 3}\,dt$

15. $\int 5x\sqrt[3]{1 - x^2}\,dx$

16. $\int u^2\sqrt{u^3 + 2}\,du$

17. $\int \dfrac{x}{(1 - x^2)^3}\,dx$

18. $\int \dfrac{x^3}{(1 + x^4)^2}\,dx$

19. $\int \dfrac{x^2}{(1 + x^3)^2}\,dx$

20. $\int \dfrac{6x^2}{(4x^3 - 9)^3}\,dx$

21. $\int \dfrac{x}{\sqrt{1 - x^2}}\,dx$

22. $\int \dfrac{x^3}{\sqrt{1 + x^4}}\,dx$

23. $\int \left(1 + \dfrac{1}{t}\right)^3\left(\dfrac{1}{t^2}\right)dt$

24. $\int \left[x^2 + \dfrac{1}{(3x)^2}\right]dx$

25. $\int \dfrac{1}{\sqrt{2x}}\,dx$

26. $\int \dfrac{x}{\sqrt[3]{5x^2}}\,dx$

Differential Equation In Exercises 27–30, solve the differential equation.

27. $\dfrac{dy}{dx} = 4x + \dfrac{4x}{\sqrt{16 - x^2}}$

28. $\dfrac{dy}{dx} = \dfrac{10x^2}{\sqrt{1 + x^3}}$

29. $\dfrac{dy}{dx} = \dfrac{x + 1}{(x^2 + 2x - 3)^2}$

30. $\dfrac{dy}{dx} = \dfrac{x - 4}{\sqrt{x^2 - 8x + 1}}$

Slope Field In Exercises 31 and 32, a differential equation, a point, and a slope field are given. A *slope field* consists of line segments with slopes given by the differential equation. These line segments give a visual perspective of the directions of the solutions of the differential equation. (a) Sketch two approximate solutions of the differential equation on the slope field, one of which passes through the given point. (To print an enlarged copy of the graph, go to *MathGraphs.com*.) (b) Use integration to find the particular solution of the differential equation and use a graphing utility to graph the solution. Compare the result with the sketches in part (a).

31. $\dfrac{dy}{dx} = x\sqrt{4 - x^2}$, $(2, 2)$

32. $\dfrac{dy}{dx} = e^{\sin x}\cos x$, $(\pi, 2)$

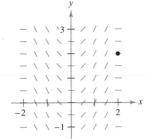
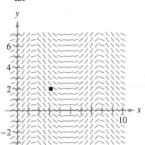

Finding an Indefinite Integral In Exercises 33–54, find the indefinite integral.

33. $\int \pi \sin \pi x\,dx$

34. $\int \sin 4x\,dx$

35. $\int \cos 8x\,dx$

36. $\int \csc^2\left(\dfrac{x}{2}\right)dx$

37. $\int \dfrac{1}{\theta^2}\cos\dfrac{1}{\theta}\,d\theta$

38. $\int x \sin x^2\,dx$

39. $\int \sin 2x \cos 2x\,dx$

40. $\int \sqrt{\tan x}\,\sec^2 x\,dx$

41. $\int \dfrac{\csc^2 x}{\cot^3 x}\,dx$

42. $\int \dfrac{\sin x}{\cos^3 x}\,dx$

43. $\int e^{7x}(7)\,dx$

44. $\int (x + 1)e^{x^2 + 2x}\,dx$

45. $\int e^x(e^x + 1)^2\,dx$

46. $\int \dfrac{2e^x - 2e^{-x}}{(e^x + e^{-x})^2}\,dx$

47. $\int \dfrac{5 - e^x}{e^{2x}}\,dx$

48. $\int \dfrac{e^{2x} + 2e^x + 1}{e^x}\,dx$

49. $\int e^{\sin \pi x}\cos \pi x\,dx$

50. $\int e^{\tan 2x}\sec^2 2x\,dx$

51. $\int e^{-x}\sec^2(e^{-x})\,dx$

52. $\int \ln(e^{2x - 1})\,dx$

53. $\int 3^{x/2}\,dx$

54. $\int (3 - x)7^{(3 - x)^2}\,dx$

Finding an Equation In Exercises 55–60, find an equation for the function f that has the given derivative and whose graph passes through the given point.

Derivative	Point
55. $f'(x) = -\sin\dfrac{x}{2}$	$(0, 6)$
56. $f'(x) = 0.4^{x/3}$	$\left(0, \dfrac{1}{2}\right)$
57. $f'(x) = 2e^{-x/4}$	$(0, 1)$
58. $f'(x) = x^2 e^{-0.2x^3}$	$\left(0, \dfrac{3}{2}\right)$
59. $f'(x) = 2x(4x^2 - 10)^2$	$(2, 10)$
60. $f'(x) = -2x\sqrt{8 - x^2}$	$(2, 7)$

Change of Variables In Exercises 61–68, find the indefinite integral by the method shown in Example 5.

61. $\displaystyle \int x\sqrt{x + 6}\, dx$

62. $\displaystyle \int x\sqrt{3x - 4}\, dx$

63. $\displaystyle \int x^2\sqrt{1 - x}\, dx$

64. $\displaystyle \int (x + 1)\sqrt{2 - x}\, dx$

65. $\displaystyle \int \frac{x^2 - 1}{\sqrt{2x - 1}}\, dx$

66. $\displaystyle \int \frac{2x + 1}{\sqrt{x + 4}}\, dx$

67. $\displaystyle \int \frac{-x}{(x + 1) - \sqrt{x + 1}}\, dx$

68. $\displaystyle \int t\sqrt[3]{t + 10}\, dt$

Evaluating a Definite Integral In Exercises 69–80, evaluate the definite integral. Use a graphing utility to verify your result.

69. $\displaystyle \int_{-1}^{1} x(x^2 + 1)^3\, dx$

70. $\displaystyle \int_{0}^{1} x^3(2x^4 + 1)^2\, dx$

71. $\displaystyle \int_{1}^{2} 2x^2\sqrt{x^3 + 1}\, dx$

72. $\displaystyle \int_{0}^{1} x\sqrt{1 - x^2}\, dx$

73. $\displaystyle \int_{0}^{4} \frac{1}{\sqrt{2x + 1}}\, dx$

74. $\displaystyle \int_{0}^{2} \frac{x}{\sqrt{1 + 2x^2}}\, dx$

75. $\displaystyle \int_{1}^{9} \frac{1}{\sqrt{x}\left(1 + \sqrt{x}\right)^2}\, dx$

76. $\displaystyle \int_{1}^{5} \frac{x}{\sqrt{2x - 1}}\, dx$

77. $\displaystyle \int_{0}^{1} e^{-2x}\, dx$

78. $\displaystyle \int_{1}^{2} e^{1-x}\, dx$

79. $\displaystyle \int_{1}^{3} \frac{e^{3/x}}{x^2}\, dx$

80. $\displaystyle \int_{0}^{\sqrt{2}} xe^{-(x^2/2)}\, dx$

Finding the Area of a Region In Exercises 81–84, find the area of the region. Use a graphing utility to verify your result.

81. $\displaystyle \int_{0}^{7} x\sqrt[3]{x + 1}\, dx$

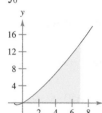

82. $\displaystyle \int_{-2}^{6} x^2\sqrt[3]{x + 2}\, dx$

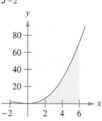

83. $\displaystyle \int_{\pi/2}^{2\pi/3} \sec^2\left(\frac{x}{2}\right) dx$

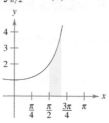

84. $\displaystyle \int_{\pi/12}^{\pi/4} \csc 2x \cot 2x\, dx$

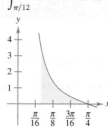

Area In Exercises 85–88, find the area of the region bounded by the graphs of the equations. Use a graphing utility to graph the region and verify your result.

85. $y = e^x, \ y = 0, \ x = 0, \ x = 5$

86. $y = e^{-x}, \ y = 0, \ x = a, \ x = b$

87. $y = xe^{-x^2/4}, \ y = 0, \ x = 0, \ x = \sqrt{6}$

88. $y = e^{-2x} + 2, \ y = 0, \ x = 0, \ x = 2$

Even and Odd Functions In Exercises 89–92, evaluate the integral using the properties of even and odd functions as an aid.

89. $\displaystyle \int_{-2}^{2} x^2(x^2 + 1)\, dx$

90. $\displaystyle \int_{-2}^{2} x(x^2 + 1)^3\, dx$

91. $\displaystyle \int_{-\pi/2}^{\pi/2} \sin^2 x \cos x\, dx$

92. $\displaystyle \int_{-\pi/2}^{\pi/2} \sin x \cos x\, dx$

93. Using an Even Function Use $\int_{0}^{4} x^2\, dx = \frac{64}{3}$ to evaluate each definite integral without using the Fundamental Theorem of Calculus.

(a) $\displaystyle \int_{-4}^{0} x^2\, dx$

(b) $\displaystyle \int_{-4}^{4} x^2\, dx$

(c) $\displaystyle \int_{0}^{4} -x^2\, dx$

(d) $\displaystyle \int_{-4}^{0} 3x^2\, dx$

94. Using Symmetry Use the symmetry of the graphs of the sine and cosine functions as an aid in evaluating each definite integral.

(a) $\displaystyle \int_{-\pi/4}^{\pi/4} \sin x\, dx$

(b) $\displaystyle \int_{-\pi/4}^{\pi/4} \cos x\, dx$

(c) $\displaystyle \int_{-\pi/2}^{\pi/2} \cos x\, dx$

(d) $\displaystyle \int_{-\pi/2}^{\pi/2} \sin x \cos x\, dx$

Even and Odd Functions In Exercises 95 and 96, write the integral as the sum of the integral of an odd function and the integral of an even function. Use this simplification to evaluate the integral.

95. $\displaystyle \int_{-3}^{3} (x^3 + 4x^2 - 3x - 6)\, dx$

96. $\displaystyle \int_{-\pi/2}^{\pi/2} (\sin 4x + \cos 4x)\, dx$

97. Using Substitution Describe why

$$\int x(5 - x^2)^3 \, dx \neq \int u^3 \, du$$

where $u = 5 - x^2$.

98. Analyzing the Integrand Without integrating, explain why

$$\int_{-2}^{2} x(x^2 + 1)^2 \, dx = 0.$$

99. Choosing an Integral You are asked to find one of the integrals. Which one would you choose? Explain.

(a) $\int \sqrt{x^3 + 1} \, dx$ or $\int x^2 \sqrt{x^3 + 1} \, dx$

(b) $\int \tan(3x) \sec^2(3x) \, dx$ or $\int \tan(3x) \, dx$

100. Comparing Methods Find the indefinite integral in two ways. Explain any difference in the forms of the answers.

(a) $\int (2x - 1)^2 \, dx$ (b) $\int \tan x \sec^2 x \, dx$

101. Depreciation The rate of depreciation dV/dt of a machine is inversely proportional to the square of $(t + 1)$, where V is the value of the machine t years after it was purchased. The initial value of the machine was $500,000, and its value decreased $100,000 in the first year. Estimate its value after 4 years.

102. HOW DO YOU SEE IT? The graph shows the flow rate of water at a pumping station for one day.

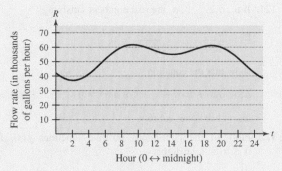

Hour (0 ↔ midnight)

(a) Approximate the maximum flow rate at the pumping station. At what time does this occur?

(b) Explain how you can find the amount of water used during the day.

(c) Approximate the two-hour period when the least amount of water is used. Explain your reasoning.

103. Sales The sales S (in thousands of units) of a seasonal product are given by the model

$$S = 74.50 + 43.75 \sin \frac{\pi t}{6}$$

where t is the time in months, with $t = 1$ corresponding to January. Find the average sales for each time period.

(a) The first quarter $(0 \leq t \leq 3)$

(b) The second quarter $(3 \leq t \leq 6)$

(c) The entire year $(0 \leq t \leq 12)$

104. Electricity The oscillating current in an electrical circuit is

$$I = 2 \sin(60 \pi t) + \cos(120 \pi t)$$

where I is measured in amperes and t is measured in seconds. Find the average current for each time interval.

(a) $0 \leq t \leq \dfrac{1}{60}$ (b) $0 \leq t \leq \dfrac{1}{240}$ (c) $0 \leq t \leq \dfrac{1}{30}$

Probability **In Exercises 105 and 106, the function**

$$f(x) = kx^n(1 - x)^m, \quad 0 \leq x \leq 1$$

where $n > 0$, $m > 0$, and k is a constant, can be used to represent various probability distributions. If k is chosen such that

$$\int_0^1 f(x) \, dx = 1$$

then the probability that x will fall between a and b $(0 \leq a \leq b \leq 1)$ is

$$P_{a,b} = \int_a^b f(x) \, dx.$$

105. The probability that a person will remember between $100a\%$ and $100b\%$ of material learned in an experiment is

$$P_{a,b} = \int_a^b \frac{15}{4} x \sqrt{1 - x} \, dx$$

where x represents the proportion remembered. (See figure.)

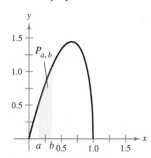

(a) For a randomly chosen individual, what is the probability that he or she will recall between 50% and 75% of the material?

(b) What is the median percent recall? That is, for what value of b is it true that the probability of recalling 0 to b is 0.5?

106. The probability that ore samples taken from a region contain between $100a\%$ and $100b\%$ iron is

$$P_{a,b} = \int_a^b \frac{1155}{32} x^3 (1-x)^{3/2}\, dx$$

where x represents the proportion of iron. (See figure.) What is the probability that a sample will contain between

(a) 0% and 25% iron?   (b) 50% and 100% iron?

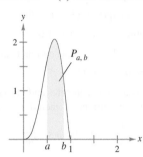

107. Graphical Analysis Consider the functions f and g, where

$$f(x) = 6 \sin x \cos^2 x \quad \text{and} \quad g(t) = \int_0^t f(x)\, dx.$$

(a) Use a graphing utility to graph f and g in the same viewing window.

(b) Explain why g is nonnegative.

(c) Identify the points on the graph of g that correspond to the extrema of f.

(d) Does each of the zeros of f correspond to an extremum of g? Explain.

(e) Consider the function

$$h(t) = \int_{\pi/2}^t f(x)\, dx.$$

Use a graphing utility to graph h. What is the relationship between g and h? Verify your conjecture.

108. Finding a Limit Using a Definite Integral Find

$$\lim_{n \to +\infty} \sum_{i=1}^n \frac{\sin(i\pi/n)}{n}$$

by evaluating an appropriate definite integral over the interval $[0, 1]$.

109. Rewriting Integrals

(a) Show that $\displaystyle\int_0^1 x^2(1-x)^5\, dx = \int_0^1 x^5(1-x)^2\, dx.$

(b) Show that $\displaystyle\int_0^1 x^a(1-x)^b\, dx = \int_0^1 x^b(1-x)^a\, dx.$

110. Rewriting Integrals

(a) Show that $\displaystyle\int_0^{\pi/2} \sin^2 x\, dx = \int_0^{\pi/2} \cos^2 x\, dx.$

(b) Show that $\displaystyle\int_0^{\pi/2} \sin^n x\, dx = \int_0^{\pi/2} \cos^n x\, dx,$ where n is a positive integer.

True or False? In Exercises 111–116, determine whether the statement is true or false. If it is false, explain why or give an example that shows it is false.

111. $\displaystyle\int (2x+1)^2\, dx = \tfrac{1}{3}(2x+1)^3 + C$

112. $\displaystyle\int x(x^2+1)\, dx = \tfrac{1}{2}x^2\left(\tfrac{1}{3}x^3 + x\right) + C$

113. $\displaystyle\int_{-10}^{10} (ax^3 + bx^2 + cx + d)\, dx = 2\int_0^{10} (bx^2 + d)\, dx$

114. $\displaystyle\int_a^b \sin x\, dx = \int_a^{b+2\pi} \sin x\, dx$

115. $4\displaystyle\int \sin x \cos x\, dx = -\cos 2x + C$

116. $\displaystyle\int \sin^2 2x \cos 2x\, dx = \tfrac{1}{3}\sin^3 2x + C$

117. Rewriting Integrals Assume that f is continuous everywhere and that c is a constant. Show that

$$\int_{ca}^{cb} f(x)\, dx = c\int_a^b f(cx)\, dx.$$

118. Integration and Differentiation

(a) Verify that $\sin u - u \cos u + C = \displaystyle\int u \sin u\, du.$

(b) Use part (a) to show that $\displaystyle\int_0^{\pi^2} \sin \sqrt{x}\, dx = 2\pi.$

119. Proof Prove the second property of Theorem 5.16.

120. Rewriting Integrals Show that if f is continuous on the entire real number line, then

$$\int_a^b f(x+h)\, dx = \int_{a+h}^{b+h} f(x)\, dx.$$

PUTNAM EXAM CHALLENGE

121. If $a_0, a_1, \ldots, a_n$ are real numbers satisfying

$$\frac{a_0}{1} + \frac{a_1}{2} + \cdots + \frac{a_n}{n+1} = 0,$$

show that the equation

$$a_0 + a_1 x + a_2 x^2 + \cdots + a_n x^n = 0$$

has at least one real root.

122. Find all the continuous positive functions $f(x)$, for $0 \le x \le 1$, such that

$$\int_0^1 f(x)\, dx = 1$$

$$\int_0^1 f(x)x\, dx = \alpha$$

$$\int_0^1 f(x)x^2\, dx = \alpha^2$$

where α is a given real number.

5.6 Numerical Integration

■ Approximate a definite integral using the Trapezoidal Rule.
■ Approximate a definite integral using Simpson's Rule.
■ Analyze the approximate errors in the Trapezoidal Rule and Simpson's Rule.

The Trapezoidal Rule

Some elementary functions simply do not have antiderivatives that are elementary functions. For example, there is no elementary function that has any of the following functions as its derivative.

$$\sqrt[3]{x}\sqrt{1-x}, \qquad \sqrt{x}\cos x, \qquad \frac{\cos x}{x}, \qquad \sqrt{1-x^3}, \qquad \sin x^2$$

If you need to evaluate a definite integral involving a function whose antiderivative cannot be found, then while the Fundamental Theorem of Calculus is still true, it cannot be easily applied. In this case, it is easier to resort to an approximation technique. Two such techniques are described in this section.

One way to approximate a definite integral is to use n trapezoids, as shown in Figure 5.42. In the development of this method, assume that f is continuous and positive on the interval $[a, b]$. So, the definite integral

$$\int_a^b f(x)\, dx$$

represents the area of the region bounded by the graph of f and the x-axis, from $x = a$ to $x = b$. First, partition the interval $[a, b]$ into n subintervals, each of width $\Delta x = (b - a)/n$, such that

$$a = x_0 < x_1 < x_2 < \cdots < x_n = b.$$

Then form a trapezoid for each subinterval (see Figure 5.43). The area of the ith trapezoid is

$$\text{Area of } i\text{th trapezoid} = \left[\frac{f(x_{i-1}) + f(x_i)}{2}\right]\left(\frac{b - a}{n}\right).$$

This implies that the sum of the areas of the n trapezoids is

$$\begin{aligned}
\text{Area} &= \left(\frac{b-a}{n}\right)\left[\frac{f(x_0) + f(x_1)}{2} + \cdots + \frac{f(x_{n-1}) + f(x_n)}{2}\right] \\
&= \left(\frac{b-a}{2n}\right)[f(x_0) + f(x_1) + f(x_1) + f(x_2) + \cdots + f(x_{n-1}) + f(x_n)] \\
&= \left(\frac{b-a}{2n}\right)[f(x_0) + 2f(x_1) + 2f(x_2) + \cdots + 2f(x_{n-1}) + f(x_n)].
\end{aligned}$$

Letting $\Delta x = (b - a)/n$, you can take the limit as $n \to \infty$ to obtain

$$\begin{aligned}
\lim_{n\to\infty} &\left(\frac{b-a}{2n}\right)[f(x_0) + 2f(x_1) + \cdots + 2f(x_{n-1}) + f(x_n)] \\
&= \lim_{n\to\infty}\left[\frac{[f(a) - f(b)]\,\Delta x}{2} + \sum_{i=1}^{n} f(x_i)\,\Delta x\right] \\
&= \lim_{n\to\infty}\frac{[f(a) - f(b)](b - a)}{2n} + \lim_{n\to\infty}\sum_{i=1}^{n} f(x_i)\,\Delta x \\
&= 0 + \int_a^b f(x)\, dx.
\end{aligned}$$

The result is summarized in the next theorem.

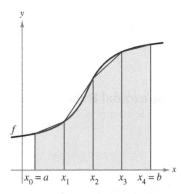

The area of the region can be approximated using four trapezoids.
Figure 5.42

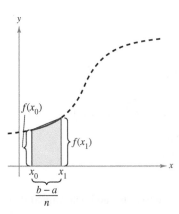

The area of the first trapezoid is
$$\left[\frac{f(x_0) + f(x_1)}{2}\right]\left(\frac{b - a}{n}\right).$$
Figure 5.43

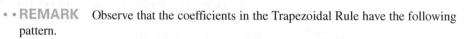

THEOREM 5.17 **The Trapezoidal Rule**

Let f be continuous on $[a, b]$. The Trapezoidal Rule for approximating $\int_a^b f(x)\, dx$ is

$$\int_a^b f(x)\, dx \approx \frac{b-a}{2n}[f(x_0) + 2f(x_1) + 2f(x_2) + \cdots + 2f(x_{n-1}) + f(x_n)].$$

Moreover, as $n \to \infty$, the right-hand side approaches $\int_a^b f(x)\, dx$.

REMARK Observe that the coefficients in the Trapezoidal Rule have the following pattern.

$$1 \quad 2 \quad 2 \quad 2 \quad \ldots \quad 2 \quad 2 \quad 1$$

EXAMPLE 1 **Approximation with the Trapezoidal Rule**

Use the Trapezoidal Rule to approximate

$$\int_0^\pi \sin x\, dx.$$

Compare the results for $n = 4$ and $n = 8$, as shown in Figure 5.44.

Solution When $n = 4$, $\Delta x = \pi/4$, and you obtain

$$\int_0^\pi \sin x\, dx \approx \frac{\pi}{8}\left(\sin 0 + 2 \sin \frac{\pi}{4} + 2 \sin \frac{\pi}{2} + 2 \sin \frac{3\pi}{4} + \sin \pi\right)$$

$$= \frac{\pi}{8}\left(0 + \sqrt{2} + 2 + \sqrt{2} + 0\right)$$

$$= \frac{\pi\left(1 + \sqrt{2}\right)}{4}$$

$$\approx 1.896.$$

When $n = 8$, $\Delta x = \pi/8$, and you obtain

$$\int_0^\pi \sin x\, dx \approx \frac{\pi}{16}\left(\sin 0 + 2 \sin \frac{\pi}{8} + 2 \sin \frac{\pi}{4} + 2 \sin \frac{3\pi}{8} + 2 \sin \frac{\pi}{2}\right.$$

$$\left. + 2 \sin \frac{5\pi}{8} + 2 \sin \frac{3\pi}{4} + 2 \sin \frac{7\pi}{8} + \sin \pi\right)$$

$$= \frac{\pi}{16}\left(2 + 2\sqrt{2} + 4 \sin \frac{\pi}{8} + 4 \sin \frac{3\pi}{8}\right)$$

$$\approx 1.974.$$

For this particular integral, you could have found an antiderivative and determined that the exact area of the region is 2.

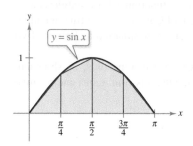

Four subintervals

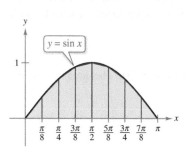

Eight subintervals

Trapezoidal approximations
Figure 5.44

▷ **TECHNOLOGY** Most graphing utilities and computer algebra systems have built-in programs that can be used to approximate the value of a definite integral. Try using such a program to approximate the integral in Example 1. How close is your approximation? When you use such a program, you need to be aware of its limitations. Often, you are given no indication of the degree of accuracy of the approximation. Other times, you may be given an approximation that is completely wrong. For instance, try using a built-in numerical integration program to evaluate

$$\int_{-1}^2 \frac{1}{x}\, dx.$$

Your calculator should give an error message. Does yours?

It is interesting to compare the Trapezoidal Rule with the Midpoint Rule given in Section 5.2. For the Trapezoidal Rule, you average the function values at the endpoints of the subintervals, but for the Midpoint Rule, you take the function values of the subinterval midpoints.

$$\int_a^b f(x)\,dx \approx \sum_{i=1}^{n} f\left(\frac{x_i + x_{i-1}}{2}\right)\Delta x \qquad \text{Midpoint Rule}$$

$$\int_a^b f(x)\,dx \approx \sum_{i=1}^{n} \left(\frac{f(x_i) + f(x_{i-1})}{2}\right)\Delta x \qquad \text{Trapezoidal Rule}$$

There are two important points that should be made concerning the Trapezoidal Rule (or the Midpoint Rule). First, the approximation tends to become more accurate as n increases. For instance, in Example 1, when $n = 16$, the Trapezoidal Rule yields an approximation of 1.994. Second, although you could have used the Fundamental Theorem to evaluate the integral in Example 1, this theorem cannot be used to evaluate an integral as simple as $\int_0^\pi \sin x^2\,dx$ because $\sin x^2$ has no elementary antiderivative. Yet, the Trapezoidal Rule can be applied to estimate this integral.

Simpson's Rule

One way to view the trapezoidal approximation of a definite integral is to say that on each subinterval, you approximate f by a *first*-degree polynomial. In Simpson's Rule, named after the English mathematician Thomas Simpson (1710–1761), you take this procedure one step further and approximate f by *second*-degree polynomials.

Before presenting Simpson's Rule, consider the next theorem for evaluating integrals of polynomials of degree 2 (or less).

THEOREM 5.18 Integral of $p(x) = Ax^2 + Bx + C$

If $p(x) = Ax^2 + Bx + C$, then

$$\int_a^b p(x)\,dx = \left(\frac{b-a}{6}\right)\left[p(a) + 4p\left(\frac{a+b}{2}\right) + p(b)\right].$$

Proof

$$\int_a^b p(x)\,dx = \int_a^b (Ax^2 + Bx + C)\,dx$$

$$= \left[\frac{Ax^3}{3} + \frac{Bx^2}{2} + Cx\right]_a^b$$

$$= \frac{A(b^3 - a^3)}{3} + \frac{B(b^2 - a^2)}{2} + C(b - a)$$

$$= \left(\frac{b-a}{6}\right)[2A(a^2 + ab + b^2) + 3B(b + a) + 6C]$$

By expansion and collection of terms, the expression inside the brackets becomes

$$\underbrace{(Aa^2 + Ba + C)}_{p(a)} + \underbrace{4\left[A\left(\frac{b+a}{2}\right)^2 + B\left(\frac{b+a}{2}\right) + C\right]}_{4p\left(\frac{a+b}{2}\right)} + \underbrace{(Ab^2 + Bb + C)}_{p(b)}$$

and you can write

$$\int_a^b p(x)\,dx = \left(\frac{b-a}{6}\right)\left[p(a) + 4p\left(\frac{a+b}{2}\right) + p(b)\right].$$

See LarsonCalculus.com for Bruce Edwards's video of this proof.

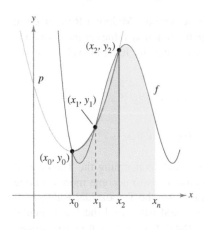

$$\int_{x_0}^{x_2} p(x)\,dx \approx \int_{x_0}^{x_2} f(x)\,dx$$

Figure 5.45

To develop Simpson's Rule for approximating a definite integral, you again partition the interval $[a, b]$ into n subintervals, each of width $\Delta x = (b - a)/n$. This time, however, n is required to be even, and the subintervals are grouped in pairs such that

$$a = \underbrace{x_0 < x_1 < x_2}_{[x_0, x_2]} < \underbrace{x_3 < x_4}_{[x_2, x_4]} < \cdots < \underbrace{x_{n-2} < x_{n-1} < x_n}_{[x_{n-2}, x_n]} = b.$$

On each (double) subinterval $[x_{i-2}, x_i]$, you can approximate f by a polynomial p of degree less than or equal to 2. (See Exercise 49.) For example, on the subinterval $[x_0, x_2]$, choose the polynomial of least degree passing through the points (x_0, y_0), (x_1, y_1), and (x_2, y_2), as shown in Figure 5.45. Now, using p as an approximation of f on this subinterval, you have, by Theorem 5.18,

$$\int_{x_0}^{x_2} f(x)\,dx \approx \int_{x_0}^{x_2} p(x)\,dx$$

$$= \frac{x_2 - x_0}{6}\left[p(x_0) + 4p\left(\frac{x_0 + x_2}{2}\right) + p(x_2)\right]$$

$$= \frac{2[(b - a)/n]}{6}[p(x_0) + 4p(x_1) + p(x_2)]$$

$$= \frac{b - a}{3n}[f(x_0) + 4f(x_1) + f(x_2)].$$

Repeating this procedure on the entire interval $[a, b]$ produces the next theorem.

▷

REMARK Observe that the coefficients in Simpson's Rule have the following pattern.

$$1 \quad 4 \quad 2 \quad 4 \quad 2 \quad 4 \quad \ldots \quad 4 \quad 2 \quad 4 \quad 1$$

THEOREM 5.19 Simpson's Rule

Let f be continuous on $[a, b]$ and let n be an even integer. Simpson's Rule for approximating $\int_a^b f(x)\,dx$ is

$$\int_a^b f(x)\,dx \approx \frac{b - a}{3n}[f(x_0) + 4f(x_1) + 2f(x_2) + 4f(x_3) + \cdots$$

$$+ 4f(x_{n-1}) + f(x_n)].$$

Moreover, as $n \to \infty$, the right-hand side approaches $\int_a^b f(x)\,dx$.

REMARK In Section 5.2, Example 8, the Midpoint Rule with $n = 4$ approximates $\int_0^\pi \sin x\,dx$ as 2.052. In Example 1, the Trapezoidal Rule with $n = 4$ gives an approximation of 1.896. In Example 2, Simpson's Rule with $n = 4$ gives an approximation of 2.005. The antiderivative would produce the true value of 2.

In Example 1, the Trapezoidal Rule was used to estimate $\int_0^\pi \sin x\,dx$. In the next example, Simpson's Rule is applied to the same integral.

EXAMPLE 2 **Approximation with Simpson's Rule**

▷ *See LarsonCalculus.com for an interactive version of this type of example.*

Use Simpson's Rule to approximate

$$\int_0^\pi \sin x\,dx.$$

Compare the results for $n = 4$ and $n = 8$.

Solution When $n = 4$, you have

$$\int_0^\pi \sin x\,dx \approx \frac{\pi}{12}\left(\sin 0 + 4\sin\frac{\pi}{4} + 2\sin\frac{\pi}{2} + 4\sin\frac{3\pi}{4} + \sin\pi\right) \approx 2.005.$$

When $n = 8$, you have $\int_0^\pi \sin x\,dx \approx 2.0003$.

Error Analysis

When you use an approximation technique, it is important to know how accurate you can expect the approximation to be. The next theorem, which is listed without proof, gives the formulas for estimating the errors involved in the use of Simpson's Rule and the Trapezoidal Rule. In general, when using an approximation, you can think of the error E as the difference between $\int_a^b f(x)\, dx$ and the approximation.

▷ •••••••••••••••••••
•• **REMARK**   In Theorem 5.20, $\max |f''(x)|$ is the least upper bound of the absolute value of the second derivative on $[a, b]$, and $\max |f^{(4)}(x)|$ is the least upper bound of the absolute value of the fourth derivative on $[a, b]$.

THEOREM 5.20   Errors in the Trapezoidal Rule and Simpson's Rule

If f has a continuous second derivative on $[a, b]$, then the error E in approximating $\int_a^b f(x)\, dx$ by the Trapezoidal Rule is

$$|E| \le \frac{(b-a)^3}{12n^2}[\max|f''(x)|], \quad a \le x \le b. \qquad \text{Trapezoidal Rule}$$

Moreover, if f has a continuous fourth derivative on $[a, b]$, then the error E in approximating $\int_a^b f(x)\, dx$ by Simpson's Rule is

$$|E| \le \frac{(b-a)^5}{180n^4}[\max|f^{(4)}(x)|], \quad a \le x \le b. \qquad \text{Simpson's Rule}$$

Theorem 5.20 states that the errors generated by the Trapezoidal Rule and Simpson's Rule have upper bounds dependent on the extreme values of $f''(x)$ and $f^{(4)}(x)$ in the interval $[a, b]$. Furthermore, these errors can be made arbitrarily small by *increasing n*, provided that f'' and $f^{(4)}$ are continuous and therefore bounded in $[a, b]$.

▷ **TECHNOLOGY**   If you have access to a computer algebra system, use it to evaluate the definite integral in Example 3. You should obtain a value of

$$\int_0^1 \sqrt{1+x^2}\, dx$$

$$= \frac{1}{2}\left[\sqrt{2} + \ln\left(1 + \sqrt{2}\right)\right]$$

$$\approx 1.14779.$$

EXAMPLE 3   **The Approximate Error in the Trapezoidal Rule**

Determine a value of n such that the Trapezoidal Rule will approximate the value of

$$\int_0^1 \sqrt{1+x^2}\, dx$$

with an error that is less than or equal to 0.01.

Solution   Begin by letting $f(x) = \sqrt{1+x^2}$ and finding the second derivative of f.

$$f'(x) = x(1+x^2)^{-1/2} \quad \text{and} \quad f''(x) = (1+x^2)^{-3/2}$$

The maximum value of $|f''(x)|$ on the interval $[0, 1]$ is $|f''(0)| = 1$. So, by Theorem 5.20, you can write

$$|E| \le \frac{(b-a)^3}{12n^2}|f''(0)| = \frac{1}{12n^2}(1) = \frac{1}{12n^2}.$$

To obtain an error E that is less than 0.01, you must choose n such that $1/(12n^2) \le 1/100$.

$$100 \le 12n^2 \quad \Longrightarrow \quad n \ge \sqrt{\tfrac{100}{12}} \approx 2.89$$

So, you can choose $n = 3$ (because n must be greater than or equal to 2.89) and apply the Trapezoidal Rule, as shown in Figure 5.46, to obtain

$$\int_0^1 \sqrt{1+x^2}\, dx \approx \frac{1}{6}\left[\sqrt{1+0^2} + 2\sqrt{1+\left(\tfrac{1}{3}\right)^2} + 2\sqrt{1+\left(\tfrac{2}{3}\right)^2} + \sqrt{1+1^2}\right]$$

$$\approx 1.154.$$

So, by adding and subtracting the error from this estimate, you know that

$$1.144 \le \int_0^1 \sqrt{1+x^2}\, dx \le 1.164.$$

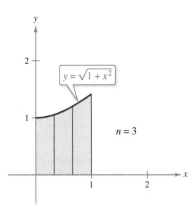

$$1.144 \le \int_0^1 \sqrt{1+x^2}\, dx \le 1.164$$

Figure 5.46

5.6 Exercises

See **CalcChat.com** for tutorial help and worked-out solutions to odd-numbered exercises.

Using the Trapezoidal Rule and Simpson's Rule In Exercises 1–10, use the Trapezoidal Rule and Simpson's Rule to approximate the value of the definite integral for the given value of n. Round your answer to four decimal places and compare the results with the exact value of the definite integral.

1. $\int_0^2 x^2 \, dx, \quad n = 4$

2. $\int_1^2 \left(\frac{x^2}{4} + 1\right) dx, \quad n = 4$

3. $\int_0^2 x^3 \, dx, \quad n = 4$

4. $\int_2^3 \frac{2}{x^2} \, dx, \quad n = 4$

5. $\int_1^3 x^3 \, dx, \quad n = 6$

6. $\int_0^8 \sqrt[3]{x} \, dx, \quad n = 8$

7. $\int_4^9 \sqrt{x} \, dx, \quad n = 8$

8. $\int_1^4 (4 - x^2) \, dx, \quad n = 6$

9. $\int_0^1 \frac{2}{(x + 2)^2} \, dx, \quad n = 4$

10. $\int_0^2 x\sqrt{x^2 + 1} \, dx, \quad n = 4$

Using the Trapezoidal Rule and Simpson's Rule In Exercises 11–22, approximate the definite integral using the Trapezoidal Rule and Simpson's Rule with $n = 4$. Compare these results with the approximation of the integral using a graphing utility.

11. $\int_0^2 \sqrt{1 + x^3} \, dx$

12. $\int_0^2 \frac{1}{\sqrt{1 + x^3}} \, dx$

13. $\int_0^1 \sqrt{x} \sqrt{1 - x} \, dx$

14. $\int_0^4 \sqrt{x} e^x \, dx$

15. $\int_0^{\sqrt{\pi/2}} \sin x^2 \, dx$

16. $\int_0^{\sqrt{\pi/4}} \tan x^2 \, dx$

17. $\int_3^{3.1} \cos x^2 \, dx$

18. $\int_0^{\pi/2} \sqrt{1 + \sin^2 x} \, dx$

19. $\int_0^2 x \ln(x + 1) \, dx$

20. $\int_1^3 \ln x \, dx$

21. $\int_0^2 xe^{-x} \, dx$

22. $\int_0^\pi f(x) \, dx, \quad f(x) = \begin{cases} \dfrac{\sin x}{x}, & x > 0 \\ 1, & x = 0 \end{cases}$

WRITING ABOUT CONCEPTS

23. Polynomial Approximations The Trapezoidal Rule and Simpson's Rule yield approximations of a definite integral $\int_a^b f(x) \, dx$ based on polynomial approximations of f. What is the degree of the polynomials used for each?

24. Describing an Error Describe the size of the error when the Trapezoidal Rule is used to approximate $\int_a^b f(x) \, dx$ when $f(x)$ is a linear function. Use a graph to explain your answer.

Estimating Errors In Exercises 25–28, use the error formulas in Theorem 5.20 to estimate the errors in approximating the integral, with $n = 4$, using (a) the Trapezoidal Rule and (b) Simpson's Rule.

25. $\int_1^3 2x^3 \, dx$

26. $\int_3^5 (5x + 2) \, dx$

27. $\int_2^4 \frac{1}{(x - 1)^2} \, dx$

28. $\int_0^\pi \cos x \, dx$

Estimating Errors In Exercises 29–32, use the error formulas in Theorem 5.20 to find n such that the error in the approximation of the definite integral is less than or equal to 0.00001 using (a) the Trapezoidal Rule and (b) Simpson's Rule.

29. $\int_1^3 \frac{1}{x} \, dx$

30. $\int_0^1 \frac{1}{1 + x} \, dx$

31. $\int_0^2 \sqrt{x + 2} \, dx$

32. $\int_0^{\pi/2} \sin x \, dx$

Estimating Errors Using Technology In Exercises 33–36, use a computer algebra system and the error formulas to find n such that the error in the approximation of the definite integral is less than or equal to 0.00001 using (a) the Trapezoidal Rule and (b) Simpson's Rule.

33. $\int_0^2 \sqrt{1 + x} \, dx$

34. $\int_0^2 (x + 1)^{2/3} \, dx$

35. $\int_0^1 \tan x^2 \, dx$

36. $\int_0^1 \sin x^2 \, dx$

37. Finding the Area of a Region Approximate the area of the shaded region using

(a) the Trapezoidal Rule with $n = 4$.

(b) Simpson's Rule with $n = 4$.

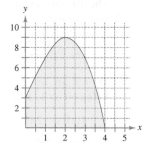

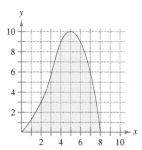

Figure for 37   Figure for 38

38. Finding the Area of a Region Approximate the area of the shaded region using

(a) the Trapezoidal Rule with $n = 8$.

(b) Simpson's Rule with $n = 8$.

39. Area Use Simpson's Rule with $n = 14$ to approximate the area of the region bounded by the graphs of $y = \sqrt{x} \cos x$, $y = 0$, $x = 0$, and $x = \pi/2$.

40. Circumference The **elliptic integral**

$$8\sqrt{3} \int_0^{\pi/2} \sqrt{1 - \tfrac{2}{3} \sin^2 \theta} \, d\theta$$

gives the circumference of an ellipse. Use Simpson's Rule with $n = 8$ to approximate the circumference.

41. Surveying

Use the Trapezoidal Rule to estimate the number of square meters of land, where x and y are measured in meters, as shown in the figure. The land is bounded by a stream and two straight roads that meet at right angles.

x	0	100	200	300	400	500
y	125	125	120	112	90	90

x	600	700	800	900	1000
y	95	88	75	35	0

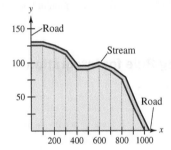

42. HOW DO YOU SEE IT? The function $f(x)$ is concave upward on the interval $[0, 2]$ and the function $g(x)$ is concave downward on the interval $[0, 2]$.

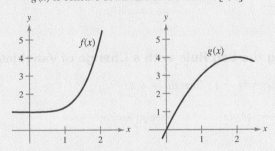

(a) Using the Trapezoidal Rule with $n = 4$, which integral would be overestimated? Which integral would be underestimated? Explain your reasoning.

(b) Which rule would you use for more accurate approximations of $\int_0^2 f(x)\, dx$ and $\int_0^2 g(x)\, dx$, the Trapezoidal Rule or Simpson's Rule? Explain your reasoning.

43. Work To determine the size of the motor required to operate a press, a company must know the amount of work done when the press moves an object linearly 5 feet. The variable force to move the object is

$$F(x) = 100x\sqrt{125 - x^3}$$

where F is given in pounds and x gives the position of the unit in feet. Use Simpson's Rule with $n = 12$ to approximate the work W (in foot-pounds) done through one cycle when

$$W = \int_0^5 F(x)\, dx.$$

44. Approximating a Function The table lists several measurements gathered in an experiment to approximate an unknown continuous function $y = f(x)$.

x	0.00	0.25	0.50	0.75	1.00
y	4.32	4.36	4.58	5.79	6.14

x	1.25	1.50	1.75	2.00
y	7.25	7.64	8.08	8.14

(a) Approximate the integral

$$\int_0^2 f(x)\, dx$$

using the Trapezoidal Rule and Simpson's Rule.

(b) Use a graphing utility to find a model of the form $y = ax^3 + bx^2 + cx + d$ for the data. Integrate the resulting polynomial over $[0, 2]$ and compare the result with the integral from part (a).

Approximation of Pi In Exercises 45 and 46, use Simpson's Rule with $n = 6$ to approximate π using the given equation. (In Section 5.8, you will be able to evaluate the integral using inverse trigonometric functions.)

45. $\pi = \int_0^{1/2} \dfrac{6}{\sqrt{1 - x^2}} \, dx$ **46.** $\pi = \int_0^1 \dfrac{4}{1 + x^2} \, dx$

47. Using Simpson's Rule Use Simpson's Rule with $n = 10$ and a computer algebra system to approximate t in the integral equation

$$\int_0^t \sin \sqrt{x} \, dx = 2.$$

48. Proof Prove that Simpson's Rule is exact when approximating the integral of a cubic polynomial function, and demonstrate the result with $n = 4$ for

$$\int_0^1 x^3 \, dx.$$

49. Proof Prove that you can find a polynomial

$$p(x) = Ax^2 + Bx + C$$

that passes through any three points (x_1, y_1), (x_2, y_2), and (x_3, y_3), where the x_i's are distinct.

5.7 The Natural Logarithmic Function: Integration

■ Use the Log Rule for Integration to integrate a rational function.
■ Integrate trigonometric functions.

Log Rule for Integration

In Chapter 3 you studied two differentiation rules for logarithms. The differentiation rule $d/dx[\ln x] = 1/x$ produces the Log Rule for Integration that you learned in Section 5.1. The differentiation rule $d/dx[\ln u] = u'/u$ produces the integration rule $\int 1/u = \ln|u| + C$. These rules are summarized below. (See Exercise 111.)

THEOREM 5.21 Log Rule for Integration

Let u be a differentiable function of x.

1. $\displaystyle\int \frac{1}{x}\, dx = \ln|x| + C$ **2.** $\displaystyle\int \frac{1}{u}\, du = \ln|u| + C$

Because $du = u'\, dx$, the second formula can also be written as

$$\int \frac{u'}{u}\, dx = \ln|u| + C. \qquad \text{Alternative form of Log Rule}$$

EXAMPLE 1 **Using the Log Rule for Integration**

To find $\int 1/(2x)\, dx$, let $u = 2x$. Then $du = 2\, dx$.

$$\int \frac{1}{2x}\, dx = \frac{1}{2}\int \left(\frac{1}{2x}\right)2\, dx \qquad \text{Multiply and divide by 2.}$$

$$= \frac{1}{2}\int \frac{1}{u}\, du \qquad \text{Substitute: } u = 2x.$$

$$= \frac{1}{2}\ln|u| + C \qquad \text{Apply Log Rule.}$$

$$= \frac{1}{2}\ln|2x| + C \qquad \text{Back-substitute.}$$

EXAMPLE 2 **Using the Log Rule with a Change of Variables**

To find $\int 1/(4x - 1)\, dx$, let $u = 4x - 1$. Then $du = 4\, dx$.

$$\int \frac{1}{4x - 1}\, dx = \frac{1}{4}\int \left(\frac{1}{4x - 1}\right)4\, dx \qquad \text{Multiply and divide by 4.}$$

$$= \frac{1}{4}\int \frac{1}{u}\, du \qquad \text{Substitute: } u = 4x - 1.$$

$$= \frac{1}{4}\ln|u| + C \qquad \text{Apply Log Rule.}$$

$$= \frac{1}{4}\ln|4x - 1| + C \qquad \text{Back-substitute.}$$

Exploration

Integrating Rational Functions

Earlier in this chapter, you learned rules that allowed you to integrate *any* polynomial function. The Log Rule presented in this section goes a long way toward enabling you to integrate rational functions. For instance, each of the following functions can be integrated with the Log Rule.

$\dfrac{1}{2x}$ Example 1

$\dfrac{1}{4x - 1}$ Example 2

$\dfrac{x}{x^2 + 1}$ Example 3

$\dfrac{3x^2 + 1}{x^3 + x}$ Example 4(a)

$\dfrac{x + 1}{x^2 + 2x}$ Example 4(c)

$\dfrac{1}{3x + 2}$ Example 4(d)

$\dfrac{x^2 + x + 1}{x^2 + 1}$ Example 5

$\dfrac{2x}{(x + 1)^2}$ Example 6

There are still some rational functions that cannot be integrated using the Log Rule. Give examples of these functions, and explain your reasoning.

Example 3 uses the alternative form of the Log Rule. To apply this rule, look for quotients in which the numerator is the derivative of the denominator.

| **EXAMPLE 3** | **Finding Area with the Log Rule** |

Find the area of the region bounded by the graph of

$$y = \frac{x}{x^2 + 1}$$

the x-axis, and the line $x = 3$.

Solution In Figure 5.47, you can see that the area of the region is given by the definite integral

$$\int_0^3 \frac{x}{x^2 + 1} \, dx.$$

If you let $u = x^2 + 1$, then $u' = 2x$. To apply the Log Rule, multiply and divide by 2 as shown.

$$\int_0^3 \frac{x}{x^2 + 1} \, dx = \frac{1}{2} \int_0^3 \frac{2x}{x^2 + 1} \, dx \qquad \text{Multiply and divide by 2.}$$

$$= \frac{1}{2} \Big[\ln(x^2 + 1) \Big]_0^3 \qquad \int \frac{u'}{u} \, dx = \ln|u| + C$$

$$= \frac{1}{2}(\ln 10 - \ln 1)$$

$$= \frac{1}{2} \ln 10 \qquad \ln 1 = 0$$

$$\approx 1.151$$

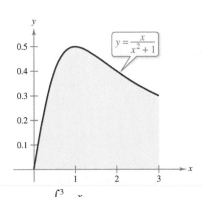

$\text{Area} = \int_0^3 \frac{x}{x^2 + 1} \, dx$

The area of the region bounded by the graph of y, the x-axis, and $x = 3$ is $\frac{1}{2} \ln 10$.

Figure 5.47

| **EXAMPLE 4** | **Recognizing Quotient Forms of the Log Rule** |

a. $\displaystyle \int \frac{3x^2 + 1}{x^3 + x} \, dx = \ln|x^3 + x| + C \qquad u = x^3 + x$

b. $\displaystyle \int \frac{\sec^2 x}{\tan x} \, dx = \ln|\tan x| + C \qquad u = \tan x$

c. $\displaystyle \int \frac{x + 1}{x^2 + 2x} \, dx = \frac{1}{2} \int \frac{2x + 2}{x^2 + 2x} \, dx \qquad u = x^2 + 2x$

$\displaystyle \qquad\qquad\qquad\quad = \frac{1}{2} \ln|x^2 + 2x| + C$

d. $\displaystyle \int \frac{1}{3x + 2} \, dx = \frac{1}{3} \int \frac{3}{3x + 2} \, dx \qquad u = 3x + 2$

$\displaystyle \qquad\qquad\qquad\quad = \frac{1}{3} \ln|3x + 2| + C$

With antiderivatives involving logarithms, it is easy to obtain forms that look quite different but are still equivalent. For instance, both

$$\ln\left|(3x + 2)^{1/3}\right| + C$$

and

$$\ln|3x + 2|^{1/3} + C$$

are equivalent to the antiderivative listed in Example 4(d).

Integrals to which the Log Rule can be applied often appear in disguised form. For instance, when a rational function has a *numerator of degree greater than or equal to that of the denominator*, division may reveal a form to which you can apply the Log Rule. This is shown in Example 5.

EXAMPLE 5 **Using Long Division Before Integrating**

⋮ ▷ *See LarsonCalculus.com for an interactive version of this type of example.*

Find the indefinite integral.

$$\int \frac{x^2 + x + 1}{x^2 + 1}\, dx$$

Solution Begin by using long division to rewrite the integrand.

$$\frac{x^2 + x + 1}{x^2 + 1} \implies x^2 + 1 \overline{\smash{)}\, x^2 + x + 1} \implies 1 + \frac{x}{x^2 + 1}$$
$$ \underline{x^2 + 1}$$
$$ x$$

Now, you can integrate to obtain

$$\int \frac{x^2 + x + 1}{x^2 + 1}\, dx = \int \left(1 + \frac{x}{x^2 + 1}\right) dx \qquad \text{Rewrite using long division.}$$

$$= \int dx + \frac{1}{2}\int \frac{2x}{x^2 + 1}\, dx \qquad \text{Rewrite as two integrals.}$$

$$= x + \frac{1}{2}\ln(x^2 + 1) + C. \qquad \text{Integrate.}$$

Check this result by differentiating to obtain the original integrand.

The next example presents another instance in which the use of the Log Rule is disguised. In this case, a change of variables helps you recognize the Log Rule.

EXAMPLE 6 **Change of Variables with the Log Rule**

Find the indefinite integral.

$$\int \frac{2x}{(x + 1)^2}\, dx$$

Solution If you let $u = x + 1$, then $du = dx$ and $x = u - 1$.

$$\int \frac{2x}{(x + 1)^2}\, dx = \int \frac{2(u - 1)}{u^2}\, du \qquad \text{Substitute.}$$

$$= 2\int \left(\frac{u}{u^2} - \frac{1}{u^2}\right) du \qquad \text{Rewrite as two fractions.}$$

$$= 2\int \frac{du}{u} - 2\int u^{-2}\, du \qquad \text{Rewrite as two integrals.}$$

$$= 2\ln|u| - 2\left(\frac{u^{-1}}{-1}\right) + C \qquad \text{Integrate.}$$

$$= 2\ln|u| + \frac{2}{u} + C \qquad \text{Simplify.}$$

$$= 2\ln|x + 1| + \frac{2}{x + 1} + C \qquad \text{Back-substitute.}$$

▷ **TECHNOLOGY** If you have access to a computer algebra system, use it to find the indefinite integrals in Examples 5 and 6. How does the form of the antiderivative that it gives you compare with that given in Examples 5 and 6?

Check this result by differentiating to obtain the original integrand.

As you study the methods shown in Examples 5 and 6, be aware that both methods involve rewriting a disguised integrand so that it fits one or more of the basic integration formulas. Throughout the remaining sections of Chapter 5 and in Chapter 8, much time will be devoted to integration techniques. To master these techniques, you must recognize the "form-fitting" nature of integration. In this sense, integration is not nearly as straightforward as differentiation. Differentiation takes the form

"Here is the question; what is the answer?"

Integration is more like

"Here is the answer; what is the question?"

Here are some guidelines you can use for integration.

GUIDELINES FOR INTEGRATION

1. Learn a basic list of integration formulas. (By the end of Section 5.8, you will have 20 basic rules.)

2. Find an integration formula that resembles all or part of the integrand, and, by trial and error, find a choice of u that will make the integrand conform to the formula.

3. When you cannot find a u-substitution that works, try altering the integrand. You might try a trigonometric identity, multiplication and division by the same quantity, addition and subtraction of the same quantity, or long division. Be creative.

4. If you have access to computer software that will find antiderivatives symbolically, use it.

| EXAMPLE 7 | *u*-Substitution and the Log Rule |

Solve the differential equation

$$\frac{dy}{dx} = \frac{1}{x \ln x}.$$

Solution   The solution can be written as an indefinite integral.

$$y = \int \frac{1}{x \ln x}\, dx$$

Because the integrand is a quotient whose denominator is raised to the first power, you should try the Log Rule. There are three basic choices for u. The choices

$$u = x \quad \text{and} \quad u = x \ln x$$

fail to fit the u'/u form of the Log Rule. However, the third choice does fit. Letting $u = \ln x$ produces $u' = 1/x$, and you obtain the following.

$$\int \frac{1}{x \ln x}\, dx = \int \frac{1/x}{\ln x}\, dx \qquad \text{Divide numerator and denominator by } x.$$

$$= \int \frac{u'}{u}\, dx \qquad \text{Substitute: } u = \ln x.$$

$$= \ln|u| + C \qquad \text{Apply Log Rule.}$$

$$= \ln|\ln x| + C \qquad \text{Back-substitute.}$$

So, the solution is $y = \ln|\ln x| + C$.

•• **REMARK**   Keep in mind that you can check your answer to an integration problem by differentiating the answer. For instance, in Example 7, the derivative of $y = \ln|\ln x| + C$ is $y' = 1/(x \ln x)$.

Integrals of Trigonometric Functions

In Section 5.1, you looked at six trigonometric integration rules—the six that correspond directly to differentiation rules. With the Log Rule, you can now complete the set of basic trigonometric integration formulas.

EXAMPLE 8 **Using a Trigonometric Identity**

Find $\int \tan x \, dx$.

Solution This integral does not seem to fit any formulas on our basic list. However, by using a trigonometric identity, you obtain

$$\int \tan x \, dx = \int \frac{\sin x}{\cos x} \, dx.$$

Knowing that $D_x[\cos x] = -\sin x$, you can let $u = \cos x$ and write

$$\int \tan x \, dx = -\int \frac{-\sin x}{\cos x} \, dx \qquad \text{Apply trigonometric identity and multiply and divide by } -1.$$

$$= -\int \frac{u'}{u} \, dx \qquad \text{Substitute: } u = \cos x.$$

$$= -\ln|u| + C \qquad \text{Apply Log Rule.}$$

$$= -\ln|\cos x| + C. \qquad \text{Back-substitute.}$$

Example 8 uses a trigonometric identity to derive an integration rule for the tangent function. The next example takes a rather unusual step (multiplying and dividing by the same quantity) to derive an integration rule for the secant function.

EXAMPLE 9 **Derivation of the Secant Formula**

Find $\int \sec x \, dx$.

Solution Consider the following procedure.

$$\int \sec x \, dx = \int \sec x \left(\frac{\sec x + \tan x}{\sec x + \tan x} \right) dx$$

$$= \int \frac{\sec^2 x + \sec x \tan x}{\sec x + \tan x} \, dx$$

Letting u be the denominator of this quotient produces

$$u = \sec x + \tan x$$

and

$$u' = \sec x \tan x + \sec^2 x.$$

So, you can conclude that

$$\int \sec x \, dx = \int \frac{\sec^2 x + \sec x \tan x}{\sec x + \tan x} \, dx \qquad \text{Rewrite integrand.}$$

$$= \int \frac{u'}{u} \, dx \qquad \text{Substitute: } u = \sec x + \tan x.$$

$$= \ln|u| + C \qquad \text{Apply Log Rule.}$$

$$= \ln|\sec x + \tan x| + C. \qquad \text{Back-substitute.}$$

With the results of Examples 8 and 9, you now have integration formulas for sin x, cos x, tan x, and sec x. The integrals of the six basic trigonometric functions are summarized below. (For proofs of cot u and csc u, see Exercises 89 and 90.)

> **· ·REMARK**   Using trigonometric identities and properties of logarithms, you could rewrite these six integration rules in other forms. For instance, you could write
>
> $$\int \csc u \, du$$
> $$= \ln|\csc u - \cot u| + C.$$
>
> (See Exercises 91–94.)

INTEGRALS OF THE SIX BASIC TRIGONOMETRIC FUNCTIONS

$$\int \sin u \, du = -\cos u + C \qquad \int \cos u \, du = \sin u + C$$

$$\int \tan u \, du = -\ln|\cos u| + C \qquad \int \cot u \, du = \ln|\sin u| + C$$

$$\int \sec u \, du = \ln|\sec u + \tan u| + C \qquad \int \csc u \, du = -\ln|\csc u + \cot u| + C$$

EXAMPLE 10   **Integrating Trigonometric Functions**

Evaluate $\displaystyle\int_0^{\pi/4} \sqrt{1 + \tan^2 x} \, dx$.

Solution   Using $1 + \tan^2 x = \sec^2 x$, you can write

$$\int_0^{\pi/4} \sqrt{1 + \tan^2 x} \, dx = \int_0^{\pi/4} \sqrt{\sec^2 x} \, dx$$

$$= \int_0^{\pi/4} \sec x \, dx \qquad \sec x \geq 0 \text{ for } 0 \leq x \leq \frac{\pi}{4}$$

$$= \ln|\sec x + \tan x| \Big]_0^{\pi/4}$$

$$= \ln(\sqrt{2} + 1) - \ln 1$$

$$\approx 0.881.$$

EXAMPLE 11   **Finding an Average Value**

Find the average value of

$$f(x) = \tan x$$

on the interval $[0, \pi/4]$.

Solution

$$\text{Average value} = \frac{1}{(\pi/4) - 0} \int_0^{\pi/4} \tan x \, dx \qquad \text{Average value} = \frac{1}{b-a}\int_a^b f(x) \, dx$$

$$= \frac{4}{\pi} \int_0^{\pi/4} \tan x \, dx \qquad \text{Simplify.}$$

$$= \frac{4}{\pi} \left[-\ln|\cos x| \right]_0^{\pi/4} \qquad \text{Integrate.}$$

$$= -\frac{4}{\pi} \left[\ln\left(\frac{\sqrt{2}}{2}\right) - \ln(1) \right]$$

$$= -\frac{4}{\pi} \ln\left(\frac{\sqrt{2}}{2}\right)$$

$$\approx 0.441$$

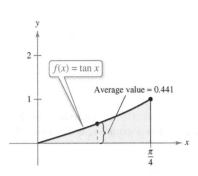

Figure 5.48

The average value is about 0.441, as shown in Figure 5.48.

Finding an Indefinite Integral In Exercises 1–26, find the indefinite integral.

1. $\int \dfrac{5}{x}\,dx$

2. $\int \dfrac{10}{x}\,dx$

3. $\int \dfrac{1}{x+1}\,dx$

4. $\int \dfrac{1}{x-5}\,dx$

5. $\int \dfrac{1}{2x+5}\,dx$

6. $\int \dfrac{9}{5-4x}\,dx$

7. $\int \dfrac{x}{x^2-3}\,dx$

8. $\int \dfrac{x^2}{5-x^3}\,dx$

9. $\int \dfrac{4x^3+3}{x^4+3x}\,dx$

10. $\int \dfrac{x^2-2x}{x^3-3x^2}\,dx$

11. $\int \dfrac{x^2-4}{x}\,dx$

12. $\int \dfrac{x^3-8x}{x^2}\,dx$

13. $\int \dfrac{x^2+2x+3}{x^3+3x^2+9x}\,dx$

14. $\int \dfrac{x^2+4x}{x^3+6x^2+5}\,dx$

15. $\int \dfrac{x^2-3x+2}{x+1}\,dx$

16. $\int \dfrac{2x^2+7x-3}{x-2}\,dx$

17. $\int \dfrac{x^3-3x^2+5}{x-3}\,dx$

18. $\int \dfrac{x^3-6x-20}{x+5}\,dx$

19. $\int \dfrac{x^4+x-4}{x^2+2}\,dx$

20. $\int \dfrac{x^3-4x^2-4x+20}{x^2-5}\,dx$

21. $\int \dfrac{(\ln x)^2}{x}\,dx$

22. $\int \dfrac{1}{x\ln x^3}\,dx$

23. $\int \dfrac{1}{\sqrt{x}\left(1-3\sqrt{x}\right)}\,dx$

24. $\int \dfrac{1}{x^{2/3}\left(1+x^{1/3}\right)}\,dx$

25. $\int \dfrac{2x}{(x-1)^2}\,dx$

26. $\int \dfrac{x(x-2)}{(x-1)^3}\,dx$

Finding an Indefinite Integral by u-Substitution In Exercises 27–30, find the indefinite integral by u-substitution. (*Hint:* Let u be the denominator of the integrand.)

27. $\int \dfrac{1}{1+\sqrt{2x}}\,dx$

28. $\int \dfrac{1}{1+\sqrt{3x}}\,dx$

29. $\int \dfrac{\sqrt{x}}{\sqrt{x}-3}\,dx$

30. $\int \dfrac{\sqrt[3]{x}}{\sqrt[3]{x}-1}\,dx$

Finding an Indefinite Integral of a Trigonometric Function In Exercises 31–42, find the indefinite integral.

31. $\int \cot \dfrac{\theta}{3}\,d\theta$

32. $\int \tan 5\theta\,d\theta$

33. $\int \csc 2x\,dx$

34. $\int \sec \dfrac{x}{2}\,dx$

35. $\int (\cos 3\theta - 1)\,d\theta$

36. $\int \left(2-\tan\dfrac{\theta}{4}\right)d\theta$

37. $\int \dfrac{\cos t}{1+\sin t}\,dt$

38. $\int \dfrac{\csc^2 t}{\cot t}\,dt$

39. $\int \dfrac{\sec x \tan x}{\sec x - 1}\,dx$

40. $\int (\sec 2x + \tan 2x)\,dx$

41. $\int e^{-x}\tan(e^{-x})\,dx$

42. $\int \sec t(\sec t + \tan t)\,dt$

Differential Equation In Exercises 43–46, solve the differential equation. Use a graphing utility to graph three solutions, one of which passes through the given point.

43. $\dfrac{dy}{dx} = \dfrac{3}{2-x}$, $(1, 0)$

44. $\dfrac{dy}{dx} = \dfrac{x-2}{x}$, $(-1, 0)$

45. $\dfrac{dy}{dx} = \dfrac{2x}{x^2-9}$, $(0, 4)$

46. $\dfrac{dr}{dt} = \dfrac{\sec^2 t}{\tan t + 1}$, $(\pi, 4)$

Finding a Particular Solution In Exercises 47 and 48, find the particular solution that satisfies the differential equation and the initial equations.

47. $f''(x) = \dfrac{2}{x^2}$, $f'(1) = 1$, $f(1) = 1$, $x > 0$

48. $f''(x) = -\dfrac{4}{(x-1)^2} - 2$, $f'(2) = 0$, $f(2) = 3$, $x > 1$

Slope Field In Exercises 49 and 50, a differential equation, a point, and a slope field are given. (a) Sketch two approximate solutions of the differential equation on the slope field, one of which passes through the given point. (b) Use integration to find the particular solution of the differential equation and use a graphing utility to graph the solution. Compare the result with the sketches in part (a). To print an enlarged copy of the graph, go to *MathGraphs.com*.

49. $\dfrac{dy}{dx} = \dfrac{1}{x+2}$

$(0, 1)$

50. $\dfrac{dy}{dx} = \dfrac{\ln x}{x}$

$(1, -2)$

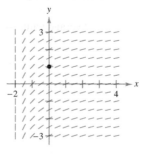

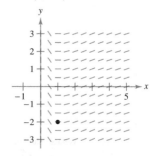

Evaluating a Definite Integral In Exercises 51–58, evaluate the definite integral. Use a graphing utility to verify your result.

51. $\displaystyle\int_0^4 \dfrac{5}{3x+1}\,dx$

52. $\displaystyle\int_{-1}^1 \dfrac{1}{2x+3}\,dx$

53. $\int_1^e \dfrac{(1 + \ln x)^2}{x}\,dx$

54. $\int_e^{e^2} \dfrac{1}{x \ln x}\,dx$

55. $\int_0^2 \dfrac{x^2 - 2}{x + 1}\,dx$

56. $\int_0^1 \dfrac{x - 1}{x + 1}\,dx$

57. $\int_1^2 \dfrac{1 - \cos \theta}{\theta - \sin \theta}\,d\theta$

58. $\int_{\pi/8}^{\pi/4} (\csc 2\theta - \cot 2\theta)\,d\theta$

Using Technology to Find an Integral In Exercises 59–64, use a computer algebra system to find or evaluate the integral.

59. $\int \dfrac{1}{1 + \sqrt{x}}\,dx$

60. $\int \dfrac{1 - \sqrt{x}}{1 + \sqrt{x}}\,dx$

61. $\int \dfrac{\sqrt{x}}{x - 1}\,dx$

62. $\int \dfrac{x^2}{x - 1}\,dx$

63. $\int_{\pi/4}^{\pi/2} (\csc x - \sin x)\,dx$

64. $\int_{-\pi/4}^{\pi/4} \dfrac{\sin^2 x - \cos^2 x}{\cos x}\,dx$

Finding a Derivative In Exercises 65–68, find $F'(x)$.

65. $F(x) = \int_1^x \dfrac{1}{t}\,dt$

66. $F(x) = \int_0^x \tan t\,dt$

67. $F(x) = \int_1^{3x} \dfrac{1}{t}\,dt$

68. $F(x) = \int_1^{x^2} \dfrac{1}{t}\,dt$

Area In Exercises 69–72, find the area of the given region. Use a graphing utility to verify your result.

69. $y = \dfrac{6}{x}$

70. $y = \dfrac{2}{x \ln x}$

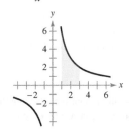

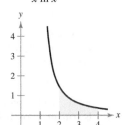

71. $y = \tan x$

72. $y = \dfrac{\sin x}{1 + \cos x}$

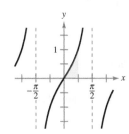

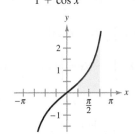

Area In Exercises 73–76, find the area of the region bounded by the graphs of the equations. Use a graphing utility to verify your result.

73. $y = \dfrac{x^2 + 4}{x}$, $x = 1$, $x = 4$, $y = 0$

74. $y = \dfrac{5x}{x^2 + 2}$, $x = 1$, $x = 5$, $y = 0$

75. $y = 2 \sec \dfrac{\pi x}{6}$, $x = 0$, $x = 2$, $y = 0$

76. $y = 2x - \tan 0.3x$, $x = 1$, $x = 4$, $y = 0$

Numerical Integration In Exercises 77–80, use the Trapezoidal Rule and Simpson's Rule to approximate the value of the definite integral. Let $n = 4$ and round your answer to four decimal places. Use a graphing utility to verify your result.

77. $\int_1^5 \dfrac{12}{x}\,dx$

78. $\int_0^4 \dfrac{8x}{x^2 + 4}\,dx$

79. $\int_2^6 \ln x\,dx$

80. $\int_{-\pi/3}^{\pi/3} \sec x\,dx$

WRITING ABOUT CONCEPTS

Choosing a Formula In Exercises 81–84, state the integration formula you would use to perform the integration. Do not integrate.

81. $\int \sqrt[3]{x}\,dx$

82. $\int \dfrac{x}{(x^2 + 4)^3}\,dx$

83. $\int \dfrac{x}{x^2 + 4}\,dx$

84. $\int \dfrac{\sec^2 x}{\tan x}\,dx$

Approximation In Exercises 85 and 86, determine which value best approximates the area of the region between the x-axis and the graph of the function over the given interval. (Make your selection on the basis of a sketch of the region, not by performing any calculations.)

85. $f(x) = \sec x$, $[0, 1]$

　(a) 6 　(b) -6 　(c) $\frac{1}{2}$ 　(d) 1.25 　(e) 3

86. $f(x) = \dfrac{2x}{x^2 + 1}$, $[0, 4]$

　(a) 3 　(b) 7 　(c) -2 　(d) 5 　(e) 1

87. Finding a Value Find a value of x such that

$$\int_1^x \dfrac{3}{t}\,dt = \int_{1/4}^x \dfrac{1}{t}\,dt.$$

88. Finding a Value Find a value of x such that

$$\int_1^x \dfrac{1}{t}\,dt$$

is equal to (a) $\ln 5$ and (b) 1.

89. Proof Prove that

$$\int \cot u\,du = \ln|\sin u| + C.$$

90. Proof Prove that

$$\int \csc u\,du = -\ln|\csc u + \cot u| + C.$$

Using Properties of Logarithms and Trigonometric Identities In Exercises 91–94, show that the two formulas are equivalent.

91. $\int \tan x \, dx = -\ln|\cos x| + C$

$\int \tan x \, dx = \ln|\sec x| + C$

92. $\int \cot x \, dx = \ln|\sin x| + C$

$\int \cot x \, dx = -\ln|\csc x| + C$

93. $\int \sec x \, dx = \ln|\sec x + \tan x| + C$

$\int \sec x \, dx = -\ln|\sec x - \tan x| + C$

94. $\int \csc x \, dx = -\ln|\csc x + \cot x| + C$

$\int \csc x \, dx = \ln|\csc x - \cot x| + C$

Finding the Average Value of a Function In Exercises 95–98, find the average value of the function over the given interval.

95. $f(x) = \dfrac{8}{x^2}$, $\ [2, 4]$

96. $f(x) = \dfrac{4(x + 1)}{x^2}$, $\ [2, 4]$

97. $f(x) = \dfrac{2 \ln x}{x}$, $\ [1, e]$

98. $f(x) = \sec \dfrac{\pi x}{6}$, $\ [0, 2]$

99. Population Growth A population of bacteria P is changing at a rate of

$$\frac{dP}{dt} = \frac{3000}{1 + 0.25t}$$

where t is the time in days. The initial population (when $t = 0$) is 1000. Write an equation that gives the population at any time t. Then find the population when $t = 3$ days.

100. Sales The rate of change in sales S is inversely proportional to time t ($t > 1$), measured in weeks. Find S as a function of t when the sales after 2 and 4 weeks are 200 units and 300 units, respectively.

101. Heat Transfer

Find the time required for an object to cool from 300°F to 250°F by evaluating

$$t = \frac{10}{\ln 2} \int_{250}^{300} \frac{1}{T - 100} \, dT$$

where t is time in minutes.

102. Average Price The demand equation for a product is

$$p = \frac{90{,}000}{400 + 3x}$$

where p is the price (in dollars) and x is the number of units (in thousands). Find the average price p on the interval $40 \le x \le 50$.

103. Area and Slope Graph the function

$$f(x) = \frac{x}{1 + x^2}$$

on the interval $[0, \infty)$.

(a) Find the area bounded by the graph of f and the line $y = \frac{1}{2}x$.

(b) Determine the values of the slope m such that the line $y = mx$ and the graph of f enclose a finite region.

(c) Calculate the area of this region as a function of m.

104. **HOW DO YOU SEE IT?** Use the graph of f' shown in the figure to answer the following.

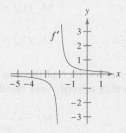

(a) Approximate the slope of f at $x = -1$. Explain.

(b) Approximate any open intervals in which the graph of f is increasing and any open intervals in which it is decreasing. Explain.

True or False? In Exercises 105–108, determine whether the statement is true or false. If it is false, explain why or give an example that shows it is false.

105. $(\ln x)^{1/2} = \dfrac{1}{2} \ln x$

106. $\int \ln x \, dx = \dfrac{1}{x} + C$

107. $\int \dfrac{1}{x} \, dx = \ln|cx|$, $\ c \ne 0$

108. $\int_{-1}^{2} \dfrac{1}{x} \, dx = \Big[\ln|x|\Big]_{-1}^{2} = \ln 2 - \ln 1 = \ln 2$

109. Napier's Inequality For $0 < x < y$, show that

$$\frac{1}{y} < \frac{\ln y - \ln x}{y - x} < \frac{1}{x}.$$

110. Proof Prove that the function

$$F(x) = \int_{x}^{2x} \frac{1}{t} \, dt$$

is constant on the interval $(0, \infty)$.

111. Proof Prove Theorem 5.21.

5.8   Inverse Trigonometric Functions: Integration

- ■ Integrate functions whose antiderivatives involve inverse trigonometric functions.
- ■ Use the method of completing the square to integrate a function.
- ■ Review the basic integration rules involving elementary functions.

Integrals Involving Inverse Trigonometric Functions

The derivatives of the six inverse trigonometric functions fall into three pairs. In each pair, the derivative of one function is the negative of the other. For example,

$$\frac{d}{dx}[\arcsin x] = \frac{1}{\sqrt{1 - x^2}}$$

and

$$\frac{d}{dx}[\arccos x] = -\frac{1}{\sqrt{1 - x^2}}.$$

When listing the *antiderivative* that corresponds to each of the inverse trigonometric functions, you need to use only one member from each pair. It is conventional to use $\arcsin x$ as the antiderivative of $1/\sqrt{1 - x^2}$, rather than $-\arccos x$. The next theorem gives one antiderivative formula for each of the three pairs. The proofs of these integration rules are left to you (see Exercises 75–77).

■ **FOR FURTHER INFORMATION**
For a detailed proof of rule 2 of Theorem 5.22, see the article "A Direct Proof of the Integral Formula for Arctangent" by Arnold J. Insel in *The College Mathematics Journal.* To view this article, go to *MathArticles.com.*

> **THEOREM 5.22   Integrals Involving Inverse Trigonometric Functions**
>
> Let u be a differentiable function of x, and let $a > 0$.
>
> **1.** $\displaystyle\int \frac{du}{\sqrt{a^2 - u^2}} = \arcsin \frac{u}{a} + C$ **2.** $\displaystyle\int \frac{du}{a^2 + u^2} = \frac{1}{a}\arctan \frac{u}{a} + C$
>
> **3.** $\displaystyle\int \frac{du}{u\sqrt{u^2 - a^2}} = \frac{1}{a}\operatorname{arcsec} \frac{|u|}{a} + C$

> **EXAMPLE 1**   **Integration with Inverse Trigonometric Functions**
>
> **a.** $\displaystyle\int \frac{dx}{\sqrt{4 - x^2}} = \arcsin \frac{x}{2} + C$
>
> **b.** $\displaystyle\int \frac{dx}{2 + 9x^2} = \frac{1}{3}\int \frac{3\,dx}{(\sqrt{2})^2 + (3x)^2}$ $u = 3x,\ a = \sqrt{2}$
>
> $= \dfrac{1}{3\sqrt{2}}\arctan \dfrac{3x}{\sqrt{2}} + C$
>
> **c.** $\displaystyle\int \frac{dx}{x\sqrt{4x^2 - 9}} = \int \frac{2\,dx}{2x\sqrt{(2x)^2 - 3^2}}$ $u = 2x,\ a = 3$
>
> $= \dfrac{1}{3}\operatorname{arcsec} \dfrac{|2x|}{3} + C$

The integrals in Example 1 are fairly straightforward applications of integration formulas. Unfortunately, this is not typical. The integration formulas for inverse trigonometric functions can be disguised in many ways.

Integration by Substitution

Find $\displaystyle\int \frac{dx}{\sqrt{e^{2x} - 1}}$.

Solution As it stands, this integral doesn't fit any of the three inverse trigonometric formulas. Using the substitution $u = e^x$, however, produces

$$u = e^x \implies du = e^x \, dx \implies dx = \frac{du}{e^x} = \frac{du}{u}.$$

With this substitution, you can integrate as shown.

$$\int \frac{dx}{\sqrt{e^{2x} - 1}} = \int \frac{dx}{\sqrt{(e^x)^2 - 1}} \qquad \text{Write } e^{2x} \text{ as } (e^x)^2.$$

$$= \int \frac{du/u}{\sqrt{u^2 - 1}} \qquad \text{Substitute.}$$

$$= \int \frac{du}{u\sqrt{u^2 - 1}} \qquad \text{Rewrite to fit Arcsecant Rule.}$$

$$= \text{arcsec} \frac{|u|}{1} + C \qquad \text{Apply Arcsecant Rule.}$$

$$= \text{arcsec } e^x + C \qquad \text{Back-substitute.}$$

▷ **TECHNOLOGY PITFALL** A symbolic integration utility can be useful for integrating functions such as the one in Example 2. In some cases, however, the utility may fail to find an antiderivative for two reasons. First, some elementary functions do not have antiderivatives that are elementary functions. Second, every utility has limitations—you might have entered a function that the utility was not programmed to handle. You should also remember that antiderivatives involving trigonometric functions or logarithmic functions can be written in many different forms. For instance, one utility found the integral in Example 2 to be

$$\int \frac{dx}{\sqrt{e^{2x} - 1}} = \arctan \sqrt{e^{2x} - 1} + C.$$

Try showing that this antiderivative is equivalent to the one found in Example 2.

Rewriting as the Sum of Two Quotients

Find $\displaystyle\int \frac{x + 2}{\sqrt{4 - x^2}} \, dx$.

Solution This integral does not appear to fit any of the basic integration formulas. By splitting the integrand into two parts, however, you can see that the first part can be found with the Power Rule and the second part yields an inverse sine function.

$$\int \frac{x + 2}{\sqrt{4 - x^2}} \, dx = \int \frac{x}{\sqrt{4 - x^2}} \, dx + \int \frac{2}{\sqrt{4 - x^2}} \, dx$$

$$= -\frac{1}{2} \int (4 - x^2)^{-1/2}(-2x) \, dx + 2 \int \frac{1}{\sqrt{4 - x^2}} \, dx$$

$$= -\frac{1}{2} \left[\frac{(4 - x^2)^{1/2}}{1/2} \right] + 2 \arcsin \frac{x}{2} + C$$

$$= -\sqrt{4 - x^2} + 2 \arcsin \frac{x}{2} + C$$

Completing the Square

Completing the square helps when quadratic functions are involved in the integrand. For example, the quadratic $x^2 + bx + c$ can be written as the difference of two squares by adding and subtracting $(b/2)^2$.

$$x^2 + bx + c = x^2 + bx + \left(\frac{b}{2}\right)^2 - \left(\frac{b}{2}\right)^2 + c = \left(x + \frac{b}{2}\right)^2 - \left(\frac{b}{2}\right)^2 + c$$

EXAMPLE 4   **Completing the Square**

⋯▷ *See LarsonCalculus.com for an interactive version of this type of example.*

Find $\displaystyle\int \frac{dx}{x^2 - 4x + 7}$.

Solution   You can write the denominator as the sum of two squares, as shown.

$$x^2 - 4x + 7 = (x^2 - 4x + 4) - 4 + 7 = (x - 2)^2 + 3 = u^2 + a^2$$

Now, in this completed square form, let $u = x - 2$ and $a = \sqrt{3}$.

$$\int \frac{dx}{x^2 - 4x + 7} = \int \frac{dx}{(x - 2)^2 + 3} = \frac{1}{\sqrt{3}} \arctan \frac{x - 2}{\sqrt{3}} + C$$

When the leading coefficient is not 1, it helps to factor before completing the square. For instance, you can complete the square of $2x^2 - 8x + 10$ by factoring first.

$$2x^2 - 8x + 10 = 2(x^2 - 4x + 5)$$
$$= 2(x^2 - 4x + 4 - 4 + 5)$$
$$= 2[(x - 2)^2 + 1]$$

To complete the square when the coefficient of x^2 is negative, use the same factoring process shown above. For instance, you can complete the square for $3x - x^2$ as shown.

$$3x - x^2 = -(x^2 - 3x) = -\left[x^2 - 3x + \left(\tfrac{3}{2}\right)^2 - \left(\tfrac{3}{2}\right)^2\right] = \left(\tfrac{3}{2}\right)^2 - \left(x - \tfrac{3}{2}\right)^2$$

EXAMPLE 5   **Completing the Square**

Find the area of the region bounded by the graph of

$$f(x) = \frac{1}{\sqrt{3x - x^2}}$$

the x-axis, and the lines $x = \frac{3}{2}$ and $x = \frac{9}{4}$.

Solution   In Figure 5.49, you can see that the area is

$$\text{Area} = \int_{3/2}^{9/4} \frac{1}{\sqrt{3x - x^2}}\, dx$$

$$= \int_{3/2}^{9/4} \frac{dx}{\sqrt{(3/2)^2 - [x - (3/2)]^2}} \qquad \text{Use completed square form derived above.}$$

$$= \arcsin \frac{x - (3/2)}{3/2} \bigg]_{3/2}^{9/4}$$

$$= \arcsin \frac{1}{2} - \arcsin 0$$

$$= \frac{\pi}{6}$$

$$\approx 0.524.$$

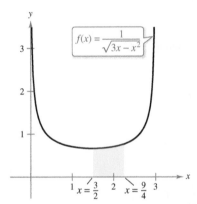

$$f(x) = \frac{1}{\sqrt{3x - x^2}}$$

$x = \frac{3}{2}$ $x = \frac{9}{4}$

The area of the region bounded by the graph of f, the x-axis, $x = \frac{3}{2}$, and $x = \frac{9}{4}$ is $\pi/6$.
Figure 5.49

▷ **TECHNOLOGY**   With definite integrals such as the one given in Example 5, remember that you can resort to a numerical solution. For instance, applying Simpson's Rule (with $n = 12$) to the integral in the example, you obtain

$$\int_{3/2}^{9/4} \frac{1}{\sqrt{3x - x^2}}\, dx \approx 0.523599.$$

This differs from the exact value of the integral $(\pi/6 \approx 0.5235988)$ by less than one-millionth.

Review of Basic Integration Rules

You have now completed the introduction of the **basic integration rules.** To be efficient at applying these rules, you should have practiced enough so that each rule is committed to memory.

BASIC INTEGRATION RULES ($a > 0$)

1. $\displaystyle\int kf(u)\,du = k\int f(u)\,du$

2. $\displaystyle\int [f(u) \pm g(u)]\,du = \int f(u)\,du \pm \int g(u)\,du$

3. $\displaystyle\int du = u + C$

4. $\displaystyle\int u^n\,du = \frac{u^{n+1}}{n+1} + C, \quad n \neq -1$

5. $\displaystyle\int \frac{du}{u} = \ln|u| + C$

6. $\displaystyle\int e^u\,du = e^u + C$

7. $\displaystyle\int a^u\,du = \left(\frac{1}{\ln a}\right)a^u + C$

8. $\displaystyle\int \sin u\,du = -\cos u + C$

9. $\displaystyle\int \cos u\,du = \sin u + C$

10. $\displaystyle\int \tan u\,du = -\ln|\cos u| + C$

11. $\displaystyle\int \cot u\,du = \ln|\sin u| + C$

12. $\displaystyle\int \sec u\,du = \ln|\sec u + \tan u| + C$

13. $\displaystyle\int \csc u\,du = -\ln|\csc u + \cot u| + C$

14. $\displaystyle\int \sec^2 u\,du = \tan u + C$

15. $\displaystyle\int \csc^2 u\,du = -\cot u + C$

16. $\displaystyle\int \sec u \tan u\,du = \sec u + C$

17. $\displaystyle\int \csc u \cot u\,du = -\csc u + C$

18. $\displaystyle\int \frac{du}{\sqrt{a^2 - u^2}} = \arcsin \frac{u}{a} + C$

19. $\displaystyle\int \frac{du}{a^2 + u^2} = \frac{1}{a}\arctan \frac{u}{a} + C$

20. $\displaystyle\int \frac{du}{u\sqrt{u^2 - a^2}} = \frac{1}{a}\text{arcsec}\frac{|u|}{a} + C$

You can learn a lot about the nature of integration by comparing this list with the summary of differentiation rules given in Section 3.6. For differentiation, you now have rules that allow you to differentiate *any* elementary function. For integration, this is far from true.

The integration rules listed above are primarily those that were happened on during the development of differentiation rules. So far, you have not learned any rules or techniques for finding the antiderivative of a general product or quotient, the natural logarithmic function, or the inverse trigonometric functions. More important, you cannot apply any of the rules in this list unless you can create the proper *du* corresponding to the *u* in the formula. The point is that you need to work more on integration techniques, which you will do in Chapter 8. The next two examples should give you a better feeling for the integration problems that you *can* and *cannot* solve with the techniques and rules you now know.

EXAMPLE 6   **Comparing Integration Problems**

Find as many of the following integrals as you can using the formulas and techniques you have studied so far in the text.

a. $\displaystyle \int \frac{dx}{x\sqrt{x^2 - 1}}$

b. $\displaystyle \int \frac{x \, dx}{\sqrt{x^2 - 1}}$

c. $\displaystyle \int \frac{dx}{\sqrt{x^2 - 1}}$

Solution

a. You *can* find this integral (it fits the Arcsecant Rule).

$$\int \frac{dx}{x\sqrt{x^2 - 1}} = \operatorname{arcsec}|x| + C$$

b. You *can* find this integral (it fits the Power Rule).

$$\int \frac{x \, dx}{\sqrt{x^2 - 1}} = \frac{1}{2}\int (x^2 - 1)^{-1/2}(2x) \, dx$$
$$= \frac{1}{2}\left[\frac{(x^2 - 1)^{1/2}}{1/2}\right] + C$$
$$= \sqrt{x^2 - 1} + C$$

c. You *cannot* find this integral using the techniques you have studied so far. (You should scan the list of basic integration rules to verify this conclusion.)

EXAMPLE 7   **Comparing Integration Problems**

Find as many of the following integrals as you can using the formulas and techniques you have studied so far in the text.

a. $\displaystyle \int \frac{dx}{x \ln x}$

b. $\displaystyle \int \frac{\ln x \, dx}{x}$

c. $\displaystyle \int \ln x \, dx$

Solution

a. You *can* find this integral (it fits the Log Rule).

$$\int \frac{dx}{x \ln x} = \int \frac{1/x}{\ln x} \, dx$$
$$= \ln|\ln x| + C$$

b. You *can* find this integral (it fits the Power Rule).

$$\int \frac{\ln x \, dx}{x} = \int \left(\frac{1}{x}\right)(\ln x)^1 \, dx$$
$$= \frac{(\ln x)^2}{2} + C$$

• • REMARK Note in Examples 6 and 7 that the *simplest* functions are the ones that you cannot yet integrate.

c. You *cannot* find this integral using the techniques you have studied so far.

5.8 Exercises

See CalcChat.com for tutorial help and worked-out solutions to odd-numbered exercises.

Finding an Indefinite Integral In Exercises 1–20, find the indefinite integral.

1. $\displaystyle\int \frac{dx}{\sqrt{9-x^2}}$

2. $\displaystyle\int \frac{dx}{\sqrt{1-4x^2}}$

3. $\displaystyle\int \frac{1}{x\sqrt{4x^2-1}}\,dx$

4. $\displaystyle\int \frac{12}{1+9x^2}\,dx$

5. $\displaystyle\int \frac{1}{\sqrt{1-(x+1)^2}}\,dx$

6. $\displaystyle\int \frac{1}{4+(x-3)^2}\,dx$

7. $\displaystyle\int \frac{t}{\sqrt{1-t^4}}\,dt$

8. $\displaystyle\int \frac{1}{x\sqrt{x^4-4}}\,dx$

9. $\displaystyle\int \frac{t}{t^4+25}\,dt$

10. $\displaystyle\int \frac{1}{x\sqrt{1-(\ln x)^2}}\,dx$

11. $\displaystyle\int \frac{e^{2x}}{4+e^{4x}}\,dx$

12. $\displaystyle\int \frac{2}{x\sqrt{9x^2-25}}\,dx$

13. $\displaystyle\int \frac{\sec^2 x}{\sqrt{25-\tan^2 x}}\,dx$

14. $\displaystyle\int \frac{\sin x}{7+\cos^2 x}\,dx$

15. $\displaystyle\int \frac{1}{\sqrt{x}\sqrt{1-x}}\,dx$

16. $\displaystyle\int \frac{3}{2\sqrt{x}(1+x)}\,dx$

17. $\displaystyle\int \frac{x-3}{x^2+1}\,dx$

18. $\displaystyle\int \frac{x^2+3}{x\sqrt{x^2-4}}\,dx$

19. $\displaystyle\int \frac{x+5}{\sqrt{9-(x-3)^2}}\,dx$

20. $\displaystyle\int \frac{x-2}{(x+1)^2+4}\,dx$

Evaluating a Definite Integral In Exercises 21–32, evaluate the definite integral.

21. $\displaystyle\int_0^{1/6} \frac{3}{\sqrt{1-9x^2}}\,dx$

22. $\displaystyle\int_0^{\sqrt{2}} \frac{1}{\sqrt{4-x^2}}\,dx$

23. $\displaystyle\int_0^{\sqrt{3}/2} \frac{1}{1+4x^2}\,dx$

24. $\displaystyle\int_{\sqrt{3}}^3 \frac{1}{x\sqrt{4x^2-9}}\,dx$

25. $\displaystyle\int_3^6 \frac{1}{25+(x-3)^2}\,dx$

26. $\displaystyle\int_1^4 \frac{1}{x\sqrt{16x^2-5}}\,dx$

27. $\displaystyle\int_0^{\ln 5} \frac{e^x}{1+e^{2x}}\,dx$

28. $\displaystyle\int_{\ln 2}^{\ln 4} \frac{e^{-x}}{\sqrt{1-e^{-2x}}}\,dx$

29. $\displaystyle\int_{\pi/2}^{\pi} \frac{\sin x}{1+\cos^2 x}\,dx$

30. $\displaystyle\int_0^{\pi/2} \frac{\cos x}{1+\sin^2 x}\,dx$

31. $\displaystyle\int_0^{1/\sqrt{2}} \frac{\arcsin x}{\sqrt{1-x^2}}\,dx$

32. $\displaystyle\int_0^{1/\sqrt{2}} \frac{\arccos x}{\sqrt{1-x^2}}\,dx$

Completing the Square In Exercises 33–42, find or evaluate the integral by completing the square.

33. $\displaystyle\int_0^2 \frac{dx}{x^2-2x+2}$

34. $\displaystyle\int_{-2}^2 \frac{dx}{x^2+4x+13}$

35. $\displaystyle\int \frac{2x}{x^2+6x+13}\,dx$

36. $\displaystyle\int \frac{2x-5}{x^2+2x+2}\,dx$

37. $\displaystyle\int \frac{1}{\sqrt{-x^2-4x}}\,dx$

38. $\displaystyle\int \frac{2}{\sqrt{-x^2+4x}}\,dx$

39. $\displaystyle\int_2^3 \frac{2x-3}{\sqrt{4x-x^2}}\,dx$

40. $\displaystyle\int \frac{1}{(x-1)\sqrt{x^2-2x}}\,dx$

41. $\displaystyle\int \frac{x}{x^4+2x^2+2}\,dx$

42. $\displaystyle\int \frac{x}{\sqrt{9+8x^2-x^4}}\,dx$

Integration by Substitution In Exercises 43–46, use the specified substitution to find or evaluate the integral.

43. $\displaystyle\int \sqrt{e^t-3}\,dt$

$u=\sqrt{e^t-3}$

44. $\displaystyle\int \frac{\sqrt{x-2}}{x+1}\,dx$

$u=\sqrt{x-2}$

45. $\displaystyle\int_1^3 \frac{dx}{\sqrt{x}(1+x)}$

$u=\sqrt{x}$

46. $\displaystyle\int_0^1 \frac{dx}{2\sqrt{3-x}\sqrt{x+1}}$

$u=\sqrt{x+1}$

WRITING ABOUT CONCEPTS

Comparing Integration Problems In Exercises 47–50, determine which of the integrals can be found using the basic integration formulas you have studied so far in the text.

47. (a) $\displaystyle\int \frac{1}{\sqrt{1-x^2}}\,dx$

(b) $\displaystyle\int \frac{x}{\sqrt{1-x^2}}\,dx$

(c) $\displaystyle\int \frac{1}{x\sqrt{1-x^2}}\,dx$

48. (a) $\displaystyle\int e^{x^2}\,dx$

(b) $\displaystyle\int xe^{x^2}\,dx$

(c) $\displaystyle\int \frac{1}{x^2}e^{1/x}\,dx$

49. (a) $\displaystyle\int \sqrt{x-1}\,dx$

(b) $\displaystyle\int x\sqrt{x-1}\,dx$

(c) $\displaystyle\int \frac{x}{\sqrt{x-1}}\,dx$

50. (a) $\displaystyle\int \frac{1}{1+x^4}\,dx$

(b) $\displaystyle\int \frac{x}{1+x^4}\,dx$

(c) $\displaystyle\int \frac{x^3}{1+x^4}\,dx$

51. Finding an Integral Decide whether you can find the integral

$$\int \frac{2\,dx}{\sqrt{x^2+4}}$$

using the formulas and techniques you have studied so far. Explain your reasoning.

52. **HOW DO YOU SEE IT?** Using the graph, which value best approximates the area of the region between the x-axis and the function over the interval $\left[-\frac{1}{2}, \frac{1}{2}\right]$? Explain.

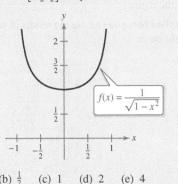

$$f(x) = \frac{1}{\sqrt{1 - x^2}}$$

   (a) -3 (b) $\frac{1}{2}$ (c) 1 (d) 2 (e) 4

Differential Equation In Exercises 53 and 54, use the differential equation and the specified initial condition to find y.

53. $\dfrac{dy}{dx} = \dfrac{1}{\sqrt{4 - x^2}}$

    $y(0) = \pi$

54. $\dfrac{dy}{dx} = \dfrac{1}{4 + x^2}$

    $y(2) = \pi$

 Slope Field In Exercises 55 and 56, a differential equation, a point, and a slope field are given. (a) Sketch two approximate solutions of the differential equation on the slope field, one of which passes through the given point. (b) Use integration to find the particular solution of the differential equation and use a graphing utility to graph the solution. Compare the result with the sketches in part (a). To print an enlarged copy of the graph, go to *MathGraphs.com*.

55. $\dfrac{dy}{dx} = \dfrac{2}{9 + x^2}$, $(0, 2)$

56. $\dfrac{dy}{dx} = \dfrac{2}{\sqrt{25 - x^2}}$, $(5, \pi)$

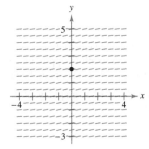 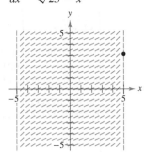

 Slope Field In Exercises 57–60, use a computer algebra system to graph the slope field for the differential equation and graph the solution satisfying the specified initial condition.

57. $\dfrac{dy}{dx} = \dfrac{10}{x\sqrt{x^2 - 1}}$

    $y(3) = 0$

58. $\dfrac{dy}{dx} = \dfrac{1}{12 + x^2}$

    $y(4) = 2$

59. $\dfrac{dy}{dx} = \dfrac{2y}{\sqrt{16 - x^2}}$

    $y(0) = 2$

60. $\dfrac{dy}{dx} = \dfrac{\sqrt{y}}{1 + x^2}$

    $y(0) = 4$

Area In Exercises 61–66, find the area of the region.

61. $y = \dfrac{2}{\sqrt{4 - x^2}}$

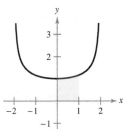

62. $y = \dfrac{1}{x\sqrt{x^2 - 1}}$

 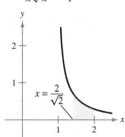

63. $y = \dfrac{1}{x^2 - 2x + 5}$

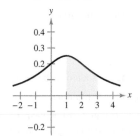

64. $y = \dfrac{2}{x^2 + 4x + 8}$

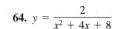 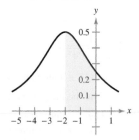

65. $y = \dfrac{3 \cos x}{1 + \sin^2 x}$

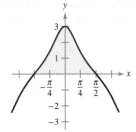

66. $y = \dfrac{4e^x}{1 + e^{2x}}$

 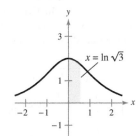

67. Area

  (a) Sketch the region whose area is represented by

$$\int_0^1 \arcsin x \, dx.$$

  (b) Use the integration capabilities of a graphing utility to approximate the area.

  (c) Find the exact area analytically.

68. Approximating Pi

  (a) Show that

$$\int_0^1 \frac{4}{1 + x^2} \, dx = \pi.$$

  (b) Approximate the number π using Simpson's Rule (with $n = 6$) and the integral in part (a).

  (c) Approximate the number π by using the integration capabilities of a graphing utility.

69. Investigation Consider the function

$$F(x) = \frac{1}{2}\int_x^{x+2} \frac{2}{t^2 + 1}\, dt.$$

(a) Write a short paragraph giving a geometric interpretation of the function $F(x)$ relative to the function

$$f(x) = \frac{2}{x^2 + 1}.$$

Use what you have written to guess the value of x that will make F maximum.

(b) Perform the specified integration to find an alternative form of $F(x)$. Use calculus to locate the value of x that will make F maximum and compare the result with your guess in part (a).

70. Comparing Integrals Consider the integral

$$\int \frac{1}{\sqrt{6x - x^2}}\, dx.$$

(a) Find the integral by completing the square of the radicand.

(b) Find the integral by making the substitution $u = \sqrt{x}$.

(c) The antiderivatives in parts (a) and (b) appear to be significantly different. Use a graphing utility to graph each antiderivative in the same viewing window and determine the relationship between them. Find the domain of each.

True or False? In Exercises 71–74, determine whether the statement is true or false. If it is false, explain why or give an example that shows it is false.

71. $\displaystyle\int \frac{dx}{3x\sqrt{9x^2 - 16}} = \frac{1}{4}\operatorname{arcsec}\frac{3x}{4} + C$

72. $\displaystyle\int \frac{dx}{25 + x^2} = \frac{1}{25}\arctan\frac{x}{25} + C$

73. $\displaystyle\int \frac{dx}{\sqrt{4 - x^2}} = -\arccos\frac{x}{2} + C$

74. One way to find $\displaystyle\int \frac{2e^{2x}}{\sqrt{9 - e^{2x}}}\, dx$ is to use the Arcsine Rule.

Verifying an Integration Rule In Exercises 75–77, verify the rule by differentiating. Let $a > 0$.

75. $\displaystyle\int \frac{du}{\sqrt{a^2 - u^2}} = \arcsin\frac{u}{a} + C$

76. $\displaystyle\int \frac{du}{a^2 + u^2} = \frac{1}{a}\arctan\frac{u}{a} + C$

77. $\displaystyle\int \frac{du}{u\sqrt{u^2 - a^2}} = \frac{1}{a}\operatorname{arcsec}\frac{|u|}{a} + C$

78. Proof Graph

$$y_1 = \frac{x}{1 + x^2}, \quad y_2 = \arctan x, \quad \text{and} \quad y_3 = x$$

on $[0, 10]$. Prove that

$$\frac{x}{1 + x^2} < \arctan x < x \quad \text{for} \quad x > 0.$$

79. Numerical Integration

(a) Write an integral that represents the area of the region in the figure.

(b) Use the Trapezoidal Rule with $n = 8$ to estimate the area of the region.

(c) Explain how you can use the results of parts (a) and (b) to estimate π.

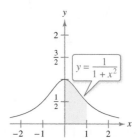

80. Vertical Motion An object is projected upward from ground level with an initial velocity of 500 feet per second. In this exercise, the goal is to analyze the motion of the object during its upward flight.

(a) If air resistance is neglected, find the velocity of the object as a function of time. Use a graphing utility to graph this function.

(b) Use the result of part (a) to find the position function and determine the maximum height attained by the object.

(c) If the air resistance is proportional to the square of the velocity, you obtain the equation

$$\frac{dv}{dt} = -(32 + kv^2)$$

where -32 feet per second per second is the acceleration due to gravity and k is a constant. Find the velocity as a function of time by solving the equation

$$\int \frac{dv}{32 + kv^2} = -\int dt.$$

(d) Use a graphing utility to graph the velocity function $v(t)$ in part (c) for $k = 0.001$. Use the graph to approximate the time t_0 at which the object reaches its maximum height.

(e) Use the integration capabilities of a graphing utility to approximate the integral

$$\int_0^{t_0} v(t)\, dt$$

where $v(t)$ and t_0 are those found in part (d). This is the approximation of the maximum height of the object.

(f) Explain the difference between the results in parts (b) and (e).

■ FOR FURTHER INFORMATION For more information on this topic, see the article "What Goes Up Must Come Down; Will Air Resistance Make It Return Sooner, or Later?" by John Lekner in *Mathematics Magazine*. To view this article, go to *MathArticles.com*.

5.9   Hyperbolic Functions

- Develop properties of hyperbolic functions.
- Differentiate and integrate hyperbolic functions.
- Develop properties of inverse hyperbolic functions.
- Differentiate and integrate functions involving inverse hyperbolic functions.

Hyperbolic Functions

In this section, you will look briefly at a special class of exponential functions called **hyperbolic functions.** The name *hyperbolic function* arose from comparison of the area of a semicircular region, as shown in Figure 5.50, with the area of a region under a hyperbola, as shown in Figure 5.51.

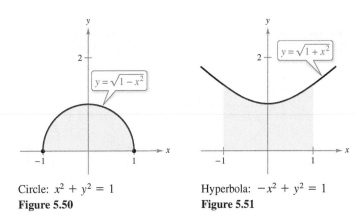

Circle: $x^2 + y^2 = 1$
Figure 5.50

Hyperbola: $-x^2 + y^2 = 1$
Figure 5.51

The integral for the semicircular region involves an inverse trigonometric (circular) function:

$$\int_{-1}^{1} \sqrt{1 - x^2}\, dx = \frac{1}{2}\left[x\sqrt{1 - x^2} + \arcsin x \right]_{-1}^{1} = \frac{\pi}{2} \approx 1.571.$$

The integral for the hyperbolic region involves an inverse hyperbolic function:

$$\int_{-1}^{1} \sqrt{1 + x^2}\, dx = \frac{1}{2}\left[x\sqrt{1 + x^2} + \sinh^{-1} x \right]_{-1}^{1} \approx 2.296.$$

This is only one of many ways in which the hyperbolic functions are similar to the trigonometric functions.

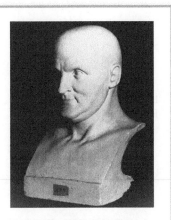

**JOHANN HEINRICH LAMBERT
(1728–1777)**

The first person to publish a comprehensive study on hyperbolic functions was Johann Heinrich Lambert, a Swiss-German mathematician and colleague of Euler. *See LarsonCalculus.com to read more of this biography.*

· · REMARK   The notation $\sinh x$ is read as "the hyperbolic sine of x," $\cosh x$ as "the hyperbolic cosine of x," and so on.

Definitions of the Hyperbolic Functions

$$\sinh x = \frac{e^x - e^{-x}}{2} \qquad\qquad \operatorname{csch} x = \frac{1}{\sinh x}, \quad x \neq 0$$

$$\cosh x = \frac{e^x + e^{-x}}{2} \qquad\qquad \operatorname{sech} x = \frac{1}{\cosh x}$$

$$\tanh x = \frac{\sinh x}{\cosh x} \qquad\qquad \coth x = \frac{1}{\tanh x}, \quad x \neq 0$$

FOR FURTHER INFORMATION   For more information on the development of hyperbolic functions, see the article "An Introduction to Hyperbolic Functions in Elementary Calculus" by Jerome Rosenthal in *Mathematics Teacher.* To view this article, go to *MathArticles.com.*

The graphs of the six hyperbolic functions and their domains and ranges are shown in Figure 5.52. Note that the graph of $\sinh x$ can be obtained by adding the corresponding y-coordinates of the exponential functions $f(x) = \frac{1}{2}e^x$ and $g(x) = -\frac{1}{2}e^{-x}$. Likewise, the graph of $\cosh x$ can be obtained by adding the corresponding y-coordinates of the exponential functions $f(x) = \frac{1}{2}e^x$ and $h(x) = \frac{1}{2}e^{-x}$.

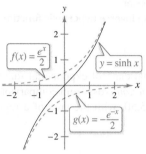

Domain: $(-\infty, \infty)$
Range: $(-\infty, \infty)$

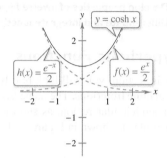

Domain: $(-\infty, \infty)$
Range: $[1, \infty)$

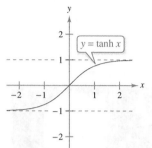

Domain: $(-\infty, \infty)$
Range: $(-1, 1)$

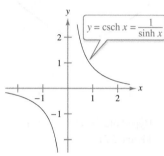

Domain: $(-\infty, 0) \cup (0, \infty)$
Range: $(-\infty, 0) \cup (0, \infty)$

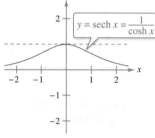

Domain: $(-\infty, \infty)$
Range: $(0, 1]$

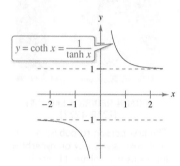

Domain: $(-\infty, 0) \cup (0, \infty)$
Range: $(-\infty, -1) \cup (1, \infty)$

Figure 5.52

Many of the trigonometric identities have corresponding *hyperbolic identities*. For instance,

$$\cosh^2 x - \sinh^2 x = \left(\frac{e^x + e^{-x}}{2}\right)^2 - \left(\frac{e^x - e^{-x}}{2}\right)^2$$

$$= \frac{e^{2x} + 2 + e^{-2x}}{4} - \frac{e^{2x} - 2 + e^{-2x}}{4}$$

$$= \frac{4}{4}$$

$$= 1.$$

■ FOR FURTHER INFORMATION
To understand geometrically the relationship between the hyperbolic and exponential functions, see the article "A Short Proof Linking the Hyperbolic and Exponential Functions" by Michael J. Seery in *The AMATYC Review*.

HYPERBOLIC IDENTITIES

$\cosh^2 x - \sinh^2 x = 1$ $\qquad$ $\sinh(x + y) = \sinh x \cosh y + \cosh x \sinh y$

$\tanh^2 x + \operatorname{sech}^2 x = 1$ $\qquad$ $\sinh(x - y) = \sinh x \cosh y - \cosh x \sinh y$

$\coth^2 x - \operatorname{csch}^2 x = 1$ $\qquad$ $\cosh(x + y) = \cosh x \cosh y + \sinh x \sinh y$

$\qquad\qquad\qquad\qquad\qquad\qquad$ $\cosh(x - y) = \cosh x \cosh y - \sinh x \sinh y$

$\sinh^2 x = \dfrac{-1 + \cosh 2x}{2}$ $\qquad$ $\cosh^2 x = \dfrac{1 + \cosh 2x}{2}$

$\sinh 2x = 2 \sinh x \cosh x$ $\qquad$ $\cosh 2x = \cosh^2 x + \sinh^2 x$

Differentiation and Integration of Hyperbolic Functions

Because the hyperbolic functions are written in terms of e^x and e^{-x}, you can easily derive rules for their derivatives. The next theorem lists these derivatives with the corresponding integration rules.

THEOREM 5.23 Derivatives and Integrals of Hyperbolic Functions

Let u be a differentiable function of x.

$$\frac{d}{dx}[\sinh u] = (\cosh u)u' \qquad\qquad \int \cosh u \, du = \sinh u + C$$

$$\frac{d}{dx}[\cosh u] = (\sinh u)u' \qquad\qquad \int \sinh u \, du = \cosh u + C$$

$$\frac{d}{dx}[\tanh u] = (\operatorname{sech}^2 u)u' \qquad\qquad \int \operatorname{sech}^2 u \, du = \tanh u + C$$

$$\frac{d}{dx}[\coth u] = -(\operatorname{csch}^2 u)u' \qquad\qquad \int \operatorname{csch}^2 u \, du = -\coth u + C$$

$$\frac{d}{dx}[\operatorname{sech} u] = -(\operatorname{sech} u \tanh u)u' \qquad \int \operatorname{sech} u \tanh u \, du = -\operatorname{sech} u + C$$

$$\frac{d}{dx}[\operatorname{csch} u] = -(\operatorname{csch} u \coth u)u' \qquad \int \operatorname{csch} u \coth u \, du = -\operatorname{csch} u + C$$

Proof Here is a proof of two of the differentiation rules. (You are asked to prove some of the other differentiation rules in Exercises 103–105.)

$$\frac{d}{dx}[\sinh x] = \frac{d}{dx}\left[\frac{e^x - e^{-x}}{2}\right]$$

$$= \frac{e^x + e^{-x}}{2}$$

$$= \cosh x$$

$$\frac{d}{dx}[\tanh x] = \frac{d}{dx}\left[\frac{\sinh x}{\cosh x}\right]$$

$$= \frac{\cosh x(\cosh x) - \sinh x(\sinh x)}{\cosh^2 x}$$

$$= \frac{1}{\cosh^2 x}$$

$$= \operatorname{sech}^2 x$$

See LarsonCalculus.com for Bruce Edwards's video of this proof.

EXAMPLE 1 **Differentiation of Hyperbolic Functions**

a. $\dfrac{d}{dx}[\sinh(x^2 - 3)] = 2x \cosh(x^2 - 3)$

b. $\dfrac{d}{dx}[\ln(\cosh x)] = \dfrac{\sinh x}{\cosh x} = \tanh x$

c. $\dfrac{d}{dx}[x \sinh x - \cosh x] = x \cosh x + \sinh x - \sinh x = x \cosh x$

d. $\dfrac{d}{dx}[(x-1)\cosh x - \sinh x] = (x-1)\sinh x + \cosh x - \cosh x = (x-1)\sinh x$

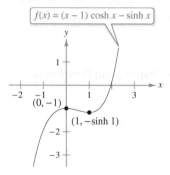

$f(x) = (x - 1) \cosh x - \sinh x$

$f''(0) < 0$, so $(0, -1)$ is a relative maximum. $f''(1) > 0$, so $(1, -\sinh 1)$ is a relative minimum.
Figure 5.53

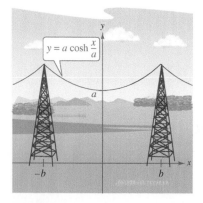

$y = a \cosh \dfrac{x}{a}$

Catenary
Figure 5.54

▆ FOR FURTHER INFORMATION
In Example 3, the cable is a catenary between two supports at the same height. To learn about the shape of a cable hanging between supports of different heights, see the article "Reexamining the Catenary" by Paul Cella in *The College Mathematics Journal.* To view this article, go to *MathArticles.com.*

EXAMPLE 2   **Finding Relative Extrema**

Find the relative extrema of

$$f(x) = (x - 1) \cosh x - \sinh x.$$

Solution   Using the result of Example 1(d), set the first derivative of f equal to 0.

$$(x - 1) \sinh x = 0$$

So, the critical numbers are $x = 1$ and $x = 0$. Using the Second Derivative Test, you can verify that the point $(0, -1)$ yields a relative maximum and the point $(1, -\sinh 1)$ yields a relative minimum, as shown in Figure 5.53. Try using a graphing utility to confirm this result. If your graphing utility does not have hyperbolic functions, you can use exponential functions, as shown.

$$f(x) = (x - 1)\left(\frac{1}{2}\right)(e^x + e^{-x}) - \frac{1}{2}(e^x - e^{-x})$$

$$= \frac{1}{2}(xe^x + xe^{-x} - e^x - e^{-x} - e^x + e^{-x})$$

$$= \frac{1}{2}(xe^x + xe^{-x} - 2e^x)$$

When a uniform flexible cable, such as a telephone wire, is suspended from two points, it takes the shape of a *catenary*, as discussed in Example 3.

EXAMPLE 3   **Hanging Power Cables**

•••▷ *See LarsonCalculus.com for an interactive version of this type of example.*

Power cables are suspended between two towers, forming the catenary shown in Figure 5.54. The equation for this catenary is

$$y = a \cosh \frac{x}{a}.$$

The distance between the two towers is $2b$. Find the slope of the catenary at the point where the cable meets the right-hand tower.

Solution   Differentiating produces

$$y' = a\left(\frac{1}{a}\right) \sinh \frac{x}{a} = \sinh \frac{x}{a}.$$

At the point $(b, a \cosh(b/a))$, the slope (from the left) is $m = \sinh \dfrac{b}{a}$.

EXAMPLE 4   **Integrating a Hyperbolic Function**

Find $\displaystyle\int \cosh 2x \sinh^2 2x \, dx.$

Solution

$$\int \cosh 2x \sinh^2 2x \, dx = \frac{1}{2}\int (\sinh 2x)^2 (2 \cosh 2x) \, dx \qquad u = \sinh 2x$$

$$= \frac{1}{2}\left[\frac{(\sinh 2x)^3}{3}\right] + C$$

$$= \frac{\sinh^3 2x}{6} + C$$

Inverse Hyperbolic Functions

Unlike trigonometric functions, hyperbolic functions are not periodic. In fact, by looking back at Figure 5.52, you can see that four of the six hyperbolic functions are actually one-to-one (the hyperbolic sine, tangent, cosecant, and cotangent). So, you can conclude that these four functions have inverse functions. The other two (the hyperbolic cosine and secant) are one-to-one when their domains are restricted to the positive real numbers, and for this restricted domain they also have inverse functions. Because the hyperbolic functions are defined in terms of exponential functions, it is not surprising to find that the inverse hyperbolic functions can be written in terms of logarithmic functions, as shown in Theorem 5.24.

••REMARK Recall from Section 1.5 that a function has an inverse function if and only if it is one-to-one.

THEOREM 5.24   Inverse Hyperbolic Functions

Function	**Domain**
$\sinh^{-1} x = \ln\left(x + \sqrt{x^2 + 1}\right)$	$(-\infty, \infty)$
$\cosh^{-1} x = \ln\left(x + \sqrt{x^2 - 1}\right)$	$[1, \infty)$
$\tanh^{-1} x = \dfrac{1}{2} \ln \dfrac{1 + x}{1 - x}$	$(-1, 1)$
$\coth^{-1} x = \dfrac{1}{2} \ln \dfrac{x + 1}{x - 1}$	$(-\infty, -1) \cup (1, \infty)$
$\text{sech}^{-1} x = \ln \dfrac{1 + \sqrt{1 - x^2}}{x}$	$(0, 1]$
$\text{csch}^{-1} x = \ln\left(\dfrac{1}{x} + \dfrac{\sqrt{1 + x^2}}{|x|}\right)$	$(-\infty, 0) \cup (0, \infty)$

Proof   The proof of this theorem is a straightforward application of the properties of the exponential and logarithmic functions. For example, for

$$f(x) = \sinh x = \frac{e^x - e^{-x}}{2}$$

and

$$g(x) = \ln\left(x + \sqrt{x^2 + 1}\right)$$

you can show that

$$f(g(x)) = x \quad \text{and} \quad g(f(x)) = x$$

which implies that g is the inverse function of f.

See LarsonCalculus.com for Bruce Edwards's video of this proof.   ■

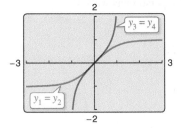

Graphs of the hyperbolic tangent function and the inverse hyperbolic tangent function
Figure 5.55

▷ **TECHNOLOGY**   You can use a graphing utility to confirm graphically the results of Theorem 5.24. For instance, graph the following functions.

$y_1 = \tanh x$ Hyperbolic tangent

$y_2 = \dfrac{e^x - e^{-x}}{e^x + e^{-x}}$ Definition of hyperbolic tangent

$y_3 = \tanh^{-1} x$ Inverse hyperbolic tangent

$y_4 = \dfrac{1}{2} \ln \dfrac{1 + x}{1 - x}$ Definition of inverse hyperbolic tangent

The resulting display is shown in Figure 5.55. As you watch the graphs being traced out, notice that $y_1 = y_2$ and $y_3 = y_4$. Also notice that the graph of y_1 is the reflection of the graph of y_3 in the line $y = x$.

The graphs of the inverse hyperbolic functions are shown in Figure 5.56.

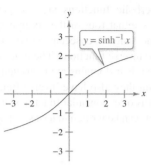

Domain: $(-\infty, \infty)$
Range: $(-\infty, \infty)$

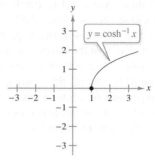

Domain: $[1, \infty)$
Range: $[0, \infty)$

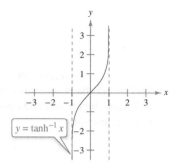

Domain: $(-1, 1)$
Range: $(-\infty, \infty)$

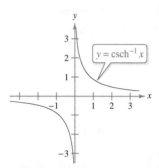

Domain: $(-\infty, 0) \cup (0, \infty)$
Range: $(-\infty, 0) \cup (0, \infty)$

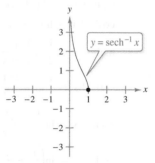

Domain: $(0, 1]$
Range: $[0, \infty)$

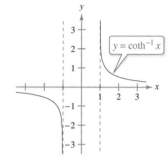

Domain: $(-\infty, -1) \cup (1, \infty)$
Range: $(-\infty, 0) \cup (0, \infty)$

Figure 5.56

The inverse hyperbolic secant can be used to define a curve called a *tractrix* or *pursuit curve*, as discussed in Example 5.

EXAMPLE 5   **A Tractrix**

A person is holding a rope that is tied to a boat, as shown in Figure 5.57. As the person walks along the dock, the boat travels along a **tractrix,** given by the equation

$$y = a \operatorname{sech}^{-1} \frac{x}{a} - \sqrt{a^2 - x^2}$$

where a is the length of the rope. For $a = 20$ feet, find the distance the person must walk to bring the boat to a position 5 feet from the dock.

Solution   In Figure 5.57, notice that the distance the person has walked is

$$y_1 = y + \sqrt{20^2 - x^2}$$

$$= \left(20 \operatorname{sech}^{-1} \frac{x}{20} - \sqrt{20^2 - x^2} \right) + \sqrt{20^2 - x^2}$$

$$= 20 \operatorname{sech}^{-1} \frac{x}{20}.$$

When $x = 5$, this distance is

$$y_1 = 20 \operatorname{sech}^{-1} \frac{5}{20} = 20 \ln \frac{1 + \sqrt{1 - (1/4)^2}}{1/4} = 20 \ln \left(4 + \sqrt{15} \right) \approx 41.27 \text{ feet.}$$

So, the person must walk about 41.27 feet to bring the boat to a position 5 feet from the dock.

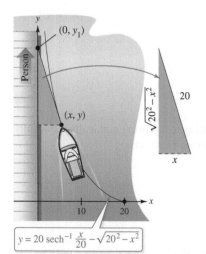

A person must walk about 41.27 feet to bring the boat to a position 5 feet from the dock.
Figure 5.57

Inverse Hyperbolic Functions: Differentiation and Integration

The derivatives of the inverse hyperbolic functions, which resemble the derivatives of the inverse trigonometric functions, are listed in Theorem 5.25 with the corresponding integration formulas (in logarithmic form). You can verify each of these formulas by applying the logarithmic definitions of the inverse hyperbolic functions. (See Exercises 106–108.)

THEOREM 5.25 Differentiation and Integration Involving Inverse Hyperbolic Functions

Let u be a differentiable function of x.

$$\frac{d}{dx}[\sinh^{-1} u] = \frac{u'}{\sqrt{u^2 + 1}} \qquad \frac{d}{dx}[\cosh^{-1} u] = \frac{u'}{\sqrt{u^2 - 1}}$$

$$\frac{d}{dx}[\tanh^{-1} u] = \frac{u'}{1 - u^2} \qquad \frac{d}{dx}[\coth^{-1} u] = \frac{u'}{1 - u^2}$$

$$\frac{d}{dx}[\operatorname{sech}^{-1} u] = \frac{-u'}{u\sqrt{1 - u^2}} \qquad \frac{d}{dx}[\operatorname{csch}^{-1} u] = \frac{-u'}{|u|\sqrt{1 + u^2}}$$

$$\int \frac{du}{\sqrt{u^2 \pm a^2}} = \ln\left(u + \sqrt{u^2 \pm a^2}\right) + C$$

$$\int \frac{du}{a^2 - u^2} = \frac{1}{2a} \ln\left|\frac{a + u}{a - u}\right| + C$$

$$\int \frac{du}{u\sqrt{a^2 \pm u^2}} = -\frac{1}{a} \ln \frac{a + \sqrt{a^2 \pm u^2}}{|u|} + C$$

EXAMPLE 6 Differentiation of Inverse Hyperbolic Functions

a. $\dfrac{d}{dx}\left[\sinh^{-1}(2x)\right] = \dfrac{2}{\sqrt{(2x)^2 + 1}}$

$\qquad\qquad\qquad = \dfrac{2}{\sqrt{4x^2 + 1}}$

b. $\dfrac{d}{dx}\left[\tanh^{-1}(x^3)\right] = \dfrac{3x^2}{1 - (x^3)^2}$

$\qquad\qquad\qquad = \dfrac{3x^2}{1 - x^6}$

EXAMPLE 7 Integration Using Inverse Hyperbolic Functions

a. $\displaystyle\int \frac{dx}{x\sqrt{4 - 9x^2}} = \int \frac{3\,dx}{(3x)\sqrt{4 - 9x^2}}$ $\qquad \displaystyle\int \frac{du}{u\sqrt{a^2 - u^2}}$

$\qquad\qquad = -\dfrac{1}{2} \ln \dfrac{2 + \sqrt{4 - 9x^2}}{|3x|} + C$ $\qquad -\dfrac{1}{a} \ln \dfrac{a + \sqrt{a^2 - u^2}}{|u|} + C$

REMARK Let $a = 2$ and $u = 3x$.

b. $\displaystyle\int \frac{dx}{5 - 4x^2} = \frac{1}{2} \int \frac{2\,dx}{(\sqrt{5})^2 - (2x)^2}$ $\qquad \displaystyle\int \frac{du}{a^2 - u^2}$

$\qquad\qquad = \dfrac{1}{2}\left(\dfrac{1}{2\sqrt{5}} \ln\left|\dfrac{\sqrt{5} + 2x}{\sqrt{5} - 2x}\right|\right) + C$ $\qquad \dfrac{1}{2a} \ln\left|\dfrac{a + u}{a - u}\right| + C$

$\qquad\qquad = \dfrac{1}{4\sqrt{5}} \ln\left|\dfrac{\sqrt{5} + 2x}{\sqrt{5} - 2x}\right| + C$

REMARK Let $a = \sqrt{5}$ and $u = 2x$.

5.9 Exercises

See CalcChat.com for tutorial help and worked-out solutions to odd-numbered exercises.

Evaluating a Function In Exercises 1–6, evaluate the function. If the value is not a rational number, round your answer to three decimal places.

1. (a) $\sinh 3$
   (b) $\tanh(-2)$

2. (a) $\cosh 0$
   (b) $\operatorname{sech} 1$

3. (a) $\operatorname{csch}(\ln 2)$
   (b) $\coth(\ln 5)$

4. (a) $\sinh^{-1} 0$
   (b) $\tanh^{-1} 0$

5. (a) $\cosh^{-1} 2$
   (b) $\operatorname{sech}^{-1} \frac{2}{3}$

6. (a) $\operatorname{csch}^{-1} 2$
   (b) $\coth^{-1} 3$

Verifying an Identity In Exercises 7–14, verify the identity.

7. $\tanh^2 x + \operatorname{sech}^2 x = 1$

8. $\coth^2 x - \operatorname{csch}^2 x = 1$

9. $\cosh^2 x = \dfrac{1 + \cosh 2x}{2}$

10. $\sinh^2 x = \dfrac{-1 + \cosh 2x}{2}$

11. $\sinh 2x = 2 \sinh x \cosh x$

12. $e^{2x} = \sinh 2x + \cosh 2x$

13. $\sinh(x + y) = \sinh x \cosh y + \cosh x \sinh y$

14. $\cosh x + \cosh y = 2 \cosh \dfrac{x + y}{2} \cosh \dfrac{x - y}{2}$

Finding Values of Hyperbolic Functions In Exercises 15 and 16, use the value of the given hyperbolic function to find the values of the other hyperbolic functions at x.

15. $\sinh x = \dfrac{3}{2}$

16. $\tanh x = \dfrac{1}{2}$

Finding a Limit In Exercises 17–22, find the limit.

17. $\lim\limits_{x \to \infty} \sinh x$

18. $\lim\limits_{x \to -\infty} \tanh x$

19. $\lim\limits_{x \to \infty} \operatorname{sech} x$

20. $\lim\limits_{x \to -\infty} \operatorname{csch} x$

21. $\lim\limits_{x \to 0} \dfrac{\sinh x}{x}$

22. $\lim\limits_{x \to 0^-} \coth x$

Finding a Derivative In Exercises 23–32, find the derivative of the function.

23. $f(x) = \sinh 3x$

24. $f(x) = \cosh(8x + 1)$

25. $y = \operatorname{sech}(5x^2)$

26. $f(x) = \tanh(4x^2 + 3x)$

27. $f(x) = \ln(\sinh x)$

28. $y = \ln\left(\tanh \dfrac{x}{2}\right)$

29. $h(x) = \dfrac{1}{4} \sinh 2x - \dfrac{x}{2}$

30. $y = x \cosh x - \sinh x$

31. $f(t) = \arctan(\sinh t)$

32. $g(x) = \operatorname{sech}^2 3x$

Finding an Equation of a Tangent Line In Exercises 33–36, find an equation of the tangent line to the graph of the function at the given point.

33. $y = \sinh(1 - x^2)$, $(1, 0)$

34. $y = x^{\cosh x}$, $(1, 1)$

35. $y = (\cosh x - \sinh x)^2$, $(0, 1)$

36. $y = e^{\sinh x}$, $(0, 1)$

Finding Relative Extrema In Exercises 37–40, find any relative extrema of the function. Use a graphing utility to confirm your result.

37. $f(x) = \sin x \sinh x - \cos x \cosh x$, $-4 \le x \le 4$

38. $f(x) = x \sinh(x - 1) - \cosh(x - 1)$

39. $g(x) = x \operatorname{sech} x$

40. $h(x) = 2 \tanh x - x$

Catenary In Exercises 41 and 42, a model for a power cable suspended between two towers is given. (a) Graph the model, (b) find the heights of the cable at the towers and at the midpoint between the towers, and (c) find the slope of the model at the point where the cable meets the right-hand tower.

41. $y = 10 + 15 \cosh \dfrac{x}{15}$, $-15 \le x \le 15$

42. $y = 18 + 25 \cosh \dfrac{x}{25}$, $-25 \le x \le 25$

Finding an Indefinite Integral In Exercises 43–54, find the indefinite integral.

43. $\displaystyle\int \cosh 2x \, dx$

44. $\displaystyle\int \operatorname{sech}^2(3x) \, dx$

45. $\displaystyle\int \sinh(1 - 2x) \, dx$

46. $\displaystyle\int \dfrac{\cosh \sqrt{x}}{\sqrt{x}} \, dx$

47. $\displaystyle\int \cosh^2(x - 1) \sinh(x - 1) \, dx$

48. $\displaystyle\int \dfrac{\sinh x}{1 + \sinh^2 x} \, dx$

49. $\displaystyle\int \dfrac{\cosh x}{\sinh x} \, dx$

50. $\displaystyle\int \operatorname{sech}^2(2x - 1) \, dx$

51. $\displaystyle\int x \operatorname{csch}^2 \dfrac{x^2}{2} \, dx$

52. $\displaystyle\int \operatorname{sech}^3 x \tanh x \, dx$

53. $\displaystyle\int \dfrac{\operatorname{csch}(1/x) \coth(1/x)}{x^2} \, dx$

54. $\displaystyle\int \dfrac{\cosh x}{\sqrt{9 - \sinh^2 x}} \, dx$

Evaluating a Definite Integral In Exercises 55–60, evaluate the integral.

55. $\displaystyle\int_0^{\ln 2} \tanh x \, dx$

56. $\displaystyle\int_0^1 \cosh^2 x \, dx$

57. $\displaystyle\int_0^4 \dfrac{1}{25 - x^2} \, dx$

58. $\displaystyle\int_0^4 \dfrac{1}{\sqrt{25 - x^2}} \, dx$

59. $\displaystyle\int_0^{\sqrt{2}/4} \dfrac{2}{\sqrt{1 - 4x^2}} \, dx$

60. $\displaystyle\int_0^{\ln 2} 2e^{-x} \cosh x \, dx$

61. Comparing Functions Discuss several ways in which the hyperbolic functions are similar to the trigonometric functions.

62. Hyperbolic Functions Which hyperbolic functions take on only positive values? Which hyperbolic functions are increasing on their domains?

63. Comparing Derivative Formulas Which hyperbolic derivative formulas differ from their trigonometric counterparts by a minus sign?

64. **HOW DO YOU SEE IT?**   Use the graphs of f and g shown in the figures to answer the following.

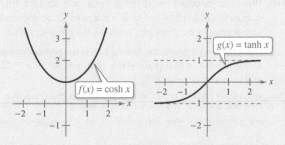

(a) Identify the open interval(s) on which the graphs of f and g are increasing or decreasing.

(b) Identify the open interval(s) on which the graphs of f and g are concave upward or concave downward.

Finding a Derivative   In Exercises 65–74, find the derivative of the function.

65. $y = \cosh^{-1}(3x)$

66. $y = \tanh^{-1}\dfrac{x}{2}$

67. $y = \tanh^{-1}\sqrt{x}$

68. $f(x) = \coth^{-1}(x^2)$

69. $y = \sinh^{-1}(\tan x)$

70. $y = \tanh^{-1}(\sin 2x)$

71. $y = (\operatorname{csch}^{-1} x)^2$

72. $y = \operatorname{sech}^{-1}(\cos 2x), \quad 0 < x < \pi/4$

73. $y = 2x \sinh^{-1}(2x) - \sqrt{1 + 4x^2}$

74. $y = x \tanh^{-1} x + \ln\sqrt{1 - x^2}$

Finding an Indefinite Integral   In Exercises 75–82, find the indefinite integral using the formulas from Theorem 5.25.

75. $\displaystyle\int \frac{1}{3 - 9x^2}\,dx$

76. $\displaystyle\int \frac{1}{2x\sqrt{1 - 4x^2}}\,dx$

77. $\displaystyle\int \frac{1}{\sqrt{1 + e^{2x}}}\,dx$

78. $\displaystyle\int \frac{x}{9 - x^4}\,dx$

79. $\displaystyle\int \frac{1}{\sqrt{x}\sqrt{1 + x}}\,dx$

80. $\displaystyle\int \frac{\sqrt{x}}{\sqrt{1 + x^3}}\,dx$

81. $\displaystyle\int \frac{-1}{4x - x^2}\,dx$

82. $\displaystyle\int \frac{dx}{(x + 2)\sqrt{x^2 + 4x + 8}}$

Evaluating a Definite Integral   In Exercises 83–86, evaluate the definite integral using the formulas from Theorem 5.25.

83. $\displaystyle\int_3^7 \frac{1}{\sqrt{x^2 - 4}}\,dx$

84. $\displaystyle\int_1^3 \frac{1}{x\sqrt{4 + x^2}}\,dx$

85. $\displaystyle\int_{-1}^1 \frac{1}{16 - 9x^2}\,dx$

86. $\displaystyle\int_0^1 \frac{1}{\sqrt{25x^2 + 1}}\,dx$

Differential Equation   In Exercises 87–90, solve the differential equation.

87. $\dfrac{dy}{dx} = \dfrac{1}{\sqrt{80 + 8x - 16x^2}}$

88. $\dfrac{dy}{dx} = \dfrac{1}{(x - 1)\sqrt{-4x^2 + 8x - 1}}$

89. $\dfrac{dy}{dx} = \dfrac{x^3 - 21x}{5 + 4x - x^2}$

90. $\dfrac{dy}{dx} = \dfrac{1 - 2x}{4x - x^2}$

Area   In Exercises 91–94, find the area of the region.

91. $y = \operatorname{sech}\dfrac{x}{2}$

92. $y = \tanh 2x$

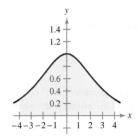

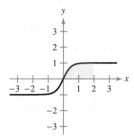

93. $y = \dfrac{5x}{\sqrt{x^4 + 1}}$

94. $y = \dfrac{6}{\sqrt{x^2 - 4}}$

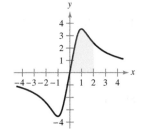

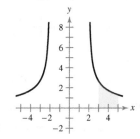

95. Chemical Reactions Chemicals A and B combine in a 3-to-1 ratio to form a compound. The amount of compound x being produced at any time t is proportional to the unchanged amounts of A and B remaining in the solution. So, when 3 kilograms of A is mixed with 2 kilograms of B, you have

$$\frac{dx}{dt} = k\left(3 - \frac{3x}{4}\right)\left(2 - \frac{x}{4}\right) = \frac{3k}{16}(x^2 - 12x + 32).$$

One kilogram of the compound is formed after 10 minutes. Find the amount formed after 20 minutes by solving the equation

$$\int \frac{3k}{16}\,dt = \int \frac{dx}{x^2 - 12x + 32}.$$

96. Vertical Motion An object is dropped from a height of 400 feet.

(a) Find the velocity of the object as a function of time (neglect air resistance on the object).

(b) Use the result in part (a) to find the position function.

(c) If the air resistance is proportional to the square of the velocity, then $dv/dt = -32 + kv^2$, where -32 feet per second per second is the acceleration due to gravity and k is a constant. Show that the velocity v as a function of time is $v(t) = -\sqrt{32/k}\tanh(\sqrt{32k}\,t)$ by performing $\int dv/(32 - kv^2) = -\int dt$ and simplifying the result.

(d) Use the result of part (c) to find $\lim_{t\to\infty} v(t)$ and give its interpretation.

(e) Integrate the velocity function in part (c) and find the position s of the object as a function of t. Use a graphing utility to graph the position function when $k = 0.01$ and the position function in part (b) in the same viewing window. Estimate the additional time required for the object to reach ground level when air resistance is not neglected.

(f) Give a written description of what you believe would happen if k were increased. Then test your assertion with a particular value of k.

97. Tractrix Consider the equation of the tractrix

$$y = a\,\text{sech}^{-1}(x/a) - \sqrt{a^2 - x^2}, \quad a > 0.$$

(a) Find dy/dx.

(b) Let L be the tangent line to the tractrix at the point P. When L intersects the y-axis at the point Q, show that the distance between P and Q is a.

98. Tractrix Show that the boat in Example 5 is always pointing toward the person.

99. Proof Prove that

$$\tanh^{-1} x = \frac{1}{2}\ln\left(\frac{1 + x}{1 - x}\right), \quad -1 < x < 1.$$

100. Proof Prove that

$$\sinh^{-1} t = \ln\left(t + \sqrt{t^2 + 1}\right).$$

101. Using a Right Triangle Show that

$$\arctan(\sinh x) = \arcsin(\tanh x).$$

102. Integration Let $x > 0$ and $b > 0$. Show that

$$\int_{-b}^{b} e^{xt}\,dt = \frac{2\sinh bx}{x}.$$

Proof In Exercises 103–105, prove the differentiation formula.

103. $\dfrac{d}{dx}[\cosh x] = \sinh x$

104. $\dfrac{d}{dx}[\coth x] = -\text{csch}^2 x$

105. $\dfrac{d}{dx}[\text{sech } x] = -\text{sech } x \tanh x$

Ken Nyborg/Shutterstock.com

Verifying a Differentiation Rule In Exercises 106–108, verify the differentiation formula.

106. $\dfrac{d}{dx}[\cosh^{-1} x] = \dfrac{1}{\sqrt{x^2 - 1}}$

107. $\dfrac{d}{dx}[\sinh^{-1} x] = \dfrac{1}{\sqrt{x^2 + 1}}$

108. $\dfrac{d}{dx}[\text{sech}^{-1} x] = \dfrac{-1}{x\sqrt{1 - x^2}}$

PUTNAM EXAM CHALLENGE

109. From the vertex $(0, c)$ of the catenary $y = c\cosh(x/c)$ a line L is drawn perpendicular to the tangent to the catenary at point P. Prove that the length of L intercepted by the axes is equal to the ordinate y of the point P.

110. Prove or disprove: there is at least one straight line normal to the graph of $y = \cosh x$ at a point $(a, \cosh a)$ and also normal to the graph of $y = \sinh x$ at a point $(c, \sinh c)$.

[At a point on a graph, the normal line is the perpendicular to the tangent at that point. Also, $\cosh x = (e^x + e^{-x})/2$ and $\sinh x = (e^x - e^{-x})/2$.]

These problems were composed by the Committee on the Putnam Prize Competition.
© The Mathematical Association of America. All rights reserved.

SECTION PROJECT

St. Louis Arch

The Gateway Arch in St. Louis, Missouri, was constructed using the hyperbolic cosine function. The equation used for construction was

$$y = 693.8597 - 68.7672\cosh 0.0100333x,$$
$$-299.2239 \le x \le 299.2239$$

where x and y are measured in feet. Cross sections of the arch are equilateral triangles, and (x, y) traces the path of the centers of mass of the cross-sectional triangles. For each value of x, the area of the cross-sectional triangle is

$$A = 125.1406\cosh 0.0100333x.$$

(Source: Owner's Manual for the Gateway Arch, Saint Louis, MO, by William Thayer)

(a) How high above the ground is the center of the highest triangle? (At ground level, $y = 0$.)

(b) What is the height of the arch? (*Hint:* For an equilateral triangle, $A = \sqrt{3}c^2$, where c is one-half the base of the triangle, and the center of mass of the triangle is located at two-thirds the height of the triangle.)

(c) How wide is the arch at ground level?

Finding an Indefinite Integral In Exercises 1–6, find the indefinite integral.

1. $\int (4x^2 + x + 3)\, dx$

2. $\int \dfrac{6}{\sqrt[3]{x}}\, dx$

3. $\int \dfrac{x^4 + 8}{x^3}\, dx$

4. $\int (5 \cos x - 2 \sec^2 x)\, dx$

5. $\int (5 - e^x)\, dx$

6. $\int \dfrac{10}{x}\, dx$

Finding a Particular Solution In Exercises 7–10, find the particular solution that satisfies the differential equation and the initial condition.

7. $f'(x) = -6x,\ f(1) = -2$

8. $f'(x) = 9x^2 + 1,\ f(0) = 7$

9. $f''(x) = 24x,\ f'(-1) = 7,\ f(1) = -4$

10. $f''(x) = 2 \cos x,\ f'(0) = 4,\ f(0) = -5$

11. **Velocity and Acceleration** A ball is thrown vertically upward from ground level with an initial velocity of 96 feet per second. Use $a(t) = -32$ feet per second per second as the acceleration due to gravity. (Neglect air resistance.)

   (a) How long will it take the ball to rise to its maximum height? What is the maximum height?

   (b) After how many seconds is the velocity of the ball one-half the initial velocity?

   (c) What is the height of the ball when its velocity is one-half the initial velocity?

12. **Velocity and Acceleration** The speed of a car traveling in a straight line is reduced from 45 to 30 miles per hour in a distance of 264 feet. Find the distance in which the car can be brought to rest from 30 miles per hour, assuming the same constant deceleration.

Finding a Sum In Exercises 13 and 14, find the sum. Use the summation capabilities of a graphing utility to verify your result.

13. $\displaystyle\sum_{i=1}^{5} (5i - 3)$

14. $\displaystyle\sum_{k=0}^{3} (k^2 + 1)$

Using Sigma Notation In Exercises 15 and 16, use sigma notation to write the sum.

15. $\dfrac{1}{3(1)} + \dfrac{1}{3(2)} + \dfrac{1}{3(3)} + \cdots + \dfrac{1}{3(10)}$

16. $\left(\dfrac{3}{n}\right)\left(\dfrac{1+1}{n}\right)^2 + \left(\dfrac{3}{n}\right)\left(\dfrac{2+1}{n}\right)^2 + \cdots + \left(\dfrac{3}{n}\right)\left(\dfrac{n+1}{n}\right)^2$

Evaluating a Sum In Exercises 17–20, use the properties of summation and Theorem 5.2 to evaluate the sum.

17. $\displaystyle\sum_{i=1}^{20} 2i$

18. $\displaystyle\sum_{i=1}^{30} (3i - 4)$

19. $\displaystyle\sum_{i=1}^{20} (i + 1)^2$

20. $\displaystyle\sum_{i=1}^{12} i(i^2 - 1)$

Finding Area by the Limit Definition In Exercises 21–24, use the limit process to find the area of the region bounded by the graph of the function and the x-axis over the given interval. Sketch the region.

21. $y = 8 - 2x,\ [0, 3]$

22. $y = x^2 + 3,\ [0, 2]$

23. $y = 5 - x^2,\ [-2, 1]$

24. $y = \tfrac{1}{4}x^3,\ [2, 4]$

25. **Finding Area by the Limit Definition** Use the limit process to find the area of the region bounded by $x = 5y - y^2$, $x = 0$, $y = 2$, and $y = 5$.

26. **Upper and Lower Sums** Consider the region bounded by $y = mx$, $y = 0$, $x = 0$, and $x = b$.

   (a) Find the upper and lower sums to approximate the area of the region when $\Delta x = b/4$.

   (b) Find the upper and lower sums to approximate the area of the region when $\Delta x = b/n$.

   (c) Find the area of the region by letting n approach infinity in both sums in part (b). Show that, in each case, you obtain the formula for the area of a triangle.

Evaluating a Definite Integral Using a Geometric Formula In Exercises 27 and 28, sketch the region whose area is given by the definite integral. Then use a geometric formula to evaluate the integral.

27. $\displaystyle\int_{0}^{5} (5 - |x - 5|)\, dx$

28. $\displaystyle\int_{-6}^{6} \sqrt{36 - x^2}\, dx$

29. **Using Properties of Definite Integrals** Given

$$\int_{4}^{8} f(x)\, dx = 12 \quad \text{and} \quad \int_{4}^{8} g(x)\, dx = 5$$

evaluate

   (a) $\displaystyle\int_{4}^{8} [f(x) + g(x)]\, dx$.

   (b) $\displaystyle\int_{4}^{8} [f(x) - g(x)]\, dx$.

   (c) $\displaystyle\int_{4}^{8} [2f(x) - 3g(x)]\, dx$.

   (d) $\displaystyle\int_{4}^{8} 7f(x)\, dx$.

30. **Using Properties of Definite Integrals** Given

$$\int_{0}^{3} f(x)\, dx = 4 \quad \text{and} \quad \int_{3}^{6} f(x)\, dx = -1$$

evaluate

   (a) $\displaystyle\int_{0}^{6} f(x)\, dx$.

   (b) $\displaystyle\int_{6}^{3} f(x)\, dx$.

   (c) $\displaystyle\int_{4}^{4} f(x)\, dx$.

   (d) $\displaystyle\int_{3}^{6} -10f(x)\, dx$.

Evaluating a Definite Integral In Exercises 31–36, use the Fundamental Theorem of Calculus to evaluate the definite integral.

31. $\displaystyle\int_{0}^{8} (3 + x)\, dx$

32. $\displaystyle\int_{2}^{3} (x^4 + 4x - 6)\, dx$

33. $\displaystyle\int_4^9 x\sqrt{x}\,dx$

34. $\displaystyle\int_{-\pi/4}^{\pi/4} \sec^2 t\,dt$

35. $\displaystyle\int_0^2 (x + e^x)\,dx$

36. $\displaystyle\int_1^6 \frac{3}{x}\,dx$

Finding the Area of a Region In Exercises 37–40, find the area of the region bounded by the graphs of the equations.

37. $y = 8 - x, \quad x = 0, \quad x = 6, \quad y = 0$

38. $y = \sqrt{x}(1 - x), \quad y = 0$

39. $y = \dfrac{2}{x}, \quad y = 0, \quad x = 1, \quad x = 3$

40. $y = 1 + e^x, \quad y = 0, \quad x = 0, \quad x = 2$

Finding the Average Value of a Function In Exercises 41 and 42, find the average value of the function over the given interval and all values of x in the interval for which the function equals its average value.

41. $f(x) = \dfrac{1}{\sqrt{x}}, \quad [4, 9]$

42. $f(x) = x^3, \quad [0, 2]$

Using the Second Fundamental Theorem of Calculus In Exercises 43–46, use the Second Fundamental Theorem of Calculus to find $F'(x)$.

43. $F(x) = \displaystyle\int_0^x t^2\sqrt{1 + t^3}\,dt$

44. $F(x) = \displaystyle\int_1^x \frac{1}{t^2}\,dt$

45. $F(x) = \displaystyle\int_{-3}^x (t^2 + 3t + 2)\,dt$

46. $F(x) = \displaystyle\int_0^x \csc^2 t\,dt$

Finding an Indefinite Integral In Exercises 47–60, find the indefinite integral.

47. $\displaystyle\int \frac{x^2}{\sqrt{x^3 + 3}}\,dx$

48. $\displaystyle\int 6x^3\sqrt{3x^4 + 2}\,dx$

49. $\displaystyle\int x(1 - 3x^2)^4\,dx$

50. $\displaystyle\int \frac{x + 4}{(x^2 + 8x - 7)^2}\,dx$

51. $\displaystyle\int \sin^3 x \cos x\,dx$

52. $\displaystyle\int x \sin 3x^2\,dx$

53. $\displaystyle\int \frac{\cos\theta}{\sqrt{1 - \sin\theta}}\,d\theta$

54. $\displaystyle\int \frac{\sin x}{\sqrt{\cos x}}\,dx$

55. $\displaystyle\int xe^{-3x^2}\,dx$

56. $\displaystyle\int \frac{e^{1/x}}{x^2}\,dx$

57. $\displaystyle\int (x + 1)5^{(x+1)^2}\,dx$

58. $\displaystyle\int \frac{1}{t^2}(2^{-1/t})\,dt$

59. $\displaystyle\int (1 + \sec \pi x)^2 \sec \pi x \tan \pi x\,dx$

60. $\displaystyle\int \sec 2x \tan 2x\,dx$

Evaluating a Definite Integral In Exercises 61–68, evaluate the definite integral. Use a graphing utility to verify your result.

61. $\displaystyle\int_0^1 (3x + 1)^5\,dx$

62. $\displaystyle\int_0^1 x^2(x^3 - 2)^3\,dx$

63. $\displaystyle\int_0^3 \frac{1}{\sqrt{1 + x}}\,dx$

64. $\displaystyle\int_3^6 \frac{x}{3\sqrt{x^2 - 8}}\,dx$

65. $2\pi\displaystyle\int_0^1 (y + 1)\sqrt{1 - y}\,dy$

66. $2\pi\displaystyle\int_{-1}^0 x^2\sqrt{x + 1}\,dx$

67. $\displaystyle\int_0^\pi \cos \frac{x}{2}\,dx$

68. $\displaystyle\int_{-\pi/4}^{\pi/4} \sin 2x\,dx$

Using the Trapezoidal Rule and Simpson's Rule In Exercises 69–72, approximate the definite integral using the Trapezoidal Rule and Simpson's Rule with $n = 4$. Compare these results with the approximation of the integral using a graphing utility.

69. $\displaystyle\int_2^3 \frac{2}{1 + x^2}\,dx$

70. $\displaystyle\int_0^1 \frac{x^{3/2}}{3 - x^2}\,dx$

71. $\displaystyle\int_0^3 \sqrt{x}\ln(x + 1)\,dx$

72. $\displaystyle\int_0^\pi \sqrt{1 + \sin^2 x}\,dx$

Finding an Indefinite Integral In Exercises 73–78, find the indefinite integral.

73. $\displaystyle\int \frac{1}{7x - 2}\,dx$

74. $\displaystyle\int \frac{x^2}{x^3 + 1}\,dx$

75. $\displaystyle\int \frac{\sin x}{1 + \cos x}\,dx$

76. $\displaystyle\int \frac{\ln\sqrt{x}}{x}\,dx$

77. $\displaystyle\int \frac{e^{2x} - e^{-2x}}{e^{2x} + e^{-2x}}\,dx$

78. $\displaystyle\int \frac{e^{2x}}{e^{2x} + 1}\,dx$

Evaluating a Definite Integral In Exercises 79–82, evaluate the definite integral.

79. $\displaystyle\int_1^4 \frac{2x + 1}{2x}\,dx$

80. $\displaystyle\int_1^e \frac{\ln x}{x}\,dx$

81. $\displaystyle\int_0^{\pi/3} \sec\theta\,d\theta$

82. $\displaystyle\int_0^\pi \tan \frac{\theta}{3}\,d\theta$

Finding an Indefinite Integral In Exercises 83–88, find the indefinite integral.

83. $\displaystyle\int \frac{1}{e^{2x} + e^{-2x}}\,dx$

84. $\displaystyle\int \frac{1}{3 + 25x^2}\,dx$

85. $\displaystyle\int \frac{x}{\sqrt{1 - x^4}}\,dx$

86. $\displaystyle\int \frac{1}{x\sqrt{9x^2 - 49}}\,dx$

87. $\displaystyle\int \frac{\arctan(x/2)}{4 + x^2}\,dx$

88. $\displaystyle\int \frac{\arcsin 2x}{\sqrt{1 - 4x^2}}\,dx$

Finding a Derivative In Exercises 89–92, find the derivative of the function.

89. $y = \operatorname{sech}(4x - 1)$

90. $y = 2x - \cosh\sqrt{x}$

91. $y = \sinh^{-1}(4x)$

92. $y = x\tanh^{-1} 2x$

Finding an Indefinite Integral In Exercises 93–96, find the indefinite integral.

93. $\displaystyle\int x^2 \operatorname{sech}^2 x^3\,dx$

94. $\displaystyle\int \sinh 6x\,dx$

95. $\displaystyle\int \frac{1}{9 - 4x^2}\,dx$

96. $\displaystyle\int \frac{x}{\sqrt{x^4 - 1}}\,dx$

P.S. Problem Solving

See **CalcChat.com** for tutorial help and worked-out solutions to odd-numbered exercises.

1. **Using a Function**   Let $L(x) = \int_1^x \frac{1}{t}\, dt, \; x > 0$.

   (a) Find $L(1)$.

   (b) Find $L'(x)$ and $L'(1)$.

   (c) Use a graphing utility to approximate the value of x (to three decimal places) for which $L(x) = 1$.

   (d) Prove that $L(x_1 x_2) = L(x_1) + L(x_2)$ for all positive values of x_1 and x_2.

2. **Parabolic Arch**   Archimedes showed that the area of a parabolic arch is equal to $\frac{2}{3}$ the product of the base and the height (see figure).

   (a) Graph the parabolic arch bounded by $y = 9 - x^2$ and the x-axis. Use an appropriate integral to find the area A.

   (b) Find the base and height of the arch and verify Archimedes' formula.

   (c) Prove Archimedes' formula for a general parabola.

3. **Using a Continuous Function**   Let f be continuous on the interval $[0, b]$, where $f(x) + f(b - x) \neq 0$ on $[0, b]$.

   (a) Show that $\displaystyle\int_0^b \frac{f(x)}{f(x) + f(b - x)}\, dx = \frac{b}{2}$.

   (b) Use the result in part (a) to evaluate

   $$\int_0^1 \frac{\sin x}{\sin(1 - x) + \sin x}\, dx.$$

   (c) Use the result in part (a) to evaluate

   $$\int_0^3 \frac{\sqrt{x}}{\sqrt{x} + \sqrt{3 - x}}\, dx.$$

4. **Fresnel Function**   The **Fresnel function** S is defined by the integral

   $$S(x) = \int_0^x \sin\!\left(\frac{\pi t^2}{2}\right) dt.$$

   (a) Graph the function $y = \sin\!\left(\dfrac{\pi x^2}{2}\right)$ on the interval $[0, 3]$.

   (b) Use the graph in part (a) to sketch the graph of S on the interval $[0, 3]$.

   (c) Locate all relative extrema of S on the interval $(0, 3)$.

   (d) Locate all points of inflection of S on the interval $(0, 3)$.

5. **Approximation**   The **Two-Point Gaussian Quadrature Approximation** for f is

   $$\int_{-1}^1 f(x)\, dx \approx f\!\left(-\frac{1}{\sqrt{3}}\right) + f\!\left(\frac{1}{\sqrt{3}}\right).$$

   (a) Use this formula to approximate

   $$\int_{-1}^1 \cos x\, dx.$$

   Find the error of the approximation.

   (b) Use this formula to approximate

   $$\int_{-1}^1 \frac{1}{1 + x^2}\, dx.$$

   (c) Prove that the Two-Point Gaussian Quadrature Approximation is exact for all polynomials of degree 3 or less.

6. **Extrema and Points of Inflection**   The graph of the function f consists of the three line segments joining the points $(0, 0)$, $(2, -2)$, $(6, 2)$, and $(8, 3)$. The function F is defined by the integral

   $$F(x) = \int_0^x f(t)\, dt.$$

   (a) Sketch the graph of f.

   (b) Complete the table.

x	0	1	2	3	4	5	6	7	8
$F(x)$									

   (c) Find the extrema of F on the interval $[0, 8]$.

   (d) Determine all points of inflection of F on the interval $(0, 8)$.

7. **Falling Objects**   Galileo Galilei (1564–1642) stated the following proposition concerning falling objects:

   The time in which any space is traversed by a uniformly accelerating body is equal to the time in which that same space would be traversed by the same body moving at a uniform speed whose value is the mean of the highest speed of the accelerating body and the speed just before acceleration began.

   Use the techniques of this chapter to verify this proposition.

8. **Proof**   Prove $\displaystyle\int_0^x f(t)(x - t)\, dt = \int_0^x \left(\int_0^t f(v)\, dv\right) dt$.

9. **Proof**   Prove $\displaystyle\int_a^b f(x) f'(x)\, dx = \frac{1}{2}\left([f(b)]^2 - [f(a)]^2\right)$.

10. **Riemann Sum**   Use an appropriate Riemann sum to evaluate the limit

   $$\lim_{n \to \infty} \frac{\sqrt{1} + \sqrt{2} + \sqrt{3} + \cdots + \sqrt{n}}{n^{3/2}}.$$

11. Riemann Sum   Use an appropriate Riemann sum to evaluate the limit

$$\lim_{n \to \infty} \frac{1^5 + 2^5 + 3^5 + \cdots + n^5}{n^6}.$$

12. Proof   Let f be integrable on $[a, b]$ and

$$0 < m \le f(x) \le M$$

for all x in the interval $[a, b]$. Prove that

$$m(a - b) \le \int_a^b f(x)\, dx \le M(b - a).$$

Use this result to estimate $\displaystyle\int_0^1 \sqrt{1 + x^4}\, dx$.

13. Velocity and Acceleration   A car travels in a straight line for 1 hour. Its velocity v in miles per hour at six-minute intervals is shown in the table.

t (hours)	0	0.1	0.2	0.3	0.4	0.5
v (mi/h)	0	10	20	40	60	50

t (hours)	0.6	0.7	0.8	0.9	1.0
v (mi/h)	40	35	40	50	65

(a) Produce a reasonable graph of the velocity function v by graphing these points and connecting them with a smooth curve.

(b) Find the open intervals over which the acceleration a is positive.

(c) Find the average acceleration of the car (in miles per hour squared) over the interval $[0, 0.4]$.

(d) What does the integral

$$\int_0^1 v(t)\, dt$$

signify? Approximate this integral using the Trapezoidal Rule with five subintervals.

(e) Approximate the acceleration at $t = 0.8$.

14. Proof   Prove that if f is a continuous function on a closed interval $[a, b]$, then

$$\left| \int_a^b f(x)\, dx \right| \le \int_a^b |f(x)|\, dx.$$

15. Verifying a Sum   Verify that

$$\sum_{i=1}^n i^2 = \frac{n(n + 1)(2n + 1)}{6}$$

by showing the following.

(a) $(1 + i)^3 - i^3 = 3i^2 + 3i + 1$

(b) $(n + 1)^3 = \displaystyle\sum_{i=1}^n (3i^2 + 3i + 1) + 1$

(c) $\displaystyle\sum_{i=1}^n i^2 = \frac{n(n + 1)(2n + 1)}{6}$

16. Area   Consider the three regions A, B, and C determined by the graph of $f(x) = \arcsin x$, as shown in the figure.

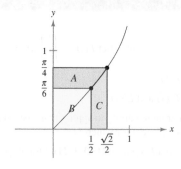

(a) Calculate the areas of regions A and B.

(b) Use your answers in part (a) to evaluate the integral

$$\int_{1/2}^{\sqrt{2}/2} \arcsin x\, dx.$$

(c) Use the methods in part (a) to evaluate the integral

$$\int_1^3 \ln x\, dx.$$

(d) Use the methods in part (a) to evaluate the integral

$$\int_1^{\sqrt{3}} \arctan x\, dx.$$

17. Area   Use integration by substitution to find the area under the curve

$$y = \frac{1}{\sqrt{x} + x}$$

between $x = 1$ and $x = 4$.

18. Area   Use integration by substitution to find the area under the curve

$$y = \frac{1}{\sin^2 x + 4\cos^2 x}$$

between $x = 0$ and $x = \dfrac{\pi}{4}$.

19. Approximating a Function

(a) Use a graphing utility to compare the graph of the function $y = e^x$ with the graph of each given function.

   (i) $y_1 = 1 + \dfrac{x}{1!}$

   (ii) $y_2 = 1 + \dfrac{x}{1!} + \dfrac{x^2}{2!}$

   (iii) $y_3 = 1 + \dfrac{x}{1!} + \dfrac{x^2}{2!} + \dfrac{x^3}{3!}$

(b) Identify the pattern of successive polynomials in part (a), extend the pattern one more term, and compare the graph of the resulting polynomial function with the graph of $y = e^x$.

(c) What do you think this pattern implies?

For this edition, we have made Appendix A, Proofs of Selected Theorems, available in video format at *LarsonCalculus.com*. When you navigate to that website, you will find a link to Bruce Edwards explaining each proof in the text, including those in this appendix. We hope these videos enhance your study of calculus. The text version of this appendix is available at *CengageBrain.com*.

**Proofs of Selected Theorems sample
at *LarsonCalculus.com***

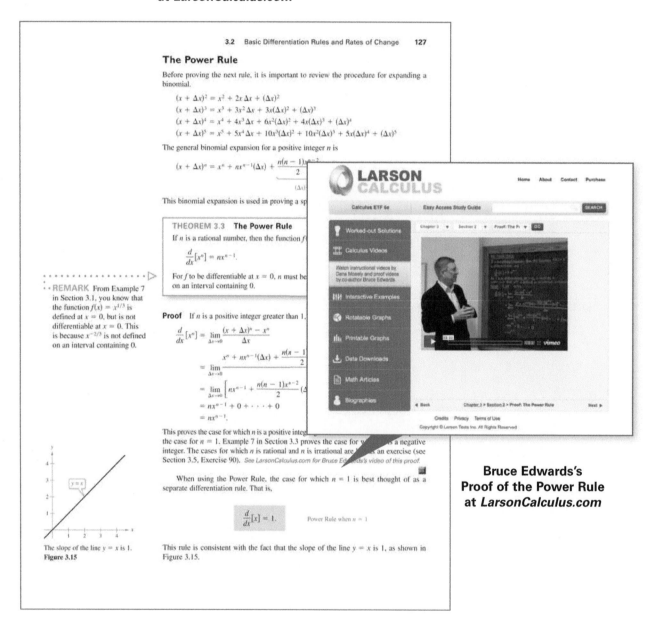

**Bruce Edwards's
Proof of the Power Rule
at *LarsonCalculus.com***

Forms Involving u^n

1. $\displaystyle\int u^n \, du = \frac{u^{n+1}}{n+1} + C, \; n \neq -1$

2. $\displaystyle\int \frac{1}{u} \, du = \ln|u| + C$

Forms Involving $a + bu$

3. $\displaystyle\int \frac{u}{a+bu} \, du = \frac{1}{b^2}\big(bu - a\ln|a+bu|\big) + C$

4. $\displaystyle\int \frac{u}{(a+bu)^2} \, du = \frac{1}{b^2}\left(\frac{a}{a+bu} + \ln|a+bu|\right) + C$

5. $\displaystyle\int \frac{u}{(a+bu)^n} \, du = \frac{1}{b^2}\left[\frac{-1}{(n-2)(a+bu)^{n-2}} + \frac{a}{(n-1)(a+bu)^{n-1}}\right] + C, \quad n \neq 1, 2$

6. $\displaystyle\int \frac{u^2}{a+bu} \, du = \frac{1}{b^3}\left[-\frac{bu}{2}(2a-bu) + a^2\ln|a+bu|\right] + C$

7. $\displaystyle\int \frac{u^2}{(a+bu)^2} \, du = \frac{1}{b^3}\left(bu - \frac{a^2}{a+bu} - 2a\ln|a+bu|\right) + C$

8. $\displaystyle\int \frac{u^2}{(a+bu)^3} \, du = \frac{1}{b^3}\left[\frac{2a}{a+bu} - \frac{a^2}{2(a+bu)^2} + \ln|a+bu|\right] + C$

9. $\displaystyle\int \frac{u^2}{(a+bu)^n} \, du = \frac{1}{b^3}\left[\frac{-1}{(n-3)(a+bu)^{n-3}} + \frac{2a}{(n-2)(a+bu)^{n-2}} - \frac{a^2}{(n-1)(a+bu)^{n-1}}\right] + C, \quad n \neq 1, 2, 3$

10. $\displaystyle\int \frac{1}{u(a+bu)} \, du = \frac{1}{a}\ln\left|\frac{u}{a+bu}\right| + C$

11. $\displaystyle\int \frac{1}{u(a+bu)^2} \, du = \frac{1}{a}\left(\frac{1}{a+bu} + \frac{1}{a}\ln\left|\frac{u}{a+bu}\right|\right) + C$

12. $\displaystyle\int \frac{1}{u^2(a+bu)} \, du = -\frac{1}{a}\left(\frac{1}{u} + \frac{b}{a}\ln\left|\frac{u}{a+bu}\right|\right) + C$

13. $\displaystyle\int \frac{1}{u^2(a+bu)^2} \, du = -\frac{1}{a^2}\left[\frac{a+2bu}{u(a+bu)} + \frac{2b}{a}\ln\left|\frac{u}{a+bu}\right|\right] + C$

Forms Involving $a + bu + cu^2, \; b^2 \neq 4ac$

14. $\displaystyle\int \frac{1}{a+bu+cu^2} \, du = \begin{cases} \dfrac{2}{\sqrt{4ac-b^2}} \arctan \dfrac{2cu+b}{\sqrt{4ac-b^2}} + C, & b^2 < 4ac \\[4mm] \dfrac{1}{\sqrt{b^2-4ac}} \ln\left|\dfrac{2cu+b-\sqrt{b^2-4ac}}{2cu+b+\sqrt{b^2-4ac}}\right| + C, & b^2 > 4ac \end{cases}$

15. $\displaystyle\int \frac{u}{a+bu+cu^2} \, du = \frac{1}{2c}\left(\ln|a+bu+cu^2| - b\int \frac{1}{a+bu+cu^2} \, du\right)$

Forms Involving $\sqrt{a+bu}$

16. $\displaystyle\int u^n \sqrt{a+bu} \, du = \frac{2}{b(2n+3)}\left[u^n(a+bu)^{3/2} - na\int u^{n-1}\sqrt{a+bu} \, du\right]$

17. $\displaystyle\int \frac{1}{u\sqrt{a+bu}} \, du = \begin{cases} \dfrac{1}{\sqrt{a}} \ln\left|\dfrac{\sqrt{a+bu}-\sqrt{a}}{\sqrt{a+bu}+\sqrt{a}}\right| + C, & a > 0 \\[4mm] \dfrac{2}{\sqrt{-a}} \arctan \sqrt{\dfrac{a+bu}{-a}} + C, & a < 0 \end{cases}$

18. $\displaystyle\int \frac{1}{u^n\sqrt{a+bu}} \, du = \frac{-1}{a(n-1)}\left[\frac{\sqrt{a+bu}}{u^{n-1}} + \frac{(2n-3)b}{2}\int \frac{1}{u^{n-1}\sqrt{a+bu}} \, du\right], \; n \neq 1$

A3

19. $\displaystyle\int \frac{\sqrt{a + bu}}{u}\, du = 2\sqrt{a + bu} + a\int \frac{1}{u\sqrt{a + bu}}\, du$

20. $\displaystyle\int \frac{\sqrt{a + bu}}{u^n}\, du = \frac{-1}{a(n - 1)}\left[\frac{(a + bu)^{3/2}}{u^{n-1}} + \frac{(2n - 5)b}{2}\int \frac{\sqrt{a + bu}}{u^{n-1}}\, du\right],\ n \neq 1$

21. $\displaystyle\int \frac{u}{\sqrt{a + bu}}\, du = \frac{-2(2a - bu)}{3b^2}\sqrt{a + bu} + C$

22. $\displaystyle\int \frac{u^n}{\sqrt{a + bu}}\, du = \frac{2}{(2n + 1)b}\left(u^n\sqrt{a + bu} - na\int \frac{u^{n-1}}{\sqrt{a + bu}}\, du\right)$

Forms Involving $a^2 \pm u^2,\ a > 0$

23. $\displaystyle\int \frac{1}{a^2 + u^2}\, du = \frac{1}{a}\arctan \frac{u}{a} + C$

24. $\displaystyle\int \frac{1}{u^2 - a^2}\, du = -\int \frac{1}{a^2 - u^2}\, du = \frac{1}{2a}\ln\left|\frac{u - a}{u + a}\right| + C$

25. $\displaystyle\int \frac{1}{(a^2 \pm u^2)^n}\, du = \frac{1}{2a^2(n - 1)}\left[\frac{u}{(a^2 \pm u^2)^{n-1}} + (2n - 3)\int \frac{1}{(a^2 \pm u^2)^{n-1}}\, du\right],\ n \neq 1$

Forms Involving $\sqrt{u^2 \pm a^2},\ a > 0$

26. $\displaystyle\int \sqrt{u^2 \pm a^2}\, du = \frac{1}{2}\left(u\sqrt{u^2 \pm a^2} \pm a^2 \ln\left|u + \sqrt{u^2 \pm a^2}\right|\right) + C$

27. $\displaystyle\int u^2\sqrt{u^2 \pm a^2}\, du = \frac{1}{8}\left[u(2u^2 \pm a^2)\sqrt{u^2 \pm a^2} - a^4 \ln\left|u + \sqrt{u^2 \pm a^2}\right|\right] + C$

28. $\displaystyle\int \frac{\sqrt{u^2 + a^2}}{u}\, du = \sqrt{u^2 + a^2} - a \ln\left|\frac{a + \sqrt{u^2 + a^2}}{u}\right| + C$

29. $\displaystyle\int \frac{\sqrt{u^2 - a^2}}{u}\, du = \sqrt{u^2 - a^2} - a \operatorname{arcsec}\frac{|u|}{a} + C$

30. $\displaystyle\int \frac{\sqrt{u^2 \pm a^2}}{u^2}\, du = \frac{-\sqrt{u^2 \pm a^2}}{u} + \ln\left|u + \sqrt{u^2 \pm a^2}\right| + C$

31. $\displaystyle\int \frac{1}{\sqrt{u^2 \pm a^2}}\, du = \ln\left|u + \sqrt{u^2 \pm a^2}\right| + C$

32. $\displaystyle\int \frac{1}{u\sqrt{u^2 + a^2}}\, du = \frac{-1}{a}\ln\left|\frac{a + \sqrt{u^2 + a^2}}{u}\right| + C$ **33.** $\displaystyle\int \frac{1}{u\sqrt{u^2 - a^2}}\, du = \frac{1}{a}\operatorname{arcsec}\frac{|u|}{a} + C$

34. $\displaystyle\int \frac{u^2}{\sqrt{u^2 \pm a^2}}\, du = \frac{1}{2}\left(u\sqrt{u^2 \pm a^2} \mp a^2 \ln\left|u + \sqrt{u^2 \pm a^2}\right|\right) + C$

35. $\displaystyle\int \frac{1}{u^2\sqrt{u^2 \pm a^2}}\, du = \mp \frac{\sqrt{u^2 \pm a^2}}{a^2 u} + C$ **36.** $\displaystyle\int \frac{1}{(u^2 \pm a^2)^{3/2}}\, du = \frac{\pm u}{a^2\sqrt{u^2 \pm a^2}} + C$

Forms Involving $\sqrt{a^2 - u^2},\ a > 0$

37. $\displaystyle\int \sqrt{a^2 - u^2}\, du = \frac{1}{2}\left(u\sqrt{a^2 - u^2} + a^2 \arcsin\frac{u}{a}\right) + C$

38. $\displaystyle\int u^2\sqrt{a^2 - u^2}\, du = \frac{1}{8}\left[u(2u^2 - a^2)\sqrt{a^2 - u^2} + a^4 \arcsin\frac{u}{a}\right] + C$

39. $\displaystyle\int \frac{\sqrt{a^2 - u^2}}{u}\, du = \sqrt{a^2 - u^2} - a \ln\left|\frac{a + \sqrt{a^2 - u^2}}{u}\right| + C$

40. $\displaystyle\int \frac{\sqrt{a^2 - u^2}}{u^2}\, du = \frac{-\sqrt{a^2 - u^2}}{u} - \arcsin\frac{u}{a} + C$

41. $\displaystyle\int \frac{1}{\sqrt{a^2 - u^2}}\, du = \arcsin\frac{u}{a} + C$

42. $\displaystyle\int \frac{1}{u\sqrt{a^2 - u^2}}\, du = \frac{-1}{a} \ln\left|\frac{a + \sqrt{a^2 - u^2}}{u}\right| + C$

43. $\displaystyle\int \frac{u^2}{\sqrt{a^2 - u^2}}\, du = \frac{1}{2}\left(-u\sqrt{a^2 - u^2} + a^2 \arcsin\frac{u}{a}\right) + C$

44. $\displaystyle\int \frac{1}{u^2\sqrt{a^2 - u^2}}\, du = \frac{-\sqrt{a^2 - u^2}}{a^2 u} + C$

45. $\displaystyle\int \frac{1}{(a^2 - u^2)^{3/2}}\, du = \frac{u}{a^2\sqrt{a^2 - u^2}} + C$

Forms Involving sin *u* or cos *u*

46. $\displaystyle\int \sin u\, du = -\cos u + C$

47. $\displaystyle\int \cos u\, du = \sin u + C$

48. $\displaystyle\int \sin^2 u\, du = \frac{1}{2}(u - \sin u \cos u) + C$

49. $\displaystyle\int \cos^2 u\, du = \frac{1}{2}(u + \sin u \cos u) + C$

50. $\displaystyle\int \sin^n u\, du = -\frac{\sin^{n-1} u \cos u}{n} + \frac{n-1}{n}\int \sin^{n-2} u\, du$

51. $\displaystyle\int \cos^n u\, du = \frac{\cos^{n-1} u \sin u}{n} + \frac{n-1}{n}\int \cos^{n-2} u\, du$

52. $\displaystyle\int u \sin u\, du = \sin u - u \cos u + C$

53. $\displaystyle\int u \cos u\, du = \cos u + u \sin u + C$

54. $\displaystyle\int u^n \sin u\, du = -u^n \cos u + n\int u^{n-1} \cos u\, du$

55. $\displaystyle\int u^n \cos u\, du = u^n \sin u - n\int u^{n-1} \sin u\, du$

56. $\displaystyle\int \frac{1}{1 \pm \sin u}\, du = \tan u \mp \sec u + C$

57. $\displaystyle\int \frac{1}{1 \pm \cos u}\, du = -\cot u \pm \csc u + C$

58. $\displaystyle\int \frac{1}{\sin u \cos u}\, du = \ln|\tan u| + C$

Forms Involving tan *u*, cot *u*, sec *u*, or csc *u*

59. $\displaystyle\int \tan u\, du = -\ln|\cos u| + C$

60. $\displaystyle\int \cot u\, du = \ln|\sin u| + C$

61. $\displaystyle\int \sec u\, du = \ln|\sec u + \tan u| + C$

62. $\displaystyle\int \csc u\, du = \ln|\csc u - \cot u| + C$ or $\displaystyle\int \csc u\, du = -\ln|\csc u + \cot u| + C$

63. $\displaystyle\int \tan^2 u\, du = -u + \tan u + C$

64. $\displaystyle\int \cot^2 u\, du = -u - \cot u + C$

65. $\displaystyle\int \sec^2 u\, du = \tan u + C$

66. $\displaystyle\int \csc^2 u\, du = -\cot u + C$

67. $\displaystyle\int \tan^n u\, du = \frac{\tan^{n-1} u}{n-1} - \int \tan^{n-2} u\, du,\ n \neq 1$

68. $\displaystyle\int \cot^n u\, du = -\frac{\cot^{n-1} u}{n-1} - \int (\cot^{n-2} u)\, du,\ n \neq 1$

69. $\displaystyle\int \sec^n u\, du = \frac{\sec^{n-2} u \tan u}{n-1} + \frac{n-2}{n-1}\int \sec^{n-2} u\, du,\ n \neq 1$

70. $\displaystyle\int \csc^n u\, du = -\frac{\csc^{n-2} u \cot u}{n-1} + \frac{n-2}{n-1}\int \csc^{n-2} u\, du,\ n \neq 1$

71. $\int \dfrac{1}{1 \pm \tan u} \, du = \dfrac{1}{2}\left(u \pm \ln|\cos u \pm \sin u|\right) + C$

72. $\int \dfrac{1}{1 \pm \cot u} \, du = \dfrac{1}{2}\left(u \mp \ln|\sin u \pm \cos u|\right) + C$

73. $\int \dfrac{1}{1 \pm \sec u} \, du = u + \cot u \mp \csc u + C$

74. $\int \dfrac{1}{1 \pm \csc u} \, du = u - \tan u \pm \sec u + C$

Forms Involving Inverse Trigonometric Functions

75. $\int \arcsin u \, du = u \arcsin u + \sqrt{1 - u^2} + C$

76. $\int \arccos u \, du = u \arccos u - \sqrt{1 - u^2} + C$

77. $\int \arctan u \, du = u \arctan u - \ln\sqrt{1 + u^2} + C$

78. $\int \text{arccot } u \, du = u \text{ arccot } u + \ln\sqrt{1 + u^2} + C$

79. $\int \text{arcsec } u \, du = u \text{ arcsec } u - \ln\left|u + \sqrt{u^2 - 1}\right| + C$

80. $\int \text{arccsc } u \, du = u \text{ arccsc } u + \ln\left|u + \sqrt{u^2 - 1}\right| + C$

Forms Involving e^u

81. $\int e^u \, du = e^u + C$

82. $\int u e^u \, du = (u - 1)e^u + C$

83. $\int u^n e^u \, du = u^n e^u - n \int u^{n-1} e^u \, du$

84. $\int \dfrac{1}{1 + e^u} \, du = u - \ln(1 + e^u) + C$

85. $\int e^{au} \sin bu \, du = \dfrac{e^{au}}{a^2 + b^2}(a \sin bu - b \cos bu) + C$

86. $\int e^{au} \cos bu \, du = \dfrac{e^{au}}{a^2 + b^2}(a \cos bu + b \sin bu) + C$

Forms Involving $\ln u$

87. $\int \ln u \, du = u(-1 + \ln u) + C$

88. $\int u \ln u \, du = \dfrac{u^2}{4}(-1 + 2 \ln u) + C$

89. $\int u^n \ln u \, du = \dfrac{u^{n+1}}{(n+1)^2}[-1 + (n+1) \ln u] + C, \quad n \neq -1$

90. $\int (\ln u)^2 \, du = u\left[2 - 2 \ln u + (\ln u)^2\right] + C$

91. $\int (\ln u)^n \, du = u(\ln u)^n - n \int (\ln u)^{n-1} \, du$

Forms Involving Hyperbolic Functions

92. $\int \cosh u \, du = \sinh u + C$

93. $\int \sinh u \, du = \cosh u + C$

94. $\int \text{sech}^2 u \, du = \tanh u + C$

95. $\int \text{csch}^2 u \, du = -\coth u + C$

96. $\int \text{sech } u \tanh u \, du = -\text{sech } u + C$

97. $\int \text{csch } u \coth u \, du = -\text{csch } u + C$

Forms Involving Inverse Hyperbolic Functions (in logarithmic form)

98. $\int \dfrac{du}{\sqrt{u^2 \pm a^2}} = \ln\left(u + \sqrt{u^2 \pm a^2}\right) + C$

99. $\int \dfrac{du}{a^2 - u^2} = \dfrac{1}{2a} \ln\left|\dfrac{a + u}{a - u}\right| + C$

100. $\int \dfrac{du}{u\sqrt{a^2 \pm u^2}} = -\dfrac{1}{a} \ln\dfrac{a + \sqrt{a^2 \pm u^2}}{|u|} + C$

C Precalculus Review

C.1 Real Numbers and the Real Number Line

- ◼ Represent and classify real numbers.
- ◼ Order real numbers and use inequalities.
- ◼ Find the absolute values of real numbers and find the distance between two real numbers.

Real Numbers and the Real Number Line

Real numbers can be represented by a coordinate system called the **real number line** or x-axis (see Figure C.1). The real number corresponding to a point on the real number line is the **coordinate** of the point. As Figure C.1 shows, it is customary to identify those points whose coordinates are integers.

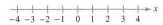

The real number line
Figure C.1

The point on the real number line corresponding to zero is the **origin** and is denoted by 0. The **positive direction** (to the right) is denoted by an arrowhead and is the direction of increasing values of x. Numbers to the right of the origin are **positive.** Numbers to the left of the origin are **negative.** The term **nonnegative** describes a number that is either positive or zero. The term **nonpositive** describes a number that is either negative or zero.

Each point on the real number line corresponds to one and only one real number, and each real number corresponds to one and only one point on the real number line. This type of relationship is called a **one-to-one correspondence.**

Each of the four points in Figure C.2 corresponds to a **rational number**—one that can be written as the ratio of two integers. $\left(\text{Note that } 4.5 = \frac{9}{2} \text{ and } -2.6 = -\frac{13}{5}.\right)$ Rational numbers can be represented either by *terminating decimals* such as $\frac{2}{5} = 0.4$, or by *repeating decimals* such as $\frac{1}{3} = 0.333 \ldots = 0.\overline{3}$.

Real numbers that are not rational are **irrational.** Irrational numbers cannot be represented as terminating or repeating decimals. In computations, irrational numbers are represented by decimal approximations. Here are three familiar examples.

$$\sqrt{2} \approx 1.414213562$$
$$\pi \approx 3.141592654$$
$$e \approx 2.718281828$$

(See Figure C.3.)

Rational numbers
Figure C.2

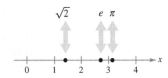

Irrational numbers
Figure C.3

Order and Inequalities

One important property of real numbers is that they are **ordered.** For two real numbers a and b, a is **less than** b when $b - a$ is positive. This order is denoted by the **inequality**

$$a < b.$$

This relationship can also be described by saying that b is **greater than** a and writing $b > a$. If three real numbers a, b, and c are ordered such that $a < b$ and $b < c$, then b is **between** a and c and $a < b < c$.

Geometrically, $a < b$ if and only if a lies to the *left* of b on the real number line (see Figure C.4). For example, $1 < 2$ because 1 lies to the left of 2 on the real number line.

Several properties used in working with inequalities are listed below. Similar properties are obtained when $<$ is replaced by $\leq$ and $>$ is replaced by $\geq$. (The symbols $\leq$ and $\geq$ mean **less than or equal to** and **greater than or equal to,** respectively.)

$a < b$ if and only if a lies to the left of b.

Figure C.4

Properties of Inequalities

Let a, b, c, d, and k be real numbers.

1. If $a < b$ and $b < c$, then $a < c$.   Transitive Property

2. If $a < b$ and $c < d$, then $a + c < b + d$.   Add inequalities.

3. If $a < b$, then $a + k < b + k$.   Add a constant.

4. If $a < b$ and $k > 0$, then $ak < bk$.   Multiply by a positive constant.

5. If $a < b$ and $k < 0$, then $ak > bk$.   Multiply by a negative constant.

Note that you *reverse the inequality* when you multiply the inequality by a negative number. For example, if $x < 3$, then $-4x > -12$. This also applies to division by a negative number. So, if $-2x > 4$, then $x < -2$.

A **set** is a collection of elements. Two common sets are the set of real numbers and the set of points on the real number line. Many problems in calculus involve **subsets** of one of these two sets. In such cases, it is convenient to use **set notation** of the form $\{x: \text{condition on } x\}$, which is read as follows.

$$\underbrace{\{}_{\text{The set of}} \underbrace{x}_{\text{all } x} \underbrace{:}_{\text{such that}} \underbrace{\text{condition on } x\}}_{\text{a certain condition is true.}}$$

For example, you can describe the set of positive real numbers as

$$\{x: \ x > 0\}. \qquad \text{Set of positive real numbers}$$

Similarly, you can describe the set of nonnegative real numbers as

$$\{x: \ x \geq 0\}. \qquad \text{Set of nonnegative real numbers}$$

The **union** of two sets A and B, denoted by $A \cup B$, is the set of elements that are members of A *or* B *or both*. The **intersection** of two sets A and B, denoted by $A \cap B$, is the set of elements that are members of A *and* B. Two sets are **disjoint** when they have no elements in common.

The most commonly used subsets are **intervals** on the real number line. For example, the **open** interval

$$(a, b) = \{x \colon a < x < b\} \qquad \text{Open interval}$$

is the set of all real numbers greater than a and less than b, where a and b are the **endpoints** of the interval. Note that the endpoints are not included in an open interval. Intervals that include their endpoints are **closed** and are denoted by

$$[a, b] = \{x \colon a \leq x \leq b\}. \qquad \text{Closed interval}$$

The nine basic types of intervals on the real number line are shown in the table below. The first four are **bounded intervals** and the remaining five are **unbounded intervals.** Unbounded intervals are also classified as open or closed. The intervals $(-\infty, b)$ and (a, ∞) are open, the intervals $(-\infty, b]$ and $[a, \infty)$ are closed, and the interval $(-\infty, \infty)$ is considered to be both open *and* closed.

Intervals on the Real Number Line

	Interval Notation	Set Notation	Graph
Bounded open interval	(a, b)	$\{x \colon a < x < b\}$	
Bounded closed interval	$[a, b]$	$\{x \colon a \leq x \leq b\}$	
Bound intervals (neither open nor closed)	$[a, b)$	$\{x \colon a \leq x < b\}$	
	$(a, b]$	$\{x \colon a < x \leq b\}$	
Unbounded open intervals	$(-\infty, b)$	$\{x \colon x < b\}$	
	(a, ∞)	$\{x \colon x > a\}$	
Unbounded closed intervals	$(-\infty, b]$	$\{x \colon x \leq b\}$	
	$[a, \infty)$	$\{x \colon x \geq a\}$	
Entire real line	$(-\infty, \infty)$	$\{x \colon x \text{ is a real number}\}$	

Note that the symbols ∞ and $-\infty$ refer to positive and negative infinity, respectively. These symbols do not denote real numbers. They simply enable you to describe unbounded conditions more concisely. For instance, the interval $[a, \infty)$ is unbounded to the right because it includes *all* real numbers that are greater than or equal to a.

| EXAMPLE 1 | **Liquid and Gaseous States of Water** |

Describe the intervals on the real number line that correspond to the temperatures x (in degrees Celsius) of water in

a. a liquid state.   **b.** a gaseous state.

Solution

a. Water is in a liquid state at temperatures greater than 0°C and less than 100°C, as shown in Figure C.5(a).

$$(0, 100) = \{x: \; 0 < x < 100\}$$

b. Water is in a gaseous state (steam) at temperatures greater than or equal to 100°C, as shown in Figure C.5(b).

$$[100, \infty) = \{x: \; x \geq 100\}$$

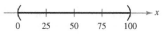

(a) Temperature range of water
(in degrees Celsius)

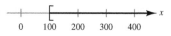

(b) Temperature range of steam
(in degrees Celsius)

Figure C.5

If a real number a is a **solution** of an inequality, then the inequality is **satisfied** (is true) when a is substituted for x. The set of all solutions is the **solution set** of the inequality.

| EXAMPLE 2 | **Solving an Inequality** |

Solve $2x - 5 < 7$.

Solution

$2x - 5 < 7$	Write original inequality.
$2x - 5 + 5 < 7 + 5$	Add 5 to each side.
$2x < 12$	Simplify.
$\dfrac{2x}{2} < \dfrac{12}{2}$	Divide each side by 2.
$x < 6$	Simplify.

The solution set is $(-\infty, 6)$.

In Example 2, all five inequalities listed as steps in the solution are called **equivalent** because they have the same solution set.

Once you have solved an inequality, check some x-values in your solution set to verify that they satisfy the original inequality. You should also check some values outside your solution set to verify that they *do not* satisfy the inequality. For example, Figure C.6 shows that when $x = 0$ or $x = 5$ the inequality $2x - 5 < 7$ is satisfied, but when $x = 7$ the inequality $2x - 5 < 7$ is not satisfied.

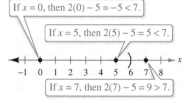

If $x = 0$, then $2(0) - 5 = -5 < 7$.

If $x = 5$, then $2(5) - 5 = 5 < 7$.

If $x = 7$, then $2(7) - 5 = 9 > 7$.

Checking solutions of $2x - 5 < 7$
Figure C.6

EXAMPLE 3 **Solving a Double Inequality**

Solve $-3 \le 2 - 5x \le 12$.

Solution

$-3 \le$	$2 - 5x$	≤ 12	Write original inequality.
$-3 - 2 \le 2 - 5x - 2 \le 12 - 2$			Subtract 2 from each part.
$-5 \le$	$-5x$	≤ 10	Simplify.
$\dfrac{-5}{-5} \ge$	$\dfrac{-5x}{-5}$	$\ge \dfrac{10}{-5}$	Divide each part by -5 and reverse both inequalities.
$1 \ge$	x	≥ -2	Simplify.

The solution set is $[-2, 1]$, as shown in Figure C.7.

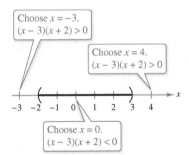

$[-2, 1]$

Solution set of $-3 \le 2 - 5x \le 12$

Figure C.7

The inequalities in Examples 2 and 3 are **linear inequalities**—that is, they involve first-degree polynomials. To solve inequalities involving polynomials of higher degree, use the fact that a polynomial can change signs *only* at its real **zeros** (the x-values that make the polynomial equal to zero). Between two consecutive real zeros, a polynomial must be either entirely positive or entirely negative. This means that when the real zeros of a polynomial are put in order, they divide the real number line into **test intervals** in which the polynomial has no sign changes. So, if a polynomial has the factored form

$$(x - r_1)(x - r_2) \cdots (x - r_n), \qquad r_1 < r_2 < r_3 < \cdots < r_n$$

then the test intervals are

$$(-\infty, r_1), \quad (r_1, r_2), \ldots, \quad (r_{n-1}, r_n), \quad \text{and} \quad (r_n, \infty).$$

To determine the sign of the polynomial in each test interval, you need to test only *one value* from the interval.

EXAMPLE 4 **Solving a Quadratic Inequality**

Solve $x^2 < x + 6$.

Solution

$x^2 < x + 6$	Write original inequality.
$x^2 - x - 6 < 0$	Write in general form.
$(x - 3)(x + 2) < 0$	Factor.

The polynomial $x^2 - x - 6$ has $x = -2$ and $x = 3$ as its zeros. So, you can solve the inequality by testing the sign of $x^2 - x - 6$ in each of the test intervals $(-\infty, -2)$, $(-2, 3)$, and $(3, \infty)$. To test an interval, choose any number in the interval and determine the sign of $x^2 - x - 6$. After doing this, you will find that the polynomial is positive for all real numbers in the first and third intervals and negative for all real numbers in the second interval. The solution of the original inequality is therefore $(-2, 3)$, as shown in Figure C.8.

Choose $x = -3$.
$(x - 3)(x + 2) > 0$

Choose $x = 4$.
$(x - 3)(x + 2) > 0$

Choose $x = 0$.
$(x - 3)(x + 2) < 0$

Testing an interval

Figure C.8

Absolute Value and Distance

If a is a real number, then the **absolute value** of a is

$$|a| = \begin{cases} a, & a \geq 0 \\ -a, & a < 0. \end{cases}$$

The absolute value of a number cannot be negative. For example, let $a = -4$. Then, because $-4 < 0$, you have

$$|a| = |-4| = -(-4) = 4.$$

Remember that the symbol $-a$ does not necessarily mean that $-a$ is negative.

• **REMARK**   You are asked to prove these properties in Exercises 73, 75, 76, and 77.

Operations with Absolute Value

Let a and b be real numbers and let n be a positive integer.

1. $|ab| = |a|\,|b|$ **2.** $\left|\dfrac{a}{b}\right| = \dfrac{|a|}{|b|}, \quad b \neq 0$

3. $|a| = \sqrt{a^2}$ **4.** $|a^n| = |a|^n$

Properties of Inequalities and Absolute Value

Let a and b be real numbers and let k be a positive real number.

1. $-|a| \leq a \leq |a|$
2. $|a| \leq k$ if and only if $-k \leq a \leq k$.
3. $|a| \geq k$ if and only if $a \leq -k$ or $a \geq k$.
4. *Triangle Inequality:* $|a + b| \leq |a| + |b|$

Properties 2 and 3 are also true when $\leq$ is replaced by $<$ and $\geq$ is replaced by $>$.

EXAMPLE 5   **Solving an Absolute Value Inequality**

Solve $|x - 3| \leq 2$.

Solution   Using the second property of inequalities and absolute value, you can rewrite the original inequality as a double inequality.

$$
\begin{array}{llll}
-2 \leq & x - 3 & \leq 2 & \quad \text{Write as double inequality.} \\
-2 + 3 \leq & x - 3 + 3 & \leq 2 + 3 & \quad \text{Add 3 to each part.} \\
1 \leq & x & \leq 5 & \quad \text{Simplify.}
\end{array}
$$

The solution set is $[1, 5]$, as shown in Figure C.9.

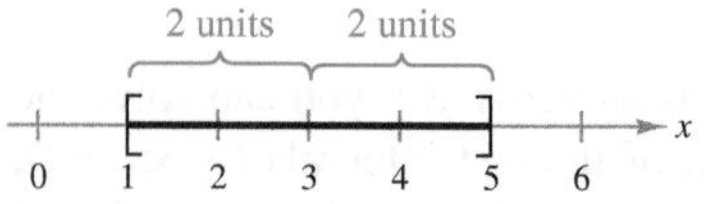

2 units   2 units

$$\begin{array}{ccccccc} + & | & | & | & | & | & + \\ 0 & 1 & 2 & 3 & 4 & 5 & 6 \end{array} \longrightarrow x$$

Solution set of $|x - 3| \leq 2$
Figure C.9

Solution set of $|x + 2| > 3$
Figure C.10

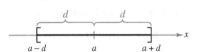

Solution set of $|x - a| \le d$

Solution set of $|x - a| \ge d$
Figure C.11

EXAMPLE 6 **A Two-Interval Solution Set**

Solve $|x + 2| > 3$.

Solution Using the third property of inequalities and absolute value, you can rewrite the original inequality as two linear inequalities.

$$x + 2 < -3 \quad \text{or} \quad x + 2 > 3$$
$$x < -5 \qquad\qquad x > 1$$

The solution set is the union of the disjoint intervals $(-\infty, -5)$ and $(1, \infty)$, as shown in Figure C.10.

Examples 5 and 6 illustrate the general results shown in Figure C.11. Note that for $d > 0$, the solution set for the inequality $|x - a| \le d$ is a *single* interval, whereas the solution set for the inequality $|x - a| \ge d$ is the union of *two* disjoint intervals.

The **distance between two points** a and b on the real number line is given by

$$d = |a - b| = |b - a|.$$

The **directed distance from a to b** is $b - a$ and the **directed distance from b to a** is $a - b$, as shown in Figure C.12.

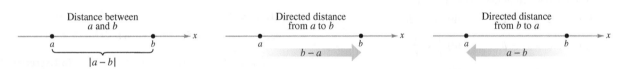

Figure C.12

EXAMPLE 7 **Distance on the Real Number Line**

a. The distance between -3 and 4 is

$$|4 - (-3)| = |7| = 7 \quad \text{or} \quad |-3 - 4| = |-7| = 7.$$

(See Figure C.13.)

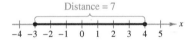

Figure C.13

b. The directed distance from -3 to 4 is

$$4 - (-3) = 7.$$

c. The directed distance from 4 to -3 is

$$-3 - 4 = -7.$$

The **midpoint** of an interval with endpoints a and b is the average value of a and b. That is,

$$\text{Midpoint of interval } (a, b) = \frac{a + b}{2}.$$

To show that this is the midpoint, you need only show that $(a + b)/2$ is equidistant from a and b.

C.1 Exercises

Rational or Irrational?   In Exercises 1–10, determine whether the real number is rational or irrational.

1. 0.7

2. -3678

3. $\dfrac{3\pi}{2}$

4. $3\sqrt{2} - 1$

5. $4.3\overline{451}$

6. $\frac{22}{7}$

7. $\sqrt[3]{64}$

8. $0.\overline{8177}$

9. $4\frac{5}{8}$

10. $\left(\sqrt{2}\right)^3$

Repeating Decimal   In Exercises 11–14, write the repeating decimal as a ratio of two integers using the following procedure. If $x = 0.6363\ldots$, then $100x = 63.6363\ldots$. Subtracting the first equation from the second produces $99x = 63$ or $x = \frac{63}{99} = \frac{7}{11}$.

11. $0.\overline{36}$

12. $0.3\overline{18}$

13. $0.\overline{297}$

14. $0.\overline{9900}$

15. Using Properties of Inequalities   Given $a < b$, determine which of the following are true.

(a) $a + 2 < b + 2$

(b) $5b < 5a$

(c) $5 - a > 5 - b$

(d) $\dfrac{1}{a} < \dfrac{1}{b}$

(e) $(a - b)(b - a) > 0$

(f) $a^2 < b^2$

16. Intervals and Graphs on the Real Number Line   Complete the table with the appropriate interval notation, set notation, and graph on the real number line.

Interval Notation	Set Notation	Graph
$(-\infty, -4]$		
	$\left\{x \colon 3 \le x \le \frac{11}{2}\right\}$	
$(-1, 7)$		

Analyzing an Inequality   In Exercises 17–20, verbally describe the subset of real numbers represented by the inequality. Sketch the subset on the real number line, and state whether the interval is bounded or unbounded.

17. $-3 < x < 3$

18. $x \ge 4$

19. $x \le 5$

20. $0 \le x < 8$

Using Inequality and Interval Notation   In Exercises 21–24, use inequality and interval notation to describe the set.

21. y is at least 4.

22. q is nonnegative.

23. The interest rate r on loans is expected to be greater than 3% and no more than 7%.

24. The temperature T is forecast to be above 90°F today.

Solving an Inequality   In Exercises 25–44, solve the inequality and graph the solution on the real number line.

25. $2x - 1 \ge 0$

26. $3x + 1 \ge 2x + 2$

27. $-4 < 2x - 3 < 4$

28. $0 \le x + 3 < 5$

29. $\dfrac{x}{2} + \dfrac{x}{3} > 5$

30. $x > \dfrac{1}{x}$

31. $|x| < 1$

32. $\dfrac{x}{2} - \dfrac{x}{3} > 5$

33. $\left|\dfrac{x - 3}{2}\right| \ge 5$

34. $\left|\dfrac{x}{2}\right| > 3$

35. $|x - a| < b, \ b > 0$

36. $|x + 2| < 5$

37. $|2x + 1| < 5$

38. $|3x + 1| \ge 4$

39. $\left|1 - \dfrac{2}{3}x\right| < 1$

40. $|9 - 2x| < 1$

41. $x^2 \le 3 - 2x$

42. $x^4 - x \le 0$

43. $x^2 + x - 1 \le 5$

44. $2x^2 + 1 < 9x - 3$

Distance on the Real Number Line   In Exercises 45–48, find the directed distance from a to b, the directed distance from b to a, and the distance between a and b.

45.

46.

47. (a) $a = 126, \ b = 75$

(b) $a = -126, \ b = -75$

48. (a) $a = 9.34, \ b = -5.65$

(b) $a = \frac{16}{5}, \ b = \frac{112}{75}$

Using Absolute Value Notation   In Exercises 49–54, use absolute value notation to define the interval or pair of intervals on the real number line.

49.

50.

51.

52.

53. (a) All numbers that are at most 10 units from 12

(b) All numbers that are at least 10 units from 12

54. (a) y is at most two units from a.

(b) y is less than δ units from c.

Finding the Midpoint In Exercises 55–58, find the midpoint of the interval.

55.

56.

57. (a) $[7, 21]$

(b) $[8.6, 11.4]$

58. (a) $[-6.85, 9.35]$

(b) $[-4.6, -1.3]$

59. Profit   The revenue R from selling x units of a product is

$$R = 115.95x$$

and the cost C of producing x units is

$$C = 95x + 750.$$

To make a (positive) profit, R must be greater than C. For what values of x will the product return a profit?

60. Fleet Costs   A utility company has a fleet of vans. The annual operating cost C (in dollars) of each van is estimated to be

$$C = 0.32m + 2300$$

where m is measured in miles. The company wants the annual operating cost of each van to be less than \$10,000. To do this, m must be less than what value?

61. Fair Coin   To determine whether a coin is fair (has an equal probability of landing tails up or heads up), you toss the coin 100 times and record the number of heads x. The coin is declared unfair when

$$\left|\frac{x - 50}{5}\right| \geq 1.645.$$

For what values of x will the coin be declared unfair?

62. Daily Production   The estimated daily oil production p at a refinery is

$$|p - 2,250,000| < 125,000$$

where p is measured in barrels. Determine the high and low production levels.

Which Number is Greater? In Exercises 63 and 64, determine which of the two real numbers is greater.

63. (a) π or $\frac{355}{113}$

(b) π or $\frac{22}{7}$

64. (a) $\frac{224}{151}$ or $\frac{144}{97}$

(b) $\frac{73}{81}$ or $\frac{6427}{7132}$

65. Approximation—Powers of 10   Light travels at the speed of 2.998×10^8 meters per second. Which best estimates the distance in meters that light travels in a year?

(a) 9.5×10^5

(b) 9.5×10^{15}

(c) 9.5×10^{12}

(d) 9.6×10^{16}

66. Writing   The accuracy of an approximation of a number is related to how many significant digits there are in the approximation. Write a definition of significant digits and illustrate the concept with examples.

True or False? In Exercises 67–72, determine whether the statement is true or false. If it is false, explain why or give an example that shows it is false.

67. The reciprocal of a nonzero integer is an integer.

68. The reciprocal of a nonzero rational number is a rational number.

69. Each real number is either rational or irrational.

70. The absolute value of each real number is positive.

71. If $x < 0$, then $\sqrt{x^2} = -x$.

72. If a and b are any two distinct real numbers, then $a < b$ or $a > b$.

Proof In Exercises 73–80, prove the property.

73. $|ab| = |a||b|$

74. $|a - b| = |b - a|$

[Hint: $(a - b) = (-1)(b - a)$]

75. $\left|\frac{a}{b}\right| = \frac{|a|}{|b|}, \quad b \neq 0$

76. $|a| = \sqrt{a^2}$

77. $|a^n| = |a|^n, \quad n = 1, 2, 3, \ldots$

78. $-|a| \leq a \leq |a|$

79. $|a| \leq k$ if and only if $-k \leq a \leq k, \quad k > 0$.

80. $|a| \geq k$ if and only if $a \leq -k$ or $a \geq k, \quad k > 0$.

81. Proof   Find an example for which $|a - b| > |a| - |b|$, and an example for which $|a - b| = |a| - |b|$. Then prove that $|a - b| \geq |a| - |b|$ for all a, b.

82. Maximum and Minimum   Show that the maximum of two numbers a and b is given by the formula

$$\max(a, b) = \tfrac{1}{2}(a + b + |a - b|).$$

Derive a similar formula for $\min(a, b)$.

C.2 The Cartesian Plane

- Understand the Cartesian plane.
- Use the Distance Formula to find the distance between two points and use the Midpoint Formula to find the midpoint of a line segment.
- Find equations of circles and sketch the graphs of circles.

The Cartesian Plane

Just as you can represent real numbers by points on a real number line, you can represent ordered pairs of real numbers by points in a plane called the **rectangular coordinate system,** or the **Cartesian plane,** after the French mathematician René Descartes.

The Cartesian plane is formed by using two real number lines intersecting at right angles, as shown in Figure C.14. The horizontal real number line is usually called the **x-axis,** and the vertical real number line is usually called the **y-axis.** The point of intersection of these two axes is the **origin.** The two axes divide the plane into four parts called **quadrants.**

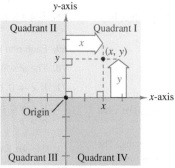

The Cartesian plane
Figure C.14

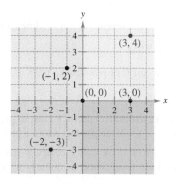

Points represented by ordered pairs
Figure C.15

Each point in the plane is identified by an **ordered pair** (x, y) of real numbers x and y, called the **coordinates** of the point. The number x represents the directed distance from the y-axis to the point, and the number y represents the directed distance from the x-axis to the point (see Figure C.14). For the point (x, y), the first coordinate is the **x-coordinate** or **abscissa,** and the second coordinate is the **y-coordinate** or **ordinate.** For example, Figure C.15 shows the locations of the points $(-1, 2)$, $(3, 4)$, $(0, 0)$, $(3, 0)$, and $(-2, -3)$ in the Cartesian plane. The signs of the coordinates of a point determine the quadrant in which the point lies. For instance, if $x > 0$ and $y < 0$, then the point (x, y) lies in Quadrant IV.

Note that an ordered pair (a, b) is used to denote either a point in the plane *or* an open interval on the real number line. This, however, should not be confusing—the nature of the problem should clarify whether a point in the plane or an open interval is being discussed.

The Distance and Midpoint Formulas

Recall from the Pythagorean Theorem that, in a right triangle, the hypotenuse c and sides a and b are related by $a^2 + b^2 = c^2$. Conversely, if $a^2 + b^2 = c^2$, then the triangle is a right triangle (see Figure C.16).

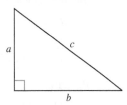

The Pythagorean Theorem:
$a^2 + b^2 = c^2$

Figure C.16

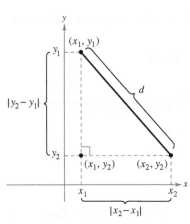

The distance between two points
Figure C.17

Now, consider the problem of determining the distance d between the two points (x_1, y_1) and (x_2, y_2) in the plane. If the points lie on a horizontal line, then $y_1 = y_2$ and the distance between the points is $|x_2 - x_1|$. If the points lie on a vertical line, then $x_1 = x_2$ and the distance between the points is $|y_2 - y_1|$. When the two points do not lie on a horizontal or vertical line, they can be used to form a right triangle, as shown in Figure C.17. The length of the vertical side of the triangle is $|y_2 - y_1|$, and the length of the horizontal side is $|x_2 - x_1|$. By the Pythagorean Theorem, it follows that

$$d^2 = |x_2 - x_1|^2 + |y_2 - y_1|^2$$
$$d = \sqrt{|x_2 - x_1|^2 + |y_2 - y_1|^2}.$$

Replacing $|x_2 - x_1|^2$ and $|y_2 - y_1|^2$ by the equivalent expressions $(x_2 - x_1)^2$ and $(y_2 - y_1)^2$ produces the **Distance Formula.**

Distance Formula

The distance d between the points (x_1, y_1) and (x_2, y_2) in the plane is given by

$$d = \sqrt{(x_2 - x_1)^2 + (y_2 - y_1)^2}.$$

EXAMPLE 1 **Finding the Distance Between Two Points**

Find the distance between the points $(-2, 1)$ and $(3, 4)$.

Solution

$$
\begin{aligned}
d &= \sqrt{(x_2 - x_1)^2 + (y_2 - y_1)^2} &&\text{Distance Formula} \\
&= \sqrt{[3 - (-2)]^2 + (4 - 1)^2} &&\text{Substitute for } x_1, y_1, x_2, \text{ and } y_2. \\
&= \sqrt{5^2 + 3^2} \\
&= \sqrt{25 + 9} \\
&= \sqrt{34} \\
&\approx 5.83
\end{aligned}
$$

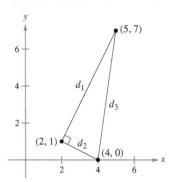

Verifying a right triangle
Figure C.18

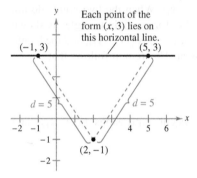

Figure C.19

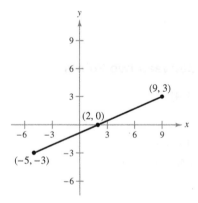

Midpoint of a line segment
Figure C.20

EXAMPLE 2   Verifying a Right Triangle

Verify that the points $(2, 1)$, $(4, 0)$, and $(5, 7)$ form the vertices of a right triangle.

Solution   Figure C.18 shows the triangle formed by the three points. The lengths of the three sides are as follows.

$$d_1 = \sqrt{(5 - 2)^2 + (7 - 1)^2} = \sqrt{9 + 36} = \sqrt{45}$$
$$d_2 = \sqrt{(4 - 2)^2 + (0 - 1)^2} = \sqrt{4 + 1} = \sqrt{5}$$
$$d_3 = \sqrt{(5 - 4)^2 + (7 - 0)^2} = \sqrt{1 + 49} = \sqrt{50}$$

Because

$$d_1^2 + d_2^2 = 45 + 5 = 50 \qquad \text{Sum of squares of sides}$$

and

$$d_3^2 = 50 \qquad \text{Square of hypotenuse}$$

you can apply the Pythagorean Theorem to conclude that the triangle is a right triangle.

EXAMPLE 3   Using the Distance Formula

Find x such that the distance between $(x, 3)$ and $(2, -1)$ is 5.

Solution   Using the Distance Formula, you can write the following.

$$5 = \sqrt{(x - 2)^2 + [3 - (-1)]^2} \qquad \text{Distance Formula}$$
$$25 = (x^2 - 4x + 4) + 16 \qquad \text{Square each side.}$$
$$0 = x^2 - 4x - 5 \qquad \text{Write in general form.}$$
$$0 = (x - 5)(x + 1) \qquad \text{Factor.}$$

So, $x = 5$ or $x = -1$, and you can conclude that there are two solutions. That is, each of the points $(5, 3)$ and $(-1, 3)$ lies five units from the point $(2, -1)$, as shown in Figure C.19.

The coordinates of the **midpoint** of the line segment joining two points can be found by "averaging" the x-coordinates of the two points and "averaging" the y-coordinates of the two points. That is, the midpoint of the line segment joining the points (x_1, y_1) and (x_2, y_2) in the plane is

$$\left(\frac{x_1 + x_2}{2}, \frac{y_1 + y_2}{2} \right). \qquad \text{Midpoint Formula}$$

For instance, the midpoint of the line segment joining the points $(-5, -3)$ and $(9, 3)$ is

$$\left(\frac{-5 + 9}{2}, \frac{-3 + 3}{2} \right) = (2, 0)$$

as shown in Figure C.20.

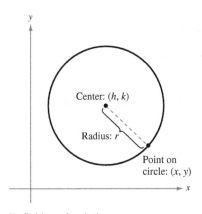

Definition of a circle
Figure C.21

Equations of Circles

A **circle** can be defined as the set of all points in a plane that are equidistant from a fixed point. The fixed point is the **center** of the circle, and the distance between the center and a point on the circle is the **radius** (see Figure C.21).

You can use the Distance Formula to write an equation for the circle with center (h, k) and radius r. Let (x, y) be any point on the circle. Then the distance between (x, y) and the center (h, k) is given by

$$\sqrt{(x - h)^2 + (y - k)^2} = r.$$

By squaring each side of this equation, you obtain the **standard form of the equation of a circle.**

Standard Form of The Equation of a Circle

The point (x, y) lies on the circle of radius r and center (h, k) if and only if

$$(x - h)^2 + (y - k)^2 = r^2.$$

The standard form of the equation of a circle with center at the origin, $(h, k) = (0, 0)$, is

$$x^2 + y^2 = r^2.$$

If $r = 1$, then the circle is called the **unit circle.**

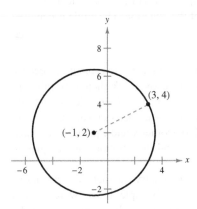

Figure C.22

EXAMPLE 4   **Writing the Equation of a Circle**

The point $(3, 4)$ lies on a circle whose center is at $(-1, 2)$, as shown in Figure C.22. Write the standard form of the equation of this circle.

Solution   The radius of the circle is the distance between $(-1, 2)$ and $(3, 4)$.

$$r = \sqrt{[3 - (-1)]^2 + (4 - 2)^2} = \sqrt{16 + 4} = \sqrt{20}$$

You can write the standard form of the equation of this circle as

$$[x - (-1)]^2 + (y - 2)^2 = (\sqrt{20})^2$$
$$(x + 1)^2 + (y - 2)^2 = 20. \qquad \text{Write in standard form.}$$

By squaring and simplifying, the equation $(x - h)^2 + (y - k)^2 = r^2$ can be written in the following **general form of the equation of a circle.**

$$Ax^2 + Ay^2 + Dx + Ey + F = 0, \quad A \neq 0$$

To convert such an equation to the standard form

$$(x - h)^2 + (y - k)^2 = p$$

you can use a process called **completing the square.** If $p > 0$, then the graph of the equation is a circle. If $p = 0$, then the graph is the single point (h, k). If $p < 0$, then the equation has no graph.

EXAMPLE 5   **Completing the Square**

Sketch the graph of the circle whose general equation is

$$4x^2 + 4y^2 + 20x - 16y + 37 = 0.$$

Solution To complete the square, first divide by 4 so that the coefficients of x^2 and y^2 are both 1.

$$4x^2 + 4y^2 + 20x - 16y + 37 = 0 \qquad \text{Write original equation.}$$

$$x^2 + y^2 + 5x - 4y + \frac{37}{4} = 0 \qquad \text{Divide by 4.}$$

$$(x^2 + 5x +) + (y^2 - 4y +) = -\frac{37}{4} \qquad \text{Group terms.}$$

$$\left(x^2 + 5x + \frac{25}{4}\right) + (y^2 - 4y + 4) = -\frac{37}{4} + \frac{25}{4} + 4 \qquad \begin{array}{l}\text{Complete the square by} \\ \text{adding } \left(\frac{5}{2}\right)^2 = \frac{25}{4} \text{ and} \\ \left(\frac{4}{2}\right)^2 = 4 \text{ to each side.}\end{array}$$

$$\underbrace{\qquad}_{(\text{half})^2} \qquad \underbrace{\qquad}_{(\text{half})^2}$$

$$\left(x + \frac{5}{2}\right)^2 + (y - 2)^2 = 1 \qquad \text{Write in standard form.}$$

Note that you complete the square by adding the square of half the coefficient of x *and* the square of half the coefficient of y to each side of the equation. The circle is centered at $\left(-\frac{5}{2}, 2\right)$ and its radius is 1, as shown in Figure C.23.

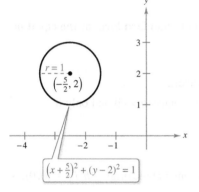

A circle with a radius of 1 and center at $\left(-\frac{5}{2}, 2\right)$

Figure C.23

You have now reviewed some fundamental concepts of *analytic geometry*. Because these concepts are in common use today, it is easy to overlook their revolutionary nature. At the time analytic geometry was being developed by Pierre de Fermat and René Descartes, the two major branches of mathematics—geometry and algebra—were largely independent of each other. Circles belonged to geometry and equations belonged to algebra. The coordination of the points on a circle and the solutions of an equation belongs to what is now called analytic geometry.

It is important to become skilled in analytic geometry so that you can move easily between geometry and algebra. For instance, in Example 4, you were given a geometric description of a circle and were asked to find an algebraic equation for the circle. So, you were moving from geometry to algebra. Similarly, in Example 5 you were given an algebraic equation and asked to sketch a geometric picture. In this case, you were moving from algebra to geometry. These two examples illustrate the two most common problems in analytic geometry.

1. Given a graph, find its equation.

Geometry ⟹ Algebra

2. Given an equation, find its graph.

Algebra ⟹ Geometry

C.2 Exercises

Using the Distance and Midpoint Formulas **In Exercises 1–6, (a) plot the points, (b) find the distance between the points, and (c) find the midpoint of the line segment joining the points.**

1. $(2, 1), (4, 5)$

2. $(-3, 2), (3, -2)$

3. $\left(\frac{1}{2}, 1\right), \left(-\frac{3}{2}, -5\right)$

4. $\left(\frac{2}{3}, -\frac{1}{3}\right), \left(\frac{5}{6}, 1\right)$

5. $\left(1, \sqrt{3}\right), (-1, 1)$

6. $(-2, 0), \left(0, \sqrt{2}\right)$

Locating a Point **In Exercises 7–10, determine the quadrant(s) in which (x, y) is located so that the condition(s) is (are) satisfied.**

7. $x = -2$ and $y > 0$

8. $y < -2$

9. $xy > 0$

10. $(x, -y)$ is in Quadrant II.

Vertices of a Polygon **In Exercises 11–14, show that the points are the vertices of the polygon. (A rhombus is a quadrilateral whose sides are all the same length.)**

Vertices	Polygon
11. $(4, 0), (2, 1), (-1, -5)$	Right triangle
12. $(1, -3), (3, 2), (-2, 4)$	Isosceles triangle
13. $(0, 0), (1, 2), (2, 1), (3, 3)$	Rhombus
14. $(0, 1), (3, 7), (4, 4), (1, -2)$	Parallelogram

15. Number of Stores The table shows the number y of Target stores for each year x from 2002 through 2011. (*Source:* Target Corp.)

Year, x	2002	2003	2004	2005	2006
Number, y	1147	1225	1308	1397	1488

Year, x	2007	2008	2009	2010	2011
Number, y	1591	1682	1740	1750	1763

Select reasonable scales on the coordinate axes and plot the points (x, y).

16. Conjecture Plot the points $(2, 1), (-3, 5)$, and $(7, -3)$ in a rectangular coordinate system. Then change the sign of the x-coordinate of each point and plot the three new points in the same rectangular coordinate system. What conjecture can you make about the location of a point when the sign of the x-coordinate is changed? Repeat the exercise for the case in which the signs of the y-coordinates are changed.

Collinear Points? **In Exercises 17–20, use the Distance Formula to determine whether the points lie on the same line.**

17. $(0, -4), (2, 0), (3, 2)$

18. $(0, 4), (7, -6), (-5, 11)$

19. $(-2, 1), (-1, 0), (2, -2)$

20. $(-1, 1), (3, 3), (5, 5)$

Using the Distance Formula **In Exercises 21 and 22, find x such that the distance between the points is 5.**

21. $(0, 0), (x, -4)$

22. $(2, -1), (x, 2)$

Using the Distance Formula **In Exercises 23 and 24, find y such that the distance between the points is 8.**

23. $(0, 0), (3, y)$

24. $(5, 1), (5, y)$

25. Using the Midpoint Formula Use the Midpoint Formula to find the three points that divide the line segment joining (x_1, y_1) and (x_2, y_2) into four equal parts.

26. Using the Midpoint Formula Use the result of Exercise 25 to find the points that divide the line segment joining the given points into four equal parts.

(a) $(1, -2), (4, -1)$ (b) $(-2, -3), (0, 0)$

Matching **In Exercises 27–30, match the equation with its graph. [The graphs are labeled (a), (b), (c), and (d).]**

(a)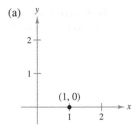

(b)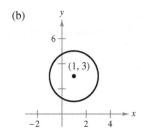

(c)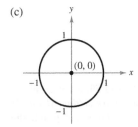

(d)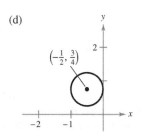

27. $x^2 + y^2 = 1$

28. $(x - 1)^2 + (y - 3)^2 = 4$

29. $(x - 1)^2 + y^2 = 0$

30. $\left(x + \frac{1}{2}\right)^2 + \left(y - \frac{3}{4}\right)^2 = \frac{1}{4}$

Writing the Equation of a Circle **In Exercises 31–38, write the general form of the equation of the circle.**

31. Center: $(0, 0)$

Radius: 3

32. Center: $(0, 0)$

Radius: 5

33. Center: $(2, -1)$

Radius: 4

34. Center: $(-4, 3)$

Radius: $\frac{5}{8}$

35. Center: $(-1, 2)$

Point on circle: $(0, 0)$

36. Center: $(3, -2)$

Point on circle: $(-1, 1)$

37. Endpoints of a diameter: $(2, 5), (4, -1)$

38. Endpoints of a diameter: $(1, 1), (-1, -1)$

39. Satellite Communication Write the standard form of the equation for the path of a communications satellite in a circular orbit 22,000 miles above Earth. (Assume that the radius of Earth is 4000 miles.)

40. Building Design A circular air duct of diameter D is fit firmly into the right-angle corner where a basement wall meets the floor (see figure). Find the diameter of the largest water pipe that can be run in the right-angle corner behind the air duct.

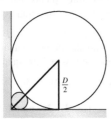

Writing the Equation of a Circle In Exercises 41–48, write the standard form of the equation of the circle and sketch its graph.

41. $x^2 + y^2 - 2x + 6y + 6 = 0$

42. $x^2 + y^2 - 2x + 6y - 15 = 0$

43. $x^2 + y^2 - 2x + 6y + 10 = 0$

44. $3x^2 + 3y^2 - 6y - 1 = 0$

45. $2x^2 + 2y^2 - 2x - 2y - 3 = 0$

46. $4x^2 + 4y^2 - 4x + 2y - 1 = 0$

47. $16x^2 + 16y^2 + 16x + 40y - 7 = 0$

48. $x^2 + y^2 - 4x + 2y + 3 = 0$

Graphing a Circle In Exercises 49 and 50, use a graphing utility to graph the equation. Use a *square setting*. (*Hint:* It may be necessary to solve the equation for y and graph the resulting two equations.)

49. $4x^2 + 4y^2 - 4x + 24y - 63 = 0$

50. $x^2 + y^2 - 8x - 6y - 11 = 0$

Sketching a Graph of an Inequality In Exercises 51 and 52, sketch the set of all points satisfying the inequality. Use a graphing utility to verify your result.

51. $x^2 + y^2 - 4x + 2y + 1 \leq 0$ **52.** $(x - 1)^2 + \left(y - \frac{1}{2}\right)^2 > 1$

53. Proof Prove that

$$\left(\frac{2x_1 + x_2}{3}, \frac{2y_1 + y_2}{3}\right)$$

is one of the points of trisection of the line segment joining (x_1, y_1) and (x_2, y_2). Find the midpoint of the line segment joining

$$\left(\frac{2x_1 + x_2}{3}, \frac{2y_1 + y_2}{3}\right)$$

and (x_2, y_2) to find the second point of trisection.

54. Finding Points of Trisection Use the results of Exercise 53 to find the points of trisection of the line segment joining each pair of points.

(a) $(1, -2), (4, 1)$

(b) $(-2, -3), (0, 0)$

True or False? In Exercises 55–58, determine whether the statement is true or false. If it is false, explain why or give an example that shows it is false.

55. If $ab < 0$, then the point (a, b) lies in either Quadrant II or Quadrant IV.

56. The distance between the points $(a + b, a)$ and $(a - b, a)$ is $2b$.

57. If the distance between two points is zero, then the two points must coincide.

58. If $ab = 0$, then the point (a, b) lies on the x-axis or on the y-axis.

Proof In Exercises 59–62, prove the statement.

59. The line segments joining the midpoints of the opposite sides of a quadrilateral bisect each other.

60. The perpendicular bisector of a chord of a circle passes through the center of the circle.

61. An angle inscribed in a semicircle is a right angle.

62. The midpoint of the line segment joining the points (x_1, y_1) and (x_2, y_2) is

$$\left(\frac{x_1 + x_2}{2}, \frac{y_1 + y_2}{2}\right).$$

C.3 Review of Trigonometric Functions

■ Describe angles and use degree measure.
■ Use radian measure.
■ Understand the definitions of the six trigonometric functions.
■ Evaluate trigonometric functions.
■ Solve trigonometric equations.
■ Graph trigonometric functions.

Angles and Degree Measure

An **angle** has three parts: an **initial ray,** a **terminal ray,** and a **vertex** (the point of intersection of the two rays), as shown in Figure C.24. An angle is in **standard position** when its initial ray coincides with the positive x-axis and its vertex is at the origin. It is assumed that you are familiar with the degree measure of an angle.* It is common practice to use θ (the lowercase Greek letter *theta*) to represent both an angle and its measure. Angles between $0°$ and $90°$ are **acute,** and angles between $90°$ and $180°$ are **obtuse.**

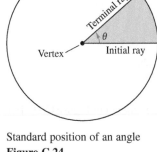

Standard position of an angle
Figure C.24

Positive angles are measured *counterclockwise*, and negative angles are measured *clockwise*. For instance, Figure C.25 shows an angle whose measure is $-45°$. You cannot assign a measure to an angle by simply knowing where its initial and terminal rays are located. To measure an angle, you must also know how the terminal ray was revolved. For example, Figure C.25 shows that the angle measuring $-45°$ has the same terminal ray as the angle measuring $315°$. Such angles are **coterminal.** In general, if θ is any angle, then

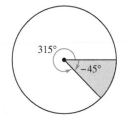

Coterminal angles
Figure C.25

$$\theta + n(360), \quad n \text{ is a nonzero integer}$$

is coterminal with θ.

An angle that is larger than $360°$ is one whose terminal ray has been revolved more than one full revolution counterclockwise, as shown in Figure C.26. You can form an angle whose measure is less than $-360°$ by revolving a terminal ray more than one full revolution clockwise.

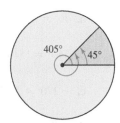

Coterminal angles
Figure C.26

Note that it is common to use the symbol θ to refer to both an *angle* and its *measure*. For instance, in Figure C.26, you can write the measure of the smaller angle as $\theta = 45°$.

---

*For a more complete review of trigonometry, see *Precalculus*, 9th edition, by Larson (Brooks/Cole, Cengage Learning, 2014).

Radian Measure

To assign a radian measure to an angle θ, consider θ to be a central angle of a circle of radius 1, as shown in Figure C.27. The **radian measure** of θ is then defined to be the length of the arc of the sector. Because the circumference of a circle is $2\pi r$, the circumference of a **unit circle** (of radius 1) is 2π. This implies that the radian measure of an angle measuring $360°$ is 2π. In other words, $360° = 2\pi$ radians.

Using radian measure for θ, the length s of a circular arc of radius r is $s = r\theta$, as shown in Figure C.28.

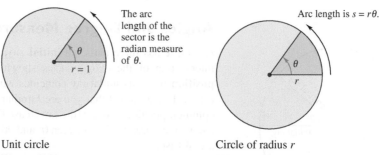

The arc length of the sector is the radian measure of θ.

Arc length is $s = r\theta$.

Unit circle
Figure C.27

Circle of radius r
Figure C.28

You should know the conversions of the common angles shown in Figure C.29. For other angles, use the fact that $180°$ is equal to π radians.

  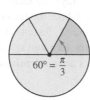 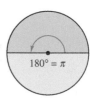 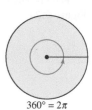

$30° = \dfrac{\pi}{6}$ $45° = \dfrac{\pi}{4}$ $60° = \dfrac{\pi}{3}$ $90° = \dfrac{\pi}{2}$ $180° = \pi$ $360° = 2\pi$

Radian and degree measures for several common angles
Figure C.29

EXAMPLE 1 **Conversions Between Degrees and Radians**

a. $40° = (40 \text{ deg})\left(\dfrac{\pi \text{ rad}}{180 \text{ deg}}\right) = \dfrac{2\pi}{9} \text{ radian}$

b. $540° = (540 \text{ deg})\left(\dfrac{\pi \text{ rad}}{180 \text{ deg}}\right) = 3\pi \text{ radians}$

c. $-270° = (-270 \text{ deg})\left(\dfrac{\pi \text{ rad}}{180 \text{ deg}}\right) = -\dfrac{3\pi}{2} \text{ radians}$

d. $-\dfrac{\pi}{2} \text{ radians} = \left(-\dfrac{\pi}{2} \text{ rad}\right)\left(\dfrac{180 \text{ deg}}{\pi \text{ rad}}\right) = -90°$

e. $2 \text{ radians} = (2 \text{ rad})\left(\dfrac{180 \text{ deg}}{\pi \text{ rad}}\right) = \dfrac{360}{\pi} \approx 114.59°$

f. $\dfrac{9\pi}{2} \text{ radians} = \left(\dfrac{9\pi}{2} \text{ rad}\right)\left(\dfrac{180 \text{ deg}}{\pi \text{ rad}}\right) = 810°$

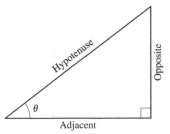

Sides of a right triangle
Figure C.30

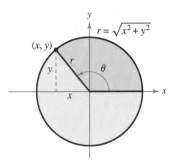

An angle in standard position
Figure C.31

The Trigonometric Functions

There are two common approaches to the study of trigonometry. In one, the trigonometric functions are defined as ratios of two sides of a right triangle. In the other, these functions are defined in terms of a point on the terminal side of an angle in standard position. The six trigonometric functions, **sine, cosine, tangent, cotangent, secant,** and **cosecant** (abbreviated as sin, cos, tan, cot, sec, and csc, respectively), are defined below from both viewpoints.

Definition of the Six Trigonometric Functions

Right triangle definitions, where $0 < \theta < \dfrac{\pi}{2}$ (see Figure C.30).

$$\sin \theta = \frac{\text{opposite}}{\text{hypotenuse}} \qquad \cos \theta = \frac{\text{adjacent}}{\text{hypotenuse}} \qquad \tan \theta = \frac{\text{opposite}}{\text{adjacent}}$$

$$\csc \theta = \frac{\text{hypotenuse}}{\text{opposite}} \qquad \sec \theta = \frac{\text{hypotenuse}}{\text{adjacent}} \qquad \cot \theta = \frac{\text{adjacent}}{\text{opposite}}$$

Circular function definitions, where θ *is any angle* (see Figure C.31).

$$\sin \theta = \frac{y}{r} \qquad\qquad \cos \theta = \frac{x}{r} \qquad\qquad \tan \theta = \frac{y}{x}, \quad x \neq 0$$

$$\csc \theta = \frac{r}{y}, \quad y \neq 0 \qquad \sec \theta = \frac{r}{x}, \quad x \neq 0 \qquad \cot \theta = \frac{x}{y}, \quad y \neq 0$$

The trigonometric identities listed below are direct consequences of the definitions. [Note that ϕ is the lowercase Greek letter *phi* and $\sin^2 \theta$ is used to represent $(\sin \theta)^2$.]

TRIGONOMETRIC IDENTITIES

Pythagorean Identities

$\sin^2 \theta + \cos^2 \theta = 1$

$1 + \tan^2 \theta = \sec^2 \theta$

$1 + \cot^2 \theta = \csc^2 \theta$

Even/Odd Identities

$\sin(-\theta) = -\sin \theta$ $\qquad$ $\csc(-\theta) = -\csc \theta$

$\cos(-\theta) = \cos \theta$ $\qquad$ $\sec(-\theta) = \sec \theta$

$\tan(-\theta) = -\tan \theta$ $\qquad$ $\cot(-\theta) = -\cot \theta$

Sum and Difference Formulas

$\sin(\theta \pm \phi) = \sin \theta \cos \phi \pm \cos \theta \sin \phi$

$\cos(\theta \pm \phi) = \cos \theta \cos \phi \mp \sin \theta \sin \phi$

$\tan(\theta \pm \phi) = \dfrac{\tan \theta \pm \tan \phi}{1 \mp \tan \theta \tan \phi}$

Power-Reducing Formulas

$\sin^2 \theta = \dfrac{1 - \cos 2\theta}{2}$

$\cos^2 \theta = \dfrac{1 + \cos 2\theta}{2}$

$\tan^2 \theta = \dfrac{1 - \cos 2\theta}{1 + \cos 2\theta}$

Double-Angle Formulas

$\sin 2\theta = 2 \sin \theta \cos \theta$

$\cos 2\theta = 2 \cos^2 \theta - 1$

$\qquad\;\; = 1 - 2 \sin^2 \theta$

$\qquad\;\; = \cos^2 \theta - \sin^2 \theta$

$\tan 2\theta = \dfrac{2 \tan \theta}{1 - \tan^2 \theta}$

Law of Cosines

$a^2 = b^2 + c^2 - 2bc \cos A$

Reciprocal Identities

$\csc \theta = \dfrac{1}{\sin \theta}$

$\sec \theta = \dfrac{1}{\cos \theta}$

$\cot \theta = \dfrac{1}{\tan \theta}$

Quotient Identities

$\tan \theta = \dfrac{\sin \theta}{\cos \theta}$

$\cot \theta = \dfrac{\cos \theta}{\sin \theta}$

Evaluating Trigonometric Functions

There are two ways to evaluate trigonometric functions: (1) decimal approximations with a calculator and (2) exact evaluations using trigonometric identities and formulas from geometry. When using a calculator to evaluate a trigonometric function, remember to set the calculator to the appropriate mode—*degree* mode or *radian* mode.

EXAMPLE 2   Exact Evaluation of Trigonometric Functions

Evaluate the sine, cosine, and tangent of $\dfrac{\pi}{3}$.

Solution   Because $60° = \pi/3$ radians, you can draw an equilateral triangle with sides of length 1 and θ as one of its angles, as shown in Figure C.32. Because the altitude of this triangle bisects its base, you know that $x = \frac{1}{2}$. Using the Pythagorean Theorem, you obtain

$$y = \sqrt{r^2 - x^2} = \sqrt{1 - \left(\frac{1}{2}\right)^2} = \sqrt{\frac{3}{4}} = \frac{\sqrt{3}}{2}.$$

Now, knowing the values of x, y, and r, you can write the following.

$$\sin\frac{\pi}{3} = \frac{y}{r} = \frac{\sqrt{3}/2}{1} = \frac{\sqrt{3}}{2}$$

$$\cos\frac{\pi}{3} = \frac{x}{r} = \frac{1/2}{1} = \frac{1}{2}$$

$$\tan\frac{\pi}{3} = \frac{y}{x} = \frac{\sqrt{3}/2}{1/2} = \sqrt{3}$$

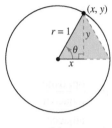

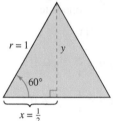

Figure C.32

Note that all angles in this text are measured in radians unless stated otherwise. For example, when sin 3 is written, the sine of 3 radians is meant, and when sin 3° is written, the sine of 3 degrees is meant.

The degree and radian measures of several common angles are shown in the table below, along with the corresponding values of the sine, cosine, and tangent (see Figure C.33).

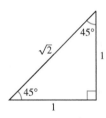

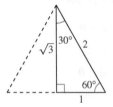

Common angles
Figure C.33

Common First-Quadrant Angles

Degrees	0	30°	45°	60°	90°
Radians	0	$\dfrac{\pi}{6}$	$\dfrac{\pi}{4}$	$\dfrac{\pi}{3}$	$\dfrac{\pi}{2}$
$\sin\theta$	0	$\dfrac{1}{2}$	$\dfrac{\sqrt{2}}{2}$	$\dfrac{\sqrt{3}}{2}$	1
$\cos\theta$	1	$\dfrac{\sqrt{3}}{2}$	$\dfrac{\sqrt{2}}{2}$	$\dfrac{1}{2}$	0
$\tan\theta$	0	$\dfrac{\sqrt{3}}{3}$	1	$\sqrt{3}$	Undefined

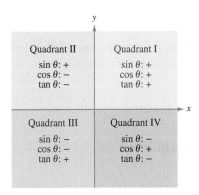

Quadrant signs for trigonometric functions

Figure C.34

The quadrant signs for the sine, cosine, and tangent functions are shown in Figure C.34. To extend the use of the table on the preceding page to angles in quadrants other than the first quadrant, you can use the concept of a **reference angle** (see Figure C.35), with the appropriate quadrant sign. For instance, the reference angle for $3\pi/4$ is $\pi/4$, and because the sine is positive in Quadrant II, you can write

$$\sin \frac{3\pi}{4} = \sin \frac{\pi}{4} = \frac{\sqrt{2}}{2}.$$

Similarly, because the reference angle for $330°$ is $30°$, and the tangent is negative in Quadrant IV, you can write

$$\tan 330° = -\tan 30° = -\frac{\sqrt{3}}{3}.$$

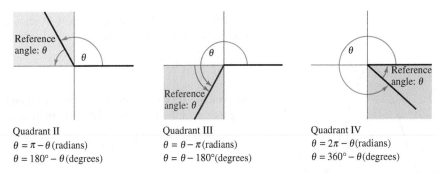

Quadrant II	Quadrant III	Quadrant IV
$\theta = \pi - \theta$ (radians)	$\theta = \theta - \pi$ (radians)	$\theta = 2\pi - \theta$ (radians)
$\theta = 180° - \theta$ (degrees)	$\theta = \theta - 180°$ (degrees)	$\theta = 360° - \theta$ (degrees)

Figure C.35

EXAMPLE 3   **Trigonometric Identities and Calculators**

Evaluate each trigonometric expression.

a. $\sin\left(-\dfrac{\pi}{3}\right)$ **b.** $\sec 60°$ **c.** $\cos(1.2)$

Solution

a. Using the reduction formula $\sin(-\theta) = -\sin \theta$, you can write

$$\sin\left(-\frac{\pi}{3}\right) = -\sin \frac{\pi}{3} = -\frac{\sqrt{3}}{2}.$$

b. Using the reciprocal identity $\sec \theta = 1/\cos \theta$, you can write

$$\sec 60° = \frac{1}{\cos 60°} = \frac{1}{1/2} = 2.$$

c. Using a calculator, you obtain

$$\cos(1.2) \approx 0.3624.$$

Remember that 1.2 is given in *radian* measure. Consequently, your calculator must be set in *radian* mode.

Solving Trigonometric Equations

How would you solve the equation $\sin \theta = 0$? You know that $\theta = 0$ is one solution, but this is not the only solution. Any one of the following values of θ is also a solution.

$$\ldots, -3\pi, -2\pi, -\pi, 0, \pi, 2\pi, 3\pi, \ldots$$

You can write this infinite solution set as $\{n\pi: n \text{ is an integer}\}$.

EXAMPLE 4   **Solving a Trigonometric Equation**

Solve the equation

$$\sin \theta = -\frac{\sqrt{3}}{2}.$$

Solution   To solve the equation, you should consider that the sine is negative in Quadrants III and IV and that

$$\sin \frac{\pi}{3} = \frac{\sqrt{3}}{2}.$$

So, you are seeking values of θ in the third and fourth quadrants that have a reference angle of $\pi/3$. In the interval $[0, 2\pi]$, the two angles fitting these criteria are

$$\theta = \pi + \frac{\pi}{3} = \frac{4\pi}{3} \quad \text{and} \quad \theta = 2\pi - \frac{\pi}{3} = \frac{5\pi}{3}.$$

By adding integer multiples of 2π to each of these solutions, you obtain the following general solution.

$$\theta = \frac{4\pi}{3} + 2n\pi \quad \text{or} \quad \theta = \frac{5\pi}{3} + 2n\pi, \quad \text{where } n \text{ is an integer.}$$

See Figure C.36.

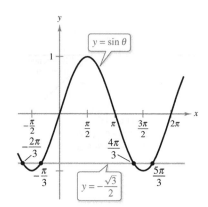

Solution points of $\sin \theta = -\dfrac{\sqrt{3}}{2}$

Figure C.36

EXAMPLE 5   **Solving a Trigonometric Equation**

Solve $\cos 2\theta = 2 - 3 \sin \theta$, where $0 \le \theta \le 2\pi$.

Solution   Using the double-angle identity $\cos 2\theta = 1 - 2 \sin^2 \theta$, you can rewrite the equation as follows.

$$\begin{aligned}
\cos 2\theta &= 2 - 3 \sin \theta & &\text{Write original equation.}\\
1 - 2 \sin^2 \theta &= 2 - 3 \sin \theta & &\text{Trigonometric identity}\\
0 &= 2 \sin^2 \theta - 3 \sin \theta + 1 & &\text{Quadratic form}\\
0 &= (2 \sin \theta - 1)(\sin \theta - 1) & &\text{Factor.}
\end{aligned}$$

If $2 \sin \theta - 1 = 0$, then $\sin \theta = 1/2$ and $\theta = \pi/6$ or $\theta = 5\pi/6$. If $\sin \theta - 1 = 0$, then $\sin \theta = 1$ and $\theta = \pi/2$. So, for $0 \le \theta \le 2\pi$, there are three solutions.

$$\theta = \frac{\pi}{6}, \frac{5\pi}{6}, \quad \text{or} \quad \frac{\pi}{2}$$

Graphs of Trigonometric Functions

A function f is **periodic** when there exists a nonzero number p such that $f(x + p) = f(x)$ for all x in the domain of f. The least such positive value of p (if it exists) is the **period** of f. The sine, cosine, secant, and cosecant functions each have a period of 2π, and the other two trigonometric functions, tangent and cotangent, have a period of π, as shown in Figure C.37.

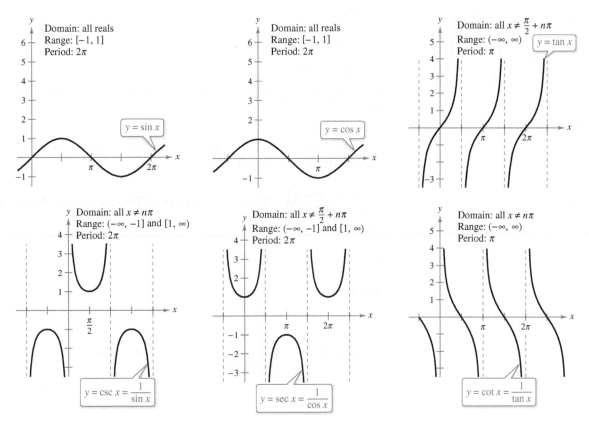

The graphs of the six trigonometric functions
Figure C.37

Note in Figure C.37 that the maximum value of $\sin x$ and $\cos x$ is 1 and the minimum value is -1. The graphs of the functions $y = a \sin bx$ and $y = a \cos bx$ oscillate between $-a$ and a, and so have an **amplitude** of $|a|$. Furthermore, because $bx = 0$ when $x = 0$ and $bx = 2\pi$ when $x = 2\pi/b$, it follows that the functions $y = a \sin bx$ and $y = a \cos bx$ each have a period of $2\pi/|b|$. The table below summarizes the amplitudes and periods of some types of trigonometric functions.

Function	Period	Amplitude
$y = a \sin bx$ or $y = a \cos bx$	$\dfrac{2\pi}{|b|}$	$|a|$
$y = a \tan bx$ or $y = a \cot bx$	$\dfrac{\pi}{|b|}$	Not applicable
$y = a \sec bx$ or $y = a \csc bx$	$\dfrac{2\pi}{|b|}$	Not applicable

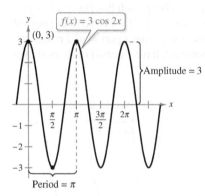

Figure C.38

EXAMPLE 6 **Sketching the Graph of a Trigonometric Function**

Sketch the graph of $f(x) = 3 \cos 2x$.

Solution The graph of $f(x) = 3 \cos 2x$ has an amplitude of 3 and a period of $2\pi/2 = \pi$. Using the basic shape of the graph of the cosine function, sketch one period of the function on the interval $[0, \pi]$, using the following pattern.

Maximum: $(0, 3)$

Minimum: $\left(\dfrac{\pi}{2}, -3\right)$

Maximum: $(\pi, 3)$

By continuing this pattern, you can sketch several cycles of the graph, as shown in Figure C.38.

Horizontal shifts, vertical shifts, and reflections can be applied to the graphs of trigonometric functions, as illustrated in Example 7.

EXAMPLE 7 **Shifts of Graphs of Trigonometric Functions**

Sketch the graph of each function.

a. $f(x) = \sin\left(x + \dfrac{\pi}{2}\right)$ **b.** $f(x) = 2 + \sin x$ **c.** $f(x) = 2 + \sin\left(x - \dfrac{\pi}{4}\right)$

Solution

a. To sketch the graph of $f(x) = \sin(x + \pi/2)$, shift the graph of $y = \sin x$ to the left $\pi/2$ units, as shown in Figure C.39(a).

b. To sketch the graph of $f(x) = 2 + \sin x$, shift the graph of $y = \sin x$ upward two units, as shown in Figure C.39(b).

c. To sketch the graph of $f(x) = 2 + \sin(x - \pi/4)$, shift the graph of $y = \sin x$ upward two units and to the right $\pi/4$ units, as shown in Figure C.39(c).

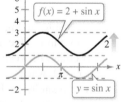 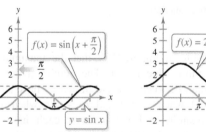 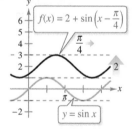

(a) Horizontal shift to the left (b) Vertical shift upward (c) Horizontal and vertical shifts

Transformations of the graph of $y = \sin x$

Figure C.39

C.3 Exercises

Coterminal Angles in Degrees **In Exercises 1 and 2,** determine two coterminal angles in degree measure (one positive and one negative) for each angle.

1. (a) 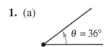 (b)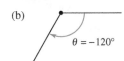

2. (a) $\theta = 300°$ (b) $\theta = -420°$

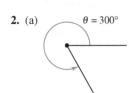

Coterminal Angles in Radians **In Exercises 3 and 4,** determine two coterminal angles in radian measure (one positive and one negative) for each angle.

3. (a) $\theta = \dfrac{\pi}{9}$ (b) $\theta = \dfrac{4\pi}{3}$

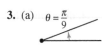 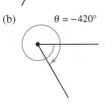

4. (a) $\theta = -\dfrac{9\pi}{4}$ (b) $\theta = \dfrac{8\pi}{9}$

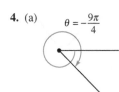 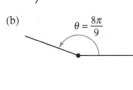

Degrees to Radians **In Exercises 5 and 6,** rewrite each angle in radian measure as a multiple of π and as a decimal accurate to three decimal places.

5. (a) $30°$ (b) $150°$ (c) $315°$ (d) $120°$

6. (a) $-20°$ (b) $-240°$ (c) $-270°$ (d) $144°$

Radians to Degrees **In Exercises 7 and 8,** rewrite each angle in degree measure.

7. (a) $3\pi/2$ (b) $7\pi/6$ (c) $-7\pi/12$ (d) -2.367

8. (a) $7\pi/3$ (b) $-11\pi/30$ (c) $11\pi/6$ (d) 0.438

9. Completing a Table Let r represent the radius of a circle, θ the central angle (measured in radians), and s the length of the arc subtended by the angle. Use the relationship $s = r\theta$ to complete the table.

r	8 ft	15 in.	85 cm		
s	12 ft			96 in.	8642 mi
θ		1.6	$\dfrac{3\pi}{4}$	4	$\dfrac{2\pi}{3}$

10. Angular Speed A car is moving at the rate of 50 miles per hour, and the diameter of its wheels is 2.5 feet.

(a) Find the number of revolutions per minute that the wheels are rotating.

(b) Find the angular speed of the wheels in radians per minute.

Finding the Six Trigonometric Functions **In Exercises 11 and 12, determine all six trigonometric functions for the angle θ.**

11. (a) (b)

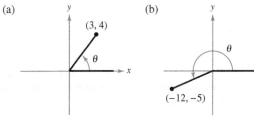

12. (a) (b)

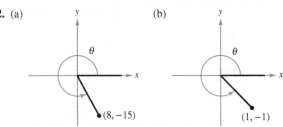

Determining a Quadrant **In Exercises 13 and 14,** determine the quadrant in which θ lies.

13. (a) $\sin \theta < 0$ and $\cos \theta < 0$ (b) $\sec \theta > 0$ and $\cot \theta < 0$

14. (a) $\sin \theta > 0$ and $\cos \theta < 0$ (b) $\csc \theta < 0$ and $\tan \theta > 0$

Evaluating a Trigonometric Function **In Exercises 15–18, evaluate the trigonometric function.**

15. $\sin \theta = \dfrac{1}{2}$

$\cos \theta = $

16. $\sin \theta = \dfrac{1}{3}$

$\tan \theta = $

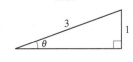

17. $\cos \theta = \dfrac{4}{5}$

$\cot \theta = $

18. $\sec \theta = \dfrac{13}{5}$

$\csc \theta = $

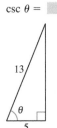

Evaluating Trigonometric Functions **In Exercises 19–22,** **evaluate the sine, cosine, and tangent of each angle** *without* **using a calculator.**

19. (a) $60°$
    (b) $120°$
    (c) $\dfrac{\pi}{4}$
    (d) $\dfrac{5\pi}{4}$

20. (a) $-30°$
    (b) $150°$
    (c) $-\dfrac{\pi}{6}$
    (d) $\dfrac{\pi}{2}$

21. (a) $225°$
    (b) $-225°$
    (c) $\dfrac{5\pi}{3}$
    (d) $\dfrac{11\pi}{6}$

22. (a) $750°$
    (b) $510°$
    (c) $\dfrac{10\pi}{3}$
    (d) $\dfrac{17\pi}{3}$

Evaluating Trigonometric Functions **In Exercises 23–26,** **use a calculator to evaluate each trigonometric function. Round your answers to four decimal places.**

23. (a) $\sin 10°$
    (b) $\csc 10°$

24. (a) $\sec 225°$
    (b) $\sec 135°$

25. (a) $\tan \dfrac{\pi}{9}$
    (b) $\tan \dfrac{10\pi}{9}$

26. (a) $\cot(1.35)$
    (b) $\tan(1.35)$

Solving a Trigonometric Equation **In Exercises 27–30,** **find two solutions of each equation. Give your answers in radians $(0 \le \theta < 2\pi)$. Do not use a calculator.**

27. (a) $\cos \theta = \dfrac{\sqrt{2}}{2}$
    (b) $\cos \theta = -\dfrac{\sqrt{2}}{2}$

28. (a) $\sec \theta = 2$
    (b) $\sec \theta = -2$

29. (a) $\tan \theta = 1$
    (b) $\cot \theta = -\sqrt{3}$

30. (a) $\sin \theta = \dfrac{\sqrt{3}}{2}$
    (b) $\sin \theta = -\dfrac{\sqrt{3}}{2}$

Solving a Trigonometric Equation **In Exercises 31–38,** **solve the equation for θ $(0 \le \theta < 2\pi)$.**

31. $2 \sin^2 \theta = 1$

32. $\tan^2 \theta = 3$

33. $\tan^2 \theta - \tan \theta = 0$

34. $2 \cos^2 \theta - \cos \theta = 1$

35. $\sec \theta \csc \theta = 2 \csc \theta$

36. $\sin \theta = \cos \theta$

37. $\cos^2 \theta + \sin \theta = 1$

38. $\cos \dfrac{\theta}{2} - \cos \theta = 1$

39. **Airplane Ascent** An airplane leaves the runway climbing at an angle of $18°$ with a speed of 275 feet per second (see figure). Find the altitude a of the plane after 1 minute.

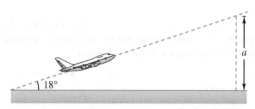

40. **Height of a Mountain** While traveling across flat land, you notice a mountain directly in front of you. Its angle of elevation (to the peak) is $3.5°$. After you drive 13 miles closer to the mountain, the angle of elevation is $9°$. Approximate the height of the mountain.

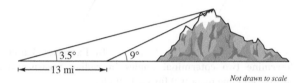

Not drawn to scale

Period and Amplitude **In Exercises 41–44, determine the period and amplitude of each function.**

41. (a) $y = 2 \sin 2x$

    (b) $y = \tfrac{1}{2} \sin \pi x$

42. (a) $y = \dfrac{3}{2} \cos \dfrac{x}{2}$

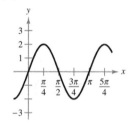

    (b) $y = -2 \sin \dfrac{x}{3}$

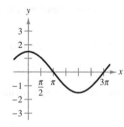

43. $y = 3 \sin 4\pi x$

44. $y = \dfrac{2}{3} \cos \dfrac{\pi x}{10}$

Period In Exercises 45–48, find the period of the function.

45. $y = 5 \tan 2x$

46. $y = 7 \tan 2\pi x$

47. $y = \sec 5x$

48. $y = \csc 4x$

Writing In Exercises 49 and 50, use a graphing utility to graph each function f in the same viewing window for $c = -2$, $c = -1$, $c = 1$, and $c = 2$. Give a written description of the change in the graph caused by changing c.

49. (a) $f(x) = c \sin x$

    (b) $f(x) = \cos(cx)$

    (c) $f(x) = \cos(\pi x - c)$

50. (a) $f(x) = \sin x + c$

    (b) $f(x) = -\sin(2\pi x - c)$

    (c) $f(x) = c \cos x$

Sketching the Graph of a Trigonometric Function In Exercises 51–62, sketch the graph of the function.

51. $y = \sin \dfrac{x}{2}$

52. $y = 2 \cos 2x$

53. $y = -\sin \dfrac{2\pi x}{3}$

54. $y = 2 \tan x$

55. $y = \csc \dfrac{x}{2}$

56. $y = \tan 2x$

57. $y = 2 \sec 2x$

58. $y = \csc 2\pi x$

59. $y = \sin(x + \pi)$

60. $y = \cos\left(x - \dfrac{\pi}{3}\right)$

61. $y = 1 + \cos\left(x - \dfrac{\pi}{2}\right)$

62. $y = 1 + \sin\left(x + \dfrac{\pi}{2}\right)$

Graphical Reasoning In Exercises 63 and 64, find a, b, and c such that the graph of the function matches the graph in the figure.

63. $y = a \cos(bx - c)$

64. $y = a \sin(bx - c)$

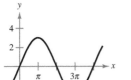

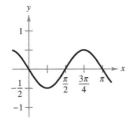

65. Think About It Sketch the graphs of $f(x) = \sin x$, $g(x) = |\sin x|$, and $h(x) = \sin(|x|)$. In general, how are the graphs of $|f(x)|$ and $f(|x|)$ related to the graph of f?

66. Think About It The model for the height h of a Ferris wheel car is

$$h = 51 + 50 \sin 8\pi t$$

where t is measured in minutes. (The Ferris wheel has a radius of 50 feet.) This model yields a height of 51 feet when $t = 0$. Alter the model so that the height of the car is 1 foot when $t = 0$.

67. Sales The monthly sales S (in thousands of units) of a seasonal product are modeled by

$$S = 58.3 + 32.5 \cos \frac{\pi t}{6}$$

where t is the time (in months), with $t = 1$ corresponding to January. Use a graphing utility to graph the model for S and determine the months when sales exceed 75,000 units.

68. Investigation Two trigonometric functions f and g have a period of 2, and their graphs intersect at $x = 5.35$.

    (a) Give one smaller and one larger positive value of x at which the functions have the same value.

    (b) Determine one negative value of x at which the graphs intersect.

    (c) Is it true that $f(13.35) = g(-4.65)$? Give a reason for your answer.

Pattern Recognition In Exercises 69 and 70, use a graphing utility to compare the graph of f with the given graph. Try to improve the approximation by adding a term to $f(x)$. Use a graphing utility to verify that your new approximation is better than the original. Can you find other terms to add to make the approximation even better? What is the pattern? (In Exercise 69, sine terms can be used to improve the approximation, and in Exercise 70, cosine terms can be used.)

69. $f(x) = \dfrac{4}{\pi}\left(\sin \pi x + \dfrac{1}{3} \sin 3\pi x\right)$

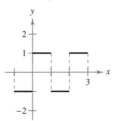

70. $f(x) = \dfrac{1}{2} - \dfrac{4}{\pi^2}\left(\cos \pi x + \dfrac{1}{9} \cos 3\pi x\right)$

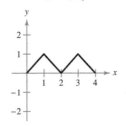

Chapter 1

Section 1.1   *(page 8)*

1. b   **2.** d   **3.** a   **4.** c

5.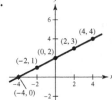

7.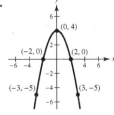

9.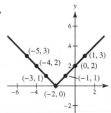

11.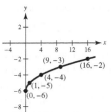

13.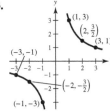

15.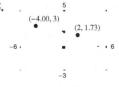

(a) $y \approx 1.73$ (b) $x = -4$

17. $(0, -5), \left(\frac{5}{2}, 0\right)$ **19.** $(0, -2), (-2, 0), (1, 0)$

21. $(0, 0), (4, 0), (-4, 0)$ **23.** $(0, 2), (4, 0)$ **25.** $(0, 0)$

27. Symmetric with respect to the y-axis

29. Symmetric with respect to the x-axis

31. Symmetric with respect to the origin   **33.** No symmetry

35. Symmetric with respect to the origin

37. Symmetric with respect to the y-axis

39.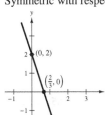

Symmetry: none

41.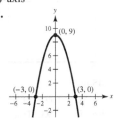

Symmetry: y-axis

43.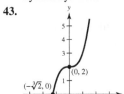

Symmetry: none

45.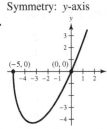

Symmetry: none

47.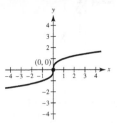

Symmetry: origin

49.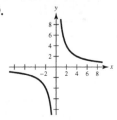

Symmetry: origin

51.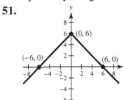

Symmetry: y-axis

53.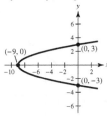

Symmetry: x-axis

55.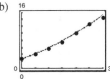

Symmetry: x-axis

57. $(3, 5)$

59. $(-1, 5), (2, 2)$

61. $(-1, -2), (2, 1)$

63. $(-1, -5), (0, -1), (2, 1)$

65. $(-2, 2), \left(-3, \sqrt{3}\right)$

67. (a) $y = 0.005t^2 + 0.27t + 2.7$

(b)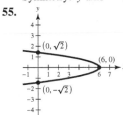

The model is a good fit for the data.

(c) \$21.5 trillion

69. 4480 units

71. (a) $k = 4$ (b) $k = -\frac{1}{8}$

(c) All real numbers k (d) $k = 1$

73. Answers will vary. Sample answer: $y = (x + 4)(x - 3)(x - 8)$

75. (a) and (b) Proofs

77. False. $(4, -5)$ is not a point on the graph of $x = y^2 - 29$.

79. True

Section 1.2   *(page 16)*

1. $m = 2$ **3.** $m = -1$

5.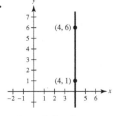

$m = 3$

7.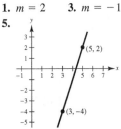

m is undefined.

9.

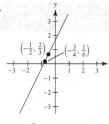

$m = 2$

11. $m = -2$ m is undefined.

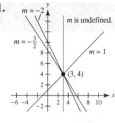

43. $x - 6 = 0$

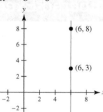

45. $22x - 4y + 3 = 0$

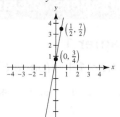

13. Answers will vary. Sample answers: $(0, 2), (1, 2), (5, 2)$
15. Answers will vary. Sample answers: $(0, 10), (2, 4), (3, 1)$
17. $3x - 4y + 12 = 0$

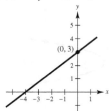

19. $2x - 3y = 0$

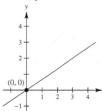

21. $3x - y - 11 = 0$

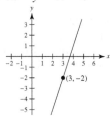

23. (a) $\frac{1}{3}$ (b) $10\sqrt{10}$ ft

25. $m = 4, (0, -3)$ **27.** $m = -\frac{1}{5}, (0, 4)$
29. m is undefined, no y-intercept

31.

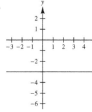

33.

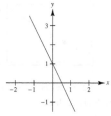

35.

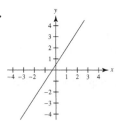

37.

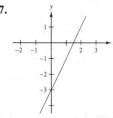

39. $2x - y = 0$

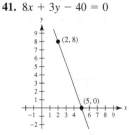

41. $8x + 3y - 40 = 0$

47. $x - 3 = 0$ **49.** $3x + 2y - 6 = 0$ **51.** $x + y - 3 = 0$
53. $x + 2y - 5 = 0$ **55.** (a) $x + 7 = 0$ (b) $y + 2 = 0$
57. (a) $x - y + 3 = 0$ (b) $x + y - 7 = 0$
59. (a) $2x - y - 3 = 0$ (b) $x + 2y - 4 = 0$
61. (a) $40x - 24y - 9 = 0$ (b) $24x + 40y - 53 = 0$
63. $V = 250t + 1350$ **65.** $V = -1600t + 20{,}400$
67. Not collinear, because $m_1 \neq m_2$
69. $\left(0, \dfrac{-a^2 + b^2 + c^2}{2c}\right)$ **71.** $\left(b, \dfrac{a^2 - b^2}{c}\right)$
73. (a) The line is parallel to the x-axis when $a = 0$ and $b \neq 0$.
(b) The line is parallel to the y-axis when $b = 0$ and $a \neq 0$.
(c) Answers will vary. Sample answer: $a = -5$ and $b = 8$
(d) Answers will vary. Sample answer: $a = 5$ and $b = 2$
(e) $a = \frac{5}{2}$ and $b = 3$
75. $5F - 9C - 160 = 0$; $72°F \approx 22.2°C$
77. (a) Current job: $W = 2000 + 0.07s$
Job offer: $W = 2300 + 0.05s$
(b)

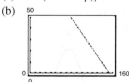

You will make more money at the job offer until you sell $\$15{,}000$. When your sales exceed $\$15{,}000$, your current job will pay you more.
(c) No, because you will make more money at your current job.
79. (a) $x = (1530 - p)/15$
(b)

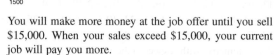

(c) 49 units

45 units
81. $12y + 5x - 169 = 0$ **83.** $\left(5\sqrt{2}\right)/2$ **85.** $2\sqrt{2}$
87–91. Proofs   **93.** True   **95.** True

Section 1.3   *(page 27)*

1. (a) -4 (b) -25 (c) $7b - 4$ (d) $7x - 11$
3. (a) 5 (b) 0 (c) 1 (d) $4 + 2t - t^2$
5. (a) 1 (b) 0 (c) $-\frac{1}{2}$ (d) 1
7. $3x^2 + 3x\,\Delta x + (\Delta x)^2, \Delta x \neq 0$
9. $\left(\sqrt{x - 1} - x + 1\right)/[(x - 2)(x - 1)]$
11. Domain: $(-\infty, \infty)$; Range: $[0, \infty)$
13. Domain: $(-\infty, \infty)$; Range: $(-\infty, \infty)$
15. Domain: $[0, \infty)$; Range: $[0, \infty)$
17. Domain: $[-4, 4]$; Range: $[0, 4]$

19. Domain: All real numbers t such that $t \neq 4n + 2$, where n is an integer; Range: $(-\infty, -1] \cup [1, \infty)$

21. Domain: $(-\infty, 0) \cup (0, \infty)$; Range: $(-\infty, 0) \cup (0, \infty)$

23. Domain: $[0, 1]$

25. Domain: All real numbers x such that $x \neq 2n\pi$, where n is an integer

27. Domain: $(-\infty, -3) \cup (-3, \infty)$

29. (a) -1 (b) 2 (c) 6 (d) $2t^2 + 4$
Domain: $(-\infty, \infty)$; Range: $(-\infty, 1) \cup [2, \infty)$

31. (a) 4 (b) 0 (c) -2 (d) $-b^2$
Domain: $(-\infty, \infty)$; Range: $(-\infty, 0] \cup [1, \infty)$

33.

Domain: $(-\infty, \infty)$
Range: $(-\infty, \infty)$

35.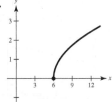

Domain: $[6, \infty)$
Range: $[0, \infty)$

37.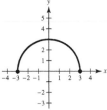

Domain: $[-3, 3]$
Range: $[0, 3]$

39.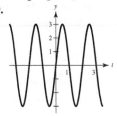

Domain: $(-\infty, \infty)$
Range: $[-3, 3]$

41. The student travels $\frac{1}{2}$ mile/minute during the first 4 minutes, is stationary for the next 2 minutes, and travels 1 mile/minute during the final 4 minutes.

43. y is not a function of x.   **45.** y is a function of x.

47. y is not a function of x.   **49.** y is not a function of x.

51. Horizontal shift to the right two units; $y = \sqrt{x - 2}$

53. Horizontal shift to the right two units and vertical shift down one unit; $y = (x - 2)^2 - 1$

55. d **56.** b **57.** c **58.** a **59.** e **60.** g

61. (a) 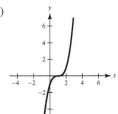   (b)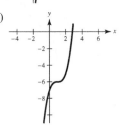

(c) 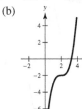   (d)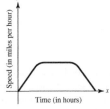

(e) 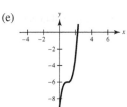   **(f)**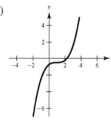

(g) 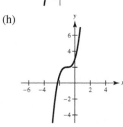   **(h)**

63. (a) $3x$ (b) $3x - 8$ (c) $12x - 16$ (d) $\frac{3}{4}x - 1$

65. (a) 0 (b) 0 (c) -1 (d) $\sqrt{15}$
(e) $\sqrt{x^2 - 1}$ (f) $x - 1 \ (x \geq 0)$

67. $(f \circ g)(x) = x$; Domain: $[0, \infty)$
$(g \circ f)(x) = |x|$; Domain: $(-\infty, \infty)$
No, their domains are different.

69. $(f \circ g)(x) = 3/(x^2 - 1)$;
Domain: $(-\infty, -1) \cup (-1, 1) \cup (1, \infty)$
$(g \circ f)(x) = (9/x^2) - 1$; Domain: $(-\infty, 0) \cup (0, \infty)$
No

71. (a) 4 (b) -2
(c) Undefined. The graph of g does not exist at $x = -5$.
(d) 3 (e) 2
(f) Undefined. The graph of f does not exist at $x = -4$.

73. Answers will vary.
Sample answer: $f(x) = \sqrt{x}; g(x) = x - 2; h(x) = 2x$

75. (a) $\left(\frac{3}{2}, 4\right)$ (b) $\left(\frac{3}{2}, -4\right)$

77. f is even. g is neither even nor odd. h is odd.

79. Even; zeros: $x = -2, 0, 2$

81. Odd; zeros: $x = 0, \frac{\pi}{2} + n\pi$, where n is an integer

83. $f(x) = -5x - 6, -2 \leq x \leq 0$ **85.** $y = -\sqrt{-x}$

87. Answers will vary.   **89.** Answers will vary.
Sample answer: Sample answer:

91. $c = 25$

93. (a) $T(4) = 16°C, T(15) \approx 23°C$
(b) The changes in temperature occur 1 hour later.
(c) The temperatures are 1° lower.

95. (a)

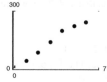

Year (0 ↔ 1960)

(b) $A(25) \approx 443$ acres/farm

97. $f(x) = |x| + |x - 2| = \begin{cases} 2x - 2, & x \geq 2 \\ 2, & 0 < x < 2 \\ -2x + 2, & x \leq 0 \end{cases}$

99–101. Proofs   **103.** $L = \sqrt{x^2 + \left(\dfrac{2x}{x - 3}\right)^2}$

105. False. For example, if $f(x) = x^2$, then $f(-1) = f(1)$.

107. True

109. False. $f(x) = 0$ is symmetric with respect to the x-axis.

111. Putnam Problem A1, 1988

Section 1.4 *(page 34)*

1. (a) and (b)   (c) $790

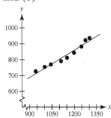

Approximately linear

3. (a) $d = 0.066F$

(b)

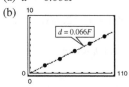

The model fits well.

(c) 3.63 cm

5. (a) $y = 0.122x + 2.07$, $r \approx 0.87$

(b)

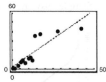

(c) Greater per capita energy consumption by a country tends to correspond to greater per capita gross national product of the country. The three countries that differ most from the linear model are Canada, Italy, and Japan.

(d) $y = 0.142x - 1.66$, $r \approx 0.97$

7. (a) $S = 180.89x^2 - 205.79x + 272$

(b)

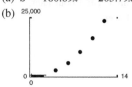

(c) When $x = 2$, $S \approx 583.98$ pounds.

(d) About 4 times greater

(e) About 4.37 times greater; No; Answers will vary.

9. (a) $y = -1.806x^3 + 14.58x^2 + 16.4x + 10$

(b)

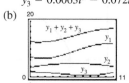

(c) 214 hp

11. (a) $y_1 = -0.0172t^3 + 0.305t^2 - 0.87t + 7.3$

$y_2 = -0.038t^2 + 0.45t + 3.5$

$y_3 = 0.0063t^3 - 0.072t^2 + 0.02t + 1.8$

(b)

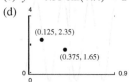

About 15.31 cents/mi

13. (a) Yes. At time t, there is one and only one displacement y.

(b) Amplitude: 0.35; Period: 0.5

(c) $y = 0.35 \sin(4\pi t) + 2$

(d)

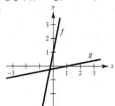

The model appears to fit the data well.

15. Answers will vary.   **17.** Putnam Problem A2, 2004

Section 1.5 *(page 44)*

1. (a) $f(g(x)) = 5[(x - 1)/5] + 1 = x$;

$g(f(x)) = [(5x + 1) - 1]/5 = x$

(b)

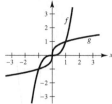

3. (a) $f(g(x)) = \left(\sqrt[3]{x}\right)^3 = x$; $g(f(x)) = \sqrt[3]{x^3} = x$

(b)

5. (a) $f(g(x)) = \sqrt{x^2 + 4 - 4} = x;$
    $g(f(x)) = \left(\sqrt{x-4}\right)^2 + 4 = x$
(b)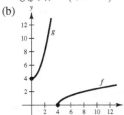

7. (a) $f(g(x)) = \dfrac{1}{1/x} = x;\ g(f(x)) = \dfrac{1}{1/x} = x$
(b)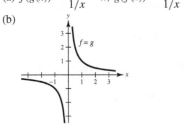

9. c   **10.** b   **11.** a   **12.** d
13. One-to-one, inverse exists.   **15.** Not one-to-one, inverse does not exist.
17. 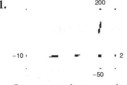   **19.**
One-to-one, inverse exists.   Not one-to-one, inverse does not exist.
21.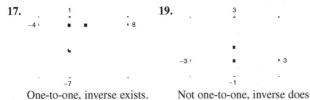
One-to-one, inverse exists.
23. Not one-to-one, inverse does not exist.
25. One-to-one, inverse exists.
27. (a) $f^{-1}(x) = (x+3)/2$
(b)   (c) f and f^{-1} are symmetric about $y = x$.
(d) Domain of f and f^{-1}: $(-\infty, \infty)$
Range of f and f^{-1}: $(-\infty, \infty)$
29. (a) $f^{-1}(x) = x^{1/5}$
(b) 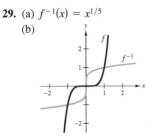   (c) f and f^{-1} are symmetric about $y = x$.
(d) Domain of f and f^{-1}: $(-\infty, \infty)$
Range of f and f^{-1}: $(-\infty, \infty)$

31. (a) $f^{-1}(x) = x^2,\ x \ge 0$
(b) 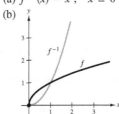   (c) f and f^{-1} are symmetric about $y = x$.
(d) Domain of f and f^{-1}: $[0, \infty)$
Range of f and f^{-1}: $[0, \infty)$
33. (a) $f^{-1}(x) = \sqrt{4 - x^2},\ 0 \le x \le 2$
(b) 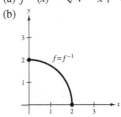   (c) f and f^{-1} are symmetric about $y = x$.
(d) Domain of f and f^{-1}: $[0, 2]$
Range of f and f^{-1}: $[0, 2]$
35. (a) $f^{-1}(x) = x^3 + 1$
(b)   (c) f and f^{-1} are symmetric about $y = x$.
(d) Domain of f and f^{-1}: $(-\infty, \infty)$
Range of f and f^{-1}: $(-\infty, \infty)$
37. (a) $f^{-1}(x) = x^{3/2},\ x \ge 0$
(b)   (c) f and f^{-1} are symmetric about $y = x$.
(d) Domain of f and f^{-1}: $[0, \infty)$
Range of f and f^{-1}: $[0, \infty)$
39. (a) $f^{-1}(x) = \sqrt{7}x/\sqrt{1 - x^2},\ -1 < x < 1$
(b) 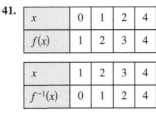   (c) f and f^{-1} are symmetric about $y = x$.
(d) Domain of f: $(-\infty, \infty)$
Range of f: $(-1, 1)$
Domain of f^{-1}: $(-1, 1)$
Range of f^{-1}: $(-\infty, \infty)$
41.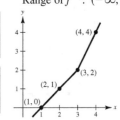

x	0	1	2	4
$f(x)$	1	2	3	4

x	1	2	3	4
$f^{-1}(x)$	0	1	2	4

43. (a) Answers will vary.
(b) $y = \frac{20}{7}(80 - x)$
x: total cost
y: number of pounds of the less expensive commodity
(c) $[62.5, 80]$; The total cost will be between $62.50 and $80.00
(d) 20 lb

45. One-to-one; $f^{-1}(x) = x^2 + 2$, $x \geq 0$　　**47.** Not one-to-one

49. One-to-one; $f^{-1}(x) = \dfrac{x - b}{a}$, $a \neq 0$

51. The function f passes the Horizontal Line Test on $[4, \infty)$, so it is one-to-one on $[4, \infty)$.

53. The function f passes the Horizontal Line Test on $(0, \infty)$, so it is one-to-one on $(0, \infty)$.

55. The function f passes the Horizontal Line Test on $[0, \pi]$, so it is one-to-one on $[0, \pi]$.

57. Answers will vary. Sample answer: $f^{-1}(x) = \sqrt{x} + 3$, $x \geq 0$

59. (a)
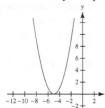

(b) Answers will vary. Sample answer: $[-5, \infty)$
(c) $f^{-1}(x) = \sqrt{x} - 5$
(d) Domain of f^{-1}: $[0, \infty)$

61. (a)
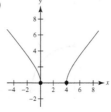

(b) Answers will vary. Sample answer: $[4, \infty)$
(c) $f^{-1}(x) = 2 + \sqrt{x^2 + 4}$
(d) Domain of f^{-1}: $[0, \infty)$

63. (a)
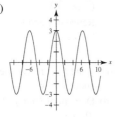

(b) Answers will vary. Sample answer: $[0, \pi]$
(c) $f^{-1}(x) = \arccos\left(\dfrac{x}{3}\right)$
(d) Domain of f^{-1}: $[-3, 3]$

65. 1　　**67.** $\dfrac{\pi}{6}$　　**69.** 2　　**71.** 32　　**73.** 600

75. $(g^{-1} \circ f^{-1})(x) = \dfrac{x + 1}{2}$　　**77.** $(f \circ g)^{-1}(x) = \dfrac{x + 1}{2}$

79. (a) f is one-to-one because it passes the Horizontal Line Test.
(b) $[-2, 2]$
(c) -4

81.
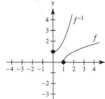

83. (a)

x	-1	-0.8	-0.6	-0.4	-0.2
y	-1.57	-0.93	-0.64	-0.41	-0.20

x	0	0.2	0.4	0.6	0.8	1
y	0	0.20	0.41	0.64	0.93	1.57

(b)　　　　(c)
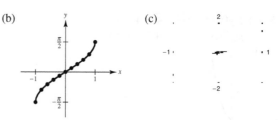

(d) Intercept: $(0, 0)$; Symmetry: origin

85. $\left(-\sqrt{2}/2, 3\pi/4\right)$, $(1/2, \pi/3)$, $\left(\sqrt{3}/2, \pi/6\right)$　　**87.** $\pi/6$

89. $\pi/3$　　**91.** $\pi/6$　　**93.** $-\pi/4$　　**95.** 2.50　　**97.** 0.66

99. -0.1　　**101.** x　　**103.** $\dfrac{\sqrt{1 - x^2}}{x}$　　**105.** $\dfrac{1}{x}$

107. (a) $\dfrac{3}{5}$　(b) $\dfrac{5}{3}$　　**109.** (a) $-\sqrt{3}$　(b) $-\dfrac{13}{5}$

111. $\sqrt{1 - 4x^2}$　　**113.** $\dfrac{\sqrt{x^2 - 1}}{|x|}$　　**115.** $\dfrac{\sqrt{x^2 - 9}}{3}$

117. $x = \frac{1}{3}\left[\sin\left(\frac{1}{2}\right) + \pi\right] \approx 1.207$　　**119.** $x = \frac{1}{3}$

121. $(0.7862, 0.6662)$

123. Let $y = f(x)$ be one-to-one. Solve for x as a function of y. Interchange x and y to get $y = f^{-1}(x)$. Let the domain of f^{-1} be the range of f. Verify that $f(f^{-1}(x)) = x$ and $f^{-1}(f(x)) = x$. Sample answer:
$$f(x) = x^3$$
$$y = x^3$$
$$x = \sqrt[3]{y}$$
$$y = \sqrt[3]{x}$$
$$f^{-1}(x) = \sqrt[3]{x}$$

125. The trigonometric functions are not one-to-one. So, their domains must be restricted to define the inverse trigonometric functions.

127. $\arcsin\left(\dfrac{9}{\sqrt{x^2 + 81}}\right)$　　**129.** Answers will vary.

131.　　　　　　　**133.**
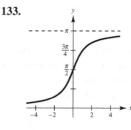

135. $f^{-1}(8) = -3$　　**137–139.** Proofs

141. False. Let $f(x) = x^2$.

143. False. $\arcsin^2 0 + \arccos^2 0 = \left(\dfrac{\pi}{2}\right)^2 \neq 1$

145. True　　**147.** Answers will vary.　　**149.** Proof

151. $f^{-1}(x) = \dfrac{-b - \sqrt{b^2 - 4ac + 4ax}}{2a}$

153. $ad - bc \neq 0$; $f^{-1}(x) = \dfrac{b - dx}{cx - a}$

Section 1.6　(page 53)

1. (a) 125　(b) 9　(c) $\frac{1}{9}$　(d) $\frac{1}{3}$
3. (a) 5^5　(b) $\frac{1}{5}$　(c) $\frac{1}{5}$　(d) 2^2

5. (a) e^6 (b) e^{12} (c) $\dfrac{1}{e^6}$ (d) e^2

7. $x = 4$ **9.** $x = 4$ **11.** $x = -5$ **13.** $x = -2$

15. $x = 2$ **17.** $x = 16$ **19.** $x = \ln 5 \approx 1.609$

21. $x = -\dfrac{5}{2}$ **23.** $2.7182805 < e$

25.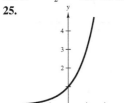

27.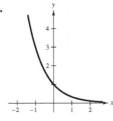

29.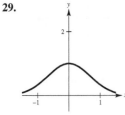

31.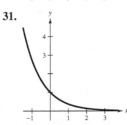

33.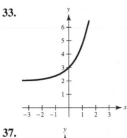

35.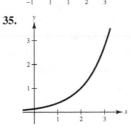

37.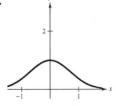

39. Domain: $(-\infty, \infty)$

41. Domain: $(-\infty, 0]$

43. Domain: $(-\infty, \infty)$

45. (a)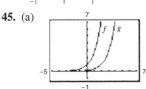

(b)

Translation two units to the right

Reflection in the x-axis and vertical shrink

(c)

Reflection in the y-axis and translation three units upward

47. c   **48.** d   **49.** a   **50.** b   **51.** $y = 2(3^x)$ **53.** b

54. d   **55.** a   **56.** c   **57.** $\ln 1 = 0$ **59.** $e^{0.6931\ldots} = 2$

61.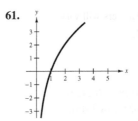

Domain: $x > 0$

63.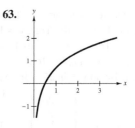

Domain: $x > 0$

65.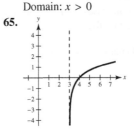

Domain: $x > 3$

67.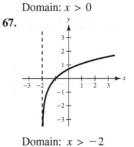

Domain: $x > -2$

69. $g(x) = -e^x - 8$ **71.** $g(x) = \ln(x - 5) - 1$

73.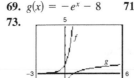

75.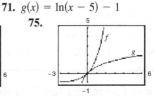

77. (a) $f^{-1}(x) = \dfrac{\ln x + 1}{4}$

(b)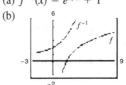

(c) Answers will vary.

79. (a) $f^{-1}(x) = e^{x/2} + 1$

(b)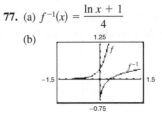

(c) Answers will vary.

81. x^2 **83.** $5x + 2$ **85.** $-1 + 2x$

87. (a) 1.7917 (b) -0.4055 (c) 4.3944 (d) 0.5493

89. $\ln x - \ln 4$ **91.** $\ln x + \ln y - \ln z$

93. $\ln x + \frac{1}{2}\ln(x^2 + 5)$ **95.** $\frac{1}{2}[\ln(x - 1) - \ln x]$

97. $2 + \ln 3$ **99.** $\ln(7x)$

101. $\ln\dfrac{x - 2}{x + 2}$ **103.** $\ln \sqrt[3]{\dfrac{x(x + 3)^2}{x^2 - 1}}$ **105.** $\ln\dfrac{9}{\sqrt{x^2 + 1}}$

107. (a) $x = 4$ (b) $x = \frac{3}{2}$

109. (a) $x = e^2 \approx 7.389$ (b) $x = \ln 4 \approx 1.386$

111. $x > \ln 5$ **113.** $e^{-2} < x < 1$

115.

117. Answers will vary.   **119.** Answers will vary.
121. (a) False   (b) True. $y = \log_2 x$
(c) True. $2^y = x$ (d) False
123. $\beta = 10 \log_{10} I + 160$
125. False. $\ln x + \ln 25 = \ln 25x$
127.

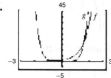

$(-0.7899, 0.2429)$,
$(1.6242, 18.3615)$,
and $(6, 46,656)$;
As x increases, $f(x) = 6^x$ grows
more rapidly.

129. (a)

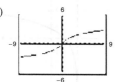

Domain: $(-\infty, \infty)$

(b) Proof

(c) $f^{-1}(x) = \dfrac{e^{2x} - 1}{2e^x}$

131. $12! = 479,001,600$
Stirling's Formula: $12! \approx 475,687,487$
133. Proof

Review Exercises for Chapter 1   *(page 56)*

1. $\left(\frac{8}{5}, 0\right), (0, -8)$ **3.** $(3, 0), \left(0, \frac{3}{4}\right)$ **5.** Not symmetric
7. Symmetric with respect to the x-axis, the y-axis, and the origin
9.

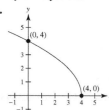

Symmetry: none

11.

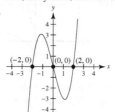

Symmetry: origin

13.

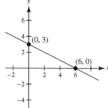

Symmetry: none

15. $(-2, 3)$
17. $(-2, 3), (3, 8)$

19.

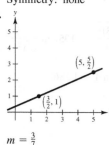

$m = \frac{3}{7}$

21. $7x - 4y - 41 = 0$

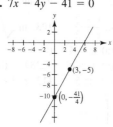

23. $2x + 3y + 6 = 0$

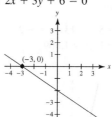

25.

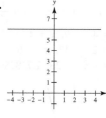

27.

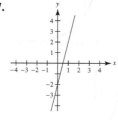

29. $x - 4y = 0$

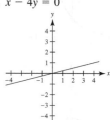

31. (a) $7x - 16y + 101 = 0$ (b) $5x - 3y + 30 = 0$
(c) $4x - 3y + 27 = 0$ (d) $x + 3 = 0$
33. $V = 12,500 - 850t$; \$9950
35. (a) 4   (b) 29   (c) -11 (d) $5t + 9$
37. $8x + 4\,\Delta x, \Delta x \neq 0$
39. Domain: $(-\infty, \infty)$; Range: $[3, \infty)$
41. Domain: $(-\infty, \infty)$; Range: $(-\infty, 0]$
43.

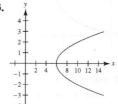

Not a function

45.

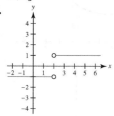

Function

47. $f(x) = x^3 - 3x^2$

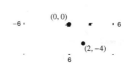

(a) $g(x) = -x^3 + 3x^2 + 1$
(b) $g(x) = (x - 2)^3 - 3(x - 2)^2 + 1$

49. (a)

(b)

(c)

51. For company (a), the profit rose rapidly for the first year and then leveled off. For company (b), the profit dropped and then rose again later.

53. (a) $y = -1.204x + 64.2667$

(b)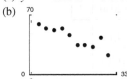

(c) The data point $(27, 44)$ is probably an error. Without this point, the new model is $y = -1.4344x + 66.4387$.

55. (a) $y = 0.61t^2 + 11.0t + 172$

(b)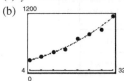

The model fits the data well.

57. (a) $f^{-1}(x) = 2x + 6$

(b) .   (c) Answers will vary.

59. (a) $f^{-1}(x) = x^2 - 1, \ x \geq 0$

(b) .   (c) Answers will vary.

61. (a) $f^{-1}(x) = x^3 - 1$

(b) .

(c) Answers will vary.

63.   **65.** $\frac{1}{2}$ **67.** d   **68.** a

69. c   **70.** b

71.

73. $\frac{1}{5}[\ln(2x + 1) + \ln(2x - 1) - \ln(4x^2 + 1)]$

75. $\ln\left(\dfrac{3\sqrt[3]{4 - x^2}}{x}\right)$ **77.** $x = e^4 - 1 \approx 53.598$

79. (a) $f^{-1}(x) = e^{2x}$

(b) 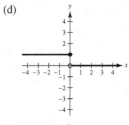   (c) Answers will vary.

81.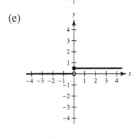

P.S. Problem Solving *(page 59)*

1. (a) Center: $(3, 4)$; Radius: 5

(b) $y = -\frac{3}{4}x$ (c) $y = \frac{3}{4}x - \frac{9}{2}$ (d) $\left(3, -\frac{9}{4}\right)$

3.

(a)   (b)

(c)   (d)

(e)   (f)

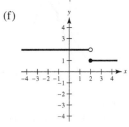

5. (a) $A(x) = x[(100 - x)/2]$; Domain: $(0, 100)$

(b)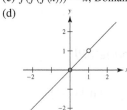

Dimensions 50 m × 25 m yield maximum area of 1250 m².

(c) 50 m × 25 m; Area = 1250 m²

7. $T(x) = \left[2\sqrt{4 + x^2} + \sqrt{(3 - x)^2 + 1}\right]/4$

9. (a) 5, less   (b) 3, greater   (c) 4.1, less

(d) $4 + h$ (e) 4; Answers will vary.

11. (a) Domain: $(-\infty, 1) \cup (1, \infty)$; Range: $(-\infty, 0) \cup (0, \infty)$

(b) $f(f(x)) = \dfrac{x - 1}{x}$; Domain: $(-\infty, 0) \cup (0, 1) \cup (1, \infty)$

(c) $f(f(f(x))) = x$; Domain: $(-\infty, 0) \cup (0, 1) \cup (1, \infty)$

(d)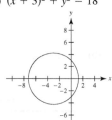

The graph is not a line because there are holes at $x = 0$ and $x = 1$.

13. (a) $x \approx 1.2426, -7.2426$ **15.** Proof

(b) $(x + 3)^2 + y^2 = 18$

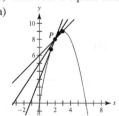

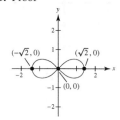

Chapter 2

Section 2.1   *(page 67)*

1. Precalculus: 300 ft

3. Calculus: Slope of the tangent line at $x = 2$ is 0.16.

5. (a) Precalculus: 10 square units

(b) Calculus: 5 square units

7. (a)

(b) $1; \dfrac{3}{2}; \dfrac{5}{2}$

(c) 2; Use points closer to P.

9. Area ≈ 10.417; Area ≈ 9.145; Use more rectangles.

Section 2.2   *(page 75)*

1.

x	3.9	3.99	3.999	4
$f(x)$	0.2041	0.2004	0.2000	?

x	4.001	4.01	4.1
$f(x)$	0.2000	0.1996	0.1961

$\displaystyle\lim_{x \to 4} \frac{x - 4}{x^2 - 3x - 4} \approx 0.2000$ $\left(\text{Actual limit is } \dfrac{1}{5}.\right)$

3.

x	-0.1	-0.01	-0.001	0
$f(x)$	0.9983	0.99998	1.0000	?

x	0.001	0.01	0.1
$f(x)$	1.0000	0.99998	0.9983

$\displaystyle\lim_{x \to 0} \frac{\sin x}{x} \approx 1.0000$ (Actual limit is 1.)

5.

x	-0.1	-0.01	-0.001	0
$f(x)$	0.9516	0.9950	0.9995	?

x	0.001	0.01	0.1
$f(x)$	1.0005	1.0050	1.0517

$\displaystyle\lim_{x \to 0} \frac{e^x - 1}{x} \approx 1.0000$ (Actual limit is 1.)

7.

x	0.9	0.99	0.999	1
$f(x)$	0.2564	0.2506	0.2501	?

x	1.001	1.01	1.1
$f(x)$	0.2499	0.2494	0.2439

$\displaystyle\lim_{x \to 1} \frac{x - 2}{x^2 + x - 6} \approx 0.2500$ $\left(\text{Actual limit is } \dfrac{1}{4}.\right)$

9.

x	0.9	0.99	0.999	1
$f(x)$	0.7340	0.6733	0.6673	?

x	1.001	1.01	1.1
$f(x)$	0.6660	0.6600	0.6015

$\displaystyle\lim_{x \to 1} \frac{x^4 - 1}{x^6 - 1} \approx 0.6666$ $\left(\text{Actual limit is } \dfrac{2}{3}.\right)$

11.

x	-6.1	-6.01	-6.001	-6
$f(x)$	-0.1248	-0.1250	-0.1250	?

x	-5.999	-5.99	-5.9
$f(x)$	-0.1250	-0.1250	-0.1252

$\displaystyle\lim_{x \to -6} \frac{\sqrt{10 - x} - 4}{x + 6} \approx -0.1250$ $\left(\text{Actual limit is } -\dfrac{1}{8}.\right)$

13.

x	-0.1	-0.01	-0.001	0
$f(x)$	1.9867	1.9999	2.0000	?

x	0.001	0.01	0.1
$f(x)$	2.0000	1.9999	1.9867

$\lim\limits_{x\to 0} \dfrac{\sin 2x}{x} \approx 2.0000$ (Actual limit is 2.)

15.

x	1.9	1.99	1.999	2
$f(x)$	0.5129	0.5013	0.5001	?

x	2.001	2.01	2.1
$f(x)$	0.4999	0.4988	0.4879

$\lim\limits_{x\to 2} \dfrac{\ln x - \ln 2}{x - 2} \approx 0.5000$ $\left(\text{Actual limit is } \dfrac{1}{2}.\right)$

17. 1   **19.** 2

21. Limit does not exist. The function approaches 1 from the right side of 2, but it approaches -1 from the left side of 2.

23. Limit does not exist. The function oscillates between 1 and -1 as x approaches 0.

25. (a) 2
(b) Limit does not exist. The function approaches 1 from the right side of 1, but it approaches 3.5 from the left side of 1.
(c) Value does not exist. The function is undefined at $x = 4$.
(d) 2

27.

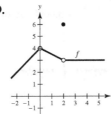

29.

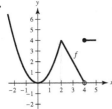

$\lim\limits_{x\to c} f(x)$ exists for all points on the graph except where $c = 4$.

31. $\delta = 0.4$ **33.** $\delta = \frac{1}{11} \approx 0.091$

35. $L = 8$; Let $\delta = 0.01/3 \approx 0.0033$.

37. $L = 1$; Let $\delta = 0.01/5 = 0.002$.   **39.** 6   **41.** -3

43. 3   **45.** 0   **47.** 10   **49.** 2   **51.** 4

53.

$\lim\limits_{x\to 4} f(x) = \frac{1}{6}$

Domain: $[-5, 4) \cup (4, \infty)$

The graph has a hole at $x = 4$.

55.

$\lim\limits_{x\to 9} f(x) = 6$

Domain: $[0, 9) \cup (9, \infty)$

The graph has a hole at $x = 9$.

57. (a)

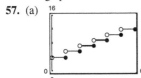

(b)

t	3	3.3	3.4	3.5
C	11.57	12.36	12.36	12.36

t	3.6	3.7	4
C	12.36	12.36	12.36

$\lim\limits_{t\to 3.5} C(t) = 12.36$

(c)

t	2	2.5	2.9	3
C	10.78	11.57	11.57	11.57

t	3.1	3.5	4
C	12.36	12.36	12.36

The limit does not exist because the limits from the right and left are not equal.

59. Answers will vary. Sample answer: As x approaches 8 from either side, $f(x)$ becomes arbitrarily close to 25.

61. (i) The values of f approach different numbers as x approaches c from different sides of c.

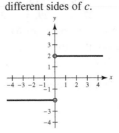

(ii) The values of f increase or decrease without bound as x approaches c.

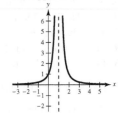

(iii) The values of f oscillate between two fixed numbers as x approaches c.

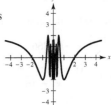

63. (a) $r = \dfrac{3}{\pi} \approx 0.9549$ cm

(b) $\dfrac{5.5}{2\pi} \le r \le \dfrac{6.5}{2\pi}$, or approximately $0.8754 < r < 1.0345$

(c) $\lim\limits_{r\to 3/\pi} 2\pi r = 6$; $\varepsilon = 0.5$; $\delta \approx 0.0796$

65.

x	-0.001	-0.0001	-0.00001	0
$f(x)$	2.7196	2.7184	2.7183	?

x	0.00001	0.0001	0.001
$f(x)$	2.7183	2.7181	2.7169

$\lim\limits_{x\to 0} f(x) \approx 2.7183$

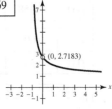

67.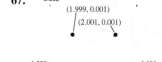

0.002
(1.999, 0.001)
(2.001, 0.001)
1.998 ⌞____×____⌟ 2.002
0

$\delta = 0.001$, $(1.999, 2.001)$

69. False. The existence or nonexistence of $f(x)$ at $x = c$ has no bearing on the existence of the limit of $f(x)$ as $x \to c$.

71. False. See Exercise 19.

73. Yes. As x approaches 0.25 from either side, $\sqrt{x}$ becomes arbitrarily close to 0.5.

75. $\lim\limits_{x \to 0} \dfrac{\sin nx}{x} = n$ **77–79.** Proofs

81. Putnam Problem B1, 1986

Section 2.3   *(page 87)*

1.

6
-4 ⌞_____⌟ 8
-6

3.

4
-π _____ π
-4

(a) 0   (b) -5 (a) 0   (b) About 0.52 or $\pi/6$

5. 8   **7.** -1 **9.** 0   **11.** 7   **13.** 2   **15.** 1   **17.** $\frac{1}{2}$

19. $\frac{1}{5}$ **21.** 7   **23.** 1   **25.** $\frac{1}{2}$ **27.** 1   **29.** $\frac{1}{2}$ **31.** -1

33. 1   **35.** $\ln 3 + e$ **37.** (a) 4   (b) 64   (c) 64

39. (a) 3   (b) 2   (c) 2   **41.** (a) 10   (b) 5   (c) 6   (d) $\frac{3}{2}$

43. (a) 64   (b) 2   (c) 12   (d) 8

45. $f(x) = \dfrac{x^2 - 1}{x + 1}$ and $g(x) = x - 1$ agree except at $x = -1$.

$\lim\limits_{x \to -1} f(x) = \lim\limits_{x \to -1} g(x) = -2$

47. $f(x) = \dfrac{x^3 - 8}{x - 2}$ and $g(x) = x^2 + 2x + 4$ agree except at $x = 2$.

$\lim\limits_{x \to 2} f(x) = \lim\limits_{x \to 2} g(x) = 12$

49. $-\dfrac{\ln 2}{8} \approx -0.0866$

$f(x) = \dfrac{(x + 4)\ln(x + 6)}{x^2 - 16}$ and $g(x) = \dfrac{\ln(x + 6)}{x - 4}$ agree except at $x = -4$.

51. -1 **53.** 1/8   **55.** 5/6   **57.** 1/6   **59.** $\sqrt{5}/10$

61. $-1/9$ **63.** 2   **65.** $2x - 2$ **67.** 1/5   **69.** 0

71. 0   **73.** 0   **75.** 1   **77.** 1   **79.** 3/2

81.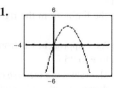

2
-3 · ▪ · 3
-2

The graph has a hole at $x = 0$.

Answers will vary. Sample answer:

x	-0.1	-0.01	-0.001	0
$f(x)$	0.358	0.354	0.354	?

x	0.001	0.01	0.1
$f(x)$	0.354	0.353	0.349

$\lim\limits_{x \to 0} \dfrac{\sqrt{x + 2} - \sqrt{2}}{x} \approx 0.354$; Actual limit is $\dfrac{1}{2\sqrt{2}} = \dfrac{\sqrt{2}}{4}$.

83.

3
-5 ▪ ▪ —▪ 1
-2

The graph has a hole at $x = 0$.

Answers will vary. Sample answer:

x	-0.1	-0.01	-0.001	0
$f(x)$	-0.263	-0.251	-0.250	?

x	0.001	0.01	0.1
$f(x)$	-0.250	-0.249	-0.238

$\lim\limits_{x \to 0} \dfrac{[1/(2 + x)] - (1/2)}{x} \approx -0.250$; Actual limit is $-\dfrac{1}{4}$.

85.

4
-2π _____ 2π
-1

The graph has a hole at $t = 0$.

Answers will vary. Sample answer:

t	-0.1	-0.01	0	0.01	0.1
$f(t)$	2.96	2.9996	?	2.9996	2.96

$\lim\limits_{t \to 0} \dfrac{\sin 3t}{t} \approx 3.0000$; Actual limit is 3.

87.

1
-2π _____ 2π
-1

The graph has a hole at $x = 0$.

Answers will vary. Sample answer:

x	-0.1	-0.01	-0.001	0
$f(x)$	-0.1	-0.01	-0.001	?

x	0.001	0.01	0.1
$f(x)$	0.001	0.01	0.1

$\lim\limits_{x \to 0} \dfrac{\sin x^2}{x} = 0$; Actual limit is 0.

89.

Answers will vary. Sample answer:

x	0.5	0.9	0.99	1
$f(x)$	1.3863	1.0536	1.0050	?

x	1.01	1.1	1.5
$f(x)$	0.9950	0.9531	0.8109

$\lim\limits_{x \to 1} \dfrac{\ln x}{x-1} \approx 1$; Actual limit is 1.

91. 3   **93.** $-1/(x+3)^2$ **95.** 4

97. 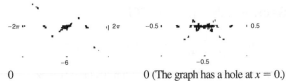 **99.**

0   0 (The graph has a hole at $x = 0$.)

101. (a) f and g agree at all but one point if c is a real number such that $f(x) = g(x)$ for all $x \neq c$.

(b) Sample answer: $f(x) = \dfrac{x^2 - 1}{x - 1}$ and $g(x) = x + 1$ agree at all points except $x = 1$.

103. If a function f is squeezed between two functions h and g, $h(x) \leq f(x) \leq g(x)$, and h and g have the same limit L as $x \to c$, then $\lim\limits_{x \to c} f(x)$ exists and equals L.

105.

The magnitudes of $f(x)$ and $g(x)$ are approximately equal when x is close to 0. Therefore, their ratio is approximately 1.

107. -64 ft/sec (speed $= 64$ ft/sec)   **109.** -29.4 m/sec

111. Let $f(x) = 1/x$ and $g(x) = -1/x$. $\lim\limits_{x \to 0} f(x)$ and $\lim\limits_{x \to 0} g(x)$ do not exist. However,

$$\lim_{x \to 0} [f(x) + g(x)] = \lim_{x \to 0}\left[\frac{1}{x} + \left(-\frac{1}{x}\right)\right] = \lim_{x \to 0} 0 = 0$$

and therefore does exist.

113–117. Proofs

119. Let $f(x) = \begin{cases} 4, & x \geq 0 \\ -4, & x < 0 \end{cases}$.

$\lim\limits_{x \to 0} |f(x)| = \lim\limits_{x \to 0} 4 = 4$

$\lim\limits_{x \to 0} f(x)$ does not exist because for $x < 0$, $f(x) = -4$ and for $x \geq 0$, $f(x) = 4$.

121. False. The limit does not exist because the function approaches 1 from the right side of 0 and approaches -1 from the left side of 0.

123. True.

125. False. The limit does not exist because $f(x)$ approaches 3 from the left side of 2 and approaches 0 from the right side of 2.

127. Proof

129. (a) All $x \neq 0, \dfrac{\pi}{2} + n\pi$

(b) 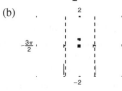 The domain is not obvious. The hole at $x = 0$ is not apparent from the graph.

(c) $\dfrac{1}{2}$ (d) $\dfrac{1}{2}$

Section 2.4   *(page 99)*

1. (a) 3   (b) 3   (c) 3; $f(x)$ is continuous on $(-\infty, \infty)$.

3. (a) 0   (b) 0   (c) 0; Discontinuity at $x = 3$

5. (a) -3 (b) 3   (c) Limit does not exist.
Discontinuity at $x = 2$

7. $\dfrac{1}{16}$ **9.** $\dfrac{1}{10}$

11. Limit does not exist. The function decreases without bound as x approaches -3 from the left.

13. -1 **15.** $-1/x^2$ **17.** $5/2$

19. Limit does not exist. The function decreases without bound as x approaches π from the left and increases without bound as x approaches π from the right.

21. 8

23. Limit does not exist. The function approaches 5 from the left side of 3 but approaches 6 from the right side of 3.

25. Limit does not exist. The function decreases without bound as x approaches 3 from the right.

27. $\ln 4$ **29.** Discontinuities at $x = -2$ and $x = 2$

31. Discontinuities at every integer

33. Continuous on $[-7, 7]$ **35.** Continuous on $[-1, 4]$

37. Nonremovable discontinuity at $x = 0$

39. Continuous for all real x

41. Nonremovable discontinuities at $x = -2$ and $x = 2$

43. Nonremovable discontinuity at $x = 1$
Removable discontinuity at $x = 0$

45. Continuous for all real x

47. Removable discontinuity at $x = -2$
Nonremovable discontinuity at $x = 5$

49. Nonremovable discontinuity at $x = -7$

51. Continuous for all real x

53. Nonremovable discontinuity at $x = 2$

55. Continuous for all real x

57. Nonremovable discontinuity at $x = 0$

59. Nonremovable discontinuities at integer multiples of $\pi/2$

61. Nonremovable discontinuities at each integer

63. $a = 7$ **65.** $a = -1, b = 1$ **67.** $a = -1$

69. Continuous for all real x

71. Nonremovable discontinuities at $x = 1$ and $x = -1$

73. 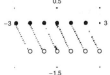 **75.**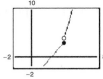

Nonremovable discontinuity   Nonremovable discontinuity
at each integer   at $x = 4$

77. Continuous on $(-\infty, \infty)$ **79.** Continuous on $[0, \infty)$
81. Continuous on the open intervals . . . , $(-6, -2)$, $(-2, 2)$, $(2, 6)$, . . .
83. Continuous on $(-\infty, \infty)$
85.

The graph has a hole at $x = 0$. The graph appears to be continuous, but the function is not continuous on $[-4, 4]$. It is not obvious from the graph that the function has a discontinuity at $x = 0$.

87.

The graph has a hole at $x = 0$. The graph appears to be continuous, but the function is not continuous on $[-4, 4]$. It is not obvious from the graph that the function has a discontinuity at $x = 0$.

89. Because $f(x)$ is continuous on the interval $[1, 2]$ and $f(1) = 37/12$ and $f(2) = -8/3$, by the Intermediate Value Theorem there exists a real number c in $[1, 2]$ such that $f(c) = 0$.
91. Because $h(x)$ is continuous on the interval $[0, \pi/2]$, and $h(0) = -2$ and $h(\pi/2) \approx 0.9119$, by the Intermediate Value Theorem there exists a real number c in $[0, \pi/2]$ such that $f(c) = 0$.
93. 0.68, 0.6823   **95.** 0.56, 0.5636   **97.** 0.79, 0.7921
99. $f(3) = 11$ **101.** $f(2) = 4$
103. (a) The limit does not exist at $x = c$.
  (b) The function is not defined at $x = c$.
  (c) The limit exists, but it is not equal to the value of the function at $x = c$.
  (d) The limit does not exist at $x = c$.
105. If f and g are continuous for all real x, then so is $f + g$ (Theorem 1.11, part 2). However, f/g might not be continuous if $g(x) = 0$. For example, let $f(x) = x$ and $g(x) = x^2 - 1$. Then f and g are continuous for all real x, but f/g is not continuous at $x = \pm 1$.
107. True
109. False. A rational function can be written as $P(x)/Q(x)$, where P and Q are polynomials of degree m and n, respectively. It can have, at most, n discontinuities.
111. The functions differ by 1 for non-integer values of x.
113. $C = \begin{cases} 0.40, & 0 < t \le 10 \\ 0.40 + 0.05[\![t - 9]\!], & t > 10, \ t \text{ is not an integer.} \\ 0.40 + 0.05(t - 10), & t > 10, \ t \text{ is an integer.} \end{cases}$

There is a nonremovable discontinuity at each integer greater than or equal to 10.

115–117. Proofs   **119.** Answers will vary.

121. (a)

(b) There appears to be a limiting speed, and a possible cause is air resistance.

123. $c = \left(-1 \pm \sqrt{5}\right)/2$
125. Domain: $[-c^2, 0) \cup (0, \infty)$; Let $f(0) = 1/(2c)$.
127. $h(x)$ has a nonremovable discontinuity at every integer except 0.

129. Putnam Problem B2, 1988

Section 2.5   *(page 108)*

1. $\lim\limits_{x \to -2^+} 2\left|\dfrac{x}{x^2 - 4}\right| = \infty$, $\quad \lim\limits_{x \to -2^-} 2\left|\dfrac{x}{x^2 - 4}\right| = \infty$

3. $\lim\limits_{x \to -2^+} \tan(\pi x/4) = -\infty$, $\quad \lim\limits_{x \to -2^-} \tan(\pi x/4) = \infty$

5. $\lim\limits_{x \to 4^+} \dfrac{1}{x - 4} = \infty$, $\quad \lim\limits_{x \to 4^-} \dfrac{1}{x - 4} = -\infty$

7. $\lim\limits_{x \to 4^+} \dfrac{1}{(x - 4)^2} = \infty$, $\quad \lim\limits_{x \to 4^-} \dfrac{1}{(x - 4)^2} = \infty$

9.

x	-3.5	-3.1	-3.01	-3.001	-3
$f(x)$	0.31	1.64	16.6	167	?

x	-2.999	-2.99	-2.9	-2.5
$f(x)$	-167	-16.7	-1.69	-0.36

$\lim\limits_{x \to -3^+} f(x) = -\infty$, $\quad \lim\limits_{x \to -3^-} f(x) = \infty$

11.

x	-3.5	-3.1	-3.01	-3.001	-3
$f(x)$	3.8	16	151	1501	?

x	-2.999	-2.99	-2.9	-2.5
$f(x)$	-1499	-149	-14	-2.3

$\lim\limits_{x \to -3^+} f(x) = -\infty$, $\quad \lim\limits_{x \to -3^-} f(x) = \infty$

13. $x = 0$ **15.** $x = \pm 2$ **17.** No vertical asymptote
19. $x = -2, x = 1$ **21.** No vertical asymptote
23. $x = 1$ **25.** $t = -2$ **27.** $x = 0$
29. $x = n$, n is an integer.   **31.** $t = n\pi$, n is a nonzero integer.
33. Removable discontinuity at $x = -1$
35. Vertical asymptote at $x = -1$ **37.** ∞ **39.** ∞
41. $-\frac{1}{5}$ **43.** $-\infty$ **45.** $-\infty$ **47.** ∞ **49.** $-\infty$
51. $-\infty$ **53.** ∞

55.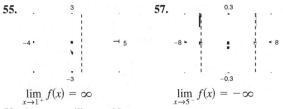

$$\lim_{x \to 1^+} f(x) = \infty$$

57.

$$\lim_{x \to 5^-} f(x) = -\infty$$

59. Answers will vary; No

61. Answers will vary. Sample answer: $f(x) = \dfrac{x-3}{x^2 - 4x - 12}$

63.

65. (a)

x	1	0.5	0.2	0.1
$f(x)$	0.1585	0.0411	0.0067	0.0017

x	0.01	0.001	0.0001
$f(x)$	≈ 0	≈ 0	≈ 0

$$\lim_{x \to 0^+} \frac{x - \sin x}{x} = 0$$

(b)

x	1	0.5	0.2	0.1
$f(x)$	0.1585	0.0823	0.0333	0.0167

x	0.01	0.001	0.0001
$f(x)$	0.0017	≈ 0	≈ 0

$$\lim_{x \to 0^+} \frac{x - \sin x}{x^2} = 0$$

(c)

x	1	0.5	0.2	0.1
$f(x)$	0.1585	0.1646	0.1663	0.1666

x	0.01	0.001	0.0001
$f(x)$	0.1667	0.1667	0.1667

$$\lim_{x \to 0^+} \frac{x - \sin x}{x^3} = 0.1667 \ (1/6)$$

(d)

x	1	0.5	0.2	0.1
$f(x)$	0.1585	0.3292	0.8317	1.6658

x	0.01	0.001	0.0001
$f(x)$	16.67	166.7	1667.0

$$\lim_{x \to 0^+} \frac{x - \sin x}{x^4} = \infty$$

For $n > 3$, $\lim\limits_{x \to 0^+} \dfrac{x - \sin x}{x^n} = \infty$.

67. (a) $\dfrac{7}{12}$ ft/sec   (b) $\dfrac{3}{2}$ ft/sec   (c) $\lim\limits_{x \to 25^-} \dfrac{2x}{\sqrt{625 - x^2}} = \infty$

69. (a) $A = 50 \tan \theta - 50\theta$; Domain: $(0, \pi/2)$

(b)

θ	0.3	0.6	0.9	1.2	1.5
$f(\theta)$	0.47	4.21	18.0	68.6	630.1

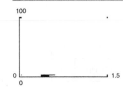

(c) $\lim\limits_{\theta \to \pi/2} A = \infty$

71. False. Let $f(x) = (x^2 - 1)/(x - 1)$.

73. False. Let $f(x) = \tan x$.

75. Let $f(x) = \dfrac{1}{x^2}$ and $g(x) = \dfrac{1}{x^4}$, and let $c = 0$. $\lim\limits_{x \to 0} \dfrac{1}{x^2} = \infty$ and

$\lim\limits_{x \to 0} \dfrac{1}{x^4} = \infty$, but $\lim\limits_{x \to 0} \left(\dfrac{1}{x^2} - \dfrac{1}{x^4} \right) = \lim\limits_{x \to 0} \left(\dfrac{x^2 - 1}{x^4} \right) = -\infty \neq 0$.

77. Given $\lim\limits_{x \to c} f(x) = \infty$, let $g(x) = 1$. Then $\lim\limits_{x \to c} \dfrac{g(x)}{f(x)} = 0$ by Theorem 2.15.

79. Answers will vary.

Review Exercises for Chapter 2   *(page 111)*

1. Calculus   Estimate: 8.3

3.

x	2.9	2.99	2.999	3
$f(x)$	-0.9091	-0.9901	-0.9990	?

x	3.001	3.01	3.1
$f(x)$	-1.0010	-1.0101	-1.1111

$$\lim_{x \to 0} \frac{x - 3}{x^2 - 7x + 12} \approx -1.0000$$

5. (a) 4   (b) 5   **7.** 5; Proof   **9.** -3; Proof   **11.** 36

13. 16   **15.** $\frac{4}{3}$ **17.** $-\frac{1}{4}$ **19.** $\frac{1}{2}$ **21.** -1 **23.** 0

25. 1   **27.** $\sqrt{3}/2$ **29.** -3 **31.** -5

33.

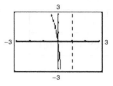

The graph has a hole at $x = 0$.

x	-0.1	-0.01	-0.001	0
$f(x)$	0.3352	0.3335	0.3334	?

x	0.001	0.01	0.1
$f(x)$	0.3333	0.3331	0.3315

$\lim\limits_{x \to 0} \dfrac{\sqrt{2x + 9} - 3}{x} \approx 0.3333$; Actual limit is $\dfrac{1}{3}$.

35.

x	-0.1	-0.01	-0.001	0
$f(x)$	0.8867	0.0988	0.0100	?

x	0.001	0.01	0.1
$f(x)$	-0.0100	-0.1013	-1.1394

$\lim\limits_{x \to 0} f(x) = 0$; Actual limit is 0.

37. -39.2 m/sec   **39.** $\frac{1}{6}$ **41.** $\frac{1}{4}$ **43.** 3   **45.** 0

47. Limit does not exist. The limit as t approaches 1 from the left is 2, whereas the limit as t approaches 1 from the right is 1.

49. Continuous for all real x

51. Nonremovable discontinuity at $x = 5$

53. Nonremovable discontinuities at $x = -1$ and $x = 1$
Removable discontinuity at $x = 0$

55. $c = -\frac{1}{2}$ **57.** Continuous for all real x

59. Continuous on $[4, \infty)$

61. Continuous on $(k, k + 1)$ for all integers k

63. Removable discontinuity at $x = 1$
Continuous on $(-\infty, 1) \cup (1, \infty)$

65. Proof   **67.** (a) -4 (b) 4   (c) Limit does not exist.

69. $x = 0$ **71.** $x = \pm 3$ **73.** $x = \pm 8$

75. $x = \pm 5$ **77.** $-\infty$ **79.** $\frac{1}{3}$ **81.** $-\infty$

83. $\frac{4}{5}$ **85.** ∞ **87.** $-\infty$

89. (a) \$14,117.65   (b) \$80,000.00   (c) \$720,000.00
(d) ∞; No matter how much the company spends, the company will never be able to remove 100% of the pollutants.

P.S. Problem Solving   *(page 113)*

1. (a) Perimeter $\triangle PAO = 1 + \sqrt{(x^2 - 1)^2 + x^2} + \sqrt{x^4 + x^2}$
Perimeter $\triangle PBO = 1 + \sqrt{x^4 + (x - 1)^2} + \sqrt{x^4 + x^2}$

(b)

x	4	2	1
Perimeter $\triangle PAO$	33.0166	9.0777	3.4142
Perimeter $\triangle PBO$	33.7712	9.5952	3.4142
$r(x)$	0.9777	0.9461	1.0000

x	0.1	0.01
Perimeter $\triangle PAO$	2.0955	2.0100
Perimeter $\triangle PBO$	2.0006	2.0000
$r(x)$	1.0475	1.0050

1

3. (a) Area (hexagon) $= (3\sqrt{3})/2 \approx 2.5981$
Area (circle) $= \pi \approx 3.1416$
Area (circle) $-$ Area (hexagon) ≈ 0.5435
(b) $A_n = (n/2) \sin(2\pi/n)$
(c)

n	6	12	24	48	96
A_n	2.5981	3.0000	3.1058	3.1326	3.1394

3.1416 or π

5. (a) $m = -\frac{12}{5}$ (b) $y = \frac{5}{12}x - \frac{169}{12}$
(c) $m_x = \dfrac{-\sqrt{169 - x^2} + 12}{x - 5}$
(d) $\frac{5}{12}$; It is the same as the slope of the tangent line found in (b).

7. (a) Domain: $[-27, 1) \cup (1, \infty)$
(b)

(c) $\frac{1}{14}$ (d) $\frac{1}{12}$

The graph has a hole at $x = 1$.

9. (a) g_1, g_4 (b) g_1 (c) g_1, g_3, g_4

11.

The graph jumps at every integer.

(a) $f(1) = 0$, $f(0) = 0$, $f\left(\frac{1}{2}\right) = -1$, $f(-2.7) = -1$
(b) $\lim\limits_{x \to 1^-} f(x) = -1$, $\lim\limits_{x \to 1^+} f(x) = -1$, $\lim\limits_{x \to 1/2} f(x) = -1$
(c) There is a discontinuity at each integer.

13. (a)

(b) (i) $\lim\limits_{x \to a^+} P_{a,b}(x) = 1$
(ii) $\lim\limits_{x \to a^-} P_{a,b}(x) = 0$
(iii) $\lim\limits_{x \to b^+} P_{a,b}(x) = 0$
(iv) $\lim\limits_{x \to b^-} P_{a,b}(x) = 1$

(c) Continuous for all positive real numbers except a and b
(d) The area under the graph of U and above the x-axis is 1.

Chapter 3

Section 3.1   *(page 123)*

1. $m_1 = 0, m_2 = 5/2$

3. (a)–(c)

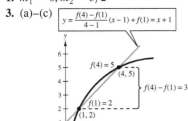

$$y = \frac{f(4)-f(1)}{4-1}(x-1)+f(1) = x+1$$

5. $m = -5$

7. $m = 4$

9. $m = 3$ **11.** $f'(x) = 0$ **13.** $f'(x) = -10$

15. $h'(s) = \frac{2}{3}$ **17.** $f'(x) = 2x + 1$ **19.** $f'(x) = 3x^2 - 12$

21. $f'(x) = \dfrac{-1}{(x-1)^2}$ **23.** $f'(x) = \dfrac{1}{2\sqrt{x+4}}$

25. (a) Tangent line:
   $y = -2x + 2$
(b)

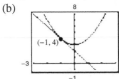

27. (a) Tangent line:
   $y = 12x - 16$
(b)

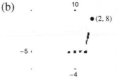

29. (a) Tangent line:
   $y = \frac{1}{2}x + \frac{1}{2}$
(b)

31. (a) Tangent line:
   $y = \frac{3}{4}x - 2$
(b)

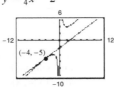

33. $y = 2x - 1$ **35.** $y = 3x - 2; y = 3x + 2$

37. $y = -\frac{1}{2}x + \frac{3}{2}$

39.

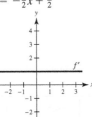

The slope of the graph of f is 1 for all x-values.

41.

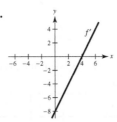

The slope of the graph of f is negative for $x < 4$, positive for $x > 4$, and 0 at $x = 4$.

43.

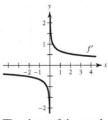

The slope of the graph of f is negative for $x < 0$ and positive for $x > 0$. The slope is undefined at $x = 0$.

45. Answers will vary.
   Sample answer: $y = -x$

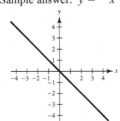

47. $g(4) = 5; g'(4) = -\frac{5}{3}$

49. $f(x) = 5 - 3x$
   $c = 1$

51. $f(x) = -x^2$
   $c = 6$

53. $f(x) = -3x + 2$

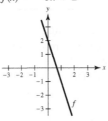

55. $y = 2x + 1; y = -2x + 9$

57. (a)

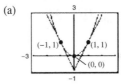

For this function, the slopes of the tangent lines are always distinct for different values of x.

(b)

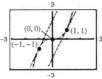

For this function, the slopes of the tangent lines are sometimes the same.

59. (a)

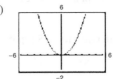

$$f'(0) = 0, f'\left(\tfrac{1}{2}\right) = \tfrac{1}{2}, f'(1) = 1, f'(2) = 2$$

(b) $f'\left(-\tfrac{1}{2}\right) = -\tfrac{1}{2}, f'(-1) = -1, f'(-2) = -2$

(c)

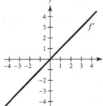

(d) $f'(x) = x$

61.

$g(x) \approx f'(x)$

63. $f(2) = 4; f(2.1) = 3.99; f'(2) \approx -0.1$

65. 6   **67.** 4

69. $g(x)$ is not differentiable at $x = 0$.

71. $f(x)$ is not differentiable at $x = 6$.

73. $h(x)$ is not differentiable at $x = -7$.   **75.** $(-\infty, 3) \cup (3, \infty)$

77. $(-\infty, -4) \cup (-4, \infty)$ **79.** $(1, \infty)$

81. 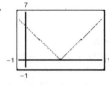   **83.**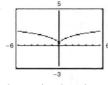

$(-\infty, 5) \cup (5, \infty)$ $(-\infty, 0) \cup (0, \infty)$

85. The derivative from the left is -1 and the derivative from the right is 1, so f is not differentiable at $x = 1$.

87. The derivatives from both the right and the left are 0, so $f'(1) = 0$.

89. f is differentiable at $x = 2$.

91. 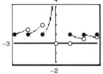   **93.** False. The slope is
$$\lim_{\Delta x \to 0} \frac{f(2 + \Delta x) - f(2)}{\Delta x}.$$

Yes, f is differentiable for all $x \neq n$, n is an integer.

95. False. For example, $f(x) = |x|$. The derivative from the left and the derivative from the right both exist but are not equal.

97. Proof

Section 3.2 *(page 135)*

1. (a) $\frac{1}{2}$ (b) 3 **3.** 0 **5.** $7x^6$ **7.** $-5/x^6$
9. $1/(5x^{4/5})$ **11.** 1 **13.** $-4t + 3$ **15.** $2x + 12x^2$
17. $3t^2 + 10t - 3$ **19.** $\frac{\pi}{2}\cos\theta + \sin\theta$ **21.** $2x + \frac{1}{2}\sin x$
23. $\frac{1}{2}e^x - 3\cos x$

Function	Rewrite	Differentiate	Simplify
25. $y = \dfrac{5}{2x^2}$	$y = \dfrac{5}{2}x^{-2}$	$y' = -5x^{-3}$	$y' = -\dfrac{5}{x^3}$
27. $y = \dfrac{6}{(5x)^3}$	$y = \dfrac{6}{125}x^{-3}$	$y' = -\dfrac{18}{125}x^{-4}$	$y' = -\dfrac{18}{125x^4}$
29. $y = \dfrac{\sqrt{x}}{x}$	$y = x^{-1/2}$	$y' = -\dfrac{1}{2}x^{-3/2}$	$y' = -\dfrac{1}{2x^{3/2}}$

31. -2 **33.** 8 **35.** 3 **37.** $\frac{3}{4}$ **39.** $2t + 12/t^4$
41. $8x + 3$ **43.** $(x^3 - 8)/x^3$ **45.** $3x^2 + 1$
47. $\dfrac{1}{2\sqrt{x}} - \dfrac{2}{x^{2/3}}$ **49.** $\dfrac{3}{\sqrt{x}} - 5\sin x$ **51.** $\dfrac{-2}{x^3} - 2e^x$
53. (a) $2x + y - 2 = 0$ **55.** (a) $2x - y + 1 = 0$
  (b)    (b)

57. $(-1, 2), (0, 3), (1, 2)$ **59.** No horizontal tangents
61. $(\ln 4, 4 - 4\ln 4)$ **63.** (π, π) **65.** $k = -8$
67. $k = 3$ **69.** $k = 4/27$
71. 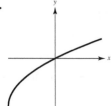   **73.** $g'(x) = f'(x)$

75.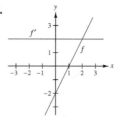
The rate of change of f is constant, and therefore f' is a constant function.

77. $y = 2x - 1$ $y = 4x - 4$
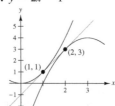   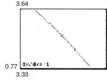

79. $f'(x) = 3 + \cos x \neq 0$ for all x.   **81.** $x - 4y + 4 = 0$
83.
$f'(1)$ appears to be close to -1.
$f'(1) = -1$

85. (a)
(3.9, 7.7019),
$S(x) = 2.981x - 3.924$

(b) $T(x) = 3(x - 4) + 8 = 3x - 4$
The slope (and equation) of the secant line approaches that of the tangent line at $(4, 8)$ as you choose points closer and closer to $(4, 8)$.

(c)
The approximation becomes less accurate.

(d)

Δx	-3	-2	-1	-0.5	-0.1	0
$f(4 + \Delta x)$	1	2.828	5.196	6.548	7.702	8
$T(4 + \Delta x)$	-1	2	5	6.5	7.7	8

Δx	0.1	0.5	1	2	3
$f(4 + \Delta x)$	8.302	9.546	11.180	14.697	18.520
$T(4 + \Delta x)$	8.3	9.5	11	14	17

87. False. Let $f(x) = x$ and $g(x) = x + 1$.
89. False. $dy/dx = 0$ **91.** True
93. Average rate: 4 **95.** Average rate: $\frac{1}{2}$
Instantaneous rates: Instantaneous rates:
$f'(1) = 4; f'(2) = 4$ $f'(1) = 1; f'(2) = \frac{1}{4}$

97. Average rate: $e \approx 2.718$
Instantaneous rates: $g'(0) = 1$; $g'(1) = 2 + e \approx 4.718$

99. (a) $s(t) = -16t^2 + 1362$; $v(t) = -32t$ (b) -48 ft/sec
(c) $s'(1) = -32$ ft/sec; $s'(2) = -64$ ft/sec
(d) $t = \dfrac{\sqrt{1362}}{4} \approx 9.226$ sec (e) -295.242 ft/sec

101. $v(5) = 71$ m/sec; $v(10) = 22$ m/sec

103.

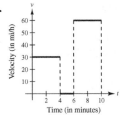

105.

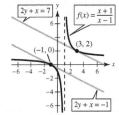

107. $V'(6) = 108$ cm³/cm

109. (a) $R(v) = 0.417v - 0.02$
(b) $B(v) = 0.0056v^2 + 0.001v + 0.04$
(c) $T(v) = 0.0056v^2 + 0.418v + 0.02$
(d)

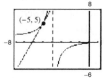

(e) $T'(v) = 0.0112v + 0.418$
$T'(40) = 0.866$
$T'(80) = 1.314$
$T'(100) = 1.538$

(f) Stopping distance increases at an increasing rate.

111. Proof   **113.** $y = 2x^2 - 3x + 1$

115. $9x + y = 0, 9x + 4y + 27 = 0$ **117.** $a = \frac{1}{3}, b = -\frac{4}{3}$

119. $f_1(x) = |\sin x|$ is differentiable for all $x \neq n\pi$, n an integer.
$f_2(x) = \sin|x|$ is differentiable for all $x \neq 0$.

121. Putnam Problem A2, 2010

Section 3.3   *(page 146)*

1. $2(2x^3 - 6x^2 + 3x - 6)$ **3.** $(1 - 5t^2)/(2\sqrt{t})$

5. $e^x(\cos x - \sin x)$ **7.** $(1 - x^2)/(x^2 + 1)^2$

9. $\dfrac{1 - 5x^3}{2\sqrt{x}(x^3 + 1)^2}$ **11.** $\dfrac{\cos x - \sin x}{e^x}$

13. $f'(x) = (x^3 + 4x)(6x + 2) + (3x^2 + 2x - 5)(3x^2 + 4)$
$= 15x^4 + 8x^3 + 21x^2 + 16x - 20$
$f'(0) = -20$

15. $f'(x) = \dfrac{x^2 - 6x + 4}{(x - 3)^2}$ **17.** $f'(x) = \cos x - x \sin x$

$f'(1) = -\dfrac{1}{4}$ $f'\left(\dfrac{\pi}{4}\right) = \dfrac{\sqrt{2}}{8}(4 - \pi)$

19. $f'(x) = e^x(\cos x + \sin x)$
$f'(0) = 1$

Function	Rewrite	Differentiate	Simplify
21. $y = \dfrac{x^2 + 3x}{7}$	$y = \dfrac{1}{7}x^2 + \dfrac{3}{7}x$	$y' = \dfrac{2}{7}x + \dfrac{3}{7}$	$y' = \dfrac{2x + 3}{7}$
23. $y = \dfrac{6}{7x^2}$	$y = \dfrac{6}{7}x^{-2}$	$y' = -\dfrac{12}{7}x^{-3}$	$y' = -\dfrac{12}{7x^3}$
25. $y = \dfrac{4x^{3/2}}{x}$	$y = 4x^{1/2},$	$y' = 2x^{-1/2}$	$y' = \dfrac{2}{\sqrt{x}},$
	$x > 0$		$x > 0$

27. $\dfrac{3}{(x + 1)^2}$, $x \neq 1$ **29.** $(x^2 + 6x - 3)/(x + 3)^2$

31. $(3x + 1)/(2x^{3/2})$ **33.** $6s^2(s^3 - 2)$

35. $-(2x^2 - 2x + 3)/[x^2(x - 3)^2]$

37. $10x^4 - 8x^3 - 21x^2 - 10x - 30$ **39.** $-\dfrac{4xc^2}{(x^2 - c^2)^2}$

41. $t(t \cos t + 2 \sin t)$ **43.** $-(t \sin t + \cos t)/t^2$

45. $-e^x + \sec^2 x$ **47.** $\dfrac{1}{4t^{3/4}} - 6 \csc t \cot t$

49. $\frac{3}{2} \sec x(\tan x - \sec x)$ **51.** $\cos x \cot^2 x$

53. $x(x \sec^2 x + 2 \tan x)$ **55.** $2x \cos x + 2 \sin x + x^2 e^x + 2xe^x$

57. $\dfrac{e^x}{(8x^{3/2})(2x - 1)}$ **59.** $\dfrac{2x^2 + 8x - 1}{(x + 2)^2}$

61. $\dfrac{1 - \sin \theta + \theta \cos \theta}{(1 - \sin \theta)^2}$ **63.** $y' = \dfrac{-2 \csc x \cot x}{(1 - \csc x)^2}$, $-4\sqrt{3}$

65. $h'(t) = \sec t(t \tan t - 1)/t^2$, $1/\pi^2$

67. (a) $y = -3x - 1$ **69.** (a) $y = 4x + 25$
(b)

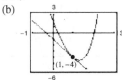

(b)

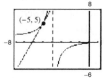

71. (a) $4x - 2y - \pi + 2 = 0$ **73.** (a) $y = e(x - 1)$
(b)

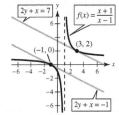

(b)

75. $2y + x - 4 = 0$ **77.** $25y - 12x + 16 = 0$

79. $(1, 1)$ **81.** $(3, 8e^{-3})$

83. Tangent lines: $2y + x = 7$; $2y + x = -1$

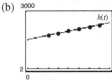

85. $f(x) + 2 = g(x)$ **87.** (a) $p'(1) = 1$ (b) $q'(4) = -1/3$

89. $(18t + 5)/(2\sqrt{t})$ cm²/sec

91. (a) $-\$38.13$ thousand/100 components
(b) $-\$10.37$ thousand/100 components
(c) $-\$3.80$ thousand/100 components
The cost decreases with increasing order size.

93. Proofs

95. (a) $h(t) = 112.4t + 1332$
$p(t) = 2.9t + 282$
(b)

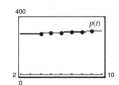

(c) $A = \dfrac{112.4t + 1332}{2.9t + 282}$

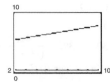

A represents the average health care expenditures per person (in thousands of dollars).

(d) $A'(t) = \dfrac{27,834}{8.41t^2 + 1635.6t + 79,524}$

$A'(t)$ represents the rate of change of the average health care expenditures per person for the given year t.

97. $12x^2 + 12x - 6$ **99.** $3/\sqrt{x}$ **101.** $2/(x - 1)^3$

103. $2\cos x - x\sin x$ **105.** $(e^x/x^3)(x^2 - 2x + 2)$

107. $2x$ **109.** $1/\sqrt{x}$ **111.** 0 **113.** -10

115. Answers will vary.   **117.**

Sample answer:
$f(x) = (x - 2)^2$

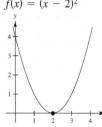

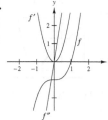

119.   **121.**

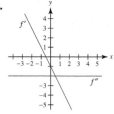   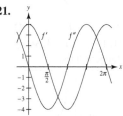

123. $v(3) = 27$ m/sec
$a(3) = -6$ m/sec^2
The speed of the object is decreasing.

125.

t	0	1	2	3	4
$s(t)$	0	57.75	99	123.75	132
$v(t)$	66	49.5	33	16.5	0
$a(t)$	-16.5	-16.5	-16.5	-16.5	-16.5

The average velocity on $[0, 1]$ is 57.75, on $[1, 2]$ is 41.25, on $[2, 3]$ is 24.75, and on $[3, 4]$ is 8.25.

127. $f^{(n)}(x) = n(n - 1)(n - 2) \cdots (2)(1) = n!$

129. (a) $f''(x) = g(x)h''(x) + 2g'(x)h'(x) + g''(x)h(x)$
$f'''(x) = g(x)h'''(x) + 3g'(x)h''(x) +$
$\qquad 3g''(x)h'(x) + g'''(x)h(x)$
$f^{(4)}(x) = g(x)h^{(4)}(x) + 4g'(x)h'''(x) + 6g''(x)h''(x) +$
$\qquad 4g'''(x)h'(x) + g^{(4)}(x)h(x)$

(b) $f^{(n)}(x) = g(x)h^{(n)}(x) + \dfrac{n!}{1!(n - 1)!}g'(x)h^{(n-1)}(x) +$

$\qquad \dfrac{n!}{2!(n - 2)!}g''(x)h^{(n-2)}(x) + \cdots +$

$\qquad \dfrac{n!}{(n - 1)!1!}g^{(n-1)}(x)h'(x) + g^{(n)}(x)h(x)$

131. $n = 1: f'(x) = x\cos x + \sin x$
$n = 2: f'(x) = x^2\cos x + 2x\sin x$
$n = 3: f'(x) = x^3\cos x + 3x^2\sin x$
$n = 4: f'(x) = x^4\cos x + 4x^3\sin x$
General rule: $f'(x) = x^n\cos x + nx^{(n-1)}\sin x$

133. $y' = -1/x^2,\ y'' = 2/x^3,$
$x^3y'' + 2x^2y' = x^3(2/x^3) + 2x^2(-1/x^2)$
$\qquad\qquad = 2 - 2 = 0$

135. $y' = 2\cos x,\ y'' = -2\sin x,$
$y'' + y = -2\sin x + 2\sin x + 3 = 3$

137. False. $dy/dx = f(x)g'(x) + g(x)f'(x)$ **139.** True

141. True   **143.** $f'(x) = 2|x|; f''(0)$ does not exist.

145. Proof

Section 3.4   *(page 160)*

$y = f(g(x))$	$u = g(x)$	$y = f(u)$
1. $y = (5x - 8)^4$	$u = 5x - 8$	$y = u^4$
3. $y = \csc^3 x$	$u = \csc x$	$y = u^3$
5. $y = e^{-2x}$	$u = -2x$	$y = e^u$

7. $12(4x - 1)^2$ **9.** $-108(4 - 9x)^3$ **11.** $-1/(2\sqrt{5 - t})$

13. $4x/\sqrt[3]{(6x^2 + 1)^2}$ **15.** $-x/\sqrt[4]{(9 - x^2)^3}$

17. $-1/(x - 2)^2$ **19.** $-2/(t - 3)^3$

21. $-3/\left[2\sqrt{(3x + 5)^3}\right]$ **23.** $2x(x - 2)^3(3x - 2)$

25. $\dfrac{1 - 2x^2}{\sqrt{1 - x^2}}$ **27.** $\dfrac{1}{\sqrt{(x^2 + 1)^3}}$

29. $\dfrac{-2(x + 5)(x^2 + 10x - 2)}{(x^2 + 2)^3}$ **31.** $\dfrac{-9(1 - 2v)^2}{(v + 1)^4}$

33. $20x(x^2 + 3)^9 + 2(x^2 + 3)^5 + 20x^2(x^2 + 3)^4 + 2x$

35. $(1 - 3x^2 - 4x^{3/2})/[2\sqrt{x}(x^2 + 1)^2]$

The zero of y' corresponds to the point on the graph of the function where the tangent line is horizontal.

37. $-\dfrac{\sqrt{\dfrac{x + 1}{x}}}{2x(x + 1)}$

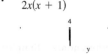

y' has no zeros.

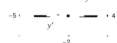

39. $-[\pi x\sin(\pi x) + \cos(\pi x) + 1]/x^2$

The zeros of y' correspond to the points on the graph of the function where the tangent lines are horizontal.

41. (a) 1   (b) 2; The slope of $\sin ax$ at the origin is a.

43. 3   **45.** 3   **47.** $-4 \sin 4x$ **49.** $15 \sec^2 3x$

51. $2\pi^2 x \cos(\pi x)^2$ **53.** $2 \cos 4x$

55. $(-1 - \cos^2 x)/\sin^3 x$ **57.** $8 \sec^2 x \tan x$

59. $10 \tan 5\theta \sec^2 5\theta$ **61.** $\sin 2\theta \cos 2\theta = \frac{1}{2} \sin 4\theta$

63. $\dfrac{6\pi \sin(\pi t - 1)}{\cos^3(\pi t - 1)}$ **65.** $\dfrac{1}{2\sqrt{x}} + 2x \cos(2x)^2$

67. $2 \sec^2 2x \cos(\tan 2x)$ **69.** $2e^{2x}$ **71.** $e^{\sqrt{x}}/(2\sqrt{x})$

73. $3(e^{-t} + e^t)^2(e^t - e^{-t})$ **75.** $2x$ **77.** $\dfrac{-2(e^x - e^{-x})}{(e^x + e^{-x})^2}$

79. $x^2 e^x$ **81.** $e^{-x}\left(\dfrac{1}{x} - \ln x\right)$ **83.** $2e^x \cos x$

85. $\dfrac{2}{x}$ **87.** $\dfrac{4(\ln x)^3}{x}$ **89.** $\dfrac{2x^2 - 1}{x(x^2 - 1)}$ **91.** $\dfrac{1 - x^2}{x(x^2 + 1)}$

93. $\dfrac{1 - 2\ln t}{t^3}$ **95.** $\dfrac{1}{1 - x^2}$ **97.** $\dfrac{\sqrt{x^2 + 1}}{x^2}$ **99.** $\cot x$

101. $-\tan x + \dfrac{\sin x}{\cos x - 1}$ **103.** $\dfrac{3 \cos x}{(\sin x - 1)(\sin x + 2)}$

105. $y' = \dfrac{x + 4}{\sqrt{x^2 + 8x}}, \dfrac{5}{3}$ **107.** $f'(x) = \dfrac{-15x^2}{(x^3 - 2)^2}, -\dfrac{3}{5}$

109. $f'(t) = \dfrac{-5}{(t - 1)^2}, -5$ **111.** $y' = -12 \sec^3 4x \tan 4x, 0$

113. (a) $8x - 5y - 7 = 0$ **115.** (a) $2x - y - 2\pi = 0$

(b) 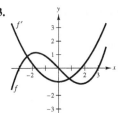   (b)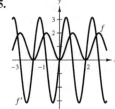

117. (a) $4x - y + (1 - \pi) = 0$

(b)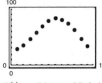

119. (a) $x + 2y - 8 = 0$ **121.** $3x + 4y - 25 = 0$

(b)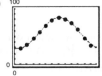

123. $\left(\dfrac{\pi}{6}, \dfrac{3\sqrt{3}}{2}\right), \left(\dfrac{5\pi}{6}, -\dfrac{3\sqrt{3}}{2}\right), \left(\dfrac{3\pi}{2}, 0\right)$ **125.** $2940(2 - 7x)^2$

127. $\dfrac{2}{(x - 6)^3}$ **129.** $2(\cos x^2 - 2x^2 \sin x^2)$

131. $3(6x + 5)e^{-3x}$ **133.** $h''(x) = 18x + 6, 24$

135. $f''(x) = -4x^2 \cos(x^2) - 2 \sin(x^2), 0$ **137.** $(\ln 4)4^x$

139. $(\ln 5)5^{x-2}$ **141.** $t2^t(t \ln 2 + 2)$

143. $-2^{-\theta}[(\ln 2) \cos \pi\theta + \pi \sin \pi\theta]$ **145.** $1/[x(\ln 3)]$

147. $\dfrac{x - 2}{(\ln 2)x(x - 1)}$ **149.** $\dfrac{x}{(\ln 5)(x^2 - 1)}$

151. $\dfrac{5}{(\ln 2)t^2}(1 - \ln t)$

153. 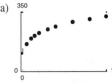   **155.**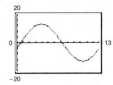

The zeros of f' correspond to the points where the graph of f has horizontal tangents.   The zeros of f' correspond to the points where the graph of f has horizontal tangents.

157. The rate of change of g is three times as fast as the rate of change of f.   **159.** 24   **161.** $\frac{4}{3}$

163. (a) $\frac{1}{2}$

(b) $s'(5)$ does not exist because g is not differentiable at 6.

165. (a) 1.461   (b) -1.016 **167.** 0.2 rad, 1.45 rad/sec

169. (a)

$$T(t) = 56.1 + 27.6 \sin(0.48t - 1.86)$$

(b)

The model is a good fit.

(c) $T'(t) \approx 13.25 \cos(0.48t - 1.86)$

(d) The temperature changes most rapidly around spring (March–May) and fall (Oct.–Nov.)

The temperature changes most slowly around winter (Dec.–Feb.) and summer (Jun.–Aug.)

Yes. Explanations will vary.

171. (a)   (b) $T'(10) \approx 4.75$ deg/lb/in.^{2}
$T'(70) \approx 0.97$ deg/lb/in.^{2}

173. 0.04224 cm/sec^2

175. (a) 0 bacteria per day   (b) 177.8 bacteria per day

(c) 44.4 bacteria per day   (d) 10.8 bacteria per day

(e) 3.3 bacteria per day

(f) The rate of change of the population is decreasing as time passes.

177. (a) $f'(x) = \beta \cos \beta x$
$f''(x) = -\beta^2 \sin \beta x$
$f'''(x) = -\beta^3 \cos \beta x$
$f^{(4)}(x) = \beta^4 \sin \beta x$

(b) $f''(x) + \beta^2 f(x) = -\beta^2 \sin \beta x + \beta^2(\sin \beta x) = 0$

(c) $f^{(2k)}(x) = (-1)^k \beta^{2k} \sin \beta x$

$f^{(2k-1)}(x) = (-1)^{k+1} \beta^{2k-1} \cos \beta x$

179. (a) $r'(1) = 0$ (b) $s'(4) = \frac{5}{8}$

181. (a) and (b) Proofs

183. $g'(x) = 3\left(\dfrac{3x-5}{|3x-5|}\right), \ x \neq \dfrac{5}{3}$

185. $h'(x) = -|x| \sin x + \dfrac{x}{|x|} \cos x, \ x \neq 0$

187. (a) $P_1(x) = 2(x - \pi/4) + 1$

$P_2(x) = 2(x - \pi/4)^2 + 2(x - \pi/4) + 1$

(b) 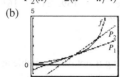   (c) P_2

(d) The accuracy worsens as you move away from $x = \pi/4$.

189. (a) $P_1(x) = x + 1$

$P_2(x) = \frac{1}{2}x^2 + x + 1$

(b) 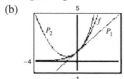   (c) P_2

(d) The accuracy worsens as you move away from $x = 0$.

191. False. If $y = (1 - x)^{1/2}$, then $y' = \frac{1}{2}(1 - x)^{-1/2}(-1)$.

193. True   **195.** Putnam Problem A1, 1967

Section 3.5   *(page 171)*

1. $-x/y$ **3.** $-\sqrt{y/x}$ **5.** $(y - 3x^2)/(2y - x)$

7. $(1 - 3x^2y^3)/(3x^3y^2 - 1)$ **9.** $(10 - e^y)/(xe^y + 3)$

11. $(\cos x)/(4 \sin 2y)$ **13.** $(\cos x - \tan y - 1)/(x \sec^2 y)$

15. $(y \cos xy)/(1 - x \cos xy)$

17. $2xy/(3 - 2y^2)$ **19.** $[y(1 - 6x^2)]/(1 + y)$

21. (a) $y_1 = \sqrt{64 - x^2}; \ y_2 = -\sqrt{64 - x^2}$

(b)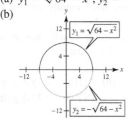

(c) $y' = \mp \dfrac{x}{\sqrt{64 - x^2}} = -\dfrac{x}{y}$ (d) $y' = -\dfrac{x}{y}$

23. (a) $y_1 = \dfrac{\sqrt{x^2 + 16}}{4}; \ y_2 = \dfrac{-\sqrt{x^2 + 16}}{4}$

(b)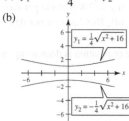

(c) $y' = \dfrac{\pm x}{4\sqrt{x^2 + 16}} = \dfrac{x}{16y}$ (d) $y' = \dfrac{x}{16y}$

25. $-\dfrac{y}{x}, -\dfrac{1}{6}$ **27.** $\dfrac{98x}{y(x^2 + 49)^2}$, Undefined

29. $-\sin^2(x + y)$ or $-\dfrac{x^2}{x^2 + 1}, 0$ **31.** $\dfrac{1 - 3ye^{xy}}{3xe^{xy}}, \dfrac{1}{9}$

33. $-\frac{1}{2}$ **35.** 0 **37.** $y = -x + 7$ **39.** $y = -x + 2$

41. $y = \left(\sqrt{3}x/6\right) + \left(8\sqrt{3}/3\right)$ **43.** $y = -\frac{2}{11}x + \frac{30}{11}$

45. $y = -\frac{9}{4}x + \frac{9}{2}$ **47.** $y = x - 1$

49. (a) $y = -2x + 4$ (b) Answers will vary.

51. $\cos^2 y, -\dfrac{\pi}{2} < y < \dfrac{\pi}{2}, \dfrac{1}{1 + x^2}$ **53.** $-4/y^3$

55. $-36/y^3$ **57.** $(3x)/(4y)$

59. At $(4, 3)$:

Tangent line: $4x + 3y - 25 = 0$

Normal line: $3x - 4y = 0$

At $(-3, 4)$:

Tangent line: $3x - 4y + 25 = 0$

Normal line: $4x + 3y = 0$

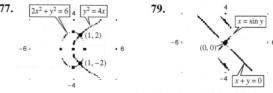

61. $x^2 + y^2 = r^2 \Rightarrow y' = -x/y \Rightarrow y/x =$ slope of normal line. Then for (x_0, y_0) on the circle, $x_0 \neq 0$, an equation of the normal line is $y = (y_0/x_0)x$, which passes through the origin. If $x_0 = 0$, the normal line is vertical and passes through the origin.

63. Horizontal tangents: $(-4, 0), (-4, 10)$

Vertical tangents: $(0, 5), (-8, 5)$

65. $\dfrac{2x^2 + 1}{\sqrt{x^2 + 1}}$ **67.** $\dfrac{3x^3 + 15x^2 - 8x}{2(x + 1)^3 \sqrt{3x - 2}}$

69. $\dfrac{(2x^2 + 2x - 1)\sqrt{x - 1}}{(x + 1)^{3/2}}$ **71.** $2(1 - \ln x)x^{(2/x) - 2}$

73. $(x - 2)^{x+1}\left[\dfrac{x + 1}{x - 2} + \ln(x - 2)\right]$ **75.** $\dfrac{2x^{\ln x} \ln x}{x}$

77. 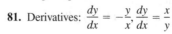   **79.**

At $(1, 2)$:

Slope of ellipse: -1

Slope of parabola: 1

At $(1, -2)$:

Slope of ellipse: 1

Slope of parabola: -1

At $(0, 0)$:

Slope of line: -1

Slope of sine curve: 1

81. Derivatives: $\dfrac{dy}{dx} = -\dfrac{y}{x}, \dfrac{dy}{dx} = \dfrac{x}{y}$

83. Answers will vary. In the explicit form of a function, the variable is explicitly written as a function of x. In an implicit equation, the function is only implied by an equation. An example of an implicit function is $x^2 + xy = 5$. In explicit form, it would be $y = (5 - x^2)/x$.

85. (a) True

    (b) False. $\dfrac{d}{dy}\cos(y^2) = -2y\sin(y^2)$

    (c) False. $\dfrac{d}{dx}\cos(y^2) = -2yy'\sin(y^2)$

87. (a)

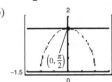

    (b)

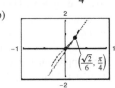

$$y_1 = \tfrac{1}{3}\left[(\sqrt{7}+7)x + (8\sqrt{7}+23)\right]$$
$$y_2 = -\tfrac{1}{3}\left[(-\sqrt{7}+7)x - (23-8\sqrt{7})\right]$$
$$y_3 = -\tfrac{1}{3}\left[(\sqrt{7}-7)x - (23-8\sqrt{7})\right]$$
$$y_4 = -\tfrac{1}{3}\left[(\sqrt{7}+7)x - (8\sqrt{7}+23)\right]$$

    (c) $\left(\dfrac{8\sqrt{7}}{7}, 5\right)$

89. $(6, -8)$ and $(-6, 8)$

91. $y = -\dfrac{\sqrt{3}}{2}x + 2\sqrt{3}$, $y = \dfrac{\sqrt{3}}{2}x - 2\sqrt{3}$

93. (a) $y = 2x - 6$

    (b)

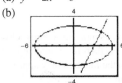

    (c) $\left(\dfrac{28}{17}, -\dfrac{46}{17}\right)$

Section 3.6 *(page 178)*

1. $\dfrac{1}{27}$ **3.** $\dfrac{1}{5}$ **5.** $\dfrac{2\sqrt{3}}{3}$ **7.** -2 **9.** $\dfrac{1}{13}$

11. $f'\left(\tfrac{1}{2}\right) = \tfrac{3}{4}$, $(f^{-1})'\left(\tfrac{1}{8}\right) = \tfrac{4}{3}$ **13.** $f'(5) = \tfrac{1}{2}$, $(f^{-1})'(1) = 2$

15. (a) $y = \dfrac{\pi}{2}$ **17.** (a) $y = 3\sqrt{2}x + \dfrac{\pi}{4} - 1$

    (b)   (b)

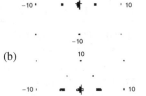

19. $-\dfrac{1}{11}$ **21.** $\dfrac{\pi + 2}{\pi}$ **23.** $\dfrac{1}{\sqrt{1-(x+1)^2}}$

25. $-\dfrac{3}{\sqrt{4-x^2}}$ **27.** $\dfrac{e^x}{1+e^{2x}}$

29. $\dfrac{3x - \sqrt{1-9x^2}\arcsin 3x}{x^2\sqrt{1-9x^2}}$

31. $e^{2x}\left[2\arcsin x + \dfrac{1}{\sqrt{1-x^2}}\right]$ **33.** $-\dfrac{6}{1+36x^2}$

35. $-\dfrac{t}{\sqrt{1-t^2}}$ **37.** $2\arccos x$ **39.** $\dfrac{1}{1-x^4}$

41. $\dfrac{1}{(1-t^2)^{3/2}}$ **43.** $\arcsin x$ **45.** $\dfrac{x^2}{\sqrt{16-x^2}}$

47. $\dfrac{2}{(1+x^2)^2}$ **49.** $y = \tfrac{1}{3}\left(4\sqrt{3}x - 2\sqrt{3} + \pi\right)$

51. $y = \tfrac{1}{4}x + (\pi - 2)/4$ **53.** $y = (2\pi - 4)x + 4$

55. $y = -2x + \left(\dfrac{\pi}{6} + \sqrt{3}\right)$

    $y = -2x + \left(\dfrac{5\pi}{6} - \sqrt{3}\right)$

57. $P_1(x) = x$; $P_2(x) = x$

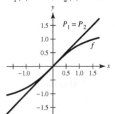

59. $P_1(x) = \dfrac{\pi}{6} + \dfrac{2\sqrt{3}}{3}\left(x - \dfrac{1}{2}\right)$

    $P_2(x) = \dfrac{\pi}{6} + \dfrac{2\sqrt{3}}{3}\left(x - \dfrac{1}{2}\right) + \dfrac{2\sqrt{3}}{9}\left(x - \dfrac{1}{2}\right)^2$

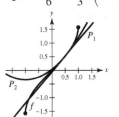

61. $y = [-2\pi x/(\pi + 8)] + 1 - [\pi^2/(2\pi + 16)]$

63. $y = -x + \sqrt{2}$

65. Many x-values yield the same y-value. For example, $f(\pi) = 0 = f(0)$. The graph is not continuous at $x = (2n-1)\pi/2$, where n is an integer.

67. Because you know that f^{-1} exists and $y_1 = f(x_1)$, by Theorem 3.17 you know that $(f^{-1})'(y_1) = \dfrac{1}{f'(x_1)}$, $f'(x_1) \neq 0$.

69. The derivatives are algebraic. See Theorem 3.18.

71. Because the slope of f at $(1, 3)$ is $m = 2$, the slope of f^{-1} at $(3, 1)$ is $\tfrac{1}{2}$.

73. (a) $\theta = \text{arccot}(x/5)$

    (b) $x = 10$: 16 rad/h; $x = 3$: 58.824 rad/h

75. (a) $h(t) = -16t^2 + 256$; $t = 4$ sec

    (b) $t = 1$: -0.0520 rad/sec; $t = 2$: -0.1116 rad/sec

77. 0.015 rad/sec **79.** Proofs **81.** True **83.** True

85. Proof

87. (a)   (b) Proof

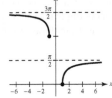

Section 3.7   *(page 186)*

1. (a) $\frac{3}{4}$ (b) 20   3. (a) $-\frac{5}{8}$ (b) $\frac{3}{2}$

5. (a) -8 cm/sec   (b) 0 cm/sec   (c) 8 cm/sec

7. (a) 12 ft/sec   (b) 6 ft/sec   (c) 3 ft/sec

9. In a linear function, if x changes at a constant rate, so does y. However, unless $a = 1$, y does not change at the same rate as x.

11. (a) 64π cm^2/min   (b) 256π cm^2/min

13. (a) 972π in.^{3}/min; $15{,}552\pi$ in.^{3}/min

   (b) If dr/dt is constant, dV/dt is proportional to r^2.

15. (a) 72 cm^3/sec   (b) 1800 cm^3/sec

17. $8/(405\pi)$ ft/min   19. (a) 12.5%   (b) $\frac{1}{144}$ m/min

21. (a) $-\frac{7}{12}$ ft/sec; $-\frac{3}{2}$ ft/sec; $-\frac{48}{7}$ ft/sec

   (b) $\frac{527}{24}$ ft^2/sec   (c) $\frac{1}{12}$ rad/sec

23. Rate of vertical change: $\frac{1}{5}$ m/sec

   Rate of horizontal change: $-\sqrt{3}/15$ m/sec

25. (a) -750 mi/h   (b) 30 min

27. $-50/\sqrt{85} \approx -5.42$ ft/sec

29. (a) $\frac{25}{3}$ ft/sec   (b) $\frac{10}{3}$ ft/sec

31. (a) 12 sec   (b) $\frac{1}{2}\sqrt{3}$ m   (c) $\sqrt{5}\pi/120$ m/sec

33. Evaporation rate proportional to $S \Rightarrow \dfrac{dV}{dt} = k(4\pi r^2)$

$$V = \left(\frac{4}{3}\right)\pi r^3 \Rightarrow \frac{dV}{dt} = 4\pi r^2 \frac{dr}{dt}. \text{ So } k = \frac{dr}{dt}.$$

35. $V^{0.3}\left(1.3p\,\dfrac{dV}{dt} + V\,\dfrac{dp}{dt}\right) = 0$ 37. $\dfrac{1}{25}$ rad/sec

39. (a) $t = 65°$: $H \approx 99.8\%$ (b) -4.7%/h
   $t = 80°$: $H \approx 60.2\%$

41. (a) $\dfrac{dx}{dt} = -600\pi \sin\theta$

   (b)

   (c) $\theta = \dfrac{\pi}{2} + n\pi$ (or $90° + n \cdot 180°$); $\theta = n\pi$ (or $n \cdot 180°$)

   (d) -300π cm/sec; $-300\sqrt{3}\pi$ cm/sec

43. $\dfrac{d\theta}{dt} = \dfrac{1}{25}\cos^2\theta$, $-\dfrac{\pi}{4} \le \theta \le \dfrac{\pi}{4}$

45. -0.1808 ft/sec^2

47. (a) $\dfrac{dy}{dt} = 3\dfrac{dx}{dt}$ means that y changes three times as fast as x changes.

   (b) y changes slowly when $x \approx 0$ or $x \approx L$. y changes more rapidly when x is near the middle of the interval.

49. (a) $A = 2xe^{-x^2/2}$ (b) $\dfrac{dA}{dt} = -3.25$ cm^2/min

Section 3.8   *(page 194)*

In the answers for Exercises 1 and 3, the values in the tables have been rounded for convenience. Because a calculator and a computer program calculates internally using more digits than they display, you may produce slightly different values from those shown in the tables.

1.

n	x_n	$f(x_n)$	$f'(x_n)$	$\dfrac{f(x_n)}{f'(x_n)}$	$x_n - \dfrac{f(x_n)}{f'(x_n)}$
1	2.2000	-0.1600	4.4000	-0.0364	2.2364
2	2.2364	0.0015	4.4728	0.0003	2.2361

3.

n	x_n	$f(x_n)$	$f'(x_n)$	$\dfrac{f(x_n)}{f'(x_n)}$	$x_n - \dfrac{f(x_n)}{f'(x_n)}$
1	1.6	-0.0292	-0.9996	0.0292	1.5708
2	1.5708	0	-1	0	1.5708

5. -1.587 7. 0.682   9. 1.250, 5.000   11. 0.567

13. 0.900, 1.100, 1.900   15. 1.935   17. 0.569

19. 4.493   21. (a) Proof   (b) $\sqrt{5} \approx 2.236$; $\sqrt{7} \approx 2.646$

23. $f'(x_1) = 0$ 25. 0.74   27. 1.12   29. Proof

31. (a) 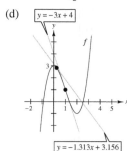   (b) 1.347   (c) 2.532

   (d)

   x-intercept of $y = -3x + 4$ is $\frac{4}{3}$.
   x-intercept of
   $y = -1.313x + 3.156$
   is approximately 2.404.

   (e) If the initial estimate $x = x_1$ is not sufficiently close to the desired zero of a function, then the x-intercept of the corresponding tangent line to the function may approximate a second zero of the function.

33. Answers will vary. Sample answer:
If f is a function continuous on $[a, b]$ and differentiable on (a, b), where $c \in [a, b]$ and $f(c) = 0$, then Newton's Method uses tangent lines to approximate c. First, estimate an initial x_1 close to c. (See graph.) Then determine

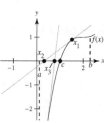

x_2 using $x_2 = x_1 - f(x_1)/f'(x_1)$. Calculate a third estimate x_3 using $x_3 = x_2 - f(x_2)/f'(x_2)$. Continue this process until $|x_n - x_{n+1}|$ is within the desired accuracy, and let x_{n+1} be the final approximation of c.

35. $(1.939, 0.240)$ 37. $x \approx 1.563$ mi

39. False. Let $f(x) = \dfrac{x^2 - 1}{x - 1}$.   41. True   43. 0.217

Review Exercises for Chapter 3   *(page 196)*

1. $f'(x) = 0$ 3. $f'(x) = 2x - 4$ 5. 5

7. f is differentiable at all $x \ne 3$.   9. 0   11. $3x^2 - 22x$

13. $\dfrac{3}{\sqrt{x}} + \dfrac{1}{\sqrt[3]{x^2}}$ **15.** $-\dfrac{4}{3t^3}$ **17.** $4 - 5\cos\theta$

19. $-3\sin t - 4e^t$ **21.** -1 **23.** 0

25. (a) 50 vibrations/sec/lb   (b) 33.33 vibrations/sec/lb

27. (a) $s(t) = -16t^2 - 30t + 600$; $v(t) = -32t - 30$

    (b) -94 ft/sec

    (c) $v'(1) = -62$ ft/sec; $v'(3) = -126$ ft/sec

    (d) About 5.258 sec   (e) About -198.256 ft/sec

29. $4(5x^3 - 15x^2 - 11x - 8)$ **31.** $\sqrt{x}\cos x + \sin x/(2\sqrt{x})$

33. $\dfrac{-(x^2 + 1)}{(x^2 - 1)^2}$ **35.** $\dfrac{4x^3\cos x + x^4\sin x}{\cos^2 x}$

37. $3x^2\sec x\tan x + 6x\sec x$ **39.** $4xe^x + 4e^x + \csc^2 x$

41. $y = 4x + 10$ **43.** $y = -8x + 1$ **45.** $-48t$

47. $\dfrac{225}{4}\sqrt{x}$ **49.** $6\sec^2\theta\tan\theta$

51. $v(3) = 11$ m/sec; $a(3) = -6$ m/sec^2 **53.** $28(7x + 3)^3$

55. $-\dfrac{2x}{(x^2 + 4)^2}$ **57.** $-45\sin(9x + 1)$

59. $\frac{1}{2}(1 - \cos 2x) = \sin^2 x$ **61.** $(36x + 1)(6x + 1)^4$

63. $\dfrac{3}{(x^2 + 1)^{3/2}}$ **65.** $\frac{1}{4}te^{t/4}(t + 8)$ **67.** $\dfrac{e^{2x} - e^{-2x}}{\sqrt{e^{2x} + e^{-2x}}}$

69. $\dfrac{x(2 - x)}{e^x}$ **71.** $\dfrac{1}{2x}$ **73.** $\dfrac{1 + 2\ln x}{2\sqrt{\ln x}}$ **75.** $\dfrac{x}{(a + bx)^2}$

77. $\dfrac{1}{x(a + bx)}$ **79.** $\dfrac{-3x^2}{2\sqrt{1 - x^3}}$; -2 **81.** $-\dfrac{8x}{(x^2 + 1)^2}$; 2

83. $-\csc 2x\cot 2x$; 0 **85.** $384(8x + 5)$ **87.** $2\csc^2 x\cot x$

89. (a) $-18.667°/h$ (b) $-7.284°/h$

    (c) $-3.240°/h$ (d) $-0.747°/h$

91. (a) $h = 0$ is not in the domain of the function.

    (b) $h = 0.8627 - 6.4474\ln p$

    (c) 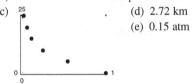   (d) 2.72 km

    (e) 0.15 atm

    (f) $h = 5$: $\dfrac{dp}{dh} = -0.0816$ atm/km

    $h = 20$: $\dfrac{dp}{dh} = -0.008$ atm/km

As the altitude increases, the rate of change of pressure decreases.

93. $-\dfrac{x}{y}$ **95.** $\dfrac{y(y^2 - 3x^2)}{x(x^2 - 3y^2)}$ **97.** $\dfrac{y\sin x + \sin y}{\cos x - x\cos y}$

99. Tangent line: **101.** Tangent line:

    $3x + y - 10 = 0$ $xe^{-1} + y = 0$

    Normal line: Normal line:

    $x - 3y = 0$ $xe - y - (e^2 + 1) = 0$

103. $\dfrac{x^3 + 8x^2 + 4}{(x + 4)^2\sqrt{x^2 + 1}}$ **105.** $\dfrac{1}{3(\sqrt[3]{-3})^2} \approx 0.160$ **107.** $\dfrac{3}{4}$

109. $(1 - x^2)^{-3/2}$ **111.** $\dfrac{x}{|x|\sqrt{x^2 - 1}} + \text{arcsec } x$

113. $(\arcsin x)^2$

115. (a) $2\sqrt{2}$ units/sec   (b) 4 units/sec   (c) 8 units/sec

117. 450π km/h   **119.** $-0.347, -1.532, 1.879$ **121.** 1.202

123. $-2.182, -0.795$ **125.** $-1.164, 1.453$ **127.** 0.567

P.S. Problem Solving   *(page 199)*

1. (a) $r = \frac{1}{2}$; $x^2 + \left(y - \frac{1}{2}\right)^2 = \frac{1}{4}$

    (b) Center: $\left(0, \frac{5}{4}\right)$; $x^2 + \left(y - \frac{5}{4}\right)^2 = 1$

3. $p(x) = 2x^3 + 4x^2 - 5$

5. (a) $y = 4x - 4$ (b) $y = -\frac{1}{4}x + \frac{9}{2}$; $\left(-\frac{9}{4}, \frac{81}{16}\right)$

    (c) Tangent line: $y = 0$; Normal line: $x = 0$

    (d) Proof

7. (a) Graph $\begin{cases} y_1 = \dfrac{1}{a}\sqrt{x^2(a^2 - x^2)} \\ y_2 = -\dfrac{1}{a}\sqrt{x^2(a^2 - x^2)} \end{cases}$ as separate equations.

    (b) Answers will vary. Sample answer:

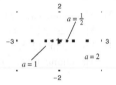

The intercepts will always be $(0, 0)$, $(a, 0)$, and $(-a, 0)$, and the maximum and minimum y-values appear to be $\pm\frac{1}{2}a$.

    (c) $\left(\dfrac{a\sqrt{2}}{2}, \dfrac{a}{2}\right)$, $\left(\dfrac{a\sqrt{2}}{2}, -\dfrac{a}{2}\right)$, $\left(-\dfrac{a\sqrt{2}}{2}, \dfrac{a}{2}\right)$, $\left(-\dfrac{a\sqrt{2}}{2}, -\dfrac{a}{2}\right)$

9. (a) When the man is 90 ft from the light, the tip of his shadow is $112\frac{1}{2}$ ft from the light. The tip of the child's shadow is $111\frac{1}{9}$ ft from the light, so the man's shadow extends $1\frac{7}{18}$ ft beyond the child's shadow.

    (b) When the man is 60 ft from the light, the tip of his shadow is 75 ft from the light. The tip of the child's shadow is $77\frac{7}{9}$ ft from the light, so the child's shadow extends $2\frac{7}{9}$ ft beyond the man's shadow.

    (c) $d = 80$ ft

    (d) Let x be the distance of the man from the light, and let s be the distance from the light to the tip of the shadow.

    If $0 < x < 80$, then $ds/dt = -50/9$.

    If $x > 80$, then $ds/dt = -25/4$.

    There is a discontinuity at $x = 80$.

11. (a) $v(t) = -\frac{27}{5}t + 27$ ft/sec   (b) 5 sec; 73.5 ft

    $a(t) = -\frac{27}{5}$ ft/sec^2

    (c) The acceleration due to gravity on Earth is greater in magnitude than that on the moon.

13. $a = 1$, $b = \frac{1}{2}$, $c = -\frac{1}{2}$

$f(x) = \dfrac{1 + \frac{1}{2}x}{1 - \frac{1}{2}x}$

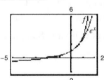

15. (a) j would be the rate of change of acceleration.

    (b) $j = 0$. Acceleration is constant, so there is no change in acceleration.

    (c) a: position function, d: velocity function, b: acceleration function, c: jerk function

Chapter 4

Section 4.1 *(page 207)*

1. $f'(0) = 0$ **3.** $f'(2) = 0$ **5.** $f'(-2)$ is undefined.

7. 2, absolute maximum (and relative maximum)

9. 1, absolute maximum (and relative maximum)
 2, absolute minimum (and relative minimum)
 3, absolute maximum (and relative maximum)

11. $x = 0, x = 2$ **13.** $t = 8/3$ **15.** $x = \pi/3, \pi, 5\pi/3$

17. $t = \frac{1}{2}$ **19.** $x = 0$

21. Minimum: $(2, 1)$ **23.** Minimum: $(2, -8)$
  Maximum: $(-1, 4)$ Maximum: $(6, 24)$

25. Minimum: $\left(-1, -\frac{5}{2}\right)$ **27.** Minimum: $(0, 0)$
  Maximum: $(2, 2)$ Maximum: $(-1, 5)$

29. Minimum: $(1, -1)$ **31.** Minimum: $(-1, -1)$
  Maximum: $\left(0, -\frac{1}{2}\right)$ Maximum: $(3, 3)$

33. Minimum value is -2 for $-2 \le x < -1$.
  Maximum: $(2, 2)$

35. Minimum: $(3\pi/2, -1)$ **37.** Minimum: $(\pi, -3)$
  Maximum: $(5\pi/6, 1/2)$ Maxima: $(0, 3)$ and $(2\pi, 3)$

39. Minimum: $(0, 0)$ **41.** Minimum: $(2, 5e^2 - e^4)$
  Maximum: $(-2, \arctan 4)$ Maximum: $\left(\ln\frac{5}{2}, \frac{25}{4}\right)$

43. Minima: $(0, 0)$ and $(\pi, 0)$
  Maximum: $\left(3\pi/4, \left(\sqrt{2}/2\right)e^{3\pi/4}\right)$

45. (a) Minimum: $(0, -3)$ (b) Minimum: $(0, -3)$
   Maximum: $(2, 1)$
 (c) Maximum: $(2, 1)$ (d) No extrema

47.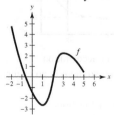
  Minimum: $(4, 1)$

49.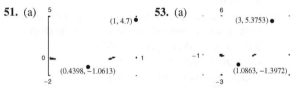
  Minimum:
  $(-0.7753, 1.9070)$

51. (a)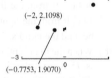
53. (a)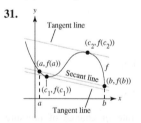

 (b) Minimum: (b) Minimum:
   $(0.4398, -1.0613)$ $(1.0863, -1.3972)$

55. Maximum: $\left|f''\left(\sqrt[3]{-10 + \sqrt{108}}\right)\right| = f''\left(\sqrt{3} - 1\right) \approx 1.47$

57. Maximum: $|f''(0)| = 1$ **59.** Maximum: $|f^{(4)}(0)| = \frac{56}{81}$

61. f is continuous on $[0, \pi/4]$ but not on $[0, \pi]$.

63. Answers will vary. Sample answer:

65. (a) Yes (b) No **67.** (a) No (b) Yes

69. Maximum: $P(12) = 72$; No. P is decreasing for $I > 12$.

71. $\theta = \operatorname{arcsec}\sqrt{3} \approx 0.9553$ rad **73.** True **75.** True

77. Proof **79.** Putnam Problem B3, 2004

Section 4.2 *(page 214)*

1. $f(-1) = f(1) = 1$; f is not continuous on $[-1, 1]$.

3. $f(0) = f(2) = 0$; f is not differentiable on $(0, 2)$.

5. $(2, 0), (-1, 0); f'\left(\frac{1}{2}\right) = 0$ **7.** $(0, 0), (-4, 0); f'\left(-\frac{8}{3}\right) = 0$

9. $f'\left(\frac{3}{2}\right) = 0$ **11.** $f'\left(\frac{6 - \sqrt{3}}{3}\right) = 0; f'\left(\frac{6 + \sqrt{3}}{3}\right) = 0$

13. Not differentiable at $x = 0$ **15.** $f'\left(-2 + 2\sqrt{2}\right) = 0$

17. $f'\left(\frac{\pi}{2}\right) = 0; f'\left(\frac{3\pi}{2}\right) = 0$ **19.** Not continuous on $[0, \pi]$

21. $f'\left(\sqrt{2}\right) = 0$

23. **25.**
  Rolle's Theorem does not   Rolle's Theorem does not
  apply.   apply.

27.
  Rolle's Theorem does not apply.

29. (a) $f(1) = f(2) = 38$
 (b) Velocity $= 0$ for some t in $(1, 2)$; $t = \frac{3}{2}$ sec

31.

33. The function is not continuous on $[0, 6]$.

35. The function is not continuous on $[0, 6]$.

37. (a) Secant line: $x + y - 3 = 0$
 (b) $c = \frac{1}{2}$
 (c) Tangent line: $4x + 4y - 21 = 0$
 (d)

39. $f'(-1/2) = -1$ **41.** $f'\left(1/\sqrt{3}\right) = 3, f'\left(-1/\sqrt{3}\right) = 3$

43. $f'\left(\frac{8}{27}\right) = 1$ **45.** f is not differentiable at $x = -\frac{1}{2}$.

47. $f'(\pi/2) = 0$ **49.** f is not continuous at $x = \pi/2$.

51. $f'(4e^{-1}) = 2$

53. (a)–(c)   **55.** (a)–(c)

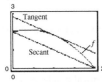
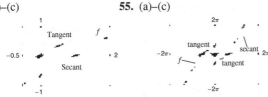

(b) $y = \frac{2}{3}(x - 1)$ (b) $y = x$

(c) $y = \frac{1}{3}(2x + 5 - 2\sqrt{6})$ (c) $y = x + 2$

57. (a)–(c)

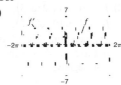

(b) $y = -x + 2$ (c) $y = -x + 2.8161$

59. (a) -14.7 m/sec   (b) 1.5 sec

61. No. Let $f(x) = x^2$ on $[-1, 2]$.

63. No. $f(x)$ is not continuous on $[0, 1]$. So it does not satisfy the hypothesis of Rolle's Theorem.

65. By the Mean Value Theorem, there is a time when the speed of the plane must equal the average speed of 454.5 miles/hour. The speed was 400 miles/hour when the plane was accelerating to 454.5 miles/hour and decelerating from 454.5 miles/hour.

67. Proof

69. (a)

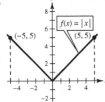

(b) Yes; yes

(c) Because $f(-1) = f(1) = 0$, Rolle's Theorem applies on $[-1, 1]$. Because $f(1) = 0$ and $f(2) = 3$, Rolle's Theorem does not apply on $[1, 2]$.

(d) $\lim\limits_{x\to 3^-} f'(x) = 0$; $\lim\limits_{x\to 3^+} f'(x) = 0$

71.   **73–75.** Proofs   **77.** $f(x) = 5$

79. $f(x) = x^2 - 1$ **81.** False. f is not continuous on $[-1, 1]$.

83. True   **85–93.** Proofs

Section 4.3 *(page 223)*

1. (a) $(0, 6)$ (b) $(6, 8)$

3. Increasing on $(3, \infty)$; Decreasing on $(-\infty, 3)$

5. Increasing on $(-\infty, -2)$ and $(2, \infty)$; Decreasing on $(-2, 2)$

7. Increasing on $(-\infty, -1)$; Decreasing on $(-1, \infty)$

9. Increasing on $(1, \infty)$; Decreasing on $(-\infty, 1)$

11. Increasing on $(-2\sqrt{2}, 2\sqrt{2})$;
Decreasing on $(-4, -2\sqrt{2})$ and $(2\sqrt{2}, 4)$

13. Increasing on $(0, \pi/2)$ and $(3\pi/2, 2\pi)$;
Decreasing on $(\pi/2, 3\pi/2)$

15. Increasing on $(0, 7\pi/6)$ and $(11\pi/6, 2\pi)$;
Decreasing on $(7\pi/6, 11\pi/6)$

17. Increasing on $(-\frac{1}{4} \ln 3, \infty)$; Decreasing on $(-\infty, -\frac{1}{4} \ln 3)$

19. Increasing on $\left(\dfrac{2}{\sqrt{e}}, \infty\right)$; Decreasing on $\left(0, \dfrac{2}{\sqrt{e}}\right)$

21. (a) Critical number: $x = 2$
(b) Increasing on $(2, \infty)$; Decreasing on $(-\infty, 2)$
(c) Relative minimum: $(2, -4)$

23. (a) Critical number: $x = 1$
(b) Increasing on $(-\infty, 1)$; Decreasing on $(1, \infty)$
(c) Relative maximum: $(1, 5)$

25. (a) Critical numbers: $x = -2, 1$
(b) Increasing on $(-\infty, -2)$ and $(1, \infty)$;
Decreasing on $(-2, 1)$
(c) Relative maximum: $(-2, 20)$;
Relative minimum: $(1, -7)$

27. (a) Critical numbers: $x = -\frac{5}{3}, 1$
(b) Increasing on $\left(-\infty, -\frac{5}{3}\right), (1, \infty)$; Decreasing on $\left(-\frac{5}{3}, 1\right)$
(c) Relative maximum: $\left(-\frac{5}{3}, \frac{256}{27}\right)$;
Relative minimum: $(1, 0)$

29. (a) Critical numbers: $x = \pm 1$
(b) Increasing on $(-\infty, -1)$ and $(1, \infty)$;
Decreasing on $(-1, 1)$
(c) Relative maximum: $\left(-1, \frac{4}{5}\right)$; Relative minimum: $\left(1, -\frac{4}{5}\right)$

31. (a) Critical number: $x = 0$
(b) Increasing on $(-\infty, \infty)$
(c) No relative extrema

33. (a) Critical number: $x = -2$
(b) Increasing on $(-2, \infty)$; Decreasing on $(-\infty, -2)$
(c) Relative minimum: $(-2, 0)$

35. (a) Critical number: $x = 5$
(b) Increasing on $(-\infty, 5)$; Decreasing on $(5, \infty)$
(c) Relative maximum: $(5, 5)$

37. (a) Critical numbers: $x = \pm\sqrt{2}/2$; Discontinuity: $x = 0$
(b) Increasing on $\left(-\infty, -\sqrt{2}/2\right)$ and $\left(\sqrt{2}/2, \infty\right)$;
Decreasing on $\left(-\sqrt{2}/2, 0\right)$ and $\left(0, \sqrt{2}/2\right)$
(c) Relative maximum: $\left(-\sqrt{2}/2, -2\sqrt{2}\right)$;
Relative minimum: $\left(\sqrt{2}/2, 2\sqrt{2}\right)$

39. (a) Critical number: $x = 0$; Discontinuities: $x = \pm 3$
(b) Increasing on $(-\infty, -3)$ and $(-3, 0)$;
Decreasing on $(0, 3)$ and $(3, \infty)$
(c) Relative maximum: $(0, 0)$

41. (a) Critical number: $x = 0$
(b) Increasing on $(-\infty, 0)$; Decreasing on $(0, \infty)$
(c) Relative maximum: $(0, 4)$

43. (a) Critical number: $x = 1$
(b) Increasing on $(-\infty, 1)$; Decreasing on $(1, \infty)$
(c) Relative maximum: $(1, 4)$

45. (a) Critical number: $x = 2$
(b) Increasing on $(-\infty, 2)$;
Decreasing on $(2, \infty)$
(c) Relative maximum: $(2, e^{-1})$

47. (a) Critical number: $x = 0$
(b) Decreasing on $[-1, 1]$
(c) No relative extrema

49. (a) Critical number: $x = 1/\ln 3$
(b) Increasing on $(-\infty, 1/\ln 3)$;
Decreasing on $(1/\ln 3, \infty)$
(c) Relative maximum: $(1/\ln 3, (3^{-1/\ln 3})/\ln 3)$ or
$(1/\ln 3, 1/(e \ln 3))$

51. (a) Critical number: $x = 1/\ln 4$
(b) Increasing on $(1/\ln 4, \infty)$;
Decreasing on $(0, 1/\ln 4)$
(c) Relative minimum: $(1/\ln 4, (\ln(\ln 4) + 1)/\ln 4)$

53. (a) No critical numbers
(b) Increasing on $(-\infty, \infty)$
(c) No relative extrema

55. (a) No critical numbers
(b) Increasing on $(-\infty, 2)$ and $(2, \infty)$
(c) No relative extrema

57. (a) Critical numbers: $x = \pi/6, 5\pi/6$;
Increasing on $(0, \pi/6), (5\pi/6, 2\pi)$;
Decreasing on $(\pi/6, 5\pi/6)$
(b) Relative maximum: $(\pi/6, (\pi + 6\sqrt{3})/12)$;
Relative minimum: $(5\pi/6, (5\pi - 6\sqrt{3})/12)$

59. (a) Critical numbers: $x = \pi/4, 5\pi/4$;
Increasing on $(0, \pi/4), (5\pi/4, 2\pi)$;
Decreasing on $(\pi/4, 5\pi/4)$
(b) Relative maximum: $(\pi/4, \sqrt{2})$;
Relative minimum: $(5\pi/4, -\sqrt{2})$

61. (a) Critical numbers: $x = \pi/4, \pi/2, 3\pi/4, \pi,$
$5\pi/4, 3\pi/2, 7\pi/4$
Increasing on $(\pi/4, \pi/2), (3\pi/4, \pi), (5\pi/4, 3\pi/2),$
$(7\pi/4, 2\pi)$;
Decreasing on $(0, \pi/4), (\pi/2, 3\pi/4), (\pi, 5\pi/4),$
$(3\pi/2, 7\pi/4)$
(b) Relative maxima: $(\pi/2, 1), (\pi, 1), (3\pi/2, 1)$;
Relative minima: $(\pi/4, 0), (3\pi/4, 0),$
$(5\pi/4, 0), (7\pi/4, 0)$

63. (a) Critical numbers: $\pi/2, 7\pi/6, 3\pi/2, 11\pi/6$
Increasing on $(0, \pi/2), (7\pi/6, 3\pi/2), (11\pi/6, 2\pi)$;
Decreasing on $(\pi/2, 7\pi/6), (3\pi/2, 11\pi/6)$
(b) Relative maxima: $(\pi/2, 2), (3\pi/2, 0)$;
Relative minima: $(7\pi/6, -1/4), (11\pi/6, -1/4)$

65. (a) $f'(x) = 2(9 - 2x^2)/\sqrt{9 - x^2}$
(b)

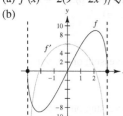

(c) Critical numbers:
$x = \pm 3\sqrt{2}/2$

(d) $f' > 0$ on $(-3\sqrt{2}/2, 3\sqrt{2}/2)$;
$f' < 0$ on $(-3, -3\sqrt{2}/2), (3\sqrt{2}/2, 3)$;
f is increasing when f' is positive and decreasing when f' is
negative.

67. (a) $f'(t) = t(t \cos t + 2 \sin t)$
(b)

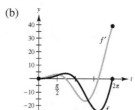

(c) Critical numbers:
$t = 2.2889, 5.0870$

(d) $f' > 0$ on $(0, 2.2889), (5.0870, 2\pi)$;
$f' < 0$ on $(2.2889, 5.0870)$;
f is increasing when f' is positive and decreasing when f' is
negative.

69. (a) $f'(x) = -\cos(x/3)$
(b)

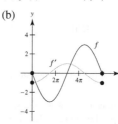

(c) Critical numbers: $x = \dfrac{3\pi}{2}, \dfrac{9\pi}{2}$
(d) $f' > 0$ on $\left(\dfrac{3\pi}{2}, \dfrac{9\pi}{2}\right)$;
$f' < 0$ on $\left(0, \dfrac{3\pi}{2}\right), \left(\dfrac{9\pi}{2}, 6\pi\right)$;
f is increasing when f' is
positive and decreasing when
f' is negative.

71. (a) $f'(x) = (2x^2 - 1)/2x$
(b)

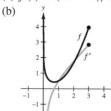

(c) Critical number: $x = \sqrt{2}/2$
(d) $f' > 0$ on $\left(\sqrt{2}/2, 3\right)$;
$f' < 0$ on $\left(0, \sqrt{2}/2\right)$;
f is increasing when f' is
positive and decreasing when
f' is negative.

73. $f(x)$ is symmetric with
respect to the origin.
Zeros: $(0, 0), (\pm\sqrt{3}, 0)$

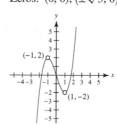

$g(x)$ is continuous on $(-\infty, \infty)$,
and $f(x)$ has holes at $x = 1$
and $x = -1$.

75.

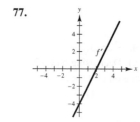

77.

79.

81. $g'(0) < 0$ **83.** $g'(-6) < 0$ **85.** $g'(0) > 0$

87. No; f has a horizontal tangent line at $x = c$, but f could be increasing (or decreasing) on both sides of the point, which would mean that f has no local extremum.

89. Answers will vary.   **91.** $(5, f(5))$ is a relative minimum.

Sample answer:

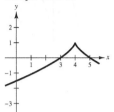

93. (a)

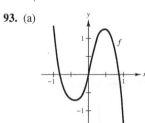

(b) Critical numbers: $x \approx -0.40$ and $x \approx 0.48$

(c) Relative maximum: $(0.48, 1.25)$;
   Relative minimum: $(-0.40, 0.75)$

95. (a) $s'(t) = 9.8(\sin \theta)t$; speed $= |9.8(\sin \theta)t|$

(b)

θ	0	$\pi/4$	$\pi/3$	$\pi/2$	$2\pi/3$	$3\pi/4$	π
$s'(t)$	0	$4.9\sqrt{2}\,t$	$4.9\sqrt{3}\,t$	$9.8t$	$4.9\sqrt{3}\,t$	$4.9\sqrt{2}\,t$	0

The speed is maximum at $\theta = \pi/2$.

97. (a)

t	0	0.5	1	1.5	2	2.5	3
$C(t)$	0	0.055	0.107	0.148	0.171	0.176	0.167

$t = 2.5$ h

(b)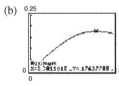

(c) $t \approx 2.38$ h

$t \approx 2.38$ h

99. $r = 2R/3$

101. (a) $v(t) = 6 - 2t$ (b) $[0, 3)$ (c) $(3, \infty)$ (d) $t = 3$

103. (a) $v(t) = 3t^2 - 10t + 4$

(b) $\left(0, (5 - \sqrt{13})/3\right)$ and $\left((5 + \sqrt{13})/3, \infty\right)$

(c) $\left(\dfrac{5 - \sqrt{13}}{3}, \dfrac{5 + \sqrt{13}}{3}\right)$ (d) $t = \dfrac{5 \pm \sqrt{13}}{3}$

105. Answers will vary.

107. (a) Minimum degree: 3

(b) $a_3(0)^3 + a_2(0)^2 + a_1(0) + a_0 = 0$
   $a_3(2)^3 + a_2(2)^2 + a_1(2) + a_0 = 2$
   $3a_3(0)^2 + 2a_2(0) + a_1 = 0$
   $3a_3(2)^2 + 2a_2(2) + a_1 = 0$

(c) $f(x) = -\frac{1}{2}x^3 + \frac{3}{2}x^2$

109. (a) Minimum degree: 4

(b) $a_4(0)^4 + a_3(0)^3 + a_2(0)^2 + a_1(0) + a_0 = 0$
   $a_4(2)^4 + a_3(2)^3 + a_2(2)^2 + a_1(2) + a_0 = 4$
   $a_4(4)^4 + a_3(4)^3 + a_2(4)^2 + a_1(4) + a_0 = 0$
   $4a_4(0)^3 + 3a_3(0)^2 + 2a_2(0) + a_1 = 0$
   $4a_4(2)^3 + 3a_3(2)^2 + 2a_2(2) + a_1 = 0$
   $4a_4(4)^3 + 3a_3(4)^2 + 2a_2(4) + a_1 = 0$

(c) $f(x) = \frac{1}{4}x^4 - 2x^3 + 4x^2$

111. True   **113.** False. Let $f(x) = x^3$.

115. False. Let $f(x) = x^3$. There is a critical number at $x = 0$, but not a relative extremum.

117–121. Proofs   **123.** Putnam Problem A3, 2003

Section 4.4   *(page 232)*

1. Concave upward: $(-\infty, \infty)$

3. Concave upward: $(-\infty, 2)$; Concave downward: $(2, \infty)$

5. Concave upward: $(-\infty, -2), (2, \infty)$;
   Concave downward: $(-2, 2)$

7. Concave upward: $(-\infty, -1), (1, \infty)$;
   Concave downward: $(-1, 1)$

9. Concave upward: $(-2, 2)$;
   Concave downward: $(-\infty, -2), (2, \infty)$

11. Concave upward: $(-\pi/2, 0)$; Concave downward: $(0, \pi/2)$

13. Point of inflection: $(2, 8)$; Concave downward: $(-\infty, 2)$;
   Concave upward: $(2, \infty)$

15. Points of inflection: $(-2, -8), (0, 0)$;
   Concave upward: $(-\infty, -2), (0, \infty)$;
   Concave downward: $(-2, 0)$

17. Points of inflection: $(2, -16), (4, 0)$;
   Concave upward: $(-\infty, 2), (4, \infty)$;
   Concave downward: $(2, 4)$

19. Concave upward: $(-3, \infty)$

21. Points of inflection: $\left(-\sqrt{3}/3, 3\right), \left(\sqrt{3}/3, 3\right)$;
   Concave upward: $\left(-\infty, -\sqrt{3}/3\right), \left(\sqrt{3}/3, \infty\right)$;
   Concave downward: $\left(-\sqrt{3}/3, \sqrt{3}/3\right)$

23. Point of inflection: $(2\pi, 0)$;
   Concave upward: $(2\pi, 4\pi)$; Concave downward: $(0, 2\pi)$

25. Concave upward: $(0, \pi), (2\pi, 3\pi)$;
   Concave downward: $(\pi, 2\pi), (3\pi, 4\pi)$

27. Points of inflection: $(\pi, 0), (1.823, 1.452), (4.46, -1.452)$;
   Concave upward: $(1.823, \pi), (4.46, 2\pi)$;
   Concave downward: $(0, 1.823), (\pi, 4.46)$

29. Point of inflection: $\left(\frac{3}{2}, e^{-2}\right)$;
   Concave upward: $(-\infty, 0), \left(0, \frac{3}{2}\right)$;
   Concave downward: $\left(\frac{3}{2}, \infty\right)$

31. Concave upward: $(0, \infty)$

33. Points of inflection:
   $\left(-\left(\frac{1}{5}\right)^{5/8}, \arcsin\left(\sqrt{5}/5\right)\right), \left(\left(\frac{1}{5}\right)^{5/8}, \arcsin\left(\sqrt{5}/5\right)\right)$;
   Concave upward: $\left(-1, -\left(\frac{1}{5}\right)^{5/8}\right), \left(\left(\frac{1}{5}\right)^{5/8}, 1\right)$;
   Concave downward: $\left(-\left(\frac{1}{5}\right)^{5/8}, 0\right), \left(0, \left(\frac{1}{5}\right)^{5/8}\right)$

35. Relative maximum: $(3, 9)$

37. Relative maximum: $(0, 3)$; Relative minimum: $(2, -1)$

39. Relative minimum: $(3, -25)$

41. Relative minimum: $(0, -3)$

43. Relative maximum: $(-2, -4)$; Relative minimum: $(2, 4)$

45. No relative extrema because f is nonincreasing.
47. Relative minimum: $\left(\frac{1}{4}, \frac{1}{2} + \ln 4\right)$
49. Relative minimum: (e, e) **51.** Relative minimum: $(0, 1)$
53. Relative minimum: $(0, 0)$;
Relative maximum: $(2, 4e^{-2})$
55. Relative maximum: $(1/\ln 4, 4e^{-1}/\ln 2)$
57. Relative minimum: $(-1.272, 3.747)$;
Relative maximum: $(1.272, -0.606)$
59. (a) $f'(x) = 0.2x(x - 3)^2(5x - 6)$;
$f''(x) = 0.4(x - 3)(10x^2 - 24x + 9)$
(b) Relative maximum: $(0, 0)$;
Relative minimum: $(1.2, -1.6796)$;
Points of inflection: $(0.4652, -0.7048)$,
$(1.9348, -0.9048), (3, 0)$

(c) 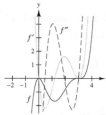 f is increasing when f' is positive and decreasing when f' is negative. f is concave upward when f'' is positive and concave downward when f'' is negative.

61. (a) $f'(x) = \cos x - \cos 3x + \cos 5x$;
$f''(x) = -\sin x + 3\sin 3x - 5\sin 5x$
(b) Relative maximum: $(\pi/2, 1.53333)$;
Points of inflection: $(\pi/6, 0.2667), (1.1731, 0.9637)$,
$(1.9685, 0.9637), (5\pi/6, 0.2667)$

(c) 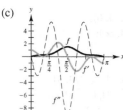 f is increasing when f' is positive and decreasing when f' is negative. f is concave upward when f'' is positive and concave downward when f'' is negative.

63. (a) 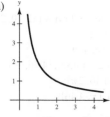   (b)

65. Answers will vary. Sample answer: $f(x) = x^4$; $f''(0) = 0$, but $(0, 0)$ is not a point of inflection.

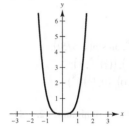

67. (a) 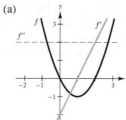   (b)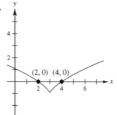

69.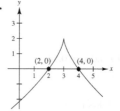

71. 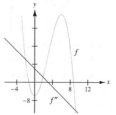   **73.** Sample answer: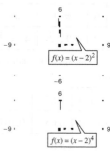

75. (a)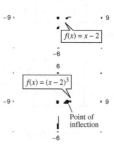

$f(x) = (x - 2)^n$ has a point of inflection at $(2, 0)$ if n is odd and $n \geq 3$.
(b) Proof
77. $f(x) = \frac{1}{2}x^3 - 6x^2 + \frac{45}{2}x - 24$
79. (a) $f(x) = \frac{1}{32}x^3 + \frac{3}{16}x^2$ (b) Two miles from touchdown
81. $x = 100$ units
83. (a)

t	0.5	1	1.5	2	2.5	3
S	151.5	555.6	1097.6	1666.7	2193.0	2647.1

$1.5 < t < 2$
(b) 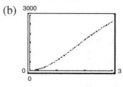   (c) About 1.633 yr

$t \approx 1.5$

85. $P_1(x) = 2\sqrt{2}$
$P_2(x) = 2\sqrt{2} - \sqrt{2}(x - \pi/4)^2$

The values of f, P_1, and P_2 and their first derivatives are equal when $x = \pi/4$. The approximations worsen as you move away from $x = \pi/4$.

87. $P_1(x) = -\pi/4 + 1/2(x + 1)$
$P_2(x) = -\pi/4 + 1/2(x + 1) + 1/4(x + 1)^2$

The values of f, P_1, and P_2 and their first derivatives are equal when $x = -1$. The approximations worsen as you move away from $x = -1$.

89.   **91.** True

$\left(\frac{1}{\pi}, 0\right)$

93. False. f is concave upward at $x = c$ if $f''(c) > 0$.
95. Proof

Section 4.5   (page 242)

1. f   **2.** c   **3.** d   **4.** a   **5.** b   **6.** e
7.

x	10^0	10^1	10^2	10^3
$f(x)$	7	2.2632	2.0251	2.0025

x	10^4	10^5	10^6
$f(x)$	2.0003	2.0000	2.0000

$$\lim_{x \to \infty} \frac{4x + 3}{2x - 1} = 2$$

9.

x	10^0	10^1	10^2	10^3
$f(x)$	-2	-2.9814	-2.9998	-3.0000

x	10^4	10^5	10^6
$f(x)$	-3.0000	-3.0000	-3.0000

$$\lim_{x \to \infty} \frac{-6x}{\sqrt{4x^2 + 5}} = -3$$

11.

x	10^0	10^1	10^2	10^3
$f(x)$	4.5000	4.9901	4.9999	5.0000

x	10^4	10^5	10^6
$f(x)$	5.0000	5.0000	5.0000

$$\lim_{x \to \infty}\left(5 - \frac{1}{x^2 + 1}\right) = 5$$

13. (a) ∞ (b) 5   (c) 0   **15.** (a) 0   (b) 1   (c) ∞
17. (a) 0   (b) $-\frac{2}{3}$ (c) $-\infty$ **19.** 4   **21.** $\frac{2}{3}$ **23.** 0
25. -1 **27.** -2 **29.** $\frac{1}{2}$ **31.** ∞ **33.** 0   **35.** 0
37. 2   **39.** 0   **41.** $-\dfrac{\pi}{2}$
43.   **45.**

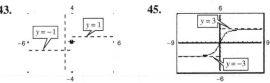

47. 1   **49.** 0   **51.** $\frac{1}{6}$
53.

x	10^0	10^1	10^2	10^3	10^4	10^5	10^6
$f(x)$	1.000	0.513	0.501	0.500	0.500	0.500	0.500

$$\lim_{x \to \infty}\left[x - \sqrt{x(x - 1)}\right] = \frac{1}{2}$$

55.

x	10^0	10^1	10^2	10^3	10^4	10^5	10^6
$f(x)$	0.479	0.500	0.500	0.500	0.500	0.500	0.500

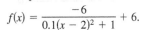

The graph has a hole at $x = 0$.

$$\lim_{x \to \infty} x \sin \frac{1}{2x} = \frac{1}{2}$$

57. (a) As x becomes large, $f(x)$ approaches 4.

(b) As x becomes very large (in absolute value) and negative, $f(x)$ approaches 2.

59. Answers will vary.
Sample answer: Let

$$f(x) = \frac{-6}{0.1(x - 2)^2 + 1} + 6.$$

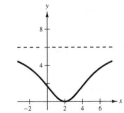

61. (a) 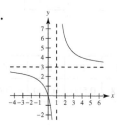   (b) Answers will vary.

63. 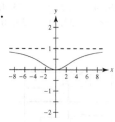   **65.**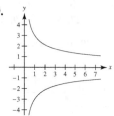

67. 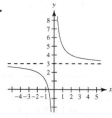   **69.**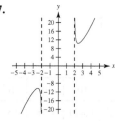

71. 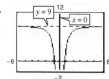   **73.**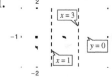

75. 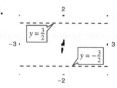   **77.**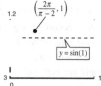

79. 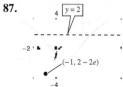   **81.**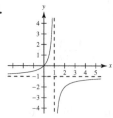

83. 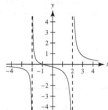   **85.** $\left(\dfrac{2\pi}{\pi-2},1\right)$
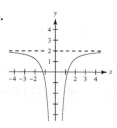

87.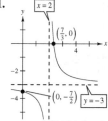

89. (a) 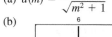   (c)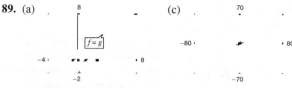

(b) Proof   Slant asymptote: $y = x$

91. 100%   **93.** $\lim\limits_{t\to\infty} N(t) = +\infty;\ \lim\limits_{t\to\infty} E(t) = c$

95. (a) 83%   (b) $P'(3) \approx 0.038;\ P'(10) \approx 0.017$

97. (a) $\lim\limits_{x\to\infty} f(x) = 2$

(b) $x_1 = \sqrt{\dfrac{4 - 2\varepsilon}{\varepsilon}},\ x_2 = -\sqrt{\dfrac{4 - 2\varepsilon}{\varepsilon}}$

(c) $\sqrt{\dfrac{4 - 2\varepsilon}{\varepsilon}}$ (d) $-\sqrt{\dfrac{4 - 2\varepsilon}{\varepsilon}}$

99. (a) Answers will vary. $M = \dfrac{5\sqrt{33}}{11}$ **101–103.** Proofs

(b) Answers will vary. $M = \dfrac{29\sqrt{177}}{59}$

105. (a) $d(m) = \dfrac{|3m + 3|}{\sqrt{m^2 + 1}}$

(b) 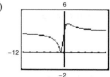   (c) $\lim\limits_{m\to\infty} d(m) = 3;$

$\lim\limits_{m\to-\infty} d(m) = 3;$

As m approaches $\pm\infty$, the distance approaches 3.

107. Proof

109. False. Let $f(x) = \dfrac{2x}{\sqrt{x^2 + 2}}.\ f'(x) > 0$ for all real numbers.

Section 4.6   *(page 253)*

1. 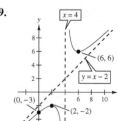   **3.**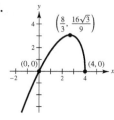

5. 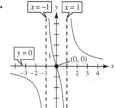   **7.**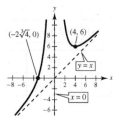

9. 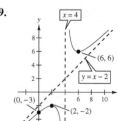   **11.**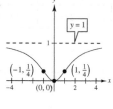

13.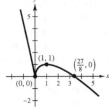

15.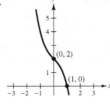

17.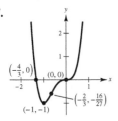

19.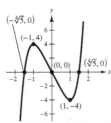

21.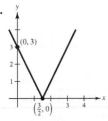

23.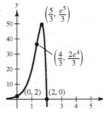

25.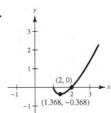

27.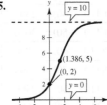

29.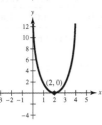

31.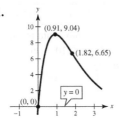

33.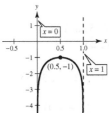

35.

Minimum: $(-1.10, -9.05)$
Maximum: $(1.10, 9.05)$
Points of inflection: $(-1.84, -7.86), (1.84, 7.86)$
Vertical asymptote: $x = 0$
Horizontal asymptote: $y = 0$

37.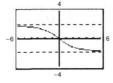

Point of inflection: $(0, 0)$
Horizontal asymptotes:
$y = \pm 2$

39.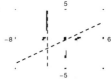

Vertical asymptotes:
$x = -3, x = 0$
Slant asymptote: $y = x/2$

41.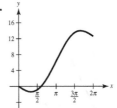

43.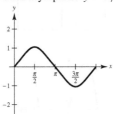

45.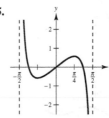

47.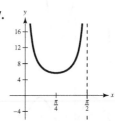

49.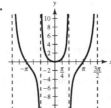

51. f is decreasing on $(2, 8)$, and therefore $f(3) > f(5)$.

53.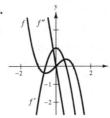

The zeros of f' correspond to the points where the graph of f has horizontal tangents. The zero of f'' corresponds to the point where the graph of f' has a horizontal tangent.

55.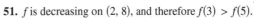

The graph crosses the horizontal asymptote $y = 4$.
The graph of a function f does not cross its vertical asymptote $x = c$ because $f(c)$ does not exist.

57.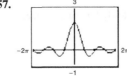

The graph has a hole at $x = 0$.
The graph crosses the horizontal asymptote $y = 0$.
The graph of a function f does not cross its vertical asymptote $x = c$ because $f(c)$ does not exist.

59.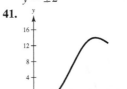

The graph has a hole at $x = 3$. The rational function is not reduced to lowest terms.

61.

The graph appears to approach the line $y = -x + 1$, which is the slant asymptote.

63.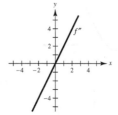

The graph appears to approach the line $y = 2x$, which is the slant asymptote.

65.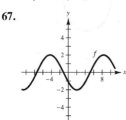

67.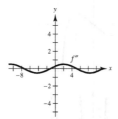

69. (a)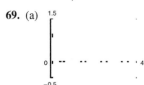

The graph has holes at $x = 0$ and at $x = 4$.

Visually approximated critical numbers: $\frac{1}{2}, 1, \frac{3}{2}, 2, \frac{5}{2}, 3, \frac{7}{2}$

(b) $f'(x) = \dfrac{-x \cos^2(\pi x)}{(x^2 + 1)^{3/2}} - \dfrac{2\pi \sin(\pi x) \cos(\pi x)}{\sqrt{x^2 + 1}}$;

Approximate critical numbers: $\frac{1}{2}, 0.97, \frac{3}{2}, 1.98, \frac{5}{2}, 2.98, \frac{7}{2}$
The critical numbers where maxima occur appear to be integers in part (a), but by approximating them using f', you can see that they are not integers.

71. Answers will vary. Sample answer: $y = 1/(x - 3)$

73. Answers will vary.
Sample answer: $y = (3x^2 - 7x - 5)/(x - 3)$

75. (a)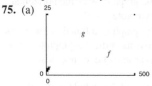

$g; f(x) = \ln x$ increases very slowly for "large" values of x.

(b)

$g; f(x) = \ln x$ increases very slowly for "large" values of x.

77. (a) x_0, x_2, x_4 (b) x_2, x_3 (c) x_1 (d) x_1 (e) x_2, x_3

79. (a)–(h) Proofs

81. Answers will vary. Sample answer: The graph has a vertical asymptote at $x = b$. If a and b are both positive or both negative, then the graph of f approaches ∞ as x approaches b, and the graph has a minimum at $x = -b$. If a and b have opposite signs, then the graph of f approaches $-\infty$ as x approaches b, and the graph has a maximum at $x = -b$.

83. $y = 4x$, $y = -4x$

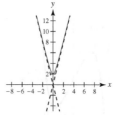

85. Putnam Problem 13(i), 1939

Section 4.7 *(page 262)*

1. (a) and (b)

First Number, x	Second Number	Product, P
10	$110 - 10$	$10(110 - 10) = 1000$
20	$110 - 20$	$20(110 - 20) = 1800$
30	$110 - 30$	$30(110 - 30) = 2400$
40	$110 - 40$	$40(110 - 40) = 2800$
50	$110 - 50$	$50(110 - 50) = 3000$
60	$110 - 60$	$60(110 - 60) = 3000$
70	$110 - 70$	$70(110 - 70) = 2800$
80	$110 - 80$	$80(110 - 80) = 2400$
90	$110 - 90$	$90(110 - 90) = 1800$
100	$110 - 100$	$100(110 - 100) = 1000$

The maximum is attained near $x = 50$ and 60.

(c) $P = x(110 - x)$

(d) 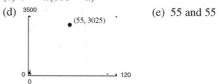   (e) 55 and 55

3. $S/2$ and $S/2$ **5.** 21 and 7   **7.** 54 and 27

9. $l = w = 20$ m   **11.** $l = w = 4\sqrt{2}$ ft

13. $(1, 1)$ **15.** $\left(\frac{7}{2}, \sqrt{\frac{7}{2}}\right)$

17. Dimensions of page: $\left(2 + \sqrt{30}\right)$ in. $\times \left(2 + \sqrt{30}\right)$ in.

19. 700×350 m

21. Rectangular portion: $16/(\pi + 4) \times 32/(\pi + 4)$ ft

23. (a) $L = \sqrt{x^2 + 4 + \dfrac{8}{x - 1} + \dfrac{4}{(x - 1)^2}}$, $x > 1$

(b)

(c) $(0, 0), (2, 0), (0, 4)$

$(2.587, 4.162)$

Minimum when $x \approx 2.587$

25. Width: $5\sqrt{2}/2$; Length: $5\sqrt{2}$

27. (a)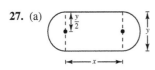

(b)

Length, x	Width, y	Area, xy
10	$2/\pi(100 - 10)$	$(10)(2/\pi)(100 - 10) \approx 573$
20	$2/\pi(100 - 20)$	$(20)(2/\pi)(100 - 20) \approx 1019$
30	$2/\pi(100 - 30)$	$(30)(2/\pi)(100 - 30) \approx 1337$
40	$2/\pi(100 - 40)$	$(40)(2/\pi)(100 - 40) \approx 1528$
50	$2/\pi(100 - 50)$	$(50)(2/\pi)(100 - 50) \approx 1592$
60	$2/\pi(100 - 60)$	$(60)(2/\pi)(100 - 60) \approx 1528$

The maximum area of the rectangle is approximately 1592 m².
(c) $A = 2/\pi(100x - x^2)$, $0 < x < 100$

(d) $\dfrac{dA}{dx} = \dfrac{2}{\pi}(100 - 2x)$ (e)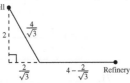

$= 0$ when $x = 50$;
The maximum value is
approximately 1592
when $x = 50$.

29. $18 \times 18 \times 36$ in.
31. No. The volume changes because the shape of the container changes when it is squeezed.
33. $r = \sqrt[3]{21/(2\pi)} \approx 1.50$ ($h = 0$, so the solid is a sphere.)
35. Side of triangle: $\dfrac{30}{9 + 4\sqrt{3}}$; Side of square: $\dfrac{10\sqrt{3}}{9 + 4\sqrt{3}}$
37. $w = \left(20\sqrt{3}\right)/3$ in., $h = \left(20\sqrt{6}\right)/3$ in.
39.

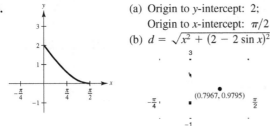

The path of the pipe should go underwater from the oil well to the coast following the hypotenuse of a right triangle with leg lengths of 2 kilometers and $2/\sqrt{3}$ kilometers for a distance of $4/\sqrt{3}$ kilometers. Then the pipe should go down the coast to the refinery for a distance of $\left(4 - 2/\sqrt{3}\right)$ kilometers.
41. (a) One mile from the nearest point on the coast   (b) Proof
43.

(a) Origin to y-intercept: 2;
   Origin to x-intercept: $\pi/2$
(b) $d = \sqrt{x^2 + (2 - 2\sin x)^2}$

(c) Minimum distance is 0.9795 when $x \approx 0.7967$.
45. About 1.153 radians or 66°   **47.** 8%   **49.** Proof
51. $y = \frac{64}{141}x$; $S \approx 6.1$ mi   **53.** $y = \frac{3}{10}x$; $S_3 \approx 4.50$ mi
55. Putnam Problem A1, 1986

Section 4.8   *(page 272)*

1. $T(x) = 4x - 4$

x	1.9	1.99	2	2.01	2.1
$f(x)$	3.610	3.960	4	4.040	4.410
$T(x)$	3.600	3.960	4	4.040	4.400

3. $T(x) = 80x - 128$

x	1.9	1.99	2	2.01	2.1
$f(x)$	24.761	31.208	32	32.808	40.841
$T(x)$	24.000	31.200	32	32.800	40.000

5. $T(x) = (\cos 2)(x - 2) + \sin 2$

x	1.9	1.99	2	2.01	2.1
$f(x)$	0.946	0.913	0.909	0.905	0.863
$T(x)$	0.951	0.913	0.909	0.905	0.868

7. $\Delta y = 0.331$; $dy = 0.3$ **9.** $\Delta y = -0.039$; $dy = -0.040$
11. $6x\, dx$ **13.** $(x \sec^2 x + \tan x)\, dx$
15. $-\dfrac{13}{(2x - 1)^2}\, dx$ **17.** $\dfrac{-x}{\sqrt{9 - x^2}}\, dx$ **19.** $(3 - \sin 2x)\, dx$
21. $\dfrac{x}{x^2 - 4}\, dx$ **23.** $\left(\arcsin x + \dfrac{x}{\sqrt{1 - x^2}}\right) dx$
25. (a) 0.9   (b) 1.04   **27.** (a) 8.035   (b) 7.95
29. (a) $\pm\dfrac{5}{8}$ in.²   (b) 0.625%
31. (a) ± 10.75 cm²   (b) About 1.19%
33. (a) ± 20.25 in.³   (b) ± 5.4 in.²   (c) 0.6%; 0.4%
35. 27.5 mi; About 7.3%   **37.** (a) $\frac{1}{4}$%   (b) 216 sec = 3.6 min
39. About -2.65%

41. $f(x) = \sqrt{x}$, $dy = \dfrac{1}{2\sqrt{x}}\, dx$

$f(99.4) \approx \sqrt{100} + \dfrac{1}{2\sqrt{100}}(-0.6) = 9.97$

Calculator: 9.97

43. $f(x) = \sqrt[4]{x}$, $dy = \dfrac{1}{4x^{3/4}}\, dx$

$f(624) \approx \sqrt[4]{625} + \dfrac{1}{4(625)^{3/4}}(-1) = 4.998$

Calculator: 4.998

45. $y - f(0) = f'(0)(x - 0)$
$y - 2 = \frac{1}{4}x$
$y = 2 + x/4$

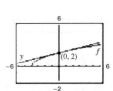

47. The value of dy becomes closer to the value of Δy as decreases.

49. (a) $f(x) = \sqrt{x}$; $dy = \dfrac{1}{2\sqrt{x}}\, dx$

$f(4.02) \approx \sqrt{4} + \dfrac{1}{2\sqrt{4}}(0.02) = 2 + \dfrac{1}{4}(0.02)$

(b) $f(x) = \tan x; dy = \sec^2 x \, dx$

$f(0.05) \approx \tan 0 + \sec^2(0)(0.05) = 0 + 1(0.05)$

51. True   **53.** True

Review Exercises for Chapter 4   *(page 274)*

1. Maximum: $(0, 0)$;   **3.** Maximum: $(4, 0)$;
   Minimum: $\left(-\frac{5}{2}, -\frac{25}{4}\right)$ Minimum: $(0, -2)$

5. Maximum: $\left(3, \frac{2}{3}\right)$;   **7.** Maximum: $(2\pi, 17.57)$;
   Minimum: $\left(-3, -\frac{2}{3}\right)$ Minimum: $(2.73, 0.88)$

9. $f(0) \neq f(4)$ **11.** Not continuous on $[-2, 2]$

13. $f'\left(\frac{2744}{729}\right) = \frac{3}{7}$ **15.** f is not differentiable at $x = 5$.

17. $f'(0) = 1$

19. No; The function has a discontinuity at $x = 0$, which is in the interval $[-2, 1]$.

21. Increasing on $\left(-\frac{3}{2}, \infty\right)$; Decreasing on $\left(-\infty, -\frac{3}{2}\right)$

23. Increasing on $(-\infty, 1)$, $\left(\frac{7}{3}, \infty\right)$; Decreasing on $\left(1, \frac{7}{3}\right)$

25. Increasing on $(1, \infty)$; Decreasing on $(0, 1)$

27. Increasing on $(-\infty, 2 - 1/\ln 2)$;
   Decreasing on $(2 - 1/\ln 2, \infty)$

29. (a) Critical number: $x = 3$
   (b) Increasing on $(3, \infty)$; Decreasing on $(-\infty, 3)$
   (c) Relative minimum: $(3, -4)$
   (d)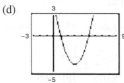

31. (a) Critical number: $t = 2$
   (b) Increasing on $(2, \infty)$; Decreasing on $(-\infty, 2)$
   (c) Relative minimum: $(2, -12)$
   (d)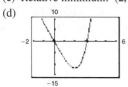

33. (a) Critical number: $x = -8$; Discontinuity: $x = 0$
   (b) Increasing on $(-8, 0)$;
      Decreasing on $(-\infty, -8)$ and $(0, \infty)$
   (c) Relative minimum: $\left(-8, -\frac{1}{16}\right)$
   (d)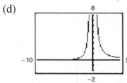

35. (a) Critical numbers: $x = \dfrac{3\pi}{4}, \dfrac{7\pi}{4}$

   (b) Increasing on $\left(\dfrac{3\pi}{4}, \dfrac{7\pi}{4}\right)$;

      Decreasing on $\left(0, \dfrac{3\pi}{4}\right)$ and $\left(\dfrac{7\pi}{4}, 2\pi\right)$

   (c) Relative minimum: $\left(\dfrac{3\pi}{4}, -\sqrt{2}\right)$;

      Relative maximum: $\left(\dfrac{7\pi}{4}, \sqrt{2}\right)$

(d)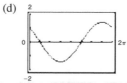

37. $(3, -54)$; Concave upward: $(3, \infty)$;
   Concave downward: $(-\infty, 3)$

39. No point of inflection; Concave upward: $(-5, \infty)$

41. $(\pi/2, \pi/2)$, $(3\pi/2, 3\pi/2)$; Concave upward: $(\pi/2, 3\pi/2)$;
   Concave downward: $(0, \pi/2)$, $(3\pi/2, 2\pi)$

43. Relative minimum: $(-9, 0)$

45. Relative maxima: $\left(\sqrt{2}/2, 1/2\right)$, $\left(-\sqrt{2}/2, 1/2\right)$;
   Relative minimum: $(0, 0)$

47. Relative maximum: $(-3, -12)$; Relative minimum: $(3, 12)$

49.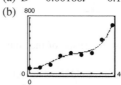

51. Increasing and concave down

53. (a) $D = 0.00188t^4 - 0.1273t^3 + 2.672t^2 - 7.81t + 77.1$
   (b)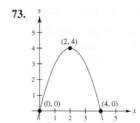

   (c) Maximum in 2010; Minimum in 1970   (d) 2010

55. 8   **57.** $\frac{2}{3}$ **59.** $-\infty$ **61.** 0   **63.** 6

65.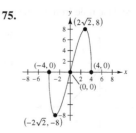

67.

69.

71.

73.

75.

77.
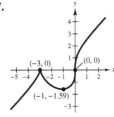

79.
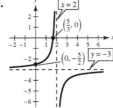

81.
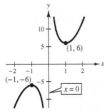

83. $x = 50$ ft and $y = \frac{200}{3}$ ft   **85.** $(0, 0), (5, 0), (0, 10)$

87. (a)

(b) $P = 10{,}957.7e^{-0.1499h}$

$y = -0.1499h + 9.3018$

(c)
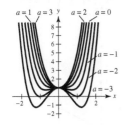
(d) $-776.3; -110.6$

89. 14.05 ft   **91.** $32\pi r^3/81$

93. $\Delta y = 0.03005; dy = 0.03$

95. $dy = (1 - \cos x + x \sin x)\,dx$

97. (a) $\pm 8.1\pi\,\text{cm}^3$ (b) $\pm 1.8\pi\,\text{cm}^2$
   (c) About 0.83%; About 0.56%

99. 267.24; 3.1%

P.S. Problem Solving   *(page 277)*

1. Choices of a may vary.

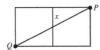

(a) One relative minimum at $(0, 1)$
   for $a \geq 0$

(b) One relative maximum at $(0, 1)$
   for $a < 0$

(c) Two relative minima for $a < 0$
   when $x = \pm\sqrt{-a/2}$

(d) If $a < 0$, then there are three
   critical points; if $a \geq 0$, then
   there is only one critical point.

3. All c, where c is a real number   **5.** Proof

7. The bug should head towards the midpoint of the opposite side.
   Without calculus, imagine opening up the cube. The shortest
   distance is the line PQ, passing through the midpoint as shown.

9. $a = 6, b = 1, c = 2$ **11.** Proof

13. Greatest slope: $\left(-\frac{\sqrt{3}}{3}, \frac{3}{4}\right)$; Least slope: $\left(\frac{\sqrt{3}}{3}, \frac{3}{4}\right)$

15. Proof   **17.** Proof; Point of inflection: $(1, 0)$

19. (a) $(0, \infty)$

(b) Answers will vary. Sample answer:
   $x = e^{\pi/2}, x = e^{(\pi/2)+2\pi}$

(c) Answers will vary. Sample answer: $x = e^{-\pi/2}, x = e^{3\pi/2}$

(d) $[-1, 1]$ (e) $f'(x) = \dfrac{\cos(\ln x)}{x}$; Maximum $= e^{\pi/2}$

(f)

$\displaystyle\lim_{x \to 0^+} f(x)$ seems to be $-\frac{1}{2}$. (This is incorrect.)

(g) The limit does not exist.

Chapter 5

Section 5.1   *(page 287)*

1. Proof   **3.** $y = 3t^3 + C$ **5.** $y = \frac{2}{5}x^{5/2} + C$

Original Integral	Rewrite	Integrate	Simplify
7. $\displaystyle\int \sqrt[3]{x}\,dx$	$\displaystyle\int x^{1/3}\,dx$	$\dfrac{x^{4/3}}{4/3} + C$	$\dfrac{3}{4}x^{4/3} + C$
9. $\displaystyle\int \dfrac{1}{x\sqrt{x}}\,dx$	$\displaystyle\int x^{-3/2}\,dx$	$\dfrac{x^{-1/2}}{-1/2} + C$	$-\dfrac{2}{\sqrt{x}} + C$

11. $\frac{1}{2}x^2 + 7x + C$ **13.** $\frac{2}{5}x^{5/2} + x^2 + x + C$

15. $\frac{3}{5}x^{5/3} + C$ **17.** $-1/(4x^4) + C$

19. $\frac{2}{3}x^{3/2} + 12x^{1/2} + C$ **21.** $x^3 + \frac{1}{2}x^2 - 2x + C$

23. $5\sin x - 4\cos x + C$ **25.** $-2\cos x - 5e^x + C$

27. $\tan y + C$ **29.** $x^2 - (4^x/\ln 4) + C$

31. $\frac{1}{2}x^2 - 5\ln|x| + C$

33. Answers will vary. Sample answer:

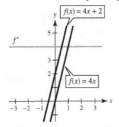

35. $f(x) = 3x^2 + 8$ **37.** $f(x) = x^2 + x + 4$

39. $f(x) = -4\sqrt{x} + 3x$ **41.** $f(x) = e^x + x + 4$

43. (a) Answers will vary.   (b) $y = \dfrac{x^3}{3} - x + \dfrac{7}{3}$
   Sample answer:

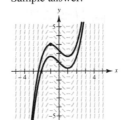

45. (a) 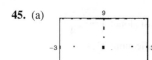   (b) $y = x^2 - 6$
(c)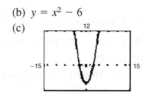

47. When you evaluate the integral $\int f(x)\,dx$, you are finding a function $F(x)$ that is an antiderivative of $f(x)$. So, there is no difference.

49.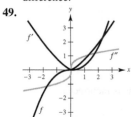

51. (a) $h(t) = \frac{3}{4}t^2 + 5t + 12$ (b) 69 cm   **53.** 62.25 ft
55. (a) $t \approx 2.562$ sec   (b) $v(t) \approx -65.970$ ft/sec
57. $v_0 \approx 62.3$ m/sec   **59.** 320 m; -32 m/sec
61. (a) $v(t) = 3t^2 - 12t + 9; a(t) = 6t - 12$
(b) $(0, 1), (3, 5)$ (c) -3
63. $a(t) = -1/(2t^{3/2}); x(t) = 2\sqrt{t} + 2$
65. (a) 1.18 m/sec^2 (b) 190 m
67. (a) 300 ft   (b) 60 ft/sec ≈ 41 mi/h
69. False. f has an infinite number of antiderivatives, each differing by a constant.

71. $f(x) = \dfrac{x^3}{3} - 4x + \dfrac{16}{3}$ **73–75.** Proofs

Section 5.2   (page 299)

1. 75   **3.** $\dfrac{158}{85}$ **5.** $4c$ **7.** $\displaystyle\sum_{i=1}^{11} \dfrac{1}{5i}$

9. $\displaystyle\sum_{j=1}^{6} \left[7\left(\dfrac{j}{6}\right) + 5 \right]$ **11.** $\dfrac{2}{n} \displaystyle\sum_{i=1}^{n} \left[\left(\dfrac{2i}{n}\right)^3 - \left(\dfrac{2i}{n}\right) \right]$

13. 84   **15.** 1200   **17.** 2470   **19.** 12,040
21. $(n + 2)/n$ **23.** $[2(n + 1)(n - 1)]/n^2$
    $n = 10$: $S = 1.2$ $n = 10$: $S = 1.98$
    $n = 100$: $S = 1.02$ $n = 100$: $S = 1.9998$
    $n = 1000$: $S = 1.002$ $n = 1000$: $S = 1.999998$
    $n = 10{,}000$: $S = 1.0002$ $n = 10{,}000$: $S = 1.99999998$
25. $13 < (\text{Area of region}) < 15$
27. $55 < (\text{Area of region}) < 74.5$
29. $0.7908 < (\text{Area of region}) < 1.1835$
31. The area of the shaded region falls between 12.5 square units and 16.5 square units.
33. $A \approx S \approx 0.768$ **35.** $A \approx S \approx 0.746$
    $A \approx s \approx 0.518$ $A \approx s \approx 0.646$

37. $\displaystyle\lim_{n\to\infty} \left[\dfrac{12(n + 1)}{n} \right] = 12$ **39.** $\displaystyle\lim_{n\to\infty} \dfrac{1}{6}\left(\dfrac{2n^3 - 3n^2 + n}{n^3} \right) = \dfrac{1}{3}$

41. $\displaystyle\lim_{n\to\infty} [(3n + 1)/n] = 3$

43. (a) 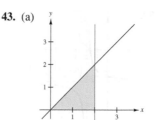   (b) $\Delta x = (2 - 0)/n = 2/n$

(c) $s(n) = \displaystyle\sum_{i=1}^{n} f(x_{i-1})\,\Delta x = \displaystyle\sum_{i=1}^{n} [(i - 1)(2/n)](2/n)$

(d) $S(n) = \displaystyle\sum_{i=1}^{n} f(x_i)\,\Delta x = \displaystyle\sum_{i=1}^{n} [i(2/n)](2/n)$

(e)

n	5	10	50	100
$s(n)$	1.6	1.8	1.96	1.98
$S(n)$	2.4	2.2	2.04	2.02

(f) $\displaystyle\lim_{n\to\infty} \displaystyle\sum_{i=1}^{n} [(i - 1)(2/n)](2/n) = 2$;

$\displaystyle\lim_{n\to\infty} \displaystyle\sum_{i=1}^{n} [i(2/n)](2/n) = 2$

45. $A = 3$ **47.** $A = \frac{7}{3}$

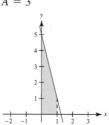 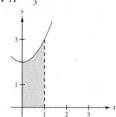

49. $A = 54$ **51.** $A = 34$

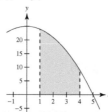 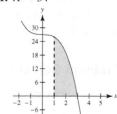

53. $A = \frac{2}{3}$ **55.** $A = 8$

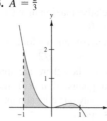 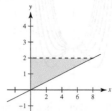

57. $A = \frac{125}{3}$ **59.** $A = \frac{44}{3}$

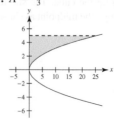 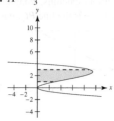

61. $\frac{69}{8}$ **63.** 0.345   **65.** 4.0786   **67.** b

69. You can use the line $y = x$ bounded by $x = a$ and $x = b$. The sum of the areas of the inscribed rectangles in the figure below is the lower sum.   The sum of the areas of the circumscribed rectangles in the figure below is the upper sum.

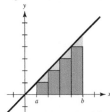

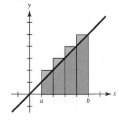

The rectangles in the first graph do not contain all of the area of the region, and the rectangles in the second graph cover more than the area of the region. The exact value of the area lies between these two sums.

71. (a)

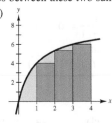

$s(4) = \frac{46}{3}$

(b)

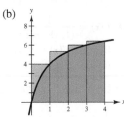

$S(4) = \frac{326}{15}$

(c)

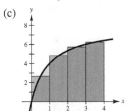

$M(4) = \frac{6112}{315}$

(d) Proof

(e)

n	4	8	20	100	200
$s(n)$	15.333	17.368	18.459	18.995	19.060
$S(n)$	21.733	20.568	19.739	19.251	19.188
$M(n)$	19.403	19.201	19.137	19.125	19.125

(f) Because f is an increasing function, $s(n)$ is always increasing and $S(n)$ is always decreasing.

73. True

75. Suppose there are n rows and $n + 1$ columns. The stars on the left total $1 + 2 + \cdots + n$, as do the stars on the right. There are $n(n + 1)$ stars in total. So, $2[1 + 2 + \cdots + n] = n(n + 1)$ and $1 + 2 + \cdots + n = [n(n + 1)]/2$.

77. For n odd, $\left(\dfrac{n + 1}{2}\right)^2$ blocks;

For n even, $\dfrac{n^2 + 2n}{4}$ blocks

79. Putnam Problem B1, 1989

Section 5.3   *(page 309)*

1. $2\sqrt{3} \approx 3.464$ **3.** 32   **5.** 0   **7.** $\frac{10}{3}$

9. $\displaystyle\int_{-1}^{5} (3x + 10)\, dx$ **11.** $\displaystyle\int_{0}^{3} \sqrt{x^2 + 4}\, dx$

13. $\displaystyle\int_{1}^{5} \left(1 + \frac{3}{x}\right) dx$ **15.** $\displaystyle\int_{0}^{4} 5\, dx$ **17.** $\displaystyle\int_{-4}^{4} \left(4 - |x|\right) dx$

19. $\displaystyle\int_{-5}^{5} (25 - x^2)\, dx$ **21.** $\displaystyle\int_{0}^{\pi/2} \cos x\, dx$ **23.** $\displaystyle\int_{0}^{2} y^3\, dy$

25. $\displaystyle\int_{1}^{4} \frac{2}{x}\, dx$

27.

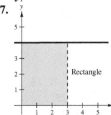

$A = 12$

29.

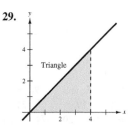

$A = 8$

31.

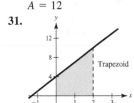

$A = 14$

33.

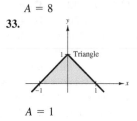

$A = 1$

35.

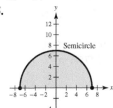

$A = 49\pi/2$

37. -6 **39.** 48   **41.** -12

43. 16   **45.** (a) 13   (b) -10 (c) 0   (d) 30

47. (a) 8   (b) -12 (c) -4 (d) 30   **49.** $-48, 88$

51. (a) $-\pi$ (b) 4   (c) $-(1 + 2\pi)$ (d) $3 - 2\pi$
(e) $5 + 2\pi$ (f) $23 - 2\pi$

53. (a) 14   (b) 4   (c) 8   (d) 0   **55.** 40   **57.** a   **59.** c

61. No. There is a discontinuity at $x = 4$.

63. $a = -2$, $b = 5$

65. Answers will vary. Sample answer: $a = \pi$, $b = 2\pi$

$$\int_{\pi}^{2\pi} \sin x\, dx < 0$$

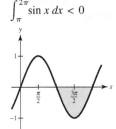

67. True   **69.** True   **71.** False. $\int_0^2 (-x)\,dx = -2$

73. 272   **75.** Proof

77. No. No matter how small the subintervals, the number of both rational and irrational numbers within each subinterval is infinite, and $f(c_i) = 0$ or $f(c_i) = 1$.

79. $a = -1$ and $b = 1$ maximize the integral.   **81.** $\frac{1}{3}$

Section 5.4   *(page 324)*

1.    **3.**

Positive   Zero

5. 12   **7.** -2 **9.** $-\frac{10}{3}$ **11.** $\frac{1}{3}$ **13.** $\frac{1}{2}$ **15.** $\frac{2}{3}$

17. -4 **19.** $-\frac{1}{18}$ **21.** $-\frac{27}{20}$ **23.** $\frac{25}{2}$ **25.** $\frac{64}{3}$

27. $\pi + 2$ **29.** $\pi/4$ **31.** $2\sqrt{3}/3$ **33.** 0

35. $(3/\ln 2) + 12$ **37.** $e - e^{-1}$ **39.** $\frac{1}{6}$ **41.** 1

43. $\frac{52}{3}$ **45.** 20   **47.** 4   **49.** $3\sqrt[3]{2}/2 \approx 1.8899$

51. $3/\ln 4 \approx 2.1640$ **53.** $\pm\arccos\sqrt{\pi}/2 \approx \pm0.4817$

55. Average value $= 6$
$x = \pm\sqrt{3} \approx \pm1.7321$

57. Average value $= e - e^{-1} \approx 2.3504$
$x = \ln((e - e^{-1})/2) \approx 0.1614$

59. Average value $= 2/\pi$ **61.** About 540 ft
$x \approx 0.690, x \approx 2.451$

63. (a) 8   (b) $\frac{4}{3}$ (c) $\int_1^7 f(x)\,dx = 20$; Average value $= \frac{10}{3}$

65. (a) $F(x) = 500 \sec^2 x$ (b) $1500\sqrt{3}/\pi \approx 827$ N

67. About 0.5318 L

69. (a) $v = -0.00086t^3 + 0.0782t^2 - 0.208t + 0.10$
(b) 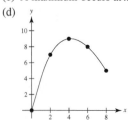   (c) 2475.6 m

71. $F(x) = 2x^2 - 7x$ **73.** $F(x) = -20/x + 20$
$F(2) = -6$ $F(2) = 10$
$F(5) = 15$ $F(5) = 16$
$F(8) = 72$ $F(8) = \frac{35}{2}$

75. $F(x) = \sin x - \sin 1$
$F(2) = \sin 2 - \sin 1 \approx 0.0678$
$F(5) = \sin 5 - \sin 1 \approx -1.8004$
$F(8) = \sin 8 - \sin 1 \approx 0.1479$

77. (a) $g(0) = 0$, $g(2) \approx 7$, $g(4) \approx 9$, $g(6) \approx 8$, $g(8) \approx 5$
(b) Increasing: $(0, 4)$; Decreasing: $(4, 8)$
(c) A maximum occurs at $x = 4$.
(d)

79. $\frac{1}{2}x^2 + 2x$ **81.** $\frac{3}{4}x^{4/3} - 12$ **83.** $\tan x - 1$
85. $e^x - e^{-1}$ **87.** $x^2 - 2x$ **89.** $\sqrt{x^4 + 1}$
91. $x \cos x$ **93.** 8   **95.** $\cos x\sqrt{\sin x}$ **97.** $3x^2 \sin x^6$
99.    **101.** (a) $\frac{3}{2}$ ft to the right
                                        (b) $\frac{113}{10}$ ft

An extremum of g occurs
at $x = 2$.

103. (a) 0 ft   (b) $\frac{63}{2}$ ft   **105.** (a) 2 ft to the right   (b) 2 ft
107. 28 units   **109.** 8190 L
111. $f(x) = x^{-2}$ has a nonremovable discontinuity at $x = 0$.
113. $f(x) = \sec^2 x$ has a nonremovable discontinuity at $x = \pi/2$.
115. $2/\pi \approx 63.7\%$ **117.** True

119. $f'(x) = \dfrac{1}{(1/x)^2 + 1}\left(-\dfrac{1}{x^2}\right) + \dfrac{1}{x^2 + 1} = 0$
Because $f'(x) = 0$, $f(x)$ is constant.

121. (a) 0   (b) 0   (c) $xf(x) + \int_0^x f(t)\,dt$ (d) 0

Section 5.5   *(page 337)*

$\int f(g(x))g'(x)\,dx$	$u = g(x)$	$du = g'(x)\,dx$
1. $\int (8x^2 + 1)^2(16x)\,dx$	$8x^2 + 1$	$16x\,dx$
3. $\int \tan^2 x \sec^2 x\,dx$	$\tan x$	$\sec^2 x\,dx$

5. $\frac{1}{5}(1 + 6x)^5 + C$ **7.** $\frac{2}{3}(25 - x^2)^{3/2} + C$
9. $\frac{1}{12}(x^4 + 3)^3 + C$ **11.** $\frac{1}{15}(x^3 - 1)^5 + C$
13. $\frac{1}{3}(t^2 + 2)^{3/2} + C$ **15.** $-\frac{15}{8}(1 - x^2)^{4/3} + C$
17. $1/[4(1 - x^2)^2] + C$ **19.** $-1/[3(1 + x^3)] + C$
21. $-\sqrt{1 - x^2} + C$ **23.** $-\frac{1}{4}(1 + 1/t)^4 + C$
25. $\sqrt{2x} + C$ **27.** $2x^2 - 4\sqrt{16 - x^2} + C$
29. $-1/[2(x^2 + 2x - 3)] + C$
31. (a) Answers will vary.   (b) $y = -\frac{1}{3}(4 - x^2)^{3/2} + 2$
Sample answer:

33. $-\cos(\pi x) + C$

35. $\int \cos 8x\,dx = \frac{1}{8}\int (\cos 8x)(8)\,dx = \frac{1}{8}\sin 8x + C$

37. $-\sin(1/\theta) + C$
39. $\frac{1}{4}\sin^2 2x + C$ or $-\frac{1}{4}\cos^2 2x + C_1$ or $-\frac{1}{8}\cos 4x + C_2$
41. $\frac{1}{2}\tan^2 x + C$ or $\frac{1}{2}\sec^2 x + C_1$ **43.** $e^{7x} + C$
45. $\frac{1}{3}(e^x + 1)^3 + C$ **47.** $-\frac{5}{2}e^{-2x} + e^{-x} + C$
49. $1/\pi e^{\sin \pi x} + C$ **51.** $-\tan(e^{-x}) + C$
53. $2/\ln 3 (3^{x/2}) + C$ **55.** $f(x) = 2\cos(x/2) + 4$

57. $f(x) = -8e^{-x/4} + 9$ **59.** $f(x) = \frac{1}{12}(4x^2 - 10)^3 - 8$

61. $\frac{2}{5}(x + 6)^{5/2} - 4(x + 6)^{3/2} + C = \frac{2}{5}(x + 6)^{3/2}(x - 4) + C$

63. $-\left[\frac{2}{3}(1 - x)^{3/2} - \frac{4}{5}(1 - x)^{5/2} + \frac{2}{7}(1 - x)^{7/2}\right] + C =$
$-\frac{2}{105}(1 - x)^{3/2}(15x^2 + 12x + 8) + C$

65. $\frac{1}{8}\left[\frac{2}{5}(2x - 1)^{5/2} + \frac{4}{3}(2x - 1)^{3/2} - 6(2x - 1)^{1/2}\right] + C =$
$\left(\sqrt{2x - 1}/15\right)(3x^2 + 2x - 13) + C$

67. $-x - 1 - 2\sqrt{x + 1} + C$ or $-\left(x + 2\sqrt{x + 1}\right) + C_1$

69. 0   **71.** $12 - \frac{8}{9}\sqrt{2}$ **73.** 2   **75.** $\frac{1}{2}$

77. $(e^2 - 1)/2e^2$ **79.** $e/3(e^2 - 1)$

81. 1209/28   **83.** $2\left(\sqrt{3} - 1\right)$

85. $e^5 - 1 \approx 147.413$ **87.** $2(1 - e^{-3/2}) \approx 1.554$

89. $\frac{272}{15}$ **91.** $\frac{2}{3}$ **93.** (a) $\frac{64}{3}$ (b) $\frac{128}{3}$ (c) $-\frac{64}{3}$ (d) 64

95. $2\displaystyle\int_0^3 (4x^2 - 6)\,dx = 36$

97. If $u = 5 - x^2$, then $du = -2x\,dx$ and
$\int x(5 - x^2)^3\,dx = -\frac{1}{2}\int(5 - x^2)^3(-2x)\,dx = -\frac{1}{2}\int u^3\,du.$

99. (a) $\displaystyle\int x^2\sqrt{x^3 + 1}\,dx$ (b) $\displaystyle\int \tan(3x)\sec^2(3x)\,dx$

101. \$340,000

103. (a) 102.532 thousand units   (b) 102.352 thousand units
(c) 74.5 thousand units

105. (a) $P_{0.50,\,0.75} \approx 35.3\%$ (b) $b \approx 58.6\%$

107. (a)

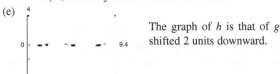

(b) g is nonnegative, because the graph of f is positive at the beginning and generally has more positive sections than negative ones.

(c) The points on g that correspond to the extrema of f are points of inflection of g.

(d) No, some zeros of f, such as $x = \pi/2$, do not correspond to extrema of g. The graph of g continues to increase after $x = \pi/2$, because f remains above the x-axis.

(e)

The graph of h is that of g shifted 2 units downward.

109. (a) and (b) Proofs

111. False. $\displaystyle\int(2x + 1)^2\,dx = \frac{1}{6}(2x + 1)^3 + C$ **113.** True

115. True   **117–119.** Proofs   **121.** Putnam Problem A1, 1958

Section 5.6   (page 346)

	Trapezoidal	Simpson's	Exact
1.	2.7500	2.6667	2.6667
3.	4.2500	4.0000	4.0000
5.	20.2222	20.0000	20.0000
7.	12.6640	12.6667	12.6667
9.	0.3352	0.3334	0.3333

	Trapezoidal	Simpson's	Graphing Utility
11.	3.2833	3.2396	3.2413
13.	0.3415	0.3720	0.3927
15.	0.5495	0.5483	0.5493
17.	-0.0975	-0.0977	-0.0977
19.	1.6845	1.6487	1.6479
21.	0.5706	0.5930	0.5940

23. Trapezoidal: Linear (1st-degree) polynomials
Simpson's: Quadratic (2nd-degree) polynomials

25. (a) 1.500   (b) 0.000   **27.** (a) $\frac{1}{4}$ (b) $\frac{1}{12}$

29. (a) $n = 366$ (b) $n = 26$ **31.** (a) $n = 77$ (b) $n = 8$

33. (a) $n = 130$ (b) $n = 12$ **35.** (a) $n = 643$ (b) $n = 48$

37. (a) 24.5   (b) 25.67   **39.** 0.701   **41.** 89,250 m²

43. 10,233.58 ft-lb   **45.** 3.1416   **47.** 2.477   **49.** Proof

Section 5.7   (page 354)

1. $5\ln|x| + C$ **3.** $\ln|x + 1| + C$ **5.** $\frac{1}{2}\ln|2x + 5| + C$

7. $\frac{1}{2}\ln|x^2 - 3| + C$ **9.** $\ln|x^4 + 3x| + C$

11. $x^2/2 - \ln(x^4) + C$ **13.** $\frac{1}{3}\ln|x^3 + 3x^2 + 9x| + C$

15. $\frac{1}{2}x^2 - 4x + 6\ln|x + 1| + C$ **17.** $\frac{1}{3}x^3 + 5\ln|x - 3| + C$

19. $\frac{1}{3}x^3 - 2x + \ln\sqrt{x^2 + 2} + C$ **21.** $\frac{1}{3}(\ln x)^3 + C$

23. $-\frac{2}{3}\ln\left|1 - 3\sqrt{x}\right| + C$ **25.** $2\ln|x - 1| - 2/(x - 1) + C$

27. $\sqrt{2x} - \ln\left|1 + \sqrt{2x}\right| + C$

29. $x + 6\sqrt{x} + 18\ln\left|\sqrt{x} - 3\right| + C$ **31.** $3\ln\left|\sin\frac{\theta}{3}\right| + C$

33. $-\frac{1}{2}\ln|\csc 2x + \cot 2x| + C$ **35.** $\frac{1}{3}\sin 3\theta - \theta + C$

37. $\ln|1 + \sin t| + C$ **39.** $\ln|\sec x - 1| + C$

41. $\ln|\cos(e^{-x})| + C$

43. $y = -3\ln|2 - x| + C$ **45.** $y = \ln|x^2 - 9| + C$

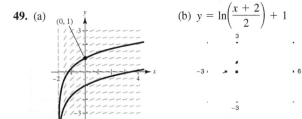

47. $f(x) = -2\ln x + 3x - 2$

49. (a)   (b) $y = \ln\left(\dfrac{x + 2}{2}\right) + 1$

51. $\frac{5}{3}\ln 13 \approx 4.275$ **53.** $\frac{7}{3}$ **55.** $-\ln 3 \approx -1.099$

57. $\ln\left|\dfrac{2 - \sin 2}{1 - \sin 1}\right| \approx 1.929$ **59.** $2\left[\sqrt{x} - \ln\left(1 + \sqrt{x}\right)\right] + C$

61. $\ln\left(\dfrac{\sqrt{x} - 1}{\sqrt{x} + 1}\right) + 2\sqrt{x} + C$ **63.** $\ln\left(\sqrt{2} + 1\right) - \dfrac{\sqrt{2}}{2} \approx 0.174$

65. $1/x$ **67.** $1/x$ **69.** $6\ln 3$ **71.** $\frac{1}{2}\ln 2$

73. $\frac{15}{2} + 8\ln 2 \approx 13.045$ **75.** $(12/\pi)\ln\left(2 + \sqrt{3}\right) \approx 5.03$

77. Trapezoidal Rule: 20.2   **79.** Trapezoidal Rule: 5.3368
Simpson's Rule: 19.4667   Simpson's Rule: 5.3632

81. Power Rule   **83.** Log Rule   **85.** d   **87.** $x = 2$

89. Proof

91. $-\ln|\cos x| + C = \ln|1/\cos x| + C = \ln|\sec x| + C$

93. $\ln|\sec x + \tan x| + C = \ln\left|\dfrac{\sec^2 x - \tan^2 x}{\sec x - \tan x}\right| + C$

$= -\ln|\sec x - \tan x| + C$

95. 1   **97.** $1/(e - 1) \approx 0.582$

99. $P(t) = 1000(12 \ln|1 + 0.25t| + 1); P(3) \approx 7715$

101. About 4.15 min

103.

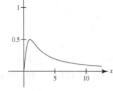

    (a) $A = \frac{1}{2} \ln 2 - \frac{1}{4}$

    (b) $0 < m < 1$

    (c) $A = \frac{1}{2}(m - \ln m - 1)$

105. False. $\frac{1}{2}\ln x = \ln x^{1/2}$ **107.** True   **109–111.** Proofs

Section 5.8   *(page 362)*

1. $\arcsin \dfrac{x}{3} + C$ **3.** $\arcsec|2x| + C$

5. $\arcsin(x + 1) + C$ **7.** $\frac{1}{2}\arcsin t^2 + C$

9. $\dfrac{1}{10} \arctan \dfrac{t^2}{5} + C$ **11.** $\dfrac{1}{4}\arctan(e^{2x}/2) + C$

13. $\arcsin\left(\dfrac{\tan x}{5}\right) + C$ **15.** $2 \arcsin\sqrt{x} + C$

17. $\frac{1}{2}\ln(x^2 + 1) - 3 \arctan x + C$

19. $8 \arcsin[(x - 3)/3] - \sqrt{6x - x^2} + C$ **21.** $\pi/6$

23. $\pi/6$ **25.** $\frac{1}{5}\arctan\frac{3}{5} \approx 0.108$

27. $\arctan 5 - \pi/4 \approx 0.588$ **29.** $\pi/4$ **31.** $\frac{1}{32}\pi^2 \approx 0.308$

33. $\pi/2$ **35.** $\ln|x^2 + 6x + 13| - 3 \arctan[(x + 3)/2] + C$

37. $\arcsin[(x + 2)/2] + C$ **39.** $4 - 2\sqrt{3} + \frac{1}{6}\pi \approx 1.059$

41. $\frac{1}{2}\arctan(x^2 + 1) + C$

43. $2\sqrt{e^t - 3} - 2\sqrt{3}\arctan\left(\sqrt{e^t - 3}/\sqrt{3}\right) + C$ **45.** $\pi/6$

47. a and b   **49.** a, b, and c

51. No. This integral does not correspond to any of the basic integration rules.

53. $y = \arcsin(x/2) + \pi$

55. (a)

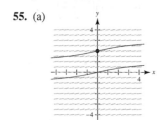

    (b) $y = \dfrac{2}{3}\arctan\dfrac{x}{3} + 2$

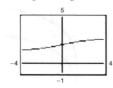

57.

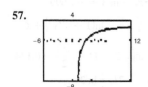

59.

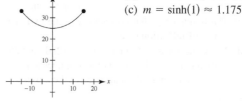

61. $\pi/3$ **63.** $\pi/8$ **65.** $3\pi/2$

67. (a)

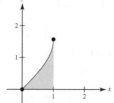

    (b) 0.5708

    (c) $(\pi - 2)/2$

69. (a) $F(x)$ represents the average value of $f(x)$ over the interval $[x, x + 2]$. Maximum at $x = -1$

    (b) Maximum at $x = -1$

71. False. $\displaystyle\int \dfrac{dx}{3x\sqrt{9x^2 - 16}} = \dfrac{1}{12}\arcsec\dfrac{|3x|}{4} + C$

73. True   **75–77.** Proofs

79. (a) $\displaystyle\int_0^1 \dfrac{1}{1 + x^2}\,dx$ (b) About 0.7847

    (c) Because $\displaystyle\int_0^1 \dfrac{1}{1 + x^2}\,dx = \dfrac{\pi}{4}$, you can use the Trapezoidal Rule to approximate $\dfrac{\pi}{4}$. Multiplying the result by 4 gives an estimation of π.

Section 5.9   *(page 372)*

1. (a) 10.018   (b) -0.964 **3.** (a) $\frac{4}{3}$ (b) $\frac{13}{12}$

5. (a) 1.317   (b) 0.962   **7–13.** Proofs

15. $\cosh x = \sqrt{13}/2$; $\tanh x = 3\sqrt{13}/13$; $\csch x = 2/3$; $\sech x = 2\sqrt{13}/13$; $\coth x = \sqrt{13}/3$

17. ∞ **19.** 0   **21.** 1   **23.** $3 \cosh 3x$

25. $-10x[\sech(5x^2)\tanh(5x^2)]$ **27.** $\coth x$ **29.** $\sinh^2 x$

31. $\sech t$ **33.** $y = -2x + 2$ **35.** $y = 1 - 2x$

37. Relative maxima: $(\pm\pi, \cosh\pi)$; Relative minimum: $(0, -1)$

39. Relative maximum: $(1.20, 0.66)$; Relative minimum: $(-1.20, -0.66)$

41. (a)

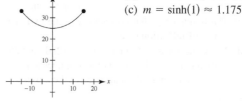

    (b) 33.146 units; 25 units

    (c) $m = \sinh(1) \approx 1.175$

43. $\frac{1}{2}\sinh 2x + C$ **45.** $-\frac{1}{2}\cosh(1 - 2x) + C$

47. $\frac{1}{3}\cosh^3(x - 1) + C$ **49.** $\ln|\sinh x| + C$

51. $-\coth(x^2/2) + C$ **53.** $\csch(1/x) + C$ **55.** $\ln(5/4)$

57. $\frac{1}{5}\ln 3$ **59.** $\pi/4$ **61.** Answers will vary.

63. $\cosh x$, $\sech x$ **65.** $\dfrac{3}{\sqrt{9x^2 - 1}}$ **67.** $\dfrac{1}{2\sqrt{x}(1 - x)}$

69. $|\sec x|$ **71.** $\dfrac{-2\,\csch^{-1} x}{|x|\sqrt{1 + x^2}}$ **73.** $2 \sinh^{-1}(2x)$

75. $\dfrac{\sqrt{3}}{18}\ln\left|\dfrac{1 + \sqrt{3}x}{1 - \sqrt{3}x}\right| + C$ **77.** $\ln\left(\sqrt{e^{2x} + 1} - 1\right) - x + C$

79. $2 \sinh^{-1}\sqrt{x} + C = 2 \ln\left(\sqrt{x} + \sqrt{1 + x}\right) + C$

81. $\dfrac{1}{4}\ln\left|\dfrac{x - 4}{x}\right| + C$ **83.** $\ln\left(\dfrac{3 + \sqrt{5}}{2}\right)$ **85.** $\dfrac{\ln 7}{12}$

87. $\dfrac{1}{4}\arcsin\left(\dfrac{4x - 1}{9}\right) + C$

89. $-\dfrac{x^2}{2} - 4x - \dfrac{10}{3}\ln\left|\dfrac{x-5}{x+1}\right| + C$

91. $8\arctan(e^2) - 2\pi \approx 5.207$ **93.** $\frac{5}{2}\ln\left(\sqrt{17} + 4\right) \approx 5.237$

95. $\frac{52}{31}$ kg   **97.** (a) $-\sqrt{a^2 - x^2}/x$ (b) Proof

99–107. Proofs   **109.** Putnam Problem 8, 1939

Review Exercises for Chapter 5   *(page 375)*

1. $\dfrac{4}{3}x^3 + \dfrac{1}{2}x^2 + 3x + C$ **3.** $\dfrac{x^2}{2} - \dfrac{4}{x^2} + C$

5. $5x - e^x + C$ **7.** $f(x) = 1 - 3x^2$

9. $f(x) = 4x^3 - 5x - 3$

11. (a) 3 sec; 144 ft   (b) $\frac{3}{2}$ sec   (c) 108 ft

13. 60   **15.** $\displaystyle\sum_{n=1}^{10}\dfrac{1}{3n}$ **17.** 420   **19.** 3310

21. $A = 15$ **23.** $A = 12$

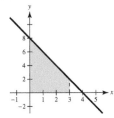   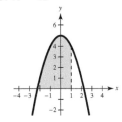

25. $\frac{27}{2}$

27.   **29.** (a) 17   (b) 7
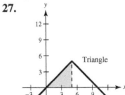   (c) 9   (d) 84

$A = \frac{25}{2}$

31. 56   **33.** $\frac{422}{5}$ **35.** $e^2 + 1$ **37.** 30

39. $2\ln 3 \approx 2.1972$ **41.** Average value $= \frac{2}{5}$; $x = \frac{25}{4}$

43. $x^2\sqrt{1 + x^3}$ **45.** $x^2 + 3x + 2$ **47.** $\frac{2}{3}\sqrt{x^3 + 3} + C$

49. $-\frac{1}{30}(1 - 3x^2)^5 + C = \frac{1}{30}(3x^2 - 1)^5 + C$

51. $\frac{1}{4}\sin^4 x + C$ **53.** $-2\sqrt{1 - \sin\theta} + C$

55. $-\dfrac{1}{6}e^{-3x^2} + C$ **57.** $\dfrac{1}{2\ln 5}(5^{(x+1)^2}) + C$

59. $\dfrac{1}{3\pi}(1 + \sec\pi x)^3 + C$

61. $\frac{455}{2}$ **63.** 2   **65.** $28\pi/15$ **67.** 2

69. Trapezoidal Rule: 0.285   **71.** Trapezoidal Rule: 3.432
Simpson's Rule: 0.284   Simpson's Rule: 3.414
Graphing Utility: 0.284   Graphing Utility: 3.406

73. $\frac{1}{7}\ln|7x - 2| + C$ **75.** $-\ln|1 + \cos x| + C$

77. $\frac{1}{2}\ln(e^{2x} + e^{-2x}) + C$ **79.** $3 + \ln 2$ **81.** $\ln\left(2 + \sqrt{3}\right)$

83. $\frac{1}{2}\arctan(e^{2x}) + C$ **85.** $\frac{1}{2}\arcsin x^2 + C$

87. $\frac{1}{4}[\arctan(x/2)]^2 + C$

89. $y' = -4\,\text{sech}(4x - 1)\tanh(4x - 1)$

91. $y' = \dfrac{4}{\sqrt{16x^2 + 1}}$ **93.** $\frac{1}{3}\tanh x^3 + C$

95. $\dfrac{1}{12}\ln\left|\dfrac{3 + 2x}{3 - 2x}\right| + C$

P.S. Problem Solving   *(page 377)*

1. (a) $L(1) = 0$ (b) $L'(x) = 1/x$, $L'(1) = 1$
(c) $x \approx 2.718$ (d) Proof

3. (a) Proof   (b) $\frac{1}{2}$ (c) $\frac{3}{2}$

5. (a) 1.6758; Error of approximation ≈ 0.0071
(b) $\frac{3}{2}$ (c) Proof

7–9. Proofs   **11.** $\displaystyle\lim_{n\to\infty}\sum_{t=1}^{n}\left(\dfrac{t}{n}\right)^5\left(\dfrac{1}{n}\right) = \dfrac{1}{6}$

13. (a)

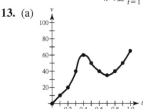

(b) $(0, 0.4)$ and $(0.7, 1.0)$ (c) $150\ \text{mi/h}^2$
(d) Total distance traveled in miles; 38.5 mi
(e) Sample answer: $100\ \text{mi/h}^2$

15. (a)–(c) Proofs   **17.** $2\ln\frac{3}{2} \approx 0.8109$

19. (a) (i)

(ii)

(iii)

(b) Pattern: $y_n = 1 + \dfrac{x}{1!} + \dfrac{x^2}{2!} + \cdots + \dfrac{x^n}{n!} + \cdots$

$y_4 = 1 + \dfrac{x}{1!} + \dfrac{x^2}{2!} + \dfrac{x^3}{3!} + \dfrac{x^4}{4!}$

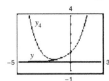

(c) The pattern implies that $e^x = 1 + \dfrac{x}{1!} + \dfrac{x^2}{2!} + \dfrac{x^3}{3!} + \cdots$

Index

A

Abel, Niels Henrik (1802–1829), 193
Absolute convergence, 622
Absolute maximum of a function, 202
  of two variables, 936
Absolute minimum of a function, 202
  of two variables, 936
Absolute value, 70, A12
  derivative involving, 157
  function, 22
  operations with, A12
  properties of inequalities and, A12
Absolute Value Theorem, 588
Absolute zero, 94
Absolutely convergent series, 622
Acceleration, 145, 833, 857
  centripetal component of, 846
  tangential and normal components of,
    845, 846, 859
  vector, 845, 859
Accumulation function, 319
Acute angle, A23
Addition of vectors, 750, 760
Additive Identity Property of Vectors, 751
Additive Interval Property, 307
Additive Inverse Property of Vectors, 751
Agnesi, Maria Gaetana (1718–1799), 238
d'Alembert, Jean Le Rond (1717–1783),
  890
Algebraic function(s), 24, 25, 177
  derivatives of, 159
Algebraic properties of the cross product,
  776
Alternating series, 619
  geometric, 619
  harmonic, 620, 622, 624
Alternating Series Remainder, 621
Alternating Series Test, 619
Alternative form
  of the derivative, 121
  of the directional derivative, 918
  of Green's Theorem, 1080
  of Log Rule for Integration, 348
  of Mean Value Theorem, 213
Amplitude of a function, A29
Angle, A23
  acute, A23
  between two nonzero vectors, 767
  between two planes, 785
  common
    cosine, A26
    sine, A26
    tangent, A26
  conversions between radians and
    degrees, A24
  coterminal, A23
  of incidence, 684
  of inclination of a plane, 931
  initial ray, A23
  obtuse, A23

  radian measure of, A24
  rainbow, 226
  reference, A27
  of reflection, 684
  standard position, A23
  terminal ray, A23
  vertex, A23
Angular speed, 999
Antiderivative, 280
  of f with respect to x, 281
  finding by integration by parts, 515
  general, 281
  notation for, 281
  representation of, 280
  of a vector-valued function, 828
Antidifferentiation, 281, 313
  of a composite function, 328
Aphelion, 694, 741
Apogee, 694
Approximating zeros
  bisection method, 98
  Intermediate Value Theorem, 97
  Newton's Method, 190
Approximation
  linear, 267, 902
  Padé, 200
  polynomial, 636
  Stirling's, 517
  tangent line, 267
  Two-Point Gaussian Quadrature, 377
Arc length, 466, 467, 852
  derivative of, 852
  parameter, 852, 853
  in parametric form, 709
  of a polar curve, 729
  of a space curve, 851
  in the xy-plane, 1003
Arccosecant function, 41
Arccosine function, 41
Arccotangent function, 41
Archimedes (287–212 B.C.), 292
  Principle, 506
  spiral of, 717, 733
Arcsecant function, 41
Arcsine function, 41
  series for, 670
Arctangent function, 41
  series for, 670
Area
  found by exhaustion method, 292
  line integral for, 1078
  of a parametric surface, 1088
  in polar coordinates, 725
  problem, 65, 66
  of a rectangle, 292
  of a region between two curves, 437
  of a region in the plane, 296
  of a surface of revolution, 471
    in parametric form, 710
    in polar coordinates, 730

  of the surface 1003
  in the xy-plane, 1003
Associative Property of Vector Addition,
  751
Astroid, 171
Astroidal sphere, 1093
Asymptote(s)
  horizontal, 236
  of a hyperbola, 689
  slant, 241, 248
  vertical, 105
Autonomous equations, 423
Average rate of change, 12
Average value of a function
  on an interval, 317
  over a region R, 982
  over a solid region Q, 1019
Average velocity, 133
Axis
  conjugate, of a hyperbola, 689
  major, of an ellipse, 685
  minor, of an ellipse, 685
  of a parabola, 683
  polar, 715
  of revolution, 446
  transverse, of a hyperbola, 689

B

Barrow, Isaac (1630–1677), 169
Base(s), 158
  of the natural exponential function, 158
  other than e
    derivatives for, 158
    exponential function, 158
    logarithmic function, 158
Basic differentiation rules for elementary
  functions, 177
Basic equation obtained in a partial
  fraction decomposition, 544
  guidelines for solving, 548
Basic integration rules, 282, 360, 508
  procedures for fitting integrands to, 511
Basic limits, 79
Basic types of transformations, 23
Bearing, 754
Bernoulli equation, 422
  general solution of, 422
Bernoulli, James (1654–1705), 702
Bernoulli, John (1667–1748), 542
Bessel function, 655
Between, A8
Bifolium, 171
Binomial series, 669
Binormal vector, 849, 866
Bisection method, 98
Bose-Einstein condensate, 94
Boundary point of a region, 880
Bounded
  above, 591

below, 591
intervals, A9
monotonic sequence, 591
region 936
sequence, 591
Brachistochrone problem, 702
Breteuil, Emilie de (1706–1749), 478
Bullet-nose curve, 161

C

Cantor set, 679
Capillary action, 1008
Cardioid, 720, 721
Carrying capacity, 399, 409
Cartesian plane, A16
    coordinates, A16
    ordered pair, A16
    origin, A16
    quadrants, A16
    x-axis, A16
    x-coordinate (abscissa), A16
    y-axis, A16
    y-coordinate (ordinate), A16
Catenary, 368
Cauchy, Augustin-Louis (1789–1857), 95
Cauchy-Riemann differential equations, 914
Cauchy-Schwarz Inequality, 774
Cavalieri's Theorem, 456
Center
    of a circle, A19
    of curvature, 856
    of an ellipse, 685
    of gravity, 488, 489
        of a one-dimensional system, 488
        of a two-dimensional system, 489
    of a hyperbola, 689
    of mass, 487, 488, 489
        of a one-dimensional system, 487, 488
        of a planar lamina, 490
            of variable density, 996
        of a solid region, 1014
        of a two-dimensional system, 489
    of a power series, 647
Centered at c, 636
Central force field, 1041
Centripetal component of acceleration, 846
Centripetal force, 850
Centroid, 491
    of a simple region, 996
Chain Rule, 150, 151, 159
    implicit differentiation, 912
    one independent variable, 907
    three or more independent variables, 910
    and trigonometric functions, 155
    two independent variables, 909
Change in x, 117
Change in y, 117
Change of variables, 331
    for definite integrals, 334
    for double integrals, 1029
    guidelines for making, 332

for homogeneous equations, 408
    to polar form, 988
    using a Jacobian, 1027
Charles, Jacques (1746–1823), 74
Charles's Law, 94
Circle, 171, 682, 721, A19
    center, A19
    equation of
        general form, A19
        standard form, A19
    radius, A19
    unit, A19, A24
Circle of curvature, 199, 856
Circulation of $\mathbf{F}$ around C_α, 1117
Circumscribed rectangle, 294
Cissoid, 171
    of Diocles, 746
Classification of conics by eccentricity, 734
Closed
    curve, 1070
    disk, 880
    interval, A9
        continuous on, 93
        differentiable on, 121
        guidelines for finding extrema on, 205
    region R, 880
    surface, 1106
Cobb-Douglas production function, 873
Coefficient, 24
    correlation, 31
    leading, 24
Collinear, 17
Combinations of functions, 25
Common first quadrant angles
    cosine, A26
    sine, A26
    tangent, A26
Common types of behavior associated with nonexistence of a limit, 71
Commutative Property
    of the dot product, 766
    of vector addition, 751
Comparison Test
    Direct, 612
    for improper integrals, 576
    Limit, 614
Competing-species equations, 426
Completeness, 97, 591
Completing the square, 359, A19
Component of acceleration
    centripetal, 846
    normal, 845, 846, 859
    tangential, 845, 846, 859
Component form of a vector in the plane, 749
Component functions, 816
Components of a vector, 770
    along $\mathbf{v}$, 770
    in the direction of $\mathbf{v}$, 771
    orthogonal to $\mathbf{v}$, 770
    in the plane, 749
Composite function, 25
    antidifferentiation of, 328

continuity of, 75
    derivative of, 150
    limit of, 81
    of two variables, 869
        continuity of, 885
Composition of functions, 25, 869
Computer graphics, 874
Concave downward, 227
Concave upward, 227
Concavity, 227
    test for, 228
Conditional convergence, 622
Conditionally convergent series, 622
Conic(s), 682
    circle, 682
    classification by eccentricity, 734
    degenerate, 682
    directrix of, 734
    eccentricity, 734
    ellipse, 682, 685
    focus of, 734
    hyperbola, 682, 689
    parabola, 682, 683
    polar equations of, 735
Conic section, 682
Conjugate axis of a hyperbola, 689
Connected region, 1068
Conservative vector field, 1043, 1065
    independence of path, 1068
    test for, 1044, 1047
Constant
    Euler's, 611
    force, 477
    function, 24
    gravitational, 479
    of integration, 281
    Multiple Rule, 129, 159
        differential form, 270
    proportionality, 390
    Rule, 126, 159
    spring, 34
    term of a polynomial function, 24
Constraint, 952
Continued fraction expansion, 679
Continuity
    on a closed interval, 93
    of a composite function, 95
        of two variables, 885
    differentiability implies, 122
    and differentiability of inverse functions, 174
    implies integrability, 304
    properties of, 95
    of a vector-valued function, 820
Continuous, 90
    at c, 79, 90
    on the closed interval $[a, b]$, 93
    everywhere, 90
    function of two variables, 884
    on an interval, 820
    from the left and from the right, 93
    on an open interval (a, b), 90
    in the open region R, 884, 886
    at a point, 820, 884, 886

vector field, 1040
Continuously differentiable, 466
Contour lines, 871
Converge, 192, 585, 595
Convergence
  absolute, 622
  conditional, 622
  endpoint, 650
  of a geometric series, 597
  of improper integral with infinite
      discontinuities, 571
  integration limits, 568
  interval of, 648, 652
  of Newton's Method, 192, 193
  of a power series, 648
  of p-series, 607
  radius of, 648, 652
  of a sequence, 585
  of a series, 595
  of Taylor series, 666
  tests for series
    Alternating Series Test, 619
    Direct Comparison Test, 612
    geometric series, 597
    guidelines, 631
    Integral Test, 605
    Limit Comparison Test, 614
    p-series, 607
    Ratio Test, 627
    Root Test, 630
    summary, 632
Convergent power series, form of, 664
Convergent series, limit of nth term of, 599
Conversions between degrees and
  radians, A24
Convex limaçon, 721
Coordinate conversion
  cylindrical to rectangular, 804
  cylindrical to spherical, 807
  polar to rectangular, 716
  rectangular to cylindrical, 804
  rectangular to polar, 716
  rectangular to spherical, 807
  spherical to cylindrical, 807
  spherical to rectangular, 807
Coordinate planes, 758
  xy-plane, 758
  xz-plane, 758
  yz-plane, 758
Coordinate of a point on the real number
  line, A7
Coordinate system
  cylindrical, 804
  polar, 715
  rectangular, A16
  spherical, 807
  three-dimensional, 758
Coordinates, A16
  x-coordinate (abscissa), A16
  y-coordinate (ordinate), A16
Coordinates, polar, 715
  area in, 725
  area of a surface of revolution in, 730
  converting to rectangular, 716

Distance Formula in, 722
Coordinates, rectangular, converting to
  polar, 716
Copernicus, Nicolaus (1473–1543), 685
Cornu spiral, 745, 865
Correlation coefficient, 31
Cosecant function, A25
  derivative of, 143, 155, 159
  graph of, A29
  integral of, 353
  inverse of, 41
    derivative of, 176
Cosine function, 22, A25
  derivative of, 131, 155, 159
  graph of, A29
  integral of, 353
  inverse of, 41
    derivative of, 176
  series for, 670
Cotangent function, A25
  derivative of, 143, 155, 159
  graph of, A29
  integral of, 353
  inverse of, 41
    derivative of, 176
Coterminal angles, A23
Coulomb's Law, 479, 1041
Critical number(s)
  of a function, 204
  relative extrema occur only at, 204
Critical point(s)
  of a function of two variables, 937
  of predator-prey equations, 424
  relative extrema occur only at, 937
Cross product of two vectors in space, 775
  algebraic properties of, 776
  determinant form, 775
  geometric properties of, 777
  torque, 779
Cruciform, 171
Cubic function, 24
Cubing function, 22
Curl of a vector field, 1046
  and divergence, 1048
Curtate cycloid, 704
Curvature, 854
  center of, 856
  circle of, 199, 856
  formulas for, 855, 859
  radius of, 856
  in rectangular coordinates, 856, 859
  related to acceleration and speed, 857
Curve
  astroid, 171
  bifolium, 171
  bullet-nose, 161
  cissoid, 171
  closed, 1070
  cruciform, 171
  eight, 199
  equipotential, 400
  folium of Descartes, 171, 733
  isothermal, 400
  kappa, 169, 172

  lateral surface area over, 1063
  lemniscate, 60, 168, 172, 721
  level, 871
  logistic, 410, 550
  natural equation for, 865
  orientation of, 1051
  piecewise smooth, 701, 1051
  plane, 696, 816
  pursuit, 370
  rectifiable, 466
  rose, 718, 721
  simple, 1075
  smooth, 466, 701, 826, 841, 1051
    piecewise, 701, 1051
  solution, 381
  space, 816
  tangent line to, 842
  velocity potential, 400
Curve sketching, summary of, 246
Cusps, 826
Cycloid, 701, 705
  curtate, 704
  prolate, 708
Cylinder, 794
  directrix of, 794
  equations of, 794
  generating curve of, 794
  right, 794
  rulings of, 794
Cylindrical coordinate system, 804
  pole of, 804
Cylindrical coordinates
  converting to rectangular, 804
  converting to spherical, 807
Cylindrical surface, 794

D

Darboux's Theorem, 278
Decay model, exponential, 390
Decomposition of $N(x)/D(x)$ into partial
  fractions, 543
Decreasing function, 217
  test for, 217
Definite integral(s), 304, 313
  approximating
    Midpoint Rule, 298
    Simpson's Rule, 344
    Trapezoidal Rule, 342
  as the area of a region, 305
  change of variables, 334
  evaluation of a line integral as a, 1053
  properties of, 308
  two special, 307
  of a vector-valued function, 828
Degenerate conic, 682
  line, 682
  point, 682
  two intersecting lines, 682
Degree of a polynomial function, 24
Delta, δ, δ-neighborhood, 880
Demand, 18
Density, 490
Density function ρ, 994, 1014

Dependent variable, 19
of a function of two variables, 868
Derivative(s)
of algebraic functions, 159
alternative form, 121
of arc length function, 852
for bases other than e, 158
Chain Rule, 150, 151, 159
implicit differentiation, 912
one independent variable, 907
three or more independent
variables, 910
two independent variables, 909
of a composite function, 150
Constant Multiple Rule, 129, 159
Constant Rule, 126, 159
of cosecant function, 143, 159
of cosine function, 131, 159
of cotangent function, 143, 159
Difference Rule, 130, 159
directional, 915, 916, 923
of an exponential function, base a, 159
of a function, 119
General Power Rule, 152, 159
higher-order, 145
of hyperbolic functions, 367
implicit, 165
of an inverse function, 174
of inverse trigonometric functions, 176
involving absolute value, 157
from the left and from the right, 121
of a logarithmic function, base a, 159
of the natural exponential function, 132
of the natural logarithmic function, 156
notation, 119
parametric form, 706
partial, 890
Power Rule, 127, 159
Product Rule, 139, 159
Quotient Rule, 141, 159
of secant function, 143, 159
second, 145
Simple Power Rule, 159
simplifying, 154
of sine function, 131, 159
Sum Rule, 130, 159
of tangent function, 143, 159
third, 145
of trigonometric functions, 143, 159
of a vector-valued function, 824
higher-order, 825
properties of, 826
Descartes, René (1596–1650), 2
Determinant form of cross product, 775
Difference quotient, 20, 117
Difference Rule, 130
differential form, 270
Difference of two functions, 25
Difference of two vectors, 750
Differentiability
implies continuity, 122, 903
and continuity of inverse functions, 174
sufficient condition for, 901
Differentiable at x, 119

Differentiable, continuously, 466
Differentiable function
on the closed interval $[a, b]$, 121
on an open interval (a, b), 119
in a region R, 901
of three variables, 902
of two variables, 901
vector-valued, 824
Differential, 268
as an approximation, 902
function of three or more variables, 900
function of three variables, 902
function of two variables, 900
of x, 268
of y, 268
Differential equation, 281, 380
Bernoulli equation, 422
Cauchy-Riemann, 914
doomsday, 433
Euler's Method, 384
modified, 433
first-order linear, 416
general solution of, 281, 380
Gompertz, 403
homogeneous, 408
change of variables, 408
initial condition, 285, 381
integrating factor, 416
logistic, 277, 409
order of, 380
particular solution of, 285
separable, 397
separation of variables, 389, 397
singular solution of, 380
solution of, 380
Differential form, 270
of a line integral, 1059
Differential formulas, 270
constant multiple, 270
product, 270
quotient, 270
sum or difference, 270
Differential operator, 1046, 1048
Laplacian, 1123
Differentiation, 119
Applied minimum and maximum
problems, guidelines for solving,
257
basic rules for elementary functions, 177
implicit, 165
Chain Rule, 912
guidelines for, 166
involving inverse hyperbolic functions,
371
logarithmic, 170
numerical, 122
partial, 890
of power series, 652
of a vector-valued function, 824
Differentiation rules
basic, 177
Chain, 150, 151, 159
Constant, 126, 159
Constant Multiple, 126, 159

cosecant function, 143, 159
cosine function, 131, 159
cotangent function, 143, 159
Difference, 130, 159
general, 159
General Power, 152, 159
Power, 127, 159
Product, 139, 159
Quotient, 141, 159
secant function, 143, 159
Simple Power, 159
sine function, 131, 159
Sum, 130, 159
summary of, 159
tangent function, 143, 159
Diminishing returns, point of, 265
Dimpled limaçon, 721
Direct Comparison Test, 612
Direct substitution, 79, 80
Directed distance, 489, A13
Directed line segment, 748
equivalent, 748
initial point of, 748
length of, 748
magnitude of, 748
terminal point of, 748
Direction angles of a vector, 769
Direction cosines of a vector, 769
Direction field, 287, 382
Direction of motion, 832
Direction numbers, 783
Direction vector, 783
Directional derivative, 915, 916
alternative form of, 918
of f in the direction of $\mathbf{u}$, 916, 923
of a function in three variables, 923
Directrix
of a conic, 734
of a cylinder, 794
of a parabola, 683
Dirichlet, Peter Gustav (1805–1859), 71
Dirichlet function, 71
Discontinuity, 91
infinite, 568
nonremovable, 91
removable, 91
Disjoint sets, A8
Disk, 446, 880
closed, 880
method, 447
compared to shell, 459
open, 880
Displacement of a particle, 322, 323
Distance
between a point and a line in space, 789
between a point and a plane, 788
between two points on the real number
line, A13
directed, 489, A13
total, traveled on $[a, b]$, 323
Distance Formula, A17
in polar coordinates, 722
in space, 759
Distributive Property

for the dot product, 766
for vectors, 751
Diverge, 585, 595
Divergence
of improper integral with infinite
discontinuities, 571
integration limits, 568
of a sequence, 585
of a series, 595
tests for series
Direct Comparison Test, 612
geometric series, 597
guidelines, 631
Integral Test, 605
Limit Comparison Test, 614
nth-Term Test, 599
p-series, 607
Ratio Test, 627
Root Test, 630
summary, 632
of a vector field, 1048
and curl, 1048
Divergence Theorem, 1080, 1106
Divergence-free vector field, 1048
Divide out like factors, 83
Domain
feasible, 256
of a function, 19
explicitly defined, 19
of two variables, 868
implied, 19
of a power series, 648
of a vector-valued function, 817
Doomsday equation, 433
Dot product
Commutative Property of, 766
Distributive Property for, 766
form of work, 772
projection using the, 771
properties of, 766
of two vectors, 766
Double integral, 974, 975, 976
change of variables for, 1029
of over R, 976
properties of, 976
Double-angle formulas, A25
Doyle Log Rule, 878
Dummy variable, 306
Dyne, 477

E

e, the number, 50
Eccentricity, 734
classification of conics by, 734
of an ellipse, 687
of a hyperbola, 690
Eight curve, 199
Electric force field, 1041
Elementary function(s), 24, 177
basic differentiation rules for, 177
polynomial approximation of, 636
power series for, 670
Eliminating the parameter, 698

Ellipse, 682, 685
center of, 685
eccentricity of, 687
foci of, 685
major axis of, 685
minor axis of, 685
reflective property of, 687
rotated, 171
standard equation of, 685
vertices of, 685
Ellipsoid, 795, 796
Elliptic cone, 795, 797
Elliptic integral, 347
Elliptic paraboloid, 795, 797
Endpoint convergence, 650
Endpoint extrema, 202
Endpoints of an interval, A9
Energy
kinetic, 1071
potential, 1071
Epicycloid, 704, 705, 709
Epsilon-delta, ε-δ, definition of limit, 72
Equal vectors, 749, 760
Equality of mixed partial derivatives, 895
Equation(s)
autonomous, 423
basic, 544
guidelines for solving, 548
Bernoulli, 422
competing-series, 426
of conics, polar, 735
of a cylinder, 794
differential, 281, 380
logistic, 409
doomsday, 433
of an ellipse, 685
general second-degree, 682
Gompertz, 403
graph of, 2
harmonic, 1123
of a hyperbola, 689
Laplace's, 1123
of a line
general form, 14
horizontal, 14
point-slope form, 11, 14
slope-intercept form, 13, 14
in space, parametric, 783
in space, symmetric, 783
summary, 14
vertical, 14
Lotka-Volterra, 423
of a parabola, 683
parametric, 696, 1084
finding, 700
graph of, 696
of a plane in space
general form, 784
standard form, 784
predator-prey, 423
primary, 256, 257
related-rate, 181
secondary, 257
separable, 397

solution point of, 2
of tangent plane, 928
Equilibrium, 487
points, of predator-prey equations, 424
Equipotential
curves, 400
lines, 871
Equivalent
conditions, 1070
directed line segments, 748
inequalities, A10
Error
in approximating a Taylor polynomial,
642
in measurement, 269
percent error, 269
propagated error, 269
relative error, 269
in Simpson's Rule, 345
in Trapezoidal Rule, 345
Escape velocity, 114
Euler, Leonhard (1707–1783), 24
Euler's
constant, 611
Method, 384
modified, 433
Evaluate a function, 19
Evaluating
a flux integral, 1100
a surface integral, 1094
Evaluation
by iterated integrals, 1010
of a line integral as a definite integral,
1053
Even function, 26
integration of, 336
test for, 26
Even/odd identities, A25
Everywhere continuous, 90
Existence
of an inverse function, 39
of a limit, 93
theorem, 97, 202
Expanded about c, approximating
polynomial, 636
Explicit form of a function, 19, 165
Explicitly defined domain, 21
Exponential decay, 390
Exponential function, 24, 48
to base a, 158
derivative of, 159
natural, derivative of, 132
notation, 37
properties of, 49
series for, 670
Exponential growth and decay model, 390
initial value, 390
proportionality constant, 390
Exponents, properties of, 48
Extended Mean Value Theorem, 277, 558
Extrema
endpoint, 202
of a function, 202, 936
guidelines for finding, 205

relative, 203
Extreme Value Theorem, 202, 936
Extreme values of a function, 202

F

Factorial, 587
Fails to exist, 103
Family of functions, 304
Famous curves
    astroid, 171
    bifolium, 171
    bullet-nose curve, 161
    circle, 171, 682, 721
    cissoid, 171
    cruciform, 171
    eight curve, 199
    folium of Descartes, 171, 733
    kappa curve, 169, 172
    lemniscate, 60, 168, 172, 721
    parabola, 2, 171, 682, 683
    pear-shaped quartic, 199
    rotated ellipse, 171
    rotated hyperbola, 171
    serpentine, 147
    top half of circle, 161
    witch of Agnesi, 147, 171, 238, 823
Faraday, Michael (1791–1867), 1071
Feasible domain, 256
Fermat, Pierre de (1601–1665), 204
Fibonacci sequence, 594, 604
Field
    central force, 1041
    direction, 287, 382
    electric force, 1041
    force, 1040
    gravitational, 1041
    inverse square, 1041
    slope, 287, 382
    vector, 1040
        over a plane region R, 1040
        over a solid region Q, 1040
    velocity, 1040, 1041
Finite Fourier series, 532
First Derivative Test, 219
First moments, 998, 1014
First partial derivatives, 890
    notation for, 891
First-order differential equations
    linear, 416
        integrating factor, 416
        solution of, 417
        standard form, 416
Fitting integrands to basic rules, 511
Fixed plane, 862
Fixed point, 194
Fluid(s)
    force, 498
    pressure, 497
    weight-densities of, 497
Flux integral, 1100
    evaluating, 1100
Focal chord of a parabola, 683
Focus

of a conic, 734
of an ellipse, 685
of a hyperbola, 689
of a parabola, 683
Folium of Descartes, 171, 733
Force, 477
    constant, 477
    exerted by a fluid, 498
    of friction, 858
    resultant, 754
    variable, 478
Force field, 1040
    central, 1041
    electric, 1041
    work, 1056
Form of a convergent power series, 664
Formula(s)
    for curvature, 855, 859
    Distance, A17
        in polar coordinates, 722
        in space, 759
    double-angle, A25
    Midpoint, A18
    power-reducing, A25
    sum and difference, A25
    summation, 291
Fourier, Joseph (1768–1830), 657
Fourier series, finite, 532
Fourier Sine Series, 523
Fraction expansion, continued, 679
Fractions, partial, 542
    decomposition of $N(x)/D(x)$, into, 543
    method of, 542
Frenet-Serret formulas, 866
Fresnel function, 377
Friction, 858
Fubini's Theorem, 978
    for a triple integral, 1010
Function(s), 6, 19
    absolute maximum of, 202
    absolute minimum of, 202
    absolute value, 22
    acceleration, 145
    accumulation, 319
    addition of, 25
    algebraic, 24, 25, 177
    amplitude of, A29
    antiderivative of, 280
    arc length, 466, 467, 852
    arccosecant, 41
    arccosine, 41
    arccotangent, 41
    arcsecant, 41
    arcsine, 41
    arctangent, 41
    average value of, 317, 982
    Bessel, 655
    Cobb-Douglas production, 873
    combinations of, 25
    component, 816
    composite, 25, 869
    composition of, 25, 869
    concave downward, 227
    concave upward, 227

constant, 24
continuous, 90
continuously differentiable, 466
cosecant, A25
cosine, 22, A25
cotangent, A25
critical number of, 204
cubic, 24
cubing, 22
decreasing, 217
    test for, 217
defined by power series, properties of,
    652
density, 994, 1014
derivative of, 119
difference of, 25
differentiable, 119
Dirichlet, 71
domain of, 19
elementary, 24, 177
    algebraic, 24, 25
    exponential, 24
    logarithmic, 24
    trigonometric, 24
evaluate, 19
even, 26
explicit form, 19, 165
exponential to base a, 24, 48, 158
extrema of, 202
extreme values of, 202
family of, 304
feasible domain of, 256
Fresnel, 377
Gamma, 566, 578
global maximum of, 202
global minimum of, 202
graph of, guidelines for analyzing, 246
greatest integer, 92
Heaviside, 59
homogeneous, 408, 913
hyperbolic, 365
identity, 22
implicit form, 19
implicitly defined, 165
increasing, 217
    test for, 217
inner product of two, 532
integrable, 268
inverse, 37
inverse hyperbolic, 369
inverse trigonometric, 41
involving a radical, limit of, 80
jerk, 200
limit of, 65, 68
linear, 24
local extrema of, 203
local maximum of, 203
local minimum of, 203
logarithmic, 24
    to base a, 158
logistic, 239, 249
natural logarithmic, 51
normal probability density, 228
notation, 19

odd, 26
one-to-one, 21
onto, 21
orthogonal, 532
period of, A29
periodic, A29
point of inflection, 229, 230
polynomial, 24, 869
position, 32, 133, 837
potential, 1043
product of, 25
pulse, 114
quadratic, 24
quotient of, 25
radius, 800
range of, 19
rational, 22, 25, 869
real-valued, 19
relative extrema of, 203, 936
relative maximum of, 203, 936
relative minimum of, 203, 936
representation by power series, 657
Riemann zeta, 611
secant, A25
signum, 102
sine, 22, A25
square root, 22
squaring, 22
step, 92
strictly monotonic, 218
sum of, 25
tangent, A25
that agree at all but one point, 82
of three variables
    continuity of, 886
    directional derivative of, 923
    gradient of, 923
transcendental, 25, 177
transformation of a graph of, 23
    horizontal shift, 23
    reflection about origin, 23
    reflection about x-axis, 23
    reflection about y-axis, 23
    reflection in the line $y = x$, 38
    vertical shift, 23
trigonometric, 24, A25
    period of, A29
of two variables, 868
    absolute maximum of, 936
    absolute minimum of, 936
    continuity of, 884
    critical point of, 937
    dependent variable, 868
    differentiability implies continuity,
        903
    differentiable, 901
    differential of, 900
    domain of, 868
    gradient of, 918
    graph of, 870
    independent variables, 868
    limit of, 881
    maximum of, 936
    minimum of, 936

nonremovable discontinuity of, 884
    partial derivative of, 890
    range of, 868
    relative extrema of, 936
    relative maximum of, 936, 939
    relative minimum of, 936, 939
    removable discontinuity of, 884
    total differential of, 900
unit pulse, 114
vector-valued, 816
Vertical Line Test, 22
of x and y, 868
zero of, 26
    approximating with Newton's
        Method, 190
Fundamental Theorem
    of Algebra, 1106
    of Calculus, 313, 314
        guidelines for using, 314
        Second, 320
    of Line Integrals, 1065, 1066

G

Gabriel's Horn, 574, 1086
Galilei, Galileo (1564–1642), 177
Galois, Evariste (1811–1832), 193
Gamma Function, 566, 578
Gauss, Carl Friedrich (1777–1855), 291,
    1106
Gaussian Quadrature Approximation,
    two-point, 377
Gauss's Law, 1103
Gauss's Theorem, 1106
General antiderivative, 281
General differentiation rules, 159
General form
    of the equation of a circle, A19
    of the equation of a line, 14
    of the equation of a plane in space, 784
    of the equation of a quadric surface, 795
    of a second-degree equation, 682
General harmonic series, 607
General partition, 303
General Power Rule
    for differentiation, 152, 159
    for Integration, 333
General second-degree equation, 682
General solution
    of the Bernoulli equation, 422
    of a differential equation, 281, 380
Generating curve of a cylinder, 794
Geometric power series, 657
Geometric properties of the cross product,
    777
Geometric property of triple scalar
    product, 780
Geometric series, 597
    alternating, 619
    convergence of, 597
    divergence of, 597
Gibbs, Josiah Willard (1839–1903), 1051
Global maximum of a function, 202
Global minimum of a function, 202

Golden ratio, 594
Gompertz growth model, 403
Grad, 918
Gradient, 1040, 1043
    of a function of three variables, 923
    of a function of two variables, 918
    normal to level curves, 921
    normal to level surfaces, 832
    properties of, 919
    recovering a function from, 1047
Graph(s)
    of absolute value function, 22
    of cosecant function, A29
    of cosine function, 22, A29
    of cotangent function, A29
    of cubing function, 22
    of an equation, 2
    of a function
        guidelines for analyzing, 246
        transformation of, 23
        of two variables, 870
    of hyperbolic functions, 366
    of identity function, 22
    intercept of, 4
    of inverse hyperbolic functions, 370
    of inverse trigonometric functions, 42
    orthogonal, 172
    of parametric equations, 696
    point of inflection, 229, 230
    polar, 717
        points of intersection, 727
        special polar graphs, 721
    of rational function, 22
    of secant function, A29
    of sine function, 22, A29
    of square root function, 22
    of squaring function, 22
    symmetry of, 5
    of tangent function, A29
Gravitational
    constant, 479
    field, 1041
Greater than, A8
    or equal to, A8
Greatest integer function, 92
Green, George (1793–1841), 1076
Green's Theorem, 1075
    alternative forms of, 1080
Gregory, James (1638–1675), 652
Growth model
    exponential, 390
    Gompertz, 403
Guidelines
    for analyzing the graph of a function,
        246
    for evaluating integrals involving
        secant and tangent, 527
    for evaluating integrals involving sine
        and cosine, 524
    for finding extrema on a closed interval,
        205
    for finding intervals on which a function
        is increasing or decreasing, 218
    for finding an inverse function, 39

for finding limits at infinity of rational functions, 238
for finding a Taylor series, 668
for implicit differentiation, 166
for integration, 351
for integration by parts, 515
for making a change of variables, 332
for solving applied minimum and maximum problems, 257
for solving the basic equation, 548
for solving related-rate problems, 182
for testing a series for convergence or divergence, 631
for using the Fundamental Theorem of Calculus, 314
Gyration, radius of, 999

H

Half-life, 391
Hamilton, William Rowan (1805–1865), 750
Harmonic equation, 1123
Harmonic series, 607
    alternating, 620, 622, 624
Heat flow, 1103
Heat flux, 1103
Heaviside, Oliver (1850–1925), 59
Heaviside function, 59
Helix, 817
Heron's Formula, 963
Herschel, Caroline (1750–1848), 691
Higher-order derivative, 145
    of a vector-valued function, 825
    partial, 894
Homogeneous of degree n, 408, 913
Homogeneous differential equation, 408
    change of variables for, 408
Homogeneous function, 408, 913
Hooke's Law, 479
Horizontal asymptote, 236
Horizontal component of a vector, 753
Horizontal line, 14
Horizontal Line Test, 39
Horizontal shift of a graph of a function, 23
Horizontally simple region of integration, 968
Huygens, Christian (1629–1795), 466
Hypatia (370–415 A.D.), 682
Hyperbola, 682, 689
    asymptotes of, 689
    center of, 689
    conjugate axis of, 689
    eccentricity of, 690
    foci of, 689
    rotated, 171
    standard equation of, 689
    transverse axis of, 689
    vertices of, 689
Hyperbolic functions, 365
    derivatives of, 367
    graphs of, 366
    identities, 366

integrals of, 367
inverse, 369
    differentiation involving, 371
    graphs of, 370
    integration involving, 371
Hyperbolic identities, 366
Hyperbolic paraboloid, 795, 797
Hyperboloid
    of one sheet, 795, 796
    of two sheets, 795, 796
Hypocycloid, 705

I

Identities, hyperbolic, 366
Identity function, 22
If and only if, 14
Image of x under f, 19
Implicit derivative, 166
Implicit differentiation, 165, 912
    Chain Rule, 912
    guidelines for, 166
Implicit form of a function, 19
Implicitly defined function, 165
Implied domain, 21
Improper integral, 568
    comparison test for, 576
    with infinite discontinuities, 571
        convergence of, 571
        divergence of, 571
    with infinite integration limits, 568
        convergence of, 568
        divergence of, 568
    special type, 574
Incidence, angle of, 684
Inclination of a plane, angle of, 931
Incompressible, 1048, 1111
Increasing function, 217
    test for, 217
Increment of z, 900
Increments of x and y, 900
Indefinite integral, 281
    pattern recognition, 328
    of a vector-valued function, 828
Indefinite integration, 281
Independence of path and conservative vector fields, 1068
Independent of path, 1068
Independent variable, 19
    of a function of two variables, 868
Indeterminate form, 83, 106, 237, 557, 560
Index of summation, 290
Inductive reasoning, 589
Inequality, A8
    Cauchy-Schwarz, 774
    equivalent, A10
    linear, A11
    Napier's, 356
    preservation of, 308
    properties, A8
    reverse the, A8
    satisfied, A10
    solution, A10
        set, A10

triangle, 753, A12
Inertia, moment of, 998, 1014
    polar, 998
Infinite discontinuities, 568
    improper integrals with, 571
        convergence of, 571
        divergence of, 571
Infinite integration limits, 568
    improper integrals with, 568
        convergence of, 568
        divergence of, 568
Infinite interval, 235
Infinite limit(s), 103
    at infinity, 241
    from the left and from the right, 103
    properties of, 107
Infinite series (or series), 595
    absolutely convergent, 622
    alternating, 619
        geometric, 619
        harmonic, 620, 622
        remainder, 621
    conditionally convergent, 622
    convergence of, 595
    convergent, limit of nth term, 599
    divergence of, 595
        nth term test for, 599
    geometric, 597
    guidelines for testing for convergence or divergence of, 631
    harmonic, 607
        alternating, 620, 622, 624
    nth partial sum, 595
    properties of, 599
    p-series, 607
    rearrangement of, 624
    sum of, 595
    telescoping, 596
    terms of, 595
Infinity
    infinite limit at, 241
    limit at, 235, 236
Inflection point, 229, 230
Initial condition(s), 285, 381
Initial point, directed line segment, 748
Initial ray of an angle, A23
Initial value, 390
Inner partition, 974, 1009
    polar, 987
Inner product
    of two functions, 532
    of two vectors, 766
Inner radius of a solid of revolution, 449
Inscribed rectangle, 294
Inside limits of integration, 967
Instantaneous rate of change, 12, 119
Instantaneous velocity, 134
Integrability and continuity, 304
Integrable function, 304, 976
Integral(s)
    definite, 304
        properties of, 308
        two special, 307
    double, 974, 975, 976

elliptic, 347
flux, 1100
of hyperbolic functions, 367
improper, 568
indefinite, 281
involving inverse trigonometric
    functions, 357
involving secant and tangent,
    guidelines for evaluating, 527
involving sine and cosine, guidelines
    for evaluating, 524
iterated, 967
line, 1052
Mean Value Theorem, 316
of $p(x) = Ax^2 + Bx + C$, 343
single, 976
of the six basic trigonometric functions,
    353
surface, 1094
trigonometric, 524
triple, 1009
Integral Test, 605
Integrand(s), procedures for fitting to
    basic rules, 511
Integrating factor, 416
Integration
    as an accumulation process, 441
    Additive Interval Property, 307
    basic rules of, 282, 360
    change of variables, 331
        guidelines for, 332
    constant of, 281
    of even and odd functions, 336
    guidelines for, 351
    indefinite, 281
        pattern recognition, 328
    involving inverse hyperbolic functions,
        371
    Log Rule, 348
    lower limit of, 304
    of power series, 652
    preservation of inequality, 308
    region R of, 967
    upper limit of, 304
    of a vector-valued function, 828
Integration by parts, 515
    guidelines for, 515
    summary of common integrals using,
        520
    tabular method, 520
Integration by tables, 551
Integration formulas
    reduction formulas, 553
    special, 537
    summary of, 1118
Integration rules
    basic, 282, 360, 508
    General Power Rule, 333
    Power Rule, 282
Integration techniques
    basic integration rules, 282, 360, 508
    integration by parts, 515
    method of partial fractions, 542
    substitution for rational functions of

sine and cosine, 554
tables, 551
trigonometric substitution, 533
Intercept(s), 4
    x-intercept, 4
    y-intercept, 4
Interior point of a region R, 880, 886
Intermediate Value Theorem, 97
Interpretation of concavity, 227
Intersection of two sets, A8
Interval(s), A9
    bounded, A9
    closed, A9
    of convergence, 648
    endpoints of, A9
    infinite, 235
    midpoint of, A13
    open, A9
    on the real number line, A9
    test, A11
    unbounded, A9
Inverse function, 37
    continuity and differentiability of, 174
    derivative of, 174
    existence of, 39
    guidelines for finding, 39
    Horizontal Line Test, 39
    reflective property of, 38
Inverse hyperbolic functions, 369
    differentiation involving, 371
    graphs of, 370
    integration involving, 371
Inverse square field, 1041
Inverse trigonometric functions, 41
    derivatives of, 176
    graphs of, 42
    integrals involving, 357
    properties of, 43
Irrational number, A7
Irrotational vector field, 1046
Isobars, 871
Isothermal curves, 400
Isothermal surface, 874
Isotherms, 871
Iterated integral, 967
    evaluation by, 1010
    inside limits of integration, 967
    outside limits of integration, 967
Iteration, 190
ith term of a sum, 290

J

Jacobi, Carl Gustav (1804–1851), 1027
Jacobian, 1027
Jerk function, 200

K

Kappa curve, 169, 172
Kepler, Johannes, (1571–1630), 737
Kepler's Laws, 737
Kinetic energy, 1071
Kirchhoff's Second Law, 418

Kovalevsky, Sonya (1850–1891), 880

L

Lagrange, Joseph-Louis (1736–1813),
    212, 952
Lagrange form of the remainder, 642
Lagrange multiplier, 952, 953
Lagrange's Theorem, 953
Lambert, Johann Heinrich (1728–1777),
    365
Lamina, planar, 490
Laplace, Pierre Simon de (1749–1827),
    1020
Laplace Transform, 578
Laplace's equation, 1123
Laplacian, 1123
Lateral surface area over a curve, 1063
Latus rectum, of a parabola, 683
Law of Conservation of Energy, 1071
Law of Cosines, A25
Leading coefficient
    of a polynomial function, 24
    test, 24
Least squares
    method of, 946
    regression, 7
    line, 946, 947
Least upper bound, 591
Left-hand limit, 92
Left-handed orientation, 758
Legendre, Adrien-Marie (1752–1833), 947
Leibniz, Gottfried Wilhelm (1646–1716),
    270
Leibniz notation, 270
Lemniscate, 60, 168, 172, 721
Length
    of an arc, 466, 467
        parametric form, 709
        polar form, 729
    of a directed line segment, 748
    of the moment arm, 487
    of a scalar multiple, 752
    of a vector in the plane, 749
    of a vector in space, 760
    on x-axis, 1003
Less than, A8
    or equal to, A8
Level curve, 871
    gradient is normal to, 921
Level surface, 873
    gradient is normal to, 932
L'Hôpital, Guillaume (1661–1704), 558
L'Hôpital's Rule, 558
Limaçon, 721
    convex, 721
    dimpled, 721
    with inner loop, 721
Limit(s), 65, 68
    basic, 79
    of a composite function, 81
    definition of, 72
    ε-δ definition of, 72
    evaluating

direct substitution, 79, 80
   divide out like factors, 83
   rationalize the numerator, 83, 84
existence of, 93
fails to exist, 103
of a function involving a radical, 80
of a function of two variables, 881
indeterminate form, 83, 106, 237
infinite, 103
   from the left and from the right, 103
   properties of, 107
at infinity, 235, 236
   infinite, 241
   of a rational function, guidelines for
      finding, 238
of integration
   inside, 967
   lower, 304
   outside, 967
   upper, 304
from the left and from the right, 92
of the lower and upper sums, 296
nonexistence of, common types of
   behavior, 71
of nth term of a convergent series, 599
one-sided, 92
of polynomial and rational functions, 80
properties of, 79
of a sequence, 585
   properties of, 586
strategy for finding, 82
three special, 85
of transcendental functions, 81
of a vector-valued function, 819
Limit Comparison Test, 614
Line(s)
   contour, 871
   as a degenerate conic, 682
   equation of
      general form, 14
      horizontal, 14
      point-slope form, 11, 14
      slope-intercept form, 13, 14
      summary, 14
      vertical, 14
   equipotential, 871
   least squares regression, 946, 947
   moment about, 487
   normal, 927, 928
      at a point, 172
   parallel, 14
   perpendicular, 14
   radial, 715
   secant, 65, 117
   slope of, 10
   in space
      direction number of, 783
      direction vector of, 783
      parametric equations of, 783
      symmetric equations of, 783
   tangent, 65, 117
      approximation, 267
      at the pole, 720
      with slope m, 117
      vertical, 118

trend, 325
Line of impact, 927
Line integral, 1052
   for area, 1078
   differential form of, 1059
   evaluation of as a definite integral, 1053
   of f along C, 1052
   independent of path, 1068
   summary of, 1103
   of a vector field, 1056
Line segment, directed, 748
Linear approximation, 267, 902
Linear combination of $\mathbf{i}$ and $\mathbf{j}$, 753
Linear function, 24
Linear inequality, A11
Local maximum, 203
Local minimum, 203
Locus, 682
Log Rule for Integration, 348
Logarithmic differentiation, 170
Logarithmic function, 24
   to base a, 158
      derivative of, 159
   natural, 51
      derivative of, 156
      properties of, 51
Logarithmic properties, 52
Logarithmic spiral, 733
Logistic curve, 410, 550
Logistic differential equation, 277, 409
   carrying capacity, 409
Logistic function, 239, 249
Lorenz curves, 444
Lotka, Alfred (1880–1949), 423
Lotka-Volterra equations, 423
Lower bound of a sequence, 591
Lower bound of summation, 290
Lower limit of integration, 304
Lower sum, 294
   limit of, 296
Lune, 541

M

Macintyre, Sheila Scott (1910–1960), 524
Maclaurin, Colin, (1698–1746), 664
Maclaurin polynomial, 638
Maclaurin series, 665
Magnitude
   of a directed line segment, 748
   of a vector in the plane, 749
Major axis of an ellipse, 685
Marginal productivity of money, 955
Mass, 486, 1100
   center of, 487, 488, 489
      of a one-dimensional system, 487,
         488
      of a planar lamina, 490
         of variable density, 996, 1014
      of a solid region Q, 1014
      of a two-dimensional system, 489
   moments of, 996
   of a planar lamina of variable density,
      994
   pound mass, 486

total, 488, 489
Mathematical model, 7, 946
Mathematical modeling, 33
Maximum
   absolute, 202
   of f on I, 202
   of a function of two variables, 936
   global, 202
   local, 203
   relative, 203
Mean Value Theorem, 212
   alternative form of, 213
   Extended, 277, 558
   for Integrals, 316
Measurement, error in, 269
Mechanic's Rule, 194
Method of
   Lagrange Multipliers, 952, 953
   least squares, 946
   partial fractions, 542
Midpoint
   Formula, 759, A18
   of an interval, A13
   of a line segment, A18
   Rule, 298
Minimum
   absolute, 202
   of f on I, 202
   of a function of two variables, 936
   global, 202
   local, 203
   relative, 203
Minor axis of an ellipse, 685
Mixed partial derivatives, 894
   equality of, 895
Möbius Strip, 1093
Model
   exponential growth and decay, 390
   mathematical, 7, 946
Modeling, mathematical, 33
Modified Euler's Method, 433
Moment(s)
   about a line, 487
   about the origin, 487, 488
   about a point, 487
   about the x-axis
      of a planar lamina, 490
      of a two-dimensional system, 489
   about the y-axis
      of a planar lamina, 490
      of a two-dimensional system, 489
   arm, length of, 487
   first, 1014
   of a force about a point, 779
   of inertia, 998, 1014, 1123
      polar, 998
      for a space curve, 1064
   of mass, 996
      of a one-dimensional system, 488
      of a planar lamina, 490
   second, 998, 1014
Monotonic sequence, 590
   bounded, 591
Monotonic, strictly, 218
Mutually orthogonal, 400

N

n factorial, 587
Napier, John (1550–1617), 318
Napier's Inequality, 356
Natural equation for a curve, 865
Natural exponential function
    derivative of, 132
    series for, 670
Natural logarithmic function, 51
    derivative of, 156
    properties of, 51
    series for, 670
Negative number, A7
Negative of a vector, 750
Net change, 322
Net Change Theorem, 322
Newton (unit of force), 477
Newton, Isaac (1642–1727), 116, 190
Newton's Law of Cooling, 393
Newton's Law of Gravitation, 1041
Newton's Law of Universal Gravitation,
    479
Newton's Method for approximating the
        zeros of a function, 190
    convergence of, 192, 193
    iteration, 190
Newton's Second Law of Motion, 417, 836
Nodes, 826
Noether, Emmy (1882–1935), 751
Nonexistence of a limit, common types
        of behavior, 71
Nonnegative number, A7
Nonpositive number, A7
Nonremovable discontinuity, 91, 804
Norm
    of a partition, 303, 974, 987, 1009
    polar, 987
    of a vector in the plane, 749
Normal component
    of acceleration, 845, 846, 859
    of a vector field, 1100
Normal line, 927, 928
    at a point, 172
Normal probability density function, 228
Normal vector(s), 768
    principal unit, 842, 859
    to a smooth parametric surface, 1087
Normalization of **v**, 752
Notation
    antiderivative, 245
    derivative, 119
    exponential, 37
    for first partial derivatives, 891
    function, 19
    Leibniz, 270
    sigma, 290
*n*th Maclaurin polynomial for *f* at *c*, 638
*n*th partial sum, 595
*n*th Taylor polynomial for *f* at *c*, 638
*n*th term
    of a convergent series, 599
    of a sequence, 584
*n*th-Term Test for Divergence, 599

Number

    critical, 204
    irrational, A7
    negative, A7
    nonnegative, A7
    nonpositive, A7
    positive, A7
    rational, A7
    real, A7
Number *e*, 50
Numerical differentiation, 122

O

Obtuse angle, A23
Octants, 758
Odd function, 26
    integration of, 336
    test for, 26
Ohm's Law, 273
One-dimensional system
    center of gravity of, 488
    center of mass of, 487, 488
    moment of, 487, 488
    total mass of, 488
One-sided limit, 92
One-to-one correspondence, A7
One-to-one function, 21
Onto function, 21
Open disk, 880
Open interval, A9
    continuous on, 90
    differentiable on, 119
Open region *R*, 880, 886
    continuous in, 884, 886
Open sphere, 886
Operations
    with absolute value, A12
    with power series, 659
Order of a differential equation, 380
Ordered pair, A16
Ordered property of real numbers, A8
Orientable surface, 1099
Orientation
    of a curve, 1051
    of a plane curve, 697
    of a space curve, 816
Oriented surface, 1099
Origin, A16
    moment about, 487, 488
    of a polar coordinate system, 715
    of the real number line, A7
    reflection about, 23
    symmetry, 5
Orthogonal
    functions, 532
    graphs, 172
    mutually, 400
    trajectory, 400
    vectors, 768
Ostrogradsky, Michel (1801–1861), 1106
Ostrogradsky's Theorem, 1106
Outer radius of a solid of revolution, 449
Outside limits of integration, 967

P

Padé approximation, 200
Pappus
    Second Theorem of, 496
    Theorem of, 493
Parabola, 2, 171, 682, 683
    axis of, 683
    directrix of, 683
    focal chord of, 683
    focus of, 683
    latus rectum of, 683
    reflective property of, 684
    standard equation of, 683
    vertex of, 683
Parabolic spandrel, 495
Parallel
    lines, 14
    planes, 785
    vectors, 761
Parameter, 696
    arc length, 852, 853
    eliminating, 698
Parametric equations, 696
    finding, 700
    graph of, 696
    of a line in space, 783
    for a surface, 1084
Parametric form
    of arc length, 709
    of the area of a surface of revolution,
        710
    of the derivative, 706
Parametric surface, 1084
    area of, 1088
    equations for, 1084
    partial derivatives of, 1087
    smooth, 1087
        normal vector to, 1087
    surface area of, 1088
Partial derivatives, 890
    first, 890
    of a function of three or more
            variables, 893
    of a function of two variables, 890
    higher-order, 894
    mixed, 894
        equality of, 895
    notation for, 891
    of a parametric surface, 1087
Partial differentiation, 890
Partial fractions, 542
    decomposition of $N(x)/D(x)$ into, 543
    method of, 542
Partial sums, sequence of, 595
Particular solution of a differential
        equation, 285, 381
Partition
    general, 303
    inner, 974, 1009
        polar, 987
    norm of, 303, 974, 1009
        polar, 987
    regular, 303

Pascal, Blaise (1623–1662), 497
Pascal's Principle, 497
Path, 881, 1051
Pear-shaped quartic, 199
Percent error, 269
Perigee, 694
Perihelion, 694, 741
Period of a function, A29
Periodic function, A29
Perpendicular
    lines, 14
    planes, 785
    vectors, 768
Piecewise smooth curve, 701, 1051
Planar lamina, 490
    center of mass of, 490
    moment of, 490
Plane
    angle of inclination of, 931
    curve, 696, 816
        orientation of, 697
        smooth, 1051
    distance between a point and, 788
    region
        area of, 296
        simply connected, 1044, 1075
    tangent, 928
        equation of, 928
    vector in, 748
Plane in space
    angle between two, 785
    equation of
        general form, 784
        standard form, 784
    parallel, 785
        to the axis, 787
        to the coordinate plane, 787
    perpendicular, 785
    trace of, 787
Planimeter, 1122
Point(s)
    critical, of predator-prey equations, 424
    as a degenerate conic, 682
    of diminishing returns, 265
    equilibrium, of predator-prey equations, 624
    fixed, 194
    of inflection, 229, 230
    of intersection, 6
        of polar graphs, 727
    moment about, 487
    in a vector field
        incompressible, 1111
        sink, 1111
        source, 1111
Point-slope equation of a line, 11, 14
Polar axis, 715
Polar coordinate system, 715
    polar axis of, 715
    pole (or origin), 715
Polar coordinates, 715
    area in, 725
    area of a surface of revolution in, 730
    converting to rectangular, 716

Distance Formula in, 722
Polar curve, arc length of, 729
Polar equations of conics, 735
Polar form of slope, 719
Polar graphs, 717
    cardioid, 720, 721
    circle, 721
    convex limaçon, 721
    dimpled limaçon, 721
    lemniscate, 721
    limaçon with inner loop, 721
    points of intersection, 727
    rose curve, 718, 721
Polar moment of inertia, 998
Polar sectors, 986
Pole, 715
    of cylindrical coordinate system, 804
    tangent lines at, 720
Polynomial
    Maclaurin, 638
    Taylor, 199, 638
Polynomial approximation, 636
    centered at c, 636
    expanded about c, 636
Polynomial function, 24, 60
    constant term of, 24
    degree of, 24
    leading coefficient of, 24
    limit of, 80
    of two variables, 869
    zero, 24
Position function, 32, 133
    for a projectile, 837
Positive number, A7
Potential energy, 1071
Potential function for a vector field, 1043
Pound mass, 486
Power Rule
    for differentiation, 127
        general, 152
    for integration, 282
        general, 333
Power series, 647
    centered at c, 647
    convergence of, 648
    convergent, form of, 664
    differentiation of, 652
    domain of, 648
    for elementary functions, 670
    endpoint convergence, 650
    geometric, 657
    integration of, 652
    interval of convergence, 648
    operations with, 659
    properties of functions defined by, 652
        interval of convergence of, 652
        radius of convergence of, 652
    radius of convergence, 648
    representation of functions by, 657
Power-reducing formulas, A25
Predator-prey equations, 423
    critical points, 424
    equilibrium points, 424
Preservation of inequality, 308

Pressure, fluid, 497
Primary equation, 256, 257
Prime Number Theorem, 55
Principal unit normal vector, 842, 859
Probability density function, 228
Procedures for fitting integrands to basic
        rules, 511
Product
    Rule, 139
        differential form, 270
    of two functions, 25
        inner, 532
    of two vectors in space, 775
Projectile, position function for, 837
Projection form of work, 772
Projection of $\mathbf{u}$ onto $\mathbf{v}$, 770
    using the dot product, 771
Prolate cycloid, 708
Propagated error, 269
Properties
    of continuity, 95
    of the cross product
        algebraic, 776
        geometric, 777
    of definite integrals, 308
    of the derivative of a vector-valued
            function, 826
    of the dot product, 766
    of double integrals, 976
    of exponential functions, 49
    of exponents, 48
    of functions defined by power series, 652
    of the gradient, 919
    of inequalities, A8
        and absolute value, A12
    of infinite limits, 107
    of infinite series, 599
    of inverse functions, 357
    of inverse trigonometric functions, 43
    of limits, 79
    of limits of sequences, 586
    logarithmic, 52
    of the natural logarithmic function, 51
    of vector operations, 751
Proportionality constant, 390
p-series, 607
    convergence of, 607
    divergence of, 607
    harmonic, 607
Pulse function, 114
    unit, 114
Pursuit curve, 370
Pythagorean identities, A25

Q

Quadrants, A16
Quadratic function, 24
Quadric surface, 795
    ellipsoid, 795, 796
    elliptic cone, 795, 797
    elliptic paraboloid, 795, 797
    general form of the equation of, 795
    hyperbolic paraboloid, 795, 797

hyperboloid of one sheet, 795, 796
hyperboloid of two sheets, 795, 796
   standard form of the equations of, 795, 796, 797
Quaternions, 750
Quotient, difference, 20, 117
Quotient identities, A25
Quotient Rule, 141, 159
   differential form, 270
Quotient of two functions, 25

R

Radial lines, 715
Radian measure, 42, A24
Radical, limit of a function involving a, 80
Radicals, solution by, 193
Radioactive isotopes, half-lives of, 409
Radius
   of a circle, A19
   of convergence, 648
   of curvature, 856
   function, 800
   of gyration, 999
   inner, 449
   outer, 449
Ramanujan, Srinivasa (1887–1920), 661
Rainbow
   angle, 226
   ray, 226
Range of a function, 19
   of two variables, 868
Raphson, Joseph (1648–1715), 190
Rate of change, 12, 119, 893
   average, 12
   instantaneous, 12, 119
Ratio, 12
   golden, 594
Ratio Test, 627
Rational function, 22, 25
   guidelines for finding limits at infinity of, 238
   limit of, 80
   of two variables, 869
Rational number, A7
Rationalize the numerator, 83, 84
Rationalizing technique, 84
Real number, A7
Real number line, A7
   coordinate, A7
   directed distance, A13
   distance between two points on, A13
   intervals, A9
   one-to-one correspondence, A7
   origin, A7
   positive direction, A7
Real numbers, completeness of, 97, 591
Real zeros of a polynomial, A11
Real-valued function f of a real variable x, 19
Reasoning, inductive, 589
Reciprocal identities, A25
Recovering a function from its gradient, 1047

Rectangle
   area of, 292
   circumscribed, 294
   inscribed, 294
   representative, 436
Rectangular coordinate system, A16
   coordinates, A16
   ordered pair, A16
   origin, A16
   quadrants, A16
   x-axis, A16
   x-coordinate (abscissa), A16
   y-axis, A16
   y-coordinate (ordinate), A16
Rectangular coordinates
   converting to cylindrical, 804
   converting to polar, 716
   converting to spherical, 807
   curvature in, 856, 859
Rectifiable curve, 466
Recursively defined sequence, 584
Reduction formulas, 553
Reference angle, A27
Reflection
   about the origin, 23
   about the x-axis, 23
   about the y-axis, 23
   angle of, 684
   in the line $y = x$, 38
Reflective property
   of an ellipse, 687
   of inverse functions, 38
   of a parabola, 684
Reflective surface, 684
Refraction, 265, 959
Region of integration R, 967
   horizontally simple, 968
   r-simple, 988
   θ-simple, 988
   vertically simple, 968
Region in the plane
   area of, 296, 968
      between two curves, 437
   centroid of, 491
   connected, 1068
Region R
   boundary point of, 880
   bounded, 936
   closed, 880
   differentiable function in, 901
   interior point of, 880, 886
   open, 880, 886
      continuous in, 884, 886
   simply connected, 1044, 1075
Regression, line, least squares, 7, 946, 947
Regular partition, 303
Related-rate equation, 181
Related-rate problems, guidelines for solving, 182
Relation, 19
Relative error, 269
Relative extrema
   First Derivative Test for, 219
   of a function, 203, 936

occur only at critical numbers, 204
occur only at critical points, 937
   Second Derivative Test for, 231
   Second Partials Test for, 939
Relative maximum
   at $(c, f(c))$, 203
   First Derivative Test for, 219
   of a function, 203, 936, 939
   Second Derivative Test for, 231
   Second Partials Test for, 939
Relative minimum
   at $(c, f(c))$, 203
   First Derivative Test for, 219
   of a function, 203, 936, 939
   Second Derivative Test for, 231
   Second Partials Test for, 939
Remainder
   alternating series, 621
   of a Taylor polynomial, 642
Removable discontinuity, 91
   of a function of two variables, 884
Representation of antiderivatives, 280
Representative element, 441
   disk, 446
   rectangle, 436
   shell, 457
   washer, 449
Resultant force, 754
Resultant vector, 750
Return wave method, 532
Reverse the inequality, A8
Review of basic integration rules, 360, 508
Revolution
   axis of, 446
   solid of, 446
   surface of, 470
      area of, 471, 710, 730
   volume of solid of
      disk method, 446
      shell method, 457, 458
      washer method, 449
Riemann, Georg Friedrich Bernhard (1826–1866), 303, 624
Riemann sum, 303
Riemann zeta function, 611
Right cylinder, 794
Right-hand limit, 92
Right-handed orientation, 758
Rolle, Michel (1652–1719), 210
Rolle's Theorem, 210
Root Test, 630
Rose curve, 718, 721
Rotated ellipse, 171
Rotated hyperbola, 171
Rotation of $\mathbf{F}$ about $\mathbf{N}$, 1117
r-simple region of integration, 988
Rulings of a cylinder, 794

S

Saddle point, 939
Satisfied inequality, A10
Scalar, 748
   field, 871

multiple, 750
multiplication, 750, 760
product of two vectors, 766
quantity, 748
Secant function, A25
derivative of, 143, 155, 159
graph of, A29
integral of, 353
inverse of, 41
derivative of, 176
Secant line, 65, 117
Second derivative, 145
Second Derivative Test, 231
Second Fundamental Theorem of
    Calculus, 320
Second moment, 998, 1014
Second Partials Test, 939
Second Theorem of Pappus, 496
Secondary equation, 257
Second-degree equation, general, 682
Separable differential equation, 397
Separation of variables, 389, 397
Sequence, 584
Absolute Value Theorem, 588
bounded, 591
bounded above, 591
bounded below, 591
bounded monotonic, 591
convergence of, 585
divergence of, 585
Fibonacci, 594, 604
least upper bound of, 591
limit of, 585
    properties of, 586
lower bound of, 591
monotonic, 590
nth term of, 584
of partial sums, 595
pattern recognition for, 588
recursively defined, 584
Squeeze Theorem, 587
terms of, 584
upper bound of, 591
Series, 595
absolutely convergent, 622
alternating, 619
    geometric, 619
    harmonic, 620, 622, 624
Alternating Series Test, 619
binomial, 669
conditionally convergent, 622
convergence of, 595
convergent, limit of nth term, 599
Direct Comparison Test, 612
divergence of, 595
    nth term test for, 599
finite Fourier, 532
Fourier Sine, 523
geometric, 597
    alternating, 619
    convergence of, 597
    divergence of, 597
    guidelines for testing for convergence
        or divergence, 631

harmonic, 607
    alternating, 620, 622, 624
infinite, 595
    properties of, 599
Integral Test, 605
Limit Comparison Test, 614
Maclaurin, 665
nth partial sum, 595
nth term of convergent, 599
power, 647
p-series, 607
Ratio Test, 627
rearrangement of, 624
Root Test, 630
sum of, 595
summary of tests for, 632
Taylor, 664, 665
telescoping, 596
terms of, 595
Serpentine, 147
Set(s), A8
disjoint, A8
intersection, A8
notation, A8
solution, A10
subset, A8
union, A8
Shell method, 457, 458
and disk method, comparison of, 459
Shift of a graph
horizontal, 23
vertical, 23
Sigma notation, 290
index of summation, 290
ith term, 290
lower bound of summation, 290
upper bound of summation, 290
Signum function, 102
Simple curve, 1075
Simple Power Rule, 159
Simple solid region, 1107
Simply connected plane region, 1075
Simpson's Rule, 344
error in, 345
Sine function, 22, A25
derivative of, 131, 155, 159
graph of, A29
integral of, 353
inverse of, 41
    derivative of, 176
series for, 670
Sine Series, Fourier, 523
Single integral, 976
Singular solution, differential equation,
    380
Sink, 1111
Slant asymptote, 241, 248
Slope(s)
field, 287, 382
of the graph of f at x = c, 117
of a line, 10
of a surface in x- and y-directions, 891
of a tangent line, 117
    parametric form, 706

polar form, 719
Slope-intercept equation of a line, 13, 14
Smooth
curve, 466, 701, 826, 841
    on an open interval, 826
    piecewise, 701
parametric surface, 1087
plane curve, 1051
space curve, 1051
Snell's Law of Refraction, 265, 959
Solenoidal, 1048
Solid region, simple, 1107
Solid of revolution, 446
volume of
    disk method, 446
    shell method, 457, 458
    washer method, 449
Solution
curves, 381
of a differential equation, 380
    Bernoulli, 422
    Euler's Method, 384
    first-order linear, 417
    general, 281, 380
    initial condition, 285, 381
    particular, 285, 381
    singular, 380
of an inequality, A10
point of an equation, 2
by radicals, 193
set, A10
Solving a polynomial inequality, A11
test intervals, A11
Some basic limits, 79
Somerville, Mary Fairfax (1780–1872),
    868
Source, 1111
Space curve, 816
arc length of, 851
moments of inertia for, 1064
smooth, 1051
Spandrel, parabolic, 495
Special integration formulas, 537
Special polar graphs, 721
Special type of improper integral, 574
Speed, 134, 832, 833, 857, 859
angular, 999
Sphere, 759
astroidal, 1093
open, 886
standard equation of, 759
Spherical coordinate system, 807
converting to cylindrical coordinates,
    807
converting to rectangular coordinates,
    807
Spiral
of Archimedes, 717, 733
cornu, 745, 865
logarithmic, 733
Spring constant, 34
Square root function, 22
Squared errors, sum of, 946
Squaring function, 22

Squeeze Theorem, 85
    for Sequences, 587
Standard deviation, 228
Standard equation of
    an ellipse, 685
    a hyperbola, 689
    a parabola, 683
    a sphere, 759
Standard form of the equation of
    a circle, A19
    an ellipse, 685
    a hyperbola, 689
    a parabola, 683
    a plane in space, 784
    a quadric surface, 795, 796, 797
Standard form of a first-order linear
        differential equation, 416
Standard position of an angle, A23
Standard position of a vector, 749
Standard unit vector, 753
    notation, 760
Step function, 92
Stirling's approximation, 517
Stirling's Formula, 55
Stokes, George Gabriel (1819–1903), 1114
Stokes's Theorem, 1080, 1114
Strategy for finding limits, 82
Strictly monotonic function, 218
Strophoid, 745
Subset, A8
Substitution for rational functions of sine
        and cosine, 554
Sufficient condition for differentiability,
        901
Sum(s)
    ith term of, 290
    lower, 294
        limit of, 296
    nth partial, 595
    Riemann, 303
    Rule, 130, 159
        differential form, 270
    of a series, 595
    sequence of partial, 595
    of the squared errors, 946
    of two functions, 25
    of two vectors, 750
    upper, 294
        limit of, 296
Sum and difference formulas, A25
Summary
    of common integrals using integration
            by parts, 520
    of curve sketching, 246
    of differentiation rules, 159
    of equations of lines, 14
    of integration formulas, 1118
    of line and surface integrals, 1103
    of tests for series, 632
    of velocity, acceleration, and curvature,
            859
Summation
    formulas, 291
    index of, 290

lower bound of, 290
upper bound of, 290
Surface
    closed, 1106
    cylindrical, 794
    isothermal, 874
    level, 873
    orientable, 1099
    oriented, 1099
    parametric, 1084
    parametric equations for, 1084
    quadric, 795
    reflective, 684
    trace of, 795
Surface area
    of a parametric surface, 1088
    of a solid, 1002, 1003
Surface integral, 1094
    evaluating, 1094
    summary of, 1103
Surface of revolution, 470, 800
    area of, 471
        parametric form, 710
        polar form, 730
Symmetric equations, line in space, 783
Symmetry
    tests for, 5
    with respect to the origin, 5
    with respect to the x-axis, 5
    with respect to the y-axis, 5

T

Table of values, 2
Tables, integration by, 551
Tabular method for integration by parts,
        520
Tangent function, A25
    derivative of, 143, 155, 159
    graph of, A29
    integral of, 353
    inverse of, 41
        derivative of, 176
Tangent line(s), 65, 117
    approximation of f at c, 267
    to a curve, 842
    at the pole, 720
    problem, 65
    slope of, 117
        parametric form, 706
        polar form, 719
    with slope m, 117
    vertical, 118
Tangent plane, 928
    equation of, 928
Tangent vector, 832
Tangential component of acceleration,
        845, 846, 859
Tautochrone problem, 702
Taylor, Brook (1685–1731), 638
Taylor polynomial, 199, 638
    error in approximating, 642
    remainder, Lagrange form of, 642
Taylor series, 664, 665

convergence of, 666
guidelines for finding, 668
Taylor's Theorem, 642
Telescoping series, 596
Terminal point, directed line segment, 748
Terminal ray of an angle, A23
Terms
    of a sequence, 584
    of a series, 595
Test(s)
    comparison, for improper integrals, 576
    for concavity, 228
    conservative vector field in the plane,
            1044
    conservative vector field in space, 1047
    for convergence
        Alternating Series, 619
        Direct Comparison, 612
        geometric series, 597
        guidelines, 631
        Integral, 605
        Limit Comparison, 614
        p-series, 607
        Ratio, 627
        Root, 630
        summary, 632
    for even and odd functions, 26
    First Derivative, 219
    Horizontal Line, 39
    for increasing and decreasing functions,
            217
    intervals, A11
    Leading Coefficient, 24
    Second Derivative, 231
    for symmetry, 5
    Vertical Line, 22
Theorem
    Absolute Value, 588
    of Calculus, Fundamental, 313, 314
        guidelines for using, 314
    of Calculus, Second Fundamental, 320
    Cavalieri's, 456
    Darboux's, 278
    existence, 97, 202
    Extended Mean Value, 277, 558
    Extreme Value, 202, 936
    Fubini's, 978
        for a triple integral, 1010
    Intermediate Value, 97
    Mean Value, 212
        alternative form, 213
        Extended, 277, 558
        for Integrals, 316
    Net Change, 322
    of Pappus, 493
        Second, 496
    Prime Number, 55
    Rolle's, 210
    Squeeze, 85
        for sequences, 587
    Taylor's, 642
Theta, θ
    simple region of integration, 988
Third derivative, 145

Three-dimensional coordinate system, 758
  left-handed orientation, 758
  right-handed orientation, 758
Three special limits, 85
Top half of circle, 161
Topographic map, 871
Torque, 488, 779
Torricelli's Law, 433
Torsion, 866
Total differential, 900
Total distance traveled on $[a, b]$, 323
Total mass, 488, 489
  of a one-dimensional system, 488
  of a two-dimensional system, 489
Trace
  of a plane in space, 787
  of a surface, 795
Tractrix, 197, 370
Transcendental function, 25, 177
  limit of, 81
Transformation, 23, 1028
Transformation of a graph of a function, 23
  basic types, 23
  horizontal shift, 23
  reflection about origin, 23
  reflection about x-axis, 23
  reflection about y-axis, 23
  reflection in the line $y = x$, 38
  vertical shift, 23
Transverse axis of a hyperbola, 689
Trapezoidal Rule, 342
  error in, 345
Trend line, 325
Triangle inequality, 753, A12
Trigonometric function(s), 24, A25
  and the Chain Rule, 155
  cosecant, A25
  cosine, 22, A25
  cotangent, A25
  derivative of, 143
  graphs of, A29
  integrals of the six basic, 353
  inverse, 41
    derivatives of, 176
    graphs of, 42
    integrals involving, 357
    properties of, 43
  limit of, 81
  secant, A25
  sine, 22, A25
  tangent, A25
Trigonometric identities, A25
  double-angle formulas, A25
  even/odd identities, A25
  Law of Cosines, A25
  power-reducing formulas, A25
  Pythagorean identities, A25
  quotient identities, A25
  reciprocal identities, A25
  sum and difference formulas, A25
Trigonometric integrals, 524
Trigonometric substitution, 533
Triple integral, 1009

in cylindrical coordinates, 1020
in spherical coordinates, 1023
Triple scalar product, 779
  geometric property of, 780
Two-dimensional system
  center of gravity of, 489
  center of mass of, 489
  moment of, 489
  total mass of, 489
Two-Point Gaussian Quadrature
    Approximation, 377
Two special definite integrals, 307

U

Unbounded intervals, A9
Union of two sets, A8
Unit circle, A19, A24
Unit pulse function, 114
Unit tangent vector, 841, 859
Unit vector, 749
  in the direction of 752, 760
  standard, 753
Universal Gravitation, Newton's Law, 479
Upper bound
  least, 591
  of a sequence, 591
  of summation, 290
Upper limit of integration, 304
Upper sum, 294
  limit of, 296
u-substitution, 328

V

Value of f at x, 19
Variable(s)
  dependent, 19
  dummy, 306
  force, 478
  independent, 19
  separation of, 389, 397
Vector(s)
  acceleration, 845, 859
  addition, 750, 751
    associative property of, 751
    commutative property of, 751
  Additive Identity Property, 751
  Additive Inverse Property, 751
  angle between two, 767
  binormal, 849, 866
  component
      of **u** along **v**, 770
      of **u** orthogonal to **v**, 770
  component form of, 749
  components, 749, 770
  cross product of, 775
  difference of two, 750
  direction, 783
  direction angles of, 769
  direction cosines of, 769
  Distributive Property, 751
  dot product of, 766
  equal, 749, 760

horizontal component of, 753
initial point, 748
inner product of, 766
length of, 749, 760
linear combination of, 753
magnitude of, 749
negative of, 750
norm of, 749
normal, 768
normalization of, 752
operations, properties of, 751
orthogonal, 768
parallel, 761
perpendicular, 768
in the plane, 748
principal unit normal, 842, 859
product of two vectors in space, 775
projection of, 770
resultant, 750
scalar multiplication, 750, 760
scalar product of, 766
in space, 760
standard position, 749
standard unit notation, 760
sum, 750
tangent, 832
terminal point, 748
triple scalar product, 779
unit, 749
    in the direction of **v**, 752, 760
    standard, 753
unit tangent, 841, 859
velocity, 832, 859
vertical component of, 753
zero, 749, 760
Vector field, 1040
  circulation of, 1117
  conservative, 1043, 1065
    test for, 1044, 1047
  continuous, 1040
  curl of, 1046
  divergence of, 1048
  divergence-free, 1048
  incompressible, 1111
  irrotational, 1046
  line integral of, 1056
  normal component of, 1100
  over a plane region R, 1040
  over a solid region Q, 1040
  potential function for, 1043
  rotation of, 1117
  sink, 1111
  solenoidal, 1048
  source, 1111
Vector space, 752
  axioms, 752
Vector-valued function(s), 816
  antiderivative of, 828
  continuity of, 820
  continuous on an interval, 820
  continuous at a point, 820
  definite integral of, 828
  derivative of, 824
    higher-order, 825

properties of, 826
differentiation of, 824
domain of, 817
indefinite integral of, 828
integration of, 828
limit of, 819
Velocity, 134, 833
average, 133
escape, 114
function, 134
instantaneous, 134
potential curves, 400
Velocity field, 1040, 1041
incompressible, 1048
Velocity vector, 832, 859
Vertéré, 238
Vertex
of an angle, A23
of an ellipse, 685
of a hyperbola, 689
of a parabola, 683
Vertical asymptote, 105
Vertical component of a vector, 753
Vertical line, 14
Vertical Line Test, 22
Vertical shift of a graph of a function, 23
Vertical tangent line, 118
Vertically simple region of integration, 968
Volterra, Vito (1860–1940), 423
Volume of a solid

disk method, 447
with known cross sections, 451
shell method, 457, 458
washer method, 449
Volume of a solid region, 976, 1009

W

Wallis, John (1616–1703), 526
Wallis's Formulas, 526, 532
Washer, 449
Washer method, 449
Weierstrass, Karl (1815–1897), 937
Weight-densities of fluids, 497
Wheeler, Anna Johnson Pell
(1883–1966), 416
Witch of Agnesi, 147, 171, 238, 823
Work, 477, 772
done by a constant force, 477
done by a variable force, 478
dot product form, 772
force field, 1056
projection form, 772

X

x-axis, A16
moment about, of a planar lamina, 490
moment about, of a two-dimensional
system, 489

reflection about, 23
symmetry, 5
x-coordinate (abscissa), A16
x-intercept, 4
xy-plane, 758
xz-plane, 758

Y

y-axis, A16
moment about, of a planar lamina, 490
moment about, of a two-dimensional
system, 489
reflection about, 23
symmetry, 5
y-coordinate (ordinate), A16
y-intercept, 4
Young, Grace Chisholm (1868–1944), 45
yz-plane, 758

Z

Zero factorial, 587
Zero of a function, 26
approximating
bisection method, 98
Intermediate Value Theorem, 97
with Newton's Method, 190
Zero polynomial, 24
Zero vector, 749, 760
Zeros of a polynomial, A11